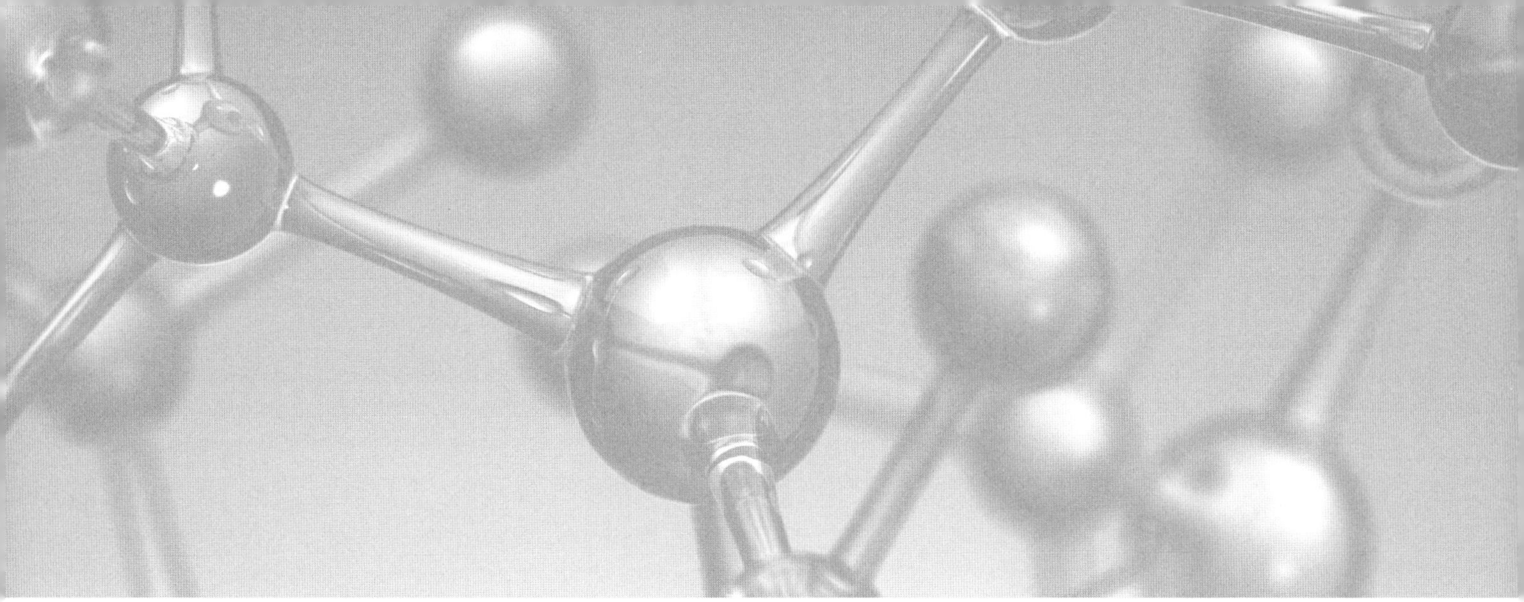

Fundamentals of **US** Regulatory Affairs

NINTH EDITION

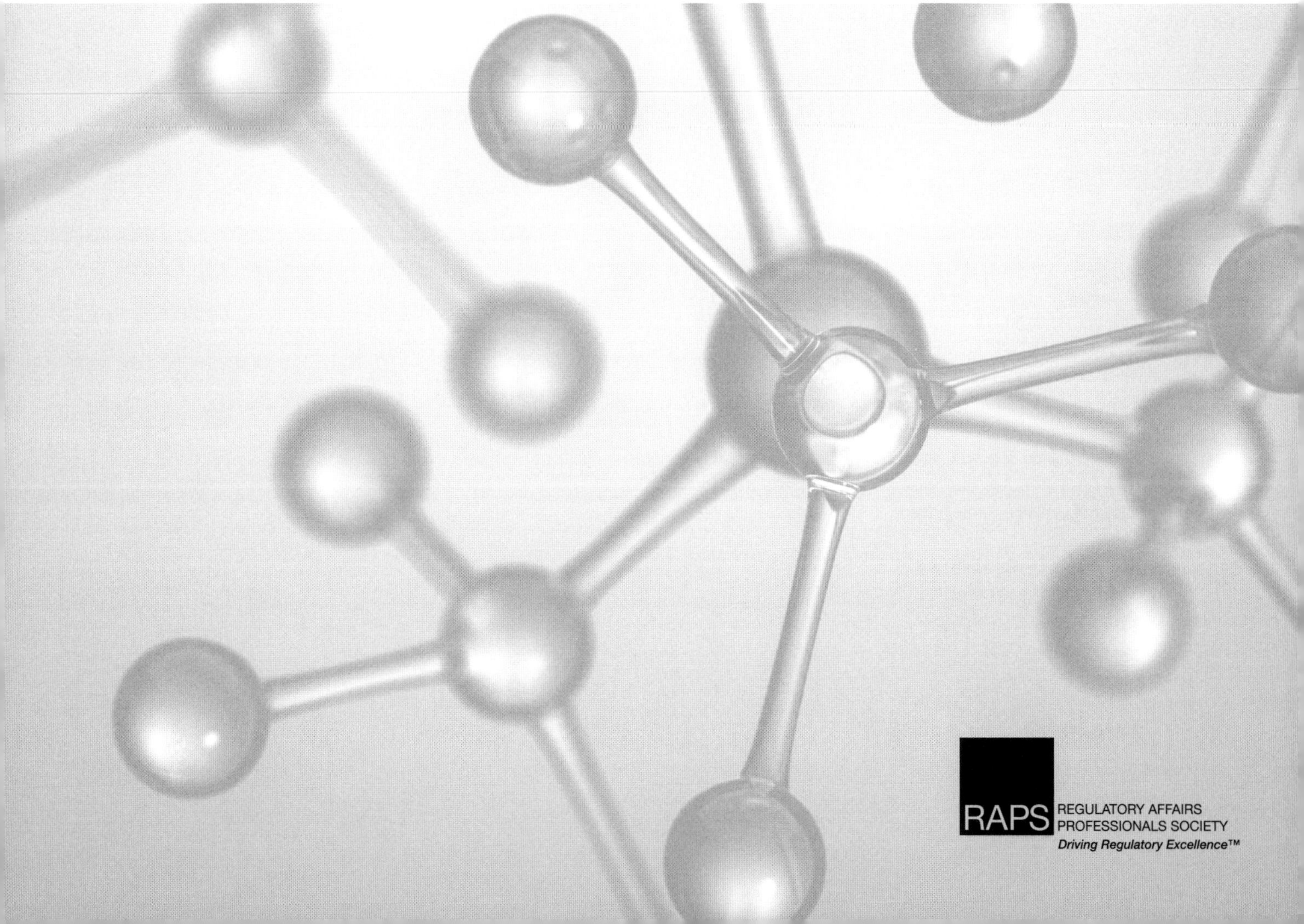

RAPS
REGULATORY AFFAIRS PROFESSIONALS SOCIETY
Driving Regulatory Excellence™

ISBN: 978-0-9673115-8-6

RAPS Global Headquarters
5635 Fishers Lane
Suite 550
Rockville, MD 20852
USA

RAPS.org

Foreword

The healthcare product regulatory environment is evolving at ever-increasing speed and FDA and other US agencies are making every effort to keep pace.

Implementation of the unique device identifier program is impacting the medical device industry and changes are afoot for companion diagnostics, as they move from one IVD therapeutic product to next generation sequencing. For the drug industry, updates to expedited approval programs for serious conditions and mandated electronic submissions are having a significant impact.

Fundamentals of US Regulatory Affairs, Ninth Edition, reflects those changes and examines what they mean for regulatory professionals. New chapters have been added to cover: all required user fees, regenerative medicine and regulatory strategy. All information in this edition is current through May 2015.

Fundamentals of US Regulatory Affairs, Ninth Edition is subdivided into seven sections:

- **Section I:** General Information—topics relating to multiple products types, such as the history of US regulations and regulatory agencies, the role of FDA and other agencies, FDA meetings and communications, health technology assessment, clinical trials, user fees, regulatory strategy, crisis management and GxPs
- **Section II:** Drugs—information on prescription, generic and over-the-counter drug product regulations and compliance, patents and pharmacovigilance
- **Section III:** Medical Devices—information on medical device and in vitro regulations and compliance
- **Section IV:** Biologics—biologics submissions, compliance and promotion
- **Section V:** Other Product Classifications—combination products, orphan products, blood and blood products, cell and tissue products, regenerative medicine, pediatric regulations, dietary supplements and homeopathic medicines, foods and medicinal foods, companion diagnostics and more
- **Section VI:** Inspection and Enforcement—FDA inspection and enforcement actions and healthcare fraud and abuse compliance
- **Section VII:** Resources—regulatory information resources

The text is accompanied by a matrix of applicable laws and regulations, a glossary and a detailed index. *Fundamentals of US Regulatory Affairs, Ninth Edition*, is an essential reference text for regulatory professionals at all levels—from those new to the field to senior level executives looking for information on an unfamiliar topic. It also is an excellent study tool for those planning to take the US RAC exam.

This publication is part of RAPS' *Fundamentals of Regulatory Affairs* series, which includes titles covering US, EU, Canadian, Japanese and international regulatory affairs. Each publication is available in print and as an e-book.

Pamela A. Jones
Senior Editor

Acknowledgements

RAPS would like to extend its thanks and appreciation to the following for contributing their time and expertise to this ninth edition of *Fundamentals of US Regulatory Affairs*.

Mujadala Abdul-Majid, MS, JD, RAC
Regulatory Counsel
US Food and Drug Administration
CDER, Office of Compliance

Maham Ansari, MS, RAC
Associate Director, Regulatory Affairs and Quality
Focal Healthcare Inc.

Maje Babatola, MS, RAC
Associate Director, Global Regulatory Affairs
Therapeutic Proteins International LLC

Rajaram Balasubramanian, RAC (US and EU)
Director, QA/RA
Elekta India

Barry Berger, JD, MBA
Professor of Regulatory Affairs
Temple University
School of Pharmacy

Mitchell Berger, MPH
Senior Policy Analyst, Consumer Safety Officer
Food and Drug Administration, Center for Biologics Evaluation and Research,
Office of Blood Research and Review

Christopher V. Braudis, Jr., MSc, RQAP-GLP
Associate Director, Research Quality Assurance
Alexion Pharmaceuticals Inc.

Charles M. Breen
Senior Consultant
EAS Consulting Group LLC

David A. Brindley, DPhil, MEng
Cooksey-Botnar-Said Fellow in Healthcare Translation
University of Oxford

Meredith Brown-Tuttle, RAC
Principal Consultant
Regulatorium

Elizabeth Campbell
Senior Advisor for Labeling and Claims
EAS Consulting Group LLC

Andy Carr, MA, ChM, Dsc, FRCS, FMedSci
Professor and Director
Botnar Research Centre
University of Oxford Institute of Musculoskeletal Sciences

Michael D'Amico
Senior Manager
Genentech Quality Assurance

Abhishek K. Gurnani, JD
Member
Amin Talati & Upadhye LLC

Brian E. Harvey, MD, PhD
Executive Vice President, Scientific & Regulatory Affairs
Global Liver Institute (GLI)

Nathalie Innocent, MS, RAC
Regulatory Associate
Teva Pharmaceuticals USA

Treena Jackson, MS, CQA, CSSGB, RAC (US)
Office of Quality Assurance
RTI-Health Solutions

Jocelyn Jennings, MS, RAC
Senior Manager, Regulatory Affairs
bioMérieux Inc.

Naseem Kabir, MS, RAC (US & EU)
Director, Global Regulatory Affairs
Amgen Inc.

Allison Komiyama, PhD, RAC
Principal Consultant
AcKnowledge Regulatory Strategies

Carrie Kuehn, MA, MPH, RAC
Senior Managing Scientist
Biomedical Engineering Practice
Exponent Inc.

Irina Kulinets, PhD, CQE, RAC
Executive VP of Regulatory and Clinical Affairs
RCCG LLC

Anne E. Maczulak, PhD, RQAP-GLP
Independent QA Consultant/ Medical Writer

Robert Martin, PhD
Senior Advisor for Food and Color Additive Safety
EAS Consulting Group LLC

Meredith May, MS, RAC
Vice President
Empirical Consulting LLC

Vic Mencarelli
Senior Manager, Regulatory Affairs–Personal Care
The Hain-Celestial Group Inc.

Shekhar Natarajan, MSc, MRSC
Director, Global Regulatory Affairs
Shire Pharmaceuticals

Maruthi Prasad Palthur, PhD, PMP, RAC (US)
VP, Technical Operations and Regulatory Affairs
Ascenthera Healthcare Inc.

Nisha Pandya, MS, RAC
Associate Director, GRA-CMC
Johnson & Johnson

Mitchell E. Parrish, JD, CIP, RAC
Life Sciences Attorney

Nancy J. Perrella, JD, RAC
Director, Regulatory Compliance and Quality Assurance
Covance Inc.

William Trey Putnam, PhD, RAC
Vice President and General Manager
Regulatory Sciences
Cardinal Health Specialty Solutions

Brock Reeve, MBA, MPhil
Executive Director
Harvard Stem Cell Insitute

Helen M. Ribbans, MBA, FRAPS
President
B&H Consulting Services Inc.

H. Carol Saul
Partner
Arnall Golden Gregory LLP

Anthony P. Schiavone
In-House Legal Counsel

Sharad Mi. Shukla, RAC (US and EU)
Regulatory Affairs Manager
Johnson & Johnson Medical India

William K. Sietsema, PhD
Senior Director, Global Regulatory Liaison
Caladrius Biosciences

Samrat Sisodia, MS, MBA, MRSC, RAC
Senior Director Regulatory Affairs
Breckenridge Pharmaceuticals Inc.

James Smith, DPhil Candidate
Nuffield Department of Orthopaedics, Rheumatology and Musculoskeletal Sciences
University of Oxford

Edward A. Steele
Chairman & CEO
EAS Consulting Group LLC

Clark G. Sullivan, JD
Partner
Troutman Sanders LLP

Ashish R. Talati, JD, MS, RAC
Member
Amin Talati & Upadhye LLC

Auresa Thomas, PhD, RAC (US, Global)
Regulatory Affairs Specialist
Trauma, Foot and Ankle
Zimmer Biomet

Adria Tyndall, RAC
Regulatory Affairs Specialist
Global Regulatory Affairs
Catalent Pharma Solutions

Richard A. Vincins, CBA, CQA, RAC (US and EU)
Vice President, QA/RA
Emergo Group

Martha Wells, MPH, RAC
VP Regulatory Affairs for Tissue & Biologics
Dohmen Life Science Services

Jennifer Wilhelm, MSc, MBA, RAC
Associate Director, Regulatory Affairs
Merck Canada Inc.

Andrew P. Zeltwanger, MS
Director of Regulatory and Quality
Rinovum Women's Health LLC

Table of Contents

Section I: General Information

Section II: Drugs

Section III: Medical Devices

Section IV: Biologics

Section V: Other Product Classifications

Section VI: Inspection and Enforcement

Section VII: Resources

Appendices

Figures

Tables

Chapter 1

FDA and Related Regulatory Agencies

Updated by Mitchell Berger, MPH and Barry Berger, JD, MBA

OBJECTIVES

- ❑ Provide an overview of the US Food and Drug Administration (FDA)
- ❑ Explain FDA's organization into offices and centers
- ❑ Provide an overview of those FDA centers
- ❑ Discuss important FDA stakeholders and partners including other federal agencies, academia, trade associations and consumer organizations
- ❑ Provide resources for readers seeking further information about FDA

LAWS, REGULATIONS AND GUIDELINES COVERED IN THIS CHAPTER

- ❑ *Virus-Toxin Law* of 1902 (*Biologics Control Act*)
- ❑ *Food and Drugs Act* of 1906
- ❑ *Food, Drug, and Cosmetic Act* of 1938 (*FD&C Act*)
- ❑ *Kefauver-Harris Amendments* of 1962
- ❑ *Hatch-Waxman, Drug Price Competition and Patent Term Restoration Act* of 1984
- ❑ *Food and Drug Administration Modernization Act* of 1997 (*FDAMA*)
- ❑ *Food and Drug Administration Amendments Act* of 2007 (*FDAAA*)
- ❑ *Patient Protection and Affordable Care Act* of 2010 (including *Biologics Price Competition and Innovation Act* (*BPCI*))
- ❑ *Food and Drug Administration Safety and Innovation Act* of 2012 (*FDASIA*) (including *Biosimilar User Fee Act*)
- ❑ *Medical Device Amendments* of 1976
- ❑ *Family Smoking Prevention and Tobacco Control Act* of 2009
- ❑ *Prescription Drug User Fee Act* of 1992 (*PDUFA*)
- ❑ *Animal Drug User Fee Act* of 2003
- ❑ *Medical Device User Fee and Modernization Act* of 2002
- ❑ *Generic Drug User Fee Act* of 2012
- ❑ *Best Pharmaceuticals for Children Act* of 2002
- ❑ *Food Safety Modernization Act* of 2011
- ❑ *Poison Prevention Act* of 1970
- ❑ *Fair Packaging and Labeling Act* of 1967 *(FPLA)*
- ❑ *Controlled Substances Act* of 1970

Introduction

The Food and Drug Administration (FDA) is part of the Department of Health and Human Services (DHHS). FDA is responsible for protecting the public health by assuring the safety, and in some cases, the efficacy of products it regulates, including foods, dietary supplements, cosmetics, veterinary products, drugs, medical devices and biologics intended for human use. As a result of recent legislation, FDA now has authority to regulate tobacco products. FDA's mission and some related key statutes and regulations are discussed below.

Historically, FDA has been focused predominately on US product manufacturing and marketing. However, FDA has evolved into a global public health agency reflecting the growing number of foods, medical products, components and active ingredients sourced or manufactured outside the US. FDA commented in a recent report, "we recognize that to successfully protect United States public health, we must think, act, and engage globally. Our interests must be broader than simply those within our borders." [1] The report notes that in 2009, FDA oversaw two trillion dollars' worth of products manufactured in more than 300,000 foreign facilities in 150 nations. More than 80% of active pharmaceutical ingredients, 40% of finished drugs, 80% of seafood and half the fresh fruit sold in the US is imported, according to the same report. More broadly, as much as 20% of all US economic spending is on products that fall within the scope of FDA regulations.[2]

The number of entities within FDA's purview is enormous. According to the agency's 2015 Annual Report on Inspections of Establishments, the official establishment inventory includes roughly 9,300 domestic and 3,600 foreign registered drug establishments, and 13,000 domestic and 10,500 foreign registered device establishments.[3] The 2013 Annual Report on Food Facilities indicated FDA regulates $417 billion in domestic foods and $49 billion in imported foods. As of 2012, there were roughly 173,000 registered domestic food and feed facilities and 285,000 foreign facilities.[4]

FDA collaborates with other federal agencies, international regulatory counterparts, academia, trade associations, consumer groups and many others to accomplish its mission. That mission is discussed on FDA's website.[5]

FDA's Mission

FDA's mission statement is: "FDA is responsible for protecting the public health by assuring the safety, efficacy, and security of human and veterinary drugs, biological products, medical devices, our nation's food supply, cosmetics, and products that emit radiation, and by regulating the manufacture, marketing, and distribution of tobacco products. FDA is also responsible for advancing the public health by helping to speed innovations that make medicines and foods more effective, safer, and more affordable, and helping the public get the accurate, science-based information they need to use medicines, and to reduce tobacco use to improve health."[5]

Brief History of Food and Drug Legislative and Regulatory Changes

A "statute" is a law or an amendment to a law passed by Congress. A "regulation" is a rule issued by a federal agency such as FDA. Proposed FDA regulations are published in the Federal Register (www.federalregister.gov) that provides both notice about the proposed rule and enables interested individuals the opportunity to comment about the proposal. If the rule is finalized, it will be included in the Code of Federal Regulations (CFR) (http://www.ecfr.gov/cgi-bin/ECFR?page=browse). FDA also issues guidance documents that provide information about how to comply with FDA regulations to agency staff and industry. Guidance documents are not legally binding, but represent FDA's "current thinking" on a given topic. However, because guidances are important and useful both to industry and agency staff, FDA policy is to issue most guidances, allowing time for public comment, then reviewing the draft as it does with regulations. In most cases, FDA staff are expected to interpret regulations and policies consistent with final guidances.[6]

Within FDA, centers have developed policies and procedures instructing staff how to deal with day-to-day issues. For instance, the Office of Regulatory Affairs (ORA) has issued compliance policy guides and manuals; the Center for Drug Evaluation and Research (CDER) has a manual of policies and procedures; and the Center for Biologics Evaluation and Research (CBER) has developed standard operating policies and procedures.[7-9] Many policies are publicly accessible and, thus, can be helpful to industry and others in understanding FDA staff expectations.

Historical Overview

Drugs and Biologics

FDA has a long and interesting history that continues to be relevant to current regulation. FDA employees assist academic researchers, FDA staff and others outside the agency in understanding this history.[10] To the founders of what was once an agrarian society, the need for a national agency to regulate foods and drugs would not have been apparent. Accordingly, until the 19th century, "[s]tates exercised the principal control over domestically produced and distributed foods and drugs."[11] Other than a few laws regarding imports, regulatory activity at the federal level was minimal and varied among states.[12] Improved medical technology, growth in food and drug marketing complexity and some high-profile incidents spurred the need for increased federal government oversight of these products.

Following one such incident in 1901, when 13 children died from a poorly manufactured tetanus antitoxin, Congress passed the *Virus-Toxin Law*, which required licensing, vaccine manufacturer inspections and premarket approval of vaccines, serums and antitoxins. This law also is referred to as the *Biologics Control Act.*[13]

As the new century began, the media reported severe problems in the food and drug industries. Upton Sinclair's *The Jungle* dramatically highlighted unsanitary practices in the nation's meat processing industry (http://www.gutenberg.org/ebooks/140?msg=welcome_stranger), Samuel Hopkins Adams' magazine articles about "The Great American Fraud" sparked similar concerns about fraudulent 'patent medicines' containing such ingredients as alcohol, cocaine, morphine and opium and advertised by their makers as cures for diseases like cancer and tuberculosis (http://www.gutenberg.org/files/44325/44325-h/44325-h.htm). The 1906 *Food and Drugs Act* prohibited the marketing of adulterated (e.g., contaminated) and misbranded (inaccurately labeled) food and drugs but did not contain required product standards and limited the extent to which the government could combat fraud.

In 1938, following more than 100 deaths due to ingestion of Elixir Sulfanilamide prepared with diethylene glycol (a component of antifreeze), President Franklin Roosevelt signed the 1938 *Food, Drug, and Cosmetic Act.* The law strengthened safety and labeling requirements and required FDA to confirm product safety. The act defined drugs as "articles intended for use in the diagnosis, cure, mitigation, treatment, or prevention of disease in man or other animals" and "articles (other than food) intended to affect the structure or any function of the body of man or other animals."[14]

Even under the 1938 law, however, most drugs still could be dispensed directly to consumers without healthcare provider oversight. In 1951, the *Durham-Humphrey Amendment* required certain medications that could be habit-forming or dangerous without medical oversight to be dispensed only with a prescription.[15]

In 1962, amid controversy about drug labeling and thalidomide side effects, Congress enacted the *Kefauver-Harris Amendments.*[16] Companies now would be required to demonstrate drug product efficacy as well as safety, and FDA was given authority to oversee drug advertising.

The *Food and Drug Administration Modernization Act* of 1997 (*FDAMA*) implemented broad changes, including permitting fast-tracking drugs and biologics intended for serious or life-threatening diseases. [17,18]

The *Food and Drug Administration Amendments Act* of 2007 (*FDAAA*) significantly impacted FDA programs intended to improve drug postmarket safety, including giving FDA the authority to impose Risk Evaluation and Mitigation Strategies (REMS). One of the more significant *FDAAA* changes was a significant expansion of clinical trial registry databases, creating a new clinical trial results database. *FDAAA* also created the FDA Office of Chief Scientist and required new steps to guard against FDA Advisory Committee members' conflicts of interest.[19]

The *Food and Drug Administration Safety and Innovation Act* of 2012 (*FDASIA*) expanded user fees from prescription drugs to generic drugs and biosimilars. Title VIII dealt with *Generating Antibiotic Incentives Now* (*GAIN*), which provides incentives for the development of new qualified infectious disease products (QIDPs), including priority review and exclusivity. This incentive added five years to other specified QIDP marketing exclusivity periods. *FDASIA* also enhanced accelerated approval pathways by providing a breakthrough therapy designation to speed access to certain drugs. Breakthrough therapies are those "intended alone or in combination with one or more other drugs to treat a serious or life threatening disease or condition" and for which "preliminary clinical evidence indicates that the drug may demonstrate substantial improvement over existing therapies on one or more clinically significant endpoints." The law also requires tighter controls to prevent drug diversion and counterfeiting and requires FDA reporting and coordination and manufacturer steps to reduce drug shortages.[20]

Medical Devices

Even as drugs and biologics became subject to more regulation, oversight of medical devices remained markedly less stringent. In 1976, Congress enacted the *Medical Device Amendments*, which divided devices into three classifications based on risk and required FDA premarketing approval of certain higher-risk devices.[21-23]

Generic Products and Biosimilars

The *Hatch-Waxman Act* or *Drug Price Competition and Patent Term Restoration Act* of 1984 allows generic drug product approval based on demonstration of bioequivalence. Currently, about 75% of written prescriptions are for generic drug products.[24] *Hatch-Waxman* added the Abbreviated New Drug Application (ANDA) pathway (505(j) to the *FD&C Act)* for approval of a generic drug with the same active ingredient as the innovator product. This approval pathway is appropriate if two products have the same active ingredient, form, route and conditions of use. FDA makes a suitability determination based on an applicant's petition (21 CFR 314.93). The generic and innovator products must be therapeutically equivalent and have equivalent labeling. Safety and efficacy data for the innovator product are required to approve the generic.[25–26]

Generic versions of most biologic products could not be approved under *Hatch-Waxman.* In 2010, the *Patient Protection and Affordable Care Act* established a process whereby FDA can approve biosimilar and interchangeable biological products. The law was based on hopes of decreasing biologic product cost as *Hatch-Waxman* had for generic pharmaceuticals. Biosimilar products must be "highly similar to the reference product, notwithstanding minor differences in clinically inactive components" and should not have any "clinically meaningful" differences in safety and effectiveness. An interchangeable product must not only be highly similar in analytical, clinical and animal study results and mechanism of action but also "can be expected to produce the same clinical result as the reference product in any given patient."[27,28]

In March 2015, FDA announced that it had approved the first biosimilar product, an anticancer drug.

Tobacco

In 2009, Congress enacted the *Family Smoking Prevention and Tobacco Control Act*, providing FDA the authority to regulate tobacco products. The agency's tobacco regulations continue to receive much public attention. In April 2014, FDA issued a proposed rule that would extend its regulatory authority to additional tobacco products such as electronic cigarettes. The *Tobacco Control Act* allows FDA to regulate tobacco products, establishes 18 as the minimum purchase age, requires certain warning labels and permits FDA to regulate tobacco advertising.[29]

FDA Budget

FDA's budget is an important resource for regulatory professionals in understanding the agency's challenges and priorities. As with the rest of the federal government, FDA's budget cycle runs from 1 October of one year to 30 September of the next (the federal fiscal year). FDA works closely with the Department of Health and Human Services (http://www.hhs.gov/budget/) and the White House Office of Management and Budget, which review FDA budget requests and help set overall department and Executive Branch priorities (http://www.whitehouse.gov/omb/overview).

At the time of publication, the most recent completed FDA budget is for Fiscal 2015, which started 1 October 2014 and will end 30 September 2015.[30] FDA's budget falls under the jurisdiction of the Senate Committee on Appropriations, Subcommittee on Agriculture, Rural Development, Food and Drug Administration, and Related Agencies and House Committee on Appropriations, Subcommittee on Agriculture, Rural Development, Food and Drug Administration, and Related Agencies. By contrast, the budgets of many other HHS agencies, such as the National Institutes for Health (NIH), fall under the jurisdiction of the House and Senate Appropriations Committees Labor, Health and Human Services, Education, and Related Agencies Subcommittees.

FDA requested a Fiscal 2015 budget of $4.74 billion, with $2.16 billion in user fees. By far the agency's largest expense is employee salaries and benefits, on which the agency will spend more than $2 billion in Fiscal 2015. Facility rental payments, contracting and consulting expenses, travel and transportation and utilities also are substantial expenses. The average FDA employee is a civil service General Schedule (GS)-13 rank; with upward locality adjustments for the expensive Washington, DC, metro area where most FDA employees work this equates to an annual salary of $89,000–$116,000.

The FDA budget provides details on the number of employees in each FDA center. In Fiscal 2015, FDA estimates it will employ 16,738 full-time equivalent (FTE) employees, including both Public Health Service Commissioned Corps staff and civilian employees. (The Public Health Service is a 6,500-person uniformed branch within HHS that is similar in scope and structure to the military (http://www.usphs.gov/)). Commissioned Corps staff are assigned to FDA in such roles as medical officer, regulatory project manager, pharmacist and scientist. FDA notes this is an increase in staff of nearly 1,000 from Fiscal 2014 and attributes the increase to new user fees and programs, including its recent focus on pharmacy compounding. FDA's ORA is the largest center, with an estimated 5,200 FTEs in Fiscal 2015, closely followed by CDER (roughly 4,500), Center for Devices and Radiological Health (CDRH) (1,720), Office of the Commissioner (OC) (1,400), Center for Food Safety and Applied Nutrition (CFSAN) (1,200), CBER (1,140), Center for Tobacco Products (CTP) (700) and Center for Veterinary Medicine (CVM) (540).

While the FDA budget may seem large, given its mission's scope and breadth, the agency can face challenges and is vulnerable to overall budget controversies such as the 2013 budget sequester, which led to two-week furloughs of many agency staff. The agency's staffing certainly has expanded in recent years but so has its workload and the complexity of the food and drug regulatory environment. Responding to such challenges as drug shortages and compounding, for instance, required additional staff time and resources. Several companies, trade associations, health professional organizations and patient groups have created the Alliance for a Stronger FDA to advocate for expanded FDA resources and ensure the agency's funding remains adequate to perform its mission (http://strengthenfda.org/).

The increasing importance of user fees in the agency's budget should be recognized. The *Prescription Drug User Fee Act* of 1992 (*PDUFA*) was the first major law to allow FDA to impose user fees for drugs and biologics and served as a template for other user fee laws.[31,32] Through user fees, companies pay FDA a certain amount to process New Drug Applications, Biologics License Applications, most Investigative New Drug Applications, and efficacy and manufacturing supplements. In Fiscal 2015, for instance, the fee for a supplement requiring clinical data is $1.16 million. FDA then agrees to meet certain performance commitments with respect to its review timeliness. For instance, one current *PDUFA* goal is to review 90% of standard original new drug applications within 10 months. User fees allow FDA to hire significant numbers of additional staff, such as regulatory project managers and medical and clinical reviewers to assist in achieving these goals. FDA notes that user fees have helped decrease drug application processing time by nearly 50%.[33–35] Many believe these user fees have numerous benefits, including more-efficient reviews and more-timely approval of new therapies.

Nonetheless, while many in industry and FDA support user fees, some critics believe the agency's increasing reliance on user fees may encourage overly rapid reviews and, while the user fees have allowed hiring by FDA in some areas, this may have resulted in less emphasis on other programs.[36–37]

Since *PDUFA*, more programs have been granted authority to levy user fees with similar approaches. These include user fees for: animal drugs (*Animal Drug User Fee Act* of 2003), animal generic drugs (*Animal Generic Drug User Fee Act* of 2013), biosimilars (*Biosimilar User Fee Act*, part of *FDASIA*), generic drugs (*Generic Drug User Fee Amendments* of 2012), medical devices (*Medical Device User Fee And Modernization Act* of 2002) and tobacco products (*Family Smoking Prevention and Tobacco Control Act* of 2009). FDA also imposes inspection fees for establishments such as mammography and food facilities. Additional user fees have been proposed for other areas as well, including cosmetics.

FDA Organization and Structure

FDA is an executive agency led by the Commissioner of Food and Drugs, who is nominated by the president and confirmed by the Senate

FDA's organization consists of the Office of the Commissioner and five offices and directorates :

- medical products and tobacco
- foods and veterinary medicine
- global regulatory operations and policy
- operations
- policy, planning, legislation and analysis

Figure 10-1 is an FDA organizational chart, but readers should note reporting structures and personnel change frequently and refer to the FDA website for the most current information.

FDA Office of the Commissioner, the Medical Products and Tobacco Directorate, Office of Foods and Veterinary Medicine and Global Regulatory Operations and Policy Directorate

Office of the Commissioner

The Office of the Commissioner includes several offices crucial to the agency's functioning.[38,39] The Office of the Commissioner provides the central agency-wide direction and management to ensure FDA's mission to protect patients and consumers is implemented effectively.

FDA's Office of the Chief Counsel, which acts as the agency's legal advisor, refers cases to the Department of Justice (DOJ) for possible prosecution and helps DOJ investigate and prosecute cases. It represents the agency in administrative hearings, helps review regulations, advises on enforcement actions and guidances and provides support to FDA programs.

The Office of the Chief Scientist provides leadership to support scientific innovation and helps the agency achieve its public health mission. The chief scientist helps oversee agency efforts to encourage scientific integrity, development of innovative new drugs and work to develop medical countermeasures for emergency preparedness. The chief scientist also oversees the Critical Path Initiative, which helps streamline and spur development of new products.[40]

Other offices within the Office of the Commissioner are:

- Office of Executive Secretariat, which helps FDA communicate with other government agencies and Freedom of Information and docket management activities
- Office of External Affairs, which helps develop communications to the media and public
- Office of Minority Health
- Office of the Counselor to the Commissioner, which oversees cross-cutting and emergency preparedness activities and includes the Office of Crisis Management, Office of Policy and Planning, which contributes to strategic planning and provides information in response to GAO requests, and Office of Women's Health

Office of Foods and Veterinary Medicine

Created as part of the commissioner's reorganization in 2009, the Office of Foods and Veterinary Medicine oversees FDA's programs in these areas. Key priorities according to the Fiscal 2015 budget include *Food Safety and Modernization Act* implementation and ensuring a coordinated response to outbreaks.[41]

The Center for Food Safety and Applied Nutrition is headquartered in College Park, MD and includes the Offices of Food Safety, Cosmetics and Colors, Food Additive Safety Nutrition, Labeling and Dietary Supplements.[42,43]

The Center for Veterinary Medicine includes the Office of New Animal Drug Evaluation, the Office of Surveillance and Compliance, which oversees product safety, and the Office of Research. FDA regulation of animal drugs expanded significantly with the enactment of *FD&C Act* Section 512 in 1968.[44] Priorities include pet food safety and labeling and antibiotic resistance.

Office of Medical Products and Tobacco

FDA's Office of Medical Products and Tobacco oversees the three medical product FDA centers, CDRH, CDER and CBER as well as the Office of Combination Products, Office of Good Clinical Practice, Office of Orphan Product Development, Office of Pediatric Therapeutics and Center for Tobacco Products (CTP). Priorities included in the Fiscal 2015 budget include pediatric medical product

Figure 1-1. FDA Organizational Chart (as of April 2015)

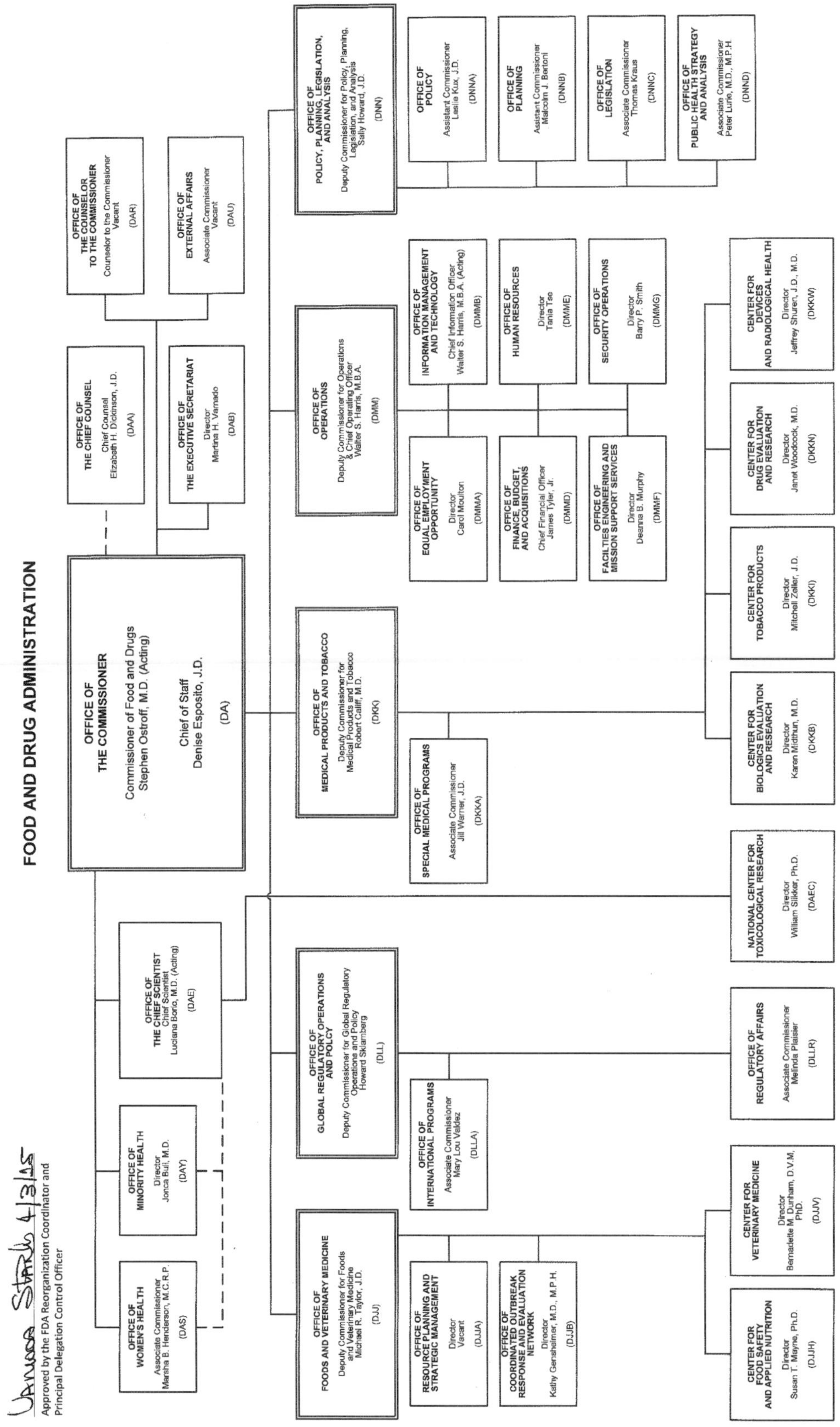

development, work with Institutional Review Boards and conflicts of interest for FDA Advisory Committee members.

CBER

CBER (http://www.fda.gov/BiologicsBloodVaccines/) has jurisdiction over blood and blood products, drugs derived from biological organisms, tissues and allergen tests and extracts used for treatment.[45,46] Offices include:

- Office of Vaccines Research and Review, which evaluates potential vaccines and conducts research
- Office of Cellular, Tissue and Gene Therapies, which regulates cell and gene therapy and human tissue products, including tissues used in transplants and stem cells (Cellular and Gene therapy products, http://www.fda.gov/biologicsbloodvaccines/cellulargenetherapyproducts/default.htm)
- Office of Blood Research and Review, which oversees blood and blood products, including blood derivatives and diagnostics
- Office of Biostatistics and Epidemiology, which supports CBER risk assessments, adverse event monitoring and surveillance
- Office of Compliance and Biologics Quality, which helps inspect biologics facilities, oversees postmarket review, publishes manufacturing guidance and includes the center's advertising and promotion staff.

In addition to biologic products, CBER regulates certain devices related to blood or cellular products.[47]

In 2003, FDA transferred jurisdiction over certain biological therapeutic products—including cytokines, enzymes, interferons, monoclonal antibodies and therapeutic proteins—from CBER to CDER.[48] As a result, many biosimilar biologic products actually fall under CDER jurisdiction.

CDRH

CDRH (http://www.fda.gov/MedicalDevices/) is charged with reviewing and regulating medical devices and radiation-emitting products, such as x-rays.[49,50]

The center's Office of Device Evaluation (ODE) includes seven divisions that help FDA assess device safety:

- Division of Cardiovascular Devices
- Division of Neurological and Physical Medicine Devices
- Division of Surgical Devices
- Division of Anesthesiology, General Hospital, Respiratory, Infection Control and Dental Devices
- Division of Ophthalmic and Ear, Nose, and Throat Devices
- Division of Orthopedic Devices
- Division of Reproductive, Gastro-Renal and Urological Devices

ODE oversees review and processing of device applications.

The Office of In Vitro Diagnostics and Radiological Health, established in November 2002, has jurisdiction over many clinical laboratory tests.[51] Radiological devices range from x-rays to microwaves and televisions.[52,53]

The Office of Communication and Education now includes communication functions such as *Freedom of Information Act* (*FOIA*) and communication of device risks and benefits as well as the agency's oversight of mammography facilities under the *Mammography Quality Standards Act* of 1992. [54]

The Office of Surveillance and Biometrics helps monitor the devices' safety after they are approved for marketing, including the new Medical Product Safety Network.

The Office of Compliance publishes guidance and helps ensure manufacturers understand FDA device regulations. The office includes CDRH's advertising and bioresearch monitoring functions.

To support its regulatory work, CDRH has a vibrant regulatory science research effort consolidated in its Office of Science and Engineering Laboratories.[55] Staff conduct research on such topics as three-dimensional printing, software and diagnostics.

At the center director level, CDRH includes policy and management staff.

CDER

CDER (http://www.fda.gov/drugs/) is charged with reviewing and ensuring the safety of new drugs, generic drugs and over-the-counter drugs.[56,57]

The Office of New Drugs is organized into six offices, which are further subdivided into nineteen divisions that review various types of drugs. For instance, the Office of Drug Evaluation I includes the Division of Cardiovascular and Renal Products, Neurology Products and Psychiatry Products. (See http://www.fda.gov/AboutFDA/CentersOffices/OfficeofMedicalProductsandTobacco/CDER/ucm075128.htm.)

The Office of Surveillance and Epidemiology helps the agency assess drug benefits and risks, risk communication and patient labeling.

The Office of Pharmaceutical Science helps evaluate New Drug Applications and Abbreviated New Drug Applications and therapeutic biologic products.

The Office of Medical Policy helps oversee product promotion to both patients and healthcare providers. Located within this office, the Office of Prescription Drug Promotion, ensures advertisements and promotional materials (labeling) to both physicians and patients is fairly balanced and accurate (this office previously was known as DDMAC, the Division of Drug Marketing, Advertising and Communication).

In 2015, CDER created the Office of Pharmaceutical Quality (OPQ), a quality-based office to focus on centralizing and standardizing how quality assurance is regulated at all relevant stages for prescription, over-the-counter and generic products.[58] OPQ, along with the Office of Compliance, is one of two CDER 'super-offices,' which reflects its importance and cross-cutting work.[59]

The Office of Compliance works with the Office of Regulatory Affairs (ORA) to enforce and interpret Good Manufacturing Practice regulations and helps design inspections of drug manufacturing facilities.[60,61]

The Office of Translational Sciences includes biostatistics and clinical pharmacology functions.

The Office of Generic Drugs has grown considerably, as generic drugs have grown to become a higher proportion of overall prescriptions.

Center for Tobacco Products (CTP)

CTP includes four offices:

- Office of Compliance and Enforcement, which includes oversight of tobacco advertising
- Office of Health Communication and Education, which helps lead tobacco control and education efforts
- Office of Science, which reviews tobacco products and investigates individual and population-level impacts
- Office of Regulations, which develops new rules and policies

CTP priorities include evaluating such products as menthol-containing cigarettes and e-cigarettes and supporting research on tobacco cessation and epidemiology.[62,63]

Office of Global Regulatory Operations and Policy (GO)

The GO consists of both ORA and the Office of International Programs (OIP). It is charged with providing oversight and policy direction for FDA's quality and safety efforts, including global collaborations, data sharing, regulatory harmonization, compliance and enforcement efforts.

ORA is the lead office for all agency field activities. ORA inspects manufacturers and products, does sample analysis of regulated products and reviews imported products seeking entry into the US. ORA includes the Office of Criminal Investigations, which helps to deter and prosecute criminal violations of the *FD&C Act,* such as counterfeiting and contamination as well as alleged criminal misconduct by FDA employees. The Office of Partnerships works with state and local governments, and the Office of Operations oversees enforcement and inspection of FDA-regulated products.[64,65]

OIP is FDA's lead on international matters. Reflecting the globalization of industry and products, FDA maintains offices with oversight over Asia-Pacific; China, Europe, India and Latin America.[66]

Regional/District Offices

According to FDA's 2015 budget and website, ORA has 20 district offices, five regional offices, 13 laboratories and 171 resident posts and border stations. Many ORA field offices include staff from FDA's Office of Criminal Investigations. ORA regional offices are based in:

- New York (Northeast region)
- Chicago (Central region)
- Oakland (Pacific region)
- Atlanta (Southeast)
- Dallas (Southwest)

These offices include contacts for such programs as retail foods and emergency response. District offices may include investigative and emergency response staff. A directory of staff can be found in the Investigations Operations Manual.[67]

FDA's National Center for Toxicological Research (NCTR)

According to its annual report, NCTR is "is a global resource for collaboration providing consultation, training, and innovative scientific solutions in support of FDA's mission to improve public health."[68,69] Established in 1971, the institute currently has approximately 280 full-time staff based in Jefferson, AR. NCTR's recent projects include studying bisphenol A and other chemicals, evaluating nanotechnology safety, identifying biomarkers, working to identify models to assess the risk of tobacco products and working with CBER and CDER to review drug labeling information.

White Oak Campus

Since 2008, FDA has been consolidating its Washington, DC area offices for drugs, devices, biologics and regulatory affairs programs at its White Oak headquarters in suburban Silver Spring, MD.[70,71] Previously, the centers were dispersed throughout the Washington metro area. Although some staff from the centers remain at other DC area locations due to space issues, most staff in the Washington area, roughly 9,000, now are at the White Oak campus, including most CBER, CDER, CTP and CDRH staff. It is hoped this co-location will lead to enhanced communication among FDA staff.

Key FDA Partners

To fulfill its mission, FDA interacts with numerous other federal agency partners, legislators, academic institutions, trade associations, regulatory agencies in other nations, state and local governments and patient and public interest groups. Some of these major FDA stakeholders are described in more detail below. In some cases, FDA has signed formal memoranda of understanding (MOU) with other agencies to define their joint work.[72] In other cases, collaboration may be more informal.

Congress

Congress is one of FDA's most important stakeholders. The House and Senate Appropriations Committees have oversight over FDA's budget. The Senate also has the responsibility of confirming the president's nominee for FDA commissioner (21 USC §393). Other committees have direct jurisdiction over specific FDA products or government operations. The Senate Health, Education, Labor and Pensions Committee is one example. Congressional committees may hold hearings about specific topics. For instance, in February 2014, the House Committee on Oversight and Government Reform held a hearing on FDA's treatment of whistleblowers, and the House Energy and Commerce Committee held a hearing on drug shortages. More recently, the same committee has held hearings on how to facilitate quicker access to FDA-regulated treatments.[73] These hearings may generate considerable media attention, help prompt new legislation and can lead to changes in FDA policy. In addition to hearings, members of Congress and congressional staff also may contact the agency about specific issues or products.

Lastly, members of Congress can request investigations of FDA by the Government Accountability Office (GAO), HHS Office of the Inspector General (OIG) or other government agencies.

The GAO, which characterizes itself as the "Congressional watchdog," investigates agencies and government programs to improve efficiency (http://www.gao.gov). GAO reports and testimony may be high-profile and drive lawmaking and policy. GAO also has an important role in ensuring government procurement complies with legal and ethical requirements. Recent reports by GAO focus on such topics as drug compounding, drug shortages, medical devices, Internet pharmacies and emergency preparedness.

White House

As with all government agencies, FDA ultimately answers to the president. However, the White House typically exercises its influence more indirectly through the HHS Secretary, who is nominated by the president and whose appointment must be confirmed by the Senate. The Office of Management and Budget, part of the White House that oversees agency budget requests and regulations and adherence to presidential Executive Orders and memoranda, also has a strong impact on FDA (http://www.whitehouse.gov/omb).

Other DHHS Agencies

The organization of DHHS is described in the DHHS Organizational Manual.[74,75] As a part of DHHS, FDA works both with departmental leadership and other DHHS agencies (operational divisions) of the department such as the National Institutes of Health (NIH). The FDA commissioner answers to the HHS secretary but, for practical reasons, DHHS leadership must delegate many duties. The DHHS Office of the Secretary and various assistant secretaries and their staff members work closely with FDA in its interactions with Congress and the media, budget and emergency preparedness activities. For instance, the Office of Human Research Protection, part of the Office of the Assistant Secretary for Health, helps oversee research conducted and supported by DHHS (http://www.hhs.gov/ohrp/about/index.html). A DHHS organizational chart is available at: http://www.hhs.gov/about/orgchart/.

NIH, which helps conduct and fund research into new therapies, complements FDA's important role in product review. NIH and FDA collaborate on workgroups, research studies, training sessions, workshops and public education efforts.[76] For example, FDA, NIH and the Defense Advanced Research Projects Agency are collaborating on an effort with industry to develop new uses for existing medical products, adaptive clinical trials and nanotechnologies. NIH has helped FDA implement the *Best Pharmaceuticals for Children Act* (*BPCA*).[77,78] *BPCA* initially was enacted in 2002, building on provisions in *FDAMA*, and was reauthorized and then made permanent as part of *FDASIA*. It provided an additional six months of marketing exclusivity to companies completing FDA-requested pediatric studies in drug development. Provisions enacted in 2007 require NIH to develop a priority list for which new therapies are needed and to ask FDA to make a written request to companies to conduct studies. NIH may conduct studies if the manufacturer does not do so, or if such products are off-patent. FDA and NIH also work together on the Cures Acceleration Network, an effort housed in NIH to develop new therapies.[79]

FDA is collaborating more frequently with the Centers for Medicare and Medicaid Services (CMS), which through the Medicare and Medicaid services, is an important payer for FDA-regulated products. FDA and CMS have developed a pilot parallel review process allowing medical devices to be reviewed by FDA while they are simultaneously considered for coverage in the Medicare program.[80] Through FDA's Sentinel Initiative, implemented following *FDAAA* in 2007, CMS, along with the Departments of Defense and Veterans Affairs and others, are sharing data that can be used to assess adverse events in FDA-regulated products.[81] CMS also has an important role in regulating laboratory tests through the Clinical Laboratory Improvement Amendments of 1988, covering 251,000 entities.[82]

FDA works as well with the DHHS Assistant Secretary for Preparedness and Response and its Biomedical Advanced Research and Development Authority on developing medical countermeasures against potential natural and manmade outbreaks. The Centers for Disease Control and Prevention (CDC) and FDA collaborate on measures to promote food safety and respond to outbreaks as well as monitoring the safety of medical products such as vaccines and compounded medications. FDA works with both CMS and CDC to help regulate diagnostic testing.

FDA and the Agency for Healthcare Research and Quality have worked together on a project to assess the safety of antipsychotics in adolescents and children.

FDA also has worked with the Office of the National Coordinator for Health Information Technology and Federal Communications Commission (FCC) on such issues as mobile medical devices and wireless technologies.[83] FCC, FDA and other agencies are part of the Radiofrequency Interagency Workgroup, which helps ensure devices such as cell phones are safe.[84]

FDA and Other Federal Agencies

In addition to working with other agencies within DHHS, FDA also collaborates with many other federal agencies, including the Departments of Agriculture, Defense and Homeland Security, the Environmental Protection Agency, Federal Trade Commission, Consumer Products Safety Commission, FCC and US Patent and Trademark Office. Some efforts, such as the National Nanotechnology Initiative, include numerous federal agencies (http://www.nano.gov/).

FDA initially was founded as the Bureau of Chemistry within the Department of Agriculture (USDA), and the two agencies, not surprisingly, continue to have a strong partnership, particularly with respect to food safety. FDA has primary jurisdiction over roughly 80% of the food supply, including dairy products, most processed foods and seafood, food ingredients, additives and colors, infant formula and dietary supplements. USDA has primary jurisdiction over meat and poultry. The two agencies share jurisdiction over shell eggs. USDA also has jurisdiction over animal biologics such as vaccines (veterinary biologics).[85–88] The two agencies also have worked together in oversight of genetically modified plants and animals, including those engineered to produce pharmaceutical products. FDA and USDA have worked with farmers and others to develop the Produce Safety Alliance.[89] FDA is working with USDA and others to implement the *Food Safety Modernization Act* of 2011, which requires identification and mitigation of potential hazards that can lead to disease outbreak.

The Department of Defense (DOD) supports research into FDA-regulated medical products. For instance, in 2014, FDA approved a DOD-developed assay for Ebola detection.[90] DOD and FDA also have signed an MOU with respect to investigational drugs and medical devices. DOD and FDA sometimes co-sponsor workshops. In addition, DOD and FDA work together to support development of medical countermeasures for emergency preparedness.

Similarly, FDA collaborates with the Department of Homeland Security (DHS) on emergency preparedness activities, including food safety and the National Infrastructure Protection Plan.[91] FDA's Office of Crisis Management also works with DHS and other agencies to plan for and respond to emergencies. DHS oversees Customs and Border Protection (CBP), which assists FDA in ensuring products under FDA jurisdiction are safe and legal. CBP will inspect imports and exports on FDA's behalf, although at some ports FDA inspectors directly inspect products. [92]

The Environmental Protection Agency (EPA) often works with FDA on issues with environmental implications. For instance, FDA and EPA recently provided guidance on fish consumption by pregnant women and young children. EPA also approves and establishes pesticide tolerances in growing crops, including antimicrobial pesticides. EPA works as well with FDA to regulate food crops genetically engineered to express or resist pesticides. EPA and FDA work together, too, in the Good Laboratory Practice area for pesticide products. [93-94]

The Consumer Product Safety Commission (CPSC), an independent agency, helps set standards for and prevent injuries caused by consumer products, ranging from food containers to bed rails. CPSC, through the *Poison Prevention Packaging Act* of 1970, also helps ensure child-resistant packaging for certain commonly used household medications, such as acetaminophen and aspirin. Other aspects of packaging and regulation are handled by FDA.[95]

FDA and Federal Trade Commission (FTC) share jurisdiction over many advertising and promotion issues. FTC has primary jurisdiction over medical product advertising, with the exception of prescription drugs and certain restricted medical devices, while FDA regulates product labeling.[96] (Restricted devices are those that can be provided only by a physician or following a physician's exam, e.g., cardiac pacemakers or hearing aids). FTC also regulates advertising of over-the-counter drugs, most medical devices, dietary supplements and foods. FTC has primary oversight responsibility for advertising of most medical devices. FDA and FTC have collaborated on issuing joint Warning Letters to distributors of products sold online allegedly to treat cold and flu. [97] FDA and FTC also coordinate to ensure consumer product labeling is accurate. FDA oversees the *Fair Packaging and Labeling Act* of 1967 for devices, drugs, food and cosmetics, ensuring consumers are aware of product identity, quantity and manufacturer; FTC is responsible for overseeing other products.

DOJ is charged with prosecuting violations of federal criminal statutes, including violations of the *FD&C Act* and related laws. When a consent decree of permanent injunction is filed, the company and, in some cases, its officials will enter into a settlement with DOJ and FDA. When a product is seized, or if FDA needs to obtain a warrant for an inspection or search, US Marshals operating under DOJ auspices may help FDA in executing the warrant or seizure.[98,99] If FDA is sued by a company or employee, DOJ will help defend the agency in court.

Under the *Controlled Substances Act* (21 USC 801 et. seq.), the Drug Enforcement Administration (DEA), part of DOJ, has a role in establishing controlled substances that can be dispensed only by practitioners with a DEA registration number. Roughly 160 substances and analogues are listed as controlled substances.[100] Substances are listed based on their potential for abuse and are subject to more rigorous controls and limited prescribing if more prone to be abused. DEA will discuss scheduling new controlled substances and reclassification of existing controlled substances with FDA. For instance, in 2014, DEA followed a DHHS/FDA recommendation to reschedule hydrocodone combination products from Schedule III to the more restrictive Schedule II.[101] FDA has worked with DEA and others to promote safe use of opioids.[102]

The US Patent and Trademark Office issues patents to inventors of a "new and useful process, machine, article of manufacture, or composition of matter, or any new and useful improvement thereof." Generally, a patent term is 20 years from the date of filing. A patent allows the holder to exclude others from manufacturing or distributing the patented object, such as a medical device, without the patent holder's license or approval. Exclusivity for drug products may be granted after approval for certain medications, such as an orphan drug, a New Chemical Entity or a qualified infectious disease product. During this time, a generic drug application cannot be filed with FDA.[103–105] A trademark is "generally a word, phrase, symbol, or design, or a combination thereof, that identifies and distinguishes the source of the goods of one party from those of others."[106] Trademarks are important to FDA-regulated entities because the names are recognized by consumers and prescribers. In many cases, a product's proprietary name for FDA purposes is registered as a trademark (e.g., Claritin®). FDA reviews proposed proprietary drug names and has guidance for how such names should be used in advertising and labeling. A copyright provides protection for work that is "tangibly expressed," such as journal article reprints, copies of print advertisements, a company's product website and product package labeling.[107]

International Collaboration

Increasingly, FDA is assuming a global role, collaborating with international organizations and other governments to promote product safety and regulatory consistency. FDA now views itself as a global agency. Globalization, therefore, is one area identified in FDA's new strategic plan. FDA has identified four "pillars" for its international work: information-sharing; data-driven risk analytics; enhanced intelligence; and smart allocation of resources through partnerships

FDA has offices focusing on Latin America, Sub-Saharan Africa, Asia-Pacific, Europe, China and India.[108,109] Permanent staff are based in such nations as Chile, Mexico, India, Jordan, Italy, China, Belgium and the UK to help with emerging issues and ensure safety of imported products. The agency's international programs are overseen by an Office of International Programs, which is led by an assistant commissioner.

FDA has signed MOUs and confidentiality commitments with several nations to promote information sharing and product safety.[110,111] For example, FDA has signed an MOU with China to promote information-sharing about issues such as product recalls and facilitating inspections. FDA and the European Medicines Agency (EMA) have established a process for developers of products such as cell therapies, gene therapies, tissue engineered products (Advanced Therapy Medicinal Products), vaccines and plasma derivatives to obtain input simultaneously from both FDA and EMA.[112] FDA is a member of the International Conference on Harmonisation, Pharmaceutical Inspection Convention, Pharmaceutical Inspection Co-operation Scheme, International Medical Device Regulators Forum and Codex Alimentarius, which promotes international food standards.

FDA also collaborates actively with the World Health Organization (WHO), which is affiliated with the United Nations. FDA has signed an MOU and collaborates to share information and promote coordination on such topics as tobacco, foods, veterinary products and drug and biologic safety. FDA staff participate as members in such efforts as the WHO Blood Regulators Network (http://www.who.int/bloodproducts/brn/en/).

FDA, EMA, Health Canada and the Japanese Pharmaceuticals and Medical Device Agency also have developed 'clusters' to permit collaboration and discussion of important topics in such areas as pharmacovigilance, biosimilars, orphan products, pediatric products and blood safety.[113]

Industry Associations

Industry trade associations and consumer and patient groups, health professional associations and academic institutions also are important stakeholders for FDA, and some have significant influence with policymakers, the media and the general public.

Trade associations allow companies to submit combined comments on regulations of interest and coordinate advocacy and public education efforts. While FDA is certainly one stakeholder, many trade associations also interact extensively with Congress, the media, patient groups and other federal agencies. For instance, many trade associations advocate on such issues as Medicare and Medicaid reimbursement, intellectual property, trade and insurance issues. Some companies may be part of more than one trade association. FDA may hold liaison meetings with trade associations to discuss important topics and participate in conferences. Regulatory professionals may work for or with companies that are members of trade associations and find these groups to be useful sources of information. Trade association officials also may serve as industry representatives on FDA Advisory Committees. Trade associations generally do not include individual members but may include associate members such as consultants, law firms, academic institutions and others who work with the industry. Some prominent trade associations include:

- Consumer Healthcare Products Association (http://www.chpa.org/), which represents manufacturers of over-the-counter drugs and dietary supplements
- Pharmaceutical Research and Manufacturers of America (http://www.phrma.org/about), representing large, brand-name pharmaceutical companies (though some members also have subsidiaries that market generic products)
- Generic Pharmaceutical Association (http://www.gphaonline.org/), which includes manufacturers of generic drug products and biosimilars
- Biotechnology Industry Organization (BIO) (http://www.bio.org), for companies manufacturing biotechnology products such as vaccines and genetically modified plants and animals
- Advanced Medical Technology Association (AdvaMed) (http://advamed.org/), which includes manufacturers of medical devices and diagnostic products

Academia

Academic institutions often partner with FDA on various initiatives and work frequently with FDA researchers on regulatory science efforts. FDA has signed memoranda of agreement with various academic institutions. For example, FDA has an agreement with Johns Hopkins to work on nanotechnology research and training. In 2009, FDA, with academic and other institutions, launched the Safety of Key Inhaled and Intravenous Drugs in Pediatrics (SAFEKIDS) Initiative to "study the effects of anesthetics and sedatives on the neurocognitive development of infants and young children."[114] FDA also has established seven regulatory centers of excellence to work with the agency on training and research.[115]

Public-Private Partnerships

Increasingly, FDA, trade associations, companies, government agencies, patient groups and professional societies are forming public-private partnerships to spur innovation and improve coordination. Examples include:

- Biomarker Consortium (http://www.fda.gov/AboutFDA/ PartnershipsCollaborations/%20PublicPrivatePartnershipProgram/ucm231115.htm)
- SmartTots, to study anesthesia and sedative use in children (http://www.smarttots.org/)
- Medical Device Epidemiology Network Initiative (http://www.fda.gov/MedicalDevices/ScienceandResearch/EpidemiologyMedicalDevices/MedicalDeviceEpidemiologyNetworkMDEpiNet/default.htm; http://www.mdepinet.org/index.php/about-us/)
- Medical Device Innovation Consortium (http://mdic.org/)

Through the Critical Path Institute established by FDA, Science Foundation Arizona and University of Arizona, FDA and its partners are working with academic, industry and government entities to study potential new approaches for Alzheimer's, kidney disease and tuberculosis as well as new testing and assessment methods (http://c-path.org/programs/). The Reagan-Udall Foundation, established by *FDAAA*, is a nonprofit foundation that is independent of FDA but works with the agency to bring stakeholders together to conduct research on such issues as tuberculosis therapies, product surveillance, toxicology and training of future regulatory scientists (http://www.reaganudall.org/about-us/frequently-asked-questions/).

Patient and Consumer Groups

Patient and health professional associations also are major FDA stakeholders. FDA's Office of Health and Constituent Affairs, part of the Office of External Affairs in the Office of the Commissioner, works with these organizations and can facilitate meetings with FDA center staff. Some patient associations are working with FDA-regulated entities to develop new treatments for such diseases as cystic fibrosis. FDA's Patient Representative Program allows patients to serve on Advisory Committees and provide patient perspectives to FDA staff.[116]

Consumer groups also play an important role in advocacy about such issues as drug pricing and approval. Prominent consumer and patient groups include:

- Public Citizen (http:www.citizen.org)
- Center for Food Safety (http://www.centerforfoodsafety.org/)
- Center for Science in the Public Interest (http://www.cspinet.org/)
- National Consumers League (http://www.nclnet.org/)
- National Center for Health Research (http://center4research.org/))

- National Women's Health Network (https://nwhn.org/)
- National Organization for Rare Disorders (https://www.rarediseases.org/)
- Friends of Cancer Research (http://www.focr.org/)

Though not directly FDA-oriented, the prestigious National Academy of Sciences (http://www.nasonline.org/) publishes reports and holds meetings relevant to FDA, such as its studies of the 510(k) clearance process for medical devices.

State and Local Governments

State and local governments work cooperatively with FDA on such issues as food safety and compounding.[117] States have authority over many product safety aspects and recalls within their jurisdictions. FDA has supported food protection task forces in 25 states and the District of Columbia.[118] It also has agreements with state and local entities to assist in sampling and inspections. FDA works as well with associations representing such entities as county and state health departments, local boards of health and public health laboratories.[119]

Summary

FDA regulation continues to evolve to reflect the complexity of regulated products, public health goals and in reaction to high-profile incidents. The agency has a complex organizational structure including six primary centers/offices. FDA's budget now is heavily reliant on industry user fees for a variety of regulated products, including drugs, devices and biologics. The budget is an important source of information about agency goals, programs and priorities. FDA collaborates extensively with other operating divisions within DHHS, other federal agencies, Congress, industry and patient and consumer groups.

References

1. Global Engagement. FDA website. http://www.fda.gov/AboutFDA/ReportsManualsForms/ Reports/ucm298576.htm. Accessed 9 April 2015.
2. FDA Strategic Priorities: 2014-2018. FDA website. http://www.fda.gov/AboutFDA/ReportsManualsForms/Reports/ucm227527.htm. Accessed 9 April 2015.
3. 2015 Annual Report on Inspection of Establishments. FDA website. http://www.fda.gov/RegulatoryInformation/Legislation/FederalFoodDrugandCosmeticActFDCAct/SignificantAmendmentstotheFDCAct/FDASIA/ucm432246.htm. Accessed 9 April 2015.
4. 2013 Annual Report on Food Facilities. FDA website. http://www.fda.gov/Food/GuidanceRegulation/FSMA/ucm271961.htm. Accessed 9 April 2015.
5. About FDA. What we do. FDA website. http://www.fda.gov/aboutfda/whatwedo/. Accessed 9 April 2015.
6. Background: Report on Good Guidance Practices. FDA website. http://www.fda.gov/AboutFDA/Transparency/TransparencyInitiative/ucm284740.htm. Updated 29 December 2011. Accessed 9 April 2015.
7. ORA Compliance Policy Guides and Manuals. FDA website. http://www.fda.gov/ICECI/ComplianceManuals/. Accessed 9 April 2015.
8. CDER, Manual of Policies and Procedures. FDA website. http://www.fda.gov/AboutFDA/CentersOffices/OfficeofMedicalProductsandTobacco/CDER/ManualofPoliciesProcedures/. Accessed 9 April 2015.
9. CBER, Standard Operating Policies and Procedures. FDA website. http://www.fda.gov/BiologicsBloodVaccines/GuidanceComplianceRegulatoryInformation/ProceduresSOPPs/default.htm. Accessed 9 April 2015.
10. History. FDA website. http://www.fda.gov/AboutFDA/WhatWeDo/History/. Accessed 9 April 2015.
11. Swann J. FDA's Origin. FDA website. http://www.fda.gov/AboutFDA/WhatWeDo/History/Origin/ucm124403.htm. Accessed 9 April 2015.
12. Background, FDA History. FDA website. http://www.fda.gov/AboutFDA/WhatWeDo/History/ResearchTools/Background/default.htm Accessed 9 April 2015.
13. Science and the Regulation of Biologics Products. FDA website. http://www.fda.gov/AboutFDA/WhatWeDo/History/ProductRegulation/100YearsofBiologicsRegulation/ucm070022.htm. Accessed 9 April 2015.
14. Definitions, Subchapter II, Federal Food, Drug and Cosmetic Act. GPO website. http://www.gpo.gov/fdsys/pkg/USCODE-2010-title21/html/USCODE-2010-title21-chap9-subchapII.htm. Accessed 9 April 2015.
15. Brass E. "Changing the Status of Drugs From Prescription to Over-the-Counter Availability." *NEJM*. 2001: 345: 810-816.
16. Kefauver-Harris Amendments Revolutionized Drug Development, Consumer Updates. FDA website. http://www.fda.gov/ForConsumers/ConsumerUpdates/ucm322856.htm. Accessed 9 April 2015.
17. *Food and Drug Administration Modernization Act* of 1997 (*FDAMA*). FDA website. http://www.fda.gov/RegulatoryInformation/Legislation/FederalFoodDrugandCosmeticActFDCAct/SignificantAmendmentstotheFDCAct/FDAMA/. Accessed 9 April 2015.
18. Fast Track Designation Request Performance. FDA website. http://www.fda.gov/AboutFDA/CentersOffices/OfficeofMedicalProductsandTobacco/CBER/ucm122932.htm. Accessed 9 April 2015.
19. *Food and Drug Administration Amendments* of 2007 (*FDAAA*). FDA website. http://www.fda.gov/regulatoryinformation/legislation/%20federalfooddrugandcosmeticactfdcact/significantamendmentstothefdcact/foodanddrugadministrationamendmentsactof2007/default.htm. Accessed 9 April 2015.
20. *Food and Drug Administration Innovation and Safety Act* of 2012 (*FDASIA*). FDA website. http://www.fda.gov/RegulatoryInformation/Legislation/FederalFoodDrugandCosmeticActFDCAct/SignificantAmendmentstotheFDCAct/FDASIA/. Accessed 9 April 2015.
21. PMA Approvals. FDA website. http://www.fda.gov/medicaldevices/productsandmedicalprocedures/deviceapprovalsandclearances/pmaapprovals/default.htm. Accessed 9 April 2015.
22. Medical Device and Radiological Health Regulations Come of Age, 2006. FDA website. http://www.fda.gov/aboutfda/whatwedo/history/productregulation/medicaldeviceandradiologicalhealthregulationscomeofage/default.htm. Accessed 9 April 2015.
23. Is The Product A Medical Device? FDA website. http://www.fda.gov/MedicalDevices/DeviceRegulationandGuidance/Overview/ClassifyYourDevice/ucm051512.htm. Accessed 9 April 2015.
24. Expanding the Use of Generic Drugs, Assistant Secretary for Planning and Evaluation (ASPE). ASPE website. http://aspe.hhs.gov/sp/reports/2010/genericdrugs/ib.shtml. Accessed 9 April 2015.
25. Schacht W and Thomas J. "The Hatch-Waxman Act: A Quarter Century Later," March 2012. Congressional Research Service report. University of Maryland website. http://www.law.umaryland.edu/marshall/crsreports/crsdocuments/R41114_03132013.pdf. Accessed 9 April 2015.

26. Facts about Generic Drugs. FDA website. http://www.fda.gov/drugs/resourcesforyou/consumers/buyingusingmedicinesafely/understandinggenericdrugs/ucm167991.htm. Accessed 9 April 2015.
27. Biosimilars. FDA website. http://www.fda.gov/drugs/developmentapprovalprocess/howdrugsaredevelopedandapproved/approvalapplications/therapeuticbiologicapplications/biosimilars/default.htm. Accessed 9 April 2015.
28. Implementation of the *Biologics Price Competition and Innovation Act*. FDA website. http://www.fda.gov/Drugs/GuidanceComplianceRegulatoryInformation/ucm215089.htm. Accessed 9 April 2015.
29. *Tobacco Control Act. FDA website.* http://www.fda.gov/TobaccoProducts/GuidanceComplianceRegulatoryInformation/ucm298595.htm. Accessed 9 April 2015.
30. 2015 Food and Drug Administration Congressional Justification. FDA website. http://www.fda.gov/AboutFDA/ReportsManualsForms/Reports/BudgetReports/ucm395076.htm. Accessed 9 April 2015.
31. User Fees. FDA website. http://www.fda.gov/ForIndustry/UserFees/. Accessed 9 April 2015.
32. *Prescription Drug User Fee Act (PDUFA)*. FDA website. http://www.fda.gov/ForIndustry/UserFees/PrescriptionDrugUserFee/UCM2005475.htm. Accessed 9 April 2015.
33. User Fees: Ensuring A Strong and Better FDA. FDA website. http://blogs.fda.gov/fdavoice/index.php/2012/06/user-fees-ensuring-a-stronger-and-better-fda/. Accessed 9 April 2015.
34. Woodcock J. and Junod S. *PDUFA* Lays the Foundation: Launching Into the Era of User Fee Act. FDA website. http://www.fda.gov/AboutFDA/WhatWeDo/History/Overviews/ucm305697.htm. Accessed 9 April 2015.
35. *PDUFA* Performance Reports. FDA website. http://www.fda.gov/AboutFDA/ReportsManualsForms/Reports/UserFeeReports/PerformanceReports/ucm2007449.htm. Accessed 9 April 2015.
36. Frank C. et al. "Era Of Faster FDA Drug Approval Has Also Seen Increased Black-Box Warnings And Market Withdrawals," Health Affairs, August 2014. vol. 33 no. 8 1453-1459. Health Affairs website. http://content.healthaffairs.org/content/33/8/1453?ijkey=176354b59ad602149715e619f269585de2bacf18&keytype2=tf_ipsecsha (paid/subscription required). Accessed 9 April 2015.
37. The State of the FDA Workforce, 2012, Partnership for Public Service. FDA website. http://ourpublicservice.org/publications/viewcontentdetails.php?id=43. Accessed 9 April 2015.
38. About FDA, Organizations and Functions, Volume 1(1000-1300). FDA website. http://www.fda.gov/AboutFDA/ReportsManualsForms/StaffManualGuides/ucm136374.htm. Accessed 9 April 2015.
39. Op cit 30.
40. FDA's Critical Path Initiative. FDA website. http://www.fda.gov/ScienceResearch/SpecialTopics/CriticalPathInitiative/ucm076689.htm. Accessed 9 April 2015.
41. Op cit 30.
42. Office of Foods and Veterinary Medicine, Overview and Mission. FDA website. http://www.fda.gov/AboutFDA/CentersOffices/OfficeofFoods/ucm196720.htm. Accessed 9 April 2015.
43. Op cit 38.
44. Chronological History of the Center for Veterinary Medicine. FDA website. http://www.fda.gov/AboutFDA/WhatWeDo/History/FOrgsHistory/CVM/ucm142587.htm. Accessed 9 April 2015.
45. Op cit 30.
46. Op cit 38.
47. Devices Regulated by the Center for Biologics Evaluation and Research. FDA website. http://www.fda.gov/BiologicsBloodVaccines/DevelopmentApprovalProcess/510kProcess/ucm133429.htm. Accessed 9 April 2015.
48. Transfer of Therapeutic Products to the Center for Drug Evaluation and Research. FDA website. http://www.fda.gov/AboutFDA/CentersOffices/OfficeofMedicalProductsandTobacco/CBER/ucm133463.htm. Accessed 9 April 2015.
49. Op cit 30.
50. Op cit 38.
51. In Vitro Diagnostics. FDA website. http://www.fda.gov/medicaldevices/productsandmedicalprocedures/invitrodiagnostics/. Accessed 9 April 2015.
52. FDA Radiological Health Program. FDA website. http://www.fda.gov/Radiation-EmittingProducts/FDARadiologicalHealthProgram/. Accessed 9 April 2015.
53. Radiation-Emitting Products. FDA website. http://www.fda.gov/Radiation-EmittingProducts/default.htm. Accessed 9 April 2015.
54. Office of Communication and Education. FDA website. http://www.fda.gov/AboutFDA/CentersOffices/OfficeofMedicalProductsandTobacco/CDRH/CDRHOffices/ucm115786.htm. Accessed 9 April 2015.
55. Office of Science and Engineering Laboratories. FDA website. http://www.fda.gov/AboutFDA/CentersOffices/OfficeofMedicalProductsandTobacco/CDRH/CDRHOffices/ucm115989.htm. Accessed 9 April 2015.
56. Op cit 30.
57. Op cit 38.
58. Office of Pharmaceutical Quality. FDA website. http://www.fda.gov/AboutFDA/CentersOffices/OfficeofMedicalProductsandTobacco/CDER/ucm418347.htm. Accessed 9 April 2015.
59. FDA Announces Major Agency Reorganization, With Focus on Drug Quality. Regulatory Focus. RAPS website. 16 October. 2014. http://www.raps.org/Regulatory-Focus/News/2014/10/16/20584/FDA-Announces-Major-Agency-Reorganization-With-Focus-on-Drug-Quality/. Accessed 9 April 2015.
60. CDER Office of Compliance. FDA website. http://www.fda.gov/AboutFDA/CentersOffices/OfficeofMedicalProductsandTobacco/CDER/ucm081992.htm.Accessed 9 April 2015.
61. FDA Office of Compliance Promoted to 'Super Office.' RAPS Weekly Update. RAPS website. 6 June 2011. http://connect.raps.org/blogs/zachary-brousseau/2011/06/09/fda-office-of-compliance-promoted-to-super-office?ssopc=1. Accessed 9 April 2015.
62. Op cit 30.
63. Op cit 38.
64. Op cit 30.
65. Op cit 38.
66. Office of International Programs. FDA website. http://www.fda.gov/AboutFDA/CentersOffices/OfficeofGlobalRegulatoryOperationsandPolicy/OfficeofInternationalPrograms/default.htm. Accessed 9 April 2015.
67. Investigations Operations Manual. FDA website. http://www.fda.gov/ICECI/Inspections/IOM/. Accessed 9 April 2015.
68. NCTR 2013-2014 Annual Report. FDA website. http://www.fda.gov/AboutFDA/CentersOffices/OC/OfficeofScientificandMedicalPrograms/NCTR/ResearchAccomplishmentsPlans/default.htm. Accessed 9 April 3015.
69. Op cit 30.
70. White Oak Campus Information. FDA website. http://www.fda.gov/AboutFDA/WorkingatFDA/BuildingsandFacilities/WhiteOakCampusInformation/. Accessed 9 April 2015.
71. Op cit 30.
72. Domestic MOUs. FDA website. http://www.fda.gov/AboutFDA/PartnershipsCollaborations/MemorandaofUnderstandingMOUs/DomesticMOUs/default.htm. Accessed 9 April 2015.
73. A Path to 21st Century Cures. House Energy & Commerce Committee website. http://energycommerce.house.gov/cures. Accessed 9 April 2015.
74. HHS Organizational Manual (April 2009). HHS website. http://www.hhs.gov/hhsmanuals/hhsorganizational/. Accessed 9 April 2015.
75. HHS Family of Agencies. HHS website. http://www.hhs.gov/about/foa/. Accessed 9 April 2015.
76. Report on NIH Collaborations with Other HHS Agencies for Fiscal Year 2013. NIH website. http://report.nih.gov/crs/Default.aspx?FY=2013. Accessed 9 April 2015.

77. *Best Pharmaceuticals for Children Act*. NIH website. http://bpca.nichd.nih.gov/about/Pages/Index.aspx. Accessed 9 April 2015.
78. FDA Pediatrics. FDA website. http://www.fda.gov/ScienceResearch/SpecialTopics/PediatricTherapeuticsResearch/default.htm. Accessed 9 April 2015.
79. Olson S. and Claiborne A. *Accelerating the Development of New Drugs and Diagnostics: Maximizing the Impact of the Cures Acceleration Network: Workshop Summary (2012)*, Institute of Medicine. National Academies Press website. http://www.nap.edu/catalog/13452/accelerating-the-development-of-new-drugs-and-diagnostics-maximizing-the. Accessed 9 April 2015.
80. FDA-CMS Parallel Review. FDA website. http://www.fda.gov/MedicalDevices/DeviceRegulationandGuidance/HowtoMarketYourDevice/PremarketSubmissions/ucm255678.htm. Accessed 9 April 2015.
81. FDA's Sentinel Initiative. FDA website. http://www.fda.gov/safety/fdassentinelinitiative/default.htm. Accessed 9 April 2015.
82. *Clinical Laboratory Improvement Act* (*CLIA*). CMS website. http://www.cms.gov/Regulations-and-Guidance/Legislation/CLIA/index.html?redirect=/clia/. Accessed 9 April 2015.
83. *FDASIA* Health IT Report. FDA website. http://www.fda.gov/aboutfda/centersoffices/officeofmedicalproductsandtobacco/cdrh/cdrhreports/ucm390588.htm. Accessed 9 April 2015.
84. Cell Phones. FDA website. http://www.fda.gov/Radiation-emittingProducts/RadiationEmittingProductsandProcedures/HomeBusinessandEntertainment/CellPhones/default.htm. Accessed 9 April 2015.
85. Food Safety. USDA website. http://www.usda.gov/wps/portal/ usda/usdahome?navid=food-safety. Accessed 9 April 2015.
86. FDA Facts, *Food Safety Modernization Act*. FDA website. http://www.fda.gov/downloads/NewsEvents/Newsroom/FactSheets/UCM305765.pdf. Accessed 9 April 2015.
87. Federal Food Safety Oversight: Food Safety Working Group Is a Positive First Step but Government-wide Planning Is Needed to Address Fragmentation, March 2011. GAO website. http://www.gao.gov/assets/320/316742.pdf. Accessed 9 April 2015.
88. Fact Sheets & Presentations. FDA website. http://www.fda.gov/Food/GuidanceRegulation/FSMA/ucm247546.htm. Accessed 9 April 2015.
89. Produce Safety Standards. FDA website. http://www.fda.gov/Food/GuidanceRegulation/FSMA/ucm304045.htm. Accessed 9 April 2015.
90. Emergency Use Authorizations. FDA website. http://www.fda.gov/MedicalDevices/Safety/EmergencySituations/ucm161496.htm. Accessed 9 April 2015.
91. National Infrastructure Protection Plan. FDA website. http://www.fda.gov/Food/FoodDefense/FoodDefensePrograms/ucm081281.htm. Accessed 9 April 2015.
92. Inspections, Compliance, Enforcement, and Criminal Investigations, Import Procedures. FDA website. http://www.fda.gov/ICECI/ComplianceManuals/RegulatoryProceduresManual/ucm179265.htm. Accessed 9 April 2015.
93. FDA and EPA issue draft updated advice for fish consumption, 10 June 2014. FDA website. http://www.fda.gov/NewsEvents/Newsroom/ PressAnnouncements/ucm397929.htm. Accessed 9 April 2015.
94. Pesticides Q&A. FDA website. http://www.fda.gov/food%20/foodborneillnesscontaminants/pesticides/ucm114958.htm. Accessed 9 April 2015.
95. *Poison Prevention Packaging Act*. CPSC website. http://www.cpsc.gov/en/Regulations-Laws--Standards/Statutes/Poison-Prevention-Packaging-Act/. Accessed 9 April 2015.
96. MOU 225-71-8003, Memorandum of Understanding Between the Federal Trade Commission and Food and Drug Administration. FDA website. http://www.fda.gov/AboutFDA/PartnershipsCollaborations/MemorandaofUnderstandingMOUs/DomesticMOUs/ucm115791.htm. Accessed 9 April 2015.
97. Gaffney A. In Midst of Crackdown, New Batch of FDA, FTC Warning Letters Target Unapproved Flu Products. RAPS website. 15 February 2013. http://www.raps.org/focus-online/news/news-article-view/article/2872/in-midst-of-crackdown-new-batch-of-fda-ftc-warning-letters-target-unapproved-fl.aspx. Accessed 9 April 2015.
98. Inspections, Compliance, Enforcement, and Criminal Investigations, Judicial Actions. FDA website. http://www.fda.gov/ICECI/ComplianceManuals/RegulatoryProceduresManual/ucm176710.htm. Accessed 9 April 2015.
99. Inspections, Compliance, Enforcement, and Criminal Investigations, Injunctions. FDA website. http://www.fda.gov/ICECI/ComplianceManuals/RegulatoryProceduresManual/ucm176734.htm. Accessed 9 April 2015.
100. Controlled Substances Schedule. DEA website. http://www.deadiversion.usdoj.gov/schedules/. Accessed 9 April 2015.
101. Schedules of Controlled Substances: Rescheduling of Hydrocodone Combination Products From Schedule III to Schedule II, Final Rule, 22 August 2014, 79 FR 49661. DEA website. http://www.deadiversion.usdoj.gov/fed_regs/rules/2014/fr0822.htm. Accessed 9 April 2015.
102. Timeline of Selected FDA Activities and Significant Events Addressing Opioid Misuse and Abuse. FDA website. http://www.fda.gov/Drugs/DrugSafety/InformationbyDrugClass/ucm338566.htm. Accessed 9 April 2015.
103. How can I better understand Patents and Exclusivity? FDA website. http://www.fda.gov/ForIndustry/FDABasicsforIndustry/ucm238582.htm. Accessed 9 April 2015.
104. Frequently Asked Questions on Patents and Exclusivity. FDA website. http://www.fda.gov/Drugs/DevelopmentApprovalProcess/ucm079031.htm. Accessed 9 April 2015.
105. Trademark, Patent, or Copyright? USPTO website. http://www.uspto.gov/trademarks/basics/definitions.jsp . Accessed 9 April 2015.
106. *Protecting Your Trademark*. USPTO website. http://www.uspto.gov/trademarks/basics/BasicFacts.pdf. Accessed 9 April 2015.
107. A Copyright Refresher. USPTO website. http://www.uspto.gov/web/offices/dcom/olia/copyright/copyrightrefresher.htm. Accessed 9 April 2015.
108. International Programs. FDA website. http://www.fda.gov/InternationalPrograms/. Accessed 9 April 2015.
109. Op cit 1.
110. Confidentiality Commitments. FDA website. http://www.fda.gov/InternationalPrograms/Agreements/ConfidentialityCommitments/default.htm. Accessed 9 April 2015.
111. Memoranda of Understanding and Other Cooperative Arrangements. FDA website. http://www.fda.gov/InternationalPrograms/Agreements/MemorandaofUnderstanding/default.htm. Accessed 9 April 2015.
112. CBER SOPP 8001.6: Procedures for Parallel Scientific Advice with European Medicines Agency (EMA). FDA website. http://www.fda.gov/biologicsbloodvaccines/guidancecomplianceregulatoryinformation/proceduressopps/ucm061218.htm. Accessed 9 April 2015.
113. FDA and European Medicines Agency strengthen collaboration in pharmacovigilance area, 19 February 2014. FDA website. http://www.fda.gov/NewsEvents/Newsroom/PressAnnouncements/ucm386372.htm. Accessed 9 April 2015.
114. FDA Launches SAFEKIDS Initiative with Academic and Clinical Partners, 13 March 2009. FDA website. http://www.fda.gov/NewsEvents/Newsroom/PressAnnouncements/ucm149543.htm . Accessed 9 April 2015.
115. Centers of Excellence in Regulatory Science and Innovation (CERSI). FDA website. http://www.fda.gov/ScienceResearch/SpecialTopics/RegulatoryScience/ucm301667.htm. Accessed 9 April 2015.
116. About the Patient Representative Program. FDA website. http://www.fda.gov/ForPatients/About/ucm412709.htm. Accessed April 9 2015.
117. For Federal, State, Local, Tribal, and Territorial Officials. FDA website. http://www.fda.gov/ForFederalStateandLocalOfficials/default.htm. Accessed 9 April 2015.

118. For Federal, State, Local, Tribal, and Territorial Officials, Food Protection Task Forces. FDA website. http://www.fda.gov/ForFederalStateandLocalOfficials/CooperativeAgreementsCRADAsGrants/ucm302069.htm . Accessed 9 April 2015.
119. For Federal, State, Local, Tribal, and Territorial Officials, Council of Association Presidents. FDA website. http://www.fda.gov/ForFederalStateandLocalOfficials/CommunicationbetweenFDAStateLocalandTribalOfficials/ucm250303.htm Accessed 9 April 2015.

Chapter 2

History of Food, Drug and Cosmetic Laws

Updated by Mujadala Abdul-Majid, MS, JD, RAC

OBJECTIVES

- ❑ Review differences between laws, regulations, guidance documents and other legal instruments affecting food, drugs and devices
- ❑ Provide an overview of laws, regulations and regulatory agencies governing food and medical products marketed in the US
- ❑ Discuss the historical context in which those laws and regulations were developed and enacted

LAWS, REGULATIONS AND GUIDELINES COVERED IN THIS CHAPTER

- ❑ *Pure Food and Drug Act* of 1906
- ❑ *Federal Food, Drug, and Cosmetic Act* of 1938
- ❑ *Durham-Humphrey Amendment* of 1951
- ❑ *Color Additive Amendment* of 1960
- ❑ *Kefauver-Harris Amendments* of 1962
- ❑ *Drug Price Competition and Patent Term Restoration Act* of 1984 (Hatch-Waxman Act)
- ❑ *Medical Device Amendments* of 1976
- ❑ *Safe Medical Devices Act* of 1990
- ❑ *Orphan Drug Act* of 1983
- ❑ *Medical Devices Amendments* of 1992
- ❑ *Prescription Drug User Fee Act* of 1992
- ❑ *Food and Drug Administration Modernization Act* of 1997
- ❑ *Medical Device User Fee and Modernization Act* of 2002
- ❑ *Food and Drug Administration Amendments Act* of 2007
- ❑ *Food Safety Modernization Act* of 2011
- ❑ *Food and Drug Administration Safety and Innovation Act* of 2012
- ❑ *Drug Quality and Security Act* of 2013

Introduction

To understand governance of food and medical products in the US, it is important to have some knowledge of legal instruments impacting drug law, the manner in which drug regulation is developed and the historical context in which food and drug laws have been established. Shifts in the food and drug regulatory paradigm often are reactions to shifts in political philosophies, economic concerns and the occurrence of significant public health events. This chapter discusses concerns and events that led to the introduction of new laws, and subsequent changes to those laws, affecting food and medical product governance.

Laws, Regulations and Guidance

In the US, federal statutes begin as bills introduced by the legislative branch. Once a member or members of Congress introduce a bill, it undergoes scrutiny in subject matter committees and public hearings may be held. Bills are subject to House and Senate votes. An approved bill then will be presented to the president who will either veto the bill or sign it into law. Statutes are published or said to be "codified" in the United States Code (U.S.C.), where they are organized by subject.

Executive agencies, such as the US Food and Drug Administration (FDA), are charged with implementing statutes through regulations. Regulations interpret laws and describe how they will be enforced. The process by which FDA proposes and establishes regulations is called rulemaking, governed by the *Administrative Procedures Act* of 1946 (*APA*). The *APA* requires agencies to keep the public informed and gives the public the right to participate in the rulemaking process by commenting on proposed rules. The public's rights were further extended through procedural rules that established a 60-day minimum public comment period for significant regulations. The enactment of the *Government in the Sunshine Act* of 1976 required both advanced notice of rulemaking meetings and those meetings to be open to the public. A regulatory agenda known as the Unified Agenda is published semi-annually and summarizes each agency's planned rulemaking activities for the following six months. New regulations or changes to existing regulations are announced in the *Federal Register*.

Guidance documents and guidelines may be used to convey FDA's current "thinking" or enforcement priorities to establish regulatory principles or practices aligned with that thinking. Guidance does not have the force of law and is not legally binding. FDA follows the procedures required by its "Good Guidance Practice" regulation (Title 21 CFR 10.115) to issue guidance.

Finally, as FDA continuously adjusts to the challenges of regulating products in a global economy, international laws and agreements play an increasing role in its activities to support its public health mission. Important international legal instruments include treaties and trade agreements. A treaty is a written agreement between sovereign states (or other international bodies) that dictates terms that will bind the parties to the agreement and become international law once the agreement is signed and ratified. A trade agreement establishes terms between parties regarding tariffs and trade restrictions. FDA monitors and negotiates international agreements, including inter-governmental agreements possibly affecting how the agency regulates its products.

Early Food and Drug Legislation

The history of modern food and drug law began in the 20th century. During the 1800s, food and drugs were largely unregulated due to concerns about government interference with free market trade and the inability of individual states to control sales of products manufactured in other states. This lack of regulation led to the use of food preservation ingredients with toxic or unknown safety profiles, and also led to unsanitary conditions in large-scale food processing plants. Public exposure of these conditions resulted in widespread outrage and a demand for legislation. In response to the demand, Congress passed the *Pure Food and Drug Act* in 1906.

Pure Food and Drug Act of 1906

In the early 1900s, concerns grew about the safety of chemicals added to food for preservation. In 1902, Harvey Wiley, the head of the Bureau of Chemistry, received federal funding to conduct studies on chemical substances used in food preservation. In the fall of 1902, he convened a group of 12 male subjects, known as the Poison Squad, to consume meals containing chemical substances with unknown health effects. In initial experiments, Borax (boric acid) was added to food in controlled settings; Wiley later extended his research to include salicylic acid, sulfuric acid, sodium benzoate and formaldehyde over the course of the five-year study.

Though the Poison Squad reported experiencing adverse effects following consumption of various tested substances, results from the laboratory analyses of fecal matter, perspiration and respiration were inconclusive. Wiley, however, continued his long-time efforts to lobby for oversight of food additives and maintained his stance that consumption of these chemicals had cumulative effects. As Wiley conducted his Poison Squad studies, investigative reports into the meat industry precipitated further support for the need to regulate the food industry. The Poison Squad studies and Wiley's activism garnered public attention for the regulation of certain food additives, laying the groundwork for US food regulation.

In 1904, Upton Sinclair, an author and member of the Socialist Party, ventured into Chicago's meat packing plants to investigate a strike undertaken by the meat packers' union. Sinclair later published a fictional novel based on his experiences in Chicago's Packingtown. His 1906 book, *The Jungle*, depicted a disturbing tale detailing not only grave working conditions for meat packers (primarily immigrants from Poland and Lithuania), but also describing unsanitary conditions in which meat sold for human consumption was prepared and packaged. Sinclair's book gained national attention as a best-seller, which brought further support for food industry regulation.

In response to public pressures, President Theodore Roosevelt appointed a special commission to investigate Chicago's meat-packing plants. The commission's report led the president to write to Congress declaring a need for a new law enabling the federal government to inspect and supervise meat preparation.

On 30 June 1906, both the *Meat Inspection Act* and the *Pure Food and Drug Act* were signed into law. The *Pure Food and Drug Act* prohibited misbranded and adulterated foods, drinks and drugs from entering interstate commerce. This act was the predecessor for the 1938 *Food, Drug, and Cosmetic Act* (*FD&C Act*). It was enforced by the Bureau of Chemistry in the Department of Agriculture, which became the Food and Drug Administration in 1930.

Sherley Amendment

On 13 May 1908, the Bureau of Chemistry seized a shipment of drugs intended for the District of Columbia from a company in Kansas City, MO. The shipment contained various packages of tablets and bottles to be used in combination for the treatment of cancer. The bureau analyzed package labels and determined the contents to be misbranded according to the *Pure Food and Drug Act*. The company's owner, O.J. Johnson, was prosecuted and convicted in the Western District of Missouri for committing six counts of willingly and knowingly violating provisions of the act by, among other things, including false and misleading statements on the drug's labeling for shipment into interstate commerce.

Johnson challenged his conviction, and in *United States v. Johnson* (1911), the Supreme Court issued a ruling against the government finding the product's claims for effectiveness were not within the scope of the *Pure Food and Drug Act*.

In response to the ruling, Congress enacted the *Sherley Amendment,* named for the legislation's sponsor, Representative Joseph Swagar Sherley. The amendment prohibited labeling medicines with false therapeutic claims intended to defraud the purchaser. The burden to prove intent to defraud remained with the government, providing easy mechanisms of defense; thus, for the next two decades, the government had little power to successfully prosecute alleged violators of the *Pure Food and Drug Act* until subsequent legislation removed this requirement.

The Federal Food, Drug, and Cosmetic Act of 1938

In 1933, shortly after Franklin Roosevelt was inaugurated, Walter Campbell, FDA's chief inspector, met with Roger Tugwell, assistant secretary of agriculture, to discuss shortcomings in food and drug regulation. Tugwell later introduced a bill to reform the 1906 Act. The "Tugwell Bill" introduced significant changes to FDA authority and was met with opposition from industry. Supporters of the bill spent the next few years altering the bill to get it to pass. During this time, a significant public health event occurred that signaled the need for greater controls.

In 1937, a chemist at a drug manufacturing company discovered sulfanilamide (a synthetic antibacterial drug originally manufactured as a tablet or injection to treat streptococcal infections) could be dissolved in diethylene glycol for oral administration as an elixir. Raspberry flavoring and red coloring were added to the product so the medication would be more appealing to children. Without undergoing safety testing, several hundred bottles of Elixir Sulfanilamide were distributed to pharmacies, and samples were sent to physician's offices.

In the fall of 1937, 71 adults and 34 children died after ingesting Elixir Sulfanilamide. The drug was recalled, and FDA inspected the drug maker; however, the agency had little authority to take action. An Oklahoma mother, whose daughter died nine days after taking Elixir Sulfanilamide, wrote a letter to President Roosevelt, which garnered significant public attention and galvanized the passage of pending legislation for drug regulation reform.

On 28 June 1938, President Roosevelt signed the *FD&C Act* into law. This new law included the following significant changes: manufacturers were required to provide scientific proof new drugs were safe for their intended use before being placed on the market; cosmetics and medical devices were regulated for the first time; the *Sherley Amendment* was removed (proof of intent to defraud no longer was required to stop false drug claims for drugs); adding poisonous substances to foods was prohibited except where unavoidable or required in production; and FDA was given authority to bring federal court injunctions, in addition to product seizures and criminal prosecutions, for violations of the *FD&C Act.*

Expansion of FDA Authority and Amendments to the FD&C Act up to the 21st Century

Public Health Service Act of 1944

In 1944, President Roosevelt signed the *Public Health Service Act* (*PHS Act*) into law. The *PHS Act* did not amend the *FD&C Act*; however, it gave FDA authority over biological products such as vaccines and serums. The *PHS Act* includes provisions for licensing new biological products through an application process.

Durham-Humphrey Amendment

Signed into law in 1951, the Durham-Humphrey Amendment clarified what constituted a prescription versus an over-the-counter drug. The amendment required any habit-forming or potentially harmful drug to be dispensed under the supervision of a health practitioner as a prescription drug. Such drugs also must carry the statement "Caution: Federal law prohibits dispensing without prescription."

Food Additives Amendment

The *FD&C Act* established criteria for food to be considered adulterated, mislabeled or harmful; however, the onus remained on the agency to demonstrate a food product was "unsafe." The act also included a requirement for "truthful" food additive labeling.

In 1958, the *Food Additives Amendment* was enacted to delineate substances added to food products generally recognized as safe (GRAS) and substances that may affect food characteristics that were not GRAS and required marketing approval. Marketing approval requires the manufacturer to prove a product is safe for human consumption.

Kefauver-Harris Amendment

In 1957, a pharmaceutical company in West Germany began marketing a patented drug containing thalidomide as its active ingredient to treat nausea and morning sickness in pregnant women. As a result of exposure to the drug in the womb, several thousand infants were born with physical defects or malformations. The most prevalent of these was phocomelia, a congenital disorder where long limbs do not form or are truncated.

By 1960, thalidomide was marketed in 46 countries, and the drugmaker had submitted an application to market the drug in the US. The application was reviewed by Frances Kelsey who, despite pressures from the drug maker, would not grant approval due to concerns over the drug's safety profile. Kelsey requested additional evidence to demonstrate the drug was safe for pregnant women. While the application was pending in the US, an Australian obstetrician, William McBride, began to associate thalidomide with severe birth defects, and eventually the German press began to report on the drug's harmful effects. By March 1962, the drug was banned in most countries where it previously had been sold.

Frances Kelsey was heralded by President John F. Kennedy and an American public that likely felt indebted to her for her role in diverting the damaging impact thalidomide caused in jurisdictions where the drug had been marketed. The tragedy surrounding thalidomide also motivated profound changes in drug approval requirements.

In the late 1950s, Senator Estes Kefauver held hearings on administered prices in the drug industry. Concerns had precipitated around price gouging in the pharmaceutical industry and, among those concerns, was the affect unsubstantiated advertising claims bore on the integrity of marketed drugs. Following the hearings, Senator Kefauver introduced a bill some considered to be sweeping reform. The bill focused on intellectual property issues in drug innovation and follow-on therapeutics. It also focused on standards for efficacy claims and proposed granting FDA power to demand proof of efficacy—in the form of "adequate and well-controlled investigations"—before approving a new drug for the US market. The bill was met with industry opposition, and was not supported by President Kennedy's Administration, which introduced an alternate bill in 1962. Kefauver's proposed legislation stalled until the thalidomide incident highlighted the need for significant drug safety reforms. In response, Congress enacted a compromised version of the legislation in the *Kefauver-Harris Amendment* to address standards for both safety and efficacy before a drug may be marketed in the US.

Medical Device Amendments

In 1938, when the *FD&C Act* was approved, medical devices were simple instruments such as scalpels and stethoscopes. While premarket approval did not apply to devices for regulatory purposes, the law equated them to drugs in every other sense. In the post-World War II years, however, a technology boom resulted in an increase in complexity and number of medical devices, including products such as heart-lung machines and dialysis equipment. In 1970, the Cooper Commission determined more than 700 deaths and 10,000 injuries were associated with medical devices. Among those, 512 deaths and injuries were attributed to heart valves, 89 deaths and 186 injuries were tied to heart pacemakers and 10 deaths and 8,000 injuries were attributed to intrauterine devices. As a result of the Cooper Report, Congress passed the 1976 *Medical Device Amendments* to the *FD&C Act*. This legislation established three classes of medical devices, each requiring a different level of regulatory scrutiny, up to premarket approval. The three classes were based on the degree of control necessary to ensure devices were safe and effective. The amendments also made provisions for device listing, establishment registration and adherence to Good Manufacturing Practices.

Orphan Drug Act of 1983

The 1983 *Orphan Drug Act* originally defined the term "orphan drug" as "a drug for a disease or condition which is rare." In October 1984, the term "rare" was defined in an amendment as "any rare disease or condition which (a) affects less than 200,000 persons in the U.S. or (b) affects more than 200,000 persons in the U.S. but for which there is no reasonable expectation that the cost of developing and making available in the U.S. a drug for such disease or condition will be recovered from sales in the U.S. of such drug." The act guarantees an orphan product developer seven years of market exclusivity following FDA's approval of the product. Incentives also include tax credits for clinical research undertaken by a sponsor to generate data required for marketing approval.

Safe Medical Devices Act of 1990 and Medical Device Amendments of 1992

Under the *Safe Medical Devices Act* of 1990 (*SMDA*), device user facilities must report device-related deaths to FDA and the manufacturer, if known. Device user facilities also must report device-related serious injuries to the manufacturer, or to FDA, if the manufacturer is not known. In addition, *SMDA* required device user facilities to submit to FDA, on a semiannual basis, a summary of all reports submitted during that time period. The device user facility reporting section of *SMDA* became effective 28 November 1991.

SMDA defined a "medical device" as "any instrument, apparatus, or other article that is used to prevent, diagnose, mitigate, or treat a disease or to affect the structure or function of the body, with the exception of drugs." It instituted device tracking, postmarket surveillance requirements and allowed FDA to temporarily suspend or withdraw approval of premarket approval applications. The rule provided civil penalties for violation of an *FD&C Act* requirement relating to devices. The act amended the *FD&C* Act to create an incentive for developing orphan or humanitarian use devices, defined as devices for use in the treatment or diagnosis of diseases or conditions affecting fewer than 4,000 patients in the US annually.

The primary impact of the 1992 *Medical Device Amendments* was to clarify certain terms and establish a single reporting standard for device user facilities, manufacturers, importers and distributors.

Drug Price Competition and Patent Term Restoration Act of 1984

Because the approval process for each new product required submission of full safety and efficacy data, economic pressures resulting from the lengthy review process led to the *Drug Price Competition and Patent Restoration Act* of 1984, also known as the *Hatch-Waxman Act*. This law established a process for approving drugs based on comparison to an already approved product and provided for exclusive marketing status for a period of time based on the length of the approval process for new drugs or the patent status of the branded drug for generics.

This act included provisions for patent term extension, which gave certain patent holders opportunity to extend patent terms by five years for human drug products, including antibiotics and biologics, medical devices, food additives and color additives. By giving inventors a portion of the patent term lost during federal regulatory review, Congress sought to restore some of the incentive for innovation to US domestic drug companies as federal premarket approval requirements became more expensive and time-consuming. The *Hatch-Waxman Act* authorized Abbreviated New Drug Applications (ANDAs) for generic drugs and specifically provided that FDA could require only bioavailability studies for ANDAs.

PDUFA, Reauthorizations and Expansion of User Fees

The *Prescription Drug User Fee Act* (*PDUFA I*) was first enacted in 1992 and authorized FDA to collect user fees from companies submitting applications to FDA for certain human drug and biological products. In addition, companies were required to pay annual fees for each manufacturing establishment and each prescription drug product marketed. Previously, taxpayers paid for product reviews through budgets provided by Congress. In this program, industry provides the funding in exchange for FDA's agreement to meet drug review performance goals, which emphasize timeliness.

The user fee concept under *PDUFA* later expanded to other product categories under FDA. In 2002, the *Medical Device User Fee and Modernization Act* (*MDUFMA*) required medical device companies to pay fees to FDA. In 2012, the *Food and Drug Administration Safety Innovation Act* (*FDASIA*) extended FDA authority to collect user fees from the generic drugs and biologics industries.

User fees are subject to reauthorization by Congress every five years. *PDUFA III* and *MDUFA II* were reauthorized under the *Food and Drug Administration Amendments Act* in 2007 and again as *PDUFA V* and *MDUFA III* under *FDASIA* in 2012.

Food and Drug Modernization Act of 1997

The Food and Drug Modernization Act of 1997 (*FDAMA*) provided additional authority for monitoring progress of drug and biologic postmarketing studies, requiring FDA to issue regulations allowing clinical study sponsors to modify any investigational device or study protocol by submitting a "Notice of Change" five days after instituting such a change, where such changes did not affect study design or patient safety significantly. The law codified the expedited review policy for certain medical devices, amended and clarified the humanitarian device provisions of *SMDA* and allowed FDA to recognize international or other national standards. *FDAMA* also directed FDA to consider the least-burdensome means of establishing substantial equivalence for certain device marketing applications. The act repealed mandatory tracking requirements for some high-risk devices imposed by *SMDA*, and instead established requirements and a process under which FDA may order device tracking.

Supply Chain Globalization and Amendments to the FD&C Act in the 21st Century

The advent of the ease of access to raw materials, goods, services and human resources through e-commerce has facilitated increasingly global food, drug and device supply chains, but not without challenges. FDA is tasked with monitoring manufacturers' compliance with programs to ensure the safety of products they place on the market. For example, tracking and tracing a drug product from its release point to its destination is important to protect against diversion, counterfeit drugs gaining market access and product quality during transport. The ability to recall items quickly for product quality safety issues is another concern. This can be challenging, particularly when a problem occurs due to materials sourced from complex networks of upstream suppliers. Challenges of a global supply chain have been the premise of much of the recent legislative changes enacted.

Food Safety Modernization Act of 2011

Food-borne illnesses due to contaminated food products have a significant impact on healthcare costs in the US each year. For example, Salmonella infection causes more hospitalizations and deaths than any other type of germ found in food. One challenging aspect of regulating food in the 21st century is the difficulty in establishing traceability in a highly technological and complex global food supply chain. To address the negative impact contaminated foods have on public health, legislation on US food supply safety has focused on the need for federal regulators to shift their priorities from responding to contamination to prevention.

The *Food Safety Modernization Act* (*FSMA*)became law on 4 January 2011 and was noted by FDA as the most sweeping reform to US food safety law in 70 years. The law provided FDA with new enforcement authorities designed to achieve higher rates of compliance with prevention- and risk-based food safety standards and new tools to respond to and contain problems when they occur. For the first time, FDA had a legislative mandate to require comprehensive, science-based preventive controls across the food supply chain. The law also gave FDA new tools to hold imported foods to the same standards as domestic foods and directed the agency to build an integrated national food safety system in partnership with state and local authorities.

Food and Drug Administration Safety and Innovation Act

The *Food and Drug Administration Safety and Innovation Act* (*FDASIA*) became law on 9 July, 2012 and became effective on 1 October 2012. It is the first major FDA legislation since the *Food and Drug Administration Amendments Act* was enacted in 2007.

Under *FDASIA*, existing user fees were reauthorized, and FDA was given authority to collect user fees to fund reviews of generics and biosimilar biologics. While House negotiations behind the legislation were focused primarily on new user fee programs under Titles III and IV, *FDASIA* ushered in several other significant changes in eleven titles under the act, such as creation of new programs to gain timely access to medicines, reporting requirements to avoid drug shortages and creation of a new drug supply chain control requirement under Title VII. For example, under Title VII, Section 711, quality manufacturing standards now include "managing the risk and establishing the safety of raw materials, materials used in the manufacturing of pharmaceuticals, and finished drug products." Thus, suppliers become part of the quality management system, and if a pharmaceutical company does not establish adequate controls over raw materials and components, its products may be deemed "adulterated."

Table 2-1. Other Laws, Regulations and Guidelines

• *Federal Meat Inspection Act* of 1906
• *Poultry Products Inspection Act* of 1957
• *Egg Products Act* of 1970
• *Dietary Supplement Health and Education Act* of 1994
• GMPs for the 21st Century (2004)
• *Wheeler-Lea Act* of 1938
• *Fair Packaging and Labeling Act* of 1967
• *Animal Drug Amendments* of 1968
• *Poison Prevention Packaging Act* of 1970
• *Infant Formula Act* of 1980
• *Generic Animal Drug and Patent Term Restoration Act* of 1988
• *Animal Medicinal Drug Use Clarification Act* of 1994
• *Food Quality Protection Act* of 1996
• *Animal Drug Availability Act* of 1996
• *Best Pharmaceuticals for Children Act* of 2002
• *Animal Drug User Fee Act* of 2003
• *Minor Use and Minor Species Animal Health Act* of 2001
• *Dietary Supplement and Nonprescription Drug Consumer Protection Act* of 2006
• *Food and Drug Administration Amendments Act* of 2007
• *Family Smoking Prevention and Tobacco Control Act* of 2009
• *Biologics Price Competition and Innovation Act* of 2010

Drug Quality and Security Act

The 2013 *Drug Quality and Security Act* (*DQSA*) contains two titles; Title I addresses pharmacy compounding and Title II addresses supply chain security. Title I of *DQSA*, also called the *Compounding Quality Act*, is a legislative response to a fungal meningitis outbreak that began in 2012 when approximately 14,000 patients received doses of contaminated lots of methylprednisolone administered by epidural injection into the spine. The lots were packaged and marketed by a small compounding pharmacy in Farmingham, MA. By 10 March 2013, 48 people had died, and 720 were being treated for persistent fungal infections.

The outbreak sparked a congressional investigation into compounding pharmacy practices, which led to significant concerns over sterile drug processing in unsanitary conditions. *DQSA* adds a new section, 503B, to the *FD&C Act* creating a new entity category called an outsourcing facility. An outsourcing facility is distinct from a traditional pharmacy and is granted certain exemptions from having to obtain drug approval and include adequate directions for use on the drug label under the *FD&C Act*, provided it meets certain other criteria, such as compliance with current Good Manufacturing Practices (CGMPs). Outsourcing facilities are not required to obtain patient-specific prescriptions to sell compounded products, although they are restricted from wholesaling.

DQSA also amends the existing Section 503A of the *FD&C Act*, under which compounded human drug products may be exempt from certain requirements of the act, including compliance with CGMPs, labeling with adequate directions for use and FDA approval prior to marketing, as long as certain condition are met. One such condition is the requirement to obtain patient-specific prescriptions for compounded drugs.

The legislation also removes a provision under Section 503A concerning commercial speech regulation. Removal of this provision is the result of a long-standing debate over severability and applicability of provisions under the section after the Supreme Court ruled in *Thomspson v. Western States Medical Center* (2002) that the provision restricting certain commercial speech under section 503A violated the First Amendment.

Title II of the *DQSA*, also called the *Drug Supply Chain Security Act*, adds a mandate to implement an electronic track and trace system to identify and trace certain prescription drugs throughout the US supply chain.

Other Food and Drug-Related Laws

More information about the laws enforced by FDA can be obtained at www.fda.gov/RegulatoryInformation/Legislation/default.htm.

While the discussion above covers many of the laws forming the basis of current regulations, many others affect foods, drugs and medical devices. **Table 2-1** lists some of these other laws.

Summary

Food and drug law, which provides a framework for regulatory practices, is closely linked to the larger historical context of the times in which the laws were enacted. Many laws, such as the *FD&C Act*, the *Kefauver-Harris Amendments* and *DQSA*, were enacted in response to specific events calling attention to the need for additional authorities or controls. Based on this history, it is likely future such events will continue to shape food and drug law and regulation.

Chapter 3

Overview of Drug, Biologic and Device Regulatory Pathways

Updated by Meredith Brown-Tuttle, RAC

OBJECTIVES

- To provide an overview of US federal regulations and processes related to the development of drugs, biologics, devices and combination products and filing of a marketing application
- To provide an overview of the scientific questions and approaches that underpin the development process
- To provide a roadmap of the facts and related decisions that define how a drug, biologic, device or combination product needs to be developed to meet US federal regulations

LAWS, REGULATIONS AND GUIDELINES COVERED IN THIS CHAPTER

- *Biologics Control Act* (1902)
- *Food and Drugs Act* (1906)
- *Federal Food, Drug, and Cosmetic Act* (*FD&C Act*; 1938, as amended)
- *Kefauver-Harris Drug Amendments to the FD&C* (1962)
- *Medical Device Amendments* (1976)
- *Orphan Drug Act* (1983)
- *Drug Price Competition and Patent Term Restoration Act* (i.e. *Hatch-Waxman Act*; 1984)
- *Safe Medical Device Act* (1990)
- *The Prescription Drug User Fee Act* (*PDUFA*; 1992; re-authorized 5 times)
- *Food and Drug Administration Modernization Act* (*FDAMA*, 1997)
- *Dietary Supplement Health and Education Act* (*DSHEA*, 1994)
- *Food and Drug Administration Amendments Act* (*FDAAA*; 2007)
- *Patient Protection and Affordable Care Act* (contains a subtitle called the *Biologics Price Competition and Innovation Act* (*BPCI Act*; 2009)
- *Food and Drug Administration Safety and Innovation Act* (*FDASIA*; January 2012)
- 21 CFR 314.92 Drug products for which abbreviated applications may be submitted
- 21 CFR 314.93 Petition to request a change from a listed drug
- 21 CFR 314.54 Procedure for submission of an application requiring investigations for approval of a new indication for, or other change from, a listed drug

- ❑ 21 CFR 310.3 Definitions and interpretations (new drugs)
- ❑ 21 CFR 316 Orphan Drugs
- ❑ 21 CFR 312 Subpart E Drugs intended to treat life-threatening and severely debilitating illnesses
- ❑ 21 CFR 314 Subpart H Accelerated approval of new drugs for serious or life-threatening illnesses
- ❑ 21 CFR 312 Investigational New Drug Application
- ❑ 21 CFR 312.50 General responsibilities of sponsors
- ❑ 21 CFR 312.60 General responsibilities of investigators
- ❑ 21 CFR 312.33 Annual reports (IND)
- ❑ 21 CFR 312.32 IND safety reports
- ❑ 21 CFR 312.23 IND content and format
- ❑ 21 CFR 312.38 Withdrawal of an IND
- ❑ 21 CFR 312.45 Inactive status (IND)
- ❑ 21 CFR 314 Applications for FDA Approval to Market a New Drug
- ❑ 21 CFR 207 Registration of Producers of Drugs and Listing of Drugs in Commercial Distribution
- ❑ 21 CFR 190.6 Requirement for premarket notification (dietary supplements)
- ❑ 21 CFR 3.2(e) Assignment of agency component for review of premarket applications—Definitions
- ❑ 21 CFR 328–358 OTC Monographs
- ❑ 21 CFR 330.11 NDA deviations from applicable monograph (OTC drugs)
- ❑ 21 CFR 10.30 Citizen petition
- ❑ 21 CFR 862–892 Device Classifications
- ❑ 21 CFR 807 Subpart E Premarket notification procedures
- ❑ 21 CFR 812 Investigational Device Exemptions
- ❑ 21 CFR 814 Subpart H Humanitarian use devices
- ❑ 21 CFR 56 Institutional Review Boards
- ❑ 21 CFR 50 Protection of Human Subjects
- ❑ 21 CFR 54 Financial Disclosure by Clinical Investigators
- ❑ 21 CFR 814 Premarket Approval of Medical Devices
- ❑ 21 CFR 807 Establishment Registration and Device Listing for Manufacturers and Initial Importers of Devices
- ❑ *Guidance for Industry: Bioavailability and Bioequivalence Studies Submitted in NDAs or INDs—General Considerations (March 2014) Guidance for Industry: Food-Effect Bioavailability and Fed Bioequivalence Studies* (December 2002)
- ❑ *Bioavailability and Bioequivalence Studies Submitted in NDAs or INDs—General Considerations (March 2014)Guidance for Industry: Statistical Approaches to Establishing Bioequivalence* (January 2001)
- ❑ *Guidance for Industry: 180-Day Exclusivity When Multiple ANDAs are Submitted on the Same Day* (July 2003)
- ❑ *Guidance for Industry: Bioequivalence Recommendations for Specific Products* (June 2010)
- ❑ *Guidance for Industry: Contents of a Complete Submission for the Evaluation of Proprietary Names* (February 2010)
- ❑ *Guidance for Industry: Formal Meetings Between the FDA and Sponsors or Applicants of PDUFA Products* (March 2015)
- ❑ *Guidance for Industry: End-of-Phase 2A Meetings* (September 2009)

- ❑ *Guidance for Industry: Special Protocol Assessment* (May 2002)
- ❑ *Guidance for Industry: Expedited Programs for Serious Conditions—Drugs and Biologics* (May 2014)
- ❑ *Guidance for Industry M4: Organization of the CTD* (August 2001)
- ❑ *Guidance for Industry M4Q: The CTD—Quality* (August 2001)
- ❑ *Guidance for Industry M4S: The CTD—Safety* (August 2001)
- ❑ *Guidance for Industry M4S: The CTD—Safety Appendices* (August 2001)
- ❑ *Guidance for Industry M4E: The CTD—Efficacy* (August 2001)
- ❑ *Guidance for Industry M2 eCTD: Electronic Common Technical Document Specification* (April 2003)
- ❑ *Draft Guidance for Industry: Product Development Under the Animal Rule* (May 2014)
- ❑ *Guidance for Industry: Estimating the Maximum Safe Starting Dose in Initial Clinical Trials for Therapeutics in Adult Healthy Volunteers* (July 2005)
- ❑ *Guidance for Industry: M3(R2) Nonclinical Safety Studies for the Conduct of Human Clinical Trials and Marketing Authorization for Pharmaceuticals* (January 2010)
- ❑ *Guidance for Industry: M3(R2) Nonclinical Safety Studies for the Conduct of Human Clinical Trials and Marketing Authorization for Pharmaceuticals - Questions and Answers(R2)* (February 2013)
- ❑ *Guidance for Industry: Immunotoxicology Evaluation of Investigational New Drugs* (October 2002)
- ❑ *Guidance for Industry: Nonclinical Evaluation of Pediatric Drug Products* (February 2006)
- ❑ *Guidance for Industry: Single Dose Acute Toxicity Testing for Pharmaceuticals* (August 1996)
- ❑ *Guidance for Industry: Dissolution Testing of Immediate Release Solid Oral Dosage Forms* (August 1997)
- ❑ *Guidance for Industry: cGMP for Phase 1 Investigational Drugs* (July 2008)
- ❑ *Draft Guidance for Industry: Analytical Procedures and Methods Validation for Drugs and Biologics* (February 2014)
- ❑ *Guidance for Industry: Collection of Race and Ethnicity Data in Clinical Trials* (September 2005)
- ❑ *Guidance for Industry: Exposure-Response Relationships—Study Design, Data Analysis, and Regulatory Applications* (April 2003)
- ❑ *Guidance for Industry: Drug-Induced Liver Injury: Premarketing Clinical Evaluation* (July 2009)
- ❑ *Guidance for Industry: S1C(R2) Dose Selection for Carcinogenicity Studies* (September 2008)
- ❑ *Draft Guidance for Industry: Drug Interaction Studies—Study Design, Data Analysis, Implications for Dosing and Labeling Recommendations* (February 2012)
- ❑ *Guidance for Industry: Pharmacokinetics in Patients with Impaired Hepatic Function: Study Design, Data Analysis, and Impact on Dosing and Labeling* (May 2003)
- ❑ *Guidance for Industry: Pharmacokinetics in Patients with Impaired Renal Function: Study Design, Data Analysis, and Impact on Dosing and Labeling* (May 2010)
- ❑ *Guidance for Industry: E7 Studies in Support of Special Populations: Geriatrics* (August 1994)
- ❑ *Guidance for Industry: E7 Studies in Support of Special Populations: Geriatrics—Questions and Answers* (February 2012)
- ❑ *Draft Guidance for Industry: How to Comply with the Pediatric Research Equity Act* (September 2005)
- ❑ *Guidance for Industry and Investigators—Safety Reporting Requirements for INDs and BA/BE Studies* (December 2012)

- *Guidance for Industry: E2F Development Safety Update Report* (August 2011)
- *Draft Guidance for Industry and Review Staff: Target Product Profile—A Strategic Development Process Tool* (March 2007)
- *Guidance for Industry: Guideline for the Format and Content of the Nonclinical Pharmacology/Toxicology Section of an Application* (February 1987)
- *Guidance for Industry: Reproductive and Developmental Toxicities—Integrating Study Results to Assess Concerns* (September 2011)
- *Guidance for Industry and Review Staff: Recommended Approaches to Integration of Genetic Toxicology Study Results* (January 2006)
- *Draft Guidance for Industry: Statistical Aspects of the Design, Analysis, and Interpretation of Chronic Rodent Carcinogenicity Studies of Pharmaceuticals* (May 2001)
- *Guideline for the Format and Content of the Clinical and Statistical Sections of an Application* (July 1988)
- *Draft Guidance for Industry: Integrated Summary of Effectiveness* (August 2008)
- *Guidance for Industry: Premarketing Risk Assessment* (March 2005)
- *Guidance for Industry: Development and Use of Risk Minimization Action Plans* (March 2005)
- *Guidance for Industry: Good Pharmacovigilance Practices and Pharmacoepidemiologic Assessment* (March 2005)
- *Guidance for Industry: Submitting Separate Marketing Applications and Clinical Data for Purposes of Assessing User Fees* (December 2004)
- *Guidance for Industry: Standards for Securing the Drug Supply Chain—Standardized Numerical Identification for Prescription Drug Packages* (March 2010)
- *Guidance for Providing Regulatory Submissions in Electronic Format—Drug Establishment Registration and Drug Listing* (May 2009)
- *Providing Regulatory Submissions in Electronic Format—Certain Human Pharmaceutical Product Applications and Related Submissions Using the eCTD Specifications* (May 2015)
- *Draft Guidance for Industry: Applications Covered by Section 505(b)(2)* (October 1999)
- *Guidance for Industry: Structure/Function Claims Small Entity Compliance Guide* (January 2002)
- *The New 510(k) Paradigm—Alternate Approaches to Demonstrating Substantial Equivalence in Premarket Notifications—Final Guidance* (March 1998)
- MAPP 6020.5: *Good Review Practice: OND Review Management of INDs and NDAs for Nonprescription Drug Products* (July 2007)
- *Guidance for Industry: How to Write a Request for Designation (RFD)* (April 2011)
- *Draft Guidance for Industry and FDA Staff: Classification of Products as Drugs and Devices & Additional Product Classification Issues* (June 2011)
- *Guidance for Industry: Nonclinical Safety Evaluation of Drug or Biologic Combinations* (March 2006)
- *Guidance for Industry Best Practices in Developing Proprietary Names for Drugs* (May 2014)

Introduction

The development of drugs, biologics and devices in the modern era is a scientific process (hypothesis testing and the recognition and control of dependent and independent variables) in the context of objective and subjective interpretations of a product's potential or actual risks and benefits. The scope, interpretation and application of US federal regulations that must be met to market a drug, biologic or device have evolved over the past century (generally in a reactive fashion, see Chapter 2 History of Food, Drug and Cosmetic Laws) and are documented in the Code of Federal Regulations (CFR). In practice, this translates into agency use of scientific review, standards, manufacturing and other inspections, advertising controls, conditional approvals, laboratory product testing and postmarketing pharmacovigilance activities. In the last quarter century, a plethora of US Food and Drug Administration (FDA) and International Conference on Harmonisation (ICH) guidelines have been issued to assist the regulatory professional in interpreting and defining the processes needed to develop drugs and devices successfully for marketing in a regulated industry. Although usually not enforceable as regulations, FDA guidelines (usually, draft versions are available for public comment before finalization) provide an understanding of the agency's current thinking on any given topic.

This chapter provides an overview of the development and approval process for prescription drug, biologic, device and combination products in an environment regulated by the US government. Other chapters in this book provide details regarding many of the development and approval aspects touched on in this chapter. The purpose of this chapter is to tie the various topics together to provide a development context and roadmap.

Regulatory professionals must understand where regulations originate and how they are organized and updated. The difference between a law and a regulation is sometimes misunderstood. Only Congress can enact laws ("acts" of Congress). Federal executive departments and agencies such as FDA write the regulations to implement the authority of laws. The US Code (USC) is the official compilation of codified laws by subject, while the CFR is the official compilation of regulations. The CFR is updated annually (on 1 April for food and drugs—Title 21) while the *Federal Register* is the daily supplement to the CFR. Thus, these two publications should be used together to find the latest version of a regulation. The original *Federal Food, Drug, and Cosmetic Act* of 1938 (*FD&C Act*) and its many subsequent amendments constitute the basic food and drug law of the US. A current version of this act can be found at www.fda.gov/RegulatoryInformation/Legislation/FederalFoodDrugandCosmeticActFDCAct/default.htm.

The CFR is divided into 50 titles that represent broad subject areas. Each title is divided into chapters, which usually bear the name of the issuing agency. Each chapter is further subdivided into parts that cover specific regulatory areas. Large parts may be subdivided into subparts. Finally, parts are divided into sections. Thus, the order for citations is: Title, CFR, Part, Section. For drugs and devices, Title 21 (Food and Drugs), and Chapter 1 (Food and Drug Administration) are the most relevant. There are 1,499 parts in Title 21 with the most applicable summarized in **Table 3-1**.

The CFR is accessible online, and the following FDA website is a convenient CFR research point for drugs and devices www.accessdata.fda.gov/scripts/cdrh/cfdocs/cfcfr/CFRSearch.cfm. The full CFR can be found and searched at http://www.ecfr.gov/cgi-bin/ECFR?page=browse.

Table 3-1. 21 CFR Parts Most Relevant to Drug and Device Development

21 CFR Parts	General Topics
1–100	Administrative Issues and Protection of Human Subjects
100s	Foods (not covered in this chapter except for dietary supplements)
200s	Labeling, CGMPs, Controlled Substances
300s	Drugs for Human Use
500s	Drugs for Animal Use
600s	Biologics
700s	Cosmetics (not covered in this chapter)
800s	Medical Devices
1000s–1400s	Contain many miscellaneous topics, but 1270 Human Tissues Intended for Transplantation and 1271 Human Cells, Tissues and Tissue-Based Products are relevant

Although this book and the current chapter describe drug, biologic and device development and approval processes in the US, modern drug development is becoming more and more globalized. Hence, in any development program, consideration should be given to the impact of regulations in other world regions (for example, the usual requirement for a positive control in safety and efficacy trials of drugs in the EU).

Finally, this chapter touches on aspects of drug, biologic and device development to explain the relationships between different technical areas. Because chemistry, manufacturing and controls (CMC) relative to drugs and biologics and Quality System Regulations (QSR) for devices involve a number of unique issues, they are covered in detail in other chapters (including Good Manufacturing Practices (GMPs) and Quality Systems), this aspect of drug development is not emphasized in this chapter.

Overview of FDA

FDA regulates more than 150,000 marketed drugs and medical devices. At any time, more than 3,000 investigational new drugs are being developed. Organizationally, FDA is part of the Public Health Service (PHS) within the Department of Health and Human Services (DHHS). PHS also oversees the Centers for Disease Control and Prevention (CDC), the National Institutes of Health (NIH) and other agencies.

The workload described above is distributed primarily across three centers and the numerous regional field offices within FDA's Office of Medical Products and Tobacco. Chapter 1 describes the primary centers and offices involved in drug and device development pathways. Since 1977, FDA centers have issued numerous guidances to increase the transparency of the development process and help move products through the process more rapidly. More recently, the Center for Drug Evaluation and Research (CDER) has developed a system of manuals of policies and procedures (MAPPs), which are written statements issued by CDER management to prescribe policies, responsibilities or procedures for the conduct of the center's work or daily operations. MAPP 4000.1—Developing and Issuing Manuals of Policies and Procedures (updated most recently in 2011) describes the guidance development process. All MAPPs can be accessed at www.fda.gov/AboutFDA/CentersOffices/CDER/ManualofPoliciesProcedures/default.htm. Several MAPPs regarding agency review processes are useful in understanding how FDA staff will use information from sponsors to make regulatory decisions and can help sponsors prepare more reviewer-friendly documents. The Center for Biologics Evaluation and Research (CBER) has a similar system, termed manuals of standard operating procedures and policies (SOPPs) (http://www.fda.gov/BiologicsBloodVaccines/GuidanceComplianceRegulatoryInformation/ProceduresSOPPs/default.htm).

Figure 3-1 shows the decision tree regarding which regulations and FDA center or office will primarily govern development and approval of any given drug, device or combination product. Because the purpose of this flow diagram is to provide a simple overview for situations that require FDA premarket review, some complexities, such as the distinction between drugs and biologics and the development of combination products, OTC drugs and dietary supplements, are not highlighted but are addressed in the text of this chapter.

Biologics and the Biologics License Application (BLA) (Public Health Service Act (PHS Act))

Biological products, or biologics, are medical products. Many biologics are made from a variety of natural sources (human, animal or microorganism). Like drugs, some biologics are intended to treat diseases and medical conditions. Other biologics are used to prevent or diagnose diseases. Examples of biological products include:

- vaccines
- blood and blood products for transfusion and/or manufacturing into other products
- allergenic extracts, which are used for both diagnosis and treatment (e.g., allergy shots)
- human cells and tissues used for transplantation (e.g., tendons, ligaments and bone)
- gene therapies
- cellular therapies
- tests to screen potential blood donors for infectious agents such as HIV

The Biologics License Application (BLA) is a request for permission to introduce, or deliver for introduction, a biologic product into interstate commerce (21 CFR 601.2). The BLA is regulated under 21 CFR 600 – 680 and is similar in content and structure to a New Drug Application (NDA) (see below).

The distinction between a drug and a biologic is based primarily on historic issues. After the St. Louis tetanus contamination due to infected serum and smaller occurrences of contaminated smallpox vaccine and diphtheria antitoxin, Congress passed the *Virus Serum and Toxin Act* (also known as the *Biologics Control Act*) in 1902. The act authorized the Hygienic Laboratory of the Public Health and Marine Hospital Service (which eventually became PHS) to issue regulations governing all aspects of commercial production of vaccines, serums, toxins, antitoxin and similar products with the objective of ensuring their safety, purity and potency. In 1934, the Hygienic Laboratory (renamed NIH in 1930 by the *Ransdell Act*) issued a regulation stating that licenses to manufacture new biologics would not be granted without evidence that the products were effective. The *Public Health Service Act* of 1944 (*PHS Act*) saw the reorganization of PHS, giving NIH the authority to license, research and develop new biological products. Hence, one of the primary historical differences between biologics and drugs has been the inherent government research component of biologics as opposed to emphasis on sponsor testing and regulation for drugs.[1] In addition, because biologics are derived from living organisms, immunogenicity issues and how they are addressed in nonclinical and clinical studies often distinguish them from small-molecule drugs.

In 1972, the Division of Biological Standards (part of NIH and in turn part of PHS) was transferred to FDA and eventually became CBER. Although the *PHS Act* established the regulation of biologics licensure, biologics are classified as drugs under the *FD&C Act*, and new biologic products require approval based on safety and efficacy prior to marketing (through a BLA as opposed to an NDA). Review and approval of these products is conducted by CBER. As technology has evolved, CBER has reviewed more therapeutic proteins. To allow CBER to focus its expertise on vaccines, blood products and other, more-complex products such as gene therapy, FDA shifted the review and approval of biological therapeutics (monoclonal antibodies, peptides or well-characterized proteins) from CBER to CDER in 2003. Chapter 1 summarizes the types of products now regulated by the two centers.

Generic Biologics and Biosimilars

The *Patient Protection and Affordable Care Act (Affordable Care Act)*, signed into law by President Obama on 23 March 2010, amends the *PHS Act* to create an abbreviated licensure pathway for biological products that are demonstrated

Figure 3-1. Decision Tree for Drug and Device Development and Approval for Situations that Require FDA Premarket Review

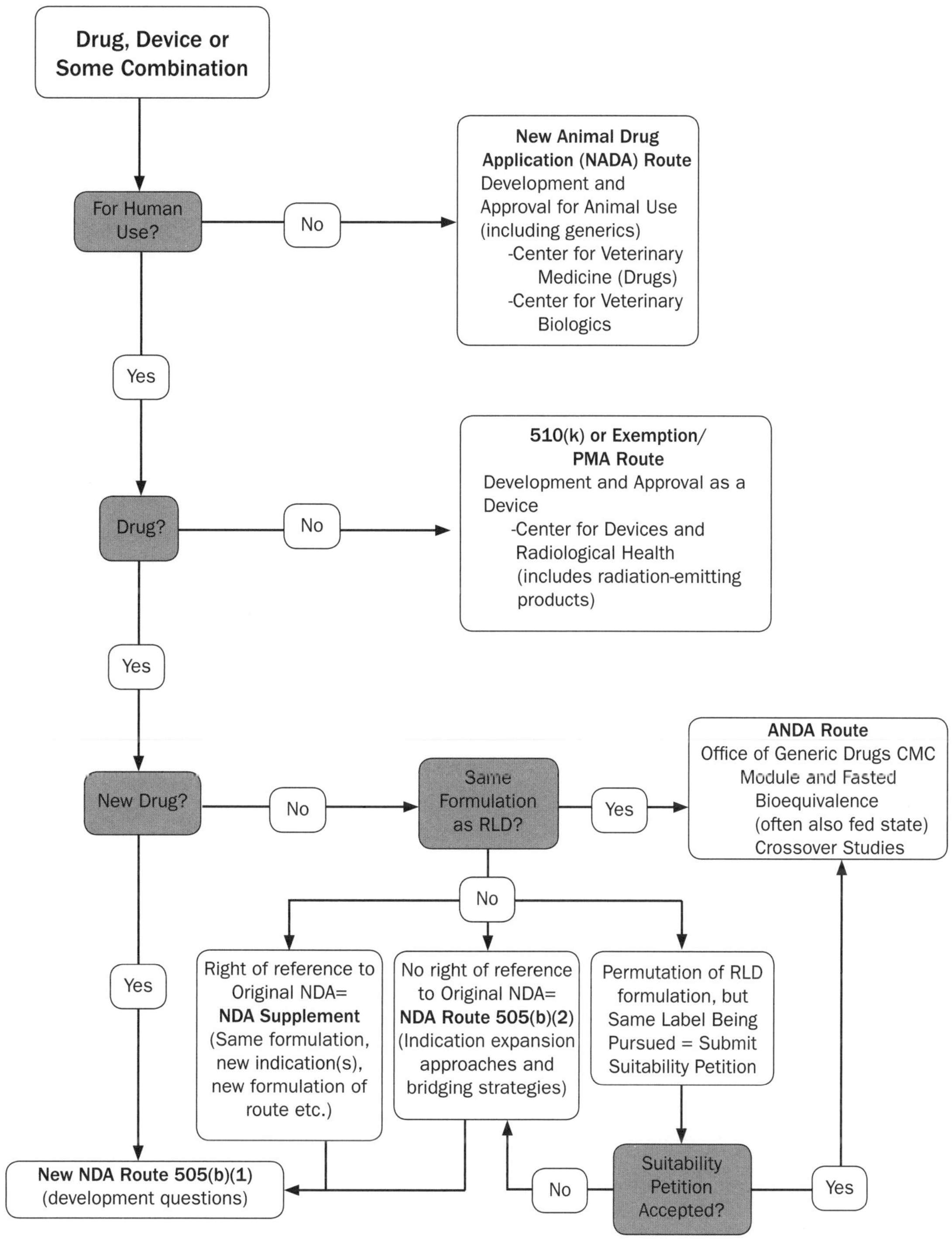

(ANDA, Abbreviated New Drug Application; CMC, Chemistry, Manufacturing, and Controls; NDA, New Drug Application; PMA, Premarket Approval; RLD, Reference Listed Drug (per *Orange Book*))

to be "biosimilar" to or "interchangeable" with an FDA-licensed biological product. This pathway is provided in the part of the law known as the *Biologics Price Competition and Innovation Act* (*BPCI Act*).

A "biosimilar" product is a biological product approved based on a showing it is "highly similar" to an FDA-approved biological product, known as a reference product, and has no clinically meaningful differences in terms of safety and effectiveness from the reference product. Only minor differences in clinically inactive components are allowable in biosimilar products.

An "interchangeable" biological product is biosimilar to an FDA-approved reference product and meets additional standards for interchangeability. An interchangeable biological product may be substituted for the reference product by a pharmacist without the intervention of the healthcare provider who prescribed the reference product.

FDA requires licensed biosimilar and interchangeable biological products to meet the agency's rigorous safety and efficacy standards. That means patients and healthcare professionals will be able to rely upon the biosimilar or interchangeable product's safety and effectiveness, just as they would the reference product.

Chapter 15 provides a more detailed discussion of the generic drug approval process.

User Fees—Biosimilar Investigational New Drug Applications (INDs)

The *FD&C Act*, as amended by the *Biosimilar User Fee Act* of 2012 (*BsUFA*), authorizes FDA to assess and collect fees for biosimilar biological products during the IND phase. For more information about the yearly cost for all biosimilar INDs, see: http://www.fda.gov/ForIndustry/UserFees/BiosimilarUserFeeActBsUFA/default.htm

New Chemical Entities and the NDA for a Marketing Application for Human Use (FD&C Act Section 505(b)(1)

Overview of the Approach to Drug Development and Approval

A "drug" is defined as a product used in diagnosing, curing, mitigating, treating or preventing a disease or affecting a structure or function of the body (21 CFR 310.3). Under the same regulation, a drug is considered a new drug if:

- There is a new drug use of any substance (e.g., active ingredient, excipient, carrier, coating etc.), which composes the drug.
- There is a new drug use of a combination of approved drugs.
- The proportion of the ingredients in combination is changed.
- There is a new intended use for the drug.
- The dosage, method or duration of administration or application is changed.

Thus, the following are subject to FDA approval:

1. a drug containing a novel chemical compound as its active ingredient (new chemical entity (NCE))
2. a drug containing an existing active ingredient that has never been approved for use as a medicine in the US
3. a drug previously approved by FDA but now proposed for a new use or indication
4. a drug previously approved by FDA but in a dosage form, route of administration or other key condition of use different from what was originally approved

The intake of any exogenous substance that has pharmacological actions on the body presents some level of risk. Drug development consists of characterizing the safety profile (risk) and the efficacy profile (benefit) as it relates to the body's exposure to the drug (pharmacokinetic profile). The most successful drugs are those with minimal risk and maximum benefit. To align development with continuous evaluation of risk and benefit, it often is productive to consider questions and answers that affect decisions on whether to continue a drug's development to the point of submitting a marketing application. The order and importance of these questions are different for each drug based on aspects such as the product (formulation) chemical and physical characteristics, the route of administration, the target patient population, the medical need, the ability to monitor safety, the ability to predict potential benefits from pharmacodynamic measures (surrogate endpoints) and the duration of treatment needed to demonstrate efficacy.

Table 3-2 lists some of the key questions FDA expects to be addressed as a drug is developed. Generally, due to risk, cost and time, evaluations are performed in the following order:

- in vitro
- live animals (juvenile if applicable)
- adult humans (often in healthy subjects before patients)
- children (if applicable)

However, as information is gained, new hypotheses may need to be tested. Therefore, drug development often is an iterative, dynamic process that involves ongoing effective communication between all the disciplines involved (i.e. clinical, nonclinical, manufacturing and regulatory).

Table 3-2 identifies key questions to be addressed in a drug development program, i.e., how a company can maximize its product's market share and realize the maximum return on investment with the least amount of risk. The sections below describe key aspects of the drug development process and regulatory tools and approaches to help reach these goals.

Table 3-2. Key Questions to be Addressed in a Drug Development Program

In Vitro—Animals—Adults—Children		
Safety (Risk)	**Pharmacokinetics** (What the body does to the drug)	**Pharmacodynamics/Efficacy** (Benefit)
How do you maximize the intellectual property aspect of the product?		
What is the known safety profile of other drugs like yours or the class of drugs in general? For a new class of drugs or mechanism of action this will not necessarily be known and hence associated with more risk.	Are there competitor drugs that have a less than ideal route of administration or pharmacokinetic profile (e.g., substrates, inhibitors or inducers of more commonly used cytochrome P [CYP] 450 isoenzyme pathways)?	What endpoints have been accepted by FDA for other drugs developed to treat the target disease, or is this a first-in-class drug?
What safety profile would provide a competitive advantage?	What pharmacokinetic (including route of administration) profile would provide a competitive advantage?	What is the potential breadth of the target indication(s)?
What do you want to say in your label? (this will drive the development of your product)		
What are the target organs/systems for toxicity?	What exposure profiles produce target organ/system effects?	What are the target organs/systems for pharmacological effects?
What toxicity is observed acutely versus chronically?	How is the time course of the effects related to the time-concentration curves of the parent drug and its metabolites?	What is the time course and duration of pharmacological/ therapeutic effects?
Can the toxicities be monitored?	Are there potential or actual interactions with other drugs (especially those most commonly used by the target patient population)?	How do you measure the benefits?
Are the toxicities reversible?	What are the single-dose versus steady-state pharmacokinetics of the drug and its metabolites?	What happens to the therapeutic effects when you stop dosing?
What is the maximum tolerated dose and what are risks of overdose?	Is the pharmacokinetic profile linear?	What is the minimal effective dose and duration of treatment?
What are the frequency and severity of safety findings?	How variable (intra- and inter-subject) are drug concentrations (may be impacted by drug bioavailability or greater involvement of the more commonly used CYP isoenzyme systems)?	How reproducible and clinically relevant are the pharmacodynamic and/or efficacy endpoints (speaks to the validity of the endpoints)?

FDA Interface and Development Leverage Options

The relationship between FDA and an investigational drug product sponsor can begin very early in the process (before the sponsor submits an IND to test the product in humans) and extends through the typical IND development process (often defined as Phases 1, 2 and 3) to a marketing application and postapproval commitments, safety surveillance and product lifecycle management. It is important to structure the presentation to meet FDA expectations. To succeed, it is important to learn—through experience or interaction—the relevant review division's approach to issues under its purview. The most effective interfaces between sponsors and FDA typically are formal meetings and Special Protocol Assessment (SPA) requests.

FDA–Sponsor Meetings

Although sponsor meetings with FDA occurred prior to 1997, it was not until the reauthorization of the 1992 *Prescription Drug User Fee Act* in 1997 (*PDUFA II*) that a formal process for meetings (with expectations and commitments from both parties) was established. Processes for meeting requests and classification are covered in *Guidance for Industry: Formal Meetings Between the FDA and Sponsors or Applicants of PDUFA Products* (March 2015). Different types of meetings are categorized as Type A, B or C, with different associated timelines (see aforementioned guidance). Meetings can be requested at any time for any valid reason, but FDA will decide whether there is sufficient justification for a face to face meeting (usually dictated by the stage of development, product background, draft questions submitted in a written meeting request and whether the sponsor already has had its allotted meeting for that development phase) or whether a written response to questions and/or a teleconference would suffice. Most commonly, meetings are classified as Pre-IND, End-of-Phase 2 (see also, *Guidance for Industry: End-of Phase 2A Meetings* (September 2009)) or Pre-NDA. For products that have been granted accelerated approval or fast track, an End-of-Phase 1 meeting generally will be granted.

For any meeting with FDA, it is important to submit clear and meaningful draft questions and a supporting pre-meeting package that is not merely a summary of what is known about a given drug (e.g., submission of only an Investigator's Brochure). Chapter 4 FDA Communications and Meetings provides a more detailed discussion of this topic.

SPA

The SPA process is described in *Guidance for Industry: Special Protocol Assessment* (May 2002). Although prior to 1997, FDA reviewed draft protocols on a case-by-case basis, the process often took several months and did not always address all the issues. As a result of *PDUFA II*, the SPA process was established. Within 45 days of receipt, FDA will evaluate certain protocols and related issues to determine whether they meet scientific and regulatory requirements identified by the sponsor (in the form of specific questions). Three types of protocols are eligible for an SPA under the *PDUFA* goals:

1. animal carcinogenicity protocols
2. final product stability protocols
3. clinical protocols for Phase 3 trials, the data from which will form the basis for an efficacy claim (i.e., a pivotal trial) if the trials were discussed at an End-of-Phase 2/Pre-Phase 3 meeting with the review division

Although FDA generally adheres to the initial 45-day period, depending on agency responses to the questions, there could be several review/response cycles (that are no longer part of the timeframe) to reach a final understanding with the sponsor. If documentation of the final agreement is not provided by the FDA review division, the sponsor should request written communication from FDA acknowledging the final agreement.

In addition, sponsors have several available avenues to help focus FDA attention on the drug development program and expedite marketing application approval. These include orphan drug designation (when eligible) and, for drugs indicated for serious or life-threatening conditions, fast track and/or Breakthrough Therapy designation with opportunities for a "rolling NDA or BLA," qualified infectious disease product (QIDP) (for antibiotic and antifungals only) and priority review (see 21 CFR 316 and *Guidance for Industry: Expedited Programs for Serious Conditions—Drugs and Biologics* (May 2014) for more information). Sponsors also may seek accelerated NDA review based on a surrogate endpoint or an effect on a clinical endpoint other than survival or irreversible morbidity. Details are described in 21 CFR 314.510, Subpart H Accelerated Approval of New Drugs for Serious or Life-threatening Illnesses. Confirmatory Phase 3 studies are likely to be required if FDA approves an NDA, under Subpart H, which typically is approved based on Phase 2 data.

Orphan Drug Designation

The *Orphan Drug Act* was signed into law in 1983 and, for the first time, provided incentives for development of drugs necessary, and often life-saving, for patients with rare diseases but with minimal prospects for commercial return on investment. The *Orphan Drug Act* is codified in 21 CFR 316.

Since 1983, Congress has amended the act several times.

- The 1984 amendment redefined "rare disease or condition" as affecting fewer than 200,000 persons in the US at a given point or for which there is no reasonable expectation of recovering development costs through US sales.
- The 1985 amendment extended the marketing exclusivity to patentable as well as unpatentable drugs and allowed federal grants for the clinical evaluation of orphan-designated drugs.
- The 1988 amendment required industry sponsors to apply for orphan designation prior to submission of a marketing application.
- The *Food and Drug Administration Modernization Act* of 1997 (*FDAMA*) included a provision that exempted manufacturers of designated orphan drug products from paying new drug application fees (user fees). It also allowed sponsors to seek waivers of annual postapproval establishment and product fees on a case-by-case, year-by-year basis.

The *Orphan Drug Act* provides a number of specific incentives for sponsors:

- seven years of exclusive marketing rights for the designated indication once the drug receives FDA marketing approval
- a tax credit for up to 50% of qualified clinical research expenses incurred in developing a designated orphan product (This tax credit has a provision that allows the sponsor to carry the excess credit back one tax year if unable to use part or all of the credit because of tax liability limits, and then to carry forward any additional unused credit for up to 20 years after the year of the credit. The latter is important to start-up companies that may not make any profits until the drug is on the market. The US Internal Revenue Service administers the tax credit provisions of the *Orphan Drug Act*.)
- eligibility to apply for orphan drug grants

An application for orphan drug designation is defined in 21 CFR 316 and includes:

- specific rare disease or condition for which designation is being requested
- sponsor contact, drug names and sources
- description of the rare disease or condition with a medically plausible rationale for any patient subset type of approach
- description of the drug and the scientific rationale for its use for the rare disease or condition
- summary of the drug's regulatory status and marketing history
- documentation that the disease or condition affects fewer than 200,000 people in the US
- alternatively, a rationale for why there is no reasonable expectation that costs of research and development for the indication can be recovered by US sales for a vaccine, diagnostic drug or preventive drug to be administered to more than 200,000 or more persons per year

Specifics on the submission format and other details are available on FDA's website (www.fda.gov/ForIndustry/DevelopingProductsforRareDiseasesConditions/default.htm). Once the request for designation has been received, OOPD will send a receipt letter, and a formal response will take one to three months. Upon notification of orphan drug designation, the sponsor's name and the proposed rare disease or condition will be entered into the searchable Orphan Drug Designations and Approvals database (http://www.accessdata.fda.gov/scripts/opdlisting/oopd/).

Once an orphan drug designation has been granted by FDA, it can only be revoked if the application is found to contain false data or material data were omitted (such as an article demonstrating a higher prevalence than that reported by the sponsor). Notably, the designation cannot be revoked even if post-designation prevalence exceeds the original estimates. Finally, the sponsor must provide annual updates that contain a brief summary of any ongoing or completed nonclinical or clinical studies; a description of the investigational plan for the coming year; as well as any anticipated difficulties in development, testing and marketing; and a brief discussion of any changes that may affect the product's orphan drug status. Further details are covered in Chapter 28 Regulation of Products for Small Patient Populations.

Fast Track Designation

The Fast Track Drug Development Program designation process is described in *Guidance for Industry: Expedited Programs for Serious Conditions—Drugs and Biologics* (May 2014). FDA better defined the program in 1997 (see 21 CFR 312 Subpart E) as a result of *FDAMA*. The fast track program is designed to facilitate the development and expedite the review of new drugs intended to treat serious or life-threatening conditions that demonstrate the potential to address unmet medical needs. A disease is considered serious if:

> "a disease or condition associated with morbidity that has substantial impact on day-to-day functioning. Short-lived and self-limiting morbidity will usually not be sufficient, but the morbidity need not be irreversible if it is persistent or recurrent. Whether a disease or condition is serious is a matter of clinical judgment, based on its impact on such factors as survival, day-to-day functioning, or the likelihood that the disease, if left untreated, will progress from a less severe condition to a more serious one."

FDA defines "an unmet medical need" as:

- has an effect on a serious outcome of the condition not known to be influenced by available therapy (e.g., progressive disability or disease progression when the available therapy has shown an effect on symptoms, but has not shown an effect on progressive disability or disease progression)
- has an improved effect on a serious outcome(s) of the condition compared with available therapy (e.g., superiority of the new drug to available therapy when either used alone or in combination with available therapy (i.e., as demonstrated in an add-on study))
- has an effect on a serious outcome of the condition in patients who are unable to tolerate or failed to respond to available therapy
- can be used effectively with other critical agents that cannot be combined with available therapy
- provides efficacy comparable to that of available therapy, while (1) avoiding serious toxicity that occurs with available therapy, (2) avoiding less-serious toxicity that is common and causes discontinuation of treatment of a serious condition or (3) reducing the potential for harmful drug interactions
- provides safety and efficacy comparable to those of available therapy but has a documented benefit, such as improved compliance, that is expected to lead to an improvement in serious outcomes
- addresses an emerging or anticipated public health need, such as a drug shortage

A sponsor may request fast track designation at any point in the development process. Depending on the drug development stage, when data become available to support the drug's potential to address unmet medical needs the development plan should be designed to assess this potential and trigger a fast track designation application. The agency will rely on summaries of available data to determine whether the potential to address unmet medical needs has been demonstrated and will provide a designation response within 60 days of receipt of the request. When emerging data no longer support fast track designation or the designated drug development program is no longer being pursued, FDA may choose to send a letter notifying the sponsor the product is no longer classified as fast track.

A product in a fast track development program is eligible for heightened interaction with FDA in sponsor meetings, a greater probability of priority review of the marketing application (six months versus the standard 10 months) and piecemeal submission of portions (complete CTD modules—constituting a "reviewable unit") of a marketing application (referred to as a "rolling NDA or BLA"). Note that this latter provision is unique to fast track and breakthrough (see below) programs, but needs to be requested specifically. Moreover, the FDA review clock for the rolling NDA does not start until the marketing application submission is complete (i.e. the last CTD module is submitted).

Breakthrough Therapy Designation

The *Food and Drug Administration Safety and Innovation Act* (*FDASIA*), signed in July 2012, expanded the accelerated approval pathway by defining a new "Breakthrough Therapy" designation to allow a sponsor increased FDA communication and attention above and beyond that provided to products designated as "Fast Track."

The breakthrough therapy initiative's goal is to expedite the development and review of a potential new medicine if it is "intended, alone or in combination with one or more other drugs, to treat a serious or life-threatening disease or condition, and preliminary clinical evidence indicates that the drug may demonstrate substantial improvement over existing therapies on one or more clinically significant endpoints, such as substantial treatment effects observed early in clinical development."

A request for breakthrough therapy designation should be submitted concurrently with, or as an amendment to an IND. No later than 60 days after receipt of the submission, a determination will be made to either grant or deny the request for breakthrough therapy designation in the form of a designation letter (for requests granted) or a non-designation letter (for requests denied). For more information about the contents of the designation requirements, see *Guidance for Industry: Expedited Programs for Serious Conditions—Drugs and Biologics* (May 2014).

FDA has posted "Fact Sheet: Breakthrough Therapies" to guide sponsors who may be seeking this designation on its website (www.fda.gov/RegulatoryInformation/Legislation/FederalFoodDrugandCosmeticActFDCAct/SignificantAmendmentstotheFDCAct/FDASIA/ucm329491.htm). Frequently asked questions about breakthrough therapies also can be found on the FDA website (www.fda.gov/RegulatoryInformation/Legislation/FederalFoodDrugandCosmeticActFDCAct/SignificantAmendmentstotheFDCAct/FDASIA/ucm341027.htm).

Generating Antibiotics Incentives Now Act (GAIN Act) and Qualified Infectious Disease Product (QIDP) Designation

Title VIII of *FDASIA*, the *Generating Antibiotic Incentives Now Act* (*GAIN Act*), provides incentives for the development of antibacterial and antifungal drugs for human use intended to treat serious and life threatening infections. Under the *GAIN Act*, a drug may be designated as a qualified infectious disease product (QIDP) if it meets the criteria outlined in the statute. A QIDP is "an antibacterial or antifungal drug for human use intended to treat serious or life-threatening infections, including those caused by an antibacterial or antifungal resistant pathogen, including novel or emerging infectious pathogens; or qualifying pathogen." A drug that receives QIDP designation is eligible under the statute for fast track designation, priority review and extends the exclusivity period for a new prescription drug by five years.

ICH and FDA Guidelines and Their Relationship to the Development Process

ICH and the CTD Format

ICH was formed in 1990. It is a unique project that brings together the regulatory authorities of EU, Japan and the US and experts from the pharmaceutical industry in the three regions to discuss scientific and technical aspects of product registration. ICH recommends ways to achieve greater harmonization in the interpretation and application of technical guidelines and requirements for product registration to reduce or avoid duplicating testing during new drug research and development. The objectives are conservation of human, animal and material resources and elimination of unnecessary delays in global development and availability of new medicines, while safeguarding quality, safety and efficacy and protecting public health.

The ICH process has resulted in numerous guidelines in four major categories:

1. Quality—topics relating to chemical and pharmaceutical quality assurance, including stability testing and impurity testing
2. Safety—topics relating to *in vitro* and *in vivo* nonclinical studies, including safety pharmacology, carcinogenicity testing, reproductive toxicology, anticancer nonclinical requirements, photosafety, chronic toxicology immunotoxicity and genotoxicity testing
3. Efficacy—topics relating to clinical studies in human subjects, including dose-response studies and GCPs
4. Multidisciplinary—topics covering cross-disciplinary issues or not uniquely fitting into one of the other categories, including *Medical Dictionary for*

Figure 3-2. CTD Organization

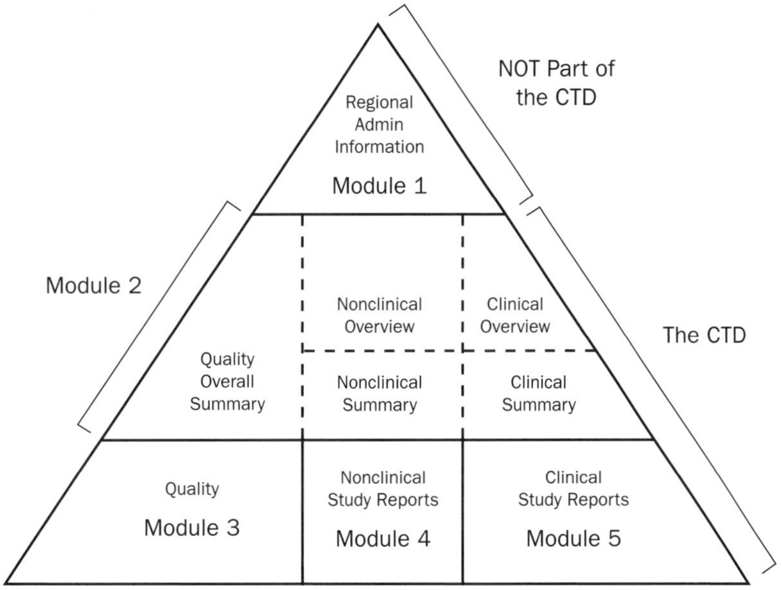

Regulatory Activities (*MedDRA*) terminology, the CTD and electronic CTD (eCTD) submissions

Copies of these guidelines and information on their history and status in the four-step review and consensus process are available at www.ich.org/products/guidelines.html. The majority of these guidelines have been accepted by FDA as reflecting current agency thinking (as documented in *Federal Register* announcements).

Two important aspects of the ICH endeavor are the CTD concept and *MedDRA*. The CTD is divided into five modules as shown in **Figure 3-2,** with a hierarchical structure with the most detail at the base leading to higher and higher level summaries and integration. *Guidance for Industry M4: Organization of the CTD* (2001) provides further details.

Module 1 is region-specific (US, EU, Japan). Modules 2, 3, 4 and 5 are intended to be common for all regions. For US submissions, Module 1 will contain various FDA forms, draft labeling, Risk Evaluation and Mitigation Strategies (REMS) plans, key FDA correspondence (e.g., FDA meeting minutes), patent information and the Investigator's Brochure (IB) (important if the CTD format is used at the IND stage). Module 2 contains CTD summaries of the three technical areas:

- Module 3 Quality (see *Guidance for Industry M4Q: The CTD—Quality* (August 2001)) and corresponding summary in Module 2.3
- Module 4 Nonclinical/Safety (see *Guidance for Industry M4S: The CTD—Safety* (August 2001) and *Guidance for Industry M4S: The CTD—Safety Appendices* (August 2001)) and corresponding summaries in Module 2.4 Nonclinical Overview and 2.6 Nonclinical Written and Tabulated Summaries
- Module 5 Clinical (see *Guidance for Industry M4E: The CTD—Efficacy* (August 2001)) and corresponding summaries in Module 2.5 Clinical Overview and 2.7 Clinical Summary

Module 2 also has several sections, the goals of which are to provide a concise context for the reviewer and integrate key benefit-risk data. The above-cited guidelines contain not only information on their respective modules, but also what should be included in the related portions of Module 2. If submitting electronically, *Guidance for Industry M2 eCTD: Electronic Common Technical Document Specification* (April 2003) is a key starting point.

MedDRA, the currently accepted international medical terminology dictionary developed by ICH, is designed to support the classification, retrieval, presentation and communication of medical information throughout the regulatory cycle for drugs and medical devices. It is particularly important in the electronic transmission of adverse event reporting and the coding of clinical trial data. Further details are available at www.meddramsso.com/public_subscribe_meddra.asp and in associated ICH *MedDRA* specific guidelines. *MedDRA* replaces the older *Coding Symbols for a Thesaurus of Adverse Reaction Terms* (COSTART) dictionary.

Guidance Documents

Collectively, CDER and CBER have issued more than 800 guidelines since 1977. These range from general topics

Table 3-3. IND Safety Reporting Timeframes

SAE Outcome	Deadline for Reporting
Fatal or life-threatening	7 calendar days, by phone or facsimile, followed by a written report within 8 additional calendar days
All other outcomes	15 calendar days, in writing

addressing a number of the issues outlined in **Table 3-4** to drug-specific issues. They are not regulations but do represent FDA's current thinking on a given topic. However, some guidelines are relatively old, so the definition of "current thinking" often needs to be validated by recent experience with the agency in the area covered by the guidance. Because they are guidance documents, they should not be followed blindly, but consideration should be given to their intent and applicability to a given development issue; however, any deviations from the guidance documents should be discussed with the agency prior to implementation.

The Initial IND and the IND Amendment Process

Before initiating a clinical trial in the US (other than bioequivalence studies to support an ANDA), the drug product sponsor must submit nonclinical, CMC and previous human experience data (if applicable) to FDA in a notice of claimed investigational exemption for a new drug in the form of an IND.

The IND application is not a request for approval; rather, it is a request for exemption from federal law. Federal law requires an NDA or BLA to be approved by FDA prior to transporting or distributing a drug in interstate commerce. Because in most cases the drug product must be shipped to investigative sites across state lines to be used in clinical trials, the sponsor must receive an exemption from this legal requirement.

After receipt of the initial IND application, FDA will send the sponsor a letter with the assigned IND number (note that an IND number with a "P" preface can be obtained at a Pre-IND meeting, and the final IND number is the same minus this preface). The letter will indicate that the proposed clinical trial cannot begin until 30 calendar days after receipt of the IND. This 30-day safety review period gives FDA an opportunity to determine whether the data in the IND application support the safety of subjects in the proposed clinical trial. Following review, rather than providing formal approval, the agency will take action on the application as follows. If the proposed study is judged not to be reasonably safe for human subjects, FDA is required to inform the sponsor within 30 calendar days of receipt of the IND application that it may not begin the clinical trial (clinical hold). If the sponsor is not contacted by FDA within 30 days, approval to initiate clinical trials is implicit, i.e. the IND goes into effect. In the latter case, it is advisable for the sponsor to contact the FDA project manager assigned to the IND to develop a relationship and to confirm the results of the review.

For the initial IND (the same is true for NDAs), FDA assigns a review team led by a regulatory project manager (RPM) that includes a medical reviewer and pharmacology/toxicology reviewer from the review division. Generally, a CMC reviewer from the Office of New Drug Quality Assessment (ONDQA) is assigned. Depending upon the proposed study, a clinical pharmacologist from the Office of Clinical Pharmacology and a statistician from the Office of Biostatistics may be assigned as well. The team generally will meet the week that the 30-day review period ends and, with the division director, decide whether the proposed study may proceed. In some cases, the RPM may contact the sponsor to request additional information or to propose that the study may be initiated if certain modifications are made to the study protocol. In the latter case, or in the case of clinical hold, FDA eventually will issue a letter containing the details of any requested modifications to the protocol or supporting data.

Where previous clinical studies have not been conducted for an NCE, the initial IND is a major milestone because it summarizes the data that support moving a drug from *in vitro* and animal testing into evaluation in humans. IND regulations are detailed in 21 CFR 312. In addition, a number of other FDA guidelines specific to certain therapeutic indications should be consulted when relevant. The content and format of an initial IND are described in 21 CFR 312.23. Traditionally, the content follows the items listed in Section 12 of Form FDA 1571 and includes an IB, clinical protocol, CMC information, nonclinical pharmacology and toxicology information and previous human experience information (the latter only if relevant). Although an initial IND still can be submitted in paper format (three copies of the submission are required), using the CTD format for the initial IND submission is becoming more common and is accepted by FDA. The advantage of this approach, especially when done electronically, is it begins building a CTD for an eventual marketing application that is updated progressively during the course of drug development under the IND. The disadvantages are the CTD structure in some areas (especially Module 1 and 2) does not easily fit the information available at an initial IND stage, and Section 12 of FDA Form 1571 (application contents) currently does not correlate directly with the CTD structure. If submitted electronically, the initial IND must be in eCTD format (with the same considerations as for an electronically submitted NDA). In addition, once an IND or IND amendment is submitted electronically, all future IND submissions also must be submitted electronically.

For active INDs (an IND can be withdrawn (21 CFR 312.38) or considered inactive (21 CFR 312.45)), sponsors are required to submit expedited safety reports for

Table 3-4. Summary of Device Classification System

Class	Required Controls			Exemptions	Examples
	General	Special	Premarket Approval		
I	X			***Exempt*** = subject to limitations on exemptions covered under 21 CFR xxx.9, where xxx refers to Parts 862–892. Class I devices are usually exempt. ***Nonexempt*** = 510(k) required for marketing	Elastic bandages, examination gloves, hand-held surgical instruments
II	X	X			Powered wheelchairs, infusion pumps, surgical drapes
III	X	X	X	Exempt if it is a preamendment device (i.e., on the market prior to the passage of the *Medical Device Amendments* in 1976 or substantially equivalent to such a device) and PMAs have not been called for. In that case, a 510(k) will be the route to market	Heart valves, silicone gel-filled breast implants, implanted cerebellar stimulators

serious, unexpected adverse reactions to the IND (IND Safety Reports) as per the definitions provided in 21 CFR 312.32. A serious adverse event (SAE) is any untoward medical occurrence that results in death, is life-threatening, requires subject hospitalization or prolongation of existing hospitalization, results in persistent or significant disability or incapacity or is a congenital anomaly or birth defect. IND safety report submission to FDA is time sensitive. The date the sponsor is notified of the SAE by the study site is considered Day 1, and all reporting timeframes are tied to this notification. **Table 3-3** summarizes these requirements. *Guidance for Industry and Investigators—Safety Reporting Requirements for INDs and BA/BE Studies* (December 2012) provides further details and covers SAE reporting requirements for bioavailability (BA) and bioequivalence (BE) studies as well.

IND sponsors are required to submit Annual Reports to the IND within 60 days of the anniversary of the date the IND went into effect (21 CFR 312.33). The Annual Report focuses on safety signals (deaths or other SAEs, dropouts due to adverse events and new nonclinical safety findings) and includes an outline of the development plan for the coming year. *Guidance for Industry: E2F Development Safety Update Report* (August 2011) describes a new approach for annual safety reporting and is intended to replace the IND Annual Report with a comprehensive, harmonized safety summary that represents a common standard for the ICH regions.

Finally, FDA requires clinical trials to be registered with the Clinical Trials Data Bank (maintained by NIH's National Library of Medicine). This initiative began in 2001 with the posting of clinical studies for serious or life-threatening diseases and, under the *Food and Drug Administration Amendments Act* of 2007 (*FDAAA*), was expanded to include all controlled clinical trials in patients (i.e., other than Phase 1 studies). The Clinical Trials Data Bank can be accessed at www.clinicaltrials.gov/. To date, the database has registered hundreds of thousands of trials in virtually every country in the world and can be a good resource for clinical study design information.

The 505(b)(1) NDA and Benefit-Risk

General Considerations

Drugs gain entry into the market via the NDA. The culmination of a drug or biologic development program is the preparation and submission of a marketing application (NDA or BLA). This is accomplished through either studies conducted by (or with a right of reference from the sponsor, i.e. the (505(b)(1) approach) or by reference to FDA's finding of safety and effectiveness for a previously approved product (i.e., the 505(b)(2) approach; see below for more information). Through frequent interactions with FDA during the development program, including a Pre-NDA meeting (usually held no later than three months prior to the target filing date), sponsor and agency expectations should be reasonably well aligned. The marketing application should contain sufficient data for FDA to decide whether the drug's benefits outweigh its risks in the context of the sponsor's proposed label; the data and content requirements are detailed in 21 CFR 314.

Package Insert

In addition to the study reports supporting the drug's safety and efficacy and the associated summaries, the NDA's core is the draft package insert (or prescribing information, also referred to as simply the "label") which, since 2005, is required to be in structured product label (SPL) format in an XML (Extensible Markup Language) backbone to meet FDA filing requirements. SPL is a model-derived standard adopted for exchange of FDA-regulated product information in the content of the labeling, coded information from the content of the labeling (data elements) and a "wrapper" for electronic listing elements. In addition, most review divisions will request a copy of the label in Microsoft Word, to be able to communicate in the label negotiation process using the track changes function, and draft SPL format with the NDA. This should be confirmed in either the Pre-NDA meeting or prior to filing with the FDA project manager. When agreement is reached on a final label, the sponsor will submit a final copy of the label to the NDA in SPL format. Moreover, since 2006, new NDAs must follow the format required by the Physician Labeling Rule (PLR), which comprises three parts: highlights (one page), contents and full prescribing information. The PLR format identifies and dates recent major changes to the prescribing information and includes the date of initial US approval for the active ingredient. Further information (including links to specific FDA guidelines on the content of different sections of the label) is available at www.fda.gov/Drugs/GuidanceComplianceRegulatoryInformation/LawsActsandRules/ucm084159.htm.

Electronic Submission

Since January 2008, sponsors submitting NDAs electronically have been required to use the eCTD format. For further information, FDA maintains a useful Electronic Regulatory Submissions and Review website at www.fda.gov/Drugs/DevelopmentApprovalProcess/FormsSubmissionRequirements/ElectronicSubmissions/UCM085361. By May 2017, all NDAs will be required to be submitted electronically in the eCTD format; in May 2018 all industry sponsored INDs will be accepted only in eCTD format.

REMS

Evaluation of a product's risk potential always has been a difficult aspect of FDA drug approval. Generally, it is difficult to extrapolate from data derived from a few thousand patients exposed to the drug under relatively well-controlled conditions to millions of patients with much less oversight. FDA's mandate to mitigate potential risks of drugs throughout their development and marketing lifecycle led to the issuance of three guidances in 2005 (*Guidance for Industry: Premarketing Risk Assessment*, *Guidance for Industry: Development and Use of Risk Minimization Action Plans* and *Guidance for Industry: Good Pharmacovigilance Practices and Pharmacoepidemiologic Assessment*). For drugs in development, FDA wanted to know how a sponsor planned to mitigate actual and potential risks (Risk MAP) if a marketing application was approved and how risk would be monitored post-approval. However, the agency did not have the statutory authority to require these assessments. This was rectified as part of *FDAAA,* which gave FDA the authority to require sponsors to submit a Risk Evaluation and Mitigation Strategy (REMS) plan prior to approval. A REMS may be as simple as inclusion of a Medication Guide with the package insert or as complex as a patient and pharmacist training program (Additional Elements to Assure Safe Use (ETASU)). The REMS includes, at minimum, sponsor postapproval evaluation at 18 months, three years and seven years.

Proprietary Name

A request for review of the sponsor's proposed proprietary name(s) should be made to the review division under the IND (*Draft Guidance for Industry: Contents of a Complete Submission for the Evaluation of Proprietary Names* (February 2010) and *Guidance for Industry Best Practices in Developing Proprietary Names for Drugs* (May 2014)) or as part of the initial NDA submission. Although the guidance states this request should be submitted at the end of Phase 2 (with a 180 day review timeframe), FDA will give only tentative name approval until 90 days after the NDA has been accepted. The review division will forward the proprietary name request to the Office of Postmarketing Drug Risk Assessment, Division of Drug Risk Evaluation, which will perform the primary review in consultation with the Office of Prescription Drug Promotion (OPDP); they will accept or reject the proposed name. If a name is rejected, a sponsor can appeal or submit one to two additional choices for review.

User Fees—Drugs

Under the original *PDUFA* (and subsequent amendments), user fees were levied on each "human drug application," including applications for:

- approval of a new drug submitted under section 505(b)(1) after 1 September 1992
- approval of a new drug submitted pursuant to section 505(b)(2) after 30 September 1992 for certain molecular entities or indications for use
- licensure of certain biological products under section 351 of the *PHS Act* submitted after 1 September 1992

PDUFA specifies different user fees for original applications depending on whether they are accompanied by clinical data on safety and/or efficacy (other than BA or BE studies). The act also levies fees on supplements to human drug applications that require clinical data. Under the fee schedules provided in the act, original applications without clinical data and supplements that require clinical data are assessed approximately one-half the fee of original applications. Further details are provided in *Guidance for Industry: Submitting Separate Marketing Applications and Clinical Data for Purposes of Assessing User Fees* (December 2004). The user fee for a full submission has increased every year since it was implemented and is currently well over $2 million. FDA also levies annual establishment and product fees. Further information on these fees can be found at www.fda.gov/Drugs/DevelopmentApprovalProcess/SmallBusinessAssistance/ucm069943.htm.

PAI

One of FDA's objectives in the NDA review process is to determine whether the methods used in manufacturing the drug and the controls used to maintain its quality are adequate to preserve the drug's identity, strength, quality, stability and purity. In conjunction with this evaluation, FDA field inspectors conduct a current Good Manufacturing Practice (CGMP) Preapproval Inspection (PAI) of the drug product manufacturing site if it has not recently been inspected by FDA with a favorable outcome. A PAI can occur as early as 90 days after an NDA submission. An adequate PAI generally is required for NDA approval.

Peri-Approval Activities

A number of peri-approval activities should be part of the overall submission and approval plan. A safety update is required to be submitted as an amendment to the NDA within 120 days of the initial NDA submission. In addition, approximately one month prior to the FDA action date, the FDA RPM will contact the sponsor and begin label negotiations. At this time (if not submitted previously), the sponsor should submit a request for a National Drug Code (NDC) assignment (*Guidance for Industry: Standards for Securing the Drug Supply Chain—Standardized Numerical Identification for Prescription Drug Packages* (March 2010)). Historically, FDA has provided these NDC numbers months before approval of the application, but recently has limited this to the peri-approval timeframe due to drug piracy concerns. Thus, the drug label, packaging artwork and labels and promotional material cannot be finalized until very near the approval date.

In 1972, Congress passed the *Federal Advisory Committee Act*, which prescribed the formal use of Advisory Committees throughout the federal government. With the increasing complexity of benefit-risk decisions, FDA increasingly has used Advisory Committees to provide independent advice that will contribute to the quality of the agency's regulatory decision making and lend credibility to the product review process in cases where additional input is desired by FDA. Chapter 5 provides a detailed description of FDA Advisory Committees and the timing of these in the peri-approval process when FDA requests such a meeting.

Establishment Listing

Under 21 CFR 207, FDA requires establishments (e.g., manufacturers, repackers and relabelers) upon first engaging in the manufacture, preparation, propagation, compounding or processing of human drugs, veterinary drugs and biological products, with certain exceptions, to register their establishments and submit listing information for all drugs and biological products in commercial distribution. Registrants also are required to submit, on or before 31 December each year, updated establishment registration information. Form FDA 2656 is used for drug establishment registration (and the labeler code assignment) and Form FDA 2657 is used for drug product listing purposes. In 2008, FDA began a pilot program to allow submission of the above information in an electronic format and, since 1 June 2009, all submissions are required to be completely electronic and in XML format, unless a waiver is granted. Further information is available in *Guidance for Industry: Providing Regulatory Submissions in Electronic Format—Drug Establishment Registration and Drug Listing (May 2009)* and at www.fda.gov/Drugs/GuidanceComplianceRegulatoryInformation/DrugRegistrationandListing/ucm084014.htm.

Patent Restoration

The passage of the *Drug Price Competition and Patent Term Restoration Act* (*Hatch-Waxman Act*) in 1984 represented a compromise between the innovator pharmaceutical industry and the generic pharmaceutical industry. It allowed innovator pharmaceutical companies to apply for up to five years of additional patent protection for new drugs to make up for time lost while their products were going through the development and regulatory review process. The drug (animal or human), medical device, biologic or food or color additive must be the first commercial marketing or use of the product under the provision of the law for which regulatory review occurred. FDA assists the Patent and Trademark Office (PTO) in determining a product's eligibility for patent extension, but PTO ultimately is responsible for determining the period of patent extension. Similarly, up to three years of exclusivity are granted for a change in an approved drug product where approval requires new clinical investigations other than BA studies (e.g., new indication, strength, dosage form or route of administration). Further details on the patent term restoration program can be found at www.fda.gov/Drugs/DevelopmentApprovalProcess/SmallBusinessAssistance/ucm069959.htm. Six months of pediatric exclusivity (FDA's incentive to conduct more studies of the use of the drug in pediatric populations) also can be requested; see www.fda.gov/Drugs/DevelopmentApprovalProcess/DevelopmentResources/UCM049867.htm for additional details.

NDA Amendments

Finally, an NDA amendment is submitted to change or add information to an unapproved NDA or NDA supplement. With the exception of the required 120-day safety update, sponsors should try to avoid initiating NDA amendments because they potentially will reset the review clock (especially if submitted in the final three months of the review period).

The 505(b)(2) NDA

Overview

The "paper" NDA approach was created after the 1962 passage of the *Drug Amendments* to the *FD&C Act*. It created a means by which duplicates (now known as generic drugs) of post-1962 drugs could be approved because the DESI program and the ANDA did not apply to drugs approved after 1962. The paper NDA policy allowed applicants to use published literature to satisfy the requirements for full reports of safety and effectiveness. The *Hatch-Waxman Act* of 1984 eliminated the paper NDA policy because it provided a mechanism to approve duplicates of post-1962 drugs, including situations where the applicant did not have the right of reference to the original NDA submitted and approved under Section 505(b)(1) of the *FD&C Act*.

The 505(b)(2) NDA is a submission type that shares characteristics of both traditional NDAs and ANDAs and is named after the section of the *FD&C Act* that describes it. **Figure 3-1** outlines how this type of NDA potentially fits into the overall development and approval scheme for a drug. As with a traditional 505(b)(1)NDA, a 505(b)(2) application is considered a complete application. Like a traditional NDA, it is approved under Section 505(c) of the act. Like an ANDA, a 505(b)(2) application may refer to FDA's finding of safety and effectiveness for a previously approved product, and its approval is subject to patent exclusivity limitations. The applicant also may rely on published literature. *Draft Guidance for Industry: Applications Covered by Section 505(b)(2)* (October 1999) provides additional details. The regulations for this type of application are codified in 21 CFR 314.54.

Bridging and Expansion Issues and Approaches

The most common uses of the 505(b)(2) route are for:

- change in drug product dosage form (including route of administration), formulation, strength and/or dosing regimen, including changes that were not accepted by FDA's Office of Generic Drugs (OGD) in a Suitability Petition
- change in active ingredient (different salt, acid or base)
- new combination product in which the active ingredients have been previously approved individually
- change from a prescription indication to an over-the-counter (OTC) indication
- indication that has not been previously approved for the active moiety
- NCE that is a prodrug or active metabolite of a drug approved in the US

If the applicant is the original NDA holder or has right of reference to that NDA from the holder, the above changes become supplements to the original NDA as outlined in **Figure 3-1**.

The data most commonly required in a 505(b)(2) approach provide a bridge between the data forming the basis for approval of the referenced NDA (and agreed to by FDA in the approved drug product label) and the different or additional claims in the 505(b)(2) NDA label. For active ingredient modifications, bridging centers on changes in impurity profiles and/or bioavailability and subsequent exposure. For drug product modifications, bridging centers on differences in the exposure profile. In both cases, a bridging toxicology program usually includes multiple-dose toxicology studies (between 14 and 90 days), with toxicokinetics in appropriate species, as well as mutagenicity and genotoxicity studies. The bridging program generally should not be initiated until agreement is reached with FDA in a formal meeting and the IND is in effect.

The above types of changes also will require additional bridging clinical pharmacokinetic studies. The product should be at least as bioavailable as the reference listed drug (RLD) unless it has some other advantage such as a smaller peak/trough exposure ratio. Moreover, the release pattern of the proposed product, although different, should be at least as favorable as that of the RLD. Clinical studies conducted for a 505(b)(2) application generally should be performed under an IND. A 505(b)(2) application may itself be granted three years of exclusivity if one or more of the clinical investigations, other than BA/BE studies, was essential to approval and was conducted for or sponsored by the applicant. A 505(b)(2) application also may be granted five years of exclusivity if it is for an NCE.

Between 1996 and 2004, 126 Section 505(b)(2) applications were filed,[2] and this continues to be a productive approach for moving older drugs into new technology platforms and/or better characterized and understood therapeutic areas. Brown-Tuttle[3] provides a concise description of how the regulatory professional can research this development approach.

Drugs

Generic Drugs for Human Use and the ANDA or 505(j) Application

Overview

In part as a result of the thalidomide tragedy, the *Kefauver-Harris Amendments* (*Drug Amendments*) to the *FD&C Act* were passed by Congress in 1962. These amendments required drug manufacturers to prove to FDA their products were both safe and effective prior to marketing (only safety was required to be demonstrated in the original *FD&C Act*). The *Drug Amendments* also gave FDA control over prescription drug advertising, established GMPs, created the IND requirement and the requirement for informed consent of clinical trial subjects. To comply, FDA contracted with the National Academy of Sciences' National Research Council in 1966 to study drugs approved for safety only between

1938 and 1962 relative to the new requirement for demonstrating efficacy. The Drug Efficacy Study Implementation (DESI) program evaluated more than 3,000 separate products and 16,000 therapeutic claims. One of the DESI program's early effects was the development of the ANDA. ANDAs were accepted for reviewed products that required changes in existing labeling to be in compliance.[4]

The modern era of generic drugs was born with passage of the *Hatch-Waxman Act*. This act expedited the availability of less-costly generic drugs by permitting FDA to approve abbreviated applications after the innovator drug's patent had expired. These are termed "abbreviated" applications because they are not required to include animal safety and clinical data to establish safety and effectiveness; but, for oral dosage forms, must demonstrate scientifically the product is bioequivalent to the innovator drug (Reference Listed Drug (RLD)). In the case of products (usually steriles, otics and ophthalmics) with a high solubility-high permeability rating (A/A rated), a waiver for *in vivo* bioequivalence testing can be obtained from FDA. To be bioequivalent, the generic drug product must deliver the same amount (within a range specified by FDA) of active ingredient into a subject's bloodstream over the same amount of time as the RLD. Specifically, a generic drug product is comparable to the innovator drug product in dosage form, strength, route of administration, quality, performance characteristics and intended use. All approved products, both innovator and generic, are listed in FDA's Approved Drug Products with Therapeutic Equivalence Evaluations (*Orange Book*), accessible on FDA's website (www.accessdata.fda.gov/scripts/cder/ob/default.cfm). The *Orange Book* identifies the RLD and provides information on applicable patents and their expiration dates. A product approved under the ANDA process will have the same labeling as the RLD. Nearly 80% of total drug prescriptions dispensed in the US are generic.

The ANDA is comprised of three primary components:

- chemistry, manufacturing and controls (CMC) information
- bioequivalence data
- administrative information (including labeling and patent certification information)

ANDA requirements for CMC information and manufacture under CGMPs do not differ significantly from NDA requirements. A relatively recent initiative in OGD to streamline the CMC section review process is submission of the ANDA Quality Overall Summary in question-based review (QbR) format (versus a more traditional non-question based summary format). The QbR questions and answers are placed in Module 2 of the Common Technical Document (CTD); therefore, QbR assumes the ANDA is submitted in CTD format, which is not mandatory until May 2017. OGD also has developed a standard group of summary tables (Model Bioequivalence Data Summary Tables) consistent with the CTD format to ensure consistent and concise data are submitted in the applicable ANDA sections.

The design, conduct and analysis of clinical bioequivalence studies are covered in *Guidance for Industry: Bioavailability and Bioequivalence Studies Submitted in NDAs or INDs—General Considerations* (March 2014) and *Guidance for Industry: Bioanalytical Method Validation* (September 2013). A third guideline, *Guidance for Industry: Bioanalytical Method Validation* (May 2001), covers the requirements for validation of bioanalytical methods used to evaluate active ingredient blood concentrations, which also applies to drugs developed through the NDA route. OGD issued *Guidance for Industry: Bioequivalence Recommendations for Specific Products* in June 2010 indicating how and where OGD will release bioequivalence recommendations for specific products in the future.

Generally, two-way crossover studies (sometimes preceded by pilot studies to determine variability and group sizes) of the generic drug product versus the RLD in the fasted state are performed. If the RLD label indicates a food effect, a second study in the fed state (using a standardized high-fat meal) typically is required. Additional studies may be needed to demonstrate bioequivalence of different strengths if the ratio of excipients to the active pharmaceutical ingredient in each generic drug dosage strength is not the same. As defined by FDA, the generic is deemed bioequivalent to the RLD in any of the above studies if the 90% confidence interval for the ratio of population geometric means between the two treatments, based on log-transformed data, is contained within the equivalence limits of 80%–125% for the area under the curve (AUC) and peak serum concentration (C_{max}). A common misinterpretation of this is active ingredient levels in generic drugs may vary from -20% to +25% compared to the innovator. In fact, those numbers relate to a derived statistical calculation and do not represent the actual difference in the amount of active ingredient in a patient's bloodstream, which generally is similar to the variation between different batches of the same innovator drug. For the statistically minded, *Guidance for Industry—Statistical Approaches to Establishing Bioequivalence* (January 2001), describes how to conduct the above analysis. If the bioequivalance studies are being conducted to support an ANDA, they do not have to be conducted under an IND, but do need to be reviewed and approved (including informed consent) by a duly constituted Institutional Review Board (IRB).

An ANDA must contain a statement by the applicant that one of the following patent certifications applies for the RLD:

- The patent information has not been filed (Paragraph I).
- The patent has expired (Paragraph II).

- The patent will expire on a specific date (Paragraph III), and the sponsor submitting the ANDA does not intend to market its product before that date.
- The patent is invalid or will not be infringed by the proposed drug product (Paragraph IV).

If the ANDA applicant certifies the patent is invalid or will not be infringed (a Paragraph IV certification), the applicant is required to notify the NDA holder and patent owner. If the NDA holder brings an action for patent infringement within 45 days of this notification, FDA will not approve the ANDA for 30 months, or such shorter or longer period as a court may order, or until the date of a court decision (known as the 30-month stay). Originally, the 180-day exclusivity for generic drugs applied only to the first company to submit an ANDA with a Paragraph IV certification. However, the current approach to 180-day exclusivity (described in *Guidance to Industry: 180-Day Exclusivity When Multiple ANDAs are Submitted on the Same Day* (July 2003)) is applicable to all cases in which multiple ANDA applicants submit Paragraph IV certifications challenging the same listed patent or patents on the same first day. This provides a shared incentive for multiple companies willing to challenge a listed patent and possibly defend a patent infringement suit.

Although the development time for a generic is relatively short, ANDA review (several hundred applications each year) and approval times average approximately two years and clearly impact the timeframe for moving generic products to the market. This suggests a proactive strategy of submitting ANDA applications well in advance of patent expiration date. A company with an approved ANDA is subject to the same postapproval reporting requirements as an NDA holder (21 CFR 314.80 Postmarketing reporting of adverse drug experiences and 21 CFR 314.81 Field alert reports and annual reports). Many of the topics above are covered in more detail in Chapter 15 Generic Drug Submissions. The OGD website also is a good resource (www.fda.gov/AboutFDA/CentersOffices/OfficeofMedicalProductsandTobacco/CDER/ucm119100.htm).

Branded and Authorized Generics

Recently, "branded" generics have become more prevalent. Branded generics are approved in the same manner as all generics, but the ANDA applicant also applies for and receives a brand (i.e., proprietary) name under the same process used for NDAs. A brand name will allow the company to distinguish its generic from others if marketing activities are contemplated.

An "authorized generic" is a drug product for which there is a licensing agreement between the innovator company and a generic drug manufacturer. It allows the innovator company to obtain revenue through the generic process by licensing a manufacturer to market the RLD as a generic using a different "trade dress" while continuing to market the innovator drug under the original proprietary name. A list (updated quarterly) of authorized generics, including the original NDA applicant name, is available on the CDER OGD website (www.fda.gov/AboutFDA/CentersOffices/OfficeofMedicalProductsandTobacco/CDER/ucm119100.htm). The appeal of this approach is avoiding the ANDA review and approval process; instead, the generic can be added to the original NDA as a supplement or described in the NDA annual report.

User Fees—Generic Drugs

The *Generic Drug User Fee Amendments* of 2012 (*GDUFA*) was designed to speed access to safe and effective generic drugs to the public and reduce costs to industry. The law requires industry to pay user fees to supplement the costs of reviewing generic drug applications and inspecting facilities. Additional resources will enable the agency to reduce a backlog of pending applications, cut the average time required to review generic drug applications for safety, and increase risk-based inspections. For more information and current *GDUFA* fees, see: http://www.fda.gov/ForIndustry/UserFees/GenericDrugUserFees/default.htm

Dietary Supplements and Natural Health Products

A dietary supplement is a product taken by mouth that contains a "dietary ingredient" intended to supplement the diet. These dietary ingredients may be vitamins, minerals, herbs or other botanicals, amino acids or substances such as enzymes, organ tissues, glandulars and metabolites.

Until 1994, dietary supplements were subject to the same regulatory requirements as other foods. Based on the belief in a positive relationship between sound dietary practices and health, Congress passed the *Dietary Supplement Health and Education Act (DSHEA)* in 1994, which amended the *FD&C Act* to create a new regulatory framework for dietary supplement safety and labeling (yet still under the regulatory umbrella of foods). *DSHEA* provisions define dietary supplements and dietary ingredients and describe the proper use of nutritional support statements. *DSHEA* also set forth new labeling requirements and required dietary supplement manufacturers to notify FDA of new dietary ingredients (after 1994; 21 CFR 190.6) prior to marketing. Interestingly, it also authorized FDA to prescribe GMPs for the industry. A final rule on this latter aspect was not forthcoming until 2007. The *Final Rule on cGMPs in Manufacturing, Packaging, Labeling, or Holding Operations for Dietary Supplements* established dietary supplement CGMPs for all domestic and foreign companies that manufacture, package, label or hold these supplements, including those involved with testing, quality control, packaging and labeling and distribution in the US. The dietary supplement CGMPs bear a stronger resemblance to drug CGMPs than to the rather general food CGMPs; however, dietary supplement CGMPs do not require process validation, which is mandated for drug CGMPs.

Dietary supplements do not require FDA premarket approval. The manufacturer is responsible for ensuring a dietary supplement is safe before it is marketed and all new dietary ingredients need notifications (NDINs) filed with the FDA 75 days prior to marketing demonstrating their safety. *DSHEA* places the burden on FDA to prove a marketed dietary supplement is unsafe prior to any action to remove the product from the market. Because of this requirement and the fact FDA received numerous reports of safety concerns for a number of products,[5] Congress passed the *Dietary Supplement and Nonprescription Drug Consumer Protection Act* in 2006. It mandates the same type of adverse event reporting for dietary supplements as for prescription drugs.

Dietary supplement claims allowed under *DSHEA* include:

- claims of benefits related to nutrient deficiencies (if the prevalence of the disease in the US is disclosed)
- claims describing the role of the dietary supplement's effects on structure or function in humans (e.g., "calcium builds strong bones")
- claims describing the mechanism of effects on structure or function (e.g., "fiber maintains bowel regularity")
- claims of general well being

Manufacturers cannot make an express or implied claim a product will diagnose, mitigate, treat, cure or prevent a specific disease or class of diseases. Examples of prohibited statements include: "protects against the development of cancer" or "reduces the pain and stiffness associated with arthritis." Examples of allowable structure/function claims include: "helps promote urinary tract health," "helps maintain cardiovascular function" or "promotes relaxation." Further details can be found in *Guidance for Industry: Structure/Function Claims Small Entity Compliance Guide* (January 2002). Also see Chapter 33 Dietary Supplements and Homeopathic Products.

Over-the-Counter (OTC) Drugs

An OTC product is a drug product marketed for use by the consumer without a healthcare professional's intervention. More than 80 therapeutic categories of OTC drugs and more than 100,000 OTC drug products are marketed in the US, encompassing approximately 800 active ingredients. OTC drug oversight is performed by CDER's Office of Nonprescription Drugs.

The distinction between drugs that do and do not require a physician prescription dates back to the 1951 *Durham-Humphrey Amendment* to the *FD&C Act*.[6] FDA applied the principle of retrospective review to OTC drugs starting in 1972. OTC review by expert panels focused on active ingredients (initially, approximately 1,000 different moieties). The agency published the results as a series of monographs in 21 CFR 328–358, specifying the active ingredient(s), restrictions on formulations and labeling by therapeutic category for those drugs deemed appropriate for OTC use.

If the relevant monograph's standards of are met, marketing preclearance of an OTC is not required. An NDA 505(b)(2) can be used to request approval of an OTC drug that deviates in any respect from a final monograph (21 CFR 330.11). However, a Citizen Petition (21 CFR 10.30) is an alternate route that bypasses the *PDUFA* user fee requirements.

"Prescription-to-OTC switch" refers to over-the-counter marketing of a former prescription drug product for the same indication, strength, dose, duration of use, dosage form, population and route of administration. An efficacy supplement to an approved NDA for a prescription product should be submitted if the sponsor plans to switch a drug product covered under an NDA to OTC status in its entirety without a change in the previously approved dosage form or route of administration. An NDA under Section 505(b)(1) should be submitted if the sponsor is proposing to convert some, but not all, of the approved prescription indications to OTC marketing status. An original NDA ((505)(b)(1) or 505(b)(2)) needs to be submitted if the sponsor plans to market a new product whose active substance, indication or dosage form previously has never been marketed OTC (refer to CDER MAPP 6020.5: "Good Review Practice: OND Review Management of INDs and NDAs for Nonprescription Drug Products" (July 2007)).

FDA has approved the switch of a number of drugs from prescription to OTC status under NDAs:

- antidiarrheals (loperamide)
- topical antifungals (clotrimazole, terbinafine)
- antihistamines (clemastine fumarate, loratadine, fexofenadine)
- vaginal antifungals (clotrimazole, miconazole nitrate)
- analgesics (ketoprofen, naproxen sodium, Ibuprofen)
- acid reducers (cimetidine, famotidine)
- hair growth treatments (minoxidil)
- smoking cessation drugs (nicotine polacrilex)
- weight reduction (orlistat)

In allowing these drugs to be sold OTC, FDA considered safety and effectiveness, benefit:risk ratio and whether clear and understandable labeling could be written to enable consumers to safely self-medicate. In 21 CFR 201.66, the agency established standardized content and format for OTC drug product labeling. In addition, manufacturers commonly are required to conduct studies to determine whether consumers understand the proposed OTC labeling and can use the products in a safe and effective manner.[7] OTC product labeling always has contained usage and safety information for consumers. With the introduction of the "Drug Facts" label regulation in 1999, the information became more uniform and easier to read and understand. Patterned after the Nutrition Facts food label, the Drug Facts label uses simple language and an easy-to-read format to help people compare and select OTC medicines and follow dosage instructions. The following information must appear in the indicated order:

- product's active ingredients, including the amount in each dosage unit
- product's purpose
- product uses (indications)
- specific warnings, including when the product should not be used under any circumstances and when it is appropriate to consult with a doctor or pharmacist; this section also describes possible side effects and substances or activities to avoid
- dosage instructions—when, how and how often to take the product
- inactive ingredients, to help consumers avoid ingredients that could cause an allergic reaction

OTC guidances can be found on the FDA website at www.fda.gov/Drugs/GuidanceComplianceRegulatoryInformation/Guidances/ucm065013.htm. See Chapter 17 Over-the-Counter Drugs for more information.

Medical Devices

Overview and Medical Device Classification

A "device" is defined by FDA as an instrument, apparatus, implement, machine, contrivance, implant, in vitro reagent or other similar or related article, including a component part, or accessory that is:

- recognized in the official *National Formulary* or the *United States Pharmacopoeia* or any supplement to them
- intended for use in the diagnosis of disease or other conditions, or in the cure, mitigation, treatment or prevention of disease in man or other animals
- intended to affect the structure or any function of the body of man or other animals, and does not achieve any of its primary intended purposes through chemical action within or on the body of man or other animals and is not dependent upon being metabolized for the achievement of any of its primary intended purposes

Devices first became subject to regulation under the *FD&C Act* (which also defined medical devices for the first time). As a result of the increasing hazards that could result from new, more-complicated devices being introduced in the 1960s and 1970s (e.g., pacemakers, kidney dialysis machines, replacement heart valves), Congress passed the *Medical Device Amendments* in 1976 and heralded the modern age of device regulation. These amendments:

- redefined medical devices to make them more distinct from drugs and expanded the definition to include diagnostics for conditions other than disease
- established safety and effectiveness requirements for devices
- established FDA premarket review
- established the medical device classification system
- created two routes to market (Premarket Notification and Premarket Approval) and established Investigational Device Exemptions (IDEs)

A second milestone in device regulation was the passage of the *Safe Medical Devices Act* (*SMDA*) in 1990. This act:

- extended adverse device incident reporting to user facilities, including hospitals, ambulatory surgical facilities and nursing homes (This was a landmark event because FDA had never extended its jurisdiction so broadly. When a user facility receives information regarding a death caused by a device, it must report it to FDA and the manufacturer. If a user facility receives information about a serious injury or illness caused by a device, it must report it to the manufacturer. A user facility must also submit to FDA an annual summary of its reports to the agency.)
- required device tracking requirements for high-risk devices
- defined substantial equivalence
- required 510(k) submitters to receive FDA clearance prior to marketing
- gave FDA the authority to regulate combination products
- defined the humanitarian device exemption
- gave FDA recall authority

These regulatory milestones gave rise to most of the modern components of the regulations used by FDA's Center for Devices and Radiological Health (CDRH) to fulfill its responsibilities for regulating firms that manufacture, repackage, relabel and/or import medical devices sold in the US.

Because medical devices vary widely in their complexity and benefits or risks, they all do not require the same degree of regulation. Thus, FDA places medical devices into one of three regulatory classes to assure their safety and effectiveness. Device classification depends on intended use and indications for use. In addition, classification is based on the risk the device poses to the patient and/or user. Class I includes devices with the lowest risk and Class III includes those with the greatest risk. The class to which a device is assigned determines the type of premarketing submission/application required. **Table 3-4** summarizes this system.

General controls for all classes include:

- establishment registration of companies required to register under 21 CFR 807.20, such as manufacturers, distributors, repackagers and relabelers; foreign establishments, however, are not required to register with FDA
- medical device listing with FDA
- manufacturing devices in accordance with GMP in 21 CFR 820
- labeling devices in accordance with labeling regulations in 21 CFR 801 or 809
- submission of a premarket notification (510(k)) (unless exempt) before marketing a device

Special controls may include special labeling requirements, mandatory performance standards and postmarket surveillance.

Premarket approval is the required scientific review process to ensure Class III devices' safety and effectiveness, the most stringent regulatory category. Class III devices are those for which insufficient information exists to assure safety and effectiveness solely through general or special controls. They usually support or sustain human life, are of substantial importance in preventing impairment of human health or present a potential, unreasonable risk of illness or injury.

FDA has established classifications for approximately 1,700 different generic types of devices and grouped them into 16 medical specialties, referred to as "panels." Classification of a device can be obtained through the CFR or the CDRH database.

CBER reviews marketing and investigational device submissions (510(k)s, PMAs and IDEs) for medical devices associated with blood collection and processing procedures, as well as those associated with cellular therapies and vaccines. Although these products are reviewed by CBER, the medical device laws and regulations still apply.

It is important for the regulatory professional to ensure a general product definition is available for new devices. Responses to the following questions will help to guide this effort:

- What will the device do? (intended use)
- For what clinical conditions or patient population will the device be used? (indications for use)
- How does the device work? (principles of operation)
- What are the product features? For example, is it electronic versus mechanical, controlled by software or other mechanism, invasive or noninvasive, implanted versus not, sterile versus nonsterile, disposable versus reusable? (product characteristics)
- What risks are inherent in the device's use? (risks)

A designation similar to that for an orphan drug provides an incentive for the development of devices for use in the treatment or diagnosis of diseases affecting small populations. A Humanitarian Use Device (HUD) is intended to benefit patients by treating or diagnosing a disease or condition that affects or is manifested in fewer than 4,000 individuals in the US per year. A request for HUD designation (21 CFR 21 CFR 814 subpart H) needs to be submitted to FDA; if so designated, the device is eligible for a humanitarian device exemption (HDE). An HDE submission is similar in both form and content to a premarket approval (PMA) application, but is exempt from the PMA effectiveness requirements.

An approved HDE authorizes marketing of the HUD. However, an HUD may be used only in facilities with an established a local IRB to supervise clinical testing of devices and after the IRB has approved the use of the device to treat or diagnose the specific disease. The device labeling must state it is an HUD and, although authorized by federal law, its effectiveness for the specific indication has not been demonstrated.

The CDRH website has a number of useful, searchable databases, including one for device classifications, one for 510(k)s, a similar one for PMAs and one for registrations and listings. There is also Device Advice (www.fda.gov/MedicalDevices/DeviceRegulationandGuidance/default.htm), which is very helpful, and a relatively new CDRH Learn site (www.fda.gov/MedicalDevices/ResourcesforYou/Industry/ucm126230.htm) that provides both visual and audio components. Finally, Chapters 20, 21, 22 and 23 of this book are devoted to devices and provide more detailed coverage.

Premarket Notification 510(k) and Exemptions

A sponsor wishing to market a Class I, II or III device intended for human use in the US, for which a PMA is not required, must submit a 510(k) exemption to FDA unless the device is exempt from those requirements and does not exceed the limitations of exemptions in the CFR device classifications as detailed below.

FD&C Act Section 513(d)(2)(A) authorizes FDA to exempt certain generic Class I devices from the 510(k) requirement. FDA has exempted more than 800 generic types of Class I devices and 60 Class II devices from the requirement. It is important to confirm the exempt status and any limitations that apply with 21 CFR 862–892, the CDRH Product Code Classification Database or subsequent *Federal Register* announcements on Class I or II exemptions. The 510(k) exemption has certain limitations, noted in ".9" of each chapter of the regulation.

There is no 510(k) form; however, 21 CFR 807 Subpart E describes requirements for a 510(k) submission. This premarket submission to FDA demonstrates the device to be marketed is as safe and effective as (i.e., substantially equivalent to) a legally marketed predicate device not subject to PMA. A predicate device can be a:

1. pre-amendment device (a currently marketed device that was on the market prior to 1976)
2. device reclassified from Class III to Class II or I
3. device found to be substantially equivalent to a device in the one of the above two categories

A device is substantially equivalent if, in comparison to a predicate, it:

- has the same intended use and the same technological characteristics as the predicate

or

- has the same intended use as the predicate and different technological characteristics and the information submitted to FDA
  - o does not raise new questions of safety and effectiveness
  - o demonstrates the device is at least as safe and effective as the legally marketed device

A claim of substantial equivalence does not mean the new device and the predicate device must be identical. Substantial equivalence is established with respect to intended use, design, energy used or delivered, materials, performance, safety, effectiveness, biocompatibility, standards and other applicable characteristics (e.g., sterility).

FDA determines substantial equivalence, usually within 90 days. If the device is determined to be substantially equivalent, it can be marketed in the US when the submitter receives a letter from the agency (and the sponsor has complied with the general controls provisions). If FDA determines that a device is **not** substantially equivalent (NSE), the applicant may:

- resubmit another 510(k) with new data
- request a Class I or II designation through the *de novo* process
- file a reclassification petition
- submit a PMA

FDASIA included the *Medical Device User Fee Amendments* of 2012 (*MDUFA III*), which introduced, in exchange for user application fees, new performance goals for FDA decision making with respect to a variety of medical device submission types (such as whether or not to clear a premarket notification or 510(k) within 90 days of active FDA review for at least 91% of submissions accepted in Fiscal 2013).

A 510(k)'s content and complexity can vary significantly depending upon the amount of information needed to establish substantial equivalence to the predicate. A typical 510(k) is between 15 and 100 pages. There are three subtypes of 510(k)s: a traditional 510(k), described in 21 CFR 807; a special 510(k); and an abbreviated 510(k) The latter two are described in *The New 510(k) Paradigm—Alternate Approaches to Demonstrating Substantial Equivalence in Premarket Notifications: Final Guidance* (March 1998).

De Novo Classification

FD&C Act Section 513(f)(2), also referred to as *de novo* classification or Evaluation of Automatic Class III Designation, was amended by *FDASIA* Section 607. This new law provides two options for *de novo* classification. First, any sponsor that receives an NSE determination in response to a 510(k) for a device not previously classified under the act, within 30 days of receiving the NSE determination notice, may request FDA to make a risk-based classification of the device under Section 513(a)(1) of the act. Alternatively, any sponsor that determines there is no legally marketed device upon which to base a determination of substantial equivalence may request FDA to make a risk-based classification of the device without first submitting a 510(k).

Investigational Device Exemption (IDE) and Premarket Approval (PMA) Process

An IDE (21 CFR 812) allows the investigational device to be used in a clinical study to collect safety and effectiveness data required to support a PMA application or a Premarket Notification (510(k)) submission to FDA. Clinical studies are conducted most often to support a PMA. Only a small percentage of 510(k)s require clinical data to support the application. Investigational use also includes clinical evaluation of certain modifications or new intended uses of legally marketed devices. All clinical evaluations of investigational devices, unless exempt, must have an approved IDE before the study is initiated. The IDE is similar in content and organization to an IND. The sponsor may begin clinical trials 30 days after FDA receives the IDE, unless the agency objects.

Clinical evaluation of devices that have not been cleared for marketing requires:

- an IDE approved by an IRB; if the study involves a significant risk device, the IDE also must be approved by FDA
- informed consent from all patients
- labeling for investigational use only
- study monitoring
- records and reports

An approved IDE permits a device to be shipped lawfully for the purpose of conducting investigations without complying with other *FD&C Act* requirements that apply to devices in commercial distribution. Sponsors need not submit a PMA or Premarket Notification 510(k), register their establishment or list the device while it is under investigation. IDE sponsors also are exempt from the Quality System Regulation (QSR) except for the requirements for design control.

In an industry of 15,000 manufacturers, where half have fewer than 10 employees, clinical study planning and conduct of a clinical study can have a serious impact on financial resources. For significant risk devices, where trials can be relatively complex and expensive, following the types of processes used for industry-sponsored drug trials is advisable to protect the validity of the company's investment. This should include the use of clinical study protocols, informed consent forms that meet FDA regulations (21 CFR 50) and are reviewed by duly constituted IRBs (21 CFR 56), source documents at the investigational sites, clinical study reports and well-written investigator agreements that include not only financial aspects (see 21 CFR 54) but also compliance with the study protocol and IDE responsibilities.

PMA is FDA's review process to evaluate Class III medical devices' safety and effectiveness. Due to the level of risk associated with Class III devices, FDA has determined that general and special controls alone are insufficient to assure their safety and effectiveness. Therefore, these devices require a PMA application (21 CFR 814).

A PMA is the most stringent device marketing application type required by FDA. The applicant must receive FDA approval of its PMA application prior to marketing the device. Approval is based on a determination by FDA the PMA contains sufficient valid scientific evidence to ensure the device is safe and effective for its intended use(s). An approved PMA is, in effect, a private license granting the applicant (or owner) permission to market the device. The PMA owner, however, can authorize use of its data by another.

The PMA application is similar in content and organization to a traditional (non-CTD format) NDA application, although with much less clinical data required. FDA has observed problems with study designs, study conduct, data analyses, presentations and conclusions. Sponsors always should consult all applicable FDA guidance documents, industry standards and recommended practices. Numerous device-specific FDA guidance documents are available. Although FDA has 180 days to review the PMA, in reality this usually takes longer, due to the frequent involvement of an Advisory Committee.

User Fees—Medical Devices

The Medical Device User Fee and Modernization Act **of 2002** (*MDUFMA*) was enacted "in order to provide the Food and Drug Administration (FDA) with the resources necessary to better review medical devices, to enact needed regulatory reforms so that medical device manufacturers can bring their safe and effective devices to the American people at an earlier time, and to ensure that reprocessed medical devices are as safe and effective as original devices." Medical device companies pay fees to FDA when they register their establishments and list their devices with the agency, whenever they submit an application or a notification to market a new medical device in the US and for certain other types of submissions. For more information on fees, by type of application, device or establishment, see: http://www.fda.gov/MedicalDevices/ResourcesforYou/Industry/ucm407660.htm and http://www.fda.gov/MedicalDevices/DeviceRegulationandGuidance/Overview/MedicalDeviceUserFeeandModernizationActMDUFMA/

Establishment Registration and Medical Device Listing

Establishments involved in the production and distribution of medical devices intended for marketing or leasing (commercial distribution) in the US are required to register with FDA. This process is known as establishment registration. Registration provides FDA with the location of medical device manufacturing facilities and importers. An establishment is defined as any place of business under one management at one physical location at which a device is manufactured, assembled or otherwise processed for commercial distribution. The "owner/operator" is defined as the corporation, subsidiary, affiliated company, partnership or proprietor directly responsible for the activities of the registering establishment. The owner/operator is responsible for registering the establishment.

The regulations for establishment registration are provided in 21 CFR 807. As of 1 October 2007, all establishment registrations and listings must be submitted electronically using FDA's Unified Registration and Listing System (FURLS)/Device Registration and Listing Module (DRLM), unless a waiver has been granted. Congress also authorized FDA to implement a user fee for certain types of establishment registrations. Establishment registration is not an FDA approval of the establishment or its products. That is, it does not provide FDA clearance to market. Unless exempt, premarketing clearance or approval is required before a device can be placed into commercial distribution in the US.

Most medical device establishments required to register with FDA also must identify the devices they have in commercial distribution, including those produced exclusively for export. This process is known as medical device listing and is a means of keeping FDA advised of the generic category(s) of devices an establishment is manufacturing or marketing. The regulations for medical device listing also are provided in 21 CFR 807.

Combination Drug-Device and Drug-Drug Products

Combination products (i.e., drug-device, drug-biologic and device-biologic products, formally defined in 21 CFR 3.2(e)) have been regulated for decades. Prior to 1990, FDA regulated such products on a case-by-case basis. Generally, the sponsor and FDA negotiated an *ad hoc* regulatory approach without explicit statutory guidance. As combination products multiplied and increased in complexity, the *ad hoc* approach no longer was satisfactory, and in 1990, Congress enacted the *SMDA*. This provision required the agency to designate a center (CDER, CBER or CDRH) with primary jurisdiction based on the product's primary mode of action. FDA issued intercenter agreements between the three centers in 1991; however, there still were a number of problems with this approach.[8]

As part of the *Medical Device User Fee and Modernization Act* of 2002 (*MDUFMA*), Congress established the Office of Combination Products (OCP) within FDA's Office of the Commissioner to ensure prompt assignment of combination products to FDA centers and oversee coordination of their development and approval processes.

By submitting a Request for Designation (RFD), a company may obtain a formal agency determination of a combination product's primary mode of action and assignment of the lead center for the its premarket review and regulation. OCP will make a determination within 60 days of receipt of the RFD. *Guidance for Industry: How to Write a Request for Designation* (April 2011) and *Draft Guidance for Industry and FDA Staff: Classification of Products as Drugs and Devices & Additional Product Classification Issues* (June 2011) each provide more specifics. Chapter 27 Combination Products provides additional details.

Summary

The development of biologics, drugs and devices is a scientific process in the context of objective and subjective interpretations of a product's potential or actual risks and benefits. The scope, interpretation and application of US federal regulations that must be met to market a drug or device have evolved over the past century and are documented in the CFR. This translates into agency use of scientific review, standards, manufacturing and other inspections, advertising controls, conditional approvals, laboratory product testing and postmarketing pharmacovigilance activities. Over the last 25 years, a plethora of FDA and ICH guidelines have been issued to assist in interpreting and defining the processes needed to develop drugs, biologics and devices successfully for marketing in a regulated industry.

A "drug" is defined as a product used in diagnosing, curing, mitigating, treating or preventing a disease or affecting a structure or function of the body. A "biologic" is defined as a substance derived from or made with the aid of living organisms. Drug development consists of characterizing the safety profile (risk) and the efficacy profile (benefit) as it relates to the body's exposure to the drug (pharmacokinetic profile). The most successful drugs are those with minimal risk and maximum benefit.

The relationship between FDA and an investigational drug product sponsor can begin very early in the process (before the sponsor submits an IND) and extend through the typical IND development process (often defined as Phases 1, 2 and 3) to a marketing application and post-approval commitments, safety surveillance and product lifecycle management. Meetings with FDA are important components of the IND process. Meetings can be requested at any time for any valid reason, but FDA will decide whether there is sufficient justification for a meeting (usually dictated by the product background and draft questions submitted in a written meeting request) or whether a written response to questions and/or a teleconference would suffice.

Sponsors can submit a request for a Special Protocol Assessment (SPA). Within 45 days of receipt, FDA will evaluate certain protocols and related issues to determine whether they meet scientific and regulatory requirements identified by the sponsor. Three types of protocols are eligible for an SPA under the *PDUFA* goals—animal carcinogenicity protocols, final product stability protocols and clinical protocols for Phase 3 trials whose data will form the basis for an efficacy claim (i.e., a pivotal trial).

The *Orphan Drug Act*, for the first time, provided incentives for the development of drugs necessary, and often life-saving, for patients with rare diseases (defined as a US prevalence of fewer than 200,000 patients) but with minimal prospects for commercial return on investment.

The fast track and Breakthrough Therapy designation programs are designed to facilitate the development and expedite the review of new drugs intended to treat serious or life-threatening conditions and demonstrate the potential to address unmet medical needs. A sponsor may request fast track or Breakthrough Therapy designation at any point in the development process. A product designated as fast track or Breakthrough Therapy is eligible for heightened FDA interest in sponsor meetings, a greater probability of priority marketing application review and piecemeal submission of portions (complete CTD modules) of a marketing application ("rolling NDA/BLA").

ICH was formed in 1990. It brings together the regulatory authorities of the EU, Japan and the US and experts from the pharmaceutical industry in the three regions to discuss scientific and technical aspects of product registration. ICH recommends ways to achieve greater harmonization in interpreting and applying technical guidelines and requirements for product registration to reduce or avoid duplicating testing during the research and development of new drugs.

The ICH process has resulted in numerous guidelines in four major categories—quality, safety, efficacy and multidisciplinary. Two important aspects of the ICH endeavor are the CTD concept and *MedDRA*.

Before initiating a clinical trial in the US (other than bioequivalence studies to support an ANDA), the sponsor must submit nonclinical, CMC and previous human experience data (if applicable) to FDA in the form of an IND. The IND application requests permission to initiate clinical trials. It is not a request for approval; rather, it is a request for exemption from federal law requiring an approved NDA or BLA prior to transporting or distributing a drug in interstate commerce. For a new chemical entity (NCE), the initial IND is a major milestone because it summarizes the data that support moving a drug from *in vitro* and animal testing into evaluation in humans. Sponsors are able to initiate their proposed clinical trial if they have not received any communication from FDA within 30 days of FDA receipt of the initial IND application.

The culmination of a drug or biologic development program is the preparation and submission of a marketing application (NDA or BLA). This is accomplished through either studies conducted by (or with a right of reference from) the sponsor (505(b)(1) approach) or by reference to FDA's finding of safety and effectiveness for a previously approved product (Section 505(b)(2) approach). Through frequent interactions with FDA during the development program, including a Pre-NDA meeting, sponsor and agency expectations should be aligned reasonably well. Items to be considered when preparing a marketing application include package inserts (labeling), electronic submissions, risk evaluation and mitigation strategies (REMS), proprietary names, user fees, preapproval inspections (PAIs), establishment listings, patent restoration, other peri-approval activities and NDA amendments and supplements.

The modern era of generic drugs was born with passage of the *Hatch-Waxman Act*. This act expedited the availability of less-costly generic drugs by permitting FDA to approve abbreviated applications after the innovator drug patent had expired. These abbreviated applications generally are not required to include animal safety and clinical data to establish safety and effectiveness. Specifically, a generic drug product is comparable to the innovator drug product in dosage form, strength, route of administration, quality, performance characteristics and intended use.

A dietary supplement is a product taken by mouth that contains a "dietary ingredient" intended to supplement the diet. *DSHEA* created a new regulatory framework for dietary supplement safety and labeling (still under the regulatory umbrella of foods). *DSHEA* provisions define dietary supplements and dietary ingredients and describe the proper use of nutritional support statements. *DSHEA* set forth new labeling requirements and required dietary supplement manufacturers to notify FDA of new dietary ingredients prior to marketing. It also authorized FDA to prescribe GMPs for the industry. Dietary supplements do not require FDA premarket approval. The manufacturer is responsible for ensuring a dietary supplement is safe before it is marketed. *DSHEA* places the burden on FDA to prove a marketed dietary supplement is unsafe (including noncompliance with CGMPs) prior to any action to remove the product from the market.

An OTC product is a drug product marketed for use by the consumer without a healthcare professional's intervention. Oversight of OTC drugs is performed by CDER's Office of Nonprescription Drugs. In allowing drugs to be sold OTC, FDA considers safety and effectiveness, benefit-risk ratio and whether clear and understandable labeling can be written to enable consumers to safely self-medicate.

A "device" is defined as an instrument, apparatus, implement, machine, contrivance, implant, in vitro reagent or other similar or related article, including a component part or accessory that meets a number of conditions.

FDA places medical devices into one of three regulatory classes based on the level of control necessary to ensure their safety and effectiveness. Device classification depends on intended use and indications for use, and the risk the device poses to the patient and/or user. Class I includes devices with the lowest risk and Class III includes those with the greatest risk. The class to which a device is assigned determines the type of premarketing submission or application required for marketing.

A sponsor wishing to market a Class I, II or III device intended for human use, for which a PMA is not required, must submit a 510(k) exemption to FDA unless the device is exempt from those requirements and does not exceed the limitations of exemptions in the CFR device classifications. A 510(k)'s content and complexity can vary significantly depending on the amount of information needed to establish substantial equivalence to the proposed predicate.

Premarket approval is the required scientific review process to ensure a Class III device's safety and effectiveness. Class III devices are those for which insufficient information exists to ensure safety and effectiveness solely through general or special controls. They usually support or sustain human life, are of substantial importance in preventing impairment of human health or present a potential, unreasonable risk of illness or injury. An IDE allows the investigational device to be used in a clinical study to collect safety and effectiveness data required to support a PMA application or a Premarket Notification (510(k)) submission.

Combination products are defined as drug-device, drug-biologic and device-biologic products. As part of *MDUFMA*, Congress established the Office of Combination Products to ensure prompt assignment of combination products to FDA centers and oversee coordination of their development and approval processes. By submitting a Request for Designation (RFD), a company may obtain a formal agency determination of a combination product's primary mode of action and assignment of the lead center for the product's premarket review and regulation.

References

1. Bren L. "The Road to the Biologic Revolution—Highlights of 100 Years of Biologics Regulation." FDA Consumer Magazine, January–February 2006. http://www.fda.gov/AboutFDA/WhatWeDo/History/FOrgsHistory/CBER/ucm135758.htm. Accessed 24 April 2013.
2. Brown-Tuttle ME. "Researching the 505(b)(2) Application." *Regulatory Affairs Focus*, May 2004; pp. 12–14.
3. Ibid.

4. FDA. Abbreviated New Drug Application (ANDA): Generics. FDA website. www.fda.gov/Drugs/DevelopmentApprovalProcess/HowDrugsareDevelopedandApproved/ApprovalApplications/AbbreviatedNewDrugApplicationANDAGenerics/. Accessed 24 April 2013.
5. Jiang T and Zhang S. "Stringent Laws and Regulations for Dietary Supplements." *Drug Information Journal*, Vol. 43; No. 1. pp. 75–81. (2009)
6. Op cit 1.
7. Hellbusch SJ. "Involving the End User in the Development of Label Wording." *Regulatory Affairs Focus*, May 2004, pp. 48–51.
8 Kahan JS and Shapiro JK. "FDA's Regulation of Combination Products: The Road Ahead." *Regulatory Compliance Newsletter*. November 2003, pp. 37–40.

Chapter 4

FDA Communications and Meetings

Updated by Helen M. Ribbans, MBA, FRAPS

OBJECTIVES

- ❑ Provide a detailed overview of the four basic types of FDA communications and meetings:
  - o administrative meetings and communications
  - o regulatory communications—FDA and company initiated
  - o product application meetings (between a sponsor and the Center for Device Evaluation and Research (CDER), the Center for Biologics Evaluation and Research (CBER) and/or the Center for Devices and Radiological Health (CDRH))
  - o public administrative proceedings

LAWS, REGULATIONS AND GUIDELINES COVERED IN THIS CHAPTER

- ❑ 21 CFR 10 Administrative Practices and Procedures
- ❑ 21 CFR 12 Formal Evidentiary Public Hearing
- ❑ 21 CFR 13 Public Hearing Before a Public Board of Inquiry
- ❑ 21 CFR 14 Public Hearing Before a Public Advisory Committee
- ❑ 21 CFR 15 Public Hearing Before the Commissioner
- ❑ 21 CFR 16 Regulatory Hearing Before the Food and Drug Administration
- ❑ 21 CFR 30 Citizen Petition
- ❑ 21 CFR 312 Investigational New Drug Application
- ❑ 21 CFR 314 Applications for FDA Approval to Market a New Drug
- ❑ 21 CFR 812 Investigational Device Exemptions
- ❑ *Guidance for Industry and Food and Drug Administration Staff: Requests for Feedback on Medical Device Submissions: The Pre-Submission Program and Meetings with Food and Drug Administration Staff* (February 2014)
- ❑ *Guidance for Industry: Expedited Programs for Serious Conditions—Drugs and Biologics* (May 2014)
- ❑ *Draft Guidance for Industry: Formal Meetings Between the FDA and Sponsors or Applicants of PDUFA Products* (March 2015)
- ❑ *Early Collaboration Meetings Under the FDA Modernization Act (FDAMA); Final Guidance for industry and CDRH Staff* (2001)

- ❑ *Guidance on PMA Interactive Procedures for Day-100 Meetings and Subsequent Deficiencies—for Use by CDRH and Industry*

- ❑ *Guidance for Industry and Food and Drug Administration Staff: Center for Devices and Radiological Health Appeals Process* (May 2013)

- ❑ *Guidance for the Public, FDA Advisory Committee Members, and FDA Staff: Public Availability of Advisory Committee Members Financial Interest Information and Waivers* (March 2014)

- ❑ *Guidance for the Public, FDA Advisory Committee Members, and FDA Staff: Procedures for Determining Conflict of Interest and Eligibility for Participation in Advisory Committee* (August 2008)

- ❑ *Guidance for FDA Advisory Committee Members and FDA Staff: Voting Procedures for Advisory Committee Meetings* (August 2008)

- ❑ *Guidance for Industry: Advisory Committee Meetings—Preparation and Public Availability of Information Given to Advisory Committee Members* (August 2008)

- ❑ *Guidance for the Public, FDA Advisory Committee Members, and FDA Staff: The Open Public Hearing at FDA Advisory Committee Meetings* (May 2013)

Introduction

Successful communication between the US Food and Drug Administration (FDA) and the industries it regulates is a key component to ensure successful product development. These communications can promote an understanding of regulatory processes and regulatory compliance.

Understanding the types of communications and meetings, and the purpose, format and timeline of each is critical to the success of regulatory professionals and companies they represent and vital to achieving desired objectives effectively and efficiently.

Types of Communications

The four primary types of communications applicable to drugs, biologics, devices and combination drug/device products are:

1. administrative meetings and communications
2. regulatory communications—FDA and company initiated
3. product application meetings (between a sponsor and CDER, CBER and/or CDRH)
4. public administrative proceedings

The various types of communications are detailed in the Code of Federal Regulations (CFR) Title 21. In addition, FDA has issued numerous guidance documents providing valuable information on mechanisms available to facilitate meetings and communications with FDA.

1. Administrative Meetings and Communications

Administrative meetings and communications can be ad hoc, private two-way communications (telephone, email or in person) between FDA and outside persons on matters within FDA's jurisdiction,[1] for example, discussions between an FDA regulatory project manager and company representative regarding any aspect of the sponsor's application. Dispute resolution utilizing an ombudsman is another example of an administrative communication between the agency and a sponsor; the ombudsman investigates and facilitates timely resolution related to issues, such as scheduling meetings, obtaining timely response to queries or obtaining timely completion of pending reviews. These administrative meetings also may be public FDA meetings to discuss matters pending before the agency; when needed, the agency will prepare a transcript, recording or memorandum summarizing the meeting's substance; the agency also will include written summaries from participants in its administrative file.

2. Regulatory Communications

Regulatory communications can be divided into those communications initiated by FDA and those initiated by a company or applicant.

FDA-initiated regulatory communications include regulations, guidance documents and recommendations.

FDA Regulations

FDA regulations are published in the *Federal Register;* proposed regulations are issued for public comment.

FDA Guidance Documents

Guidance documents describe the agency's interpretation of regulatory issues or policies and are positioned as recommendations.[2] Guidances are prepared by FDA staff and may include input from sponsors or the public. Compared to regulations, guidances are non-binding (not legally enforceable). However, when sponsors choose to follow an alternate approach, the agency expects appropriate justification to be provided.

FDA Recommendations

FDA recommendations provide advice on specific regulatory policy. They may be disseminated in the *Federal Register* or via

Figure 4-1. Timeline for Meetings During Drug and Biologics Development

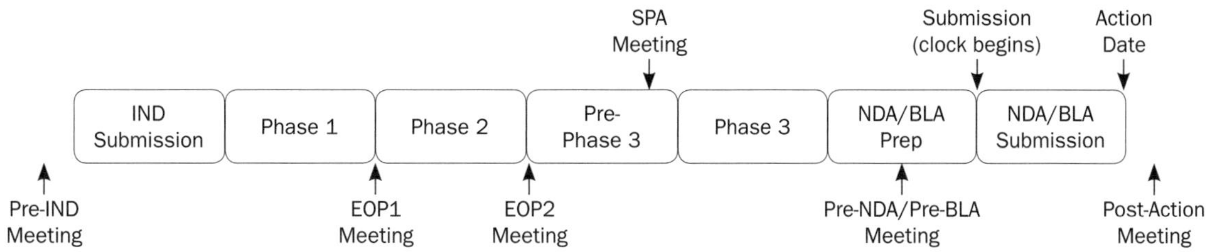

emails to a specific audience. Generally, they provide advice that does not involve direct regulatory action under law.

Company- or applicant-initiated regulatory communications include Citizen Petitions and Suitability Petitions, a type of Citizen Petition.

Citizen Petitions

A Citizen Petition is a formal written request to FDA asking the agency to take or refrain from taking an administrative action. A Citizen Petition is submitted to the Division of Dockets Management where it is assigned a docket number. Interested parties' comments on a Citizen Petition, or subsequent submissions related to the petition, should reference the docket number. FDA must respond within 180 days of receipt by: approving the petition, denying the petition and providing the rationale for the denial, or providing a tentative response explaining why the agency is unable to reach a decision on the Citizen Petition. A Citizen Petition should contain:[3]

- action requested
- statement of grounds
- environmental impact
- economic impact
- a certification (by the submitter)

Suitability Petitions

This is a specific type of Citizen Petition allowing the sponsor to file an abbreviated application for either a human or animal drug whose active ingredient(s), route of administration, dosage form or strength differ from the approved drug. FDA will approve or deny a Suitability Petition within 90 days of receipt.

3. Product and Device Application Meetings

Product Application Meetings

Three main types of product application meetings for drugs and biologics can be requested: Type A, Type B and Type C *(Draft Guidance for Industry: Formal Meetings Between the FDA and Sponsors or Applicants of PDUFA Products)*. These are formal meetings held with FDA at critical points during product development and regulatory review to discuss the sponsor's marketing applications for investigational drugs and biologics.

These application meetings are requested by the sponsor and usually are conducted in person or by telephone. As per the March 2015 draft guidance, FDA also has the option of providing written responses to the sponsor rather than granting a live (in person or by phone) meeting for Type B pre-Investigational New Drug (IND) and Type C guidance meetings.[4]

The meetings follow a systematic approach and well-defined procedures.

An overview of the timeline for drug and biologic submissions and meetings is shown in **Figure 4-1**.

Type A meetings are critical meetings to address a stalled development program. Examples include: dispute resolution, clinical hold, Special Protocol Assessment (SPA) and post-action meetings. FDA guidance suggests the sponsor first contact the review division within CDER or CBER prior to requesting a meeting. Type A meetings usually are held within 30 days of FDA's receipt of the written request and briefing package.

Type B meetings are pivotal meetings that may occur: prior to submission of the IND Application (pre-IND meeting); in some cases, at the End-of-Phase 1 (EOP1); at the conclusion of Phase 2 (End-of-Phase 2 (EOP2)/Pre-Phase 3 Meetings); and before submission of the New Drug Application (NDA) or Biologics License Application (BLA) (pre-NDA or pre-BLA meeting). In addition, pre-emergency use authorization meetings, post-action meetings, and meetings regarding REMS or postmarketing requirements are considered Type B meetings. According to FDA guidance, Type B meetings should be scheduled within 60 days of FDA's receipt of the meeting request. Generally, FDA does not grant more than one of each Type B meeting for a drug or biologic under development for a single application.

Type C meetings are any other product development or guidance meeting not included as Type A or Type B. As per FDA guidance, Type C meetings should be scheduled within 75 days of FDA's receipt of the written meeting request.

If a meeting date is requested for a Type A, B or C meeting beyond 30, 60 or 75 days, respectively, the meeting date should be within 14 days of the requested date.[5]

For drugs and biologics being developed to treat serious conditions, additional opportunities are available for frequent interactions between sponsors and FDA, to expedite development and regulatory review. These are defined in *Guidance for Industry: Expedited Programs for Serious Conditions–Drugs and Biologics.* Fast Track Designation is granted for drugs or biologics intended to treat a serious condition, when nonclinical or clinical data demonstrate the potential to address an unmet medical need or for a drug designated a qualified infectious disease product. Breakthrough Designation is granted for drugs or biologics intended to treat a serious condition where preliminary clinical evidence suggests substantial improvement over available therapies;[6] products granted Breakthrough Designation qualify for Type B meetings to discuss the overall development program[7] and may qualify for Type A meetings as well.

Each written meeting request should include the meeting's objective(s) and rationale, issues to be discussed and a list of questions the sponsor wishes to address. Upon receipt, the meeting request is reviewed, and the CDER or CBER division director or designee determines whether the meeting will be granted or denied. FDA intends to notify the sponsor within 14 days for Type A meetings and 21 days for Type B and C meetings. If the meeting is granted, CDER or CBER will provide the sponsor with meeting details including meeting type, date, time, length, location and expected FDA participants.

After a meeting is granted, the sponsor prepares a meeting/briefing package. The meeting package, which reiterates the meeting's objectives, includes the final list of questions to be addressed or resolved at the meeting and sufficient details to allow FDA to prepare for the meeting and provide responses to the sponsor's questions. The briefing package for a Type A meeting should be included as part of the Type A meeting request. For Type B and Type C meetings, the briefing package should be submitted at least one month before the formal meeting.

Per FDA guidance, the meeting request should include sufficient information for FDA to assess the meeting's utility and determine the FDA staff needed to discuss and resolve the sponsor's issues and respond to questions. FDA suggests the following components be included in the written meeting request:[8]

1. product name
2. application number (if applicable)
3. chemical name and structure
4. proposed indication(s) or context of product development
5. type of meeting requested (Type A, B or C); if Type A, include the rationale and meeting package
6. a brief statement of the meeting's purpose and objectives; the statement should include a brief background of the issues underlying the agenda, i.e., enough information to facilitate understanding the issues
7. proposed agenda with estimated times for each item
8. list of proposed questions listed by discipline; for each question, include a brief explanation of the question's context and purpose
9. list of individuals representing the sponsor (with titles and affiliations) who will attend the meeting
10. list of FDA staff, by title or discipline, sponsor requests to attend the meeting
11. suggested date(s) and time (morning or afternoon) for the meeting within or beyond the meeting type timeframe; include nonavailable dates and times
12. meeting format (written response, face-to-face or teleconference)

The meeting package should provide summary information relevant to the product under development; this includes much of the same information (in a slightly different order) included in the meeting request as well ast sufficient background and supplementary data to allow FDA to reply to sponsor issues and questions raised in the agenda. Meeting packages should be limited to a single volume. In addition to submitting the appropriate number of copies of the meeting package to the referenced application, desk copies for the agency meeting attendees also are provided. The agency prefers the archival copy of the meeting package to be submitted electronically[9] (in PDF format).

The meeting package generally includes the following information:[10]

1. product name and application number (if applicable)
2. chemical name and structure
3. proposed indication
4. dosage form, route of administration and dosing regimen (frequency and duration)
5. updated list of sponsor attendees, affiliations and titles
6. background section that includes:
    - a brief history of the development program and events leading up to the meeting
    - product development status (target indication for use)
7. brief statement summarizing the meeting's purpose
8. proposed agenda with estimated times for each item
9. list of final questions, grouped by discipline, with a brief summary prior to each question to explain its rationale or context
10. data to support discussion organized by discipline and question

Table 4-1. Description of FDA Product Application Meetings and Associated Timelines

	Type A Meeting	Type B Meeting	Type C Meeting
Meeting Description	• Dispute resolution • Clinical holds • Pre-emergency use authorization • Special Protocol Assessment (SPA) • Post-action meeting*	• Pre-IND • Breakthrough Designation • EOP1 • EOP2 • Pre-NDA/Pre-BLA • REMs • Post-action meeting*	• Any other meeting not identified as Type A or B
Confirmation of scheduling following sponsor request	14 days from time of request	21 days from time of request	21 days from time of request
Timing window for meeting to occur	30 days from time of request	60 days from time of request	75 days from time of request
Relevant questions and sufficient briefing information for discussions with FDA	Included in meeting request	At least one month prior to meeting	At least one month prior to meeting
*Post-action meetings can be granted as Type A or Type B depending on the elapsed time between the meeting request and the regulatory action other than approval, i.e., within three months for Type A and ≥ three months for Type B.			

Table 4-1 summarizes each meeting type and provides an overview of the associated timelines.

Communications During and After Product Application Meetings with FDA

FDA's goal is to provide preliminary comments to the sponsor's questions no later than two days[11] before Type A, B or C meetings. These preliminary comments result from internal discussions between agency personnel prior to the meeting, to promote collaborative and successful discussions between the agency and sponsor. Advance receipt of the preliminary meeting comments also provides an opportunity for the sponsor to cancel the meeting (if all answers are clear and no further discussion is needed), change the meeting format (e.g., from face-to face to teleconference) or adjust the agenda to focus on those questions and responses requiring further discussion or clarification.

The agency's preliminary meeting comments help the sponsor prepare for the meeting. Preparation usually includes formal rehearsal meetings where the sponsor carefully reviews the preliminary comments and determines which questions and responses require further discussion or clarification, allowing it to focus on the most important issues to be discussed at the meeting.

It is important for the sponsor to assign a meeting attendee to take notes of the discussions, agreements and action items. Although FDA will update its preliminary meeting comments to reflect the meeting with the goal of issuing its official meeting minutes within 30 days,[12] it is prudent for sponsors to document and retain their own meeting minutes. In addition, although FDA's meeting minutes are the official meeting record, the sponsor also can submit its minutes. When FDA's final meeting minutes are received, the sponsor should review them carefully and notify the agency of any significant differences in understanding regarding the meeting outcomes.

Medical Device Application Meetings

Multiple types of meetings and feedback mechanisms are available to sponsors of medical device applications submitted to CDRH. As detailed in *Guidance for Industry and Food and Drug Administration Staff: Requests for Feedback on Medical Device Submissions: The Pre-Submission Program and Meetings with Food and Drug Administration Staff* (February 2014), these include:[13]

1. presubmissions
2. formal early collaboration meetings (agreement and determination meetings)
3. submission issue meetings
4. PMA Day-100 meetings

Presubmissions

Presubmissions provide the sponsor an opportunity to obtain feedback and advice prior to submitting an Investigational Device Exemption (IDE) or marketing application.[14] This voluntary program allows sponsors to receive guidance regarding questions related, but not limited, to product development, planned nonclinical evaluations, proposed clinical study protocols and statistical design. Feedback can be received in writing (email or facsimile) or via a face-to-face meeting or teleconference. FDA strives to provide complete feedback within 75–90 days of receipt of a Presub package.

The Presub package should include relevant background information and questions for FDA. The preferred content should include:[15]

1. cover letter

2. table of contents
3. device description
4. proposed intended use or indications for use
5. previous discussions or agreements
6. overview of product development
7. specific questions
8. method of feedback; include proposed dates and times, planned attendees and duration of meeting if a meeting or teleconference is requested

A Presub package for a PMA also should include a summary of general considerations with an overview of the proposed application's format and content for nonclinical, clinical, statistical, labeling and postapproval study (if applicable) sections.

Formal Early Collaboration Meetings

The two types of formal early collaboration meetings are Agreement Meetings and Determination Meetings.[16] These meetings provide clear direction regarding testing and development of devices requiring clinical investigations prior to marketing. The timeframe for the meeting or teleconference is generally 30 days. Determinations or agreements resulting from these meetings are binding.

An Agreement Meeting's objective is to reach agreement with FDA on key parameters of the investigational plan, including clinical protocol, for a Class III device or implant.

Determination Meetings are applicable to PMAs or Product Development Protocol (PDP) applications. These meetings provide the sponsor with valid scientific evidence necessary to demonstrate the device is effective for its intended use. Discussions at these meetings focus on whether clinical studies are needed to establish effectiveness; in consultation with the sponsor, FDA seeks to determine the least burdensome way of evaluating effectiveness.

Submission Issue Meetings

Submission Issue Meetings are held at a sponsor's request to discuss deficiencies identified by FDA during review of a premarket submission, i.e., 510(k), IDE, PMA, etc. FDA's goal is to grant the meeting within 21 days of the request's receipt.[17] The objective of the in-person meeting or teleconference is to discuss the agency's requests for additional information and ensure the sponsor's planned approach for a formal response fully address the application's deficiencies.

PMA Day-100 Meetings

PMA Day-100 Meetings are held to discuss the PMA's review status.[18] To allow sufficient time for scheduling, FDA prefers requests for this type of meeting be included in the original PMA. Alternatively, the meeting can be requested no later than 70 days from the date of the PMA submission. Prior to the meeting, FDA will conduct an interim review of the application to identify any deficiencies and the information needed to correct the deficiencies. FDA provides this information to the sponsor either by day 90 in the review cycle or at least 10 days prior to the scheduled meeting to facilitate a meaningful dialog during the meeting.

4. Public Administrative Proceedings

In response to the public's demand for FDA policy and procedure transparency, formal public administrative proceedings (meetings) have been established. Five types of Public Administrative Proceedings (meetings) are held (the first three are more frequently than the last two):

1. Advisory Committee Meeting
2. Public Regulatory Hearing
3. Public Workshop
4. Board of Inquiry
5. Evidentiary Hearing

Advisory Committee Meeting

Subject matter experts provide recommendations and advice to the agency on food, drug, biologic and medical device safety and efficacy and policy in areas related to product approvals, labeling, scientific issues and research projects.[19] Advisory Committees are composed of independent experts and public representatives. The *Food and Drug Administration Amendment Act* of 2007 (*FDAAA*) mandates FDA to convene an Advisory Committee for all new molecular entities or provide an explanation as to why one is not required.[20] Although Advisory Committees provide recommendations to FDA, the agency makes the final decision.

As with the other types of sponsor and FDA communications and meetings discussed in this chapter, Advisory Committee Meetings follow established policies and procedures.[21,22]

See Chapter 5 Preparing for Key FDA Meetings and Advisory Committee Meetings for details regarding these meetings.

Public Regulatory Hearing

The commissioner holds a public regulatory hearing to obtain additional information before making a decision or taking a regulatory action, providing a forum for individuals to present information and views on matters pending at the agency. Under 21 CFR 16, public regulatory hearings are called at the commisioner's discretion. A PMA withdrawal or IRB disqualification are examples of possible regulatory hearings.

Public Workshop

FDA Public Workshops are held to share information and gather information. Notification of public workshops appears in the *Federal Register*.

Board of Inquiry

A public hearing before a Board of Inquiry is convened at the FDA commissioner's discretion when authorized by regulation or as an alternative to a formal evidentiary hearing.[23] Most often, the purpose is to review medical, scientific or scientific issues. Notice of Board of Inquiry hearings is published in the *Federal Register*. The proceedings are informal; it is not a legal trial.

Evidentiary Hearing

A formal evidentiary hearing[24] occurs when specifically provided by law, when mandated by Congress or when ordered by the FDA commissioner to discuss public health concerns about a product.

Summary

Collaborative communications between FDA, sponsors and the public generally are divided into four categories: administrative meetings or communications, regulatory communications, product application meetings and public administrative proceedings. Each type of communication has a specific objective and purpose. It is critical for regulatory professionals' success to become familiar with the expectations and responsibilities for each type of meeting.

FDA publishes guidance documents on how to successfully communicate with the agency. Prior to meeting or communicating with FDA, regulatory professionals should ensure they and their organizations are up-to-date on the FDA's most recent guidances on meetings and communications. Regulatory professionals should ensure all participating parties are trained in procedures and proper conduct for the meeting or communication. The sponsor's records of the meeting and communications should be compared carefully to FDA's records. If discrepancies are found, the sponsor should notify the agency to discuss differences so an addendum to FDA's official meeting minutes, effecting a change to the minutes or documentation of any continued objections by the sponsor, can be issued.

References

1. 21 CFR 10.65(a) Meetings and Correspondence. FDA website. www.accessdata.fda.gov/scripts/cdrh/cfdocs/cfcfr/CFRSearch.cfm?fr=10.65. Accessed 30 March 2015.
2. 21 CFR 10.115 Good Guidance Practices. FDA website. www.accessdata.fda.gov/scripts/cdrh/cfdocs/cfcfr/cfrsearch.cfm?fr=10.115. Accessed 30 March 2015.
3. 21 CFR 10.30 Citizen Petition. FDA website. www.accessdata.fda.gov/scripts/cdrh/cfdocs/cfcfr/cfrsearch.cfm?fr=10.30. Accessed 30 March 2015.
4. FDA. *Guidance for Industry: Formal Meetings Between the FDA and Sponsors or Applicants of PDUFA Products (Draft Guidance* March 2015*)*. FDA website. www.fda.gov/downloads/drugs/guidancecomplianceregulatoryinformation/guidances/ucm153222.pdf. Accessed 1 April 2015.
5. Ibid, page 4.
6. Section 902 of the *Food and Drug Administration Safety and Innovation Act (FDASIA)*, in effect January 2012.
7. FDA. *Guidance for Industry: Expedited Programs for Serious Conditions – Drugs and Biologics*. FDA website. www.fda.gov/downloads/drugs/guidancecomplianceregulatoryinformation/guidances/ucm358301.pdf. Accessed 1 April 2015.
8. Op cit 4, pages 6–7.
9. Ibid, page 10.
10. Ibid, pages 10–11.
11. Ibid, page 11.
12. Ibid, page 12.
13. FDA. *Guidance for Industry and Food and Drug Administration Staff: Requests for Feedback on Medical Device Submission: The Pre-Submission Program and Meetings with Food and Drug Administration Staff.* FDA website. www.fda.gov/ucm/groups/fdagov-public/@fdagov-meddev-gen/documents/document/ucm311176.pdf. Accessed 1 April 2015.
14. Ibid, page 8.
15. Ibid, page 12–17.
16. FDA. *Early Collaboration Meetings Under the FDA Modernization Act (FDAMA); Final Guidance for Industry and CDRH Staff.* FDA website. www.fda.gov/downloads/MedicalDevices/DeviceRegulationandGuidance/GuidanceDocuments/ucm073611.pdf. Accessed 1 April 2015.
17. Op cit 13, page 24.
18. Ibid.
19. 21 CFR 14 Public Hearing Before a Public Advisory Committee. FDA website. www.accessdata.fda.gov/scripts/cdrh/cfdocs/cfcfr/CFRSearch.cfm?CFRPart=14&showFR=1. Accessed 1 April 2015.
20. Section 918 of the *Food and Drug Administration Amendment Act of 2007.*
21. FDA. *Guidance for Industry: Advisory Committee Meetings—Preparation and Public Availability of Information Given to Advisory Committee Members* (August 2008). FDA website. www.fda.gov/ucm/groups/fdagov-public/@fdagov-afda-gen/documents/document/ucm125650.pdf. Accessed 1 April 2015.
22. FDA. *Guidance for the Public, FDA Advisory Committee Members, and FDA Staff: The Open Public Hearing at FDA Advisory Committee Meetings.* FDA website. www.fda.gov/ucm/groups/fdagov-public/@fdagov-afda-gen/documents/document/ucm236144.pdf. Accessed 1 April 2015.
23. FDA. *Guidance for Industry and Food and Drug Administration Staff: Center for Devices and Radiological Health Appeals Process* (May 2013). FDA website. Accessed 1 April 2015.
24. Ibid.

Chapter 5

Preparing for Key FDA Meetings and Advisory Committee Meetings

Updated by William K. Sietsema, PhD

OBJECTIVES

- Provide general recommendations for preparing for FDA meetings
- Detail the extensive preparation process for Advisory Committee presentations

LAWS, REGULATIONS AND GUIDELINES COVERED IN THIS CHAPTER

- *Guidance for Industry: Formal Meetings Between the FDA and Sponsors or Applicants of PDUFA Products* (May 2015)
- *Guidance for the Public, FDA Advisory Committee Members, and FDA Staff on Procedures for Determining Conflict of Interest and Eligibility for Participation in FDA Advisory Committee* (August 2008)
- *Public Availability of Advisory Committee Members' Financial Interest Information and Waivers. Guidance for the Public, FDA Advisory Committee Members, and FDA Staff* (March 2014)
- *Guidance for FDA Advisory Committee Members and FDA Staff: Voting Procedures for Advisory Committee Meetings* (August 2008)
- *Guidance for Industry: Advisory Committee Meetings—Preparation and Public Availability of Information Given to Advisory Committee Members* (August 2008)
- *Guidance for the Public, FDA Advisory Committee Members, and FDA Staff: The Open Public Hearing at FDA Advisory Committee Meetings* (May 2013)
- *Guidance for the Public and FDA Staff on Convening Advisory Committee Meetings* (August 2008)
- *Procedures for Meetings of the Medical Devices Advisory Committee. Draft Guidance for Industry and Food and Drug Administration Staff* (April 2015)
- *21 CFR §14* Public Hearing Before a Public Advisory Committee
- *21 CFR §20.118* Advisory Committee Records

Introduction

The various types of meetings with the US Food and Drug Administration (FDA) outlined in Chapter 4 require different levels of preparation by the company, ranging from regulatory communications, which require less preparation, to highly publicized Advisory Committee meetings, requiring intensive preparation.

All meetings should begin with a goal of maximizing the opportunities provided by FDA interaction. Establishing an open and forthright relationship with the FDA division and demonstrating credibility for the company's product or issue is paramount in every interaction.

This chapter highlights the general steps companies should consider in preparing for all FDA meetings and outlines the more detailed and comprehensive process of preparing for an Advisory Committee meeting.

General Preparation for FDA Meetings

Importantly, before requesting any meeting, make sure the company actually is ready to have a meeting, as briefing packages generally are due four weeks prior to meeting (two weeks for Type A). Regardless of the meeting type, the product category for which a company may be requesting approval, or any issues playing out in the external environment, there is one commonality for all FDA meetings—the need to tell a clear story and set the data or issue in context. Just as FDA has a process for determining whether a drug or device should be approved, a company needs a process to keep its team on track and prepare in the most efficient and effective way. A good process will incorporate the following objectives: developing a strategy to attain company goals best; understanding the various audiences; prioritizing data and other information; preparing speakers to articulate the information and answer questions effectively; and testing and measuring progress with well-organized practice and rehearsals.

Prior to all meetings with FDA, whether in person or by telephone, companies should consider the following 10 steps:

1. *Know Your Audience*

- Research FDA and other personnel who will be in attendance at the meeting. Learn about their experiences, biases and backgrounds to anticipate their opinions better.

2. *Know the Issues*

- Review recent relevant precedents and actions by FDA, especially by the division responsible for evaluating the product; understand published or implied FDA guidance and consider incorporating them explicitly into the sponsor's strategy or presentation.

3. *Set a Goal for Each Conversation or Meeting*

- Determine the meeting's objective or purpose, whether it is to obtain guidance, present the development program or obtain agreement.
- Determine which issues and questions will be addressed and who will attend on behalf of the company and the agency.
- Stay focused on the goal during each meeting. Seek specific answers and commitments from the agency to achieve that goal.
- Strive for agreement on the main issues. Try to get clarity, direction and, if possible, commitment on these issues.

4. *Know Your Position*

- Conduct a high-level messaging session before filing a new drug or device application for consistency across all communications. In this session:
  - o Analyze key data with a public forum and media in mind.
  - o Brainstorm and identify potential issues among all stakeholders.
  - o Develop high-level messages to provide the basis for conversations with FDA.
  - o Make sure the team clearly understands and is aligned with the company's position and knows how to articulate it.

5. *Provide Pertinent Materials for Each Meeting in a Timely Manner to Allow the Agency to Adequately Analyze the Information*

- Be succinct. Do not overwhelm agency representatives with thousands of pages of background information; streamline the information, and focus on the meeting's issues and goal. Include a preliminary proposed agenda, focused questions and a background package or briefing document that includes the sponsor's position, an outline of the product data and the sponsor's development recommendation.

6. *Anticipate Concerns and Interests; Be Prepared to Sufficiently Answer Likely Questions*

- Understand potential risks that could result from differences in data interpretation, or recommended data requests and proactively prepare acceptable contingency scenarios that could resolve them.
- In addition to concerns a regulator could raise, proactively address resolutions to any issues regarding therapeutic area, class perception and public concern.

7. *Be Organized*

- Manage the meeting time carefully to ensure adequate discussion and clear understanding of answers and recommendations within the allotted meeting time.
- Define attendees' roles in advance and bring the appropriate people to the meeting to discuss the

sponsor's questions and provide any necessary clarifications to the audience.

8. Listen Carefully to What is Actually Being Said

- During in-person meetings, pay attention to body language, internal dynamics and offhand remarks. During phone meetings, listen to voice tone.
- Immediately correct any misinterpretations or misconceptions the audience may have.

9. Record Feedback

- Strive for clear agreement on critical decisions and make sure they are documented in the meeting minutes.
- Keep an ongoing list of all issues raised during the meetings and conference calls. Record how many times specific issues are raised to gauge their importance. Remember to note which agency representative or participant is raising them.
- In a teleconference, explicitly document when FDA representatives mute the phone. This usually indicates either an important question they want to refine, or internal disagreement, and may help determine what issues still are causing internal dissent or confusion at the agency. Consider additional data or programs that could clarify or resolve these issues.
- Save the last five minutes of the meeting to summarize the discussion and obtain agreement on action steps.

10. Foster a Flexible, Collaborative and Nonadversarial Relationship

- Keep the lines of communication open—even if a negative message is received.
- Do not take a divergent point of view personally. Always retain composure if the agency takes the opposite position. Do not debate policy—unless it is clearly on the agenda and has been "briefed."
- Listen to the agency's requests and provide answers where possible. Look for opportunities to resolve issues before they become obstacles to approval.
- Be respectful but not meek.
- Be prepared to calibrate the communication strategy in light of shifting issues, an evolving environment and changes within the agency review team.
- Anticipate potential data requirements beyond those being articulated in case the agency shifts direction or changes its mind.
- Do not include any off-agenda items—avoid surprises.
- Do not hide information—the last thing a sponsor wants is for the agency to find out about a negative issue it has not introduced.
- Do not stress commercial or corporate concerns over science.

Overview of Advisory Committee Meetings

The *Food and Drug Administration Amendments Act* of 2007 (*FDAAA*) first mandated convening Advisory Committees for all new molecular entities, or FDA must provide a written explanation as to why it will not convene a meeting. The sponsor of a new drug or device must plan for the likelihood an Advisory Committee will be part of the regulatory process. However, a sponsor often does not know whether its product will have to face a committee hearing until a few months before the actual event. Thus, strategic planning for a potential meeting must be an integral part of any product's development process.

An Advisory Committee meeting to review a new drug or device application is unlike most other FDA meetings. It is not only a scientific discussion of the data and issues surrounding a drug or device, it is also a high-profile regulatory, financial and legal event—a very public day in court for the sponsor and its product.

Advisory Committee meetings typically are attended by rival pharmaceutical or device companies, the media, investment communities and key stakeholders, including patient and advocacy groups. The voting members on an Advisory Committee are not typical scientific advisors. Due to concerns regarding conflicts of interest, FDA often is prohibited from including any experts on the panel who may have collaborated on the study or contributed to the product's development. This means the panel's clinicians, academicians and statisticians, while experts in their respective fields, may know little more about the specific issues other than what they read in the FDA and sponsor briefing books and will hear at the meeting. Sponsors need to be aware of this and be careful not to assume in-depth, product-specific knowledge on the part of the committee members.

The order of events for Advisory Committee meetings can vary considerably. Most meetings begin with a call to order by the chairperson, followed by an introduction of the panel and its members. A statement regarding committee members' conflicts of interest is read. The chairperson will welcome attendees on behalf of FDA and review the issues on the meeting agenda. The opening events are followed by sponsor and FDA presentations, as listed in the meeting agenda. When these are completed, an open public hearing is held (minimum of one hour). The committee discussions and a question and answer session ensue, followed by a committee vote and, finally, meeting adjournment. "Affected persons" are then informed of the agency's decision (i.e., the committee recommendation) within 90 days of the meeting.

Figure 5-1. Major Milestone Timeline

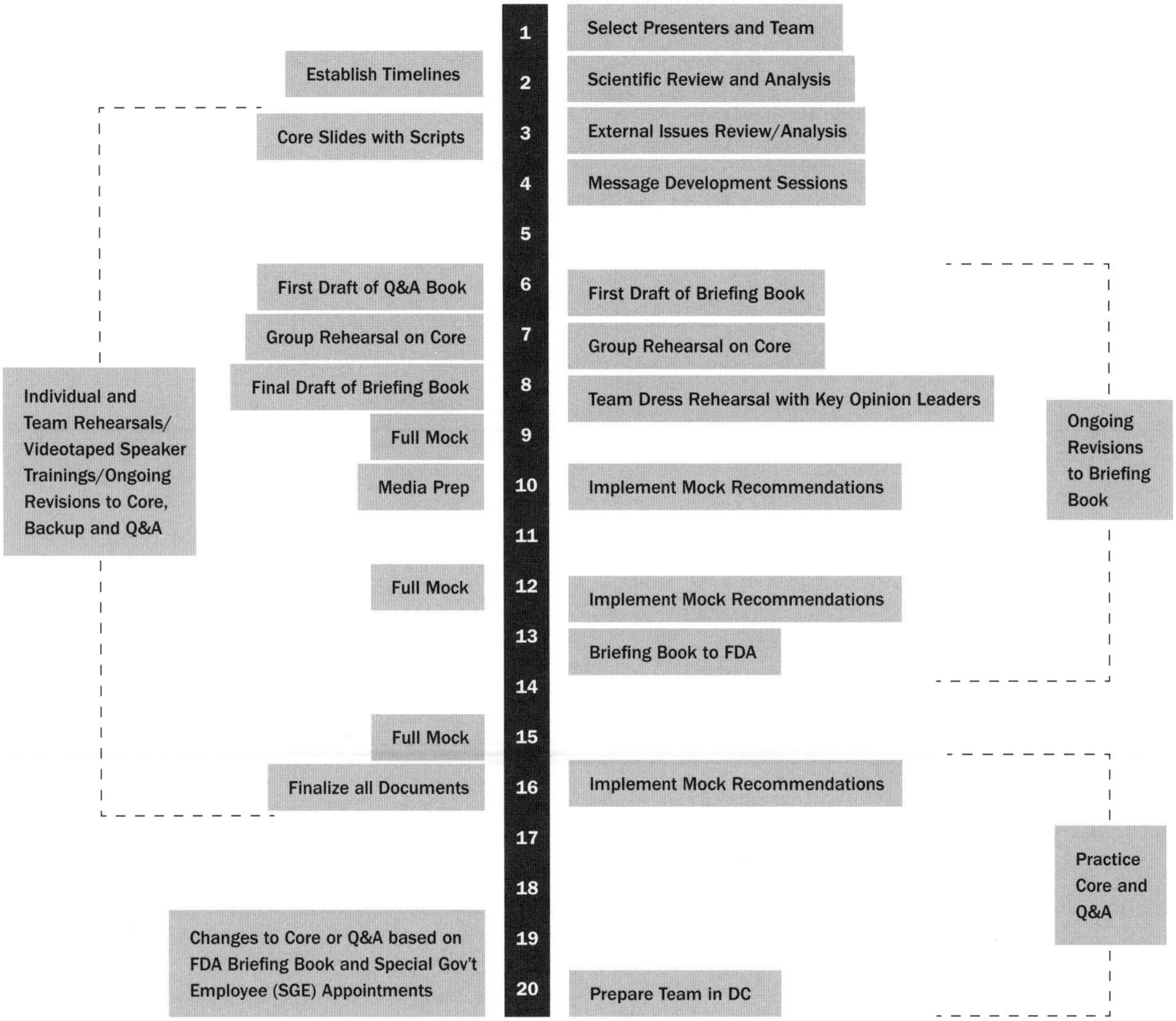

Under the *Federal Advisory Committee Act*, a part of each Advisory Committee meeting must be open to the public. Examples of "open sessions" are those in which NDAs, supplements, postapproval safety and risk versus benefit issues are discussed. Sessions not open to the public are the so-called "closed sessions," including those in which trade secrets or commercial confidential information (e.g., INDs and review division updates to the committee) are discussed. Only special government employees (SGEs), FDA employees and invited sponsor representatives are allowed to attend closed sessions of Advisory Committee meetings. (See Chapter 4 for more detailed information on the purpose and format of Advisory Committee meetings.)

Preparing for an Advisory Committee Meeting

A three-step approach to preparing for an Advisory Committee meeting comprises analysis, content development and testing the strategy and materials.

The analysis step includes: understanding the audience (FDA division heads, medical reviewers and Advisory Committee members); evaluating the data and science; analyzing the external environment and assembling the preparation team. The content development step involves creating a communication strategy and materials, including the core presentation, slides, briefing materials and advocacy outreach. The testing step comprises rehearsals, expert feedback and, ultimately, adjustment of the strategy and materials.

Selecting the Team

Most sponsors underestimate the amount of time it will take to prepare sufficiently for an FDA Advisory Committee meeting. Thus, it is critical to select the right team, assign them the proper roles and set ground rules and realistic expectations. A key starting point in team selection is identifying a senior person in research and development or regulatory to champion the project and ensure Advisory Committee preparation is the presentation team's top priority. The ideal team should include representatives from a variety of areas: regulatory, medical, clinical, manufacturing, toxicology, statistics, pharmacovigilance and commercial. Each brings individual expertise and a unique perspective that can help secure a positive recommendation from the committee and attain the target label. Orchestrating the team, considering and weighing its input and selecting the proper role for each team member are as much an art as a science.

The size of an Advisory Committee preparation team will vary according to the company and its resources. Frequently, an overlap of responsibilities will exist among subteams, with some people performing more than one role. Although there are many ways to organize a team, a typical breakdown of roles and responsibilities follows:

- presentation team—core presenters and back-up presenters
- data/slide triage team—people who compile and organize data and slides
- briefing book team—main author and data triage team members
- internal and/or external scientific advisors—content experts and responders for question and answer development
- regulatory team—regulatory executives who manage communication and scheduling with FDA throughout the Advisory Committee process
- communications team—presentation support team of writers, editors, presentation coaches, marketing, brand, public relations executives and media trainers
- slide development and slide logistics team
- logistics team—project manager, meeting organizers, schedulers and administrative support

Once the team members have been selected, it is important to brief members on what to expect during the preparation process and at the hearing. Team members should be briefed on everything from how the slide process will work and the room layout, to how the Advisory Committee hearing schedule will flow and anticipated media interest.

Organizational tools such as a major milestone timeline (**Figure 5-1**) and a project management chart (**Figure 5-2**) are highly effective ways to orient the team and keep it on track. These tools provide an overview of the process, the tasks, the assignments and the schedule and provide a realistic view of the required team member time commitment and how their roles are critical to achieving the goal.

Researching and Analyzing the Advisory Committee Members

Each Advisory Committee member has his or her own individual style and concerns, which can affect what questions are asked during the meeting, how they are asked and how members ultimately vote. Knowing the committee members, their backgrounds and how they may influence one another is critical, as it helps frame a relevant presentation, predict questions and prepare answers.

To analyze Advisory Committee members, the team may:

- Study past votes and discussions around issues similar to the sponsor's. Companies can gain a wealth of information by reviewing transcripts of previous meetings from FDA's website (www.fda.gov) or viewing videos of meetings on FDA Live (www.fdalive.com). Panel members often ask similar questions at different meetings, so it is highly instructive to learn what they have asked in the past and, of equal importance, to analyze their comments.
- Analyze their interests and positions on specific issues, including scientific studies they have authored, associations with which they are affiliated, practice guideline committees on which they serve, public comments in presentations and media interviews on specific issues.
- Identify the relationships among committee members, including what associations, universities and company affiliations they may have in common.
- See the committee in action. Reviewing old Advisory Committee recordings and taking the team on a "field trip" to an Advisory Committee meeting are invaluable ways to analyze what types of questions are being asked, how they are being asked and give the team the full flavor and experience of the event.

Leveraging Advocacy

Because FDA and Advisory Committee members are influenced by the public and the political environment, sponsors must consider these external influences in the planning process. Sponsors should have a well-thought-out plan to communicate with key stakeholders—from patient advocacy groups and healthcare associations to key opinion leaders and policy groups.

Third-party advocates, key opinion leaders and medical experts can fill a variety of valuable roles in supporting the sponsor's goals. Assuming all ties with the sponsor are clearly revealed, they can publish articles on the data or the need for the product, speak at medical symposia, answer highly technical or specific questions from the Advisory

Figure 5-2. Sample Project Management Chart

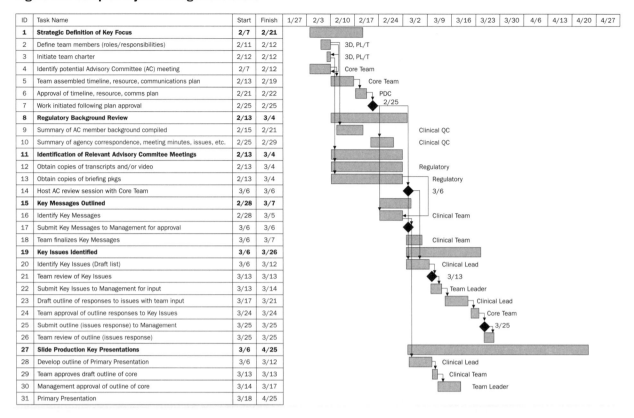

ID	Task Name	Start	Finish
1	**Strategic Definition of Key Focus**	**2/7**	**2/21**
2	Define team members (roles/responsibilities)	2/11	2/12
3	Initiate team charter	2/12	2/12
4	Identify potential Advisory Committee (AC) meeting	2/7	2/12
5	Team assembled timeline, resource, communications plan	2/13	2/19
6	Approval of timeline, resource, comms plan	2/21	2/22
7	Work initiated following plan approval	2/25	2/25
8	**Regulatory Background Review**	**2/13**	**3/4**
9	Summary of AC member background compiled	2/15	2/21
10	Summary of agency correspondence, meeting minutes, issues, etc.	2/25	2/29
11	**Identification of Relevant Advisory Commitee Meetings**	**2/13**	**3/4**
12	Obtain copies of transcripts and/or video	2/13	3/4
13	Obtain copies of briefing pkgs	2/13	3/4
14	Host AC review session with Core Team	3/6	3/6
15	**Key Messages Outlined**	**2/28**	**3/7**
16	Identify Key Messages	2/28	3/5
17	Submit Key Messages to Management for approval	3/6	3/6
18	Team finalizes Key Messages	3/6	3/7
19	**Key Issues Identified**	**3/6**	**3/26**
20	Identify Key Issues (Draft list)	3/6	3/12
21	Team review of Key Issues	3/13	3/13
22	Submit Key Issues to Management for input	3/13	3/14
23	Draft outline of responses to issues with team input	3/17	3/21
24	Team approval of outline responses to Key Issues	3/24	3/24
25	Submit outline (issues response) to Management	3/25	3/25
26	Team review of outline (issues response)	3/25	3/25
27	**Slide Production Key Presentations**	**3/6**	**4/25**
28	Develop outline of Primary Presentation	3/6	3/12
29	Team approves draft outline of core	3/13	3/13
30	Management approval of outline of core	3/14	3/17
31	Primary Presentation	3/18	4/25

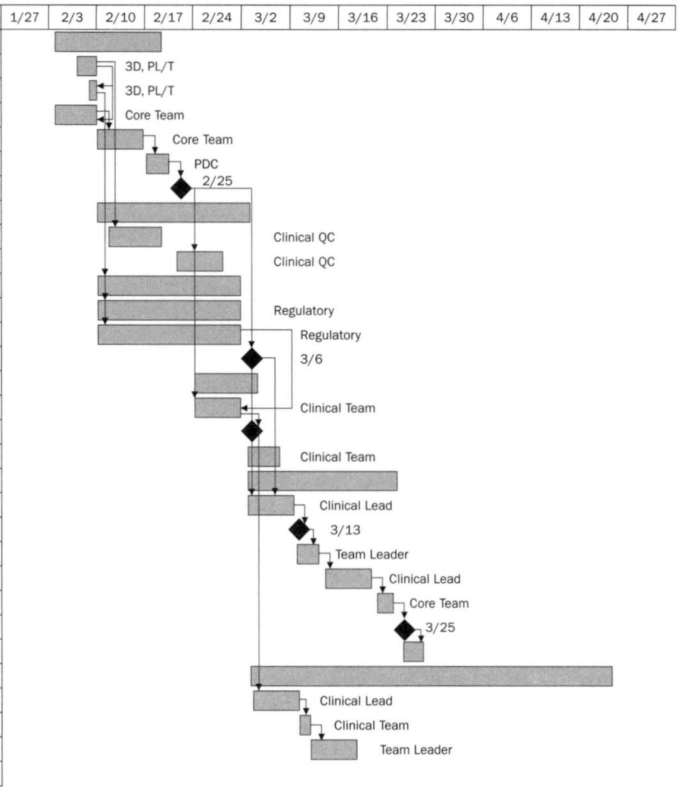

Committee during the hearing, testify during the public comment period and speak to the media. Sponsors should utilize the experience offered by such experts as much as possible. Key opinion leaders also should be considered as presenters at the Advisory Committee meeting, as they can bring a great deal of credibility to a company's presentation.

It is important to note engaging key opinion leaders and groups has never been more complicated, so any compensation must come with no strings attached. All financial relationships should be disclosed appropriately. In today's environment, transparency is extremely important.

Some key steps in creating an effective advocacy program are:

- identifying the most influential patient and consumer groups and healthcare associations and ranking them in terms of leadership and influence
- assessing opinions of medical experts in the field, as well as the position statements of medical societies
- listening to what financial analysts are saying about the product and how they are characterizing its impact on the company

Finally, it is important to prioritize the information and factor it into the communications strategy and core messages for all communications, including the Advisory Committee presentation, the briefing book, the Q&A book and media outreach. As part of this process, it also is important to brief advocacy groups and, when appropriate, enlist their support.

Preparing the Briefing Materials, Core Presentation, and Q&A Book

There is no substitute for good data. But good data alone are not always sufficient to secure a positive recommendation at an Advisory Committee meeting. A well-constructed scientific story that provides context for that data is the backbone of a sponsor's briefing book and presentation.

To ensure message consistency across all materials, no content should be developed until a strategic messaging session is conducted. The messaging should drive the direction of the briefing book, the presentation script, the slides and answers to key questions. This process should begin as soon as the sponsor has selected and organized its team and is analyzing the environment, the audiences and its issues.

The primary steps in creating, prioritizing and harmonizing content are:

- Conduct a brainstorming session with key sponsor team members. Set a goal for the content. What does the sponsor really want to communicate to the audience about its product? Focus on high-level messages that will serve as the foundation for the Advisory Committee presentation. These messages

should be based on unmet patient medical needs, the product's benefits and risks and the strength of the data.
- Discuss and prioritize the data, outlining all relevant studies, data sets and other information for easy reference and key metrics of each (e.g., meaningful endpoints, results, sample size, demographics). Rank the messages to determine which to emphasize during the presentation.
- Incorporate the data into a message matrix to serve as a guide to outline and develop the presentations and the questions and answers (Q&A), and prioritize the messages by rating what is most important, considering the product strengths and science, the issues FDA officials have highlighted and the Advisory Committee members' areas of interest.
- Finally, assign individual issue "owners" by topic, assigning responsibility and accountability to specific team members for gathering data, drafting answers to questions and developing supporting documentation in the form of charts, graphs or tables for slides.

Once the key messages and data for the briefing materials and presentation have been determined, it is time to construct the flow of the presentation and the briefing book. Although the content and flow of both will vary depending on the product and the issues, there are some general guidelines to follow.

For both the presentation and the briefing book, follow the rules of clear writing and logical organization. Headline main points. Be succinct and write in short sentences. Summarize key messages at the beginning and end of the documents.

Writing the Briefing Book

Because Advisory Committee members will get briefing books from both FDA and the sponsor, it is best to keep the book short, concise and well-organized, so it can be read and understood easily. The book should be approximately 100 to 150 pages in length, depending on the extent of the clinical program.

For purposes of efficiency, consistency and clarity, be sure the briefing book is based on the clinical section of the New Drug Application (NDA), Biologics License Application (BLA) or Premarket Approval Application (PMA), focusing on information directly related to the issues being considered by the committee. Edit out information and data not directly related to these issues. Consider how the product will fit into current treatment patterns to address treatment issues, barriers or beliefs. Never include new data that have not been reviewed already by FDA in the book. Finally, avoid any statements or suggestions that can be viewed as misleading or promotional or be misconstrued as a recommendation of off-label product use.

Structure the book in an organized way by dividing it into distinct sections, beginning with a clear executive summary that provides an overview of the book's main points and makes the best case for the product or issue. Summarize and synthesize the data within each section. In all cases, sponsors should bear in mind Advisory Committee members have limited time to prepare for the meeting, so the briefing package should be a well-organized and easy-to-read summary of the data. Engaging a fresh set of eyes from a non-team member will help optimize the briefing package's readability.

Ensure all presenters know the briefing book's contents and can answer questions that arise from both the book and presentation.

Scripting the Core Presentation

Sponsors typically have between 45 and 90 minutes to deliver the core presentation, something that can be negotiated with the agency in advance. As a result, every word counts. The core presentation is the sponsor's opportunity to make its strongest case to a "jury" deciding its fate. Because this is not a typical scientific presentation, but a persuasive argument with a singular goal, controlling the story around the data is critical. The science does not speak for itself; not everyone will interpret the data the same way; therefore, context and clear explanation are essential components of success. In general, all Advisory Committee members want to see and hear a clear, concise and convincing scientific story that creates confidence the team knows its product well and has shared fully the product's positive, negative and unknown attributes with the committee.

While sponsors routinely create core presentations from pre-developed slides, outlining and scripting the presentation before developing core slides will allow the messages to drive the presentation. Without this scripting, it may come across as presenting data without context. Scripting every word of the presentation also is a must, as this will ensure the message's precision and clarity and reduce the chances of "surprises" surfacing during the presentation.

As previously mentioned, the most effective and efficient way to develop a core presentation is to start with the goal and high-level messages from the brainstorming session. From those messages, create an outline to develop a story flow for the overall presentation and then do the same for each individual presentation. Look for opportunities to weave in and reinforce the main messages of the overall presentation for consistency.

Because the core is delivered as the spoken versus the written word, it is important the script be written for the ear and not the eye. That means using short sentences and an active voice to deliver a message that can be easily understood by the audience the first time. The presentation's goal is for everyone listening to understand the data in the same way.

Writing the Q&A Book

The same rules apply when developing answers to questions. Answers should be headlined clearly so the responses and messages are clear and direct. In addition, the questions and answers should be ordered in a well-organized book, so responders learn the answers and identify the appropriate slides. The book should serve as a practice tool as well as a map for the day of the hearing. This dynamic document will change as information is incorporated from agency feedback and external sources, such as stakeholders and the media. The Q&A book should be organized by topic and identify not only the question and answer but also the appropriate responder and what, if any, slides support the point.

Developing and Managing Slides

Once the script is written, and as answers to questions are being crafted, slides should be developed to visually reinforce the information. A slide's purpose is to support the presenter's message—not confuse it. As a result, slides should follow the same rules of clear communication. Choose a simple, clear slide template with mid- to dark blue backgrounds and a font and size to reduce eye strain. For graph slides, make sure the x- and y-axes are thick and vibrant enough to be seen in the back of a large meeting room and are clearly labeled with easy-to-find legends. For text slides, fewer words are better. The goal of any slide is to pass the "glance test," so the audience immediately understands the slide's message. It is better to have multiple slides that "build" and explain a point than to crowd too much information onto one slide. Too much information on one slide can lead committee members to focus on different information and confuse the message. With slides, as with writing, less is more.

To help in both slide development and management, a specific process should be followed and a team assigned. This team has several important functions. One is to compile and organize data and slides for each component of the core presentation. A second is to gather data and prepare backup slides for the questions Advisory Committee members may ask. A third function is to locate a requested backup slide for responders during the Q&A sessions. A fourth is to help a presenter answer a question by prompting the presenter with an appropriately chosen slide on the preview monitor.

It is common for sponsors to have several thousand backup slides for the Q&A portion of the Advisory Committee meeting. Ideally, a slide should be displayed within a few seconds of the question being asked. For this to occur, it is best for sponsors to use an automated slide recall process. This system should allow responders to preview a slide on a monitor only they can see, and then, in real time, decide whether to show that slide or call for another.

The intricate and important process of developing and locating the right slide at the right moment starts with the data triage team. The backup slides typically are organized by topic matter (e.g., safety, efficacy, unmet need, postmarketing surveillance). Each team member is responsible for at least one of these areas and is an expert.

Conducting Perfect Practice Through Rehearsals

As the content is being developed, it also needs to be tested. Sponsor teams frequently wait too long in the process to begin testing. This is a lost opportunity because testing through practice is the best way to refine content. In addition to internal team rehearsals, sponsors should also run several realistic rehearsals with external experts in the role of Advisory Committee members.

A mock Advisory Committee hearing is a rehearsal "on steroids" and is where the sponsor's team gets its first taste of what it is like to present to a potentially critical audience and answer questions under pressure. If done correctly, it will provide a reality check for the sponsor. The more realistic the mock panel, the better prepared the presenters and other responders will be for the actual hearing.

The key to a realistic mock panel is to mirror the actual Advisory Committee as closely as possible. This increases the opportunity for mock members to examine, interpret and challenge the data in the same way as Advisory Committee members. This is one area in which effective profiles of committee members provide benefits. The mock Advisory Committee hearing should be constructed like a dress rehearsal. The room should be set up in the same formation as it will be on the day of the hearing. Mock members should stay in role to provide presenters with a realistic run-through. The sponsor should provide briefing books to the mock Advisory Committee members prior to the rehearsal, so they will go into the meeting with the same information as the actual committee. This book should be a near-complete draft of the final briefing book that will be submitted. The panel should critique the value of the book and the consistency of information provided with the presentations.

Following the rehearsal, the mock panelists should provide a tough, insightful critique and give honest feedback about the presenters and the presentation. This feedback should be used to adjust and enhance strategy, core messages and responses for the Q&A session. Ineffective presenters should be replaced or coached.

The sponsor's internal team should schedule a debrief immediately following each mock hearing and document what worked well and what can de done differently in preparation for the next mock hearing.

Maximizing the Final Days before the Advisory Committee Meeting

In the few days leading up to the meeting, sponsor teams should set up rehearsals on or near the FDA meeting site, near Washington, DC. Forty-eight hours before the meeting, FDA will release final names of the Advisory Committee members, as well as the specific questions they will pose to the committee. This is the time to readjust strategy, if necessary, edit the final presentations and refine Q&A responses.

A logistics plan should be in place to help facilitate and control communications among team members during the meeting. Given the pressure and time constraints of Advisory Committee day, discipline in communications is critical. Only vital issues should be discussed, and the discussion should be fast, focused and confidential.

Whatever system is chosen, it must be thought through in advance and communicated to everyone involved. This includes everything from ensuring the availability of enough meeting rooms with working computers, printers, copiers and faxes, to ensuring the presence of a solid security system to guard against breaches. Whether a company hires a professional meeting planning company or security firm, or handles these tasks internally, organization and security are crucial components to ensuring that the meeting runs smoothly.

Summary

With Advisory Committee meetings becoming more like adversarial proceedings than presentations of scientific data, companies must prepare as they would for a big court case with major implications for everything from the company's stock price to its reputation. Clear and persuasive communication is the key to success in this challenging environment.

Strategic communications planning is critical and must begin early in the product's lifecycle. Companies must assess and analyze their products honestly and be open to criticism and perceptions, right or wrong, that exist in the external environment. It is imperative to understand the various audiences' concerns and to be proactive and persuasive in addressing those issues through an effective communication plan. By applying these principles zealously to the Advisory Committee meeting preparation process, companies can hope to achieve their goal of a positive Advisory Committee recommendation and, ultimately, FDA approval of their products.

Chapter 6

Crisis Management

Updated by Meredith May, MS, RAC

OBJECTIVES

- ❑ Review types of crises common to all industries, as well as those specific to the healthcare products industry
- ❑ Provide some perspective on how to address issues and potential crises that may arise in the healthcare products industry
- ❑ Learn how to apply proven management techniques to handle a crisis
- ❑ Understand management and regulatory affairs responsibilities for averting crises
- ❑ Understand specific tools available for effective communication and management during a company crisis

Introduction

There are two kinds of companies: those that have dealt with crisis and those that have not been in business very long. All businesses can expect to deal with a crisis of some kind; it is only a matter of time. How organizations handle crisis differentiates the long-term survivors from the short-lived failures. Organizations providing healthcare products, like medical devices and pharmaceuticals, experience all the crises typical for any organization, but they also have additional concerns related to regulatory and patient care. Successful management of a crisis requires communication and prior planning, both of which can be improved by understanding crisis management and leadership activities. The consummate regulatory professional must be able to lead and participate in any crisis management activity. In addition, it should be understood regulatory responsibilities in managing and averting crises involve almost all other disciplines within an organization, including nonclinical, clinical, product development, compliance and marketing.

Types and Examples

A crisis, as defined by *Merriam-Webster*, is a difficult or dangerous situation that needs serious attention. According to the *Oxford Dictionaries*, a crisis is a time when a difficult or important decision must be made. These and other definitions encapsulate the challenges an organization faces during a crisis situation. Naturally, various crises reflect a range of conditions as well as decisions. While this chapter includes discussions about many types of crises, the focus is on those issues specific to pharmaceutical and medical device companies, where actions have potentially significant adverse implications for regulatory agencies, healthcare providers, patients, media and the public.

A regulatory crisis can occur at any phase of product lifecycle from feasibility through marketing and postmarket surveillance. All businesses, regardless of industry, share risks associated with internal and external factors such as market changes, employee misconduct and environmental events. Medical device and pharmaceutical businesses are no exceptions. Various types of crises are discussed, stemming from regulatory, legal or financial issues. Environmental crises, i.e., hurricanes or wildfires, are not addressed in this chapter, as those types of crises are considered a discipline in their own right. The tools presented in this chapter can, however, be used to address environmental crises.

Regulatory Crises

Inspection Observations

Current Good Manufacturing Practices (CGMP) are designed to provide a framework for a good quality system that can reduce the number of errors during all product development and commercialization phases. During onsite inspections, FDA inspectors evaluate company policies, procedures and processes to ensure the company has adequate procedures in place and is following them. When CGMPs are not in place or followed, FDA can take escalating actions such as issuance of FDA Form 483s, Warning Letters, forced recalls and/or consent decrees. CGMPs and FDA compliance activities can be found in Chapters 10 and 39, respectively. The Notified Body (NB) inspecting the facility can rescind or limit ISO certifications for the facility or CE marking for products if the quality system is not compliant with applicable CGMP-related international standards. A company must respond immediately to inspection deficiencies with executable plans that include action items, responsibilities and deadlines. Inadequate responses can escalate to more severe consequences including legal injunctions and facility closures.

Submission Failures

The majority of product development projects involve a submission (i.e., 510(k), new drug application, premarket approval, technical file, etc.) to a regulatory agency, whether that body is FDA in the US or an NB in the EU. Submission of a regulatory application often comes toward the end of the development cycle, which means that a company already may have invested considerable amounts of time and money before application submission. If a submission is not successful, a company must expend additional resources to organize the company's response, which may or may not be successful. For smaller companies, a failed submission could mean severe financial deficits leading to cutbacks, layoffs and even bankruptcy. This is an example of how a crisis in one department—regulatory affairs—can easily lead to a company-wide crisis.

Recalls

A product recall, especially when in response to a potential or actual patient injury, is an event that companies seek to avoid by following processes and procedures; however, recalls do happen. A company must be prepared to address product recalls efficiently and completely to avoid further risk of patient injury and legal or financial repercussions. Dealing with a crisis related to patient injury or death can be emotional on both a professional and personal level, which is why it is often used as the worst-case scenario for crisis management training in the medical device and pharmaceutical fields. One extreme real-life example is a recall of a hydrocephalus shunt used in infants. Failures of these devices can lead to infant brain damage or death, a devastating consequence for both the patient and the company. No company wants to be left unprepared to deal with a crisis of this emotional, legal and financial magnitude; the external communications that will be required throughout the process are considerable.

Because product recalls in the US are public and listed in FDA's database, they can move quickly from an internal regulatory issue to a publicity crisis with legal implications. A recent example of this is the metal-on-metal hip implant recall. The series of events leading to the recall has affected more than one large orthopedic company in the past five years. While the public does not have access to what corrective and preventive actions were completed internally during the crisis, the regulatory, legal and financial repercussions can be found in FDA's database. Additionally, recall events have been featured prominently in legal advertisements seeking potential clients in lawsuits against the orthopedic companies. It is likely this crisis started as a clinical one (reports of patients having negative clinical outcomes after surgery), moved into a regulatory crisis and became an industry-wide crisis due to the scope and severity of the device's failure.

Legal Crises

Although this book and chapter provide a regulatory perspective, it should be noted that quality and regulatory departments are often involved in the business, legal and financial aspects of the company's management and growth. Trademark and intellectual property protection is an extremely important part of business growth and security, and there are times when the company must protect itself from infringement of those legal rights. Cases of infringement vary in severity and required actions or reactions, but both parties involved in lawsuits stand to gain or lose financially. A well-written non-disclosure agreement provides the company with documentation in the case of confidential information being shared illegally outside the company; it is important that all non-disclosure agreement breaches be considered crises until they are investigated fully. As with a regulatory crisis, a legal crisis can lead to injunctions or cease and desist orders, which prevent a company from selling some or all of its products. Depending on the importance of the identified product sales and the handling of the legal crisis, the loss of revenue can lead to a company-wide financial crisis.

Financial Crises

Startup companies are greatly affected by investor support and small sales fluctuations, but a company of any size can be driven into a financial crisis by sales deficiencies, economic slowdowns or stock market crashes if they are not handled correctly. Financial crises, regardless of the cause, can result in cutbacks, layoffs or even bankruptcy. A financial crisis affects every organization department and employee, which is why it is the most likely to have the greatest emotional impact. During a financial crisis, true leaders within the organization will rise above the fray and prove their worth. Internal communication is as critical as external communication during a financial crisis because the decisions made can impact employee confidence in the organization directly, including concerns about its longevity.

Crisis Management Communication

Communication is an important aspect of any business activity, from product development through distribution, but it certainly is the most critical factor in successful crisis management. As such, companies cannot wait until a crisis emerges before communication takes place. While both internal and external communications are important in crisis solution and mitigation, they have different audiences and, therefore, different messages.

Internal Communications

Internal communications include written and verbal communications between any and all company departments and employees, from the moment of crisis discovery through the conclusion of all mitigation activities. It is important to understand the majority of communications between team members are considered discoverable during legal proceedings, so all internal communications should be filled with facts and not supposition. Employees must be aware of the need to avoid inferences or assumptions in these communications.

Leadership

An organization's leadership is required to help employees understand the role of internal communications in dealing with a crisis in the present or the future. Most written internal communications focus on planning, facts, actions and outcomes, but equally important for internal crisis communication is the need to humanize communications for employees who may be under considerable stress due to the crisis. Leaders should focus on working with employees to relieve or minimize that stress, where possible. Quality leadership at such pivotal points is vital in helping the organization and individuals understand the situation and to determine appropriate actions. People are capable of making better decisions in highly emotionally charged situations when there is strong leadership, preparation and a sense of community ("we are all in this together"). The crisis management team's (CMT) role is to lead a company through a crisis and encourage others in accomplishing a common task by providing clear, calm leadership focused on solving the problem.

Full Disclosure

The most important rule during a crisis is to "Fully disclose all facts, even if there is a chance they are irrelevant." While having more facts than necessary to sort through during the investigation can be cumbersome, the intentional or unintentional omission of facts can later be construed as being nefarious or even criminal. Employee understanding of the review process is connected directly to how information is disclosed and to the leadership qualities mentioned above. The mantra of full disclosure has to be reinforced at all times at all levels; this serves to prevent employees from withholding information for the purpose of protecting the company.

CMT

Not all crises affect the whole company, but they can quickly become company-wide because businesses are living organisms; if one organ fails, the rest will follow. As soon as the scope of a crisis is identified, a CMT should be designated and assembled. The departments represented will vary, depending on the crisis type and scope, but some departments to consider are management, regulatory, quality, design, manufacturing, legal, marketing and clinical. The CMT is responsible for leading and monitoring the activities, creating the internal crisis plan and communicating applicable information up and down the organization's chain of command. The regulatory representative is responsible for communicating with external regulatory agencies. It is likely the CMT also will spearhead external communications with the press, patients, healthcare providers, etc.

Crisis Plan

Document, document, document. If the activity is not documented, it did not happen.

As with any other major project or company activity, creating and executing a solid plan can prevent oversights and missteps along the way. A documented plan provides all team members, stakeholders and management an opportunity to buy into the strategy, actions and deadlines.

A crisis plan should include the following elements:

- introductory statement and scope
- CMT identification and responsibilities
- documentation
    - fact sheets
    - question sheets
    - investigation
    - meeting minutes
- crisis procedures and templates
- internal communication requirements
- external communication requirements

The plan can be a physical document in a binder or an electronic one in a network folder, but it should be available for review by CMT members and updated regularly.

Fact and Question Sheets

Each CMT meeting should include the creation and analysis of running fact and question sheets. The fact sheet will grow as the investigation continues and questions are answered. These fact and question sheets help guide discussions and provide pertinent information in a timely manner, while serving as a log of the source and timing of information. It also should be noted these sheets help reduce the stress mentioned above; they keep participants focused on the actual event and the organization's response.

A fact sheet includes the following questions and answers:

- What do we know?
- When did we know about it?
- What are we doing about it?

A question sheet includes the following questions:

- What do we need to know?
- Who will get the answers?
- When will we have those answers?

Investigation

The investigation should include such activities as root cause analysis and corrective and preventive actions (CAPA). More in-depth information about risk assessment and CAPA can be found in Chapters 19 and 10, respectively. Documentation of the investigation and related activities likely will be reviewed by many people during and after the crisis, so it is imperative all procedures, guidance documents and standards be followed. Documentation must be impeccable to withstand scrutiny in future regulatory or legal audits.

In the example of the metal-on-metal hip implants discussed earlier, it is likely the investigation included some or all of the following activities, which would have been documented in the company files:

- collection of clinical data, including patient characteristics
- *in vitro* bench testing to quantify and qualify metal particulate
- animal testing of particulate responses *in vivo*
- manufacturing records evaluation
- engineering specifications review
- material standards and specifications confirmation
- inspection of failed implants
- risk assessment activities

All these documents would have been needed to fully understand the crisis, from product design through clinical and patient use of the marketed device. This underscores the importance and need for other activities mentioned in this chapter, including documentation.

External Communications

Regulatory Authorities

It is critical to inform FDA as soon as possible about a new potential patient harm issue or an issue identified externally. How the issue is presented and proposals for remediation will be important for an effective crisis management program. Depending on the issue's details, FDA discussions may start with a notification of a potential concern and an overview of what is being done to investigate and remediate the situation. A comprehensive plan and regular updates are critical for establishing a partnership between the agency and the company. All external communications should be reviewed and discussed by the CMT to ensure they are factual and complete before release outside the organization.

Public Communications

Crisis management often requires communication with external stakeholders other than regulatory agencies. For example, patients and the healthcare community must receive communications related to a marketed product issue and its resolution. The company should provide support to patients and physicians for any identified risk requiring clinical mitigation. Other stakeholders include vendors, partners, shareholders, media and the general public. It is important to understand the financial and legal compliance and ethics requirements that could affect the organization and its employees if not handled correctly (e.g., insider trading, discovery for litigation). Stakeholder involvement in the understanding of the fundamental issue is central to success.

The same work must be done for external stakeholders in managing a crisis. Effective communications will need to reach multiple audiences with varying levels of understanding. The communications need to inform, explain and educate. The CMT, including regulatory staff, should be involved in preparing or reviewing these communications to ensure the message is clear, appropriate for the audience and includes solutions.

Crisis Prevention

Operating Procedures

Quality system regulations, guidance documents and standards are established by regulatory or independent agencies to help companies develop their own company procedures. Following well-developed procedures, like those listed below, can greatly reduce the risk of a crisis by reducing the chance for patient harm and product failure:

- design controls
- quality data collection and analysis
- CAPA
- internal auditing
- postmarket surveillance
- supplier qualification
- risk assessment

It is not enough to have procedures in place; a company must feel confident the procedures are followed and revisited regularly. The company is responsible for ensuring all employees are trained on internal procedures and also have the educational background appropriate for their assigned responsibilities. A well-trained and prepared employee can prevent product, personnel and process failures that can ultimately lead to a company crisis.

It is imperative the regulatory professional, as well as other CMT members, has analytical, negotiation and conflict-handling skills to communicate successfully with both internal and external personnel. Trust and respect are built on integrity, personal commitment and initiative. Teamwork and excellent communication skills provide opportunities for success. Adaptability and flexibility of all CMT members are needed to manage the situation as the crisis resolution project unfolds.

Crisis Kit

A common risk mitigation catch-phrase called the 5Ps is "Prior Planning Prevents Poor Performance." While this is a true and valid concept, it is not always easy to implement without a structure around which to build the crisis management process. A crisis kit is a preparation method that can be created using the following steps:

- identify common crises based on brainstorming, personal experience and industry research
- develop a step-by-step action plan with checklists for each crisis type
- create internal and external communication templates for each crisis type
- assemble a folder (physical or electronic) for each crisis type, including:
  - crisis plan
  - internal communication templates
  - external communications templates
  - comments

A crisis kit can be extremely beneficial because it provides consistency in both actions and communications, regardless of who is immediately available to handle the crisis. Examples of types of potential crisis kits are: product recall, patient injury report, bad publicity news story, employee violence or extreme weather. A vulnerability audit conducted by an outside consultant can help identify potential "red flag" areas of the organization that require pre-written crisis kits.

At the conclusion of any crisis, a review of lessons learned (post-mortem review) can improve the crisis planning process and available crisis kits. The metal-on-metal hip implant crisis provided the entire implant industry with an opportunity to create crisis kits specific to patient harm due to implant failure.

Conclusions

The crisis types and examples discussed in this chapter are wide-ranging and generic enough to be a starting point for determining real-life potential for crises within a specific organization. It is only a matter of time before a company faces a crisis, and it is during that stressful time that leaders will emerge within the organization to use these or similar tools to navigate the crisis. The proven crisis management techniques presented here can be used to handle an existing crisis as well as to avert any in the future.

Honesty, integrity and full disclosure are critical when handling any crisis aspect. Lying or falsifying documentation can deepen or even criminalize any crisis. Negative publicity from improper crisis management can lead to difficulties in recruiting future employees, loss of sales revenue, legal actions and loss of investors or potential investors. Proper crisis planning and honest communications will prevent fear, confusion and skepticism. A good plan also considers the employees and the stress they may experience; stress is not conducive to level-headed issue assessment or resolution. Effective internal and external communications—professional, sensitive, complete, not false or misleading—provide the basis for success when managing a crisis.

Chapter 7

Health Technology Assessment

Updated by Richard A. Vincins, CBA, CQA, RAC (US and EU)

OBJECTIVES

- Introduce regulatory professionals to the concept of health technology assessment (HTA) methods and principles
- Describe the increasing importance of HTA in bringing new and novel pharmaceuticals, medical devices, biologics and other healthcare products to market
- Understand basic HTA terminology and methodology
- Understand the use and impact of HTA on healthcare product development and the decision-making process for key persons

HTA GUIDELINES

- World Health Organization 2011 (http://whqlibdoc.who.int/publications/2011/9789241501361_eng.pdf)
- (Børlum KF and Sigmund G, eds.) Copenhagen, National Board of Health (http://sundhedsstyrelsen.dk/publ/publ2008/mtv/metode/hta_handbook_net_final.pdf)
- National Institute for Health and Care Excellence, September 2014 (https://www.nice.org.uk/article/pmg19/chapter/acknowledgements)

Introduction

The development and use of health technology (HT) present greater challenges due to increasing evidence requirements for new technologies and justification for balancing economic factors. Payers, politicians, government agencies and others increasingly insist, prior to the approval, acquisition or payment for a healthcare technology, on the use of well-founded data to support its use in a specific healthcare environment. The growth and development of health technology assessment (HTA) is in response to that need. The US Food and Drug Administration (FDA) is not primarily involved in this type of assessment, nor is it within the agency's current scope or regulatory requirements. Other regulatory agencies around the world, such as the European Medicines Agency (EMA), the UK's Medicines and Healthcare products Regulatory Agency (MHRA) and Sweden's Medical Product Agency (MPA) are collaborating actively with HTA agencies and allowing joint Scientific Advice meetings with HT manufacturers or sponsors.

HTA is defined by the International Network of Agencies for Health Technology Assessment (INHATA) as the "systematic evaluation of properties, effects and/or impacts of healthcare technology. It may address the direct, intended consequences of technologies as well as their indirect, unintended consequences. Its main purpose is to inform technology-related policymaking in healthcare. HTA is conducted by interdisciplinary groups using explicit analytical frameworks drawing from a variety of methods."[1] The European network for Health Technology Assessment (EUnetHTA) provides a similar definition, stating "HTA is a multidisciplinary process that summarizes information about the medical, social, economic and ethical issues related to the use of a health technology in a systematic, transparent, unbiased, robust manner" with the aim "to

Table 7-1. Comparison of HT Regulation and HTA Regulation

Characteristics	Health Technology Regulations	Health Technology Assessment
Perspective	Safety and efficacy	Efficacy, effectiveness and appropriateness
Requirement	Mandatory	Recommendation on complex technologies
Role	Prevent harm	Maximize clinical and cost effectiveness

inform the formulation of safe, effective health policies that are patient focused and seek to achieve best value."[2]

HTA methods have been evolving over the last few decades, and their applications vary depending on the healthcare sector and the regulatory agency. This chapter introduces fundamental HTA aspects and issues related to these methods. The demand for HTA, in particular from the for-profit private sector as well as from government agencies, is pushing the field to develop overall HTA process and analysis reports. HTA methods vary by organization; a few organizations, such as the National Institute for Health and Care Excellence (NICE) in the UK and the Canadian Agency for Dugs and Technologies in Health (CADTH) in Canada, have been utilizing HTA methods for many years. Many other countries are in the process of developing or refining methods for conducting HTAs to inform HT decision making or policy.

A word of caution on the contents of this chapter: the process is explained at an introductory level. The processes involved for HT regulatory, HT assessment and HT management can be very complex and requires increased levels of technical expertise.

Defining the HTA Process

HTA began in the 1970s when concerns were raised about the high cost per patient for the then-new technology of computer-assisted tomography (CT-scans). The process for evaluating the impact of HT needed to be defined, to establish a systematic method for assessing new HT in addition to providing assurance of the standard product quality, safety and efficacy. Thus, HTA became known as the "fourth hurdle" for the introduction of new healthcare products to the market, demanding an effective process for evaluating new HT. The World Health Organization document, *Health Technology Assessment of Medical Devices*, provides a comparison of the different HTA characteristics; this is summarized in **Table 7-1**.

All the documents indicated in the example HTA guidelines provide an excellent overview of HTA methodologies. Because many HTA processes vary, this chapter focuses on the processes described in the *Health Technology Assessment Handbook* by the Danish Centre for Health Technology Assessment. It should be noted the US does not have a formally defined HTA process but informally follows many of these principles. **Figure 7-1** is from the Danish Handbook and provides a simplified HTA process flow.

More recently, new processes referred to as single technology appraisal (STA) and multiple technology appraisal (MTA) have been identified. These two evidence-gathering and appraisal methods use different processes because organizations may no longer be assessing single products. The STA process is designed specifically to evaluate a single product or device for a single indication. The MTA process is designed to evaluate single or multiple products with more than one related indication or combination of technologies. MTA is more time-consuming, requiring more evidence to be gathered to support how different products or technologies work together, e.g., introduction of a new diagnostic test to be used with a drug as a companion diagnostic.

Step 1—Formulation of the Policy Questions

Carefully formulating the policy question is a critical factor to ensure an appropriate, useful HTA, since decision makers focus on policy questions to form their eventual conclusions. The policy question is an iterative process that should be formulated by a professional, cross-functional team that considers the stakeholder's different interests. Policy questions are aimed at general, administrative and local decision levels in the HTA process; an example is provided from the Danish Handbook:

If a public offer of vaccination against HPV is requested, who should receive the offer, how should it be organized and with what effects and costs?

Step 2—Ask the HTA Questions

The HTA question must be phrased carefully, so the assessment will provide the information needed by the decision makers or the target group deciding on the policy question. To that end, HTA questions must be clearly formulated, defined and answerable. The HTA process usually encompasses technology, patient, organization and economy as well as any ethical aspects, although other approaches are also used.

As described in the Danish Handbook, for the policy question posed previously in the Step 1 example, the following derived HTA questions can be asked:

- What are the effects and side effects of HPV vaccination?
- Are there any interactions with other vaccines in the childhood immunization program?

- Are any ethical problems related to the HPV vaccination?
- What organizational consequences will different vaccination strategies have?
- What are the benefits compared with the costs for different models of the vaccination program?

Step 3—Gather Evidence for the Analysis

Four Basic Areas Related to HTA

The HTA model described in the Danish Handbook is a process of gathering evidence in the four basic areas related to the derived HTA question:

- technology
- organization
- patient
- economy

Technology

HT properties include performance characteristics and conformity with specifications for design, composition, manufacturing, tolerances, reliability, ease of use and/or maintenance. Three technology aspects need to be considered for the product: safety, efficacy and quality. These aspects are all part of evaluating an HT so it can be accepted by policy makers for patient use, and the new technology's economic viability will be maintained; the economic viability often is referred to as the HT's clinical and economic value.

Safety is the assessment of the acceptability of a risk (a measure of the probability of an adverse outcome and its severity) associated with using a technology in a specific environment or situation, e.g., for a patient with a particular health problem attended by a clinician with certain training and/or experience with a specific treatment setting.

Comparative efficacy and effectiveness define how well a technology works to improve patient health, usually based on changes in health outcomes or "endpoints." A technology that works under controlled conditions with carefully selected patients, such as in a clinical trial, may not always work when put into application over the greater population once on the market.

Multiple factors are considered for the HTA's quality, including type of evidence, studies performed, clinical outcomes and evaluation of the research on the HT product. Often, complete information is not available at the beginning of the HTA process, which may require discussion or advice from an assessment expert. The process can begin with preliminary searches to review health economic analysis and published articles, although often information is missing such as organizational factors.

Organization

HTs cannot merely be implemented anywhere since technologies introduced into an organization, e.g., a hospital or healthcare system, may influence organizational structures, tasks and staff (personnel) and vice versa.[3] For example, a new surgical technology may change how physicians perform surgical procedures. Thus, the organization or firm(s) where the technology will be introduced must be taken into consideration due to the impact on that organization. During evidence gathering, it may become apparent that some information requires additional consideration or further investigation during the HTA process.

One HT assessment task is preparing a workflow diagram[4] that shows specifically how the technology will be applied for the users and patients. This diagram identifies control points to explain how the technology affects the organization's work processes. The new technology must be assessed for its impact on new resource management requirements such as additional staffing and training, and its effect on the overall decision process for patient care. Finally, HT interaction and communication need to be assessed for any changes and new requirements. Fundamentally, any new technology is going to impact a healthcare organization's operation, e.g., financial management, funding, budgets, knowledge, information and interaction with external factors.

Patient

One core element is the patient receiving new HT treatment, as illustrated in **Figure 7-2**, which shows the different areas relevant to the HTA process. Often, these areas will focus on a patient's knowledge of and experience with a given technology, patient resources and the technology's importance in the patient's everyday life, i.e., the various focus areas cannot be considered in isolation. The areas listed in **Figure 7-2** are investigated for their direct or indirect influences from a patient perspective.

Figure 7-1. An HTA Model

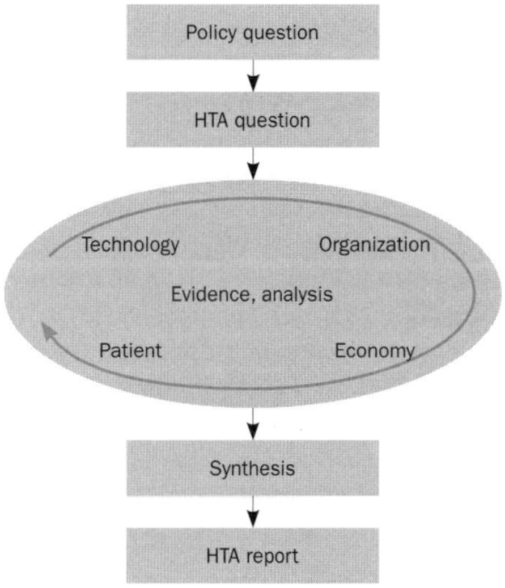

Table 7-2. Types of HTA Products and Search Approaches

HTA Product	Terms for Initial Search
Technology alert (early warning)	Primary studies*
Mini-HTA	Secondary or primary studies***
Cancer drug HTA	Primary studies
Focused HTA	Secondary studies**
Broad HTA	Secondary studies

* Primary studies are the individual scientific primary articles in the form, e.g., randomized clinical trials or cohort studies.

** Secondary studies are systematic reviews and assessments of other types of published material, e.g., HTA reports, clinical guidelines and systematic reviews.

*** In the case of new technologies, start with a search of primary studies. In the case of known technologies with a new indication, start with a search of secondary studies.

Economy

Economic analyses may help determine how resources can be used best in the healthcare sector. While economic analyses are not included in all HTAs, many agencies consider this a critical aspect of the decision-making process. Once the policy and HTA questions are defined, the next step is to gather available evidence on the HT and conduct the assessment.

Literature Assessment

Careful formulation of a literature search strategy, including the selection of studies to include in the analysis, are usual first steps in the HTA process. This step may, in fact, be circular since the research reveals information that stimulates further requirements to investigate, such as when a reviewed article provides additional references that may be valuable. A systematic approach to literature evaluation is important to ensure an unbiased assessment of the available evidence, and the literature review steps should be documented fully to enable replicable results. The Danish Handbook describes the starting point for search studies that will provide the greatest return on the effort (see **Table 7-2**). Search criteria should correlate directly with the HTA product being assessed, from specific technology to broad HT. A full review will include information from "gray literature" or sources not available in peer-reviewed publications.

Some useful advice and suggestions for this step include: primarily select literature with the highest class of evidence, such as randomized controlled trials (primary sources); use the focused HTA question when assessing whether the article is of relevance; use checklists when reviewing the individual articles; and use internationally recognized standards to assess the articles.

Information obtained for an HTA often is classified in the hierarchy of evidence, ranked from most to least important:

- meta-analyses and systematic reviews
- randomized controlled trials (RCTs)
- non-randomized controlled trials
- cohort studies
- case control studies
- descriptive studies, limited series
- position papers, non-systematic reviews, expert opinions, presentations

The information's quality often is assessed using quality assessment tools, such as the NICE or Grading of Recommendations Assessment, Development and Evaluation (GRADE) rating tools,[5] since literature quality can vary widely. These tools evaluate evidence quality and strength of individual studies' recommendations and provide a systematic method of evaluating studies.

Step 4—Synthesis Process in the HTA

The synthesis process is designed to summarize and assess the findings from the evidence gathered in Step 3 while also providing one or more summary conclusions and, possibly, stakeholder recommendations. This process requires transparency in terms of documents and methodology. The advantages and disadvantages of various HT solutions also must be described.

Various methods are available for data generation, analysis, assessment and use for an HTA. Quantitative and qualitative methods involve interviews, participant observation, fieldwork, ranking and registry studies. This should include a detailed description of the methods encompassing both the quantitative and qualitative approaches related to the HTA elements noted in Step 3.

Conducting primary HTA investigations typically is considered only if the knowledge cannot be gained from a thorough literature review, and then only if the information is of vital importance. The remaining HTA assessment basis or summary statement may not be conclusive enough without the proper data, analysis and assessment.

Step 5—The HTA Report

Numerous organizations have stressed the idea that an HTA is not a decision, but rather provides input or recommendations for the decision-making process. Decision makers, therefore, are the primary target user group for an HTA, with input from various stakeholders. The HTA may go directly to the decision makers or go through several administrative stages where it is adapted or supplemented before the final decision is made. The difference between conducting HTAs and making decisions on the basis of HTAs is that they produce different outcomes. HTA development is based primarily in a research domain, while HTA outputs are used in decision-making domains; examples of HTA reports can found on various websites.[6]

Further Analysis Methods in HTA Process

Qualitative Methods

There are different methods for generating data and different approaches to how these methods are used by researchers in different disciplines, e.g., individual interviews, observation or individual assessments. Qualitative methods can vary from an HTA process that strictly provide literature assessments. Literature reviews often are quantitative in nature due to the variables in scoring or grading an article's relevancy. Additional qualitative methods from different evidence areas, e.g., interviews or focus groups, then must be analyzed. The two primary empirical data interpretation methods are theory-based analyses and qualitative computer-based data programs.

Theory-based analysis and interpretation is based on the relevant theory linking back to the policy and HTA questions. Based on the research hypotheses made for the HT, the information related to the HTA assessment is used to determine whether the qualitative methods are valid or a new theory must be formulated. Qualitative computer-based data programs utilizing the same analysis and interpretation methods can be completed using a more-automated method.

Questionnaire-Based Surveys

Another method of gathering additional HT information is collecting questionnaires from the target audience or population about their understanding of the technology. These can be issued to large populations or targeted groups but must be used with caution because source objectivity is not always reliable.

Despite the difficulties with questionnaires, methods are available to ensure results' validity and reproducibility. The design of the questionnaire should include a base requirement that covers precision, bias and understandability.[7] Any questionnaire-based study must be evaluated to ensure it contains the following elements:

- description of the study showing the relevant selection of respondents, not just a limited representation
- participation rate must be stated for those who answered and those who did not
- lack of or deficient answers to individual questions
- information reported must be assessed using valid scientific methodology

Register Analyses

Published literature reviews typically are based on clinical studies published in peer-reviewed journals. Another method that can be used is analyzing registry data as part of HTA assessment along with previously gained knowledge, e.g., literature reviews and qualitative methods. National patient registry data differ from pure clinical research, as the information is not regulated like clinical data, and the information is obtained voluntarily. However, the wealth of information from registries may be appropriate for review, analysis and linkage to new technology or development of new HT from existing healthcare products. The following information, in the context of the HT, can help make appropriate use of registers:

- diagnosis of disease-specific causes
- morbidity or mortality rates associated with diseases

Figure 7-2. Importance of the Relevant Technology for the Patient's Everyday Life (Børlum 2007)

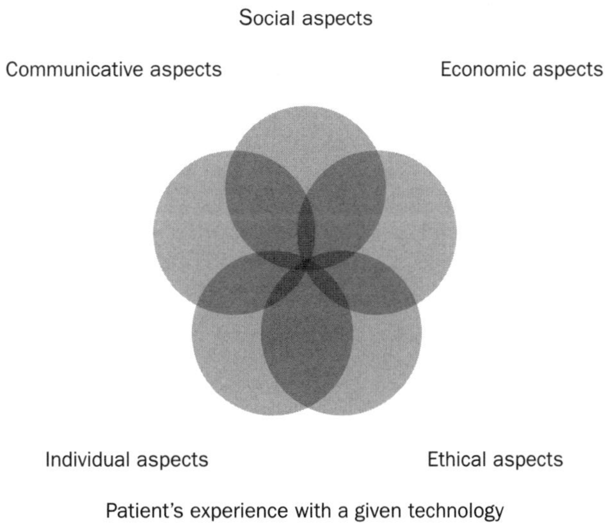

Figure 7-3. The Overall Synthesis Process as Shown in the HTA Danish Handbook

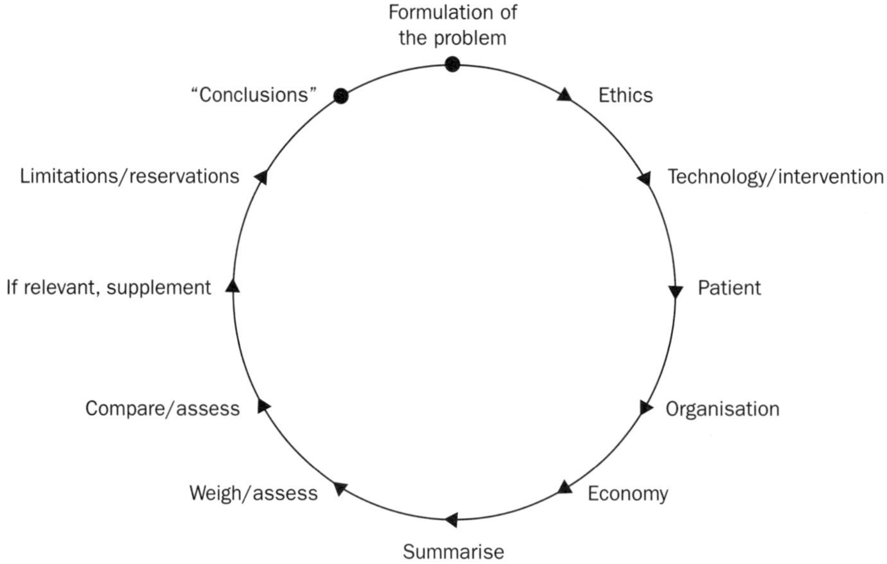

- procedures utilized for patient health
- admission times, length of stay and/or discharge methods
- identification of diseases, endemic rates and treatments

Patient registries must be used with caution, as data contained in registers often are used for purposes other than HTA. Determining whether data validation is required when using registry data is an important aspect of ensuring the data are appropriate.

Technology Assessment

The HT must be identified and linked through each of the HTA process steps, as this is the exercise's main point. The HTA process also can be applied to multiple technologies, defined in the Danish Handbook as "collective term for procedures and methods for examination, treatment, care and rehabilitation of patients, including instruments, drugs and preventative procedures." As previously mentioned, the HTA question is the starting point for the assessment, which ensures the evaluation, analysis and reporting tie back to the technology element of the HTA process.

New or novel technology must be clearly defined for the device, pharmaceutical, techniques or procedures being assessed. When there is one indication for a single product, an STA is performed. When there are multiple products involved with one or more indications, an MTA is performed. MTAs can be more complex because a multi-modal system can have numerous composites and complex technologies to be assessed. An example is a device that inserts a drug product into the patient, automatically measures the amount and then uploads data to an electronic medication system. The inclusion of new technology utilizing an electronic delivery system or electronic monitoring applied to a traditional drug delivery system would be prime HTA assessments.

During the HTA process, the assessment team continually must consider the HT's technical properties and how they are related. The HTA process may take considerable time to complete; therefore, the technology's maturity level must be assessed throughout the entire cycle (**Figure 7-3**). The technology's nature, its application, its diffusion and comparison of best practices must be considered at all times.

Importance of HTA to Decision Makers

The final step in the HTA process after synthesis is to summarize the analysis, weigh all of the factors and complete the HT assessment. As mentioned previously, in the HTA process,[8] the aspect of synthesis is not automatically a decision making process but an assessment for imparting knowledge in the decision. This is a systematic approach based on scientific methods to assure decision makers have the required information to answer new policy questions, answer the HTA questions and determine the type of decision to be made. The synthesis process is an iterative process encompassing a loop system (**Figure 7-3**) that ultimately provides a conclusion. Conclusions are the input for the decision makers in assessing the HT based on the HTA process's "recommendations;" a number of different HT solutions or scenarios may be presented for the HT.

Policy making or the decision to introduce policy is an output of the HTA process that facilitates the decision makers' understanding of all the components used to make the decision. In the US, there is no formal HTA assessment process; therefore, following a structured process helps decision makers reach informed HT recommendations that can impact health practices, patient quality of life,[8,9] reimbursement and other economic factors. Even though no formal process exists, national and state agencies have incorporated elements of the HTA process in assessing technologies.

HTA's importance is reflected in the elements of evidence and analysis steps analyzed independently, which have overlapping attributes that must be considered through the whole process.

The first element is ethics, which stretches across the entire HTA process; this must be included in all steps, with primary importance given to the patient. Decision makers must ensure the recommendations and the HTA conclusions incorporate ethically relevant characteristics and consider ethical problems. Fundamentally, individuals incorporate ethics into their everyday decision making; the patient and doctor relationship must be at the forefront of HTA.

Technology is the next element at the center of the HTA process, particularly the clinical, social and economic aspects. The technology must be described adequately to allow the decision makers to conclude the HTA step. Some regulatory agencies, such as FDA, need to understand a new technology's safety and efficacy, which must be characterized as completely as possible. In addition, the technology's medical utility must relate to how patients are affected by the technology, who can benefit from it and other treatment alternatives. The technology's relationship to the HTA question and the patient is important for decision makers, as technologies can vary significantly and must be described clearly.

The impact of patient aspects extends across all elements, from ethics to economic concerns. Patient aspects must be analyzed to provide decision makers with information necessary to make the proper conclusions (**Figure 7-2**). Not understanding or stating the individual, group and social perspectives of the HT impact can have a detrimental effect on HTA question parameters.

Organization is the next element required for the decision makers, which impacts the healthcare system, including both the healthcare system and organizations within it. When considering a new HT, decision makers have to understand the effects on various organizational actions or structures; some technologies may be appropriate for large organizations (e.g., US facility with 1,000+ beds) and not for small organizations (50-bed clinic in Greece).

The final element is economy, which analyzes costs associated with the HT and their impact on resources and/or budgets. Decision makers' main focus is understanding the new HT's impact in relation to the costs and the consequences compared to current practices or alternative treatments. This can be a complicated part of the HTA process because cost analysis involves socioeconomic issues, including resource and costs limits for organizational budgets. The HTA report's conclusions on economic factors must be appropriate for the technology, patient and organization.

Agencies Using HTA Process in Decision Making

In most cases in the US, an informal HTA process is used in the decision making for new technologies; other countries such as Canada, Sweden and the UK have more formal processes. However, even in the US, public and private healthcare organizations perform HTA evaluations and utilize these evaluations in their decision making.

Agency for Healthcare Research and Quality

The Agency for Healthcare Research and Quality (AHRQ) is the primary US government agency responsible for developing and funding HTA. AHRQ conducts technology assessments in-house and externally through research networks. AHRQ assessments typically focus on a systematic review of literature and data synthesis from multiple studies.[10]

Medicare/Medicaid

The Centers for Medicare and Medicaid Services (CMS), which provides coverage policies for national and local Medicare programs,[11] is the primary user of AHRQ technology assessment. Medicare and Medicaid are the largest government-sponsored healthcare organizations, providing coverage for US citizens aged 65 and over and young, indigent and disabled people, and thus have a major impact on the US healthcare system. CMS is the agency responsible for oversight, financing and implementation of Medicare and Medicaid programs. The Medicare Evidence Development and Coverage Advisory Committee (MedCAC) is a group of external experts that conducts open public meetings to review and weigh evidence from HTAs, such as those produced by AHRQ.

Drug Effectiveness Review Project

The state of Oregon started the Drug Effectiveness Review Project (DERP) in 2000 to manage increasing Medicaid program costs by assessing pharmaceuticals for the state Medicaid Preferred Drug List.[12] DERP is a collaboration between the Oregon Evidence-based Practice Center (EPC) at the Oregon Health Sciences University and several states. Currently, multiple state Medicaid programs and other organizations participate in DERP and utilize its assessments in their decision-making processes. Current participants include CADTH (Canada), Oregon, Washington, Idaho, Missouri, Montana, New York, Arkansas, Colorado, Wisconsin and Wyoming.

Other Federal Programs

The Department of Veterans Affairs (VA) includes the VA Technology Assessment Program (VATAP). VATAP produces technology assessments, including systematic reviews and evidence-based reports targeted at informing VA program decisions.[13]

Agencies Outside the US

UK—National Institute for Health and Care Excellence

The National Institute for Health and Care Excellence (NICE)[14] was established by the UK National Health Services (NHS) as a special interest health authority responsible for providing national guidance on the promotion of health and prevention and/or treatment of health conditions. One of the charters of NICE is to establish national guidance on specific health technologies, including drugs, medical devices and clinical practices. Since 2002, the NHS has provided mandatory healthcare funding, including new technology that is assessed and recommended by NICE through its technology appraisal guidance and clinical guidelines that are published from these HTA assessments.[15] NICE has developed guidance documents that describe the methods for appraising single and multiple technology to provide recommendations for new and existing medicines, products and treatments in the NHS.

Canada—Canadian Agency for Drugs and Technologies in Health

The Canadian Agency for Drugs and Technologies in Health (CADTH)[16] provides methods and processes for decision-making concerning drugs and medical devices for healthcare in Canada. This organization, funded by the federal, provincial and territorial governments, produces health technology reports for recommendations on healthcare decisions crucial to the quality and sustainability of healthcare in Canada. CADTH publishes guidance documents for persons undertaking HTAs for drugs, medical devices and other health technologies. These guidance documents and published HTA reports provide healthcare decision makers with credible, reliable and standardized information concerning recommendations on healthcare technologies.

Sweden—Swedish Council on Health Technology Assessment

The Swedish Council on Health Technology Assessment (SBU)[17] is one of the oldest HT groups in the world providing technology assessments through an informed decision making process. This is an independent national authority group that publishes recommendations on healthcare through a rigorous HTA review process. These SBU reports are used by decision-making authorities for new HTs and provide the basis for new HTAs to be published. The organization has developed a staged approach to assess new HTs, which are published with conclusions and used by experts in making decisions concerning treatment methods, diagnostic methods and best use of resources in the healthcare paradigm.

Conclusions

- HTAs and the resulting policy decisions are a growing consideration for the development and ongoing lifecycle of healthcare technologies.
- The HTA process is a tool for regulatory professionals that, when used properly, can provide a thorough understanding for developing healthcare technologies.
- The five steps in the HTA process provide a structured and formal process for decision makers in generating recommendations for new technologies.
- Decision makers can consider the important aspects of a technology, its impact on the patient and on an organization and delineate the economic concerns for implementing policy or decisions based on it.
- Many countries have no formal HTA regulatory requirements. As new technology is introduced more quickly through continued innovation, the lack of requirements can be a challenge for regulatory professionals, healthcare practitioners and policy makers.

References

1. INAHTA (International Network of Agencies for Health Technology Assessment). (8 June 2009). "HTA glossary.". INAHTA. http://inahta.episerverhotell.net/Glossary/. Accessed 11 March 2015.
2. Børlum KF. Presentation on "Better Use of New Technologies Through Collaboration on HTA." Learning from differences – European collaboration on health systems research conference. Montreux 16 November 2010. EC website. http://ec.europa.eu/research/health/public-health/public-health-and-health-systems/pdf/finn-borlum-kristensen_en.pdf. Slide 3. Accessed 17 May 2015.
3. Børlum KF, Sigmund H, eds. *Health technology assessment handbook*. Copenhagen, National Board of Health. 2007. http://sundhedsstyrelsen.dk/publ/publ2008/mtv/metode/hta_handbook_net_final.pdf. Accessed 11 March 2015.
4. Ibid.
5. Guyatt GH, Oxman AD, Schünemann HJ, Tugwell P, Knotterus A. "GRADE guidelines: a new series of articles in the Journal of Clinical Epidemiology." *J Clin Epidemiol* 2011, 64:380-382.
6. NHS. Centre for Reviews and Dissemination. University of York website. http://www.crd.york.ac.uk/crdweb/. Accessed 11 March 2015.
7. Stone DH. Design a questionnaire. *BMJ* 1993;307:1264-1266.
8. Hawthorne G, Richardson J, Osborne R. "The Assessment of Quality of Life (AQoL) instrument: a psychometric measure of health-related quality of life." *Qual Life Res* 1999 May;8(3):209-224.
9. Hawthorne G, Osborne R. "Population norms and meaningful differences for the Assessment of Quality of Life (AQol) measure." *Aust N Z J Public Health* 2005 Apr;29(2):136-142.
10. AHRQ Technology Assessments. AHRQ website. http://www.ahrq.gov/research/findings/ta/index.html. Accessed 11 March 2015.
11. Ibid.
12. About DERP. Oregon Health & Science University website. http://www.ohsu.edu/xd/research/centers-institutes/evidence-based-policy-center/derp/about/index.cfm. Accessed 11 March 2015.

13. VA Technology Assessment Program. US Department of Veterans Affairs website. http://www.research.va.gov/programs/tech_transfer/. Accessed 17 May 2015.
14. National Institute for Health and Care Excellence. NICE website. http://www.nice.org.uk. Accessed 11 March 2015.
15. National Institute for Health and Care Excellence. NICE and the NHS. http://www.nice.org.uk/aboutnice/whatwedo/niceandthenhs/nice_and_the_nhs.jsp. Accessed 11 March 2015.
16. Canadian Agency for Drugs and Technologies in Health. CADTH website. https://www.cadth.ca/resources/hta-database-canadian-search-interface. Accessed 17 May 2015.
17. Swedish Council on Health Technology Assessment. SBU website. http://www.sbu.se/en/. Accessed 11 March 2015.

Chapter 8

Good Laboratory Practice Regulations

Updated by Christopher V. Braudis, Jr., MSc, RQAP-GLP and Anne E. Maczulak, PhD, RQAP-GLP

OBJECTIVES

- Review the history, purpose and projected future of GLP regulations
- Differentiate between the EPA, FDA and OECD GLPs
- Explore the FDA GLP BIMO Compliance Program
- Examine implications of noncompliance with GLP regulations

LAWS, REGULATIONS AND GUIDELINES COVERED IN THIS CHAPTER

- Section 701(a) of the *Federal Food, Drug, and Cosmetic Act* of 1938
- US Food and Drug Administration, 21 CFR Part 58, Good Laboratory Practice for Nonclinical Laboratory Studies, Final Rule (1987)
- US Food and Drug Administration, 21 CFR Part 11, Electronic Records; Electronic Signatures (20 March 1997)
- Organization for Economic Cooperation and Development, Principles of Good Laboratory Practice (Revised 1997)
- US Environmental Protection Agency, 40 CFR Part 160, Federal Insecticide, Fungicide, and Rodenticide Act, Good Laboratory Practice Standards (2 May 1984)
- US Environmental Protection Agency, 40 CFR Part 792, Toxic Substances Control Act, Good Laboratory Practice Standards (29 December 1983)
- US Food and Drug Administration, Office of Regulatory Affairs, Bioresearch Monitoring Good Laboratory Practice Compliance Program Guidance 7348.808 (Nonclinical Laboratories) (21 February 2001)
- Food and Drug Administration Compliance Program Guidance Manual, Program 7348.808A, Good Laboratory Practice Program (Nonclinical Laboratories) EPA Data Audit Inspections (25 August 2000)
- US Department of Health and Human Services, Food and Drug Administration, Office of Regulatory Affairs, Comparison Chart of FDA and EPA Good Laboratory Practice (GLP) Regulations and the OECD Principles of GLP (June 2004)

Introduction

Good Laboratory Practice (GLP) regulations were developed in the 1970s to improve the trustworthiness of safety data on new drugs and chemicals submitted to US regulatory agencies for marketing in the US.[1] Regulatory professionals in organizations that produce or test the safety of human drugs, biological products, medical devices for human use, veterinary drugs, cosmetics, food and color additives, animal food additives and electronic products should have knowledge of the US Food and Drug Administration (FDA) GLP regulations for nonclinical laboratory studies. Likewise, regulatory professionals in industries producing commercial chemicals, including pesticides, are expected to be aware of the GLP requirements of the Environmental Protection Agency (EPA).

Known throughout these industries as GLPs, these regulations define a quality system to be used in nonclinical studies for assuring the study data's accuracy and integrity. FDA frequently uses the acronym ALCOA (attributable, legible, contemporaneous, original and accurate) to describe data quality. GLPs also ensure a study could be reproduced in its entirety at a future time with similar results. To achieve the study data's accuracy and integrity and overall study reproducibility, GLPs require thorough documentation of all activities comprising a study while ensuring the ALCOA principles are maintained. Additionally, the secure storage and archiving of the raw data, documentation, protocol, final report, specimens and samples of test and control articles for the required retention time will ensure the report reconstruction and evaluation can be completed during an inspection.

FDA and EPA GLP regulations parallel each other in content and wording, differing only in areas specific to the type of studies they cover.[2,3] This similarity serves two purposes. First, many US laboratories conduct studies for both agencies. Similar regulations help these laboratories meet the requirements of both without undue expense or redundancy in allocating resources. Second, any organization conducting GLP studies is open to inspection by either agency. Although these cross-agency inspections are rare, any organization conducting GLP studies should be aware of the basic requirements of both sets of regulations.

Regulatory professionals also must have knowledge of GLP requirements and expectations in countries outside the US, especially those individuals working in global industries. This chapter discusses the future of GLPs in an international framework, including an important agreement already in place for coordinating GLP studies and data acceptance across borders.

GLPs regulated and enforced by FDA are under the authority of the *Federal Food, Drug, and Cosmetic Act* (*FD&C Act*) and the *Public Health Service Act* (*PHS Act*). Both acts are intended to ensure consumers receive products that meet minimum safety and effectiveness standards. FDA's GLPs provide the quality framework for the conduct and reporting of nonclinical laboratory studies, typically on animals, for testing the safety of applicable products intended for further study in human volunteers (clinical studies) before the product is marketed to the general public. Nonclinical laboratory study results help in deciding whether a product is safe for first-in-human (FIH) clinical trials to determine its potential use and side effects as a therapeutic agent. Nonclinical studies typically are in the scientific disciplines of toxicology and pharmacology, which is comprised of pharmacokinetics and pharmacodynamics. Nonclinical and clinical study data are collectively evaluated by FDA to assure the safety of the product being submitted for a research or marketing authorization.

GLPs regulated and enforced by EPA are detailed in the *Federal Insecticide, Fungicide, and Rodenticide Act* (*FIFRA*) and the *Toxic Substances Control Act* (*TSCA*). Each law controls two separate but very similar sets of GLP regulations covering agricultural and industrial chemicals, respectively. *FIFRA* controls pesticide safety and efficacy testing, which include insecticides, herbicides, fungicides, rodenticides and antimicrobial products claiming to control the growth of microorganisms. *TSCA* controls the safety of new commercial chemicals and their effect on human health and the environment. Overall, EPA enforces these two laws to ensure all pesticides and chemicals meet minimum standards of safety in humans, animals and the environment and to demonstrate the impact of these chemicals on the environment is known and within acceptable limits.

In some instances, the EPA regulations provide more detail in particular types of laboratory testing than the FDA regulations. For example, EPA GLPs contain information on analytical reference standards.[4] In cases where an FDA GLP laboratory requires guidance on managing reference standards, the laboratory would refer to the EPA regulations.

Before the 1970s, drugs and chemicals received little or no safety testing. Illness and deaths resulted from substances that had not been evaluated thoroughly for safety compared to the rigor required for today's medicines. In the 1960s and early 1970s, awareness grew about product safety and concern for the environment, which led to the passage of new federal laws calling for stronger product testing by pharmaceutical and chemical companies. These companies were not prepared to conduct such tests, and many of them outsourced the studies to contract laboratories. With little oversight, these laboratories fell into a pattern of faulty reporting, erroneous data and outright falsification of study results. In the mid-1970s, FDA became aware of possible scientific misconduct at Industrial Bio-Test Laboratories (IBT) in Northbrook, IL. When staff from FDA's Office of Compliance inspected IBT, they found deplorable housing conditions for the laboratory animals and thousands of instances of data falsification, errors, false reporting and more egregious examples of scientific misconduct. Less than one quarter of IBT's pesticide studies could be used for evaluating safety. In 1981, the IBT president and two company managers were indicted by a federal grand jury. Ultimately, one defendant was sentenced to a year in prison; two others were jailed for several months.[5]

Additional FDA inspections of drug companies in the 1970s revealed serious problems in the industry, prompting Senator Edward Kennedy (D-MA) to convene a hearing on pharmaceutical testing to assure the American public it could count on safe and effective medications. By 1976, FDA proposed GLP regulations to ensure nonclinical laboratory study quality and integrity. These regulations became law in 1979. Proposed changes were published in 1984, and the revised GLP Final Rule was published in 1987. Subsequently, EPA issued drafts of its own GLP regulations in 1979 and 1980. It enacted its Final Rule in two parts (*FIFRA* and *TSCA*) in 1983, made extensive revisions, and published the amended regulations in 1989. The FDA and EPA GLPs are similar in format and wording. They follow the same principles for assuring data accuracy and integrity and contain the same key GLP study elements.

Regulatory oversight of GLP studies is important to ensure companies wishing to market a product have thoroughly evaluated the product's safety profile. The GLP regulations ensure the laboratory testing is performed in a way that produces accurate and reliable data, reproducible results and clear and accurate reporting. Nonclinical laboratory studies performed according to GLPs therefore are important to ensure the product is safe enough to move forward into Phase 1 clinical trials and also provide a measure of confidence the product will be safe when marketed to the general public. By providing oversight of these studies, regulatory agencies remove the burden of self-policing from drug and chemical manufacturers. Nevertheless, GLP core principles can be extended to all types of scientific research, i.e., accuracy and reproducibility of lab studies, accurate and transparent reporting, thorough and legible documentation, accountability and secure long-term retention of all study records. The GLP regulations also establish the requirement for an independent quality assurance unit (QAU) to monitor each study and assure management the facilities, equipment, personnel, methods, practices, records and controls are in conformance with GLP regulations.

The globalization of business has increasingly affected how companies follow GLP regulations. For example, many pharmaceutical companies synthesize, test and manufacture new drug active ingredients in Asia or Europe before selling their drugs in the US. The regulatory landscape for conducting such multi-site and multinational studies has made the "one shop does all" business environment of decades past increasingly rare.

To meet this changing business and regulatory landscape, the Organization for Economic Cooperation and Development (OECD) member countries throughout North America (including the US), Europe and Asia, have developed a set of GLP principles similar to the US GLP regulations. These principles cover the safety testing of pharmaceuticals, animal drugs, food additives, pesticides and industrial chemicals. Member countries without a specific set of national GLP regulations follow OECD GLP principles.[6] Other member countries, such as Japan, have regulations based on the US regulations. Mutual recognition agreements have been established for most of these different but similar GLP regulations, so US agencies generally will accept GLP studies performed under the country's national regulations where the study was conducted. In 1981, OECD adopted the Mutual Acceptance of Data (MAD) document that states study data generated in an OECD member country may be accepted by other member countries.[6] Most multinational companies conducting GLP studies have some familiarity with OECD and other international GLP regulations. An international effort has been underway for several years, with the goal of harmonizing the GLPs into a single set of regulations.

GLP Regulations and Guidelines

US GLP regulations are to be followed by companies, contract laboratories, academic laboratories or any other organization conducting studies to support an application for research (clinical trial) or a marketing application for a regulated product. In the drug product development process, these studies immediately precede the Investigational New Drug (IND) Application. FDA refers to GLP studies as nonclinical studies; EPA refers to them simply as studies.

All US and international GLP regulations contain the same key elements that make up a GLP-compliant study. In FDA and EPA GLP regulations, these elements are described in specific subparts of 21 CFR Part 58 for FDA and 40 CFR Part 160 (*FIFRA*) and 40 CFR Part 792 (*TSCA*) for EPA.[7,8] The key elements can be summarized as:

- facility where the study or delegated study phases are conducted
- standard operating procedures (SOPs)
- personnel involved in the study
- equipment
- test article (FDA) or test substance (EPA) being studied
- biological system in which the articles or substances are tested
- documentation of the study from planning to final results
- retention of study records

These key elements also appear in the OECD principles, although the terminology used to describe them varies from US regulations.[9]

Nonclinical laboratory studies expected to be in compliance with FDA 21 CFR Part 58 include, but are not limited to:

- acute, subchronic and chronic toxicology studies, including developmental, reproductive, carcinogenic, mutagenic and degenerative toxicology studies based on appearance of these effects in laboratory animals

- *in vivo* or *in vitro* medical device safety testing as well as device physical and chemical characteristics' testing
- *in vivo* and *in vitro* biochemistry, nutrition, immunology and microbiology studies
- dermal, eye, venous or muscle irritation studies
- pharmacology studies, including toxicology, pharmacokinetics, pharmacodynamics and therapeutics
- bioanalytical studies of samples from study animal dose groups
- test and control article characterization and stability
- if the target species in an animal drug study is a food-producing animal, the data related to human safety
- animal testing for establishment of color and food additive safety
- validation of methods to be used for sample analysis from GLP studies (bioanalysis); not specifically stated as a requirement in FDA regulations but recommended for bioanalytical laboratories

EPA GLP studies are intended to show any potential hazards from the pesticide or chemical to human health, the health of domestic animals and the environment. Studies expected to be in compliance with EPA 40 CFR Part 160 or 40 CFR Part 792 include, but are not limited to:

- target organism pesticide efficacy studies
- acute, subchronic and chronic toxicology studies, including developmental, reproductive, carcinogenic, mutagenic and degenerative toxicology studies based on appearance of these effects in laboratory animals
- potential exposure studies by various routes, such as oral, dermal or inhalation
- product chemistry studies, including chemical and physical characterization studies of the product's active and inert ingredients
- environmental fate studies of the chemical's effect on non-target organisms and their habitat
- residue chemistry testing on treated food or feed
- physical and chemical test substance characterization studies (also applicable to control and reference substances)

US GLP regulations do not cover the following study types: human clinical trials, field trials in animals, method development and basic exploratory studies. Exploratory studies may include research and development testing to determine a particular drug or substance's usefulness or initial laboratory testing to determine a substance's physical or chemical characteristics. Preliminary *in vivo* feasibility medical device testing and preliminary *in vivo* drug dose range testing do not have to be conducted under GLP.

The data obtained from GLP nonclinical studies and submitted to FDA are used to make decisions on a product's overall safety or toxicity profile. FDA considers parameters such as the maximum dose level with no observed adverse effects, the potential adverse effects and risks determined in human clinical trials or in animal tests, the optimum dose level, dosing frequency and duration of use and the product's teratogenicity or carcinogenic potential.

EPA evaluates similar safety issues associated with chemicals tested in GLP studies but does not require human clinical trials. EPA puts greater emphasis, however, on a chemical's effect on the environment and its environmental fate. Thus, in addition to GLP study data, EPA evaluates product chemistry, residue chemistry, environmental chemistry, physical hazards and risks associated with residential and occupational exposure.

Overview of FDA and EPA GLP Subparts and Sections

The US GLP regulations are very specific on the responsibilities of three personnel functions in a GLP study: testing facility management, study director and the QAU. The GLPs also have specific requirements that must be fulfilled for animal care and SOPs. GLPs tend to be less specific on technology and instrumentation. The US GLP regulations were written decades ago with the understanding technology, equipment and instrumentation likely would change in the future. The general GLP concepts for ensuring test method and equipment operation and reliability are described in the regulations; however, the GLPs lack specific requirements. Many of the specific methodology and equipment questions that arise in regulated laboratories often are addressed in published agency guidance and new rules (e.g., FDA's *Guidance for Industry: Bioanalytical Method Validation*, 2013). These help bridge gaps between the GLP regulations and FDA's current thinking on specific topics that were not available when the GLPs were first written and published.

The FDA and EPA GLP regulations are divided into subparts to cover key GLP compliance elements. Each subpart contains sections providing specific requirements for GLP studies or the facility and personnel involved in GLP studies. The FDA subparts and sections are described below with the corresponding EPA GLP sections shown in parentheses. Gaps in section numbers were included intentionally to allow future additions to these regulations.

Subpart A—General Provisions

§58.1 Scope (§160.1, §792.1)

This section describes the types of products regulated by the respective agency, all of which, by law, must comply with the GLPs.

§58.3 Definitions (§160.3, §792.3)
Specific definitions related to GLPs are described in this section. The list of definitions covers the item to be tested, controls, the test system, specimen, batch, raw data, study start date and study end date. Certain key elements and personnel are defined, such as testing facility, study sponsor, testing facility management, study director and QAU. The specific laws or acts covering the testing also are defined here, as is related terminology such as new drug application and application for research or marketing permit.

§58.10 Applicability to Studies Performed under Grants and Contracts (§160.10, §792.10)
The sponsor is responsible for informing all contract organizations that a study is intended for submission to a regulatory agency, and the contract laboratory must follow all applicable regulations.

Though not stated specifically, the agencies expect the sponsor to ensure the contract facility's GLP capabilities before beginning study activities. A sponsor accomplishes this by conducting a prequalification audit to determine the contracted facility's GLP compliance status and identify whether it has qualified personnel and adequate quality systems in place to conduct GLP-regulated studies. Thereafter, sponsors and contract facilities hold equal responsibility for ensuring the contracted study's GLP compliance.

§58.15 Inspection of a Testing Facility (§160.15, §792.15)
The testing facility is the location where the test article or test substance is applied to the test system. This section delineates testing facility responsibilities and those of the agency when inspecting such facilities. It describes testing facility management's responsibility to permit entrance to an authorized FDA or EPA employee at reasonable times. The section also describes the ramifications of refusing such entrance. The types of records and specimens agency representatives are permitted to inspect are described as well as those records agencies are not permitted to inspect.

Subpart B—Organization and Personnel

§58.29 Personnel (§160.29, §792.29)
The GLPs state the requirements for showing personnel involved in a GLP study have the appropriate education, experience and overall qualifications to perform their assigned tasks. Each GLP study should have an adequate number of study personnel, appropriately trained in a technical discipline corresponding with their roles and responsibilities as well as general training in laboratory safety, GLP regulations and site-specific SOPs, protocols and policies. The section emphasizes maintaining each individual's training documentation, which typically includes curriculum vitae, job description and training records. It also points out the need for good hygiene and health among study personnel to ensure they can perform their duties to the best of their ability.

§58.31 Testing Facility Management (§160.31, §792.31)
Testing facility management has considerable responsibility for ensuring specific GLP studies follow the regulations, and facility operations and personnel meet minimum GLP compliance requirements. This section lists the main management responsibilities, but those responsibilities are not limited to this list. Testing facility management should receive periodic GLP regulation training to understand all their responsibilities fully. The need for this training becomes clear when regulatory agencies repeatedly cite management as one of the major noncompliance areas found during facility inspections.

The specific testing facility management responsibilities described in this section are to designate a study director and replace that director if necessary and ensure:

- the presence of a QAU
- the QAU reports any deviations from the GLP regulations to the study director and follows up to confirm appropriate corrective actions have been made
- all test and control articles have been fully characterized
- personnel, equipment, materials, resources and facilities are ready for the GLP activities
- all methods and SOPs are available for study personnel to follow
- study personnel understand their functions in the study and the facility

§58.33 Study Director (§160.33, §792.33)
The study director has sole responsibility for the GLP study's technical conduct and the study results' interpretation, analysis, documentation and reporting. GLP regulations give the study director authority over all aspects of a study from the time the protocol is signed until the final report is signed.

In addition to clearly stating the study director's role, this section also elaborates on specific responsibilities. The study director is responsible for approving the protocol and any subsequent amendments as well as assuring study personnel follow the study protocol and GLP regulations. The study director oversees all data collection, study conduct and reporting and ensures any excursions from the protocol are documented, and a corrective action is followed. This responsibility extends to any other sites participating in the study. By signing the final study report, the study director accepts full legal responsibility for study data accuracy and integrity and conclusions drawn from the results, as well as the study's GLP compliance status by issuing a compliance statement within the final report.

The study director usually resides at the testing facility, but there is no GLP requirement for this. Some study directors reside at the sponsor's site or another location separate from the testing facility. In studies across multiple sites, individuals (contributing scientists or Principal Investigators) oversee the work conducted at their respective sites. These individuals carry out the study director's responsibilities but with the study director ultimately retaining all authority over the study conduct.

§58.35 Quality Assurance Unit (§160.35, §792.35)
The QAU is an individual or a group trained in GLPs, responsible for ensuring the facilities, equipment, personnel, methods, practices, records and controls are in conformance with the regulations. This section lists the detailed QAU responsibilities to fulfill their roles.

The QAU does not evaluate the scientific merit of studies or question the science used to draw study conclusions. This section states unequivocally the QAU must be entirely separate from and independent of the study's direction and conduct. This means a QAU cannot report to a study director or any other person involved in an open GLP study. The QAU must not participate in a study in any way, including but not limited to data collection, handling of test articles, controls or test systems, or any documentation intended as part of the study file.

QAU personnel maintain the facility's master schedule, study protocol and protocol amendment copies, and all facility and study inspection reports. In addition to inspecting individual studies and laboratory processes, the QAU periodically inspects the entire facility. All QAU inspection outcomes are reported in writing to management and the study director (GLP studies only). Additionally, the QAU writes periodic overall GLP compliance status reports for each study and sends these reports to management and the study director.

With GLP studies, the QAU inspects important phases of each study and ensures the protocol is being followed. If certain processes are guided by an SOP rather than the protocol, the QAU ensures these written procedures also are being followed. The QAU determines whether protocol or SOP deviations have occurred. If they have, the QAU makes certain the study director has been notified, the deviation has been documented and corrective actions taken. Finally, the QAU signs a statement for each final study report to specify the study inspection dates and when findings were reported to the testing facility management and the study director.

The QAU also usually is involved in hosting inspectors during regulatory inspections or sponsor audits. Though not a GLP requirement, having a QAU representative present to answer questions about a facility's GLP compliance program and inspection processes can facilitate communications between a facility and the regulatory agency.

Organizations sometimes mistakenly assign QAU the responsibility for maintaining study archives. Management assigns an archivist the responsibility of limiting archive entry, maintaining an indexing system, and assuring records and specimens are protected from deterioration (described later). Someone other than a QAU member should be designated as archivist.

Subpart C—Facilities

§58.41 General (§160.41, §792.41)
All facilities conducting GLP studies must be of suitable construction and size to accommodate the regulated activities.

§58.43 Animal Care Facilities (§160.43, §792.43)
This section provides detailed instructions on how test systems are to be managed and maintained and requirements for the facilities that house test systems. FDA's GLP regulations focus mainly on laboratory animal husbandry and care. EPA's regulations cover laboratory animal and non-laboratory animal test systems, such as aquatic species and microorganisms.

§58.45 Animal Supply Facilities (§160.45, §792.45)
The FDA GLP section includes brief requirements for animal feeding, bedding and other housing accommodations. EPA's section provides more detail by covering the care of non-laboratory animal test systems.

§58.47 Facilities for Handling Test and Control Articles (§160.47, §792.47)
Certain practices should be followed for maintaining a study's test article and the control article. Receipt, storage and mixing requirements (if applicable) are discussed. The EPA regulations also describe the requirements for reference standards for analytical methods.

§58.49 Laboratory Operation Areas (§160.49, §792.49)
This concise section describes separate laboratory space requirements, as needed, for GLP study routine or specialized procedures.

§58.51 Specimen and Data Storage Facilities (§160.51, §792.51)
Facilities involved in GLP studies must provide suitable archive space for the safe and secure storage of raw data, specimens and other materials necessary for study reproducibility.

Subpart D—Equipment

§58.61 Equipment Design (§160.61, §792.61)
Considering the US GLP regulations were written before the personal computer was introduced, Subpart D focuses

mainly on analytical instruments and other laboratory equipment for collecting study data. Computer systems and computer operations are, however, part of GLP inspections, and this subpart provides the framework for assessing GLP compliance. Despite the consternation this has caused in some laboratories, Subpart D provides basic guidelines that work as well for computer systems as they do for traditional laboratory equipment.

Equipment should be designed appropriately and have the capacity to function as intended according to the GLP study protocol. All data collection equipment also must be located in the laboratory to allow proper inspection, maintenance, repair and cleaning.

§58.63 Maintenance and Calibration of Equipment (§160.63, §792.63)

This section describes equipment testing and calibration requirements to ensure study data accuracy. Testing and calibration methods must be described in written SOPs and must also state the procedures to be taken if equipment fails or malfunctions. Finally, all routine maintenance, testing and calibration and non-routine actions such as repairs must be documented in written records. These written records usually are documented within an equipment log that provides a history of every critical piece of equipment in a testing facility. Newly purchased and older equipment even if received from another laboratory (legacy systems or "grandfathered" equipment) must follow these regulations.

The term "equipment qualification" is not used in the GLP regulations, but this section describes the agencies' expectations for thorough equipment qualification and testing before it is used in a GLP study. This requirement extends to computerized systems involved in study data collection, calculations and storage.

Subpart E—Testing Facilities Operation

§58.81 Standard Operating Procedures (§160.81, §792.81)

Regulatory agencies expect all testing facilities to have complete written records of their operations, test methods and equipment calibration, maintenance and operation procedures. Included in this list of expected SOPs are procedures describing all facets of animal care; data and specimen handling, storage and retrieval; and test and control article management. This section provides a detailed list of SOPs required by GLP regulations, but many additional expected SOPs are not listed. Specific procedures the SOPs should capture are guided by industry standards and common sense. For example, an SOP would be expected for any procedure performed routinely in a facility and needed to conduct a GLP study. Computerized system validation is one example of a procedure an inspector would expect the testing facility to have; however, this SOP requirement is not stated directly within the GLP regulations. However, the *Bioresearch Monitoring Good Laboratory Practice Compliance Program 7348.808*, Appendix A, shows computer system validation and computer operations are in the scope of an FDA GLP inspection.

Each testing facility should have an established lifecycle document management system that covers SOP and study method development, review, approval, distribution, revision and retirement. SOPs and study methods are controlled documents that require unique document numbers and versioning appropriate to the document type. For instance, SOPs and study methods are revised by sequential versioning (e.g., Version 1.0, Version 2.0, etc.) after changes or modifications are made. Management should approve all new SOPs and study methods as well as any significant changes made to ensure the quality and integrity of data generated during a study. SOPs and study methods for the tasks to be performed should be available to all personnel involved in conducting a study. All deviations from SOPs must be documented in the raw data and authorized by the study director.

§58.83 Reagents and Solutions (§160.83, §792.83)

This section describes labeling requirements for all reagents and solutions held in a laboratory that conducts GLP activities.

§58.90 Animal Care (§160.90, §792.90)

One of the most essential sections written by the agencies in the 1970s, following egregious drug safety testing errors and fraud in the first half of the 20th century, covers animal care. The GLP regulations provide specific recordkeeping and test animal handling expectations to avoid errors and ensure study results are reliable. The section details requirements for identification and housing of laboratory animals and treatment of sick animals. EPA's regulations provide slightly more detail on additional test systems.

Subpart F—Test and Control Articles

§58.105 Test and control Article Characterization (§160.105, §792.105)

Much like the animal care section, the regulatory agencies included specific details on tracking and handling GLP study test and control articles. Previous safety testing history indicated this was a source of major errors. Even today, the test and control article chain of custody remains an area most laboratories need to improve to meet GLP requirements. This section discusses labeling, characterization and test article and control article storage requirements.

Many laboratories use their Good Manufacturing Practice (GMP) facilities to characterize the GLP study test articles. This is a common error. A GLP study test article must be characterized by following the GLP regulations. GMP characterization, by contrast, is to be used only for finished products to be marketed. Further, the test article's stability testing must show unequivocally that the article was stable during the GLP study test period

This EPA regulation subpart provides further detail on the management of reference standards used in analytical methods. Laboratories following FDA regulations may refer to these EPA requirements as guidance when using any type of reference standards for analysis of test articles, samples or specimens.

§58.107 Test and Control Handling (§160.107, §792.107)

This section discusses additional requirements on maintaining error-free test and control article identity and purity from the start of the study to the final disposition.

§58.113 Mixtures of Articles with Carriers (§160.113, §792.113)

The regulations provide additional details on agencies' expectations for proper test and control article handling. In this case, the section offers specifics on how to test mixtures' purity and stability prior to a GLP study.

Subpart G—Protocol for and Conduct of a Nonclinical Laboratory Study

§58.120 Protocol (§160.120, §792.120)

Of all the GLP regulations, Subpart G may be the most referenced by both GLP and non-GLP organizations because it outlines basic study documentation steps. Forward-thinking laboratories that do not run GLP studies but do conduct basic patient substantiation research or studies refer to these sections. Good Documentation Practices refers mainly to Subpart G principles.

Each GLP study and, indeed any research study, is conducted according to a formal written plan, i.e., the study protocol. There is only one protocol per study, just as there is only one study director per study and (as discussed below) one final report per study. This section provides a detailed list of items to be included in every GLP study protocol. The order of these items may vary, provided all relevant information is included.

The sponsor must approve the protocol, and the approval date must be noted in the document. Although a signature is not required, almost all protocol approvals are authorized by the sponsor representative's (person responsible for the nonclinical toxicology program) signature and the date. Following this approval, the study director signs and dates the protocol, which is the study initiation or start date. No study-related data collection may begin before the signature date, and all activities after the protocol is signed are part of the study, must be recorded properly and are open to regulatory agency inspection.

Regulatory agencies understand things can change quickly in multi-phase studies involving multiple analytical methods, living test systems and multiple sites. The regulations, therefore, include provisions for circumstances when a protocol must be changed after the study has begun. Planned protocol changes (i.e., changes before they occur) are made via protocol amendments. Amendments are approved by the sponsor and signed by the study director just like the protocol. All study participants then must be notified of the amendment. An unplanned excursion from the protocol must be documented as a protocol deviation. The study director must evaluate these events to determine their effect on the study; events must be documented in the raw data and reviewed by the QAU. GLP study-related SOP deviations must be managed in exactly the same manner.

§58.130 Conduct of a Nonclinical Laboratory Study (§160.130, §792.130)

The GLP regulations' objective is to employ requirements to ensure the quality and integrity of data submitted as part of a research or marketing application. GLP-compliant nonclinical laboratory studies shall be reproducible, and the report shall be able to be evaluated at a later date, for example during an inspection (**Figure 8-1**). The final report should describe the test methods, SOPs and raw data accurately. Nonclinical studies may be conducted far in advance of a submission, making it crucial that all records are archived in a secure manner to ensure their long-term preservation and retrieval for further evaluation when submitted to the agency when the final report is issued. To this end, Section 58.130 is very specific about handling raw data and labeling of specimens generated in a study. These raw data and specimens are the primary items required to recreate the study at a later date, if necessary.

The regulations were written to cover data collected by hand. Thus, this section states all raw data "shall be recorded directly, promptly, and legibly in ink." Data dating and signing at the time of its generation equates to an audit trail. Any changes to entries must not obscure the original data; a reason for the change must be recorded; the change date included; and a signature included to identify the responsible person.

The introduction of computerized systems to laboratory work prompted a considerable amount of angst in laboratories. How would the Section 58.130 requirements apply to electronic data collection systems? In fact, the requirements remain exactly the same. All electronic data collected must be permanent, provide an audit trail and be unchangeable. If changes are warranted, they must be managed the same way as written entries described in this section of the regulations.

As computerized systems developed and advanced, new questions arose on electronic data management. FDA issued 21 CFR Part 11 Electronic Records; Electronic Signatures to clarify the finer points of electronic data handling and

Figure 8.1. Study Reconstruction and Evaluation

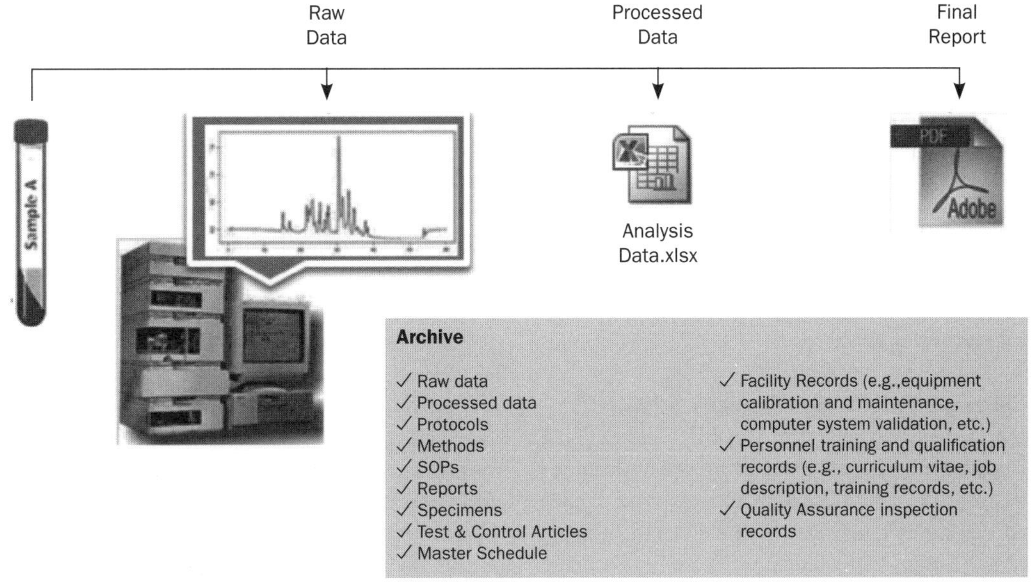

storage. Electronic systems continue to advance at a much faster pace than regulatory agencies can react. The regulations in 21 CFR 58.130 and 21 CFR Part 11 remain the requirements for electronic records generated during GLP studies.

Subpart J—Records and Reports

§58.185 Reporting of Nonclinical Laboratory Study Results (§160.185, §792.185)

Similar to the section listing required study protocol elements, this section lists the required final study report content. Each study with a study director-signed protocol also must have a signed final report. This includes completed studies as well as studies that were terminated early. The date the study director signs the final report is the study completion date. No further data may be collected or information inserted into the report after this signature. In the event new information becomes available that affects a completed study's outcome, a report amendment should be prepared, signed by the study director and kept with the original final report.

The final report is not approved by the sponsor in the same manner as the protocol. All data, results, discussion and conclusions in the report are the study director's responsibility. Sponsors, therefore, must refrain from approving the report to avoid any undue pressure they might exert on the study director to draw favorable conclusions for their products.

In addition to specific items, such as the report title and description of the methods used in the study, the regulations also state the requirements for reports submitted by other key contributing scientists. These scientists may be from the testing facility or elsewhere and bring particular scientific expertise needed for a GLP study. For example, contributing scientists in GLP studies often are pathologists, histopathologists, microbiologists, analytical chemists, engineers and statisticians. The contributing scientists who will submit a report to the study director at the end of the study's experimental phase should be listed in the protocol. Only after all contributing scientist reports have been submitted to the study director can the study director draw full and accurate study conclusions.

The regulations require two additional signed pages to be included with every report: the compliance statement and the QA statement. This section specifies the compliance statement is "a description of all circumstances that may have affected the quality and integrity of the data." This statement ensures the study has complied with GLP regulations; any protocol deviations and any circumstances that may have affected data quality or integrity are listed. The study director must sign and date the compliance statement. The QAU also prepares a statement indicating study compliance and includes a list of inspection dates, the part of the study it inspected and the dates the inspection findings were reported to testing facility management and the study director. Each contributing scientist report also should have a compliance statement signed by the scientist and a corresponding QA statement. These documents provide confirmation to the study director all study phases were completed in full compliance with GLP regulations.

In recent years, many laboratories have assumed not all study phases need to be conducted under GLPs. As long as the noncompliant phases are reported on the compliance statement, these laboratories believe an agency will accept the study results. There is, in fact, no guarantee of any study's acceptance. Regulatory agencies expect full compliance with the regulations from all study phases. Doing otherwise risks the study being rejected.

§58.190 Storage and Retrieval of Records and Data (§160.190, §792.190)
The final piece in reproducibility of GLP studies involves secure storage of all study records. This section describes the raw data, documentation and specimens that must be retained as well as the storage conditions to ensure they are protected from deterioration but also easily retrievable during an inspection. The requirement for an archivist dedicated to this task is described.

§58.195 Retention of Records (§160.195, §792.195)
Record retention requirements differ for FDA and EPA. In each set of regulations, this section describes the minimum number of years sponsors must hold records. The regulations also detail the specific records to be stored, how to retain study specimens and what to do if a record storage facility goes out of business.

Subpart K—Disqualification of Testing Facilities

Subpart K is contained in FDA GLP regulations, not EPA regulations. Its nine sections describe reasons a laboratory can be disqualified from running GLP studies and the steps required for reinstatement.

Differentiating FDA and EPA GLP Regulations

The FDA and EPA GLP regulations parallel each other in most sections but differ where they are unique to the types of studies they cover.[10] FDA issued a "Comparison Chart of FDA and EPA Good Laboratory Practice (GLP) Regulations and the OECD Principles of GLP" in June 2004. The list of subparts and comparisons between each section of the GLPs from FDA, EPA and OECD can be found at http://www.fda.gov/ICECI/EnforcementActions/BioresearchMonitoring/ucm135197.htm. One of the major differences is FDA has dedicated Subpart K in its entirety to testing facility disqualification, while the EPA GLP regulations do not. Instead, the EPA GLP regulations discuss the effects of noncompliance within Subpart A General Provisions.

Ancillary GLP Quality System Components

GLP quality systems must keep up with new technologies, even though the regulations were introduced decades ago. US regulations can change only as fast as laws change. For this reason, new regulations, rules and guidances have been issued to cover new technologies that have evolved since the introduction of the GLPs.

Regulations represent the intent of specific laws, such as the *FD&C Act,* and are legally binding.[11] FDA centers issue specific rules to clarify the requirements of 21 CFR Part 58 and these, too, are legally binding once they have been published. FDA guidances are not laws and are issued to describe the agency's current thinking on a specific topic. Nevertheless, laboratories are strongly encouraged to follow any FDA guidances. In fact, FDA considers some guidances to be requirements in support of GLP regulations, and a facility risks disciplinary action if it chooses to ignore such a guidance.

All laboratories running GLP studies today should be familiar with FDA 21 CFR Part 11.[12] This law covers facility requirements for maintaining computerized systems, electronic data collection and electronic record storage. The scope section of Part 11 describes the types of records this regulation covers and the electronic signatures required to establish an audit trail for data captured electronically rather than in handwritten records. Currently, facilities that run FDA GLP studies must follow 21 CFR Part 11 to ensure their computers and other electronic data systems are maintained, tested and protected properly by rigorous user-specific security. Part 11 also describes the requirements for electronic signatures to establish a data audit trail.

Although not specifically mentioned in the GLP regulations, additional ancillary components of GLP quality systems are seen throughout industry and described in guidances, including processes for equipment qualification and test method validation. Equipment qualification ensures all data collection equipment has been installed properly, operates according to manufacturer specifications and performs according to the user requirement specifications for its intended use prior to being used in a nonclinical study. This equipment qualification process is often described in three components: installation qualification (IQ), operational qualification (OQ) and performance qualification (PQ). Ultimately, this process ensures the quality and integrity of data generated during the course of the nonclinical laboratory study. Test methods also must be validated to ensure their accuracy, reproducibility and suitability for the type of study in which they will be used. Test method validations are run as separate studies following all applicable GLP requirements. FDA's *Guidance for Industry for Bioanalytical Method Validation* (2013) provides recommendations for the design of a bioanalytical method validation study (i.e., method validation parameters and acceptance criteria).[13]

OECD GLP Principles

With the expanding globalization of commerce, clinical and nonclinical studies increasingly are conducted as multi-site studies in more than one country. Regulatory and quality assurance professionals now must be familiar with the international regulations that impact their organizations' studies. The GLP principles published by the Organisation for Economic Co-operation and Development (OECD) play an important role as resources for topics not covered by the US regulations. To find resources on topics not covered by FDA GLP regulations, quality assurance professionals know a hierarchy is to be followed. The hierarchy for GLP resources, from highest priority to lowest priority, is: FDA GLP regulations, FDA rulings and guidances, EPA GLP regulations and OECD GLP principles.

OECD GLP principles have been useful particularly for laboratories conducting multi-site studies, even if all sites are within the US. The OECD GLP principles clarify the roles and responsibilities of test sites performing GLP study phases. OECD makes the need for open communication among test sites and the study director clear as well as the importance of all sites complying with GLP requirements.

To date, OECD has issued 15 separate documents on GLP principles. The main value of these GLP principles resides in the speed with which OECD can issue documents to address new technologies and business models. By contrast, US regulations change very slowly after long periods of agency review and public comment. The OECD documents used most by US laboratories to supplement FDA's GLP regulations are:

- Number 1: OECD Principles on Good Laboratory Practice
- Number 7: The Application of the GLP Principles to Short Term Studies
- Number 13: The Application of the GLP Principles to the Organisation and Management of Multi-Site Studies
- Number 14: The Application of the GLP Principles to in Vitro Studies

Other GLP principles can be found on the OECD website (http://www.oecd-ilibrary.org/environment/oecd-series-on-principles-of-good-laboratory-practice-and-compliance-monitoring_2077785x). In addition, FDA provides a comparison chart showing the specific differences between US GLP regulations and OECD GLP principles.[14]

Guidance for Industry—Purpose and Relevance in GLP

FDA has issued guidance periodically to clarify its current thinking on topics related to GLP studies and how they should be conducted. One of the first attempts at helping industry understand compliance to 21 CFR Part 58 was a Question and Answer document.[15] The document consolidated all GLP questions answered by FDA during the two-year period after 20 June 1979, the date the FDA GLP regulations came into law. Issued in June 1981, the *Good Laboratory Practice Questions and Answers (GLP Q&A)* guidance document underwent minor revisions in 1999 and 2007. Despite FDA's intention to clarify parts of the GLP regulations, various industries remain confused on points specific to their niches in GLP studies.

Each FDA center now provides additional directed GLP communications and guidance specific to the products under its authority. Thus, regulatory and quality assurance professionals should refer to the website of the center that regulates their products for the latest communications and guidances. Each of the following centers provides information on its current thinking on GLP compliance for safety testing of specific products:

- Center for Drug Evaluation and Research
- Center for Biologics Evaluation and Research
- Center for Devices and Radiological Health
- Center for Veterinary Medicine
- Center for Food Safety and Applied Nutrition

The Center for Tobacco Products has not yet issued guidances on GLP-compliant testing of tobacco products in toxicology, chemistry, exposure and other studies. A regulatory framework is underway in this area.

In addition to the general GLP Q&A on 21 Part 58, FDA has issued guidances on conducting bioanalytical activities. Bioanalytical samples are taken from human volunteers in clinical studies but not used for health assessment or disease diagnosis. These specimens do not fall under *Clinical Laboratory Improvement Amendments* (*CLIA*) requirements. Bioanalytical laboratories long have needed regulations to cover analysis and handling of these specimens and historically have adapted certain elements of 21 CFR Part 58 to their activities.

FDA continues to understand the need for guidance on bioanalytical specimen handling and analysis. To start addressing that goal, FDA issued a draft guidance[16] in 2001 on bioanalytical method validation. In September 2013, FDA issued an updated draft of this guidance to provide specifics on the six fundamental validation parameters:

- accuracy—closeness of mean test results to the actual value
- precision—closeness of individual repeated measurements to each other
- selectivity—ability of a test method to differentiate and quantify a given substance (the analyte) in the presence of other substances
- sensitivity—lowest analyte concentration that can be measured with acceptable accuracy and precision
- reproducibility—ability of replicate measurements to achieve the same accurate results
- stability—test method's ability to measure an analyte with the same accuracy and precision over a prescribed time period and exposure to different environmental conditions

These six parameters are essential for all GLP laboratory method validations, not solely bioanalytical work. FDA expects additional analyte and equipment qualification measurement parameters for a GLP study method to be acceptable. Many analytical laboratories conduct method validations as independent GLP studies.

FDA does not require organizations to follow draft guidances if a laboratory prefers a reasonable alternative approach, but that alternative must satisfy the requirements of the GLP regulations and be justified. Quality assurance professionals strongly advise their organizations to follow all applicable FDA guidances whenever possible.

Inspection of GLP Laboratories and Consequences of Noncompliance

All laboratories operating within the US that perform GLP studies are subject to inspection by FDA or EPA. FDA also has authority to conduct inspections of non-US laboratories if they are following US GLP regulations to conduct safety studies on substances intended for marketing in the US. These inspections are to confirm facilities and personnel engaged in GLP safety studies follow all applicable regulations. The main GLP inspection objectives, as specified in the Bioresearch Monitoring (BIMO) compliance program guidance manual, [17] are:

- to verify the quality and integrity of data submitted in a research or marketing application
- to inspect (approximately every two years) nonclinical laboratories conducting safety studies intended to support applications for regulated product research or marketing
- to audit safety studies and determine the degree of compliance with GLP regulations (The ultimate goal is to ensure products have met all required safety testing to protect public health before being marketed in the US.)

A valuable resource for such laboratories is BIMO. Part of FDA's compliance program, BIMO provides instructions to FDA personnel on how to evaluate an organization's compliance with the *FD&C Act* and other laws administered by the agency, including GLP regulations. Facilities conducting GLP studies should be familiar with the following applicable BIMO compliance program documents, available on FDA's website (http://www.fda.gov/ICECI/ComplianceManuals/ComplianceProgramManual/ucm255614.htm):

- 7348.808—Good Laboratory Practice (Nonclinical Laboratories)
- 7348.808A—Good Laboratory Practice Program (Nonclinical Laboratories) EPA Data Audit Inspections

The BIMO documents provide insight into the agency's focus areas for both laboratory inspections and data audits and how it will evaluate the facilities' GLP compliance.

US regulatory agencies conduct four main types of GLP inspections: routine or surveillance inspections of specific studies or entire facilities; data audits; for-cause (directed) inspections; and follow-up inspections. A facility inspection assesses the facility's compliance with GLP regulations and its physical capabilities in supporting studies, personnel training and qualification and equipment. Data audits focus on one or more particular studies either in progress or completed. Data audits cover only the documentation of specific completed studies. For-cause inspections occur when an agency has been alerted to serious organizational noncompliance issues. Follow-up inspections occur when serious compliance infractions previously have been found in a facility, and FDA believes another inspection is needed to ensure the facility has made the appropriate changes and corrections to its operations.

An FDA inspection at a facility's site begins when an inspector presents a Form 482, Notice of Inspection, and appropriate FDA credentials to facility personnel. At the end of the inspection, the inspector will notify facility personnel of all findings. At this time, an inspector also may issue a Form 483, Inspectional Observations. This form lists all findings the inspector felt were noncompliant with GLP regulations at the time of the inspection. The issuance of a Form 483 does not represent the agency's final determination of the facility's compliance status.

A facility receiving a Form 483 is not required to respond; however, a response providing corrective action, responsible personnel and completion date is strongly recommended to maintain a good working relationship with the agency.[18] Facility management must address each finding on the Form 483 in a written response. Each Form 483 contains the contact information for the FDA District Office to which the response can be sent.

Following the completion of an inspection the appropriate FDA center issues an Establishment Inspection Report (EIR) to the facility which documents all the inspection findings. The EIR is issued whether or not the inspector completed a Form 483.

Facilities inspected by FDA receive one of three classifications based on the number and severity of the inspector's findings. These classifications represent the agency's final determination regarding compliance based on the inspection (**Figure 8-2**).

No Action Indicated (NAI) classifications are most common across all FDA centers (about 63%). Voluntary Action Indicated (VAI) classifications usually make up about 35% of all inspections results and Official Action Indicated (OAIs) comprise about 2%.

Serious noncompliance infractions are documented officially in a Warning Letter issued to facility management. Warning Letters from a regulatory agency must be answered in writing within a specified time period. Under the *Freedom of Information Act*, the public may access all 483s and

Figure 8-2. FDA Inspection Classifications

Inspection Classifications	Description
NAI	No Action Indicated – No objectionable conditions or practices were found during the inspection, or the objectionable practices did not justify further regulatory action
VAI	Voluntary Action Indicated – Some objectionable conditions or practices were found and need correction by the facility, but no further regulatory action is likely
OAI	Official Action Indicated – Regulatory actions will be forthcoming from the FDA center or district due to objectionable conditions or practices at the facility

Warning Letters on FDA's website. This public disclosure, as well as Warning Letter responses, plays a valuable role in encouraging GLP compliance among all facilities conducting these studies. Egregious noncompliance problems may lead to study rejection, product submission withdrawal, facility disqualification from further regulated studies, prosecution or fines. FDA GLP regulations (Subpart K) provide information on the disqualification process for laboratories from further GLP studies due to serious compliance problems. This subpart also provides steps a facility must take to be reinstated. To date, FDA has disqualified no testing facility from conducting nonclinical laboratory studies.

Inspection observation trends and the most common GLP deficiencies seen by FDA and EPA remain remarkably consistent from year to year:

- organization and personnel deficiencies
- incomplete, inadequate or no study records
- inadequate study record archiving
- inadequate or no SOPs
- protocol deviations not properly documented or authorized by the study director

Regarding study personnel, most noncompliance issues are related to management deficiencies; namely, a failure to carry out all responsibilities associated with GLP compliant facilities and studies.

The Future of GLPs

Business globalization and the increased use of multi-site international safety and efficacy studies have increased the need, in the opinion of many sponsors, for seamless testing under a harmonized set of GLP regulations. In the early 1990s, industries began approaching regulatory agencies to ask them to begin working together to standardize regulations. The idea was standardized global GLP regulations would reduce confusion and allow sponsors to avoid the problem of conflicting requirements when a single study is conducted in different countries with different GLP regulations.

Most would agree confusion has arisen in the past and may continue into the future regarding GLPs and how they are enforced worldwide. Inconsistent interpretations of vague GLP areas exist in individual laboratories. Further, although all GLPs have the same overall intent of encouraging high quality and accurate study data, the means to achieving this goal can vary among countries following different rules. National monitoring authorities also can vary in how they enforce GLP regulations, including noncompliance penalties.

In the mid-1990s, the International Conference on Harmonization (ICH) began coordinating regulatory agencies in developing harmonized rules for testing pharmaceutical products, with the overall goal of reducing duplicate testing under different national guidelines. ICH since has developed several guidelines covering pharmaceutical product testing, particularly in areas related to emerging safety and efficacy study technologies. In 2010, EU, Japanese and US regulatory authorities revised an existing 1997 ICH guideline on nonclinical safety study recommendations. The guidance provides specific recommendations for various aspects of toxicology, pharmacology, carcinogenicity and other nonclinical studies to support human clinical studies. The US uses this document as guidance. Its overall intent remains the same as all harmonization efforts—to protect the safety of clinical trial participants and people taking marketed pharmaceuticals while avoiding unnecessary test animal and GLP resource use.

Despite ICH's efforts to bring pharmaceutical testing under a common implementation umbrella, a standardized set of GLP regulations has not yet appeared on the horizon. Sponsors, laboratories and various regulatory agencies have come to realize a complete harmonization of these regulations requires revisions in specific GLP topics, such as:

- master schedule content requirements
- study protocol, amendment and deviation approval process
- quality assurance role and assignment
- management roles and responsibilities
- test and control article characterization requirements
- final study report management
- closed study amendment methods
- study record archiving parameters and minimum required archiving time
- laboratory disqualification and reinstatement methods

This is hardly an exhaustive list of topics to be harmonized across all national monitoring authorities enforcing GLP regulations. These authorities also have different approaches to enforcement within their jurisdictions.

GLP harmonization remains a long-term task, and current thinking on its role in the future of GLPs is unclear. The original idea of harmonization as a tool to ease the burden of multinational companies still may hold true. The actual implementation of a standardized set of regulations, along with their testing or trouble-shooting, may be one of the biggest hurdles ever to arise in the evolution of GLPs.

Conclusion

The core GLP regulation principles are universal, regardless of the study type or site where it occurs. These principles are intended to ensure the following goal: to conduct studies with sufficient independent oversight and management authority that the data produced are accurate, reproducible and stored securely to enable their long-term preservation of documentation and specimens for future review. FDA focuses on five main areas that support each GLP study to assess whether this goal is being met:

- trained scientists
- maintained equipment and computerized systems
- written procedures
- accurate recordkeeping and reporting
- archiving to prevent loss or deterioration of study records and specimens

Any trained scientist undoubtedly understands well-run and documented studies can be conducted without following GLPs. Likewise, a GLP study does not necessarily ensure all results are flawless. GLPs' value comes from providing a framework for reducing error and strengthening each study's overall management and oversight. GLPs primarily accomplish this by emphasizing accountability in each study phase and providing an audit trail of all study activities to help regulatory agencies ensure the data are accurate, traceable and complete.

GLP studies help ensure the data related to safety testing of applicable products are accurate and reliable. These studies are essential to a comprehensive evaluation of a product prior to being marketed to the public. The testing and evaluation's ultimate goal is a product that is safe and effective for humans, animals and the environment.

References

1. Baldeshwiler A. "History of FDA Good Laboratory Practices." *Qual Assur J.* 7: 157-161 (2003).
2. 21 CFR Part 58, Good Laboratory Practice for Nonclinical Laboratory Studies, Final Rule, 1987. FDA website. http://www.accessdata.fda.gov/scripts/cdrh/cfdocs/cfcfr/CFRsearch.cfm?CFRPart=58. Accessed 13 March 2015.
3. 40 CFR Part 160, Federal Insecticide, Fungicide and Rodenticide Act (FIFRA): Good Laboratory Practice Standards. Government Publishing Office website. http://www.gpo.gov/fdsys/pkg/CFR-2011-title40-vol24/xml/CFR-2011-title40-vol24-part160.xml. Accessed 12 March 2015.
4. US Department of Health and Human Services, Food and Drug Administration, Office of Regulatory Affairs, Comparison Chart of FDA and EPA Good Laboratory Practice (GLP) Regulations and the OECD Principles of GLP (Issue date: June 2004). FDA website. http://www.fda.gov/downloads/ICECI/EnforcementActions/BioresearchMonitoring/UCM133724.pdf. Accessed 12 March 2015.
5. Organization for Economic Cooperation and Development, Environment Directorate, OECD Series on Principles of Good Laboratory Practice (GLP) and Compliance Monitoring. Number 1. OECD Principles on Good Laboratory Practice (as revised in 1997). OECD website. http://www.oecd.org/officialdocuments/publicdisplaydocumentpdf/?cote=env/mc/chem(98)17&doclanguage=en. Accessed 12 March 2015.
6. Organization for Economic Cooperation and Development, Environment Directorate, Decision of the Council concerning the Mutual Acceptance of Data in the Assessment of Chemicals. OECD website. http://acts.oecd.org/Instruments/ShowInstrumentView.aspx?InstrumentID=263&InstrumentPID=339&Lang=en&Book=False. Accessed 12 March 2015.
7. Op cit 3.
8. 40 CFR Part 792, Toxic Chemicals Control Act (TSCA): Good Laboratory Practice Standards. Government Publishing Office website. http://www.gpo.gov/fdsys/pkg/CFR-2011-title40-vol32/xml/CFR-2011-title40-vol32-part792.xml. Accessed 12 March 2015.
9. Op cit 4.
10. Ibid.
11. US Department of Health and Human Services, Food and Drug Administration, Bioresearch Monitoring Staff (HFC-30), GLP Regulations (Management Briefings) Post Conference Report, Rockville, MD. August 1979: 5–12.
12. 21 CFR Part 11, Electronic Records; Electronic Signatures. FDA website. http://www.accessdata.fda.gov/scripts/cdrh/cfdocs/cfcfr/CFRSearch.cfm?CFRPart=11. Accessed 12 March 2015.
13. Guidance for Industry, Bioanalytical Method Validation. May 2001, revised September 2013. FDA website. http://www.fda.gov/downloads/drugs/guidancecomplianceregulatoryinformation/guidances/ucm368107.pdf. Accessed 12 March 2015.
14. Op cit 4.
15. *Guidance for Industry, Good Laboratory Practices Questions and Answers.* June 1981, revised December 1999 and July 2007. FDA website. http://www.fda.gov/downloads/ICECI/EnforcementActions/BioresearchMonitoring/UCM133748.pdf. Accessed 12 March 2015.
16. Op cit 13.
17. US Department of Health and Human Services, Food and Drug Administration, Office of Regulatory Affairs, Compliance Program Guidance 7348.808, Bioresearch Monitoring, Good Laboratory Practice, Compliance Program Guidance 7348.808 (Nonclinical Laboratories) (Issued 21 February 2001).
18. Cooper R., Fleder J. "Responding to a Form 483 or Warning Letter: A Practical Guide." *Food and Drug Law J.* 40: 479-493 (2005).

Recommended Reading

- Brunetti M., Albertini P., Andreozzi D. et al. "GIQAR Position Paper on 'Arching and Good Laboratory Practice.'" *Qual Assur J* 9: 283-293 (2005).
- Cwiertniewicz J. "Introduction to the Good Laboratory Practice Regulations." *Lab Animal* 34: 305-329 (2005).
- Garvin D. "Harmonization with the OECD Principles of GLP – Friend of Foe?" Editorial. *Qual Assur J.* 12: 107-108 (2009).
- Herman D., Usher, R. "Good Research Practices: A Commonsense Approach to Ensuring Quality in Research Facilities." *Qual Assur: Good Practice Regulation and Law* 3: 355-359 (1994).
- Swidersky P. "Quality Assurance and Good Lab Practice, Examining the FDA's & OECD's GLPs." *Contract Pharma.* 76-83, May 2007.

Chapter 9

Clinical Trials: GCPs, Regulations and Compliance

Updated by Nancy J. Perrella, JD, RAC

OBJECTIVES

- ❑ Define Good Clinical Practices (GCPs)
- ❑ Discuss the purpose of GCPs
- ❑ Provide a historical overview of GCPs
- ❑ Provide an overview of clinical trials
- ❑ Define the requirements and responsibilities of the Institutional Review Board (IRB), sponsors, CROs and principal investigators
- ❑ Discuss clinical trial monitoring and auditing
- ❑ Define and discuss Good Documentation Practice (GDP)

US LAWS, REGULATIONS AND GUIDANCE DOCUMENTS COVERED IN THIS CHAPTER

- ❑ *Pure Food and Drug Act* of 1906
- ❑ *Federal Food, Drug, and Cosmetic Act* of 1938 (*FD&C Act*)
- ❑ *National Research Act* of 1974
- ❑ 21 CFR 50, Protection of Human Subjects
- ❑ 21 CFR 54, Financial Disclosure by Clinical Investigators
- ❑ 21 CFR 56, Institutional Review Board
- ❑ 21 CFR 312, Investigational New Drug Application
- ❑ 21 CFR 812, Investigational Device Exemptions
- ❑ 45 CFR 45, Public Welfare
- ❑ 45 CFR 46, Protection of Human Subjects
- ❑ *E6 Good Clinical Practice: Consolidated Guidance* (April 1996)
- ❑ *Guidance for Industry: Submitting and Reviewing Complete Responses to Clinical Holds* (October 2000)
- ❑ *Guidance for Industry and Clinical Investigators: The Use of Clinical Holds Following Clinical Investigator Misconduct* (September 2004)
- ❑ *Guidance for Industry, Investigators, and Reviewers: Exploratory IND Studies* (January 2006)
- ❑ *Guidance for Industry: Using a Centralized IRB Review Process in Multicenter Clinical Trials* (March 2006)
- ❑ *Guidance for Industry: Computerized Systems Used in Clinical Investigations* (May 2007)

- *Guidance for Clinical Investigators, Sponsors, and IRBs: Adverse Event Reporting to IRBs—Improving Human Subject Projection* (January 2009)
- *Guidance for Institutional Review Boards (IRBs): Frequently Asked Questions—IRB Registration* (July 2009)
- *Draft Guidance for Industry: Investigator Responsibilities—Protecting the Rights, Safety, and Welfare of Study Subjects* (October 2009)
- *Guidance for Sponsors, Investigators, and Institutional Review Boards: Informed Consent Elements, 21 CFR 50.35(c), Questions and Answers* (February 2012)
- *Guidance for Clinical Investigators, Industry, and FDA Staff: Financial Disclosure by Clinical Investigators* (February 2013)
- *Guidance for IRBs, Clinical Investigators, and Sponsors: IRB Responsibility for Reviewing Qualifications of Investigators, Adequacy of Research Sites, and the Determination of Whether an IND/IDE is Needed* (August 2013)
- *Guidance for Industry: Oversight of Clinical Investigations—A Risk-Based Approach to Monitoring* (August 2013)
- *Guidance for Industry: Electronic Source Data in Clinical Investigations* (September 2013)
- *Guidance for Industry and Food and Drug Administration Staff: Investigational Device Exemptions (IDEs) for Early Feasibility Medical Device Clinical Studies, Including Certain First in Human (FIH) Studies* (October 2013)
- *Guidance for IRBs, Clinical Investigators, and Sponsors: Informed Consent Information Sheet* (July 2014)
- *A Guide to Informed Consent—Information Sheet* (January 1998)
- *Institutional Review Boards Frequently Asked Questions—Information Sheet* (January 1998)
- *Sponsor—Investigator—IRB Interrelationship—Information Sheet* (January 1998)
- *Information Sheet Guidance For Sponsors, Clinical Investigators, and IRBs: Waiver of IRB Requirements for Drug and Biological Product Studies* (January 2006)
- *Information Sheet Guidance For IRBs, Clinical Investigators, and Sponsors: Frequently Asked Questions about Medical Devices* (January 2006)
- *Information Sheet Guidance For IRBs, Clinical Investigators, and Sponsors: Significant Risk and Nonsignificant Risk Medical Device Studies* (January 2006)
- *Information Sheet Guidance For IRBs, Clinical Investigators, and Sponsors: FDA Institutional Review Board Inspections* (January 2006)
- *Information Sheet Guidance for Sponsor, Clinical Investigators, and IRBs, Frequently Asked Questions - Statement of Investigator (Form FDA 1572)* (May 2010)
- *Information Sheet Guidance For IRBs, Clinical Investigators, and Sponsors: FDA Inspections of Clinical Investigators* (June 2010)
- *Information Sheet Guidance for Institutional Review Boards, Clinical Investigators, and Sponsors: Clinical Investigator Administrative Actions—Disqualification* (March 2014)

Introduction

Clinical trials are conducted to assess whether a new drug, device or biologic provides a safe and effective way to treat, prevent or diagnose a disease. Good Clinical Practice (GCP) is an internationally accepted, scientific and ethical quality standard for the design, conduct, performance, auditing, recordkeeping, analysis and reporting of clinical trials involving human subjects.[1] Although global regulatory authorities (e.g., US Food and Drug Administration (FDA), European Medicines Agency (EMA), UK Medicines and Healthcare products Regulatory Agency (MHRA), Japan's Pharmaceuticals and Medical Devices Agency (PMDA)) have published numerous regulations, reflection papers, guidance documents and information sheets defining GCP requirements, it generally is accepted that many industry standards for conducting clinical trials are "best practices," based on regulations and guidance documents, but not found in the black letter text of the regulations. When a GCP compliance issue or event is not addressed specifically by local GCP regulations and guidelines, regulatory professionals should consult internal and external resources, including their companies' quality assurance, regulatory compliance and regulatory intelligence departments and/or local Ethics Committee (EC)/Institutional Review Board (IRB) and regulatory authority.

Purpose of GCPs

GCPs establish the minimum standards and guidelines for conducting human clinical research. Compliance with GCP regulations and guidance documents provides assurance the rights, safety, confidentiality and well-being of human subjects participating in clinical research are protected.[2] Subjects' rights include the right to be informed, the right not to participate, the right to withdraw at any time and the right to privacy. GCPs also ensure the data collected and reported during the trial are of high quality, as well as credible, accurate and reliable. Regulatory agencies rely on data integrity to make scientifically sound decisions on sponsors' marketing applications. GCPs also serve to define the roles and responsibilities of the groups involved in clinical research, including study sponsors, clinical research investigators, IRBs and monitors. All parties involved in conducting clinical research are required to comply with applicable laws and regulations and ensure subjects' risks are minimized.

Historical Overview of GCPs

GCPs were developed, primarily, in response to tragic events where individuals' rights and safety were ignored or put at risk. Examples are described below, including but not limited to, the 1937 Sulfanilamide disaster, experiments performed during World War II and the Tuskegee Syphilis Study.

Sulfanilamide Disaster and the Food, Drug and Cosmetic Act (1937–38)

Prior to the *Pure Food and Drug Act*, which was passed in 1906, there were no US regulations regarding the ethical use of human subjects in clinical research.[3] The most widely recognized standard was the Hippocratic Oath, an oath traditionally taken by physicians, which indicated that a physician's primary duty was to cause no harm to the patient.

In 1937, the S.E. Massengill Company produced a treatment for streptococcal infections, composed of the antimicrobial, sulfanilamide, dissolved in diethylene glycol (i.e., a chemical analog of antifreeze) and raspberry flavoring. The elixir was tested for appearance, flavor and fragrance. However, under the *Pure Food and Drug Act*, toxicity testing was not required and was not performed.[4] Two hundred and forty gallons of the elixir were distributed in 15 states. One hundred five people, including 34 children, died. FDA was able to retrieve 228 gallons of the elixir. It was estimated that if all 240 gallons had been consumed, the number of deaths would have exceeded 4,000. In response to the sulfanilamide disaster, Congress passed the *Federal Food, Drug, and Cosmetic Act* in 1938 (*FD&C Act*), which required manufacturers to show a drug was safe before it could be marketed.[5]

WW II Holocaust (1938–45)

During WW II, the German Nazi party systematically persecuted and killed six million Jewish and five million non-Jewish victims.[6] Many were subjects of medical experiments designed to advance German medicine and the German war effort. Victims were exposed to high altitude and extreme cold, in an effort to aid the German Air Force's investigation into the effects of high-altitude flying. Subjects were exposed to mustard gas and were burned with materials used in incendiary bombs to investigate treatments of injuries resulting from air-raid and battlefield conditions. They also were infected with malaria, epidemic jaundice, tuberculosis and typhus, in search for treatments for diseases to which the German military were exposed in occupied territories. Rapid, large-scale sterilization experiments were conducted to ensure the eventual elimination of enemy populations, while maintaining a captive labor force during the war. Individuals who survived the experiments almost always were killed and dissected shortly afterward to determine the reason for their survival.[7,8] While some of these experiments may have had a legitimate scientific purpose, they were conducted without the subjects' consent and with total disregard for their suffering or survival.

Nuremberg Doctors' Trials (1946) and the Nuremberg Code (1947)

On 9 December 1946, an American military tribunal began criminal proceedings against 23 German physicians and administrators for their willing participation in WW II war crimes and crimes against humanity.[9] Sixteen doctors were found guilty, and seven were sentenced to death. In their defense, several doctors argued that no international law or standard existed to differentiate between legal and illegal human experimentation.[10]

Dr. Andrew Ivy, an American doctor working with the US Counsel for War Crimes during the trial, was disturbed by the legitimacy of this defense, and on 17 April 1947, submitted a memorandum to the Counsel defining legitimate research. Information from Dr. Ivy's memorandum was included in the trial's verdict in a section entitled "Permissible Medical Experiments," which subsequently became known as the *Nuremberg Code*.[11]

The *Nuremberg Code* lists 10 basic moral, ethical and legal principles for human medical research:

1. Voluntary consent is essential. The individual must have "sufficient knowledge and comprehension of the research to make an understanding and enlightened decision."
2. Research must benefit the good of society, unprocurable by other means.

3. Research must be based on a preclinical animal study.
4. Research should avoid all unnecessary physical and mental suffering and injury.
5. Research should not be conducted when there is reason to believe death or a disabling injury will occur.
6. Research risk must be minimized and relative to the anticipated research benefit.
7. Proper preparations and adequate facilities are required to ensure subjects are protected against even the remote possibilities of injury, disability or death.
8. Research should be conducted only by scientifically qualified persons.
9. Subjects have the right to end their participation in research.
10. Research should be terminated if, at any time, continuation is likely to result in subject injury, disability or death.[12]

Declaration of Helsinki (1964)

In 1964, the World Medical Association (WMA), an international organization representing physicians, established ethical principles for medical doctors involved in human biomedical research. Between 1964 and 2013, the *Declaration of Helsinki* was revised seven times. The original declaration was divided into three sections: Basic Principles, Medical Research Combined with Professional Care (Clinical Research) and Non-Therapeutic Biomedical Research Involving Human Subjects (Nonclinical Biomedical Research), and included 22 points, including 10 from the *Nuremberg Code*.[13] The 2013 declaration was expanded into nine sections, containing 37 points. Sections in the 2013 declaration include Preamble, General Principles, Risks, Burdens and Benefits, Vulnerable Groups and Individuals, Scientific Requirements and Research Protocols, Research Ethics Committees, Privacy and Confidentiality, Informed Consent, Use of Placebo, Post-Trial Provisions, Research Registration and Publication and Dissemination of Results and Unproven Interventions in Clinical Practices.[14]

The declaration includes a number of important human research ethical codes of practice, including the necessity of informed consent, review of research protocols by an independent committee prior to initiation, ensuring research risk does not exceed its benefits, precedence of subjects' well-being over the interests of science and society, confidentiality of subjects' personal information, provisions for post-trial access for subjects still needing intervention identified as beneficial during the trial, and the ethical obligation to publish and disseminate research results.

While the declaration has been codified in or influenced national and regional legislation and regulations, by itself, it is not a legally binding instrument in international law. Regulatory professionals should regard the declaration as an important human research guidance document that does not supersede local regulations and laws.

Tuskegee Syphilis Study (1932–72)

In 1932, the US Department of Health sponsored the Tuskegee Syphilis Study in Tuskegee, Alabama to study the effects of untreated syphilis in 400 low-income African American men for 40 years to assess the natural history of syphilis. Researchers did not tell the subjects they were participating in an experiment. Instead, most of the subjects thought they were receiving treatments for "bad blood." Researchers withheld treatment even after penicillin became the standard treatment for syphilis in the 1940s. Many subjects died of syphilis during the study, over 40 of their wives contracted syphilis and 19 babies were born with congenital syphilis.[15]

The study was stopped in 1972, after its existence was publicized by the media. By that time, only 74 of the subjects were still alive.[16] In 1970, the US government compensated the surviving subjects and the families of those who died in the study.[17] In May 1997, President Clinton apologized to the subjects and their families, acknowledging the government's actions were morally wrong and an outrage to the US commitment to integrity and equality for all citizens.[18]

National Research Act (1974)

Due to the publicity of the Tuskegee Syphilis Study, the *National Research Act* of 1974 was passed, which authorized federal agencies to develop human research regulations for government-funded research involving human subjects. It also required the development of Institutional Review Boards (IRBs) for the protection of human research subjects.

The act also established the US Office for Human Research Protection and created the National Commission for the Protection of Human Subjects of Biomedical and Behavioral Research, which created the Belmont Report, a foundational document for the ethical treatment of human research participants in the US.[19]

Belmont Report (1979)

In 1979, the National Commission released the Belmont Report, which established principles of ethical research in human subjects. The report is a key document in US human research ethics regulations, emphasizing three basic ethical principles: respect for persons, beneficence (i.e., the moral obligation to act for the benefit of others) and justice.[20]

Under respect for persons, there is a duty to respect subjects' autonomy and their choices, as well provide extra protections to those with diminished autonomy (e.g., vulnerable populations—prisoners, children, cognitively impaired individuals, etc.). Key to beneficence is to do no harm, protect subjects' welfare and maximize possible benefits while minimizing possible harms. Duties under justice include treating people fairly, distributing benefits and burdens fairly and allowing individuals who do not want to participate in the study, but would like treatment, to receive the usual standard of care and not be turned away. The application of these principles is seen in the informed consent process and respect for privacy (respect for persons), good research design, competent investigators and favorable risk-benefit analysis (beneficence) and the equitable selection of study subjects (justice).[21]

Common Rule (1981–91)

In 1981, the Department of Health and Human Services (DHHS) issued regulations based on the Belmont Report and Code of Federal Regulations (CFR), Part 45 (public welfare) and Part 46 (protection of human subject). In 1991, core DHHS regulations (45 CFR 46 Subpart A) were adopted formally by more than 17 departments and agencies. Most universities and agencies have adopted this rule (Common Rule). DHHS also has promulgated regulations providing additional protections for vulnerable populations involved in research, codified as Subpart B (pregnant women, human fetuses and neonates), Subpart C (prisoners) and Subpart D (children).[22]

In 2011, the Office of Human Research Protections (OHRP) announced proposed changes to the Common Rule, which had not changed significantly since 1981, to enhance human subject protections and reduce investigator burden. In its Advanced Notice of Proposed Rulemaking (ANPRM), DHHS invited comments on proposed changes, including:

- All studies conducted at institutions receiving federal funding from a Common Rule agency must comply with the Common Rule for research. Currently, compliance is required only for federally funded studies.
- A single IRB review would be required for multi-site studies; currently, this is optional.
- Data security and information protection standards, consistent with those of the Health Insurance Portability and Accountability Act (HIPAA), would be mandatory for all studies involving identifiable or potentially identifiable data.
- Study participants would have an opportunity to decide whether their biological specimens may be used for future research and, if so, to specify the research types in which their biospecimens may be used.
- Forms and processes used for informed consent would be updated.
- A systematic approach to data collection and analysis on unanticipated problems and adverse effects occurring during clinical trials would be implemented.[23]

1990 International Standards

In 1990, global activity associated with GCP compliance increased. In Japan, the Ministry of Health and Welfare published the GCP Handbook, and the European Commission published the GCP guidance for the EU. Additionally, the International Conference on Harmonization (ICH) Steering Committee was formed.[24]

International Ethical Guidelines for Biomedical Research (CIOMS) (1993)

In 1993, the Council for International Organization of Medical Science (CIOMS), in collaboration with the World Health Organization (WHO), developed an international ethics guideline for biomedical research, with special attention on protecting subjects' rights in developing counties. An updated version was released in 2002. Important elements include:

1. Any intervention, product or knowledge generated will be made available for the benefit of the population or community (Guideline 10).
2. Placebo control is justified when (Guideline 11):
   - there is no established intervention
   - withholding an established intervention would expose the subject to temporary discomfort
   - use of an established intervention would not yield scientifically reliable results
   - use of a placebo does not present a risk of serious irreversible harm to the subject
3. Compensation for research injury (Guideline 19).[25]

ICH Good Clinical Practice (ICH-GCP) (1996)

In 1996, ICH published the GCP (E6) guideline to eliminate unnecessary delay in the global development and availability of new medicines, while maintaining appropriate safeguards on quality, safety and efficacy and regulatory obligations to protect public health. By establishing a minimum acceptable standard, the guideline allows for the mutual acceptance of clinical trial data by regulatory agencies, avoiding redundancies and duplicative requirements in different regions. However, regulatory professionals should remember compliance with ICH GCP alone is not sufficient. Clinical trials also must comply with local regulations where the trial is being conducted.

ICH GCP is the official GCP guideline adopted by the regulatory agencies of the EU, Japan and the US. Through the ICH Global Cooperation Group, many other countries, including Australia, Canada, China, Russia, South Korea and others, also recognize ICH GCP as an international standard for clinical trial conduct.[26]

ICH GCP also forms the basis of:

- World Health Organization (WHO) Technical Report Series No. 850 Annex 3, 1995—Guidelines for good clinical practice (GCP) on pharmaceutical products http://apps.who.int/medicinedocs/en/d/Jh3009e/22.9.html
- WHO Handbook for Clinical Research Practice (GCP) Guidance for Implementation, 2005 http://whqlibdoc.who.int/publications/2005/924159392X_eng.pdf
- Pan-American Network for Drug Regulatory Harmonization (PANDRH) Good Clinical Practices "Document of Americas" http://www.anvisa.gov.br/medicamentos/pesquisa/goodclinicalpractices_english.pdf

The ICH GCP guideline consists of 13 principles and details the responsibilities of Ethics Committees (ECs)/Institutional Review Boards (IRBs), investigators and sponsors/CROs. The principles of ICH GCP include:

1. Clinical trials should be conducted in accordance with the ethical principles that have their origin in the *Declaration of Helsinki*, and are consistent with GCP and the applicable regulatory requirement(s).
2. Before a trial is initiated, foreseeable risks and inconveniences should be weighed against the anticipated benefit for the individual trial subject and society. A trial should be initiated and continued only if the anticipated benefits justify the risks.
3. The rights, safety and well-being of the trial subjects are the most important considerations and should prevail over interests of science and society.
4. The available nonclinical and clinical information on an investigational product should be adequate to support the proposed clinical trial.
5. Clinical trials should be scientifically sound and described in a clear, detailed protocol.
6. A trial should be conducted in compliance with the protocol that has received prior IRB/EC approval/favorable opinion.
7. The medical care given to, and medical decisions made on behalf of, subjects always should be the responsibility of a qualified physician or, when appropriate, a qualified dentist.
8. Each individual involved in conducting a trial should be qualified by education, training and experience to perform his or her respective task(s).
9. Freely given informed consent should be obtained from every subject prior to clinical trial participation.
10. All clinical trial information should be recorded, handled and stored in a way that allows its accurate reporting, interpretation and verification.
11. The confidentiality of records that could identify subjects should be protected, respecting the privacy and confidentiality rules in accordance with the applicable regulatory requirement(s).
12. Investigational products should be manufactured, handled and stored in accordance with applicable Good Manufacturing Practice (GMP). They should be used in accordance with the approved protocol.
13. Systems with procedures to assure the quality of every aspect of the trial should be implemented.[27]

First published in 1996, ICH GCP has not undergone revision. However, the guideline currently is under review, and the revised guideline is expected to be published in 2016.

Clinical Trial Overview

Clinical Trials—Drugs and Biologics

Clinical trials for drugs and biologics are conducted in phases. Each phase describes the general information being collected about a new treatment in a clinical trial, such as the dose, safety and efficacy and is designed to answer a separate research question.

Preclinical

During the Preclinical Phase, the drug is tested in animals, in order to collect efficacy, toxicology and pharmacokinetic information.[28]

Phase 1

Phase 1, or first-in-human trials, represent the initial human exposure to an investigational drug. Researchers test a new drug or treatment, which has proven to be safe for use in animals, in a small group of usually healthy human volunteers (i.e., 10–80 subjects). The objective in a Phase 1 trial is to evaluate the drug's metabolism and pharmacologic action, determine a safe dosage range, identify side effects and, if possible, gain early evidence on effectiveness. In some circumstances, real patients are used when the treatment is likely to make healthy individuals ill. Subjects in Phase 1 studies usually receive 24-hour medical attention and monitoring. Doses in Phase 1 often are sub-therapeutic, but with ascending or escalating doses, so the best and safest dose can be established.[29]

In 2006, FDA recognized "exploratory IND study," a new category of early-Phase 1 studies used to collect baseline information, such as biodistribution of an extremely low dose of the new agent. Investigators use this information to determine whether to pursue additional human trials. Exploratory IND studies are smaller and shorter than the usual Phase 1 study, often involving fewer than 10 subjects and lasting a week or less.[30]

Phase 2

Once a dose or range of doses has been established, the drug or treatment is given to a larger group of subjects (i.e.,

100–300) to study its effectiveness and further evaluate its safety. Genetic testing is not uncommon at this stage. Doses in Phase 2 are at a therapeutic level, although at this stage the drug is not presumed to have any therapeutic effect. Phase 2 studies are sometimes separated into Phase 2a or 2b studies, with dosing requirements assessed in Phase 2a and study efficacy evaluated in Phase 2b.[31]

Phase 3

During Phase 3 studies, the drug or treatment is given to large groups of subjects (1,000–2,000) to confirm its effectiveness, monitor side effects, compare it to commonly used treatments and collect information to allow the drug or treatment to be used safely. Phase 3 studies are randomized, multicenter trials and usually have a longer duration, sometimes lasting several years. Phase 3 studies of chronic conditions or diseases often have a short follow-up period, three to six months, for ongoing evaluation.[32]

Drug manufacturers often will continue enrollment in Phase 3 trials while the marketing application is undergoing regulatory review. These studies are usually categorized as Phase 3b studies and allow patients to continue to receive beneficial investigational drugs until the drug is available commercially.

Phase 4

Phase 4 studies are postmarketing studies used to gather information on the drug's effect in various populations and any side effects associated with long-term use. Regulatory authorities may require manufacturers to conduct Phase 4 studies to collect additional safety information among the general population or in specific populations (e.g., pregnant or nursing women) normally excluded from the clinical trials.[33]

Medical Device Clinical Trials

Not every device is required to go through the clinical trial process. This determination is based on a device risk assessment. Class I, or minimal risk devices (e.g., bandages and tongue depressors), do not require a clinical trial. Class II devices (e.g., powered wheelchairs and pregnancy test kits) are considered to be of intermediate risk and may require a clinical trial. Class III devices (e.g., implantable pacemakers and breast implants) are substantial-risk devices and always require a clinical trial.

Clinical trials for medical devices differ from those for drugs in that drug trials focus on dose response, whereas medical device trials focus on prototype development. Some medical devices (e.g., implants) require substantial bench and animal testing for reliability and biocompatibility data. While the drug development process uses Phase 1 through Phase 4 clinical trials to determine toxicity, safety and efficacy of the drug or biologic, medical devices follow early feasibility, feasibility and pivotal study models.[34]

Early Feasibility Studies

These studies occur early in device development, typically before the device design has been finalized. An early feasibility study may be used to evaluate the device design concept with respect to initial clinical safety and device functionality in a small number of subjects (generally fewer than 10), when this information cannot be provided through additional nonclinical assessments, or appropriate nonclinical tests are not available.[35]

Feasibility Studies

Feasibility studies are clinical investigations, not intended to be the primary support for a marketing application, generally used to answer basic research questions about the device and to provide support for a future pivotal study. Feasibility studies often are required by FDA to assess preliminary safety and potential for effectiveness on a near final or final device design. They generally involve a small number of subjects (i.e., 10–40), but may be larger. Feasibility studies do not always need to be proceeded by an early feasibility study.[36]

Pivotal Studies

Pivotal studies are clinical trials designed to collect definitive evidence of device safety and effectiveness for a specific intended use, typically in a statistically justified number of subjects. They generally are intended as the primary clinical support for a marketing application and may or may not be preceded by an early feasibility and/or feasibility study.[37]

Protocols and Protocol Amendments

FDA regulations require both drug and device studies to be conducted in compliance with the investigational plan, signed agreement, federal regulations and conditions of approval imposed by the IRB. Prior to starting a clinical trial, drug and device sponsors must submit a protocol for the planned study to FDA.

Protocols for drug studies are required to contain:

- a statement of the study's objectives and purpose
- the name and address and a statement of qualification for each investigator, the name of each sub-investigator, the name and address of the research facilities to be used and the name and address of each IRB reviewing the study
- criteria for subject selection (i.e., inclusion and exclusion criteria) and the estimated number of subjects to be enrolled in the study
- the study design, including the control group type to be used, if any, and a description of the methods (e.g., blinding) to be used to minimize bias on the part of subjects, investigators and analysts
- the method for determining the dose(s) to be administered, the planned maximum dosage and the duration of individual subject's exposure to the drug

- a description of the observations and measurements to be made during the study
- a description of clinical procedures, lab tests or other measures taken to monitor the drug's effects on the subjects and to minimize risk[38]

Drug study sponsors must submit protocol amendments to describe any changes that significantly affect subject safety (Phase 1) or any change in a Phase 2 or 3 protocol that significantly affects subject safety, scope of the investigation or the study's scientific quality. Examples include:

- increase in drug dosage or duration of exposure of individual subjects to the drug or a significant increase in the number of subjects to be enrolled in the study
- significant change in the study design (e.g., addition or dropping of a control group)
- adding a new test or procedure to improve monitoring for, or reduce the risk of, a side effect or adverse event, or dropping a test intended to monitor subject safety
- a new investigator added to a previously submitted protocol[39]

Protocol amendments can be implemented once the sponsor has submitted the amendment to FDA for review, and the IRB responsible for reviewing the study has approved the change. However, sponsors may implement the change to the protocol immediately if it is intended to eliminate an apparent immediate hazard to subjects, provided FDA and the reviewing IRB subsequently are notified in a timely manner.[40]

For device studies, the protocol is included in the investigational plan submitted by sponsors as part of the IDE application for a Class II or III device. The protocol describes the methodology to be used and includes protocol analysis, demonstrating its scientific soundness.

Other elements of the investigational plan include:

- purpose (device name and intended use and the study's objectives and duration)
- risk analysis (description and analysis of all increased risks to research subjects and how these risks will be minimized; a justification for the investigation; and a description of the patient population including the number, age, sex and condition)
- device description (each important component, ingredient, property and principle of device operation and any anticipated changes in the device during the investigation)
- monitoring procedures and each monitor's name and address
- copies of all device labeling
- copies of all informed consent forms and informational materials to be provided to subjects
- IRB information, including names, locations and chairpersons, and a certification of any action taken by any IRBs with respect to the study
- name and address of each institution at which a part of the investigation may be conducted
- additional records and reports (a description of any records or reports of the investigation other than those required in Subpart G of the IDE regulations)[41]

In general, sponsors must obtain approval of a supplemental application from both FDA and the IRB, when appropriate, prior to implementing a change to an investigational plan. However, FDA regulations allow an exception to this requirement, when:

- The change to the investigational plan is made to protect the life or physical well-being of a subject in an emergency. The change must be reported to FDA within five business days after the sponsor learns of it.
- The change is a developmental change in the device that does not represent a significant change in design or basic principles of operation and is made in response to information gathered during the course of the investigation.
- Changes to the protocol do not affect data validity, patient risk-benefit relationship, scientific soundness of the plan, or subjects' rights, safety or welfare in the investigation.[42]

Additionally, sponsors may make changes, based on credible information, without prior approval of the supplemental application, provided the sponsor submits a notice of the change to the IDE within five business days after making the change. Credible information is defined as documentation supporting the sponsor's conclusion that a change does not have a significant impact on the study design or planned statistical analysis and the change does not affect the subjects' rights, safety or welfare. Supporting documentation can include peer-reviewed published literature, clinical investigator(s)' recommendations, and data gathered during the trial or marketing.[43]

Informed Consent

Informed consent from prospective subjects is required for participation in FDA-regulated clinical investigations, except in limited circumstances, such as life-threatening situations, military operations or public health emergencies and emergency research. FDA has stated informed consent involves more than just obtaining the subject's or legally authorized representative's signature on the informed consent form (ICF); it is an information exchange between the individual obtaining the subject's consent and the subject.

The consent process involves providing a potential subject with sufficient information to allow an informed decision about their participation in the clinical investigation, facilitating the potential subject's understanding of the information, providing adequate opportunity for a potential subject to ask questions and consider whether to participate, obtaining the potential subject's voluntary agreement to participate and continuing to provide information as the clinical investigation progresses or as the subject or situation requires.[44] To be effective, the process must provide sufficient opportunity for the subject to consider whether to participate and must occur under circumstances that minimize the possibility of coercion or undue influence.[45]

The ICF serves multiple purposes. It ensures the subject is presented with the required information about the drug or device and the trial, allowing the subject to make an informed decision about participating in a clinical investigation. The ICF also provides the subject with a take-home reminder of the clinical investigation's elements, as well as contact information in case additional questions or concerns arise. Additionally, it documents the subject's voluntary agreement to participate. The consent process often continues after the ICF is signed. Through the course of the trial, additional information may need to be given to the subject, and the subject may need additional opportunities to ask questions and receive answers.

FDA regulations do not specifically require drug study sponsors to submit a copy of the ICF with the IND application. However, if FDA determines a review of the ICF is necessary to determine whether the clinical investigation may safely proceed, the agency will request the sponsor to submit the ICF. This is likely to occur for treatment INDs, treatment protocols and INDs conducted under the exception from informed consent requirements for emergency research. In contrast, device clinical trial sponsors are required to submit all forms and information materials that will be provided to the subjects to obtain informed consent as part of the IDE application. FDA reviews the ICF to ensure it conforms to the requirements of 21 CFR 50. After review, FDA may send the sponsor a letter citing deficiencies regarding the ICF, in which case the clinical investigation may not begin until the sponsor has corrected them. In the event an IRB makes substantive changes to the ICF after IDE approval by FDA (i.e., changes that affect subjects' rights, safety or welfare), the sponsor must submit the revised ICF to FDA for review and approval prior to implementing the document changes.[46]

All parties involved in clinical research (i.e., sponsors/CROs, IRBs, clinical investigators) share responsibility for ensuring the informed consent process is adequate. For example, FDA's review of the consent form does not negate or replace the IRB's responsibility to review and approve the consent form, all materials used in the consent process and the consent process itself, as a condition for the clinical investigation to begin. FDA regulations require an IRB to review and approve, require modifications in (to secure approval), or disapprove all research activities covered by the IRB regulations. IRB oversight is critical to ensuring an adequate informed consent process is in place to protect clinical investigation subjects' rights and welfare.[47]

The IRB's review ensures the ICF given to subjects contains the eight required elements (e.g., description of the clinical investigation, risks and discomforts, benefits, alternate procedures or treatments, confidentiality, compensation and medical treatment in the event of injury, contacts and voluntary participation) identified in 21 CFR 50.25, as well as any additional elements (e.g., unforeseeable risks, involuntary termination of subject's participation, additional costs to subjects, consequences of subject's decision to withdraw, provision of significant new findings to subjects and approximate number of subjects involved in the trial) required under 21 CFR 50.25(b), as appropriate.

The IRB also has the authority to require information, in addition to that specifically mentioned in 21 CFR 50.25, be given to subjects when, in the IRB's judgment, the information would add meaningfully to the protection of subjects' rights and welfare. Additionally, the IRB should be aware of who will conduct the consent interview on site, the timing for obtaining informed consent and any waiting period (between informing the subject and obtaining the consent) that will be observed.

The clinical investigator is responsible for protecting subjects' rights, safety and welfare during a clinical investigation and for ensuring a legally effective ICF is obtained from each subject prior to study participation. Although the investigator may delegate the task of obtaining consent to another study staff member who has the appropriate training, credentials, medical expertise and protocol knowledge, the investigator retains ultimate responsibility for the consent process.[48]

Sponsors often provide clinical investigators with a model consent form they may adapt to meet local needs. Because the clinical investigator must receive IRB approval before starting the clinical investigation, the sponsor should work closely with the clinical investigator to ensure the modified consent form is reviewed and approved by the IRB. FDA recommends the clinical investigator provide the sponsor with a copy of the consent form approved by the IRB.[49]

Responsibilities

Institutional Review Boards (IRBs)

Organization and Purpose

Under FDA regulation, an IRB is an appropriately constituted group formally designated to review and monitor biomedical research involving human subjects to ensure that subjects' rights and welfare are protected.[50]

An institutional IRB is designated or formed by an institution to review research conducted at that institution or with its support. For multicenter studies, an institution's IRB can serve as a central IRB or it can rely on a centralized IRB's review (in whole or in part) in place of its own study review; or it can conduct its own study review. Because the goal of the centralized process is to increase efficiency and decrease duplicative efforts, it may be more effective for a central IRB to take responsibility for all aspects of IRB review at each site. Other approaches may be appropriate as well. For example, an institution may permit a central IRB to take responsibility for initial and ongoing study review, or apportion IRB review responsibilities between the central IRB and its own.[51]

Whether the study utilizes a central or institutional IRB or a combination of both, FDA regulations require each IRB to have at least five members, with varying backgrounds (i.e., no IRB can consist entirely of members of one profession) to promote complete and adequate research activity review. The IRB must be sufficiently qualified through its members' experience, expertise, and their diversity, including race, gender, cultural backgrounds and sensitivity to such issues such as community attitudes.[52] When a centralized IRB is used, the review process should include mechanisms to ensure meaningful consideration of relevant local factors. Possible mechanisms include:

- providing relevant local information to the central IRB in writing by individuals or organizations familiar with the local community, institution and/or clinical research
- participation of consultants with relevant expertise or members from the institution's IRB in the central IRB's deliberations
- limited review of a central IRB-reviewed study by the institution's IRB, focused on issues of concern to the local community[53]

IRBs must include at least one member whose primary concern is in the scientific area, and at least one whose primary concern is in nonscientific areas. The IRB also must include at least one member who is not otherwise affiliated with the institution and whose immediate family does not include a person affiliated with the institution. FDA regulations allow convened IRBs to review and approve studies if at least a majority of the total number of members, including the non-scientific member, is present.[54]

IRB members with conflicting interests associated with the study may not participate in the IRB's initial or continuing study review, except to provide information requested by the IRB. For example, a clinical investigator involved with a study may be a member of the IRB but would have to absent him- or herself from deliberation and abstain from voting due to potential conflicts of interest.[55]

IRB Review

The three types of IRB review are: exempt from IRB review, expedited review and full board (convened) IRB review. The review type is driven by the study type and associated risk. An exemption from the prospective IRB review requirement is permitted for one emergency use of a test article in an institution, provided the product's emergency use is reported to the IRB within five working days. An emergency use is defined as a single use (or single course of treatment, e.g., multiple doses of antibiotic) with one subject. Subsequent use would be a second use with that subject or the use with another subject.

In its review of emergency use, if it is anticipated the test article may be used again, the IRB would ask the sponsor to develop a protocol and consent document(s) so an approved protocol would be in place when the next need arises. However, FDA notes in spite of the clinical investigator and IRB's best efforts, a situation may arise requiring a second emergency use. FDA has stated it is inappropriate to deny emergency treatment to an individual when the only obstacle is lack of time for the IRB to convene to review and approve the use.[56]

Expedited review is a procedure through which certain kinds of research may be reviewed and approved without convening an IRB meeting. FDA regulations permit, but do not require, an IRB to review certain categories of research through an expedited procedure if the research involves no more than minimal risk. Examples of activities eligible for expedited review include:

- research on drugs for which an IND is not required
- research on medical devices for which an investigational device exemption application is not required, or the medical device is cleared or approved for marketing and the medical device is being used in accordance with its cleared or approved labeling
- collection of blood samples by finger, heel or ear stick or by venipuncture from subjects meeting defined age, weight and heath criteria, and the blood draws do not exceed volume/frequency limits
- prospective collection of biological specimens (i.e., hair or nail clippings, saliva, sweat, etc.) for research purposes by noninvasive means

The IRB also may use the expedited review procedure to review minor changes to previously approved research during the period covered by the original approval. Under an expedited review procedure, research review may be carried out by the IRB chairperson or by one or more experienced IRB members designated by the chairperson. The reviewer(s) may exercise all the authorities of the IRB, except disapproval. Research may be disapproved only following review by the full committee, and the IRB is required to adopt a method to keep all members advised of research studies that have been approved by expedited review.[57]

Although IRB review and approval generally is required before a study can be initiated under an IND, FDA may waive any of the IRB requirements for specific research activities or classes of research activities otherwise covered by the IRB regulations. The waiver provision is used only when alternative mechanisms are available to ensuring protection of human subjects' rights and welfare. The most common circumstance for a waiver request is when a sponsor wishes to conduct a foreign clinical study under an IND. In this case, sponsors typically utilize an Independent EC (IEC) that operates in accordance with GCP. Although its membership and functions for assuring human subject protection are comparable to those of an IRB, an IEC may not meet all the IRB requirements contained in Part 56.[58]

Regulatory Oversight

In January 2009, FDA issued a final rule requiring all US IRBs that review FDA-regulated clinical studies to register through a system maintained by DHHS. Registration information includes:

- contact information (i.e., addresses and telephone numbers)
- number of active protocols involving FDA-regulated products reviewed during the preceding 12 months
- description of the types of FDA-regulated products involved in the protocols reviewed

IRB registration provides FDA and other interested parties (e.g., sponsors, clinical investigators) with a comprehensive listing of all US IRBs that review FDA-regulated research, as well as non-US IRBs, Independent or Research Ethics Committees (IEC/REC) that review FDA-regulated research and voluntarily choose to register. This makes it easier for FDA to inspect IRBs and convey educational information to them.[59]

FDA conducts IRB inspections to determine whether IRBs are operating in compliance with current agency regulations and statutory requirements and are following their own written procedures.

FDA inspections of IRBs generally fall into two categories:

- surveillance inspections—periodic, scheduled inspections to review the IRB's overall operations and procedures
- directed inspections—unscheduled inspections focused on the IRB's review of a specific clinical trial(s) (Directed inspections generally result from a complaint, clinical investigator misconduct, or safety issue pertaining to a trial or site.)

During an inspection, FDA will interview IRB personnel to obtain information about the IRB's policies and procedures. The IRB's performance is evaluated by tracking one or more studies subject to IRB review under FDA regulations. During the inspection, FDA typically reviews:

- records of IRB membership
- IRB procedures and guidelines
- minutes of IRB meetings for the past year
- study documents sent by the clinical investigator to the IRB
- study documents sent by the IRB to the clinical investigator
- other study materials[60]

At the end of the inspection, FDA will discuss inspection findings and, if deficiencies are found, issue a written Form FDA 483 (inspectional observations) to the responsible IRB representative. The IRB can respond to the observations verbally during the exit interview and/or in writing. After the inspection, FDA personnel will forward the Establishment Inspection Report (EIR), the 483 (if issued), copies of materials collected during the inspection and any IRB responses to the appropriate FDA center for further evaluation. Following this review, the center will send one of three types of letters to the IRB chairperson:

- a letter stating FDA observed no significant deviations from the regulations
- an Informational or Untitled Letter identifying deviations, for which voluntary corrective action is sufficient; these letters may request an IRB response
- a Warning Letter, which identifies serious deviations; a Warning Letter generally requests prompt correct by the IRB and a formal written response

In addition to issuing letters, FDA can take other administrative actions against IRBs, including:

- withholding approval of new studies conducted at the institution or reviewed by the IRB
- direct that no new subjects be added to ongoing studies
- terminate ongoing studies, when doing so would not endanger the subjects
- notify relevant state and federal regulatory agencies and other parties with direct interest in the agency's action on the IRB's operational deficiencies, in instances when the apparent noncompliance creates a significant threat to human subjects' rights and welfare

The FDA commissioner also can begin disqualification proceedings against an IRB or the institution if the IRB has refused or repeatedly failed to comply with FDA's IRB regulations, and the noncompliance adversely affects human subjects' rights or welfare.

IRB violations cited most commonly in FDA inspections include:

- failure to have adequate written procedures governing the IRB's functions and operations
- failure to ensure the IRB reviews proposed research at convened meetings at which a majority of the members are present
- failure to prepare and maintain IRB meeting minutes in sufficient detail
- failure to prepare and maintain adequate documentation of IRB activities, including a list of IRB members identified by: name, earned degrees, representative capacity, indications of experience and any other employment or other relationship between each member and the institution
- failure to conduct continuing research reviews at intervals appropriate to the degree of risk but not less than once per year[61]

One of the most publicized IRB Warning Letters was the Coast IRB letter, issued 14 April 2009. In 2009, after concerns were raised in Congress that many for-profit IRBs routinely approved clinical trials' design and conduct without adequately monitoring subjects' safety, the Government Accountability Office (GAO) created a fictitious clinical trial for a fake surgical adhesive gel, conducted by a non-existent medical device company. The GAO wrote a fake protocol, based on an actual high-risk study for a product FDA ultimately withdrew from the market because of deaths and infections among patients, and submitted the package to three central IRBs. Two of the IRBs declined approval, citing serious subject safety concerns. However, Coast IRB of Colorado Springs, CO, approved the study.

The FDA Warning Letter cited Coast for failing to determine risks to subjects were minimized and those risks were reasonable in relation to anticipated benefits, failing to make a risk determination, failing to ensure basic informed consent elements were present in the ICF and failing to demonstrate its ability to ascertain the acceptability of the proposed research. Coast was instructed to halt all new IRB operations, including enrolling additional subjects to ongoing studies.[62] As a result of the GAO actions and FDA's Warning Letter, several companies withdrew their business from Coast IRB, resulting in the IRB's closure on 29 April 2009.[63]

Sponsors and CROs

Responsibilities

Under FDA regulations, the sponsor is responsible for all the trial's operational aspects. Specifically, sponsors are responsible for ensuring: 1) the proper conduct of clinical studies for submission to FDA and 2) the protection of clinical study subjects' rights and welfare. These regulations are designed to protect human subjects and promote quality data collection.[64]

Drug Studies

FDA regulations define a sponsor as "a person who takes responsibility for and initiates a clinical investigation. The sponsor may be an individual or a pharmaceutical company…" Sponsors' regulatory responsibilities are identified in 21 CFR 312 and include:

- obtaining agency approval, where necessary, before studies begin
- manufacturing and labeling investigational products appropriately
- initiating, withholding or discontinuing clinical trials as required
- refraining from investigational product commercialization
- selecting investigators qualified by training and experience as appropriate experts to investigate the drug
- providing investigators with the information needed to conduct an investigation
- ensuring proper investigation monitoring by trained and experienced monitors
- ensuring the investigation(s) is conducted in accordance with the IND's general investigational plan and protocols
- maintaining an effective IND with respect to the investigations
- ensuring FDA and all participating investigators are informed promptly of significant new adverse effects or risks with respect to the drug
- shipping the investigational drug only to investigators participating in the trial
- reviewing and evaluating the evidence relating to the drug's safety and effectiveness as it is obtained from the investigator (If determining its investigational drug presents an unreasonable and significant risk to subjects, the sponsor will discontinue those investigations that present the risk, notify FDA, all IRBs and all investigators who have at any time participated in the investigation of the discontinuance.)
- maintaining and retaining adequate records and reports and permitting FDA to inspect records and reports relating to the clinical investigations
- maintaining written records of the investigational drug's disposition

Under 21 CFR 312.52, the sponsor may transfer responsibility for any or all of its obligations, with the exception of overall study oversight, to a contract research organization (CRO). All obligations transferred by the sponsor to a CRO must be documented in writing. If the sponsor is transferring only some obligations, the documentation must describe each of the obligations being transferred. If all obligations are transferred, a general statement that all obligations have been transferred is acceptable. Any obligation not documented in the written description will remain with the sponsor. A CRO that assumes any sponsor obligations must comply with the regulations applicable to those obligations and shall be subject to the same regulatory action as a sponsor for failure to comply with any regulations related to the obligation.

Devices

Similar to drug studies, device clinical trial sponsors' responsibilities are designed to protect human subjects and promote the quality data collection. Device sponsors are responsible for all trial operational aspects, including ensuring: 1) proper conduct of clinical studies for submission to FDA and 2) protection of clinical study subjects' rights and welfare.[65]

Device trials sponsors' regulatory responsibilities are identified in 21 CFR 812.40 and 43 and include:

- selecting qualified investigators
- providing investigators with the information needed to conduct the investigation properly
- ensuring proper investigation monitoring
- ensuring IRB review and approval are obtained
- submitting an IDE application to FDA
- ensuring any reviewing IRB and FDA are promptly informed of significant new information about an investigation
- shipping investigational device(s) only to qualified investigators
- obtaining signed investigator agreements and financial disclosure documentation
- selecting trained and experienced monitors

Unlike drug regulations, device regulations do not define or delineate CRO responsibilities. Therefore, device study sponsors are responsible for any CRO regulatory noncompliance.

Recordkeeping and Record Retention

Drug and device sponsors must retain all records associated with a clinical study, including:

- all correspondence with another sponsor, monitor, clinical investigator, IRB and FDA
- receipt, shipment and disposition of the investigational drug or device
- signed investigator agreements and financial disclosure information

Drug study sponsors also must retain reserve samples of any test article or reference standards associated with the trial. Device study sponsors also must retain records of nonsignificant risk devices and adverse events and complaints.

Drug study sponsors must retain all records and reports for two years after a marketing application is approved or, if the application is not approved, until two years after discontinuing drug shipment and delivery and FDA has been notified.[66] Device study sponsors must retain all records for two years after either: 1) the date on which the investigation is terminated or completed or 2) the date the records no longer are required for purposes of supporting a premarket approval application or a notice of completion of a product development protocol, whichever is the latter.[67]

Regulatory Oversight

FDA conducts various types of sponsor inspections, the most common being a routine surveillance inspection, a preapproval inspection used to determine whether a product approval is granted, delayed or denied, or a for cause inspection arising from a product complaint, a recall or information provided to FDA by a whistleblower. FDA sponsor inspections are used to confirm the subjects' rights, safety and welfare were appropriately protected, to determine the accuracy and reliability of the clinical data submitted in support of marketing applications and to assess compliance with FDA regulations. In addition to determining whether FDA violations occurred during the course of the trial, FDA inspections are used to obtain voluntary corrections by the inspected entity and to obtain the evidence necessary to support FDA enforcement action if voluntary correction is ineffective or does not occur.[68]

The most frequent findings cited during sponsor regulatory inspections include: 1) failure to ensure proper monitoring and 2) failure to ensure the trial was conducted in accordance with the investigational plan or protocol. Examples of both types of compliance issues were cited in the October 2007 Sanofi-Aventis Warning Letter,[69] the August 2009 Johnson & Johnson Pharmaceuticals Warning Letter,[70] the November 2009 Icon Clinical Research Inc. Warning Letter[71] and the April 2010 Pfizer Inc. Warning Letter.[72]

FDA enforcement actions (e.g., 483s, Untitled Letters, Warning Letters, Notice of Initiation of Disqualification Proceedings and Opportunity to Explain (NIDPOE) letters, debarment, etc.) against clinical trial sponsors and CROs are similar to those used to IRBs. Additionally, FDA can utilize the Application Integrity Policy (AIP), formally titled "Fraud, Untrue Statement of Material Facts, Bribery, and Illegal Gratuities Policy," implemented in 1991. Under the AIP, FDA can stop all scientific review of a pending submission when an applicant commits a "wrongful act" that raises significant questions about the data and information integrity submitted to the agency in support of marketing approval. FDA will not resume substantive scientific review until all the data in question have been validated. If the data are not validated, the applicant must withdraw the submission, conduct additional clinical trials, or abandon the product altogether. If FDA detects a pattern or practice of wrongful conduct, it can freeze review of all pending submissions until the integrity of the company's entire quality assurance system is verified. FDA also may require previously approved products to be recalled from the market.

Currently, 12 firms have been included on the AIP list from the various FDA centers (i.e., the Center for Drug Evaluation and Research (CDER)—five, two of which are no longer in business; the Center for Biologics Evaluation and Research (CBER)—one, which is no longer in business; and the Center for Devices and Radiological Health (CDRH)—six, two of which are no longer in business). This list represents firms notified by FDA it is deferring substantive scientific review of one or more of the firm's applications and/or is proceeding to withdraw the approved applications.[73]

Clinical Investigators

Responsibilities

Although investigator responsibilities in drug and biologic clinical trials are not identical to the investigator responsibilities for medical devices, the general responsibilities are essentially the same. Investigators of drug, biologic and device studies are responsible for:

- ensuring the trial is conducted according to the signed investigator statement for clinical investigations of drugs, including biological products, or agreement for clinical investigations of medical devices, the investigational plan and applicable regulations
- protecting study subjects' rights, safety and welfare
- controlling the drugs, biological products and devices under investigation
- ensuring informed consent is obtained from each subject in accordance with 21 CFR 50[74]

Clinical investigators for drug studies must ensure an IRB complies with FDA regulations, conducts initial and continuing ethical review of the study. They also must notify the IRB of changes in the research activity or unanticipated problems involving risks to human subjects or others, and must not make any changes in the protocol without IRB and sponsor approval, unless necessary to eliminate apparent immediate hazards to human subjects. Investigators also are responsible for following the signed investigator statement (Form FDA 1572) and the investigational plan. Investigators also must report their financial interests to the sponsor to permit assessment of conflicts of interest.[75]

Investigators for device trials also must obtain IRB and any necessary FDA approval before initiating the clinical trial. Device investigators must agree to conduct the investigation in accordance with the signed sponsor agreement, the investigational plan, applicable FDA regulations and any other conditions of approval imposed by the IRB or FDA.[76]

Recordkeeping and Retention

Investigators for drug studies are required to maintain the following records:

- disposition of the drug, including dates, quantity and subject use
- adequate and accurate case histories, recording all observations and other data pertinent to the investigation on each subject involved in the clinical trial
- annual clinical trial progress reports
- safety reports
- final report when the investigator's involvement in the trial is completed
- financial disclosure reports, including any updates for relevant changes occurring during the investigation and for one year following completion of the trial

The investigator is responsible for retaining all relevant records for two years following the date the drug marketing application is approved for the indication under investigation or, if no application is filed or the application is not approved for the indication, until two years after the investigation is discontinued and FDA is notified.[77]

Device study investigators are required to maintain complete and accurate records relating to their participation in the clinical trial. These include:

- correspondence with other investigators, IRB, sponsor, monitor or FDA
- records relating to device receipt, use or disposition
- records of each subject's case history and exposure to the device
- protocol and documentation of the date and reason for each protocol deviation
- any other records required by FDA

Similar to drug sponsors, device study investigators must retain all records for two years after either: 1) the date on which the investigation is terminated or completed or 2) the date the records are no longer required for purposes of supporting a premarket approval application or a notice of completion of a product development protocol, whichever is the latter.[78]

Regulatory Oversight

The various types of FDA investigator inspections include: data audits, in which the focus is on verification of study data submitted as part of a marketing application; information gathering; and for-cause inspections, where the focus is on the study's conduct by the investigator and usually is triggered by FDA's notification of a problem or complaint about the investigator. Generally, FDA conducts inspections of investigator sites to determine whether clinical investigators are conducting studies in accordance with applicable regulations.

FDA conducts both announced and unannounced clinical investigator site inspections for various reasons, including:

- verifying the accuracy and reliability of data submitted to the agency
- in response to a complaint about the study conduct at the site
- in response to sponsor concerns about the site
- upon termination of the clinical site
- during ongoing clinical trials to provide real-time assessment of the investigator's conduct of the trial and protection of human subjects
- at the request of an FDA review division
- related to certain classes of investigational products FDA has identified as products of special interest in its current work plan (i.e., targeted inspections based on current public health concerns)[79]

At the end of an inspection, the FDA investigator conducts an exit interview with the clinical investigator to review the findings and, if deficiencies are found, issues a written Form FDA 483. Common deficiencies observed by FDA investigators during clinical investigator inspections include:

- failure to follow the investigational plan and signed investigator statement/agreement (e.g., failure to conduct or supervise the study in accordance with the relevant, current protocol)
- failure to appropriately document and report medically necessary protocol deviations
- inadequate recordkeeping
- inadequate accountability for the investigational product
- inadequate subject protection, including informed consent issues

FDA enforcement actions (e.g., 483s, Untitled Letters, Warning Letters, NIDPOE letters, debarment, etc.) against investigators are similar to those used against clinical trial sponsors and CROs. If FDA determines there have been serious violations, and corrective action by the investigator cannot resolve the matter, FDA may elect to initiate an enforcement action against the investigator. If the findings indicate the investigator has violated FDA regulations or submitted false information repeatedly or deliberately, the agency may disqualify the investigator from conducting future studies it regulates. Additionally, FDA may initiate a civil or criminal enforcement action in federal court. However, both of these types of actions can take several months, or years, to complete.[80]

In the interim, FDA can issue a clinical hold, which will immediately suspend or impose restriction on an ongoing or proposed drug or biologics clinical study. The clinical hold order may apply to one or more of the investigations covered by an IND. When a proposed study is placed on clinical hold, subjects may not be given the investigational drug. When an ongoing study is placed on clinical hold, no new subjects may be recruited to the study and placed on the investigational drug; patients already in the study should be taken off therapy involving the investigational drug unless specifically permitted by FDA in the interest of patient safety. A clinical hold may be complete or partial; delay or suspension of all clinical work under an IND is considered a complete clinical hold, while delay or suspension of only part of the clinical work under an IND is considered a partial clinical hold. A partial clinical hold could be imposed to delay or suspend one of several protocols in an IND, a part of a protocol or a specific study site (i.e., investigator) in a multi-site investigation.

FDA will impose a clinical hold if it finds subjects are or would be exposed to an unreasonable and significant risk of illness or injury. Examples of investigator actions that may result in a clinical hold include:

- failure to report serious or life-threatening adverse events
- serious protocol violations (e.g., enrolling subjects who do not meet the entrance criteria, failing to carry out critical safety evaluations)
- repeated or deliberate failure to obtain adequate informed consent
- failure to obtain IRB review and approval for significant protocol changes
- failure to supervise the clinical trial adequately such that human subjects are or would be exposed to an unreasonable and significant risk of illness or injury

FDA will lift a clinical hold when the grounds for the hold no longer apply. The sponsor of the affected study may, while the clinical hold is in place, present evidence to FDA to show it has taken steps to protect study subjects, e.g., by replacing the investigator who is charged with misconduct. If FDA concludes the study subjects no longer are exposed to an unreasonable and significant risk of illness or injury, the hold will be lifted.[81]

Monitors and Monitoring

Purpose of Monitoring

Effective clinical investigation monitoring is critical to protecting human subjects; collecting complete, accurate and verifiable study data; and conducting high-quality studies, compliant with the protocol, applicable regulations and GCPs. Sponsors of clinical investigations for drugs, biologics and medical devices are required to provide adequate oversight of trials to ensure human subjects' rights, welfare and safety are protected and ensure the quality of the clinical trial data submitted to FDA. FDA regulations require sponsors to monitor the conduct and progress of their clinical investigations. While the task of monitoring can be delegated, it ultimately remains the sponsor's responsibility.[82]

Monitor Qualifications

Monitors appointed by the sponsor should be trained appropriately and have the scientific and/or clinical knowledge to monitor the trial adequately. Monitors should be thoroughly familiar with the investigational product(s), the protocol, written informed consent form and any other written information to be provided to subjects, the sponsor's SOPs, GCP and the applicable regulatory requirement(s).[83]

Monitor Responsibilities

While the sponsor determines the appropriate extent and nature of monitoring, the monitor, by following the sponsor's monitoring plans, ensures the trial is conducted and documented properly. The monitor's responsibilities include:

- acting as the main line of communication between the sponsor and the investigator
- verifying the investigator has adequate qualifications and resources and these remain in force throughout the trial period
- verifying investigational product storage time and conditions are acceptable and a sufficient supply is available throughout the trial
- verifying the investigational product is only supplied to eligible subjects and the subjects are provided with necessary instruction on the investigational product's proper use, handling, storing and return
- verifying the investigational product's receipt, use, return and disposition at the trial sites are controlled and documented adequately
- verifying the investigator and the trial staff follow the approved protocol and all approved amendment
- verifying written informed consent was obtained before each subject's participation in the trial
- ensuring the investigator receives the current Investigator's Brochure, all documents and all trial supplies needed to conduct the trial properly and to comply with the applicable regulatory requirements for the trial
- verifying source data and documents and other trial records are accurate, complete, kept up-to-date and maintained
- checking the accuracy and completeness of case report form (CRF) entries, source data and documents and other trial-related records against each other
- determining whether all adverse events (AEs) are reported appropriately within the required time periods[84]

Monitoring Activities

On-Site Monitoring

On-site monitoring is an in-person visit to the clinical investigation site. On-site monitoring is important early in a study, especially if the protocol is complex and includes novel procedures with which the investigator and site staff may be unfamiliar. On-site monitoring is used to:

- verify appropriate study subject enrollment
- assess the site's consenting process
- identify data entry errors (e.g., discrepancies between source records and CRFs, and missing data in source records or CRFs)
- verify the presence of study documentation
- assess the site's familiarity with the protocol and required procedures
- assess the site's compliance with the protocol, investigational product control and GCPs

Experienced on-site monitors also can provide the sponsor with an overall sense of the quality of the trial conduct at a site (e.g., investigator oversight, attention to detail, thoroughness of study documentation and appropriate delegation of study tasks).[85]

Remote or Centralized Monitoring

Centralized or remote monitoring is an off-site evaluation performed by clinical monitors, data management personnel, medical monitors and/or statisticians. Centralized monitoring depends on various factors, including the sponsor's use of electronic systems, the sponsor's access to the site's data (i.e., either through electronic records or timely data entry from paper CRFs) and communication tools available to the sponsor and study site.

Centralized monitoring is used to supplement or reduce the frequency and extent of on-site monitoring by replacing the on-site activities with those that can be done as well or better remotely. Examples of activities well suited for remote monitoring include:

- monitoring data quality through routine review of submitted data to identify and follow-up on missing data, inconsistent data, data outliers and potential protocol deviations that may indicate systemic or significant errors in site data collection and reporting
- conducting statistical analyses to identify data trends not easily detected by on-site monitoring, such as checks of data range, consistency and completeness; and checks for unusual data distribution within and between study sites
- analyzing site characteristics, performance metrics (e.g., high screen failure or withdrawal rates, high frequency of eligibility violations, delays in reporting data) and clinical data to identify trial sites with characteristics correlated with poor performance or noncompliance
- verifying critical source data remotely[86]

Risk-Based Monitoring

Risk assessment generally involves identifying risks, analyzing them and determining whether they need to be modified by implementing controls (e.g., processes, policies or practices). In a recent guidance document, FDA stated risk-based monitoring could improve sponsor's clinical investigation oversight. FDA recommended sponsors prospectively identify critical data and processes, perform a risk assessment to identify and understand risks that could affect the collection of critical data or the performance of critical processes and develop a monitoring plan focusing on the important and likely risks to critical data and processes. Risk-based monitoring activities focus on preventing or mitigating important and likely sources of error in the conduct, collection and reporting of critical data and processes necessary for human subject protection and trial integrity.

Under risk-based monitoring, sponsors prospectively identify critical data and processes which, if inaccurate, not performed or performed incorrectly, would threaten human subjects' protection or study result integrity. Examples of critical data and processes include:

- verification informed consent was obtained appropriately
- adherence to protocol eligibility criteria designed to exclude individuals for whom the investigational product may be less safe than the protocol intended and to include only subjects from the targeted study population for whom the test article is most appropriate
- procedures for documenting appropriate investigational product accountability and administration (e.g., ensuring the integrity of randomization at the site level, where appropriate)
- conduct and documentation of procedures and assessments related to study endpoints—protocol-required safety assessments—evaluating, documenting and reporting serious adverse events and unanticipated adverse device effects, subject deaths and withdrawals, especially when a withdrawal may be related to an adverse event
- conduct and documentation of procedures essential to trial integrity, such as ensuring the study blind is maintained, both at the site level and at the sponsor level, as appropriate, referring specified events for adjudication and allocation concealment[87]

Monitor Reports

To ensure the sponsor remains informed on clinical trial progress, monitors submit a written report after each trial-site visit or trial-related communication. These reports include the date, site, monitor name and name of the investigator or other individual(s) contacted. They also summarize what the monitor reviewed and the monitor's statements concerning the significant findings or facts, deviations and deficiencies, conclusions, actions taken or to be taken and/or actions recommended to secure compliance.[88]

Consequences of Inadequate Monitoring

FDA clearly signaled the consequences of inadequate monitoring practices in the August 2009 Johnson & Johnson Pharmaceuticals Warning Letter, the November 2009 Icon Clinical Research Inc. Warning Letter and the April 2010 Pfizer Inc. Warning Letter. In all three cases, the first deficiency cited was "Failure to ensure proper monitoring of the clinical investigation (21 CFR 312.50; 312.56(a))."[89,90,91] Additionally, in the J&J and Icon letters, many observations start with the words, "Study monitors failed to identify that ...."

The monitor's role is to ensure human subjects' protection; complete, accurate and verifiable study data collection; and the conduct of high-quality studies, compliant with the protocol, applicable regulations and GCPs. Considering the approval of any drug, diagnostic test or medical device marketing application will depend on the quality of the scientific evidence that supports such use, the criticality of the monitor's role and activities cannot be over-emphasized.[92]

Quality Assurance (Auditing)

No general guidance or industry standard clarifies the requirements for a quality assurance program for clinical trials. FDA's *Compliance Program Guidance Manual 7348.810 (Sponsors, CROs, and Monitors)* notes clinical trial quality assurance units (QAUs) are not required by regulation. However, where the sponsor utilizes audits to determine protocol compliance, GCPs, clinical trial regulations and SOPs, auditing personnel should be independent of, and separate from, routine monitoring or quality control functions.

ICH E6, Section 5.19, Audit, notes sponsors should select qualified auditors who are trained and experienced and have written procedures, describing what to audit, how to audit, audit frequency and audit report's form and content. The audit plan should be guided by the importance of the trial to regulatory submissions, the number of subjects in the trial, the trial's type and complexity, the level of risks to trial subjects and any identified problem(s). Additionally, all audit observations and findings must be documented.

Good Documentation Practices (GDPs)

All individuals associated with a clinical trial are responsible for creating and maintaining complete and accurate records. The IRB is required to create and maintain complete and accurate records of all its activities, including its members and procedures, research proposals reviewed, meeting minutes, correspondence with investigators and ongoing review activities. The investigator is required to create and maintain complete and accurate records of the investigational drug or device's disposition and case histories that record all observations and data pertinent to the investigation. The sponsor is required to create and maintain complete and accurate records of the investigational drug or device's receipt, shipment and disposition, agreement of obligations transferred to a CRO, and all records associated with clinical study's oversight, including but not limited to investigator selection, monitoring activities, quality assurance, safety reporting and data handling. The monitor is required to create and maintain complete and accurate records of all trial-site visits and trial-related communications.

Good documentation practices are important because the regulatory agency's ultimate decision to approve a marketing application is based on the accuracy and integrity of the data submitted, which should allow an independent observer to reconstruct the trial as it occurred by examining the study records.

FDA uses the acronym ALCOA (attributable, legible, contemporaneous, original and accurate) to describe the key attributes of good documentation practices.[93]

- Attributable—Does the document clearly indicate who observed and recorded the information, and the time?
- Legible—Can the information be understood easily? Is it recorded permanently on a durable medium? Are the original entries clearly readable (e.g., not obscured)?
- Contemporaneous—Was the information recorded at the time of the occurrence or observation?
- Original—Is the source information accessible and preserved in its original form?
- Accurate—Does the recorded information clearly, and without error, describe the documented study events?

Conclusion

GCPs establish the minimum standards and guidelines for conducting clinical research. GCP is an internationally accepted, scientific and ethical quality standard for the design, conduct, performance, auditing, recordkeeping, analysis and reporting of clinical trials involving human subjects. Compliance with GCP regulations and guidance documents provides assurance human subjects' rights, safety, confidentiality and well-being are protected. GCPs also serve to ensure data collected and reported during the trial are high quality, credible, accurate and reliable.

Although this chapter provides a basic overview of the requirements for drug and device clinical trials, due to regulatory requirements' complexity, regulatory professionals are advised to consult internal and external resources, including their companies' quality assurance, regulatory compliance and regulatory intelligence departments and/or local EC/IRB and regulatory authorities, when resolving GCP compliance issues.

References

1. FDA. *Guidance for Industry E6 Good Clinical Practice: Consolidated Guidance*, FDA Website. http://www.fda.gov/downloads/Drugs/Guidances/ucm073122.pdf. Accessed 15 February 2015.
2. Ibid.
3. Sulfanilamide Disaster. FDA website. http://www.fda.gov/aboutfda/whatwedo/history/productregulation/sulfanilamidedisaster/default.htm. Accessed 13 February 2015.
4. Ibid.
5. Jarrell K. "Regulatory History: Elixir Sulfanilamide." *Journal of GXP Compliance*, Summer 2012 Vol. 16 No 3: 12-14. Institute of Validation Technology website. http://www.ivtnetwork.com/sites/default/files/IVTGXPxxxx_CoverStory-2%20pr1.pdf. Accessed 13 February 2015.
6. US Holocaust Memorial Museum website. http://www.ushmm.org/wlc/en/article.php?ModuleId=10005137. Accessed 15 February 2015.
7. National WWII Museum website. http://www.nationalww2museum.org/learn/education/for-students/research-starters/holocaust.html. Accessed 15 February 2015.
8. Wikipedia, free encyclopedia. Nazi human experimentation. Wikipedia website: http://en.wikipedia.org/wiki/Nazi_human_experimentation. Accessed 15 February 2015.
9. Library of Congress. Military Legal Resources. Nuremberg Trails. Library of Congress website. http://www.loc.gov/rr/frd/Military_Law/Nuremberg_trials.html. Accessed 15 February 2015.
10. National University of Singapore website. http://www.nus.edu.sg/irb/Articles/Nuremberg.pdf. Accessed 15 February 2015.
11. Ibid.
12. US Department of Health & Human Services. The *Nuremberg Code*. DHHS website. http://www.hhs.gov/ohrp/archive/nurcode.html . Accessed 15 February 2015.
13. World Medical Organization. *Declaration of Helsinki. British Medical Journal* (7 December) 1996;313(7070):1448-1449. Wayne State University website. http://wayne.edu/search/?q=declaration+of+helsinki&type=all.. Accessed 16 May 2015.
14. World Medical Association. "*Declaration of Helsinki* – Ethical Principles for Medical Research Involving Human Subjects." 2013. WMA website. http://www.wma.net/en/30publications/10policies/b3/. Accessed 15 February 2015.
15. The New Social Worker. The Tuskegee Syphilis Study and Its Implications for the 21st Century. The New Social Worker website. http://www.socialworker.com/feature-articles/ethics-articles/The_Tuskegee_Syphilis_Study_and_Its_Implications_for_the_21st_Century/. Accessed 15 February 2015.
16. Explorable Psychology Experiments. Tuskegee Syphilis Study. Explorable website. https://explorable.com/tuskegee-syphilis-study. Accessed 15 February 2015.
17. Op cit. 15.
18. Centers for Disease Control and Prevention. US Public Health Service Syphilis Study at Tuskegee, Presidential Apology. CDC website. http://www.cdc.gov/tuskegee/clintonp.htm. Accessed 15 February 2015.
19. US Department of Health and Human Services. *The Belmont Report*. 18 April 1979. DHHS website. http://www.hhs.gov/ohrp/humansubjects/guidance/belmont.html. Accessed 15 February 2015.
20. Ibid.
21. Ibid.
22. US Department of Health and Human Services. Federal Protection for the Protection of Human Subjects ('Common Rule'). DHHS website. http://www.hhs.gov/ohrp/humansubjects/commonrule/. Accessed 15 February 2015.
23. US Department of Health and Human Services. ANPRM for Revision to Common Rule. DHHS website. http://www.hhs.gov/ohrp/humansubjects/anprm2011page.html. Accessed 15 February 2015.
24. International Conference on Harmonisation of Technical Requirements for Registration of Pharmaceuticals for Human Use (ICH) website. http://www.ich.org/home.html. Accessed 15 February 2015.
25. CIOMS. *International Ethical Guidelines for Biomedical Research Involving Human Subjects*. CIOMS website. http://www.cioms.ch/

publications/guidelines/guidelines_nov_2002_blurb.htm. Accessed 15 February 2015.
26. Op cit. 24.
27. Op cit. 1.
28. FDA website. http://www.fda.gov/ForPatients/Approvals/Drugs/ucm405658.htm. Accessed 15 February 2015.
29. FDA website. http://www.fda.gov/drugs/resourcesforyou/consumers/ucm143534.htm. Accessed 15 February 2015.
30. FDA. *Guidance for Industry, Investigators, and Reviewers Exploratory IND Studies.* Accessible at: www.fda.gov/downloads/drugs/guidancecomplianceregulatoryinformation/guidances/ucm078933.pdf. FDA website. Accessed 17 May 2015.
31. Op cit. 29.
32. Ibid.
33. Clinical trials.gov website. https://www.clinicaltrials.gov/ct2/about-studies/glossary#P. Accessed 15 February 2015.
34. FDA. Device Advice, Investigational Device Exemption. FDA website. http://www.fda.gov/medicaldevices/deviceregulationandguidance/howtomarketyourdevice/investigationaldeviceexemptionide/default.htm. Accessed 15 February 2015
35. FDA. *Guidance for Industry and Food and Drug Administration Staff, Investigational Device Exemptions (IDEs) for Early Feasibility Medical Device Clinical Studies, Including Certain First in Human (FIH) Studies.* FDA website. http://www.fda.gov/downloads/medicaldevices/deviceregulationandguidance/guidancedocuments/ucm279103.pdf. Accessed 30 March 2015.
36. Op cit. 34
37. Ibid
38. FDA. Title 21—Food and Drug Administration, Department of Health and Human Services, Part 312: Investigational New Drug Applications. FDA website. http://www.accessdata.fda.gov/scripts/cdrh/cfdocs/cfcfr/CFRsearch.cfm?CFRPart=312. Accessed 30 March 2015.
39. Ibid.
40. Ibid.
41. FDA. Title 21 – Food and Drug Administration, Department of Health and Human Services, Part 812 Investigational Device Exemptions. FDA website. http://www.accessdata.fda.gov/scripts/cdrh/cfdocs/cfcfr/CFRSearch.cfm?CFRPart=812. Accessed 30 March 2015.
42. Ibid.
43. Ibid.
44. FDA. Informed Consent Information Sheet. FDA website. http://www.fda.gov/downloads/RegulatoryInformation/Guidances/UCM405006.pdf. Accessed 22 February 2015.
45. FDA. Title 21 – Food and Drug Administration, Department of Health and Human Service, Part 50, Protection of Human Subjects. FDA website. http://www.accessdata.fda.gov/scripts/cdrh/cfdocs/cfcfr/CFRSearch.cfm?CFRPart=50. Accessed 22 February 2015.
46. Op cit. 44
47. FDA. Title 21 – Food and Drug Administration, Department of Health and Human Services, Part 56 Institutional Review Boards. FDA website. http://www.accessdata.fda.gov/scripts/cdrh/cfdocs/cfcfr/CFRSearch.cfm?CFRPart=56. Accessed 13 March 2015.
48. Op cit. 44
49. Ibid.
50. Op cit. 47
51. FDA. *Guidance for Industry, Using a Centralized IRB Review Process in Multicenter Clinical Trials.* FDA website. http://www.fda.gov/downloads/RegulatoryInformation/Guidances/ucm127013.pdf. Accessed 13 March 2015.
52. FDA. Institutional Review Boards Frequently Asked Questions—Information Sheet. FDA website. http://www.fda.gov/RegulatoryInformation/Guidances/ucm126420.htm. Accessed 13 March 2015.
53. Op cit. 51.
54. Op cit. 47
55. Ibid
56. FDA. *Information Sheet Guidance for Sponsors, Clinical Investigators and IRBs, Waiver of IRB Requirements for Drug and Biological Product Studies.* FDA website. http://www.fda.gov/downloads/RegulatoryInformation/Guidances/UCM126500.pdf. Accessed 13 March 2015.
57. FDA. *Conditions for IRB Use of Expedited Review.* FDA website. http://www.fda.gov/ScienceResearch/SpecialTopics/RunningClinicalTrials/GuidancesInformationSheetsandNotices/ucm118099.htm. Accessed 13 March 2015.
58. FDA. *Information Sheet Guidance for Sponsors, Clinical Investigators, and IRBs, Frequently Asked Questions – Statement of Investigator (Form FDA 1572).* FDA website. http://www.fda.gov/downloads/RegulatoryInformation/Guidances/UCM214282.pdf. Accessed 13 March 2015.
59. Federal Register, Volume 74, No. 10:2358 – 2369. FDA. Title 21 Food and Drug Administration, Department of Health and Human Services, Part 56 Institutional Review Boards. GPO website. http://www.gpo.gov/fdsys/pkg/FR-2009-01-15/html/E9-682.htm. Accessed 13 March 2015.
60. FDA. *Information Sheet guidance for IRBs, Clinical Investigators, and Sponsors, FDA Institutional Review Board Inspections.* FDA website. http://www.fda.gov/downloads/RegulatoryInformation/Guidances/UCM126555.pdf. Accessed 13 March 2015.
61. Ibid.
62. FDA. Inspections, Compliance, Enforcements, and Criminal Investigations. FDA website. http://www.fda.gov/ICECI/EnforcementActions/WarningLetters/ucm136673.htm. Accessed 13 March 2015.
63. Citizens for Responsible Care and Research. Coast Institutional Review Board. FDA website. http://www.circare.org/info/coastirb.htm. Accessed 13 March 2015.
64. Op cit.38
65. Op cit. 41
66. Op cit. 38
67. Op cit. 41
68. FDA. *Compliance Program 7348.810 Bioresearch Monitoring, Sponsors, Contract Research Organizations and Monitors,* FDA website. http://www.fda.gov/ICECI/EnforcementActions/BioresearchMonitoring/ucm133777.htm. Accessed 13 March 2015.
69. FDA. Inspections, Compliance, Enforcements, and Criminal Investigations. FDA website. http://www.fda.gov/ICECI/EnforcementActions/WarningLetters/2006/ucm076552.htm. Accessed 13 March 2015.
70. FDA. Inspections, Compliance, Enforcements, and Criminal Investigations. FDA website. http://www.fda.gov/ICECI/EnforcementActions/WarningLetters/ucm177398.htm. Accessed 13 March 2015.
71. FDA. Inspections, Compliance, Enforcements, and Criminal Investigations. FDA website. http://www.fda.gov/ICECI/EnforcementActions/WarningLetters/ucm193156.htm. Accessed 13 March 2015.
72. FDA. Inspections, Compliance, Enforcements, and Criminal Investigations. FDA website. http://www.fda.gov/ICECI/EnforcementActions/WarningLetters/ucm208976.htm. Accessed 13 March 2015.
73. FDA. Application Integrity Policy. FDA website. http://www.fda.gov/ICECI/EnforcementActions/ApplicationIntegrityPolicy/ucm2005394.htm. Accessed 13 March 2015.
74. Op cit. 38.
75. Ibid.
76. Op cit. 41.
77. Op cit. 38
78. Op cit. 41
79. FDA. *Information Sheet Guidance for IRBs, Clinical Investigators, and Sponsors FDA Inspection of Clinical Investigators.* FDA website.

http://www.fda.gov/downloads/RegulatoryInformation/Guidances/UCM126553.pdf. Accessed 13 March 2015.
80. Ibid.
81. FDA. *Guidance for Industry and Clinical Investigators, The Use of Clinical Holds Following Clinical Investigator Misconduct.* FDA website. http://www.fda.gov/downloads/RegulatoryInformation/Guidances/UCM126997.pdf. Accessed 13 March 2015.
82. Op cit. 1.
83. Ibid.
84. Ibid.
85. FDA. *Guidance for Industry Oversight of Clinical Investigations—A Risk-Based Approach to Monitoring.* FDA website. http://www.fda.gov/downloads/Drugs/Guidances/UCM269919.pdf. Accessed 13 March 2015.
86. Ibid.
87. Ibid.
88. Op cit. 1.
89. Op cit. 70.
90. Op cit. 71.
91. Op cit. 72.
92. Op cit. 1
93. FDA. *Guidance for Industry Electronic Source Data in Clinical Investigations.* FDA website. http://www.fda.gov/downloads/drugs/guidancecomplianceregulatoryinformation/guidances/ucm328691.pdf. Accessed 13 March 2015.

Chapter 10

Current Good Manufacturing Practices and Quality System Design

Updated by Jocelyn Jennings, MS, RAC and Carrie Kuehn, MA, MPH, RAC

OBJECTIVES

- ❑ Understand current Good Manufacturing Practice (CGMP) requirements for medical devices, drugs and biologics
- ❑ Understand the concept of "quality-by-design" and how it is embodied in CGMP regulations
- ❑ Understand the concept of a "quality system" and how it ensures product safety and efficacy
- ❑ Recognize the need for CGMP compliance at all levels of an organization
- ❑ Describe how CGMP regulations go beyond just the "manufacture" of a product and how they impact all levels of an organization
- ❑ Understand the difference between medical device verification and validation
- ❑ Develop awareness of the management responsibilities defined by the CGMP regulations
- ❑ Differentiate between medical device and pharmaceutical/biologics CGMP regulations
- ❑ Understand pharmaceutical GMPs
- ❑ Understand biologic GMP
- ❑ Understand the differences and similarities among pharmaceutical, biologic and medical device GMPs
- ❑ Understand the most significant GMP regulations and guidance documents affecting drug and biologic manufacturing

LAWS, REGULATIONS AND GUIDELINES COVERED IN THIS CHAPTER

- ❑ 21 CFR 820 Quality System Regulations
- ❑ Design Control Guidance for Medical Device Manufacturers (March 1997)
- ❑ Compliance Program Guidance Manual, Program 7382.845: Inspection of Medical Device Manufacturers (February 2011)
- ❑ Guide to Inspections of Medical Device Manufacturers (December 1997)
- ❑ Quality System Inspection Technique—QSIT (August 1999)
- ❑ *Quality System Information for Certain Premarket Application Reviews; Guidance for Industry and FDA Staff* (February 2003)
- ❑ *Guidance for Industry: Quality Systems Approach to Pharmaceutical CGMP Regulations* (September 2006)

- 21 CFR 210, Current Good Manufacturing Practice in manufacturing, processing, packing, or holding of drugs: General
- 21 CFR 211, current Good Manufacturing Practice for Finished Pharmaceuticals
- 21 CFR 600, Biological products: General
- *Guidance for Industry: Q7A Good Manufacturing Practice Guidance for Active Pharmaceutical Ingredients (August 2001)*
- *Guidance for Industry: Q10 Pharmaceutical Quality System (April 2009)*
- Guidance for Industry: CGMP for Phase 1 Investigational Drugs (July 2008)
- Questions and Answers on Current Good Manufacturing Practice (CGMP) for Drugs (updated 2014)

Introduction

Title 21 of the Code of Federal Regulations (CFR) provides specific regulations that define the minimum requirements for current Good Manufacturing Practices (CGMPs) for drugs, biologics and medical devices. For example, 21 CFR 210, 211 and 600 provide the framework within which drug and biologics manufacturers must operate to manufacture their products in compliance with CGMPs. Similarly, 21 CFR 820 provides a detailed framework for the manufacture of medical devices under CGMPs with which device manufacturers must comply to market their devices in the US. These regulations exist to ensure healthcare products in the US are manufactured according to a standard of quality to meet their intended safety and effectiveness profiles.

The CGMP regulations are based on the philosophical principle of "quality-by-design." This principle is based on the idea that "quality should be built into the product, and testing alone cannot be relied on to ensure product quality."[1] Using a quality-by-design approach means the product is developed to achieve conformance with its specifications consistently upon completion of the manufacturing process. Therefore, CGMPs do not apply just to how a drug, biologic or medical device is manufactured; rather, CGMPs apply to the entire product design, development, testing, manufacturing and commercialization process. FDA intended the CGMP regulations to be flexible enough to allow each manufacturer to determine the controls that are necessary commensurate with risk, using scientifically sound design, processing methods, and testing procedures.[2,3] CGMPs are intended to prevent manufacturing defects, failures of performance or efficacy, contamination, mix-ups, deviations and errors. Although different regulations apply to medical devices and pharmaceuticals, the intention of these regulations is the same: to ensure the safety and effectiveness of healthcare products on the US market.

Quality Management System

CGMP regulations require the establishment of a Quality Management System (QMS). The QMS is the means by which healthcare product manufacturers implement CGMP regulations. The QMS is a framework or organizational structure that maximizes conformity with policies and procedures, process efficiency and accuracy and product safety and efficacy. The QMS impacts an organization's daily activities at every level, from the manufacturing floor to executive leadership. Manufacturers with robust QMS processes are able to ensure a quality-by-design approach to product development and manage risk and initiate continuous improvement activities better, when necessary. If the QMS is implemented robustly and maintained, a manufacturer may experience fewer product failures and recalls and be subject to shorter and less frequent FDA inspections.

Management Responsibility

A critical aspect of the CGMP regulations is management responsibility for QMS establishment, implementation and maintenance. The regulations clearly hold executive leadership accountable for compliance with FDA CGMP regulations. The implication is management must be actively involved with the organization's QMS; although it can delegate authority, it cannot abdicate responsibility for organizational compliance with these regulations. Management can participate actively by establishing quality policies, modeling compliance in its organizational role, leading management reviews and making compliant quality management a company priority.

Documentation: SOPs, Work Instructions, Policies

All aspects of a manufacturer's QMS must be governed by policies, standard operating procedures (SOPs), work instructions or other types of process documents (**Figure 10-1**). Under the regulations, each of these documents must be controlled. When controlled, each policy, procedure or process document must undergo a review and approval process before being implemented and must have a revision history. Using controlled documents ensures everyone is using the most recent and approved version of a particular procedure, policy instruction or process.

Change Control

FDA also requires manufacturers to implement change control for any QMS-related controlled document. When executed properly, change control ensures any changes being made are reviewed and approved prior to implementation

Figure 10-1. Quality System Elements

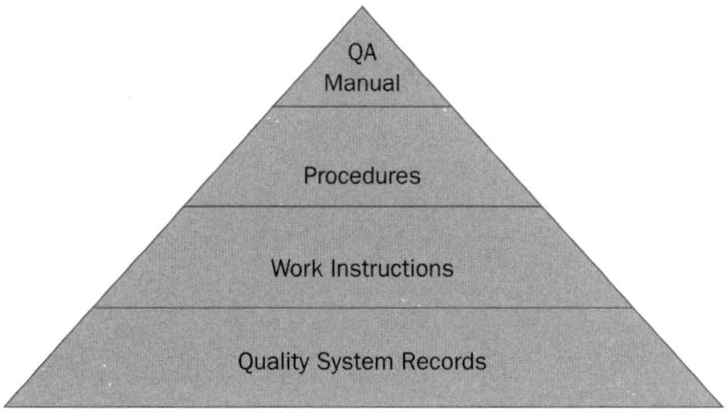

and are communicated appropriately. In some cases, if a change is being made to a process, that process may need to be revalidated before it can be used to manufacture a product. Similarly, changes to suppliers, raw materials or inspection criteria also may require validation before implementation. As such, change control is critical to ensuring that revisions are implemented only following appropriate review and approval.

Medical Device CGMP

Quality System Regulation

Medical device CGMP regulations are encompassed by the Quality System Regulation (QSR), in 21 CFR 820. The QSR details how FDA expects manufacturers to implement quality-by-design activities throughout the product lifecycle. Depending on a device's type and class, a manufacturer must implement the relevant QSR parts applicable to the product. Detailed FDA guidance provides insight into the agency's thinking about implementing these important regulations.

Design Control

One important aspect of the QSR is the regulations regarding design control, which detail the activities FDA requires for medical device design and development. Design control regulations effectively provide specific details on how FDA expects manufacturers to implement quality-by-design during the design phase of the product lifecycle. Design control is an iterative process that allows feedback throughout the design process to ensure the device under development will be safe, effective and meet end user needs (**Figure 10-2**). These regulations typically apply to all Class II and III devices. Most Class I devices are exempt from this part of the QSRs, though there are exceptions including devices automated with software, tracheobronchial suction catheters, surgeons' gloves, protective restraints, manual radionuclide applicator systems and radionuclide teletherapy sources. Design control activities must be documented and recorded in a Design History File (DHF).

Design and Development Plan

FDA regulations require manufacturers to establish a detailed plan for each product's design and development. The plan must specify the development process in terms of design control and assign responsibility for each activity. It also must detail how different development groups will interact with each other and provide a review and approval schedule. The development plan is a dynamic, living document and should be maintained and updated throughout the design control process.

Design Inputs and Outputs

Design inputs are the requirements for the device and should encompass the wants and needs of both the end user and patient. Inputs may include specific performance characteristics, reliability requirements, clinical constraints (e.g., must be sterile) and handling and storage requirements, among others. Design inputs can be informed by many different information sources, including requests from physicians and surgeon, regulations, published literature or the emergence of a new medical need. Design outputs are specifications that manifest the design inputs in the form of device specifications. These include things like materials, geometry, power source and electronic components, sterility, packaging and usability, etc. Design outputs must be objectively measureable to determine whether they correlate with design inputs. Design outputs often are captured in descriptive materials such as design/assembly drawings, material specifications, production specifications and software code, among others.

Verification and Validation

Verification and validation are critical aspects of the iterative design control process and typically are accomplished via bench, animal and/or clinical testing. Although they may appear similar, verification and validation are distinctly different activities in the design control process. Verification is the process of determining whether the design outputs match the design inputs. Verification is when the manufacturer ensures it made the product correctly and the specified requirements have been fulfilled. In contrast, validation is the process of determining whether the device meets its intended use and function. Validation is when a manufacturer determines whether it made the right product. Verification and validation are key points in the design control process during which feedback and iterative change happen. If either process results in failure (e.g., the device fails to achieve performance specifications or does not meet the user need), design control ensures the device process cycles back to a point where changes can be made and further testing can occur.

Figure 10-2. Design Control Process Required by FDA for Medical Device Design and Development (21 CFR § 820)

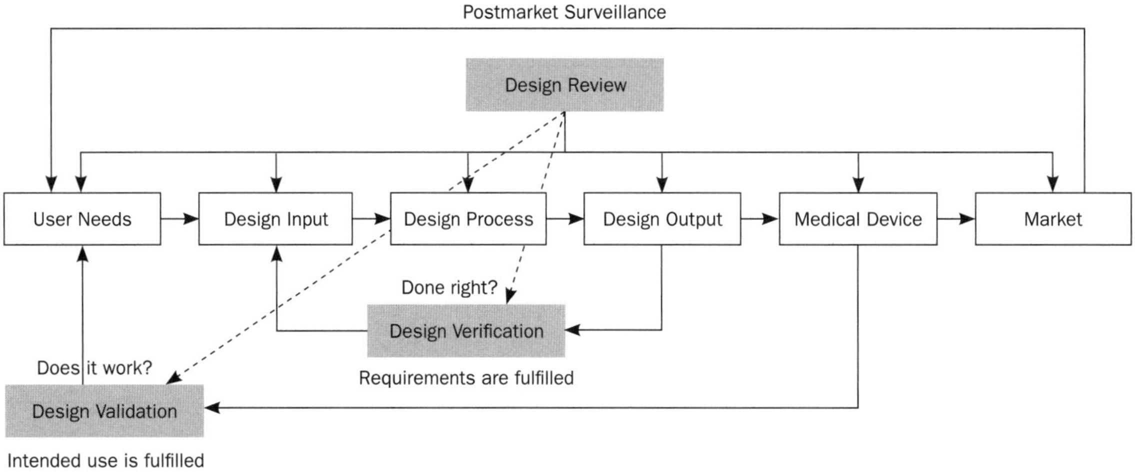

Design Transfer and Changes

Design transfer is the process by which final device specifications are transferred to manufacturing. How this transfer takes place should be detailed specifically in standard operating procedures (SOPs) that ensure information is transferred accurately between the development team and manufacturing.

Design Review

Pre-planned and documented design reviews must occur at stages throughout the design and development process. These reviews should be included in the design plan and attended by those responsible for the design stage being reviewed, at least one individual not responsible for the design stage being reviewed and anyone with specialized knowledge needed to thoroughly review the device design at that point. Design review meetings should be documented thoroughly.

Production and Process Controls

As part of device CGMP practices, manufacturers are required to conduct all manufacturing and production processes to ensure the final device meets specifications. Manufacturers are expected to establish, implement and maintain procedures, instructions, specifications, inspection criteria and methods under strict control to ensure each lot is manufactured uniformly. There also must be monitoring practices in place, such as in-process inspections, to ensure each product meets production specifications. Where appropriate, processes must conform to reference standards or codes. Whenever changes are made to a process, change control procedures must be followed.

Production and process control regulations also refer to facility and equipment controls. These include requirements for establishing and maintaining procedures to prevent equipment or product contamination if such contamination would affect device quality. Similarly, regulations require manufacturing sites to be located in buildings sufficient to achieve device manufacture to meet specifications and in compliance with the QSR. Equipment must be installed, inspected, calibrated and validated. This often is called "Installation Qualification, Operational Qualification, Process Qualification" or "IQ-OQ-PQ." Each piece of equipment must be qualified and calibrated when it is installed (IQ). Its ability to perform the function for which it was designed then must be validated (OQ). Finally, the manufacturing process it is to perform must be validated (PQ). Periodic inspections are required to ensure all equipment performs the function for which it is purposed to ensure devices are manufactured to specification. Equipment software also must be validated to ensure automated processes are functioning as intended. All of these activities must be planned and documented under a manufacturer's QMS.

Other regulations under this part include posting acceptable equipment and process tolerances visibly so operators can refer to them, making sure personnel follow cleanliness and behavior procedures in the manufacturing space, and implementing methods to remove manufacturing material that could affect device quality. Personnel also are required to be trained fully for the jobs they perform or supervised when working in specialized environments or conditions.

Acceptance Activities and Non-Conforming Product

Device CGMP regulations require manufacturers to establish procedures and criteria for acceptance activities associated with receiving, in-process and final inspections of product. Acceptance criteria must be objective criteria and may include testing, visual inspection or other means of establishing the product meets specifications. Receiving acceptance may apply when raw materials or components are received initially or when the device comes back to the manufacturer after being treated or sterilized, depending on the product's needs. In-process inspection occurs during the manufacturing process to ensure the device is being made to specification. Final acceptance occurs at the completion of the manufacturing process, when the decision is made as to whether the product is ready to be released to market.

Any product not meeting specifications is considered nonconforming product. FDA requires manufacturers to establish handling procedures for nonconforming products, which include means to identify nonconforming product as different from accepted product, designating space to quarantine nonconforming products and processes for reviewing nonconforming product for disposition. In addition, manufacturers must determine whether an investigation is necessary to identify the nonconformity's root and whether to initiate corrective or preventive action. All nonconforming product handling and disposition must be documented (see Device History Record below).

Labeling and Packaging Control

All device labeling and packaging must be controlled to ensure proper labels are affixed to each product and labels meet specifications and FDA requirements. In addition, labeling must be inspected for accuracy, contain all required information and be approved prior to product release. Labels are controlled documents and subject to change control. Further, manufacturers must ensure packaging and shipping containers will protect the device, allow for proper sterilization (when required) and maintain device integrity during processing, storage, handling and distribution.

CAPA

Corrective and preventive action (CAPA) is a critical component of the CGMP regulations and impacts all aspects of a device manufacturer's operations. CAPA is the means by which device manufacturers implement continuous improvement in operations, QMS compliance, device performance, manufacturing process function, personnel training, etc. An effective CAPA program can have a tremendous impact on a medical device manufacturer's compliance.

Under the QSR, a device manufacturer must establish, implement and maintain CAPA procedures and policies, including ongoing analysis of information from operations, complaints, records, published literature, management and design reviews, or any other quality information source about a company or its products. This information should be reviewed and analyzed statistically when possible to identify deficiencies or quality problems. Once a problem is identified, a CAPA procedures should be initiated. These may include establishing a CAPA team, conducting an investigation, running tests or gathering additional quality data from multiple sources. If CAPA corrective or preventive action is deemed necessary, the regulations require all actions be verified or validated to ensure the action corrects the problem effectively. Management review should be an integral part of a CAPA program; FDA expects activities to undergo management to review and approval. All CAPA-related actions, including trending reports, analyses, testing, meeting minutes and review, must be documented fully.

Complaint Handling

Proper product complaint handling is one of the few CGMP regulations required by all device manufacturers regardless of device class. All device manufacturers must have policies and procedures in place to handle product complaints. Each complaint must be reviewed to determine whether it must be reported to FDA under 21 CFR 803, Medical Device Reporting. In addition, each complaint must be evaluated to determine whether an investigation is necessary; if no investigation is needed, the rationale for this decision and the person responsible for the decision must be recorded in the complaint file. It is important to note proof a device was involved in a complaint does not need to be provided, only the possibility a device may have been involved in the complaint. Manufacturers must treat every complaint as though their device were involved and report to FDA if the complaint meets reporting requirements. FDA regulations are very specific about the details required for each complaint, including the context in which the device problem occurred, and whether the device failed to meet specifications, was in clinical use at the time the problem occurred, an investigation or a Medical Device Report (MDR) was required and any corrective or preventive action was needed.

Documentation

Each QSR section provides detailed expectations for the documentation level required for compliance. Every aspect of design and development, continuous improvement, review, complaint handling, training and any other device manufacturing activities must be documented. All quality system documents must be maintained per QSR requirements (**Figure 10-2**), and must be retained for a period of time equivalent to the design and device's expected life, but no less than two years. This record is the means by which all controlled documents are established, implemented, maintained, revised, reviewed, approved and distributed. Records should be accurate, complete, traceable and have dates and signatures. The QSR must be accessible easily for from locations controlled documents use is needed and to FDA should it come for an inspection. Documents should be kept in a safe place to prevent damage or loss.

In addition to the QSR, FDA requires three specific document assemblies to be compiled and maintained. These are the Design History File (DHF), the Device Master Record (DMR) and the Device History Record (DHR).

Design History File (DHF)

The DHF is the assembly of documents detailing a device's entire design and development process and demonstrating accordance with an approved design plan and product requirements. The DHF should document every design control step and should be readily accessible if FDA conducts an inspection. A device DHF should, at minimum, include multiple iterations of the design plan such as the development, design outputs and product specifications; verification and validation testing protocols and reports; processes evolved; evidence of design transfer; and design and review minutes. A DHF also may include drawings, equipment qualifications (IQ/OQ/PQ), labeling and packaging specifications and manufacturing process validations. Inspection and acceptance criteria for a specific device also may appear in a DHF. It is common for multiple iterations and revisions of each of the design and development step to appear in a DHF, thus documenting the cyclical design process expected under the design control regulations. For manufacturers marketing multiple devices, a DHF is expected for each device for which these regulations apply. Similarly, for devices marketed before QSR implementation in 1998, a retrospective DHF should be in place documenting to the best of the manufacturer's ability, the design and development history of each device is produced.

Device Master Record (DMR)

The DMR contains all the necessary information to manufacture a particular device. The DMR is the device recipe, containing all specifications and steps needed to achieve a finished device that conforms to all specifications and performance criteria. The DMR is created during the design transfer process (see Design Control). This assembly of documents should contain only the most recent and approved revisions of all procedures, work instructions, drawings, inspection and acceptance criteria, tolerances, equipment controls and settings and any other methods or procedures needed to manufacture the device. As such, the DMR must be updated and approved whenever changes are made.

Device History Record (DHR)

The DHR, also known as a lot or batch record, is a record of a specific device or device lot's manufacture. This record should include the date of products manufactured, travelers (documents showing the progression of the device through manufacturing steps), forms detailing in-process inspection and acceptance activities, detailed manufacturing information, copy of the label affixed to the device and/or device packaging, evidence of sterilization, if applicable, and final acceptance and approval for release to market. The DHR also must contain UDI information, when appropriate, and, in the case of surgical implants or devices that support or sustain life, full traceability data. In addition, the DHR must include the number of devices in the lot and of those passing final acceptance and released to market.

Other Device CGMP Requirements

A few additional requirements apply to medical device manufacture including regulations for device handling, storage, distribution and installation as well as servicing devices once they are installed. In addition, the QSR requires valid statistical techniques to be implemented, including the use of appropriate sampling plans and methods. Device manufacturers must determine which QSR parts apply to their products and establish appropriate compliance programs.

Pharmaceutical CGMP

Definitions

Per 21 CFR 210.3, drug product means a finished dosage form, e.g., tablet, capsule, solution, etc., that generally contains an active drug ingredient, but not necessarily, in association with inactive ingredients. The term also includes a finished dosage form that does not contain an active ingredient but is intended to be used as a placebo.

Active pharmaceutical ingredient (API) means any component intended to furnish pharmacological activity or other direct effect in the diagnosis, cure, mitigation, treatment or prevention of a disease, or to affect the structure or any function of the body of man or other animals. APIs also include those components that may undergo chemical change in the drug product's manufacture and be present in the drug product in a modified form intended to furnish the specified activity or effect.

A batch is a specific quantity of a drug or other material intended to have uniform character and quality, within specified limits, and produced according to a single manufacturing order during the same manufacturing cycle.

A lot refers to a batch, or a specific identified portion thereof, having uniform character and quality within specified limits; or, in case of a drug product produced by continuous process, a specific identified amount produced in a unit of time or quantity in a manner that ensures its uniform character and quality within specified limits.

Lot, control or batch number is any distinctive combination of letters, numbers, symbols or any combination of these, from which any drug product or other material's complete batch or lot manufacturing, processing, packing, holding and distribution history can be determined.

Strength is the drug substance's concentration (e.g., weight/weight, weight/volume, or unit dose/volume basis), and/or the drug product's potency (therapeutic activity) as indicated by appropriate laboratory tests or adequately developed and controlled clinical data (expressed, for example in terms of units by reference to a standard).

Organization and Personnel

A quality assurance (QA) unit is the group that is responsible for overseeing the administration and adherence to CGMPs within a pharmaceutical or biological facility. All quality-related drug product matters must be maintained by QA, including documents, internal audits, batch record reviews, vendor and supplier audits and proper stability and storage requirements. Complaint investigations also are under QA's purview.

Under CGMP, a quality control (QC) unit is required to be established (with written procedures) and has the responsibility and authority to approve or reject all components including drug products, containers, closures, in-process materials, packaging materials and labeling. Adequate laboratory facilities must be available for testing the items listed above. If procedures or specifications impact the drug product's identity, purity, strength or quality, the QC unit can approve or reject those procedures or specifications.

QA and QC form the quality unit for a pharmaceutical organization. The two entities can be one group, separate groups or a single individual or group, depending on the organization's size and structure.

Every person involved in drug product manufacture, processing, packing or holding must have the education, training and experience necessary to carry out their duties. Additionally, they must wear the correct personal protective equipment to ensure the drug product is free from contamination. Personnel with illnesses, open lesions or not practicing good hygiene habits will not be allowed access to or contact with drug products. It is imperative personnel follow all necessary steps and procedures to prevent drug product contamination.

Facilities and Equipment

Buildings and facilities should be located, designed and constructed to facilitate cleaning, maintenance and operations as appropriate for the manufacturing, packing, processing and holding type and stage. Adequate space must be available for the necessary equipment and materials to prevent mix-ups or contamination. Adequate cleaning and toilet facilities for personnel must be provided.

Equipment should be of an adequate size and design and be placed in the proper environment to ensure it works properly. Any part of the equipment that touches the drug product or API cannot be reactive, additive or absorptive. This ensures strength, purity, identity, safety and quality are not compromised. Equipment must be cleaned and maintained regularly to ensure proper function and prevent contamination issues.

Water

Any water used in drug product manufacture should meet drinking water standards, be free of contaminants and be tested to ensure it meets the required quality and purity standards. If drinking water does not meet standards, tighter microbiological and chemical specifications may be needed. If a treatment process is needed to ensure the specifications are met, it must be validated and monitored.

Air

Adequate ventilation, air filtration and exhaust systems should be provided in the manufacturing facility including any testing laboratories. These systems should be designed and constructed to minimize risks of contamination and cross-contamination. Equipment to ensure adequate control over air pressure, microorganisms, dust, humidity and temperature must be provided as appropriate for the drug product's manufacture, processing, packing or holding.

Air filtration systems, including pre-filters and particulate matter air filters, must be used on air supplied to all production areas. If recirculated air is used in production areas, measures must be taken to control recirculation of dust and other contaminants from production.

Sanitation and Cleaning

Any building used for drug product manufacture, packing, processing or holding must be maintained in a sanitary and clean condition. The facility should be free of infestation from rodents, birds, insects and other vermin. Trash and organic waste matter should be held and disposed of in a timely and sanitary manner.

Written sanitation procedures should be available including responsibilities and descriptions of cleaning schedules, methods, equipment and materials to be used in cleaning the buildings and facilities. Procedures should cover the usage of appropriate rodenticides, insecticides, fungicides, fumigating agents and cleaning and sanitizing agents. The procedures should describe how to prevent equipment, components, drug product containers, closures, packaging, labeling material and drug product contamination adequately. These procedures apply not only to employees but also to contractors and temporary staff.

Material System

Raw Materials

Written procedures should be in place describing materials' receipt, identification, quarantine, storage, handling, sampling, testing and approval or rejection. Raw materials should be purchased only from suppliers or vendors approved by the QA unit.

There should be a designated area to receive incoming raw materials. The raw materials should be inspected upon receipt to ensure the correct product has been delivered. Additionally, containers should be inspected for damage, broken seals and evidence of tampering or contamination. Tests should be performed on raw materials before they are mixed with existing stock. The certificate of analysis from the vendor or supplier can be used in lieu of testing as long as processes and procedures are in place at the manufacturing facility to ensure the the certificate is sufficient.

Containers and Closures

Written procedures should be in place that describe component receipt, identification, storage, handling, sampling, testing and approval or rejection and drug product containers and closures in sufficient detail. Components and drug product containers and closures should be handled at all times in a manner that prevents contamination.

Containers and closures should be identified by a unique code for each lot in each shipment that is used to record the disposition of each lot. Each lot shall be identified appropriately as quarantined, approved or rejected. Each lot of containers and closures should be withheld from use until the lot has been sampled, tested or examined, and released for use by the QC unit.

Drug product containers and closures should not be reactive, additive or absorptive as that may alter the drug's safety, purity, identity, strength or quality beyond the official or established requirements. Container closure systems should provide adequate protection against foreseeable external factors in storage and use that can cause drug product deterioration or contamination. If applicable, containers and closures should be sterilized and processed to remove pyrogenic properties to ensure they are suitable for their intended use. The sterilization and pyrogenic removal processes must be validated.

Production System

Batch Records

Batch production records should be prepared for each intermediate and API and include complete information relating to each batch's production and control. These records should be numbered with a unique batch or identification number, dated and signed when issued. Batch records may contain:

- identity of major equipment
- date and, if appropriate, times
- any sampling performed
- weights, measures and batch numbers of raw materials, intermediates or any reprocessed materials used during manufacturing
- signatures of personnel performing and directly supervising or checking each critical step in the operation
- actual yield
- release testing results

Packaging and Labeling System

Written procedures must be in place to describe packaging and labeling material receipt, identification, quarantine, sampling, examination and/or testing, release and handling. Packaging and labeling should adhere to established specifications. Records should be maintained for each shipment of labels and packaging materials showing receipt, examination or testing, and whether the shipment was accepted or rejected.

Label and packaging material storage areas should be limited to authorized personnel. Any obsolete or outdated labels should be destroyed. Excess labels bearing batch numbers or other batch-related printing should be destroyed. Labels or labeling materials for each drug product, strength, dosage form or quantity of contents shall be stored separately with appropriate identification.

Printing devices on or associated with manufacturing lines used to imprint labeling on drug product unit labels or cases shall be monitored to ensure all imprinting conforms to the print specified in the batch production record. Strict control must be exercised over labeling issued for use in drug product labeling operations.

Laboratory Control System

Establishment of specifications, standards, sampling plans, test procedures or other required laboratory control mechanisms must be reviewed and approved by the QC unit. Laboratory controls should include scientifically sound and appropriate specifications, standards, sampling plans, and test procedure designed to ensure components, drug product containers, closures, in-process materials, labeling and drug products conform to appropriate identity, strength, quality, and purity standards.

Instruments, apparatus, gauges and recording devices must be calibrated at appropriate intervals in accordance with established written procedures containing specific directions, schedules, limits of accuracy and precision, and provisions for remedial action in the event accuracy and/or precision limits are not met. If the instruments, apparatus, gauges and recording devices do not meet established specifications they cannot be used.

Method Validation

Any test (including in-process control tests) or analytical method used must be validated. Written procedures describing how to conduct method validation for the specific tests also should contain acceptance criteria for the results. Typically, a method validation protocol or procedure will contain all the information necessary to perform the method validation. If the test results do not meet the predefined acceptance criteria set out in the protocol or procedure, the test fails. Retesting can be conducted only if the validation protocol or procedure that provides guidance on restesting steps.

If the analytical method being used is included in a relevant pharmacopoeia or recognized standard reference then method validation does not need to be conducted.

However, the suitability of the test method used should be verified under actual use conditions and documented.

Stability Testing

A written testing program designed to assess the drug product's stability characteristics must be established. Stability testing results shall be used to determine appropriate storage conditions and expiration dates. The written testing program should include:

- sample size and test intervals based on statistical criteria for each attribute examined to ensure valid stability estimates
- storage conditions for samples retained for testing
- reliable, meaningful and specific methods
- drug product testing in the same container-closure system as that in which the drug product is marketed
- drug product testing for reconstitution at the time of dispensing (as directed in the labeling) as well as after they are reconstituted

The number of drug product batches shall be tested to determine an appropriate expiration date and a record of such data shall be maintained. Accelerated studies, combined with basic stability information on the components, drug products and container-closure system, may be used to support tentative expiration dates if full shelf-life studies are not available and are being conducted.

Training

As mentioned above all personnel involved in any aspect of drug product manufacturing must be trained to perform their specific job functions and tasks. Personnel should not conduct any tests without proper training on the instrumentation and methods to be used. Training must be documented and reviewed by an authorized person.

Records

Master Production

To ensure uniformity from batch to batch, master production instructions for each intermediate and API should be prepared, dated and signed by one person and independently checked, dated and signed by a person in the QA unit. Master production records should contain:

- name of the intermediate or API being manufactured and an identifying document reference code
- complete list of raw materials and intermediates designated by names or codes sufficiently specific to identify any special quality characteristics
- production location and major production equipment to be used
- where appropriate, special notations and precautions to be followed, or cross-references to them
- instructions for intermediate of API storage to ensure its suitability for use, including the labeling and packaging materials and special storage conditions with time limits, if applicable

Distribution

These records should contain the product's name and strength and description of dosage form, consignee name and address, date and quantity shipped and the drug product's lot or control number.

Complaint Files

Written procedures describing how all written and oral drug product complaints are handled must be established and followed. The procedures should contain review provisions for the QC unit of any complaint involving a drug product's possible failure to meet any of its specifications and, for such drug products, a determination as to the need for an investigation. Complaint records should contain:

- complainant's name and address
- name, title (if applicable) and phone number of the person submitting the complaint
- complaint nature (include the API name and batch number)
- date the manufacturer, agent or manufacturer employee receives the complaint
- action initially taken (including dates and identity of the person taking the action)
- any follow-up action taken
- responses provided to the complaint originator (including the date the response was sent)
- final decision on the intermediate or API batch or lot

Complaint records should be retained to evaluate trends, product-related frequencies and severity, with a view to taking additional and, if appropriate, immediate corrective action.

Additionally, written procedures should define the circumstances under which an intermediate or drug product recall should be considered. The procedure should designate who should evaluate the information, how a recall should be initiated, who should be informed and how the recalled material should be disposed.

Investigational Use Only

Investigational use only (IUO) drug products and biologics are not required to be manufactured according to 21 CFR 211 if used in a Phase 1 clinical trial. Because a Phase 1 clinical trial initially introduces an investigational new drug into human subjects, appropriate CGMPs must be applied to assure subject safety. Therefore, IUO products are required to comply with GMP requirements in Section 501(a)(2)(B) of the *Federal Food, Drug, and Cosmetic Act*. However, drug products to be used in Phase 2 and Phase 3 trials are subject to 21 CFR 210 and 21 CFR 211. In addition, any already approved drug or biologic used in a Phase 1 clinical trial must comply with 21 CFR 210 and 21 CFR 211.

Adherence to CGMPs during Phase 1 IUO drug manufacture occurs mostly through:

- well-defined written procedures
- adequately controlled equipment and manufacturing environment
- accurately and consistently recorded data from manufacturing (including testing)

Methods, facilities and manufacturing controls must be in place to meet the appropriate standards for IUO product identity, safety, purity, strength and quality. The important GMP aspects that should be adapted for IUO products are:

- personnel
- QC function
- facility and equipment
- component, containers and closure control
- manufacturing and records
- laboratory controls (including testing and stability)
- packaging, labeling and distribution
- recordkeeping

Chemistry, manufacturing and controls (CMC) information must be submitted to FDA as part of an Investigational New Drug (IND) application. FDA will determine whether the IUO drug or biologic to be used in a Phase 1 clinical trial is sufficiently safe to permit the trial to proceed. The agency can conduct an inspection if insufficient information is submitted in the IND to allow it to determine the risks to clinical trial subjects or if clinical trial subjects could be subjected to unreasonable and significant risk. A manufacturer's or sponsor's clinical trial could be put on hold or the IND could be terminated if sufficient information concerning the IUO drug or biologic's CMC is not provided in the IND.

Biologics CGMP

Definitions

The term "biological product" is defined in Section 351(i)(1) of the *PHS Act* to mean:

> "a virus, therapeutic serum, toxin, antitoxin, vaccine, blood, blood component or derivative, allergenic product, protein (except any chemically synthesized polypeptide), or analogous product, or arsphenamine or derivative of arsphenamine (or any other trivalent organic arsenic compound), applicable to the prevention, treatment, or cure of a disease or condition of human beings."

General Information

The GMP requirements discussed above also applicable to biologics and biotechnology products. However, because biologic products are made from living organisms, additional GMP requirements specific to biologics apply. This is true especially when using live viruses, spore-forming microorganisms and animals to manufacture a biologic product. Ensuring facilities are well maintained and do not promote contamination is extremely important as are animal care and handling. Adequate space to quarantine animals and perform necropsy is equally essential. It is critical that these areas separate from the actual manufacturing or processing areas and equipment. GMP requirements specific to biologics are discussed below.

Personnel

Personnel working with pathogenic viruses or spore-forming microorganisms for man who are engaged in the care of animals or animal quarters should be excluded from areas where other products are manufactured, or shall change outer clothing, including shoes, or wear protective covering prior to entering such areas.

Personnel cannot enter live vaccine processing areas if they have been working with other infectious agents during the same workday. Only personnel actually performing culture propagation, vaccine production and unit maintenance should be allowed in the live vaccine processing area. Personnel caring for animals used in the live vaccine manufacture are excluded from other animal quarters and from contact with other animals during the same working day.

Plant and Facilities

As stated above, all equipment, manufacturing facilities and structures must be of a size and construction conducive to the product being manufactured. Additionally, manufacturing facilities must have proper air handling (i.e., ventilation, exhaust system) and water. For biologics manufacturing, the ventilation system must be arranged to prevent dissemination of microorganisms from one manufacturing area to another and to avoid other conditions affecting product safety. Cleaning procedures must ensure that airborne contaminants are minimized.

Laboratory and Bleeding Rooms

Any room used for product processing, including bleeding rooms, must be fly-proofed and kept free of vermin. The rooms should be constructed to ensure no dust, smoke or other deleterious substances are present and to permit thorough cleaning and disinfection.

Animal Quarters and Stables

Animal quarters, stables and food storage must be of appropriate construction, fly-proofed, adequately lighted and ventilated, and maintained in a clean, vermin-free and sanitary condition.

There must be sufficient personnel caring for animals to ensure adequate care. The animals must be inspected daily if they are used in production to check of any ill effects of the production. If an animal falls ill, it must be quarantined and cannot be used for production until its recovery is complete.

Any cases of actual or suspected infection with foot and mouth disease, glanders, tetanus, anthrax, gas gangrene, equine infection anemia, equine encephalomyelitis or any of the pock diseases among animals intended for manufacture or used in manufacture of products require the manufacturer to notify the directors of both CBER and CDER.

Spore-Forming Microorganisms

Some spore-forming microorganisms are used as controls in the sterilization process. They can be introduced only into manufacturing facility areas where they will be used and only immediately prior to being used. They cannot be pathogenic to man or animals and cannot produce pyrogens or toxins. Steps must be taken to avoid spore contamination of other manufacturing facility areas.

GMP for Blood and Blood Components

Definitions

21 CFR 606.3 describes blood as whole blood collected from a single donor and process either for transfusion or further manufacturing. A component is the part of a single donor's blood separated by physical or mechanical means.

Personnel

GMPs require that all personnel, regardless of the product being manufactured, to have the necessary education, experience and training to perform their specific job duties. There is no exception for manufacturing blood or blood components.

Equipment

A table in In 21 CFR 606.60(b) details the frequency for observing, standardizing and calibrating different types of equipment.

Supplies and Reagents

As discussed earlier, GMPs require supplies to be stored in a safe, sanitary and orderly manner. Additionally, any surface that comes into contact with blood and blood components intended for transfusion must be sterile, pyrogen-free and cannot interact with the product in a manner that would adversely affect its safety, purity, potency or effectiveness. Blood collection containers should be examined for seal breakage, abnormal discoloration or any other defects. If defects are noted, then containers cannot be used.

Certain reagents and solutions used in manufacturing blood and blood components must be tested on a regularly scheduled basis per the manufacturers SOPs to determine their capacity to perform as required. The list of reagents and solutions with testing frequency is contained in 21 CFR 606.65(c).

Production and Process Controls

Standard Operating Procedures

Medical device, pharmaceutical and biologic GMPs are require the manufacturing facility to have written procedures in place for QC, methods, testing and labeling. These procedures are required for manufacturers of blood and blood components as well. For these specific products, which will be used in transfusion and further manufacturing purposes, written procedures must cover collection, processing, compatibility testing, storage and distribution. They also need to cover consignee notification of test results of tests (HIV or HCV) on donor blood, notification of the transfusion recipient's physician of record or legal representative and for donor deferral.

Labeling

Special Labeling

There are a number of uses for blood and blood components; therefore, the labeling requirements reflect the products' uniqueness. The usual labeling information (i.e., product name, expiration date, etc.) applies to these products, but other information is required depending on the product's after manufacture. For example, if the product will not be used for transfusion, the following statement must be present on the label, "Caution: For Manufacturing Use Only" or "Caution; For Use in Manufacturing Noninjectable Products Only."

Circular of Information

This document must be available for distribution if the product is intended for transfusion. It must contain adequate instructions for use. Additional information required in a circular of information can be found at 21 CFR 606.122.

Laboratory Control System

Laboratory Controls

Laboratory controls described above for pharmaceutical products also apply to these products. Scientifically sound and appropriate standards and test procedures must be established.

Compatibility Testing

Compatibility testing must be performed according to written and approved SOPs. A method for collecting and identifying recipients' blood samples to ensure positive identification must be in place. There also should be a procedure to expedite transfusion in life-threatening emergencies.

Records

Donor Records

While not inclusive, the following information is required to be collected:

- donor selection, including medical interview, examination and, if necessary, informed consent
- donor adverse reaction complaints and reports, including results of all investigations and follow-up
- immunization, including informed consent, identification of the antigen, dosage and route of administration
- records to relate the donor with the unit number of each previous donation from that donor

Other Records

Other types of records the manufacturer must maintain for blood or blood components per GMP are: processing, storage and distribution, compatibility, quality control and general records.

Adverse Event Files

Per 21 CFR 606.170, records shall be maintained of any adverse reaction complaint reports regarding each unit of blood or blood product arising as a result of blood collection or transfusion. A thorough investigation of each reported adverse reaction is required.

If a complication of blood collection or transfusion results in a fatality, CBER must be notified immediately with a written report detailing the investigation to follow within seven days.

Summary

FDA CGMP regulations exist to ensure the safety and effectiveness of all pharmaceutical, biologic and medical device products manufactured and commercialized in the US. The importance of compliance with these regulations cannot be minimized. Quite simply, failure to adhere to CGMP requirements results in adulterated product, and puts public health at risk. Compliance with all CGMP regulations is the responsibility of every manufacturer that commercializes pharmaceutical, biologic and medical device products in the US. QMS process and procedure establishment, implementation and maintenance must be management priorities to ensure a culture of compliance exists at all levels within their organizations.

As regulations change, it is imperative manufacturers stay informed and have regulatory intelligence operations to provide timely updates to leadership and compliance teams. Training personnel training on the importance of and requirements for operating in a CGMP environment will ensure everyone understands their roles in the compliance program. Attention to process and procedure validation is critical, as are the timely identification of and response to deviations and failures. Continuous improvement activities following internal audits, CAPA activities and FDA inspections will help ensure all products are manufactured under the "quality-by-design" objectives of these regulations.

References

1. FDA. *Guidance for Industry: Quality Systems Approach to Pharmaceutical CGMP Regulations* (September 2006). FDA website. http://www.fda.gov/downloads/Drugs/.../Guidances/UCM070337.pdf Accessed 27 May 2015.
2. FDA. *Guidance for Industry: Quality Systems Approach to Pharmaceutical CGMP Regulations* (September 2006). http://www.fda.gov/downloads/Drugs/.../Guidances/UCM070337.pdf Accessed 27 May 2015.
3. FDA. *Design Control Guidance for Medical Device Manufacturers* (11 March 1997).FDA website. http://www.fda.gov/RegulatoryInformation/Guidances/ucm070627.htm. Accessed 27 May 2015.

Chapter 11

FDA User Fees

By Allison C. Komiyama, PhD, RAC

OBJECTIVES

- ❑ Provide background of user fee programs and their origins
- ❑ Provide overview of individual FDA user fee programs
- ❑ Define user fee requirements

LAWS, REGULATIONS AND GUIDANCES COVERED IN THIS CHAPTER

- ❑ *Prescription Drug User Fee Act* of 1992
- ❑ *Food and Drug Administration Safety and Innovation Act* of 2012
- ❑ *Medical Device User Fee Modernization Act* of 2002
- ❑ *Medical Device User Fee Amendments* of 2007
- ❑ *Generic Drug User Fee Amendments* of 2012
- ❑ *Biosimilar User Fee Act* of 2012
- ❑ *Animal Drug User Fee Act* of 2003
- ❑ *Animal Generic Drug User Fee Act* of 2008
- ❑ 21 CFR 80.10 *Fees for certification services*
- ❑ *Family Smoking Prevention and Tobacco Control Act* of 2009
- ❑ *Food Safety Modernization Act* of 2011
- ❑ *Freedom of Information Act* of 1966
- ❑ *Drug Quality and Security Act* of 2013
- ❑ *Mammography Quality Standards Act* of 1992
- ❑ 21 CFR 1150 User Fees

Introduction

Congress has authorized the US Food and Drug Administration (FDA) to collect user fees to supplement its federally appropriated funds. Most of the submissions FDA reviews require user fee payment before they are processed. In addition, prescription drugs, biologics and medical device manufacturers are required to pay an establishment registration fee before marketing their products. FDA's Office of Financial Management (OFM) is responsible for administering the user fee programs. OFM maintains an accounts receivable system used for user fee invoicing, collections, reporting and data maintenance.

User fees are collected with the following goals:

- to augment FDA resources
- to improve the efficiency and timeliness of the review/approval process
- to hold FDA responsible for maintaining performance goals and timelines
- to increase interaction between FDA and sponsors, and enhance transparency during the review process

Background of User Fees

FDA user fees originated from the accumulated frustrations of consumers, industry and FDA itself. Each group recognized the length of time it took to move a drug or biologic marketing application through the agency was steadily on the rise. The process had become unpredictable and slow, forcing patients to wait for access to products and delaying manufacturers in recovering their development costs. In the late 1980s, FDA reported the average time from submission to decision was 29 months.[1] It was estimated that each one-month delay cost the manufacturer an average of $10 million.[2]

For many years, FDA had been unsuccessful in petitioning Congress to grant it the power to require user fees from industry. FDA argued it had not received sufficient funds to hire more reviewers to sift through the backlog and review incoming submissions. Industry generally opposed user fees, assuming the additional revenue simply would be used to reduce the federal debt instead of improve the review process.

In 1992, the *Prescription Drug User Fee Act* (*PDUFA*) was enacted when FDA and industry finally agreed on two key provisions: 1) there would be target completion times, or performance goals, for FDA on select review processes; and 2) the user fees would supplement, instead of replace, FDA's congressional funding. These provisions gave FDA the funding it needed to hire new staff and gave industry hope the review times would be significantly reduced.

In the first five years after *PDUFA* was enacted, the median total approval time for New Drug Applications (NDAs) and Biological License Applications (BLAs) decreased from 29 months to 15.[3] In addition, the backlog of applications from the pre-*PDUFA* years was eliminated, and the number of staff devoted to the drug review process increased from 1,300 to 2,000.[4] It was widely agreed the user fee program was a success for both industry and FDA. To provide feedback on the program's performance, *PDUFA* requires FDA to submit two annual reports to the president and Congress for each fiscal year: 1) a performance report; and 2) a financial report. The performance report outlines FDA's ability to meet annual *PDUFA* goals, while the financial report illustrates program activities, collections and spending.

Since 1992, user fees have been expanded to include other products beyond prescription drugs and biologics. User fee programs now include medical devices, generic drugs, biosimilars and animal drugs. Funds also are collected now for a variety of initiatives to allow FDA to recover costs or to spearhead new programs. These fees include mammography facility fees to pay for routine inspections and tobacco product fees to provide new regulatory authority.

User fee programs are evaluated annually and are subject to reauthorization by Congress every five years. A brief history of each program and a description of the most current versions are discussed in the following sections. More information about FDA user fees is available at www.fda.gov/ForIndustry/UserFees/.

Principal User Fee Programs

Prescription Drug User Fee Act

Every five years, *PDUFA* has been reauthorized with new goals: *PDUFA II* (Fiscal 1997–2002) focused on reducing application review time; *PDUFA III* (Fiscal 2003–07) focused on refining the drug development to application review to postmarket surveillance process; *PDUFA IV* (Fiscal 2008–12) focused on enhancing overall drug safety. On 9 July 2012, President Obama signed the *Food and Drug Administration Safety and Innovation Act* (*FDASIA*) into law, which included the reauthorization and expansion of *PDUFA* (Fiscal 2013–17) as well as other user fees described in the following sections. FDA established the *PDUFA V* proposals with input from drug industry representatives, patient and consumer advocates, healthcare professionals and other public stakeholders. *PDUFA V* continued the rigorous performance goals established under *PDUFA IV*, such as modernizing postapproval safety monitoring and expanding FDA's role in risk evaluation and mitigation. In addition, *PDUFA V* added new programs to enhance the review of new molecular entities and biologics, and increased the utilization of the electronic submissions system.

Medical Device User Fee Modernization Act/Medical Device User Fee Amendments

On 26 October 2002, the *Medical Device User Fee Modernization Act* (*MDUFMA I*) was signed into law. It was enacted for similar reasons as *PDUFA* almost a decade earlier, to provide FDA with additional resources to ensure adequate submission reviews. The ultimate goal was to help bring safe and effective medical devices to market in a more-timely manner. In particular, *MDUFMA I* incorporated user fees for medical device applications, allowed establishment inspections to be conducted by accredited third parties, created new requirements for reprocessed single-use devices and designated performance goals for decisions and review times. The *Medical Device User Fee Amendments* of 2007 (*MDUFA II,* Fiscal 2008–12) established more rigorous FDA performance goals and required a performance report and financial report (similar to *PDUFA* requirements) be submitted to Congress annually. *FDASIA* included the reauthorization of *MDUFA* (*MDUFA III*, Fiscal 2013–17), again committing the agency to certain performance goals (which will increase each year of the program), and vowing to improve the overall review experience for industry.

Generic Drug User Fee Amendments

The *Generic Drug User Fee Amendments* of 2012 (*GDUFA*) began a new program included in the *FDASIA* legislation.

Table 11-1 Cost of Principal User Fee Programs for Fiscal 2014 and Fiscal 2015*

Activity	Fiscal 2014	Fiscal 2015
***PDUFA V*[5]**		
• New Drug Application (With Clinical Data)	$2,169,100	$2,335,200
• New Drug Application (Without Clinical Data)	$1,084,550	$1,167,600
• New Drug Application Supplement (With Clinical Data)	$1,084,550	$1,167,600
• New Drug Application Establishment	$554,600	$569,200
• Annual Product Registration	$104,060	$110,370
***MDUFA III*[6]**		
• Premarket Application	$258,520	$250,895
• Product Development Protocol	$258,520	$250,598
• Biologics Licensing Application	$258,520	$250,598
• Premarket Report	$258,520	$250,598
• Biologics Licensing Application Efficacy Supplement	$258,520	$250,598
• Panel-Track Supplement	$193,890	$188,171
• 180-Day Supplement	$38,778	$37,634
• Real-Time Supplement	$18,096	$17,563
• 510(k) Premarket Notification Submission	$5,170	$5,018
• 30-Day Notice	$4,136	$4,014
• 513(g) Request for Classification Information	$3,490	$3,387
• Annual Fee for Class III Device	$9,048	$8,781
• Annual Establishment Registration	$3,313	$3,646
GDUFA[7]		
• Abbreviated New Drug Application	$63,860	$58,730
• Prior Approval Supplement	$31,930	$29,370
• Drug Master File	$31,460	$26,720
• Finished Dosage Form Facility (Domestic)	$220,152	$247,717
• Finished Dosage Form Facility (Foreign)	$235,152	$262,717
• Active Pharmaceutical Ingredient Facility (Domestic)	$34,515	$41,926
• Active Pharmaceutical Ingredient Facility (Foreign)	$49,515	$56,926
BsUFA[8]		
• Biosimilar Application (Requiring Clinical Data)	$2,169,100	$2,335,200
• Biosimilar Application (Not Requiring Clinical Data)	$1,084,550	$1,167,600
• Biosimilar Supplement (Requiring Clinical Data)	$1,084,550	$1,167,600
• Biological Product Development (Initial)	$216,910	$233,520
• Biological Product Development (Annual)	$216,910	$233,520
• Biological Product Development (Reactivation)	$433,820	$467,040
• Establishment Fee	$554,600	$569,200
• Product Fee	$104,060	$110,370
***ADUFA III*[9]**		
• Animal Drug Application (New)	$396,600	$400,600
• Animal Drug Application (Supplement)	$198,300	$200,300
• Animal Drug Product Fee	$9,075	$8,075
• Animal Drug Establishment Fee	$105,800	$104,150
• Animal Drug Sponsor Fee	$101,150	$94,450
***AGDUFA II*[10]**		
• Abbreviated Application Fee for Generic New Animal Drug [except those subject to the criteria in section 512(d)(4)]	$177,900	$189,200
• Abbreviated Application Fee for Generic New Animal Drug [those subject to the criteria in section 512(d)(4)]	$88,950	$94,600
• Generic New Animal Drug Product Fee	$8,035	$8,500
• Sponsor Fee (Seven or More Approved Products)	$72,800	$80,900
• Sponsor Fee (Two to Six Approved Products)	$54,600	$60,675
• Sponsor Fee (One or Fewer Approved Products)	$36,400	$40,450

*Discounted rates are available to some sponsors that receive a small-business designation or are first-time filers.

It was designed to speed access to safe and effective generic drugs to the public and reduce costs to industry. Using the success of *PDUFA* as its model, the law requires industry to pay user fees to supplement the costs of reviewing generic drug applications. Two of the key goals are to reduce the backlog of current applications and decrease the overall time required for a decision. Additionally, *GDUFA* aims to endorse the consistency and increase the frequency of inspections for both domestic and foreign facilities. With this added focus on inspections, FDA hopes to enhance the safety of the global supply chain for generic drugs.

Biosimilar User Fee Act

On 23 March 2010, President Obama signed the *Affordable Care Act* into law, which contained a subtitle called the *Biologics Price Competition and Innovation Act* (*BPCI Act*). The *BPCI Act* amended the *Public Health Service Act* to create an abbreviated licensure pathway for products shown to be "biosimilar to" or "interchangeable with" an existing FDA-licensed biological product. The resulting *Biosimilar User Fee Act* (*BsUFA*) was enacted as part of *FDASIA* and allows FDA to collect fees for the efficient review of biosimilar submissions and to facilitate development of these products. FDA requires that these biosimilar and interchangeable biological products meet the same standards as their FDA-approved reference products. Key goals of *BsUFA* include outlining application review timelines for manufacturers, reviewing proprietary names to reduce medication errors, quickly resolving any major disputes and meeting management objectives.

Animal Drug User Fee Act

The *Animal Drug User Fee Act* of 2003 (*ADUFA I*) was enacted on 18 November 2003 and authorized FDA to collect fees to build and modernize the animal drug review program. Similar to other user fee programs, under *ADUFA I* (Fiscal 2004–08), FDA was required to meet specific performance goals to demonstrate improvement in the timeliness and predictability of the new animal drug review process. During the first five years of the program, FDA was able not only to reduce the review time of New Animal Drug Applications but also eliminate the backlog of submissions. With *ADUFA II* (Fiscal 2009–13), FDA enhanced the review process by enabling sponsors to use an electronic submission tool, allowing amendments to pending submissions if minor changes were necessary (called the "End-Review Amendment" or ERA), and developing processes to simplify scheduling and conduct preapproval inspections of foreign facilities. *ADUFA III* (Fiscal 2014–18) made only minor refinements to the *ADUFA II* goals, namely focusing on phasing out the ERA process by allowing "resubmissions" and "reactivations" of files that had been deemed incomplete.

Animal Generic Drug User Fee Act

President Obama signed the *Animal Generic Drug User Fee Act* (*AGDUFA I*) into law on 14 August 2008. FDA agreed to meet specific performance goals to reduce the review time for generic animal drug submissions. By improving the approval of submissions and eliminating its backlog, FDA also was able to provide quicker access to safe and effective animal drugs at lower cost for both farmers and pet owners. In 2013, *AGDUFA II* (Fiscal 2014–18) was reauthorized; it aimed to sustain the core goals of *AGDUFA I* with setting predictable review times, scheduling meetings in a timely manner and maintaining work queue procedures. FDA also agreed to work on more-timely foreign preapproval inspections, decrease review times for certain resubmissions and reactivations and develop a question-based review (QbR) process for bioequivalence submissions. The goal is to have the QbR process implemented by the end of Fiscal 2016 to allow FDA to answer critical scientific and regulatory review questions regarding animal generic drug product quality.

Other User Fee Programs

FDA also has the right to collect specific fees to spearhead new programs and recover costs for personnel, equipment, supplies, printing and overhead.

Color Additive Certification Fee

Under the *Food, Drug, and Cosmetic Act* (*FD&C Act*), color additives intended for use in FDA-regulated products are subject to batch certification by the agency. Fees for color certification are set forth in 21 CFR 80.10 *Fees for certification services.*

Export Certificate Fee

US companies that export products often are asked by foreign customers to supply a certificate for their FDA-regulated product. This certificate is prepared by FDA and contains information about the product's regulatory or marketing status. Under provisions in the *FD&C Act*, FDA is authorized to collect user fees for these certificates.

Family Smoking Prevention and Tobacco Control Act Fee

The *Family Smoking Prevention and Tobacco Control Act* of 2009 (*FSPTCA*) granted FDA the authority to regulate tobacco products. 21 CFR 1150 allows FDA to collect user fees from manufacturers and importers of tobacco products. *FSPTCA* (Fiscal 2009–18), and the funds generated helped establish FDA's Center for Tobacco Products.

Food Safety Modernization Act Fee

The *FDA Food Safety Modernization Act* (*FSMA*) enables FDA to collect funds, with the goal of preventing food safety problems before they occur. *FSMA* provides FDA with new enforcement authority designed to improve food safety standards, order food recalls and hold imported foods to the same standards as domestic foods.

Freedom of Information Act Fee

The *Freedom of Information Act* of 1966 (*FOIA*) allowed for the full or partial disclosure of previously unreleased information and documents controlled by the US government. *FOIA* fees for services provided, paid by the requestor, are outlined in 15 CFR 4.11 *Fees.*

Human Drug Compounding Outsourcing Facility Fees

The *Drug Quality and Security Act* of 2013 (*DQSA*) added Section 503B(d)(4) to the *FD&C Act,* creating a category of entities called "*outsourcing facilities.*" Drugs compounded in these facilities are not exempt from current Good Manufacturing Practices for drugs, and an annual establishment fee must be paid.

Mammography Quality Standards Act Fee

The *Mammography Quality Standards Act* of 1992 (*MQSA*) was enacted to help regulate the quality of mammography facilities and to ensure compliance with quality standards. Under *MQSA*, FDA is allowed to assess and collect fees from facilities to cover the costs of facility inspections.

Guidelines on Paying User Fees

To pay the appropriate FDA user fee, a cover sheet must be created with the necessary information to determine whether a fee is required. These cover sheets can be accessed at www.fda.gov/ForIndustry/UserFees/default.htm. A user name and password are required to proceed. Sponsors can pay online using a credit card or electronic check or they can pay by check via mail. If a sponsor receives an invoice in the mail for outstanding FDA fees, the same link can be used to access and pay the invoice online.

Summary

FDA's user fee programs are intended to help the agency fulfill its mission of protecting the public health while helping advance medical innovations. FDA is allowed to mandate user fees based on laws enacted by Congress, the first of which, *PDUFA*, was passed in 1992. These fees enable FDA to supplement its federally appropriated funds to augment FDA resources. These resources often can involve hiring additional staff, generating new guidance literature for industry, introducing public outreach initiatives and designing training programs to improve the quality of review standards. User fees have enabled FDA to improve the predictability, consistency and transparency of its review processes. Both industry and FDA believe these improvements have given the American people quicker access to safe and effective new medical technologies.

References

1. Food and Drug Administration (FDA), *Third Annual Performance Report: Prescription Drug User Fee Act of 1992, Fiscal Year 1995 Report to Congress* (1 December 1995).
2. Hilts PJ. "Plan to Speed Approval of Drugs: Makers Would Pay Fees to U.S.," *The New York Times*, 11 August 1992.
3. Calculations based on data from US Food and Drug Administration, "CDER Approval Times for Priority and Standard NDAs and BLAs Calendar Years 1993–2008."
4. Food and Drug Administration (FDA), White Paper, *Prescription Drug User Fee Act (PDUFA): Adding Resources and Improving Performance in FDA Review of New Drug Applications.*
5. "Prescription Drug User Fee Rates for Fiscal Year 2015," 79 *Federal Register* 44807 (1 August 2014), pp. 44807–44811.
6. "Medical Device User Fee Rates for Fiscal Year 2015," 79 *Federal Register* 44178 (30 July 2014), pp. 44178–44184.
7. "Generic Drug User Fee-Abbreviated New Drug Application, Prior Approval Supplement, Drug Master File, Final Dosage Form Facility, and Active Pharmaceutical Ingredient Facility Fee Rates for Fiscal Year 2015," 79 *Federal Register* 44797 (1 August 2014), pp. 44797–44800.
8. "Biosimilar User Fee Rates for Fiscal Year 2015," 79 *Federal Register* 44795 (1 August 2014), pp. 44795–44797.
9. "Animal Drug User Fee Rates and Payment Procedures for Fiscal Year 2015," 79 *Federal Register* 44787 (1 August 2014), pp. 44787–44792.
10. "Animal Generic Drug User Fee Rates and Payment Procedures for Fiscal Year 2015," 79 *Federal Register* 44792 (1 August 2014), pp. 44792–44795.

Chapter 12

Regulatory Strategy

By Maje Babatola, MS, RAC and Naseem Kabir, MS, RAC (US & EU)

OBJECTIVES

- ❑ Understand the definition of regulatory strategy
- ❑ Understand how to develop a regulatory strategy
- ❑ Learn the tools available to help develop a regulatory strategy
- ❑ Understand the role of the regulatory strategist or scientist within a pharmaceutical or medical device company

REGULATIONS AND GUIDELINES COVERED IN THIS CHAPTER

- ❑ 21 CFR 312 Investigational New Drug Application
- ❑ 21 CFR 314 Applications for FDA Approval of New Drug
- ❑ 21 CFR 601 Licensing
- ❑ 21 CFR 316 Orphan Drugs
- ❑ ICH, *Q8 (R2) Pharmaceutical Development,* November 2009
- ❑ *Guidance for Industry and Review Staff: Target Product Profile—A Strategic Development Process Tool—Draft Guidance* (March 2007)
- ❑ *Guidance for Industry: Labeling for Human Prescription Drug and Biological Products—Implementing the PLR Content and Format Requirements* (February 13)
- ❑ *Guidance for Industry: Dosage and Administration Section of Labeling for Human Prescription Drug and Biological Products—Content and Format* (March 2010)
- ❑ *Guidance for Industry: Warnings and Precautions, Contraindications, and Boxed Warning Sections of Labeling for Human Prescription Drug and Biologic Products—Content and Format* (October 2011)
- ❑ *Guidance for Industry: Labeling for Human Prescription Drug and Biological Products Approved Under the Accelerated Approval Regulatory Pathway* (March 2014)
- ❑ *Guidance for Industry and Review Staff and Food and Drug Administration Staff: The 510(k) Program: Evaluating Substantial Equivalence in Premarket Notifications [510(k)]* (July 2014)
- ❑ *Guidance for Industry: Expedited Programs for Serious Conditions—Drugs and Biologics* (May 2014)
- ❑ *Guidance for Industry: How to Comply with the Pediatric Research Equity Act* (September 2005)
- ❑ *Guidance for Industry: Patient-Reported Outcome Measures: Use in Medical Product Development to Support Labeling Claims* (December 2009)

Introduction

Numerous definitions of "strategy" are available on the Internet, and many books have been written on the topic (a classic example is *Art of War,* Sun Tzu). Broadly defined, strategy is a holistic and proactive plan developed to prepare for and perform a project or to address and resolve a problem, so it achieves the predefined desired outcomes successfully. Developing a strategy involves analyzing problems or projects from a broad perspective and identifying solutions and a plan to accomplish them, while at the same time creating opportunities and taking full advantage of the possibilities and options that present themselves. A good strategy articulates a credible vision of how to achieve a future state and anticipates consequences, risks and trends accurately, while still being realistic and solidly grounded. It considers the larger environment, adjusts as circumstances change and is aligned with moral values. Therefore, strategy is not the tactical "here and now" of completing tasks, but rather a holistic plan of tactical maneuvers to achieve the predefined desired outcomes.

Regulatory strategy involves the same basic principles - and focuses on the process of achieving marketing approval for drugs, biologics and medical devices (hereafter collectively referred to in this chapter as products) and ensuring the approved products comply with the laws and regulations of the countries where they are marketed. From a global perspective, it is important to understand not only the laws and regulations but also the societal and cultural differences; regulatory strategies that adapt to these nuances are the most successful in achieving product approval and maintaining compliance with local requirements. Developing a successful regulatory strategy requires the ability to research, review, formulate, defend and negotiate key regulatory positions to support product development, registration and lifecycle maintenance activities, in one market or globally. Further, the regulatory professional provides input on a daily basis on regulatory decisions, which can have critical short- and long-term financial consequences and implications for the company. Thus, regulatory strategy can be developed to address either a transient problem or can be a comprehensive plan tailored to a specific product; in either case, the broad steps in developing a strategy essentially are the same.

When developing a regulatory strategy, the following steps generally are followed:

- Understand what is being requested and define the request's parameters and scope. This is a critical step as the actual information requested will be delivered (as opposed to extraneous or inaccurate information); it also helps check scope creep and allows proper allocation of resources.
- Predefine success and create a scorecard to track important measures to communicate progress.
- List the critical information needed to start to build the strategy, with key milestones.
- Ask questions, challenge assumptions and identify issues, problems and their root causes.
- Seek opinions from subject matter experts—be flexible and open to suggestion and remain patient and objective when listening to other points of view.
- Gather data (which can be complex and often ambiguous) and interpret it. Weed out irrelevant facts and pull together a draft strategy that identifies and prioritizes the step-by-step tasks, timelines and resource needs at each milestone.
- Identify the stakeholders who will ensure the strategy is accepted, funded and will support its successful implementation. Think through what is valued and what is gained.
- Gain alignment with these stakeholders on the draft strategy and incorporate feedback as needed.
- Ultimately, get confirmation from decision makers, as they are critical to the strategy's success.
- Communicate decisions to those responsible for implementing the strategy and completing tasks.
- Execute the strategy and measure progress periodically. No amount of planning can make up for weak execution and implementation; solid implementation is key to overall success.
- Track and monitor the strategy for continued viability and course correct and update it as necessary.

Why is Regulatory Strategy Important?

A good regulatory strategy is critical on several fronts; most importantly, when executed successfully, it allows patients faster access to the product while providing assurance it has met regulatory approval criteria for efficacy, benefit-risk and quality standards when used or administered in accordance with the label. It also builds credibility and trust with regulatory agencies by demonstrating the company has evaluated product risks carefully, has the proper risk mitigation strategies in place and is being transparent and collaborative in its interactions. From the company's perspective, a strong regulatory strategy is key to maximizing the product's marketing potential and sustains the company's profit and loss ratio; it also allows the company to optimize internal efficiencies, which benefit its patients, shareholders, partners and its reputation as a whole.

Tools to Develop a Regulatory Strategy

A few tools are used routinely by the regulatory strategist to create, implement and update a regulatory strategy.

The Regulatory Landscape Document

A regulatory landscape document provides the background and context around the disease area or condition the product treats, prevents or diagnoses. It describes in very broad terms the standard of care (as well as differences in standards of care from one country to another), reviews the laws, regulations and guidance documents that apply to the product in each country and summarizes competitive intelligence relevant to the product. A solid regulatory landscape document is recommended prior to finalizing the Target Product Profile (TPP) and the Global Regulatory Plan (GRP) because it helps the strategist focus on the various moving pieces of the regulatory environment surrounding the product to position the product uniquely in terms of its benefits and showcases how it differs from competitors' products. The company then can design a clinical development plan around product claims. As such, it is recommended the regulatory landscape document be written during early Phase 1 clinical trials or sooner. Some sources for the regulatory landscape are provided in **Figure 12-1**.

A regulatory landscape document may contain the following key sections:

- Disease Overview—This should be brief, as it likely will be covered under the Global Development Plan (GDP), which usually is developed by the clinical development lead. It is helpful to include a brief summary of the symptoms and methods of diagnosis, overview of the current standard of care and differences in the standard of care from one region to another (to better understand the impact on clinical trial design). Finally, it is useful to describe in broad terms the endpoints, biomarkers and/or tools commonly used in the diagnosis or treatment that potentially could be useful in clinical trial design and endpoint establishment.
- Regulatory Environment—This section describes the current regulatory environment, as well as relevant facts regarding the regulatory environment's evolution and future goals. The strategist researches applicable regulations and guidance documents and previous positions or feedback for the disease area using information available from major regulatory agencies. For example, the regulatory strategist can review Advisory Committee Meeting summaries using an online repository of all FDA meeting documents, as well as Advisory Committee members' profiles and voting results. Similarly, the regulatory strategist can use online resources to research competitors' inspection and compliance documents, e.g., Establishment Inspection Reports (EIR), FDA Form 483s, compliance manuals, inspection guides, compliance letters (Warning Letters, Untitled Letters, etc.). Finally, this section also should include a brief description of any new or upcoming legislation, regulations or guidance documents that may impact the product's regulatory pathway.
- Regulatory Precedents—Last, but not least, the regulatory landscape document also contains a thorough assessment of publicly available information on regulatory precedents; for example, the document may list already marketed competitive products and how they were approved in major markets (perhaps by referring to the US Package Insert (USPI); Summary of Product Characteristics (SmPC); Medical, Chemistry, Manufacturing, and Controls (CMC) Reviews; EU Public Assessment Reports (EPARs), etc.) to gain valuable information about competitors, including clinical development programs, number of clinical trial patients, endpoints approved by FDA, as well as other approval issues that may have impacted the precedent manufacturer's labeling claims (e.g., What is competitor product's efficacy and safety profile? Any other claims such as good patient compliance?). Importantly, the regulatory strategist will gain valuable insight into a regulator's thinking at the time it approved the precedent product, which may be of value in understanding the agency's expectations and facilitate future discussions and negotiations. This information also is invaluable for grounding and managing stakeholders' expectations.

  The regulatory precedents section should provide a thorough review of the competitor's products still under investigation and describe where they are in the development phase. This section should contain output from clinical trial disclosure site information searches (e.g., clinicaltrials.gov) to provide intelligence on the competitor's study design, results and endpoints; this may provide insight into potential label claims, and knowledge of where trials are being conducted will help to inform investigator and site selection. Study results on competitor products can be found online, in competitor companies' press releases and in presentations at clinical meetings (e.g., ASH and ASCO for cancer products), which showcase their positive clinical study data.

Figure 12-1. Tools for Regulatory Landscape

- Clinical Trial Registries
- Health Authority Websites
- Drugs.com
- FDLI SmartBrief
- IDRAC
- NDA Pipeline Information Database

Sometimes, the regulatory strategist may choose to apply previously successful methods and techniques to new regulatory strategies; when duplicating a strategy, understanding the rationale supporting that precedent and assessing new variables in the current or projected environment is important.[1]

Figure 12-2. Risk Tool

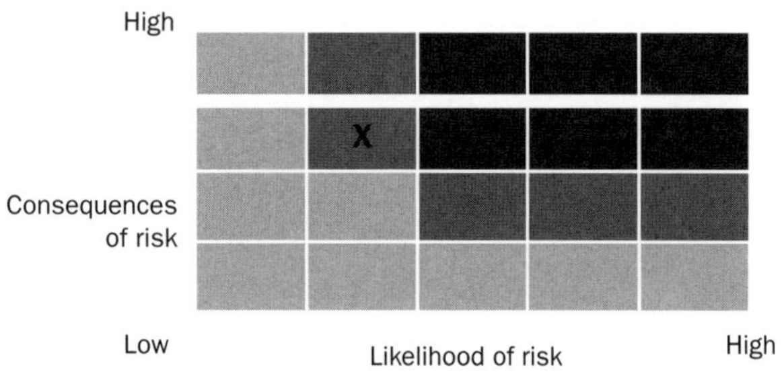

- List risk event and indicators
- Create a chart (as above) and map the likelihood and consequences of risk
- List out controls and mitigation strategies

Target Product Profile (TPP)

A proper regulatory strategy must take into consideration the product's intended use. The TPP is a labeling concept document that creates a "desired" label for the product early in its development phase, usually well before actual clinical data have been collected. Creating the TPP with the end label in mind clarifies the sponsor's intent in FDA discussions. The sponsor uses the TPP to demonstrate product claims clearly and, by working backward, is able to describe the data needed to obtain regulatory approval successfully. The TPP (which can be submitted to FDA as part of the briefing book prior to any meeting) can be used by the sponsor to initiate product development discussions with reviewers (e.g., sharing the TPP with FDA in preparation for the End-of-Phase 2 (EOP2) meeting). Note FDA does not require a TPP, but in the authors' experience, it is a vital tool to communicate the regulatory strategy for drug, biologic and device products. The TPP allows FDA reviewers, who usually receive study protocols in piecemeal fashion, to understand the overarching regulatory strategy behind the various studies and provide more informed guidance and feedback to the regulatory strategist.

The TPP is a living document that can be used throughout the drug development process, from the pre-IND stage through postmarket submissions for future label expansions. Since it is a living document, it should be updated periodically during the drug development process.

A TPP should encompass key product label sections and, ideally, should be based on the Company Core Data Sheet (CCDS). FDA's *Guidance for Industry and Review Staff—Target Product Profile—A Strategic Development Process Tool—Draft Guidance,* recommends using key sections that include but are not limited to:

- indications and usage
- contraindications
- dosage and administration
- dosage forms and strengths
- warnings and precautions
- adverse reactions
- drug interactions
- use in specific populations
- drug abuse and dependence
- overdosage
- description of the drug/biologic molecule
- nonclinical toxicology (list the studies that will be conducted)
- clinical pharmacology (list each study that will be conducted, their endpoints and the desired labeling claims, for completed studies and those under development)
- clinical studies (provide a list of Phase 1, 2 and 3 studies that will support registration, the endpoints, study populations, and brief descriptions of major safety and efficacy labeling claims to be demonstrated)
- references
- how supplied/storage and handling
- patient counseling information

If used efficiently, the TPP can be a valuable tool to address issues early in the product development process and prevent late-stage development failures.

GRP

The GRP is an internal company document that provides the regulatory strategies for a product from early development to registration worldwide to lifecycle management plan. It is not a regulated document and is highly confidential in nature. The GRP details the regulatory strategies, with instructions and timelines for execution. A thoroughly prepared GRP will help align the clinical and CMC development plan with business goals. Regulatory risk assessment and mitigation are the most critical GRP components. The GRP should capture all risks (safety, regulatory, operational, manufacturing and supply) that may prevent or delay approval and/or negatively impact product label and marketing. Alternate approaches and critical decision points should be included in the GRP. The GRP format can be either a PowerPoint presentation or a Word document. Information should be presented concisely and clearly. The GRP is reviewed by different functions within regulatory and is aligned with the product's Global Strategic Plan's manufacturing/quality, supply, commercial and reimbursement strategies. The GRP should be reviewed and updated at key milestones, such as after critical FDA meetings or on a yearly basis.

A good GRP should contain, at a minimum:

- executive regulatory summary

Figure 12-3. Decision Tree

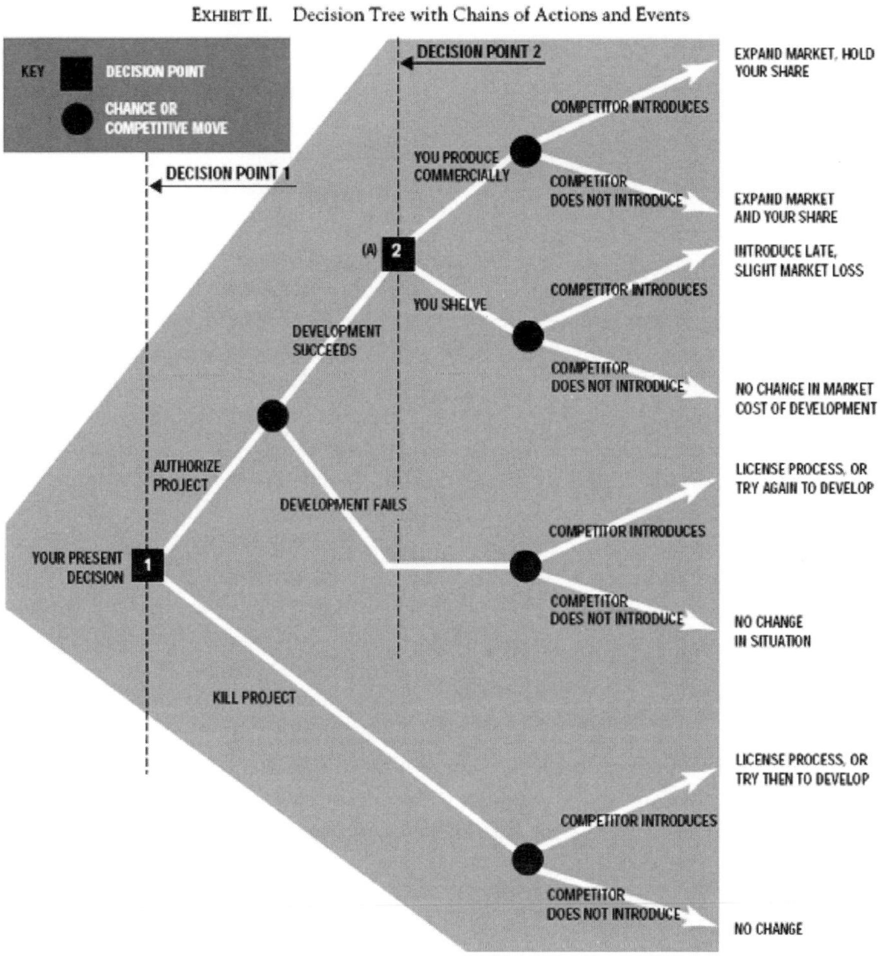

Image Source: *Harvard Business Review*, Decision Trees for Decision Making – July 1964

- o product description, target indications and key regulatory issues that must be resolved
- o opportunities available and the related events and/or tasks required to fully realize those opportunities
- o key meetings with regulatory agencies, their timeframes and their desired outcomes
- o timeframes for upcoming FDA submissions

- project deliverables: both short-term (3–12 months) and long-term deliverables (greater than two years)
- submission planning and timelines (after careful review and confirmation with all major stakeholders and regulators, where possible)
- key program issues and risk mitigation options
  - o effective risk management system to assess regulatory risk types the program faces
  - o probability assessment of each risk and its impact on the program
  - o risk mitigation options[2] (Scenario planning and analysis also is an effective way of addressing risk. **Figure 12-2** provides a risk tool example. **Figure 12-3** includes a decision tree, useful when conducting contingency and scenario-planning exercises to clarify the outcomes related to each decision.[3])
- list of all applicable regulations and guidance documents
- Target Product Label (TPL), including any regional labeling considerations (see TPP section above)
- regulatory intelligence (relevant details from the regulatory landscape document)
- regulatory pathways to expedite marketing goals, including data and market exclusivities
  - o expanded access programs
  - o special designations such as orphan drug status

Figure 12-4. Quality Target Product Profile

- Intended Use
- Route of Administration
- Delivery
- Dosage Form
- Bioavailability
- Container Closure
- Stability
- Strength

  - o expedited review and approval pathways (e.g., breakthrough therapy, fast track, priority review and accelerated approval)
- pediatric development strategy
  - o discussion of the pediatric strategy, as well as the applicability of laws such as *Best Pharmaceuticals for Children Act* (*BPCA*) and *Pediatric Research Equity Act* (*PREA*). Age-appropriate formulations and the need for long-term safety studies in children
  - o TPL description of the pediatric information on the desired label
- regulatory CMC strategy for drugs and biologics
  - o creating a Quality Target Product Profile (QTPP) (**Figure 12-4**)
  - o CMC strategy outline based on clinical development phase, clinical size and duration (Dosage forms and prior dosing history should be considered, and the target Stock Keeping Units (SKU) should be listed.)
  - o critical drug product, drug substance, intermediate and excipient quality attributes (CQA) and control strategy identity
  - o sufficient CMC information to ensure proper drug identification, quality, potency, purity and strength
  - o global cold chain distribution, process validation and shelf life regulations
  - o drug substance and drug product process performance qualification (PPQ) strategy
- device strategy, when a device is intended to be distributed with a drug or biologic product
  - o global device regulations and requirements for verification, validation and human factor evaluation
  - o assessment of any timelines for required extractable and leachable studies
- clinical strategy
  - o endpoints, comparators and statistical criteria based on not only approved products but also ongoing competing clinical programs
  - o strategies to support use of Patient-Reported Outcome (PRO) instruments in evaluating treatment efficacy
- FDA interactions (timing and strategy validation)
- plans for lifecycle management (LCM) activities, as appropriate

Postapproval Regulatory Strategy

While this chapter mainly discusses tips for creating a regulatory strategy for a new marketing application, a large part of the regulatory function also involves creating strategies for postapproval variations or supplements to assess the change objectively and create global strategies and risk maps associated with the change. Postapproval regulatory plans are not as detailed but can require strategic thinking to present the change most effectively to regulators; in some countries the variation can be a notification, while in others, it is a prior approval supplement. It also is important the postapproval regulatory strategy takes into consideration the way to ensure uninterrupted supply while the variations are submitted and approved by regulatory agencies worldwide. In some countries, product made by the new process may be commercially released in a few months, while in other countries it could take two years to get regulatory approval; hence product made by the old process and by the new process must be available for that time in accordance with the approval schedule. Comparability Protocols (CPs) or Postapproval Change Management Protocols (PACMP) may need to be submitted to FDA for some postapproval changes. Examples of postapproval changes are:

- addition of new indications
- postmarket commitment filings
- change in formulation
- technology transfers of drug substance or drug product
- addition of a new SKU or Working Cell Bank (WCB)
- alternate container closure systems
- label revisions for new safety information or any other new information
- dosing changes
- addition of fill lines

Implementing the Strategy

Implementing the strategy often is the hardest part. While planning extensively and thoroughly helps nail down the strategy, plan execution must be flawless for the regulatory strategy to be successful. Often, even the best laid plans encounter difficulties; in such cases, it is important to course correct and continue to achieve the ultimate objectives while remaining alert and flexible to developing opportunities. As a strategic document, the GRP is also a living document. Expect to update the GRP and strategy execution

Figure 12-5. Regulatory Strategist—Skills

Leadership Skills

- Knows how to build and support a strong team
- Is a "followable" leader
- Credible (e.g., makes good on promises)
- Far-sighted
- Passionate
- Courageous
- Wise
- Generous
- Trustworthy
- Listens

Executive Presence

- Technically knowledgeable/ credible
- Professional attitude
- Self aware of body language/voice tone
- Confident (not arrogant), yet realistic
- Collaboration, communication and concern
- Positive energy (enthusiasm, motivation)
- Adaptability and ability to work within the situation to make the situation work for you
- Knows when to delegate

Soft Skills

- Knows what he/she knows and does not know and seeks help
- Prioritizes effectively or escalates for prioritization
- Recognizes relevance of task to role/strategy and says no when needed
- Recognizes the winds of change and adapts

as the product progresses through development and to adapt to changing regulatory and product development environment. Monitor the environment (external, internal, regulatory), as it will impact the regulatory strategy. Use regulatory intelligence tools as a way to keep abreast of all landscape changes that could impact the strategy (an Excel spreadsheet is useful). Routinely review past decisions and course correct as needed. Importantly, notify and involve stakeholders as needed.

Key Competencies of the Regulatory Strategist

Good regulatory strategists are valued for the research and analytical skills they bring to medical product manufacturers. The regulatory strategist often is the product regulatory lead and is responsible not only for developing regulatory opinions, positions and strategy but also obtaining stakeholder agreement on the proposed regulatory strategy. The regulatory strategist should have adequate scientific education, training and experience, as well as a technical understanding of the product and how it is used to treat the disease area or condition. Developing a robust regulatory strategy, "selling" it to stakeholders and getting buy-in from FDA are important in establishing the regulatory strategist as a leader in the regulatory field. Skills for a good regulatory strategist are listed in **Figure 12-5.**

Conclusion

A good regulatory strategist not only creates a product development plan, but also anticipates and prepares for regulatory agency questions, shortens regulatory review and approval timelines and predicts and addresses the various stakeholder needs (patients, healthcare providers, regulators, payers, etc.).

Developing and implementing a solid regulatory strategy with a plan to communicate proactively and address new issues in a timely way is key to getting on-time, first-cycle regulatory approvals. A strategy that changes weekly, or even monthly, suggests the team has not understood the strategy's importance and the plan may require course correction to re-sell the strategy and ensure stakeholder acceptance. As the strategy is implemented, it is important promises made during the earlier buy-in or negotiation phases are kept to maintain credibility with regulatory agencies, team members and senior management and will enhance future interactions with these stakeholders and improve the probability of success of future projects.[4]

Regulatory strategy is important throughout a product's lifecycle because it facilitates optimized study designs to meet regulatory endpoints, increases task and work process efficiencies and increases the likelihood of product approval and compliance with all state and federal laws.

Disclaimer: The views expressed herein represent those of the authors and do not necessarily represent the views or practices of the authors' employers or any other party.

References

1. Brown-Tuttle M. *Regulatory Intelligence 101.* Regulatory Affairs Professionals Society ©2014.
2. Kaplan RS and Mikes M. "Managing Risks: A New Framework." *Harvard Business Review.* June 2012
3. Magee JF. "Decision Trees for Decision Making." *Harvard Business Review.* July 1964.
4. Binder B and Bashe P. *Science lessons: What the Business of Biotech Taught Me About Management.*Harvard Business School Publishing, ©2008.

Chapter 13

Prescription Drug Product Submissions

Updated by Wm. Trey Putnam, PhD, RAC

OBJECTIVES

- ❑ Define the regulatory submission requirements associated with the development and approval of new therapeutic entities
- ❑ Define and describe the components and review process of Investigational New Drug Applications (IND), including descriptions of the different types of INDs
- ❑ Explain the reasons for clinical holds
- ❑ Define maintenance submissions for INDs
- ❑ Define and describe the components and review process of New Drug Applications (NDAs)
- ❑ Define maintenance submissions for NDAs
- ❑ Describe programs for expediting drug development and review

LAWS, REGULATIONS, GUIDANCES DOCUMENTS COVERED IN THIS CHAPTER

- ❑ *Federal Food, Drug, and Cosmetic Act* of 1938
- ❑ *Public Health Service Act* of 1944
- ❑ *Drug Price Competition and Patent Term Restoration Act* of 1984 (*Hatch-Waxman Act*)
- ❑ *Prescription Drug Marketing Act* of 1987
- ❑ *Prescription Drug User Fee Act* of 1992
- ❑ *Federal Advisory Committee Act* of 1972
- ❑ *Food and Drug Administration Modernization Act* of 1997
- ❑ *Food and Drug Administration Amendments Act* of 2007
- ❑ *Food and Drug Administration Safety and Innovation Act* of 2012
- ❑ 21 CFR 310 New Drugs
- ❑ 21 CFR 312 Investigational New Drug Application
- ❑ 21 CFR 314 Applications for FDA Approval to Market a New Drug
- ❑ 21 CFR 601 Licensing (biological products)
- ❑ FDA *Guidance for Industry: Providing Clinical Evidence for Effectiveness for Human Drugs and Biological Products* (May 1998)
- ❑ FDA *Guidance for Industry on the Disclosure of Materials Provided to Advisory Committees in Connection with Open Advisory Committee Meetings Convened by the Center for Drug Evaluation and Research Beginning on January 1, 2000* (November 1999)

- FDA *Guidance for Industry: Reports on the Status of Postmarketing Study Commitments—Implementation of Section 130 of the Food and Drug Administration Modernization Act of 1997* (February 2006)
- FDA *Guidance for Industry: Postmarketing Studies and Clinical Trials—Implementation of Section 505(o)(3) of the Federal Food, Drug, and Cosmetic Act* (April 2011)
- FDA *Guidance for Review Staff and Industry: Good Review Management Principles and Practices for PDUFA Products* (April 2005)
- FDA *Guidance for Industry: Fixed Dose Combinations, Co-Packaged Drug Products, and Single-Entity Versions of Previously Approved Antiretrovirals for the Treatment of HIV* (October 2006)
- FDA *Guidance for Industry: Fast Track Drug Development Programs—Designation, Development, and Application Review* (January 2006)
- FDA *Draft Guidance for Industry: Accelerated Approval Products—Submission of Promotional Materials* (March 1999)
- FDA *Guidance for Industry: Formal Meetings with Sponsors and Applicants for PDUFA Products* (May 2009)
- FDA *Draft Guidance for Industry: Applications Covered by Section 505(b)(2)* (October 1999)
- Manual of Policies and Procedures 6020.3: Review Classification Policy: Priority (P) and Standard (S)
- FDA *Guidance for Industry: Providing Regulatory Submissions in Electronic Format—Human Pharmaceutical Product Applications and Related Submissions Using the eCTD Specifications* (June 2008)
- FDA *Guidance for Industry: Providing Regulatory Submissions in Electronic Format—Content of Labeling* (April 2005)
- FDA *Guidance for Industry: Contents for a Complete Submission for the Evaluation of Proprietary Names* (February 2010)
- FDA *Guidance for Industry: M4: Organization of the CTD* (August 2001)
- FDA *Draft Guidance for Industry: How to Comply with the Pediatric Research Equity Act* (September 2005)
- FDA *Draft Guidance for Industry: Qualification Process for Drug Development Tools* (October 2010)
- FDA *Draft Guidance for Industry Format and Content of Proposed Risk Evaluation and Mitigation Strategies (REMS), REMS Assessments, and Proposed REMS Modifications* (September 2009)
- FDA *Draft Guidance for Industry and Review Staff: Target Product Profile—A Strategic Development Process Tool* (March 2007)
- FDA *Draft Guidance for Industry: Labeling for Human Prescription Drug and Biological Products-Implementing the PLR Content and Format Requirements* (February 2013)
- FDA *Guidance for Industry: Dosage and Administration Section of Labeling for Human Prescription Drug and Biological Products Content and Format* (March 2010)
- FDA *Guidance for Industry: Information Program on Clinical Trials for Serious or LifeThreatening Diseases and Conditions* (March 2002)
- FDA *Guidance for Industry: Changes to an Approved NDA or ANDA* (April 2004)
- FDA *Guidance for Industry: Content and Format of Investigational New Drug Applications (INDs) for Phase 1 Studies of Drugs, Including Well-Characterized, Therapeutic, Biotechnology-Derived Products* (November 1995)
- FDA *Guidance for Industry: Meetings With Sponsors and Advocates for PDUFA Products* (May 2009)
- FDA *Guidance for Industry: Indexing Structured Product Labeling* (June 2008)
- FDA *Guidance for Industry: Part 11, Electronic Records; Electronic Signatures-Scope and Application* (August 2003)

- FDA *Guidance for Industry: Providing Regulatory Submissions in Electronic Format-General Considerations* (January 1999)
- FDA *Guidance for Industry: Expedited Programs for Serious Conditions– Drugs and Biologics* (May 2014)
- FDA *Guidance for Industry (Draft): Providing Regulatory Submissions in Electronic Format-Postmarketing Expedited Safety Reports* (June 2014)
- FDA *Guidance for Industry: Providing Regulatory Submissions in Electronic Format—Submissions Under Section 745A(a) of the Federal Food, Drug, and Cosmetic Act* (December 2014)
- FDA *Guidance for Industry: Providing Regulatory Submissions In Electronic Format—Standardized Study Data* (December 2014)

(Note: The Center for Drug Evaluation and Research (CDER) website has an index with links to all guidance documents relevant to new drug development and approval: http://www.fda.gov/Drugs/GuidanceComplianceRegulatoryInformation/Guidances/. As new guidance documents are added frequently and older ones occasionally withdrawn, it is important to check for current guidance documents when planning and preparing an IND or NDA.)

Introduction

This chapter provides an overview of the regulations, regulatory process and submission requirements associated with developing new therapeutic entities (i.e., new prescription products or new drugs). Specifically, this chapter covers submissions at the investigational stage of development and requirements associated with obtaining commercial marketing approval. It focuses on the requirements for drug manufacturers seeking approval through a New Drug Application (NDA), although high-level information associated with biologic products also is presented. Full information regarding biologic products is found in Chapter 24. For full information on generic submissions, see Chapter 15.

Overall, as described in Chapters 2 and 3, prescription drug products are regulated under the *Federal Food, Drug, and Cosmetic Act* of 1938 (*FD&C Act*) and its subsequent amendments. The *FD&C Act* also applies to biological products subject to regulation under Section 351 of the *Public Health Service Act* (*PHS Act*). A new drug generally is any drug that contains an ingredient or combination of ingredients for which the safety and effectiveness under the labeled conditions for use are not previously known. However, a new drug also may be a drug that has a known safety and effectiveness profile under the labeled conditions for use but has not been in use to a material extent or for a material time under those conditions.

The *FD&C Act* prohibits the introduction of a prescription drug into interstate commerce unless the drug manufacturer has submitted an NDA to the US Food and Drug Administration (FDA) and obtained agency approval. Likewise, the *PHS Act* prohibits the introduction of any biologic product into interstate commerce unless a biologic license is in effect and each package is plainly and properly marked with specific requirements (e.g., proper name). The NDA or Biologics License Application (BLA) must contain substantial evidence from adequate and well-controlled investigations, including clinical investigations, conducted by qualified experts. These investigations should demonstrate the drug is safe and effective under conditions for use described in the labeling, and can be manufactured consistently, in a manner that will preserve its identity, strength, quality and purity.

Aside from effectiveness, the application must provide evidence the prescription drug is reasonably safe when used under the conditions described in the labeling. Although a new drug's safety is assiduously studied through clinical trials (which often enroll several thousand patients), the reality is the variables in a clinical trial are specified and controlled, and the results relate only to the populations studied within the trial. Therefore, adverse drug reactions (ADRs) reported to occur less frequently in the trial population become more apparent and sometimes more frequent or severe only after a drug enters the market and is used by millions of people who likely have different demographic profiles than the clinical trial populations. Nevertheless, evidence from clinical trials is critical in identifying ADRs associated with the drug and establishing its benefit-risk profile. The benefit-risk profile evaluates all known data for the drug and attempts to provide answers to such key questions as: does the drug do more good than harm, and if so, how much more good? If the drug has a potential for harm, how probable and how serious is the harm? So, although clinical trials do not tell the whole story of the drug's effects in all populations and all situations, they provide a good indication of the drug's safety that can be extrapolated from the populations studied to larger populations.

To enhance FDA's oversight of drug safety issues, Congress gave the agency new authorities under the *Food and Drug Administration Amendments Act* of 2007 (*FDAAA*). If FDA becomes aware of new safety information about a serious risk associated with a drug's use, it can require a manufacturer to implement safety labeling changes, conduct postmarketing studies or clinical trials, or establish Risk Evaluation and Mitigation Strategies (REMS). *FDAAA* also mandated that FDA establish an active, integrated, electronic surveillance system for continuously monitoring the safety of drugs and other medical products in real time. FDA is working toward this mandate and, in May 2008, launched the Sentinel Initiative to strengthen the agency's ability to track how drugs and other healthcare products perform once they are approved. Although the Sentinel System is being developed and implemented in stages, ultimately, it will help monitor healthcare products throughout the entire lifecycle. It will allow FDA to communicate the risks associated with the product to the public effectively, thus better achieving its mission of protecting and promoting public health.

The *Food and Drug Administration Safety and Innovation Act* (*FDASIA*), signed into law in July 2012, includes the reauthorization of the *Prescription Drug User Fee Act* (*PDUFA V*). Although *FDASIA* includes numerous changes that will benefit patients, industry and FDA, a main component affecting the prescription drug review process is the establishment of a new review model referred to as the Program. This new review model applies to all New Molecular Entity NDAs (NME NDAs) and original BLAs, including applications resubmitted after a refuse-to-file (RTF) action, received from 1 October 2012 through 30 September 2017. Applicants who submit applications in the Program will experience greater transparency, with two meetings held during the review process (i.e., the mid-cycle meeting and the late-cycle meeting). Additionally, Program applications with a priority review designation have an eight-month action goal, and standard applications have a 12-month action goal.

Regulatory Strategy

Compiling a new marketing application is a highly complex activity requiring much preparation and early and effective communication with FDA. A clear and well-planned strategy is essential for navigating the prescription drug submission regulatory process and ultimately for obtaining timely and smooth FDA drug product approval. FDA, in turn, is committed to and responsible for bringing healthcare products, particularly innovative healthcare products, to the market as expeditiously as possible. To achieve this objective, several pathways and tools should be considered carefully when formulating a regulatory strategy. A sound regulatory strategy should underlie the applicant's drug development program, linking the different activities and drug development phases, assessing the challenges along the way and formulating appropriate risk mitigation activities, all with the ultimate goal of obtaining FDA approval for the desired indications within the desired timeframe. Applicants should develop their regulatory strategy years before the actual application is submitted and as early as Phase 1 of the drug development clinical studies. The strategy often is expanded during clinical drug development Phase 2 or Phase 3 to a global strategy, so drug approval may be obtained in the major commercial markets. Throughout drug development, applicants are encouraged to design trials and collect data to ultimately support planned marketing claims as well as product labeling.

Target Product Profile

The Target Product Profile (TPP) was developed in the late 1990s as a joint initiative between FDA and industry to improve sponsor-FDA interaction during the drug development process. Pilots were conducted between 1997 and 2003, and a draft guidance was issued in 2007.

The TPP is a format for a drug development program summary described in terms of labeling concepts, i.e., organized according to the key sections of the drug's intended labeling. It is prepared by the sponsor, and submission is voluntary.

The TPP links each specific labeling concept to a specific study or other data source intended to support the labeling concept. The TPP is a dynamic summary that will change as knowledge of the drug increases. It is intended to eliminate the need to revisit development issues already discussed with FDA, unless development goals change, and to facilitate final labeling discussions related to both initial approvals and labeling supplements. Moreover, it helps update FDA quickly on revised development goals and facilitates rapid orientation for new personnel. A TPP does not, however, represent a commitment or obligation on the part of either the sponsor or FDA to the drug development strategy or eventual drug approval. A TPP can be discussed at key development meetings with FDA.

Drug Development Tools

Another critical component of regulatory strategy is the use of drug development tools (DDT), such as animal models, biological markers (biomarkers) and clinical outcomes assessments (COA) (e.g., patient reported outcome (PRO) measures). A biomarker is defined as a characteristic that is objectively measured and evaluated as an indicator of normal biologic processes, pathogenic processes or biological responses to a therapeutic intervention. Thus, a change to a biomarker following treatment with the drug product can predict or identify safety problems related to the drug or reveal a pharmacological activity expected to predict an eventual benefit from treatment. Biomarkers may reduce uncertainty in drug development and evaluation by providing quantitative predictions about drug performance.

Although there are several types of COAs, this section focuses on PROs. A PRO is an instrument that captures drug intervention outcomes during a clinical trial from the patient's perspective (e.g., change in pain or depression over time from before the therapy began to after it is administered). The PRO uses a questionnaire that is self-administered by the patient or through interviews by other parties that report on patient perspectives. Questionnaires measure characteristics (or constructs) with sound theoretical bases, relevant to the patient group in which they are to be used. Questionnaires can be designed to provide data in any disease population and cover a broad aspect of the construct measured, or can be developed specifically to measure those outcome aspects of importance for people with a particular medical condition. In any case, a PRO tool should be tested thoroughly using appropriate methodology and validated to justify its use. Results from properly validated PRO instruments can be used to support drug approval and claims in approved medical product labeling. Examples of characteristics assessed by PRO questionnaires include symptoms and other aspects of well-being, functionality (disability) and quality of life (QoL).

In addition to PRO tools, FDA also will consider qualification of other DDTs to support labeling claims, such as clinician or caregiver rating scales, where a respondent is asked to rate a concept using a process similar to that used for PROs.

With proper qualification, analytically valid DDT measurements can be expected to have a specific use and interpretable meaning and be used broadly in drug development. Once a DDT is qualified for a specific context of use, industry can use it for the qualified purpose during drug development, and reviewers from CDER's Study Endpoints and Labeling Development Team (SEALD) can apply the DDT for the qualified use confidently, without the need to reconfirm its utility.

FDA Meetings

As presented in Chapter 4, FDA Communications and Meetings, sponsors are encouraged to request and obtain certain meetings with the agency. Three kinds of meetings advisable in most cases are the Pre-IND, End-of-Phase 2 (EoP2) and PreNDA or Pre-BLA Meetings.

Investigational New Drug Applications

An investigational new drug is a potential therapy a sponsor would like to use in human clinical trials. Such use in the US must be covered by an INDA (synonymous with a Notice of Claimed Investigational Exemption for a New Drug, Form FDA 1571), commonly referred to as an IND. Essentially, the IND is a claim of exemption from certain *FD&C Act* labeling requirements, allowing drug shipment in interstate commerce for the purpose of conducting clinical trials. An IND sponsor may be a company, institution or individual physician.

Nonclinical Testing

Prior to submitting an IND, a sponsor conducts nonclinical (also called preclinical) testing to develop the basic toxicological and pharmacological understanding (data) FDA requires to evaluate the new drug's safety before initiating human clinical trials. Nonclinical testing can take one to four years, including one to two years before filing an IND, with further testing conducted in parallel with the clinical testing. Nonclinical biosafety studies consist of *in vitro* and *in vivo* animal toxicology and pharmacology tests. Studies of the mechanism of action and animal models of efficacy in specific indications also may be conducted.

Nonclinical studies are used to:

- assess pharmacodynamic activity and mechanism of action
- assess drug absorption, distribution to organ systems and tissues, and metabolism and excretion pathways (ADME)
- assess pharmacokinetics
- detect overt toxicity, and identify toxic effects and principal target organs
- assess genotoxic or mutagenic potential
- assess carcinogenicity
- assess reproductive toxicity and teratogenic potential
- assess the safety of drug impurities
- estimate dose-response relationships of pharmacological and toxic effects
- estimate a safe starting dose for study in humans
- suggest clinical safety assessments

Toxicity

The International Conference on Harmonisation (ICH) M3 guidance discusses animal toxicity study types and durations required to support safe human clinical trials. Toxicology studies must be conducted in accordance with Good Laboratory Practice (GLP) if they are intended to support safety assessments, or FDA requires a reason why an alternate standard was utilized.

Subacute toxicity testing must be conducted in two mammalian species (one nonrodent) and usually involves rats and dogs. In general, 30- to 90-day subacute toxicity studies are required for the full drug development program, although shorter-duration studies may support initial human trials. For example, studies lasting two to four weeks may be sufficient to support Phase 1 and Phase 2 human trials of up to two weeks' duration.

The recommended duration of repeated-dose toxicity studies usually is related to the proposed clinical trial's duration, therapeutic indication and scale. In principle, the duration of animal toxicity studies should equal or exceed that of proposed human clinical trials (up to the maximum recommended duration of the repeated-dose toxicity studies).

Longer-term, repeat-dose toxicity studies are required prior to Phase 3 trials and marketing approval; these can be as long as six months' duration in a rodent species and for chronic administration in a nonrodent species. ICH guidance recommends nine months for the nonrodent, chronic studies. However, FDA has stated that as little as six months may be acceptable (e.g., for chronic conditions with short-term, intermittent exposure or life-threatening disease). As much as 12 months may be appropriate (for example, for New Chemical Entities (NCEs) where no long-term human experience is available in the pharmacological class).

Genotoxicity

A standard test battery of *in vitro* genotoxicity studies generally is required prior to initial clinical testing and includes assessment of mutagenicity in bacteria and chromosomal damage in mammalian cells. *In vivo* assessments of genotoxicity typically are required prior to conducting Phase 2 clinical trials.

Carcinogenicity

Carcinogenicity studies usually are not required prior to initial clinical testing and even may be postponed to postapproval or are not required for some products (e.g., known carcinogens or life-threatening diseases). Carcinogenicity studies are conducted for two years in rats and 18 months in mice. A shorter mouse study (six months) using knockout mice may be negotiated.

Reproductive Toxicity

Fertility and reproduction studies are divided into three segments:

- segment I: fertility and early embryonic development to implantation
- segment II: embryo-fetal development
- segment III: prenatal and postnatal development, including maternal function, in addition to a requirement for mutagenicity studies

IND Application Preparation and Submission

Regulations pertaining to INDs can be found in 21 CFR 312. The IND utilizes Form FDA 1571, which lists the aspects and applicable Code of Federal Regulations (CFR) section as outlined below:

1. Form FDA 1571 [21 CFR 312.23(a)(l)]
2. Table of Contents [21 CFR 312.23(a)(2)]
3. Introductory Statement [21 CFR 312.23(a)(3)]
4. General Investigational Plan [21 CFR 312.23(a)(3)]
5. Investigator's Brochure [21 CFR 312.23(a)(5)]
6. Protocol(s) [21 CFR 312.23(a)(6)]
    a. Study Protocol(s) [21 CFR 312.23(a)(6)]
    b. Investigator Data [21 CFR 312.23(a)(6)(iii)(b)] or Completed Form(s) FDA 1572
    c. Facilities Data [21 CFR 312.23(a)(6)(iii)(b)] or Completed Form(s) FDA 1572
    d. Institutional Review Board Data [21 CFR 312.23(a)(6)(iii)(b)] or Completed Form(s) FDA 1572
7. Chemistry, Manufacturing, and Control Data [21 CFR 312.23(a)(7)]
    a. Environmental Assessment or Claim for Exclusion [21 CFR 312.23(a)(7)(iv)(e)]
8. Pharmacology and Toxicology Data [21 CFR 312.23(a)(8)]
9. Previous Human Experience [21 CFR 312.23(a)(9)]
10. Additional Information [21 CFR 312.23(a)(10)]

The IND should be submitted electronically or in triplicate for paper format (an original for archives and two review copies), generally starting with serial number 0000 (unless a previous submission such as a pre-IND meeting document was submitted as 0000, although this is rare). All subsequent submissions to the IND (whether an amendment, report or other correspondence) are assigned sequential serial submission numbers.

After publication of a final guidance document in May 2015, FDA will require all drug product submissions made under Sections 505(b), 505(i), 505(j), 351(a) and 351(k) of the *Federal Food, Drug and Cosmetic Act (FD&C Act)* to be made electronically using the electronic common technical document (eCTD) format by 5 May 2017. All investigational new drug (IND) submissions must be submitted using the eCTD format as of 5 May 2018.

After receiving the IND, FDA assigns it to a reviewing division, which then assigns a review team consisting of at least a medical officer, pharmacologist and chemist. A project manager will work with the team to handle administrative matters, including sponsor contact. An acknowledgment letter, stating the date on which the IND was received and identifying the project manager, is sent to the sponsor.

FDA Review of the Investigational New Drug Application

INDs are not approved; instead, the IND becomes effective within 30 days of FDA receipt unless the agency places the proposed trial on clinical hold (**Figure 13-1**). If deficiencies are found in the IND, FDA generally will contact the sponsor and provide an opportunity to respond within the 30-day review time, although it is not required to contact the sponsor during the 30-day review with respect to deficiencies. If issues cannot be resolved within 30 days, FDA may place a clinical hold on the IND or study. A clinical hold differs from the 30-day review period following IND submission to FDA, and can apply to one or more proposed or ongoing studies submitted to the open IND. A clinical hold can be complete or partial. The hold order explains the basis for FDA's action and is followed within 30 days by a written explanation of the reasons for the hold. FDA lifts the clinical hold after it determines the sponsor has satisfactorily corrected

Figure 13-1. FDA IND Review Process

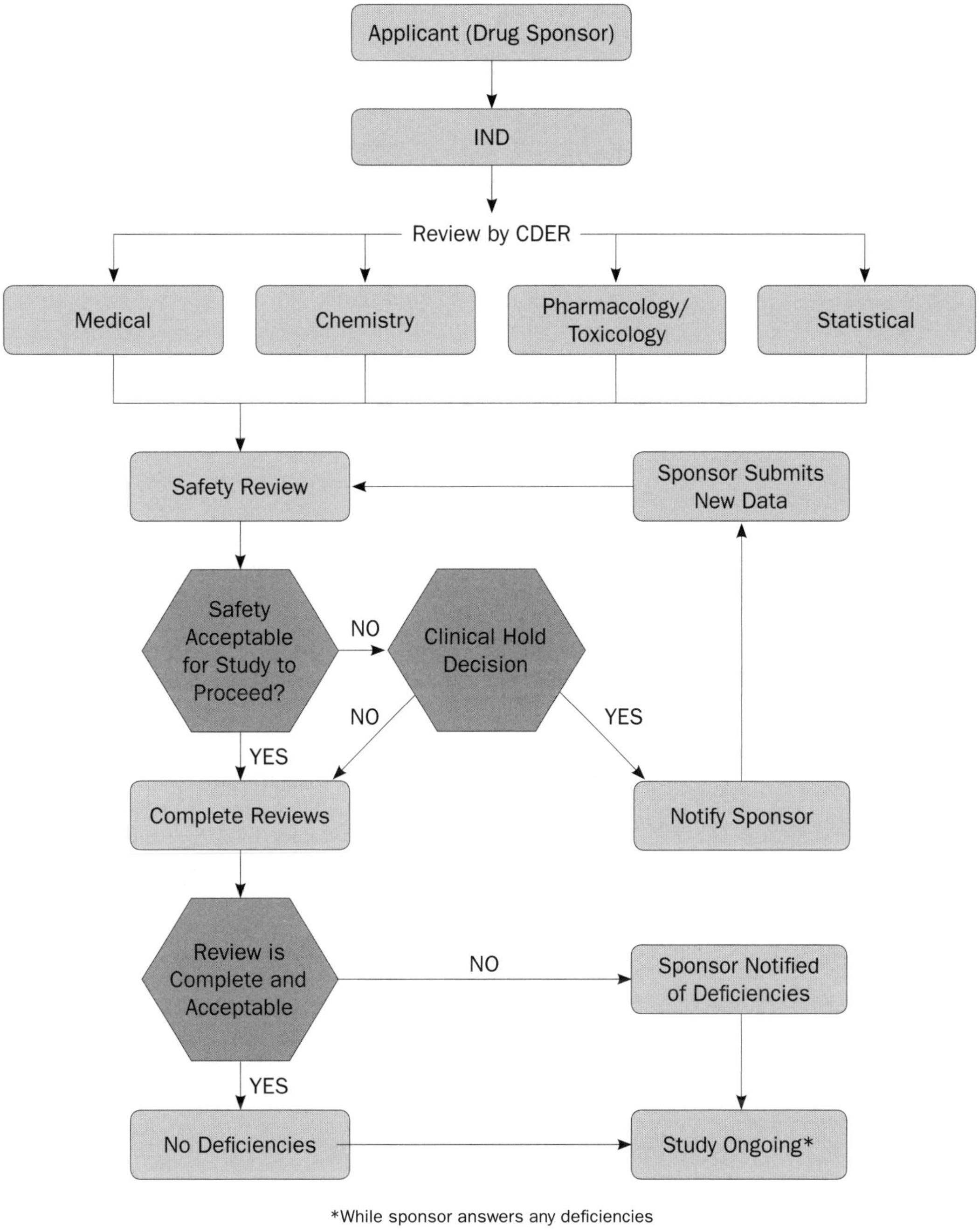

the deficiencies and the investigation may proceed safely. Reasons for Phase 1 clinical study holds include:

- unreasonable risk of human subject harm
- unqualified investigators
- misleading, incomplete or erroneous Investigator's Brochure
- insufficient information to allow assessment of risk
- gender bias in a study of patients with a life-threatening disease that affects both genders

These and additional factors may generate clinical holds on:

- Phase 2 and Phase 3 studies
- treatment protocols and INDs

- studies involving exceptions from informed consent

Once the IND is open, the sponsor may conduct human clinical trials. It is also the sponsor's responsibility to keep the IND updated through the amendment process, as described below. No public communication should promote an investigational drug as safe and effective for use, and no advertising or promotion is allowed during the drug's clinical testing. Study recruitment advertising is reviewed and approved by site Institutional Review Boards (IRB) prior to use.

IND Amendments

During development, the IND must be updated continually. Each submission is an IND amendment and must include a consecutively assigned serial number and a signed Form FDA 1571. There are five types of submissions following opening of the IND:

1. Protocol amendments are used to change a previously submitted protocol, submit a new study protocol and/or add investigator information. Protocols for new investigations must be submitted prior to the study's start; however, there is no 30-day review period after the initial IND review. The protocol must be approved by an IRB for study initiation. If adding new investigators or updating investigator information (e.g., Form FDA 1572) to a previously submitted protocol, the investigator's information may be batched and submitted every 30 days.
2. Information amendments include new animal toxicology, chemistry, technical information or discontinued clinical trials, and generally should be submitted no more frequently than every 30 days.
3. IND safety reports must be communicated in writing to FDA and all participating investigators within 15 calendar days of the sponsor's initial receipt of the following kinds of information:
   a. any adverse event, considered both serious and unexpected, associated with the drug's use (including information from non-IND studies)
   b. any finding in laboratory animals that suggests a significant risk for human subjects

   The sponsor also must notify FDA by telephone or fax of any fatal or life-threatening experience associated with the use of the drug within seven calendar days of receipt (expedited report). In addition, the sponsor is required to submit 15-day follow-up safety reports if new information is made available on an initial 15-day safety report. After the initial IND safety report submission, subsequent safety reports should include an analysis of previously submitted, similar events that evaluates the significance of the new experience in light of previous, similar reports. The sponsor is required to review all information relevant to the drug's safety received from any source, foreign or domestic promptly.
4. Annual reports to the IND must be submitted to FDA within 60 days of the anniversary date of the IND becoming effective, and must include all of the following:
   a. individual study information, including the identification of each study, its purpose, patient population, enrollment status and demographics, number completed, and number dropped out
   b. a brief description of any available study results, including:
      i. a summary showing the most frequent and most serious adverse experiences by body system
      ii. a summary of IND safety reports submitted during the year
      iii. a list of all subjects who died during participation, including cause of death
      iv. a list of all subjects who dropped out due to any adverse experience
      v. a brief description of what, if anything, has been learned that is pertinent to understanding the drug's action
      vi. a list of nonclinical studies completed or in progress during the past year and a summary of their major findings
      vii. a summary of any significant manufacturing or microbiological changes
   c. a general investigational plan for the coming year
   d. a description of any Investigator's Brochure revisions and a copy of the new brochure
   e. a description of any significant Phase 1 modifications not previously reported through a protocol amendment(s)
   f. a summary of such significant foreign marketing developments as marketing approvals or withdrawals in any country
   g. a log of any outstanding IND business for which the sponsor expects or requests a response from FDA also may be included
5. General correspondence can be submitted to the IND. These submissions generally include

all other types of miscellaneous correspondence. These can be requested by FDA or be unsolicited.

INDs can be withdrawn by the sponsor or terminated by FDA. If no subjects are entered into clinical studies for a period of two years, or all investigations are on clinical hold for one year or more, the IND may be placed on inactive status, either at the sponsor's request or at FDA's initiative. If the IND remains on inactive status for five years, or if FDA is unable to resolve deficiencies through a clinical hold or other alternative, it is terminated.

Clinical Trials Data Bank (clinicaltrials.gov)

The Clinical Trials Data Bank was created under *Food and Drug Administration Modernization Act* (*FDAMA*) Section 113 to provide the public with current clinical trial information for drugs to treat serious or life-threatening diseases and conditions. Sponsors are required to submit information to the data bank about clinical trials (usually Phase 2 and Phase 3 trials) conducted under an IND to test a drug's effectiveness. Information on non-effectiveness trials or trials for drugs to treat conditions not considered serious or life-threatening also may be submitted. Data requested include brief descriptions of clinical study protocols that include the following information:

- summary of the study's purpose
- recruiting status
- patient participation criteria
- research study design
- trial phase
- disease or condition and drug or therapy under study
- trial investigational site locations and specific contact information

If the sponsor does not want to disclose the information, it must submit a detailed certification to FDA that the disclosure will interfere substantially with timely subject enrollment. However, FDA makes the final determination of whether to disclose the information.

The Clinical Trials Data Bank is maintained by the National Institutes of Health (NIH) and is available on the internet at http://clinicaltrials.gov/. FDA guidance on requirements and procedures for submitting trial information is available on the CDER guidance page. To submit clinical trial information to the data bank, study sponsors register with the Protocol Registration System at http://prsinfo.clinicaltrials.gov/.

Special INDs

An IND sponsored by a pharmaceutical company or other organization seeking to develop evidence to support a drug marketing application is known as a commercial IND. The sponsor also may be an individual, such as an investigator (also called sponsor-investigator), in which case, the term "investigator's IND" often is used. An investigator's IND may reference a commercial IND or NDA for the technical information required to support the proposed clinical investigation. Generally, the commercial IND or NDA holder provides a letter to the sponsor-investigator, authorizing FDA to access its application.

Compassionate-use IND is an old term used to describe the use of a drug outside the clinical study environment, usually on a single-patient basis. This could be an investigator-sponsored IND.

Treatment INDs were introduced as part of the IND rewrite of 1987. These can be submitted by either the commercial IND holder or a licensed medical practitioner wishing to obtain an investigational drug to treat a patient when the sponsor will not establish a treatment protocol and the patient is not eligible for ongoing clinical trials. A treatment use protocol is required to identify the drug's use; explain the rationale for such use in relation to available, marketed treatments; and contain certain other information pertinent to such use (see 21 CFR 312.35). Each licensed practitioner receiving the drug for use under a treatment protocol is considered an investigator under the protocol and must meet all the attendant responsibilities of such. Under 21 CFR 312 subpart E (Section 312.83), FDA may ask the sponsor to submit a treatment protocol for a promising drug.

Use under a treatment protocol is subject to the standard 30-day IND review period. Sponsors are not required to supply investigational drug for a treatment IND and usually decide whether to do so on a case-by-case basis. The criteria for the treatment use of an investigational new drug are listed in 21 CFR 312.34:

- The drug is intended for a serious or immediately life-threatening disease.
- No comparable or satisfactory alternative drug or other therapy is available to treat the disease stage in the intended patient population.
- The drug is under investigation in a controlled clinical trial under an effective IND, or all clinical trials must have been completed.
- The sponsor of the controlled clinical trial is pursuing marketing approval with due diligence.

In addition, there must be sufficient evidence the drug may offer a benefit to some patients, and the investigator must comply with the regulations concerning IRB review, approval and informed consent. The FDA commissioner may deny use under a treatment protocol or IND for a serious disease if there is insufficient safety and efficacy evidence. It also may be denied for an immediately life-threatening disease if no scientifically reasonable basis exists for concluding the drug will be effective for its intended use or would expose the patients to unreasonable and significant additional risk of harm.

Specific emergency use of an investigational new drug (21 CFR 312.36) may be authorized by FDA when there is insufficient time to submit and review a treatment IND. However, an IND must be submitted as soon as practicable after receiving the emergency authorization. The regulation provides telephone numbers for communicating such requests during or after normal working hours.

Drugs for Serious or Life-Threatening Diseases: Expanded Access and Expedited Procedures

The laws and regulations administered by FDA include provisions to make experimental drugs for lifethreatening diseases more widely available to severely ill patients (expanded access), and to speed up the development, review and approval of the applications for these products (expedited procedures). These provisions include the following.

Expanded Access Mechanisms

21 CFR 312 Subpart E-Drugs Intended to Treat Life-threatening and Severely Debilitating Illness:

- Early Consultation and Expedited Approval: 21 CFR 312.82 allows meetings with FDA reviewing officials at the pre-IND stage and again at the End-of-Phase 1 (EoP1), at the sponsor's request. The pre-IND meeting's purpose is to review and agree on animal study designs needed to initiate human testing, and to discuss Phase 1 trial scope and design and IND content and format. The EoP1 Meeting is to finalize the design of controlled Phase 2 trials, to ensure data will be sufficient to support marketing approval.
- Treatment Protocols: As discussed under Special INDs, an IND sponsor or sponsor-investigator may submit a treatment protocol for an investigational drug, subject to the criteria in 21 CFR 312.34. In addition, under 21 CFR 312.83, FDA may ask a sponsor to submit a treatment protocol for a promising drug.
- Parallel Track: This policy, finalized in the 15 April 1992 *Federal Register*, permits wider access to promising new drugs for Autoimmune Deficiency Syndrome (AIDS)/human immunodeficiency virus (HIV)-related diseases under a separate expanded access protocol that parallels the controlled clinical trials essential to establish a new drug's safety and effectiveness. Under this policy, patients with these illnesses who have no therapeutic alternatives and who cannot participate in the controlled clinical trials can receive investigational drugs that preliminary studies show to be promising.

New Drug Applications

Presubmission Activities

The applicant needs to complete many activities prior to an application submission, including proprietary name submission and review, establishment registration, labeler code assignment and request for a presubmission meeting with the review division.

Proprietary Name Submission and Review

One important activity during the drug development phase is crafting the product's proprietary name (i.e., brand name). The proprietary name is one of the product's critical identifiers for healthcare professionals and consumers. Companies expend a lot of time and money creating the perfect proprietary name. Equally, FDA allocates substantial resources to review a proposed proprietary name to help prevent medication errors.

The applicant should submit proposed proprietary names for FDA review either as part of the original submission or during the review. Submitting the proposed proprietary name is recommended as early as possible. The proprietary name approval request must be submitted no later than when the application is submitted, although applicants may submit the request prior to application submission (perhaps as early as completion of Phase 2 trials) under the NDA, Abbreviated NDA (ANDA) or BLA, or for which proposed indications are not yet sufficiently clear to form the basis of a name evaluation to prevent potential medication errors, FDA does not evaluate proposed names until products have completed Phase 2 trials.

A proprietary name submission should include primary and alternate proposed proprietary names, the proprietary name's intended pronunciation, name derivation, intended proprietary name modifier meanings, the name's pharmacologic/therapeutic category and draft labeling and package insert (if available).

An FDA review of proprietary names includes an evaluation of both the proposed name's safety and promotional aspects. The safety review focuses primarily on preventing medication errors and evaluating other products that may have similar dosage regimens, overlapping strengths, similar names when spoken or a similar appearance when written by hand. The promotional review is to determine whether the name implies superiority, attempts to minimize risk or overstates efficacy.

For a proposed proprietary name submitted during the IND phase, FDA will review and communicate a decision about the name within 180 days of the submission's receipt date. For a proposed proprietary name submitted with the original NDA or BLA, or as a part of a supplement, FDA will review and communicate a decision within 90 days of the submission's receipt date. Proprietary names accepted during a pre-review will be re-reviewed 90 days before the action date to ensure they still are acceptable.

Establishment Registration and National Drug Code

A company manufacturing human drugs, certain biological products and animal drugs must register the manufacturing facility before FDA will approve a marketing application. Specifically, owners or operators of all drug establishments not exempt under *FD&C Act* Section 510(g) or Subpart B of Part 207 that engage in the drug manufacture, preparation, propagation, compounding or processing shall register and submit a list of every drug in commercial distribution [21 CFR 207.20(a)].

Prior to 1 June 2009, paper forms for Drug Establishment Registration and Drug Product Listing were completed and submitted to FDA. Changes to the *FD&C Act* under *FDAAA* require drug establishment registration and drug listing information to be submitted electronically. Therefore, as of 1 June 2009, FDA began accepting only electronic submissions for registration and listing unless a waiver is granted.

The National Drug Code (NDC) system is designed to provide drugs in the US with a specific number that describes the product. Per 21 CFR 207.35, the NDC is limited to 10 digits; however, the passing of the *Health Insurance Portability and Accountability Act* of 1996 (*HIPAA*) propagated more-consistent 11-digit codes to allow for proper reimbursement billing. The first NDC segment is assigned by FDA and identifies the vendor (or labeler) involved in the drug's manufacture, packaging or distribution. The second segment conveys the product codes and comprises the entity, strength, dosage form and formulation. The third segment, or package code, indicates the package forms and sizes. The manufacturer assigns the second and third segments of a given product's code

Prior to June 2009, FDA would input the full NDC number and information into a database known as the Drug Registration and Listing System (DRLS). However, with electronic submissions and electronic DRLS (eDRLS), this now is done automatically. More recently, *FDASIA* amended the *FD&C Act* by requiring additional information to be submitted to register domestic or foreign drug facilities. This additional information includes each drug establishment's unique facility identifier and a point of contact email address. Further, as of 1 October 2012, the re-registration period for domestic and foreign drug manufacturers has been changed to 1 October to 31 December of each year, instead of the previously more open-ended period of on or before 31 December. A link providing more direction on how to list and register products properly is included under Electronic Drug Registration and Listing Instructions below.

Since June 2009, eDRLS has included prescription and over-the-counter (OTC) products, as well as finished and unfinished drug products. FDA utilizes information from the eDRLS database to update the NDC directory on a daily basis (see the NDC Directory at www.accessdata.fda.gov/scripts/cder/ndc/default.cfm). Additionally, FDA relies on establishment registration and drug listing information to administer many of its programs, such as postmarketing surveillance (including risk-based scheduling and inspection planning), protection against bioterrorism, drug shortage prevention, drug recall management and user fee assessment.

Presubmission Meeting

Sponsors can request meetings with FDA at various stages during the drug development process. A Presubmission Meeting, considered a Type B Meeting (see Chapter 4), is highly recommended prior to NDA or BLA submission. It generally is advisable to hold such a meeting four to six months prior to the anticipated submission date.

The New Drug Application or Biologics License Application

Goals

An NDA or BLA's goals are to provide enough information to permit FDA reviewers to reach key decisions on whether: the drug is safe and effective when used for the indications described in the labeling; the drug's benefits outweigh its risks; the proposed labeling is appropriate; and the drug's manufacturing methods and the controls used to maintain drug quality are adequate to preserve its identity, strength, quality and purity.

Content and Format

An application must provide all pertinent drug development information. The quantity of information can vary from one application to another; however, the application structure is consistent. Per 21 CFR 314.50 and 601 (NDA and BLA, respectively), a submission must include an application form, an index, a summary, five or six technical sections, case report forms and tabulations, patent information, financial disclosure or certification and labeling. Technical sections may include product quality, nonclinical pharmacology and toxicology, human pharmacokinetics and bioavailability, microbiology, statistical and clinical data. The product quality section should describe the composition, manufacture and specifications of both the drug substance and the drug product, as well as fairly detailed descriptions of all manufacturing controls and stability data. The nonclinical pharmacology and toxicology section should describe any animal and *in vitro* drug studies that help define the drug's pharmacologic properties and address toxicity related to its administration. The clinical section should include a description of all clinical investigations completed in support of the drug's efficacy and safety, as well as the study protocols and copies of case report forms

Figure 13-2. Diagrammatic Representation of the ICH Common Technical Document (CTD)

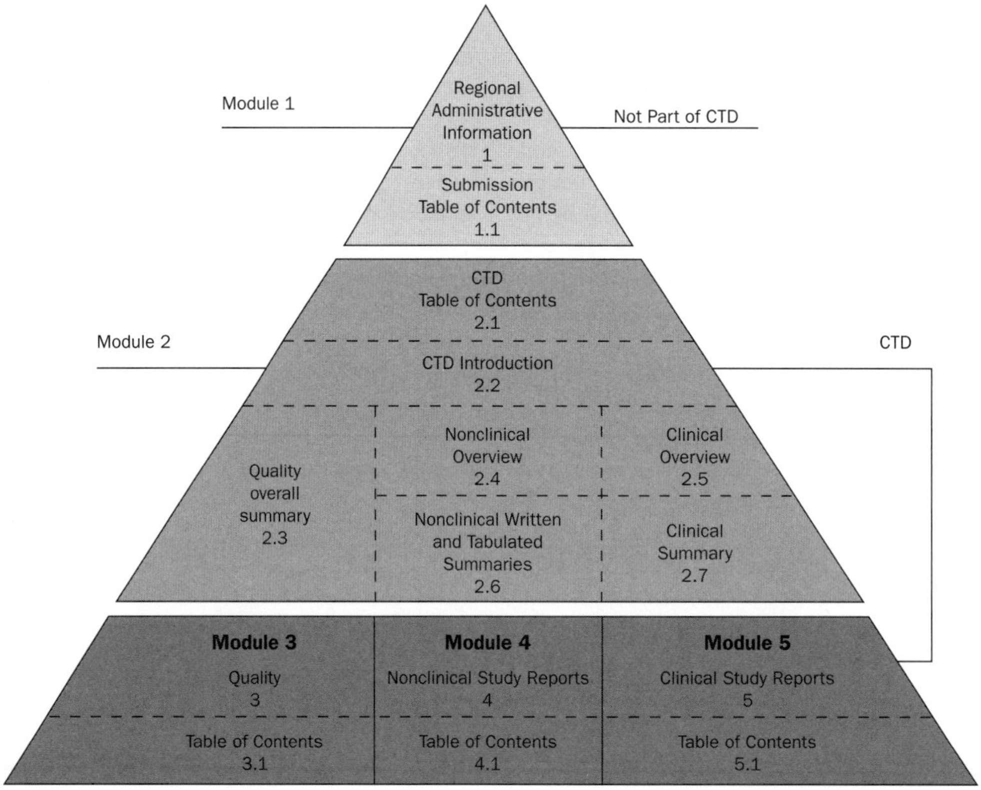

for each patient who died during a clinical study or did not complete a study because of an adverse event, regardless of the incident's relationship to the study drug.

Copies of the proposed drug product labeling—including the package insert, carton and container labels and Medication Guide—should be included in the application. FDA requires labeling to be submitted electronically in a format the agency can review and process. The labeling content must utilize structured product labeling (SPL) format with an extensible markup language (XML) backbone. SPL has several advantages: the exchange of information between computer systems, text comparison automation by section, and exchange of information needed for other submissions (i.e., cross-referencing). SPL allows labeling content to be searched, moved between systems and combined with other data sources, and lends itself to supporting electronic healthcare initiatives.

Labeling is required to be in Physician Labeling Rule (PLR) format, as described in the February 2013 FDA *Guidance for Industry: Labeling for Human Prescription Drug and Biological Products—Implementing the PLR Content and Format Requirements.* The guidance notes that on 24 January 2006, FDA published a final rule amending the requirements for the labeling content and format for human prescription drugs and biological products. The rule commonly is referred to as the PLR because it addresses prescription drug labeling used by prescribers and other healthcare practitioners. The rule was designed to make prescription drug labeling information easier for healthcare practitioners to access, read and use to facilitate their prescribing decisions.

Common Technical Document Format

As outlined above, a huge amount of information is submitted to support a marketing application. Generally, essentially similar scientific and clinical information is required in countries where a manufacturer (or applicant) plans to market the drug. Because the information is similar, and to allow manufacturers to proceed more quickly and consistently with the submission and application process, ICH developed the Common Technical Document (CTD) format (**Figure 13-2**). The CTD provides a harmonized structure and format for new marketing applications submitted in the US, EU, Japan and other countries that adhere to ICH guidance.

Per the CTD format, an application is divided into five modules. Module 1 contains region-specific information, and Modules 2 through 5 are intended to be common across all regions. Module 1 contains administrative and prescribing information (e.g., application forms, proposed labeling and applicable patent information). Module 2 contains CTD summaries (e.g., a quality overall summary and nonclinical and clinical overview and summaries). Module 3 is quality data or product quality information (e.g., drug substance and drug product data). Module 4 includes nonclinical study reports (e.g., pharmacodynamic, pharmacokinetic and toxicology data, as well as relevant literature references cited in the Module 2 nonclinical summaries). Module 5 contains clinical study reports (e.g., study protocols, case report forms, integrated safety and efficacy summaries and relevant clinical literature references and references cited in the Module 2 clinical summaries).

Electronic Common Technical Document Format

Historically, submissions to FDA have been in paper format. Paper submissions not only require many sponsor and FDA resources but also a lot of storage space. FDA attempted to address this issue by creating electronic submission standards (eSubs). FDA started accepting electronic CTDs (eCTD) in 2003, and they became the recommended standard in 2008.

The value of electronic submissions is well recognized. Under *FDASIA*, FDA, working with stakeholders, will issue draft and final guidance on e-submission standards and format. E-submission requirements will be phased in over the next few years, starting with original NDA and BLA submissions, and eventually requiring all original commercial INDs and their amendments to be submitted electronically, as well.

The formats of the paper CTD and eCTD submissions are different. With an eCTD submission, each document is separate (granular) and named according to ICH specifications. Each submission has its own eCTD XML backbone file, which allows FDA to receive, archive and review the submission. Once an application is submitted in electronic format, all subsequent submissions to the application also are submitted electronically and should include eCTD backbone files (once eCTD, always eCTD). Without these backbone files, FDA will be unable to process subsequent submissions. Unless submitted through the electronic submission gateway (ESG) as described below, FDA also recommends electronic file cover letters include a description of the submission's approximate size (e.g., 4 gigabytes), the type and number of electronic media used (e.g., two DVDs), a regulatory and technical point of contact, and a statement the submission is virus free, with a description of the software used to virus-check the file.

At any time, a sponsor can decide to convert its paper application to an electronic filing. Should a sponsor decide to do so, it is not necessary to provide all previous submissions in electronic format with eCTD backbone files; instead, the electronic filing may begin with the planned submission. For ease of conversion, the Comprehensive Table of Contents Headings and Hierarchy maps the application to the eCTD format. When converting and cross-referencing to past submissions, the applicant should be sure to include specific information, such as the date of the previous submission, document name, page numbers, volume number and approval dates, or may consider including any items critical for review of the current submission within the electronic format submission in order for the reviewer to find it more easily.

Types of Applications

There are several types of drug applications:

- Traditional 505(b)(1) NDA—*FD&C Act*, Section 505(b)(1)
- 505(b)(2) NDA—*FD&C Act*, Section 505(b)(2)
- Abbreviated NDA (ANDA)—*FD&C Act*, Section 505(j)
- Original BLA—*PHS Act*, Section 351(a)
- Biosimilar BLA—*PHS Act*, Section 351(k)

505(b)(1) NDA (Traditional NDA)

A 505(b)(1) application is a complete NDA that contains all the applicant's studies necessary to demonstrate a drug's safe and effective use. A 505(b)(1) application contains all information as outlined in 21 CFR 314.50.

505(b)(2) NDA

A 505(b)(2) application also contains information required in a 505(b)(1) application necessary to demonstrate safe and effective use of a drug; however, the applicant can provide some of the information required for approval in the application from studies it did not conduct and for which it has not obtained a right of reference.

Section 505(b)(2) was added to the *FD&C Act* by the *Drug Price Competition and Patent Term Restoration Act* of 1984 (*Hatch-Waxman Act*) to allow companies to develop alternative therapies more quickly by relying on existing data. Applicants may rely on published literature that supports approval of an application and/or on FDA's previous findings of safety and effectiveness of an approved drug. For example, a 505(b)(2) application can be submitted if the applicant has changed a product's route of administration from an oral form to an intramuscular injection. In this instance, the applicant can rely on the efficacy data and some of the safety data established for the drug's oral formulation already approved by FDA but will have to conduct studies showing safety and efficacy that relate to the change to the intramuscular dosage form. In addition, the applicant will have to establish a bridge (e.g., via comparative bioavailability data) between the proposed drug and the approved listed drug to demonstrate that reliance on FDA's previous findings of safety and effectiveness is scientifically justified.

Sections 505(b)(2) and 505(j) of the *FD&C Act* together replaced FDA's paper NDA policy, which had permitted an applicant to rely on studies published in the scientific literature to demonstrate the safety and effectiveness of duplicates of certain post-1962 pioneer drug products.

505(j) Abbreviated NDA (ANDA)

A 505(j) application is considered abbreviated because, generally, the applicant is not required to include nonclinical and clinical data necessary to demonstrate safety and effectiveness. Instead, it contains chemistry and bioequivalence data to show the proposed product is identical in active ingredient, dosage form, strength, route of administration, labeling, quality, performance characteristics and intended use to the previously-approved reference listed drug (RLD). Additional detailed information on generic drug submissions can be found in Chapter 15.

351(a) BLA (Original BLA)

A 351(a) application is a complete BLA that contains all the applicant's studies conducted to demonstrate a drug's safe and effective use. A 351(a) BLA contains all information as outlined in 21 CFR 601.2. Additional detailed information on biologics submissions can be found in Chapter 24.

351(k) BLA (Biosimilar BLA)

A 351(k) application is an abbreviated BLA for a biological product that is demonstrated to be biosimilar to or interchangeable with an FDA-licensed biological product. For additional information, see Chapter 24.

Submission of the Marketing Application and Next Steps

Once the paper application has been compiled and is ready for dispatch, it can be submitted by regular post or express mail to FDA's Document Control Room.

Electronic CTD submissions are submitted either on electronic media or through the FDA ESG. If submitted on electronic media, it should be sent by regular post or express mail just like the paper submission. The ESG is a centralized, agency-wide communications point for receiving secure electronic regulatory submissions. It electronically receives, acknowledges, routes to and notifies a reviewing center of the receipt of an electronic submission. The ESG is a conduit, or highway, along which submissions travel to reach their final destinations within FDA. ESG staff do not open or review submissions.

Upon receipt of the application, FDA has 60 days to determine whether the application is sufficiently complete to allow for a substantive review. If FDA determines the application is complete, it will be filed on day 60. If FDA determines the application is not complete (see 21 CFR 314.101[d]), FDA may Refuse to File (RTF) it and, if so, will issue a formal RTF letter by day 60 providing the reasons for the decision. By eliminating incomplete applications from the review queue, FDA is able to focus its resources on complete applications.

Note FDA tends to be more flexible in accommodating drugs intended for critical diseases, particularly when there is no alternative therapy. In such cases, the agency and applicant often will work together to find a balanced resolution to allow application review to begin as quickly as possible. Note also, FDA may accept some parts of an application and RTF others (e.g., file one of two proposed indications for use and RTF the other). The applicant may resubmit the application after addressing FDA's RTF issues; FDA then determines whether the resubmitted application can be filed.

If an applicant strongly disagrees with FDA's decision to RTF an application, the applicant has 30 days after receiving the RTF letter to request a meeting with the agency. Following the meeting, the applicant can request the agency to file the application over protest. In this event, the date of filing will be 60 days after the date the applicant requested the meeting.

For applications that will be filed, FDA performs an initial filing review by day 60 to identify filing review issues, which are substantive deficiencies or concerns that may have significant impact on FDA's ability to complete the review and approval of the application. Filing review issues are distinct from application deficiencies that serve as the basis for an RTF action. Note FDA's initial filing review represents a preliminary application review and is not indicative of deficiencies that may be identified later in the review cycle.

FDA then will inform the applicant in writing whether there are filing review issues by issuing a letter mandated by *PDUFA* within 14 days of the determination (also called a day 74 letter). The day 74 letter states the date the application was received, which is also the date the review clock begins. The day 74 letter provides the planned review timeline and includes an action date, when FDA will provide a decision on the application, as well as dates when the applicant can expect to receive feedback from the review division on proposed labeling and postmarketing requirements or commitments. The day 74 letter also identifies the review classification granted by FDA (i.e., Standard Review or Priority Review). For applications reviewed under the *PDUFA V* Program, the day 74 letter also will state whether the division is considering convening an Advisory Committee Meeting.

For additional information on filing review issues and the day 74 letter, refer to MaPP 6010.5 NDAs: Filing Review Issues.

During the review period, FDA may ask the applicant for additional information (solicited information), or the applicant may submit additional information on its own initiative (unsolicited information). If the new information constitutes a major amendment, FDA may determine an extension to the *PDUFA* action date is needed to review the new information. Only one three-month extension can be given per review cycle. For a solicited major amendment

Figure 13-3. Timeline and Product Review Clock

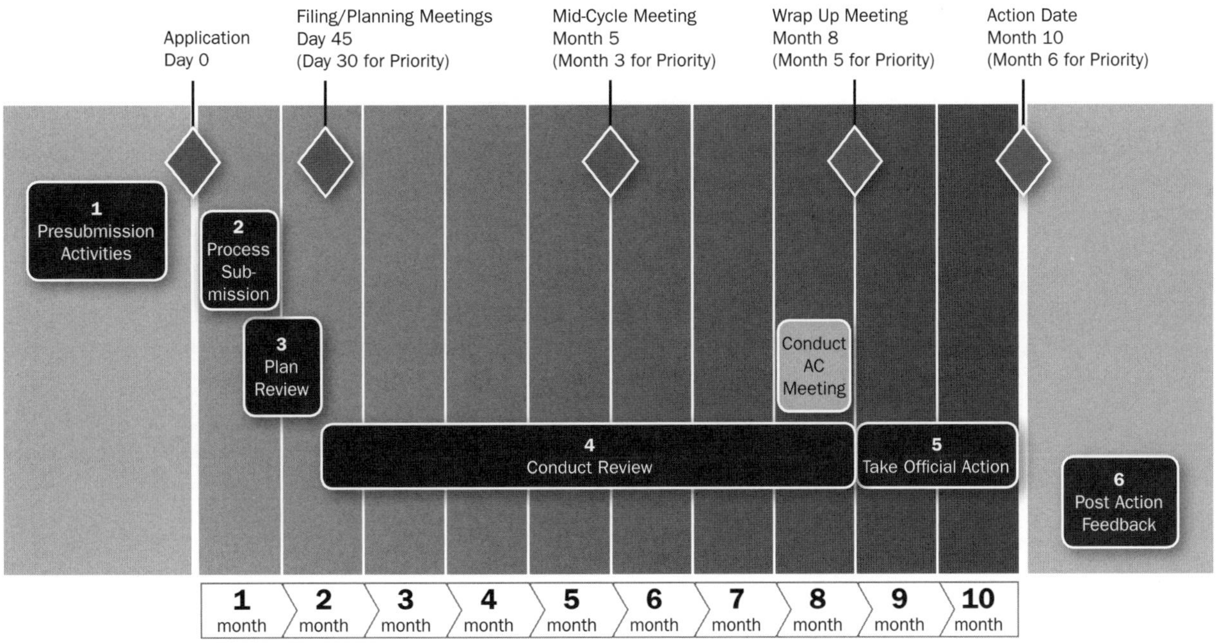

that extends the *PDUFA* action date, FDA also will provide a new timeline for feedback on proposed labeling and postmarketing requirements or commitments. Thus, an applicant's strategy for providing information contained in the application should be planned very carefully.

Food and Drug Administration Review Process

Once an application is received and validated, it is routed to the regulatory project manager (RPM) in the appropriate review division. The RPM will ask supervisory team leaders from appropriate disciplines to assign reviewers. The first review task is to determine, from each specific discipline, whether the application is fileable (see Submission of the Marketing Application and Next Steps above).

The review team consists of various disciplines, such as clinical, pharmacology and toxicology, chemistry, clinical pharmacology, etc.

It is recommended the number of NDA amendments after submission be minimized, with the exception of the 120-Day Safety Update. Specifically, for all filed NDAs, a Safety Update is required 120 days after the NDA is submitted.

Each disciplinary group completes its review and determines whether the data can support the drug's approval. During the review process, a reviewer may identify a minor deficiency, may need a topic clarified or may need additional information to facilitate his or her review. These requests for additional information usually are communicated through an information request, or advice letter, and these letters generally are handled via email, telephone or regular mail. As the regulatory contact for the application, the RPM facilitates these communications. Applicants submit amendments to the application in an attempt to address all additional information requests. If serious deficiencies exist, the review division has the option of notifying applicants via a discipline review (DR) letter after each discipline has finished the initial review of its section of the pending application. DR letters had been used sparingly since the release of the 2001 FDA *Guidance for Industry Information Request and Discipline Review Letters Under the Prescription Drug User Fee Act* (2001).

PDUFA V led to a renewed focus on DR letters for applications in the Program, as outlined in the *PDUFA Reauthorization Performance Goals and Procedures Fiscal years 2013 Through 2017*. FDA intends to complete primary and secondary discipline reviews of the application and issue DR letters in advance of the planned late-cycle meeting.

If additional scientific expertise is needed outside the core review team, the review division may consult other parts of the center or beyond (e.g., the Center for Devices and Radiological Health). For certain applications, opinions from outside experts also may be sought through the advisory committee process or by special government employees (SGEs).

As the review proceeds, FDA determines whether any bioresearch monitoring (BIMO) or current Good Manufacturing Practice (CGMP) inspections are required prior to approval. The results of these inspections will allow the agency to determine the credibility and accuracy of the data submitted in the application (see Preapproval Inspections (PAI) below).

Figure 13-4. Timeline and PDUFA Review Clock for Products Under "The Program" Described in *PDUFA V*

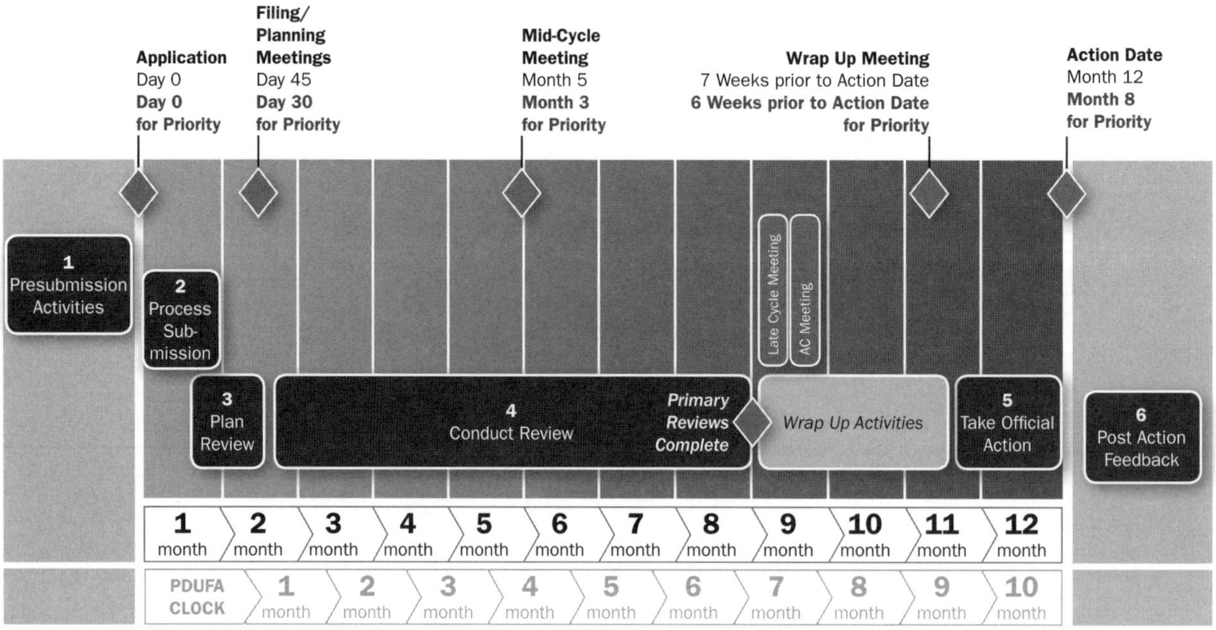

Source: CDER 21st Century Review Process Desk Reference Guide

FDA will determine whether Postmarketing Requirements (PMRs) and/or Postmarketing Commitments (PMCs) are necessary. If so, this is communicated to the applicant, and FDA and the applicant discuss and agree on specific studies and specific milestone dates, including dates for final protocol submission, study or trial completion and final report submission.

In parallel, with PMR and PMC determinations, FDA reviews the product labeling and determines whether it accurately reflects the product's safety and efficacy and allows physicians, healthcare professionals and consumers to determine whether the drug's benefits outweigh its risks. The agency then will decide if it is ready to take action on the application.

Application review consists of several stages and involves a multidisciplinary team (see **Figures 13-3** and **13-4**). The primary review staff summarize preliminary review findings at a mid-cycle meeting. Discussions at the mid-cycle meeting can include the need for additional information from the applicant and/or additional scientific expertise within the center and, potentially, initial discussions regarding the need for a REMS, or potential postmarketing commitments or requirements, if the product is approved. During the review, the applicant's proposed labeling is reviewed, and comprehensive comments are conveyed to the applicant. At the wrap-up meeting, discussions can include issues that preclude the application's approvability and details of the REMS or postmarketing commitments or requirements, as needed.

If the product is an NME or an original BLA, the signatory authority for the application is the office director; the signatory authority for all other applications, including efficacy supplements, is usually the division director.

Risk Evaluation and Mitigation Strategies

Title IX, Subtitle A, Section 901 of *FDAAA* amended the *FD&C Act* by creating Section 505-1, which authorizes FDA to require applicants of certain prescription drug products to submit a proposed REMS if the agency determines one is necessary to ensure a drug's benefits outweigh its risks. An applicant also may voluntarily submit a proposed REMS without having been required to do so by FDA. FDA can request the REMS at the time of the original application's initial submission or at any time after its approval (if FDA becomes aware of new safety information and determines a REMS is necessary). Once FDA notifies the applicant a REMS is necessary, the applicant must submit a proposed REMS within 120 days.

The proposed REMS' content should describe its proposed goals adequately and its specific elements. The proposed REMS must include, at a minimum, a timetable for the submission of strategy assessments at 18 months, three years and seven years after FDA approves the REMS. The proposed REMS also may include one or more of the following elements: Medication Guide (21 CFR 208); Patient Package Insert; communication plan to healthcare providers; and Elements to Assure Safe Use (ETASU). The proposed REMS also should contain a thorough explanation of the rationale for, and supporting information about, the content of the proposed REMS, and a timetable specifying when each element will be implemented.

ETASU may be required if a drug has been shown to be effective but is associated with a serious adverse event. In such a case, the drug can be approved only if, or would be withdrawn unless, elements are included in the REMS to mitigate the specific serious risks listed in the product's labeling. ETASU may be required for approved products when an assessment and Medication Guide, Patient Package Insert or communication plan are not sufficient to mitigate these risks. An example of an ETASU would be a system or process to ensure certain laboratory test result outcomes are obtained before a drug may be dispensed.

The applicant must reach agreement with FDA on REMS submission elements and the implementation timelines. FDA will determine which REMS elements are necessary to ensure the drug's benefits outweigh its risks and decide on the approvability of the REMS. FDA also must approve voluntarily submitted REMS. An approved REMS submitted voluntarily is subject to the same requirements and enforcement as a required REMS. FDA will notify applicants who voluntarily submit a proposed REMS whether the strategy will be required. If FDA determines a REMS is not required, an applicant may undertake voluntary risk management measures to be performed without a REMS.

Once FDA approves the REMS, the strategy will serve as the basis for inspection and enforcement. A drug will be considered to be misbranded if the applicant fails to comply with a requirement of the approved REMS. An applicant who violates a REMS requirement also is subject to civil monetary penalties of up to $250,000 per violation, not to exceed $1 million in a single proceeding. These penalties increase if the violation continues more than 30 days after FDA notifies the applicant. Penalties double for the second 30-day period, and continue to double for subsequent 30-day periods, up to $1 million per period and $10 million per proceeding. In addition, the sponsor may not introduce into interstate commerce an approved drug noncompliant with REMS' conditions. For additional information on REMS, refer to MaPP 6700.6 REMS Questions and Answers.

Advisory Committee Meeting

Advisory Committee Meetings are an integral part of the approval process and are discussed in Chapter 5. Situations that frequently lead FDA to convene an Advisory Committee meeting are described in the relevant draft guidance. According to *FDAAA* (2007), a drug characterized by "...no active ingredient (including any ester or salt of the active ingredient) of which has been approved in any other application under this section or section 351 of the Public Health Service Act" needs to be evaluated by an independent FDA Advisory Committee, unless FDA delineates why such a review will be unnecessary.

FDAAA also amended the *FD&C Act* to limit conflicts of interest and restrict the eligibility criteria for serving on FDA Advisory Committees. It was felt these provisions made the recruitment of suitable individuals for Advisory Committees more difficult. More recently, *FDASIA* largely eliminated those restrictions. Detailed discussions and analysis of the changes can be found in a number of recent third-party newsletters.

PAIs

FDA may approve a drug product if, among other requirements, the methods used in, and the facilities and controls used for, the drug's manufacture, processing, packing and testing are found adequate, and ensure and preserve its identity, strength, quality and purity.

Prior to approving an application, FDA may inspect manufacturing facilities (CGMP inspections), as well as facilities or sites where the drug was tested in nonclinical or clinical studies (BIMO inspections). A PAI is performed to contribute to FDA's assurance a manufacturing establishment listed in a drug product application is capable of manufacturing a drug, and data are accurate and complete.

Although the risk-based decision is left to the agency's discretion, BIMO and CGMP inspections generally are conducted for most new NDA and original BLA applications. FDA is likely to conduct PAI inspections in the following instances:

- NMEs or original BLAs
- priority reviews
- the first application filed by an applicant
- for-cause inspections (e.g., if one clinical site has a significantly better trial outcome than other sites)
- original or supplemental applications, if the CGMP status is unknown (e.g., it has been more than two years since the domestic facility was last inspected, or the establishment is new and has yet to be inspected by FDA or another global regulatory authority)

CDER evaluates the adequacy of the applicant's data and relies on facility inspections to verify that data's authenticity and accuracy. This ensures applications are not approved if it is determined the applicant cannot demonstrate the ability to operate with integrity and in compliance with all applicable requirements.

Per *FDASIA*, all applicants are expected to include a comprehensive and readily located list of facilities and establishments. FDA will use this list to determine the need for potential inspections of foreign and domestic sites that will manufacture a drug for the US market, or have completed a study to support the approval of a drug that will be marketed in the US.

FDA Decision on the Application

One of two actions may be taken on an application, namely an approval action or a complete response. The latter lists all review deficiencies identified by FDA and identifies steps the applicant should take to address these deficiencies in a future submission before the application can be approved.

Approval letters are issued when FDA has determined a drug is safe and effective, can be manufactured acceptably and is labeled appropriately. An approval is effective on the date of approval letter issuance, granting authorization to market the drug for sale in the US.

Postmarketing Requirements and Commitments

The approval letter also stipulates any postmarketing requirements and commitments. A postmarketing requirement is a study (e.g., an observational epidemiologic study, an animal study or a laboratory experiment) or clinical trial the applicant must conduct after the application is approved. It includes studies that may be required under the *Pediatric Research Equity Act* (*PREA*, 21 CFR 314.55[b]), the Animal Efficacy Rule (21 CFR 314.610[b][1]), Accelerated Approval regulations (21 CFR 314.510 and 601.41), or *FDAAA* (Title IX, Section 901). The applicant must report the status of each postmarketing requirement annually.

A postmarketing commitment is a written commitment by the applicant to FDA to provide additional information after application approval. It is not a postmarketing requirement, although 506B-reportable postmarketing commitments require annual status reports to be submitted by the applicant (*FD&C Act* Section 506B mandates annual status reports and obligates FDA to make certain information about postmarketing commitments publicly available).

Maintenance of the Application

After the application is approved, the applicant is expected to continue a number of activities, including the submission of expedited reporting of serious, unexpected adverse events that occur in the postmarketing setting; Periodic Safety Update Reports that provide a review of the drug's safety profile since approval; and Annual Reports. Updated stability data and annual updates to establishment registrations and drug listings also may be necessary. Please refer to Chapter 13 for more information on postmarketing activities.

Programs for Expediting Drug Development and Review

FDA currently uses four programs to expedite the development and review of new drugs for serious and life-threatening diseases with an unmet medical need:

1. Fast Track Designation
2. Accelerated Approval
3. Priority Review
4. Breakthrough Therapy Designation

An investigational agent may be eligible for any combination of these programs if it meets the requirements. For example, approximately 80% of applications approved under a Fast Track designation were also Priority Review drugs, and sponsors need to apply for these different programs separately. A novel agent with breakthrough designation is subject to the same drug development and review programs as those agents with Fast Track designation, although breakthrough products receive more development advice and are assigned top division reviewers. Accelerated Approval will apply if appropriate, and all the criteria under 21 CFR 314 Subpart H or Subpart E are met.

A comprehensive guidance has been issued on this subject, FDA *Guidance for Industry: Expedited Programs for Serious Conditions—Drugs and Biologics* (May 2014). A summary of the programs and their impact follows.

Fast Track Designation

Fast Track designation is designed to facilitate the development and expedite the review of drugs 1) to treat serious or life-threatening diseases, and 2) that have the potential to address unmet medical needs. Addressing an unmet medical need is defined as providing a therapy where none exists or one that may be potentially superior to an existing therapy. Fast Track designation may apply to drugs or biologics intended to treat a broad range of serious diseases, including AIDS, Alzheimer's disease, cancer, epilepsy and diabetes. Once a drug receives Fast Track designation, FDA offers the sponsor early and frequent communication to facilitate an efficient development program. The frequency of communications ensures questions and issues are resolved in a timely manner, often leading to earlier drug approval. Fast Track drug sponsors also are eligible for Rolling Reviews of applications, allowing earlier submission and review initiation.

The request for Fast Track designation can be submitted simultaneously with the IND, or at any time thereafter, prior to receiving marketing approval. To maximize the use of the Fast Track incentives, it is best to include the designation request in the original IND submission or as soon as possible thereafter. Note the request for Fast Track designation can be granted by FDA only upon submission of an IND.

FDA will respond to a request for Fast Track designation within 60 days of receipt. If FDA determines Fast Track criteria have been met, the review division will issue a designation letter stating Fast Track designation is granted for the product's development for treating the specific serious or life-threatening condition. The letter also will request sponsors to design and perform studies that can show whether the product fulfills unmet medical needs. FDA can issue a nondesignation letter either because the Fast Track request package was incomplete, or the drug development program failed to meet the required criteria. The nondesignation letter will explain the reasons for FDA's decision.

FDA will respond to a subsequent request for Fast Track designation after a nondesignation determination within 60 days of receiving the new request. Sponsors must continue to meet the Fast Track criteria throughout product development to retain the designation. The sponsor should expect the appropriateness of continuing the drug development program's Fast Track designation to be discussed and evaluated at different times during the process, including at the EoP2 Meeting and the Presubmission Meeting. If FDA determines a product is no longer eligible, it will notify the sponsor the product is no longer part of the Fast Track drug development program. Sponsors can appeal FDA's decision through the dispute resolution process (21 CFR 10.75, 312.48, and 314.103).

Accelerated Approval

The Accelerated Approval process under Subpart H (Drugs, 21 CFR 314) and Subpart E (Biologics, 21 CFR 601) was created by FDA in 1992 at the height of the HIV/AIDS crisis. It allows drug approvals based on surrogate endpoints that are reasonably likely to predict clinical benefit under the following conditions: the disease to be treated must be serious or life-threatening, and the treatment must provide meaningful therapeutic benefit over existing treatments. In cancer drug development, a surrogate endpoint could be tumor shrinkage and the clinical benefit increased overall survival.

Under these provisions, approval requires the applicant to study the drug further to verify and describe its clinical benefit where there is uncertainty about the relation of the surrogate end point to clinical benefit, or the observed clinical benefit to ultimate outcome.

Priority Review

In 1992, under *PDUFA*, FDA agreed to specific goals for improving drug review times using a two-tiered review time system: Priority Review and Standard Review. Priority Review designation is given to drugs that offer major advancements in treatment or provide a treatment where no adequate therapy exists. FDA reviews priority applications more quickly than standard applications, in six months versus 10 months (in eight months versus 12 months for applications in the Program). Prior to the enactment of *PDUFA*, CDER application review was subject to the 180-day review period described in 21 CFR 314.100 (the regulatory clock), with review extensions allowed for receipt of major amendments. In addition, prior to 1992, CDER used a three-tiered therapeutic-potential classification system (type A—important therapeutic gain; type B—modest therapeutic gain; and type C—little or no therapeutic gain) to determine application review priorities. Potentially eligible for Priority Review are drugs with the potential to provide significant advances in treatment in at least one of the following instances:

- provide evidence of increased effectiveness in treatment, prevention or disease diagnosis
- eliminate or substantially reduce a treatment-limiting drug reaction
- provide documented evidence of enhanced patient compliance to treatment schedule and dose
- provide evidence of safety and effectiveness in a new subpopulation, such as children

An applicant may submit a request for Priority Review to FDA, providing adequate evidence that its drug product meets one of the criteria listed above. Although Fast Track- and Breakthrough Therapy-designated products generally are eligible for Priority Review, because they are intended to treat serious or life-threatening conditions and address unmet medical needs, Fast Track or Breakthrough Therapy designation does not automatically convey a Priority Review. The applicant should request Priority Review with appropriate justification in the cover letter. CDER currently grants Priority Review for drugs that provide a significant improvement, compared to marketed products, in the treatment, diagnosis or prevention of a disease, i.e., eligibility is not limited to drugs for a serious or life-threatening disease. A Fast Track- or Breakthrough Therapy-designated product ordinarily would meet Priority Review criteria.

FDA determines within 60 days whether a Priority Review or Standard Review designation will be assigned. If Priority Review is granted, the applicant still must provide the same amount of scientific and medical evidence as required under Standard Review classification for FDA to approve the drug.

Breakthrough Therapy Designation

In 2012, *FDASIA* gave FDA a new pathway to expedite the development of therapies that show substantial promise in early clinical trials. This new authority arose from discussions between FDA, the National Institutes of Health (NIH), industry, academia and patient groups on how to create a novel pathway for developing breakthrough therapies. A drug company may seek Breakthrough Therapy designation of a drug if: it is for a serious and life-threatening disease, and preliminary clinical evidence shows the drug may offer substantial improvement over existing therapies on one or more clinically significant endpoints. Once FDA designates a drug as a Breakthrough Therapy, the drug qualifies for the same benefits as Fast Track-designated products, in addition to an organizational commitment from FDA and intensive FDA guidance and interaction throughout the development process to streamline the drug's clinical trials and review.

Rolling Review

In addition to the standard expedited programs, FDA may consider reviewing portions of a marketing application before the complete NDA or BLA is submitted (Rolling

Review). To qualify for a Rolling Review, Fast Track designation must have been granted. In addition, the pivotal study must be complete or near completion. A sponsor seeking a Rolling Review may submit a Rolling Review request simultaneously with a Fast Track designation request. The sponsor should provide a schedule for submission of portions of the application. If the Rolling Review request is granted, FDA may review portions of the application as they become available. However, FDA is not obligated to start the review upon receipt of a portion. The *PDUFA* goal date is determined upon receipt of the application's final portion, whereas the user fee is due upon receipt of the first portion. Applicants are advised to initiate discussion about their plans for submitting a Rolling Review NDA or BLA at the Presubmission Meeting.

Special Drug Development Incentive Programs

Orphan Drug Act and *PREA* programs are the most well-known special incentive programs and will be discussed in detail in other chapters of this book. This section briefly introduces programs designed to stimulate the development of new antimicrobial drugs, drugs for certain tropical diseases and the Presidential Emergency Plan for AIDS Relief (PEPFAR).

Antibiotics

FDASIA contains specific provisions to incentivize development of antibiotics, known as Generating Antibiotic Incentives Now (GAIN). GAIN is designed to stimulate development of drugs for the treatment of serious or life-threatening infections caused by bacteria or fungi. Eligible drugs must be designated as qualified infectious disease products (QIDPs). QIDP designation benefits include Fast Track designation, FDA Priority Review and a five-year marketing exclusivity extension granted at the time of NDA approval (e.g., five-year New Chemical Entity (NCE) exclusivity, three-year new product exclusivity, seven-year orphan drug exclusivity). CDER has created an Antibacterial Drug Development Task Force (www.fda.gov/Drugs/DevelopmentApprovalProcess/DevelopmentResources/ucm317207.htm). As part of its work, the task force will assist in developing and revising guidance related to antibacterial drug development, as required by GAIN.

Tropical Diseases

A guidance describing tropical disease priority review voucher policies and procedures described in *FD&C Act* Section 524(a)(3) [21 79 U.S.C. 360n(a)(3)] is available and should be used in conjunction with FDA's *Guidance for Industry: Neglected Tropical Diseases of the Developing World: Developing Drugs for Treatment or Prevention* (July 2014).

Briefly, under the law, sponsors of certain marketing applications approved for the prevention or treatment of designated tropical diseases (e.g., malaria, tuberculosis and cholera) receive Priority Review Vouchers (PRVs) from FDA to be used with products of their choice. These vouchers can be transferred to other developers. A PRV entitles the bearer to Priority Review for a future new drug application that would not otherwise qualify for the program. The PRV holder must pay FDA an additional user fee and provide FDA with a one-year notice before redeeming the voucher. Thus far, two manufacturers have been granted PRVs: Novartis for the malaria drug Coartem and Johnson & Johnson for the antimycobacterial drug Sirturo. *FDASIA* includes Section 908, the Rare Pediatric Disease Priority Review Voucher Incentive Program, which extends the voucher program on a trial basis to rare pediatric diseases.

AIDS Relief

Working with implementing organizations and governments in more than 32 countries, PEPFAR has contributed to the rapid acceleration of HIV treatment access, availability of care and support services and HIV prevention interventions. To support PEPFAR's goals, FDA introduced an initiative in 2004 to ensure antiretroviral drugs produced by manufacturers worldwide could be reviewed rapidly, their quality assessed and their acceptability for purchase with PEPFAR funds supported.

As of 2 July 2012, FDA had approved or tentatively approved a total of 152 antiretroviral drugs in association with PEPFAR. Tentative approval means, although existing patents and/or marketing exclusivity prevent the product from being approved for marketing in the US, FDA has found the product meets all manufacturing quality, safety and effectiveness requirements for marketing in the US.

New Drug Product Exclusivity (Hatch-Waxman Exclusivity)

New Drug Product Exclusivity, under Sections 505(c)(3)(E) and (j)(5)(F) of the *FD&C Act* (*Hatch-Waxman Act*), provides the approved NDA holder limited protection from new marketplace competition for the innovation its approved drug product represented. A five-year exclusivity period is granted for drugs containing an NCE. An NCE is a drug containing no active moiety approved by FDA in any other application submitted under *FD&C Act* Section 505(b). An active moiety is the molecule or ion responsible for the drug substance's physiological or pharmacological action. Excluded from the active moiety concept are those appended portions of the molecule that cause the drug to be an ester, salt (including a salt with hydrogen or coordination bonds) or other noncovalent derivative (such as a complex, chelate or clathrate) of the molecule (see 21 CFR 314.108).

A three-year period of exclusivity may be granted for drug products containing an active moiety that has been approved previously, but the applications contain reports of new clinical investigations (other than bioavailability studies) conducted or sponsored by the applicant and essential to the application's approval. For example, changes in an approved drug product that affect its active ingredient, strength, dosage form, route of administration or conditions of use may be granted exclusivity if the application meets the criteria.

Summary

- A prescription drug is any drug approved or licensed for distribution by FDA that requires a healthcare practitioner's authorization before it can be obtained.
- The *FD&C Act* prohibits introduction of a prescription drug product into interstate commerce unless the drug manufacturer has submitted an application and obtained FDA approval.
- An *FD&C Act* exemption can be obtained through the IND to allow sponsors to conduct clinical trials to demonstrate a proposed product's safety and efficacy.
- A well-thought-out regulatory strategy is essential to the ultimate success of an applicant's drug development program and could shave months, or even years, off the product launch timeline.
- A marketing application is required to contain all information pertaining to the drug's development, including chemistry, manufacturing and controls; nonclinical; and clinical data. The application's ultimate goal is to provide adequate information to allow FDA to complete its review and provide a decision on the drug's safety, effectiveness and quality.
- There are three types of NDAs and two types of BLAs. All of these applications should provide adequate information to allow FDA reviewers to conclude the drug is safe and effective when used for the proposed indication and can be manufactured consistently under controlled conditions.
- FDA will take action on a submitted application by issuing either a complete response letter or an approval letter, based on its application assessment. Complete response letters are issued when deficiencies are identified. Approval letters are issued once FDA has determined the drug is safe, effective, can be acceptably manufactured and is labeled appropriately. FDA can require a REMS be implemented or postmarketing studies or clinical trials be conducted after approval.
- Ongoing maintenance of the application is required for as long as it is active. Maintenance includes, but is not limited to, adverse event reporting, submission of Annual Reports and submission of advertising and promotional labeling.
- Many incentives and programs are available to expedite drug development, review and approval. Many of these incentives focus on the development, review and approval of drugs intended to treat serious or life-threatening conditions and/or address an unmet medical need.

Acknowledgements

The author would like to thank the previous authors and reviewers of this chapter including Klaus Gottlieb, MD, MS, MBA, RAC; Giuseppe Randazzo, MS; Maria Walsh, RN, MS; and Karen Meier, MS, RAC, whose work provided an excellent foundation for this chapter. The author also would like to thank Lavonne Patton, PhD; Wayne Vallee, RAC; and Rebecca Lamb-Wharton, PhD and all of Cardinal Health Regulatory Sciences, for their editorial contributions to this work.

Chapter 14

Postapproval Prescription Drug Submissions and Compliance

Updated by Nathalie Innocent, MS, RAC

OBJECTIVES

- ❑ Define and review postmarketing requirements and commitments
- ❑ Define and review the postapproval reporting requirements for prescription drug marketing applications, including chemistry, manufacturing and controls (CMC) and labeling changes, safety reporting and annual reports
- ❑ Understand the impact of changes to an approved product and the information that must be communicated to the agency when such changes are made

LAWS, REGULATIONS AND GUIDANCE COVERED IN THIS CHAPTER

- ❑ 21 CFR 7.40–7.59 Recalls (Including Product Corrections)—Guidance on Policy, Procedures, and Industry Responsibilities
- ❑ 21 CFR 201.122 Exemptions From Adequate Directions for Use—Drugs for processing, repacking, or manufacturing
- ❑ 21 CFR 207 Registration of Producers of Drugs and Listing of Drugs in Commercial Distribution
- ❑ 21 CFR 210 Current Good Manufacturing Practice in Manufacturing, Processing, Packing, or Holding of Drugs; General
- ❑ 21 CFR 211 Current Good Manufacturing Practice for Finished Pharmaceuticals
- ❑ 21 CFR 312.32 IND Safety Reports
- ❑ 21 CFR 314.70 Supplements and other changes to an approved application
- ❑ 21 CFR 314.71 Procedures for submission of a supplement to an approved application
- ❑ 21 CFR 314.72 Change in ownership of an application
- ❑ 21 CFR 314.80 Postmarketing reporting of adverse drug experiences
- ❑ 21 CFR 314.81 Other postmarketing reports
- ❑ 21 CFR 314.420 Drug Master Files
- ❑ 21 CFR 314.550 Accelerated approval of new drugs for serious or life-threatening illnesses—promotional materials
- ❑ *Guidance for Industry: Changes to an Approved NDA or ANDA* (April 2004)
- ❑ *Guidance for Industry: Changes to an Approved NDA or ANDA; Specifications—Use of Enforcement Discretion for Compendial Changes* (November 2004)

- ❑ *Guidance for Industry: SUPAC-IR: Immediate-Release Solid Oral Dosage Forms, Scale-Up and Postapproval Changes: Chemistry, Manufacturing, and Controls, In Vitro Dissolution Testing and In Vivo Bioequivalence Documentation* (November 1995)
- ❑ *SUPAC-IR: Questions and Answers about SUPACIR Guidance* (February 1997)
- ❑ *Guidance for Industry: SUPAC-MR: Modified-Release Solid Oral Dosage Forms: Scale-Up and Postapproval Changes: Chemistry, Manufacturing, and Controls, In Vitro Dissolution Testing and In Vivo Bioequivalence Documentation* (September 1997)
- ❑ *Guidance for Industry: SUPAC-SS: Nonsterile Semisolid Dosage Forms; Scale Up and Postapproval Changes: Chemistry, Manufacturing, and Controls, In Vitro Release Testing and In Vivo Bioequivalence Documentation* (May 1997)
- ❑ *Guidance for Industry: SUPAC: Manufacturing Equipment Addendum* (December 2014)
- ❑ *Guidance for Industry: PAC-ATLS: Postapproval Changes—Analytical Testing Sites* (April 1998)
- ❑ *Draft Guidance for Industry: Comparability Protocols—Chemistry, Manufacturing, and Controls Information* (February 2003)
- ❑ *Guidance for Industry: Format and Content of the CMC Section of an Annual Report* (September 1994)
- ❑ *Guidance for Industry: CMC Postapproval Manufacturing Changes Reportable in Annual Reports* (March 2014)
- ❑ *Draft Guidance for Industry: Established Conditions: Reportable CMC Changes for Approved Drug and Biologic Products* (May 2015)
- ❑ *Guidance for Industry: Providing Regulatory Submissions in Electronic Format—Drug Establishment Registration and Drug Listing* (May 2009)
- ❑ Guideline for Drug Master Files (September 1989) ICH, Good Manufacturing Practice Guidance for Active Pharmaceutical Ingredients Q7A (August 2001)
- ❑ ICH, *Pharmaceutical Development Q8* (R2) (August 2009)
- ❑ *Guideline for Postmarketing Reporting of Adverse Drug Experiences* (March 1992)
- ❑ *Guidance for Industry: Postmarketing Adverse Experience Reporting for Human Drugs and Licensed Biological Products: Clarification of What to Report* (August 1997)
- ❑ *Draft Guidance for Industry: Postmarketing Safety Reporting for Human Drug and Biological Products Including Vaccines* (March 2001)
- ❑ *Draft Guidance for Industry: Providing Regulatory Submissions in Electronic Format - Postmarketing Individual Case Safety Reports* (June 2014)
- ❑ *Draft Guidance for Industry: Format and Content of Proposed Risk Evaluation and Mitigation Strategies (REMS), REMS Assessments, and Proposed REMS Modifications* (September 2009)
- ❑ ICH, *Draft of the ICH Guideline on Clinical Safety Data Management—Data Elements for Transmission of Individual Case Safety Reports E2B(R3)* (October 2005)
- ❑ ICH, Medical Terminology (MedDRA) M1

Introduction

Prescription drug manufacturers, distributors and marketers are required to comply with regulations throughout the product lifecycle, starting from early development and extending through commercial marketing of the product. Requirements at the preapproval stage differ from requirements in the postapproval stage; however, both stages are focused on product safety and quality. As in the clinical development phases, manufacturers of approved products are required to adhere to current Good Manufacturing Practice (CGMP) regulations, and sponsors are required to report changes that have a potential effect on the product's safety and quality to the US Food and Drug Administration (FDA). Postapproval requirements for marketing applications, and requirements for the production of commercial products, are similar for products approved under either a New Drug Application (NDA) or an Abbreviated New Drug Application (ANDA).

This chapter discusses prescription drug postapproval activities, including postmarketing requirements, postmarketing commitments and drug establishment listing. It also examines the application holder's postapproval responsibilities. The holder of an approved marketing application is required to comply with CGMP, communicate any changes made to the application that may impact the product to FDA, establish procedures to monitor product complaints and promptly investigate reports of adverse drug experiences.

Postmarketing Requirements and Commitments

Postmarketing requirements and commitments are studies and clinical trials conducted after a product is approved, to collect additional safety, efficacy or optimal use data.

A drug sponsor may commit to conducting postapproval studies or clinical trials for a product, known as postmarketing commitments (PMC). Alternately, in some instances, FDA may require certain studies or clinical trials, referred to as Postmarketing Requirements (PMR). The 2007 *Food and Drug Administration Amendments Act (FDAAA)* expanded FDA's authority to mandate postmarketing studies and clinical trials to assess possible serious risks associated with certain drugs.

Postmarketing studies the agency may require include:[1]

- postmarketing studies or clinical trials to demonstrate clinical benefit for drugs approved under the accelerated approval requirements in 21 CFR 314.510 and 21 CFR 601.41
- deferred pediatric studies (21 CFR 314.55(b) and 601.27(b)), where studies are required under the *Pediatric Research Equity Act* (*PREA*)
- studies or clinical trials to demonstrate safety and efficacy in humans that must be conducted at the time of use of products approved under the Animal Efficacy Rule (21 CFR 314.610(b)(1) and 601.91(b)(1))
- studies to assess a known serious risk related to the drug's use
- studies to assess signals of serious risk related to the drug's use
- studies to identify a potential unexpected serious risk indicated by available data

To keep the public informed, the agency maintains a database of postmarketing requirements and commitments, including study status, at http://www.accessdata.fda.gov/scripts/cder/pmc/index.cfm.

Changes to an Approved Application

Obtaining 'approved application' status does not preclude the application holder from making changes to the drug product. On the contrary, the regulations take the need for changes to an approved application into consideration. For example, changes in availability of raw materials, compendial updates, technological advances, or the need for manufacturing process improvements may require a sponsor to make changes to the approved application.

A drug sponsor should have a robust change management process in place to ensure changes made to the approved application are assessed appropriately for impact and well documented. A successful change management process will ensure the change's impact is classified correctly to reduce the risk of agency reclassification, which can lead to delays in product distribution. Additionally, good postapproval change documentation will ensure necessary information is available when preparing supplements to the application or the Annual Report.

Under the *Food, Drug, and Cosmetic Act* of 1938 (*FD&C Act*), nearly all changes to an approved marketing application, for either an NDA or ANDA, must be reported to FDA. This may be accomplished in an Annual Report or by submitting a supplement to the application. Procedures for supplementing an approved marketing application are addressed in 21 CFR 314.71, which specifies:[2]

- only the sponsor, or its designated agent, can supplement the application
- only information related to the proposed change(s) is required to be submitted
- requirements for archival, review and field copies are the same as for original applications

Postapproval CMC and labeling change reporting requirements are discussed in 21 CFR 314.70. The regulations set forth in the section require reporting drug substance and drug product CMC changes that may affect the marketed product's identity, strength, quality, purity or potency. Editorial changes, such as correction of typographical and spelling errors or changes in formatting to standard operating procedures or batch records, are not required to be submitted.[3]

Three postapproval CMC change categories are described in 21 CFR 314.70: major (314.70(b)), moderate (314.70(c)) and minor (314.70(d)). These changes are categorized based on their potential to negatively impact the drug product's identity, strength, quality, purity or potency. **Figure 14-1** summarizes the reporting categories for changes to approved applications.

Proposed changes to product labeling also must be evaluated with respect to reporting category. Labeling changes are classified as major, moderate or minor. For example, a change to the clinical pharmacology or clinical study section of the product labeling would be classified as a major change; such a change would require submission of a Prior Approval Supplement (PAS) for FDA approval before the new labeling is distributed. Alternatively, an editorial change, such as adding a distributor's name, is an annual reportable change.

Figure 14-1. Summary of Reporting Categories for Postapproval Changes

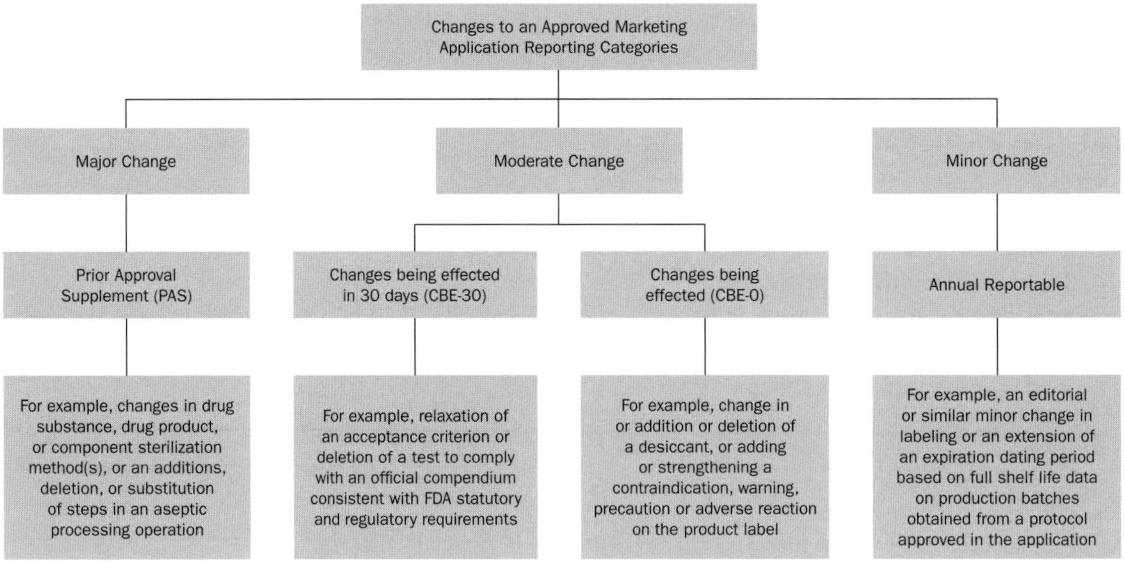

Source: Guidance for Industry: Format and Content for the CMC Section of an Annual Report (September 1994)

FDA will review each supplement and Annual Report. If FDA determines a supplement or Annual Report is deficient, the sponsor cannot distribute the product manufactured until it addresses the deficiency as required by the agency. If the product with the proposed change is in commercial distribution already (e.g., the product was distributed after a Changes Being Effected (CBE) supplement was submitted), and FDA believes the supplement is deficient, the agency may order the manufacturer to cease product distribution until the supplement is amended.

To aid sponsors in interpreting the regulations set forth in 21 CFR 314.70, FDA has issued several guidance documents:

- *Guidance for Industry: Changes to an Approved NDA or ANDA* (April 2004)
- *Guidance for Industry: Changes to an Approved NDA or ANDA: Questions and Answers* (January 2001) *Guidance for Industry: Changes to an Approved NDA or ANDA: Specifications—Use of Enforcement Discretion for Compendial Changes* (November 2004)
- *Guidance for Industry: PAC-ATLS: Postapproval Changes—Analytical Testing Sites* (April 1998)

Additionally, the agency issued *Guidance for Industry: CMC Postapproval Manufacturing Changes Reportable in Annual Reports* (March 2014) to further clarify the agency's thinking on annual reportable CMC changes.

These guidance documents provide direction on postapproval changes to:

- components and composition
- manufacturing sites
- analytical testing sites
- manufacturing process
- specifications
- container closure systems
- labeling
- miscellaneous changes
- multiple related changes

It is important to note when changes are not addressed directly by regulations, FDA guidance documents or are multifactorial in nature, the application holder should consult with the agency.

FDA also has issued guidance documents to aid manufacturers in determining the data amount and type required to support certain postapproval changes. The most notable of these regarding drug products are the Scale-Up and Postapproval Changes (SUPAC) guidance documents, which detail the chemistry information and potential bioequivalence study requirements associated with scale-up postapproval changes. Additionally, these documents assess the risk level associated with changes (e.g., manufacturing process, manufacturing site, product formula, equipment, batch size, etc.). The SUPAC documents classify changes into three levels: 1, 2 and 3, which correspond to minor, moderate and major changes, respectively. Level 1 changes are annual reportable changes, e.g., site changes within a single facility or process changes within validated ranges. Level 2 changes, such as composition changes or changes in manufacturing equipment, are filed in a CBE-0 or CBE-30 supplement (Changes Being Effected immediately or in 30 days, respectively). Level 3 changes require a PAS and can range from site changes to the use of a new manufacturer with no experience with the product type.

The SUPAC guidance documents include:

- *Guidance for Industry: SUPAC-IR: Immediate-Release Solid Oral Dosage Forms, Scale-Up and Postapproval Changes: Chemistry, Manufacturing, and Controls, In Vitro Dissolution Testing and In Vivo Bioequivalence Documentation* (November 1995)
- *SUPAC-IR: Questions and Answers about SUPAC-IR* (February 1997)
- *Guidance for Industry: SUPAC-MR: Modified-Release Solid Oral Dosage Forms: Scale-Up and Postapproval Changes: Chemistry, Manufacturing, and Controls, In Vitro Dissolution Testing and In Vivo Bioequivalence Documentation* (September 1997)
- *Guidance for Industry: SUPAC-SS: Nonsterile Semisolid Dosage Forms; Scale-Up and Postapproval Changes: Chemistry, Manufacturing, and Controls; In Vitro Release Testing and In Vivo Bioequivalence Documentation* (May 1997)
- *Guidance for Industry: SUPAC: Manufacturing Equipment Addendum* (December 2014)

A sponsor can reduce postapproval change reporting requirements if the change is implemented under an approved comparability protocol. A comparability protocol, submitted at the time of initial application or as a PAS, is a well-defined, detailed plan for assessing the effect of specific CMC changes on a specific drug product's identity, strength, quality, purity and potency. A comparability protocol describes changes covered in the protocol and specifies the tests and studies to be performed, including the analytical methods to be used and acceptance criteria to demonstrate specified CMC changes do not adversely affect the product. Submission of a comparability protocol is optional.[4]

Postapproval changes in a Quality by Design (QbD) development and validation program, as detailed in the International Conference on Harmonisation's (ICH) *Pharmaceutical Development Q8 (R2), Quality Risk Management Q9,* and *Pharmaceutical Quality System Q10,* also may reduce reporting requirements. FDA issued *Draft Guidance for Industry: Established Conditions: Reportable CMC Changes for Approved Drug and Biologic Products* (May 2015) to provide additional clarification on which CMC changes the agency considers reportable or may be managed by the sponsor's Pharmaceutical Quality System (PQS).

A supplement or Annual Report must include a list of all changes being proposed or implemented, respectively. FDA recommends the applicant describe each change in enough detail to allow the agency to determine quickly whether the appropriate reporting category has been used. If the agency determines an incorrect reporting category has been assigned to a change, the change will be reclassified, and the sponsor must adhere to the new classification's distribution requirements. For example, if FDA reclassifies a change from a CBE-30 to a PAS, the product incorporating the change cannot be marketed until the agency reviews and approves it. For supplements, the cover letter must list the changes.[6] In Annual Reports, the CMC summary section should include the list.[7]

The applicant must describe each change fully in the supplement or Annual Report body.[8] An applicant making a change to an approved application under *FD&C Act* Section 506A also must conform to other applicable laws and regulations, including CGMP requirements under the act (21 U.S.C. 351(a)(2)(B)) and applicable regulations in 21 CFR 210, 211 and 314.

Compliance with CGMPs for Manufacturing, Processing, Packing or Holding of Drugs and for Finished Pharmaceuticals

Manufacturers of approved products and those undergoing human clinical trials are required to adhere to CGMP regulations. CGMP regulations for drugs establish minimum requirements for manufacturing, personnel, equipment, product containers/closures controls, facilities, packaging, holding and distribution procedures and associated process controls. The regulations are intended to ensure drugs are safe and quality, identity, strength and purity requirements are met. Additionally, CGMP regulations require all manufacturing and testing equipment to be qualified as suitable for use, and all operational methodologies and procedures (such as manufacturing, cleaning and analytical testing) utilized in the drug manufacturing process to be validated (according to predetermined specifications) to demonstrate they can perform their purported function(s) in a reliable and consistent manner. Active Pharmaceutical Ingredients (APIs) are subject to the adulteration provisions of *FD&C Act* Section 501(a)(2)(B), which requires all drugs to be manufactured in conformance with CGMPs. The act makes no distinction between an API and a finished pharmaceutical, and failure of either to comply with CGMPs violates the act. FDA has not promulgated CGMP regulations specifically for APIs or drug components (as it has for finished pharmaceuticals). It has recognized for a long time the CGMP regulations for finished pharmaceuticals (21 CFR 210 and 211) are valid and applicable in concept to API manufacturing. These concepts include building quality into the drug by using suitable equipment and employing appropriately qualified and trained personnel, establishing adequate written procedures and controls to ensure manufacturing processes are valid, establishing a system of in-process material testing and final drug tests and ensuring drugs' stability for their intended period of use. In 2001, FDA adopted an internationally harmonized guidance for industry on API

CGMPs in conjunction with ICH regulatory partners. This guidance, *Good Manufacturing Practice Guidance for Active Pharmaceutical Ingredients Q7A*, also referred to as ICH Q7, represents FDA's current thinking on API CGMPs. Thus, API and related manufacturing and testing facilities following this guidance generally will be considered to comply with the statutory CGMP requirements.

Adverse Drug Experience Reports (ADE)

An "unexpected" ADE is defined as an ADE not listed in the drug product's current labeling. A "serious" ADE is defined as an experience occurring at any dose that results in:

- death
- a life-threatening event
- in-patient hospitalization or prolongation of existing hospitalization
- a persistent or significant disability/incapacity
- a congenital anomaly/birth defect

In addition, other medical events may be considered serious ADEs if, based on appropriate medical judgment, they may jeopardize the patient or subject, and medical intervention is required to prevent one of the outcomes listed above.

Postmarketing reporting requirements for ADEs are outlined in 21 CFR 314.80. These regulations require the holder of an approved application under 21 CFR 314.50 or an effective 505 (b)(2) to review all reports of adverse experience received regardless of the source (foreign or domestic) promptly.

Potential ADE information sources cited in 21 CFR 314.80 include:

- information derived from commercial marketing experience
- postmarketing clinical investigations
- postmarketing epidemiological/surveillance studies
- reports in scientific literature
- unpublished scientific papers

Although the applicant is not required to resubmit information FDA has forwarded to it, regulations do require the applicant to provide all follow-up information on such reports to FDA.

It is important to recognize the existence of additional adverse experience data sources not specified in the regulations. For example, the Internet and social media play significant roles in how patients interact with each other and their care providers. Approved application holders should review ADE reports received on websites they sponsor; however, the agency currently does not hold sponsors responsible for ADEs posted to sites they do not sponsor.[5] Approved applications holders should, at a minimum, assess the information to determine whether it should be reported to FDA.

In addition to ADE review requirements, the application holder is required to develop written procedures for surveillance, receipt, evaluation and reporting postmarketing adverse drug experiences to FDA.[9]

Postmarketing ADE reporting requirements apply to any company whose name appears on an approved drug product label as a manufacturer, packer or distributor.[10] However, the regulations permit non-applicants to satisfy these reporting requirements by submitting all serious ADE reports to the applicant. If a non-applicant chooses to submit ADE reports to the applicant rather than FDA, the non-applicant must submit each report to the sponsor within five calendar days of receipt of the report, and then is responsible for submitting these ADE reports to FDA.

The applicant is required to submit the following ADE reports to FDA within the specified timeframes:

- Postmarketing 15-Day Alert Reports—A sponsor must report all ADEs (foreign or domestic) that are both serious and unexpected to FDA within 15 days of receipt of the information. The applicant must investigate all ADE reports promptly and submit any additional information obtained during the investigation within 15 days of receipt as follow-up reports or as requested by FDA.
- Periodic Adverse Drug Experience Reports (PADER)—For the first three years following a drug's approval, a sponsor shall submit PADERs on a quarterly basis. Unless otherwise requested by FDA, after three years, the sponsor shall submit a PADER at annual intervals. The PADER should contain:
  - o a narrative summary and analysis of the report's information, including all ADE information obtained during the reporting period and analysis of 15-Day Alert Reports submitted during the reporting interval
  - o any Form FDA 3500A (MedWatch) for an ADE not submitted as a 15-Day Alert Report
  - o any actions taken during the reporting period due to ADEs (e.g., labeling changes or additional studies initiated)

FDA has provided guidance regarding submitting ADE reports in electronic format in *Draft Guidance for Industry: Providing Regulatory Submissions in Electronic Format—Postmarketing Individual Case Safety Reports* (June 2014).

To encourage healthcare professionals to collect, evaluate and report serious ADEs, FDA developed the MedWatch educational and publicity program in 1993. The MedWatch webpage can be found at www.fda.gov/Safety/MedWatch/default.htm. Sponsors, manufacturers, distributors and user facilities use MedWatch Form 3500A for mandatory reporting of both adverse events and problems with human drugs and other FDA-regulated products. Healthcare professionals, consumers and patients may use MedWatch Form 3500 for spontaneous ADE reporting to the sponsor or directly to FDA. Foreign reportable ADEs also may be submitted on forms developed by the Council for International Organizations of Medical Sciences (CIOMS).

FDA tracks adverse drug reaction reports by entering all safety reports for approved drugs and therapeutic biological products into the FDA Adverse Event Reporting System (FAERS) database, which uses standardized international terminology from the Medical Dictionary for Regulatory Activities (MedDRA). FDA uses FAERS to facilitate post-marketing drug surveillance and compliance activities. The FAERS goal is to improve the public health by providing the best available tools for storing and analyzing safety data and reports. Data and trends from FAERS may lead to FDA action on products, such as safety alerts communicated via FDA's website, "Dear Health Care Professional" letters or requests to sponsors for additional safety studies. This is part of an FDA initiative to collect, analyze and disseminate drug safety information rapidly and is highlighted in FDA's *Guidance: Drug Safety Information—FDA's Communication to the Public* (March 2007).

Similar adverse event reporting requirements are associated with clinical trial conduct (21 CFR 312.32); these requirements are discussed in Chapter 9 Clinical Trials: GCPs, Regulations and Compliance.

Risk Evaluation and Mitigation Strategies

FDAAA, which included renewal of the *Prescription Drug User Fee Act* (*PDUFA IV*), gave FDA authority to require manufacturers to create a Risk Evaluation and Mitigation Strategy (REMS) to ensure a drug or biological product's benefits outweigh its risks. A sponsor may propose a REMS as part of an application (NDA, ANDA or Biologics License Application (BLA)) if it is deemed necessary. FDA also can require a REMS during initial application review or any time after a drug is approved for marketing if the agency becomes aware of new safety information and determines a REMS is necessary to ensure the drug's benefits continue to outweigh its risks.

The sponsor must assess a REMS' effectiveness in achieving its stated goals and submit the assessment to FDA by 18 months, three years and seven years after its initial approval. Additional dates can be added if more frequent assessments are required to ensure the product's benefits continue to outweigh its risks.[11]

Elements of a REMS may include:

- Medication Guide and/or a patient package insert—materials written for the patient to help ensure the drug's safe use
- Communication Plan to healthcare providers—an explanation of the strategy being employed to ensure the drug's benefits outweigh its risks
- Elements to Assure Safe Use (ETASU)—e.g., requiring healthcare providers who prescribe the drug to have particular training or experience, or be specially certified; only dispensing the drug to patients in certain healthcare settings, such as hospitals; monitoring patients using the drug

FDA maintains a list of approved REMS at http://www.fda.gov/Drugs/DrugSafety/PostmarketDrugSafetyInformationforPatientsandProviders/ucm111350.htm.

A sponsor may propose modifying an approved REMS and must include a REMS assessment at the time of this proposal. Additionally, FDA may determine new safety information requires an element of the REMS to be modified; this also will require the sponsor to assess the REMS. A proposal to modify an approved REMS should be submitted in a new PAS if it is not already associated with an existing application.[12]

Reporting Field Alert Events

The purpose of Field Alert Reports (FARs), required under 21 CFR 314.81(b), is to quickly identify drug products that pose potential safety threats. Holders of approved NDAs or ANDAs are required to submit FARs within three days of becoming aware of any significant problem with a distributed drug product.[13]

FARs may be communicated to the district FDA office by telephone or other rapid means, but must be followed by a written report.

21 CFR 314.81(b) requires the following information be reported in an FAR:[14]

- incidents causing the drug product or its labeling to be mistaken for or applied to another article
- bacterial contamination
- significant chemical, physical or other change, deterioration in the distributed drug product
- failure of one or more distributed drug product batches to meet the specifications established in the approved application

Annual Reports

As outlined in 21 CFR 314.81(b)(2) holders of approved applications are required to submit Annual Reports to FDA. The Annual Report is sent to the division responsible for the application's review. The reporting period is defined as one full year from the anniversary date of the application's approval; the Annual Report must be submitted within 60 days of this anniversary date. The content of an Annual Report is outlined below:

FDA Forms and Cover Letter

The Annual Report should include a cover letter, which indicates product name, application number, reporting period and any additional information the sponsor may wish to bring to the agency's attention. Additionally, a completed Form FDA 2252 (Transmittal of Annual Reports for Drugs and Biologics for Human Use) is to be submitted with the Annual Report.[15]

Summary of Significant New Information[16]

- summary of significant new information possibly affecting the drug product's safety, effectiveness or labeling, and a description of actions the sponsor has taken or intends to take as a result of this new information
- indication of whether labeling supplements for pediatric use have been submitted, and whether new studies in the pediatric population have been initiated to support appropriate labeling for the pediatric population

Distribution Data[17]

- quantity of product distributed under the approved application including amounts provided to distributors. (The distribution data must include the National Drug Code (NDC) number, total number of dosage units of each strength or potency.)
- quantities distributed for domestic and foreign use

Labeling[18]

- current professional labeling, patient brochures or package inserts and representative samples of package labels
- content of labeling required under 21 CFR 201.100(d)(3) (i.e., the package insert or professional labeling), including all text, tables and figures provided in electronic format
- a summary of any labeling changes made since the last report, listed by date in the order in which they were implemented or, if no changes, a statement of that fact

Chemistry, Manufacturing and Controls[19]

- reports of experiences, investigations, studies or tests involving physical, chemical, or any other properties of the drug
- CMC index: a current list of approved CMC information, which is intended to aid the agency's review of the Annual Report (i.e., list of approved analytical methods, specifications, manufacturing sites, etc.) The index should include the type and date of each change to each component, the type of submission used to report the change (original, supplement, or Annual Report), and the date the change was reported and approved, if an application was submitted. (See **Figure 14-2** for an example of a CMC index.)
- a complete description of CMC changes not requiring a supplemental application under 21 CFR 314.70(b) (i.e., "Annual Reportable" changes)
- stability data obtained during the reporting period

Nonclinical Laboratory Studies[20]

The application holder should provide copies of unpublished reports and summaries of published reports of new toxicological findings in animal studies or in vitro studies.

Nonclinical laboratory study reports should include all studies conducted by, or otherwise obtained by, the application holder.

Clinical Data[21]

- published clinical trials (or abstracts) of the drug, including clinical trials on safety and effectiveness; clinical trials on new uses; biopharmaceutic, pharmacokinetic and clinical pharmacology studies; and reports of clinical experience related to safety, conducted by the sponsor or found in the public domain
- summaries of completed unpublished clinical trials or available prepublication manuscripts conducted by the sponsor or found in the public domain
- analysis of available safety and efficacy data in the pediatric population and changes in labeling based on this information (This also should include an assessment of data needed to ensure appropriate labeling for the pediatric population.)

Status Reports of Postmarketing Study Commitments[22]

- status report on each postmarketing requirement (PMR) or postmarketing commitment (PMC) concerning clinical safety, clinical efficacy, clinical pharmacology and nonclinical toxicology

Status of Other Postmarketing Studies[23]

- status report of any postmarketing study not included in the PMR/PMC section above; primarily relates to CMC postmarketing studies and product stability studies

Figure 14-2. Example of CMC Index

ATTACHMENT 1

NDA/ANDA/AADA ######
INDEX OF APPROVED CHEMISTRY, MANUFACTURING AND CONTROLS INFORMATION

		SUBMISSION		APPROVAL
		TYPE	DATE	DATE
I.	**DRUG SUBSTANCE**			
	A. Manufacturer(s)	______	______	______
	B. Method(s) of Manufacture	______	______	______
	C. Container and Closure	______	______	______
	D. Stability Protocol	______	______	______
	E. Specifications and Analytical Methods *			
II.	**DRUG PRODUCT**			
	A. Composition	______	______	______
	B. Manufacturer(s)	______	______	______
	C. Method(s) of Manufacture and Packaging	______	______	______
	D. Specifications and Analytical Methods *			
	E. Container(s) and Closure(s)	______	______	______
	F. Expiration Dating Period ______ Months	______	______	______
	G. Stability Protocol	______	______	______

*Please attach a complete listing of the Specifications and Analytical Methods for the drug substance and drug product in the format provided.

Source: *Guidance for Industry: Format and Content for the CMC Section of an Annual Report* (September 1994)

Log of Outstanding Regulatory Business[24]

At the sponsor's discretion, the Annual Report also may include a listing of any open regulatory business with FDA concerning the application (e.g., a list of unanswered correspondence between the sponsor and FDA, or vice-versa).

Advertising and Labeling

Under 21 CFR 314.81(b)(3)(i), the sponsor must submit specimens of mailing pieces and any other labeling or advertising devised for drug product promotion at the time of the promotional material's initial use and at the time of initial publication of a prescription drug advertisement. A copy of the current labeling and a completed Form FDA 2253 (Transmittal of Advertisements and Promotional Labeling for Drugs for Human Use) are required for each submission. These submissions are made to the Office of Prescription Drug Promotion (OPDP; formerly known as the Division of Drug Marketing, Advertising and Communications (DDMAC)) for products regulated by CDER, and to the Advertising and Promotional Labeling Branch (APLB) for products regulated by CBER.[25]

Submission of Patents to the Orange Book for Patent Exclusivity

Upon marketing application approval, the product is listed in the FDA reference book, *Approved Drug Products with Therapeutic Equivalence Evaluations*. Commonly referred to as the "The Orange Book" because the original print version had an orange cover, this reference lists patent and marketing exclusivity information associated with each approved drug product. FDA maintains an electronic version of the Orange Book at www.accessdata.fda.gov/scripts/cder/ob/default.cfm.

Patent information is listed in the Orange Book by completing Form FDA 3542, which is submitted with an application, amendment, or supplement, and Form FDA 3452a, which is submitted upon approval of an application, amendment or supplement.

Product Complaints

The regulations outlining CGMPs for finished pharmaceuticals require the sponsor and manufacturing/control sites to establish and follow written procedures describing the handling of all written and oral product complaints. Established procedures should include a mechanism for review by the organization's quality control unit of any complaint involving a drug product's possible failure to meet any of its specifications.[26] Additionally, the procedures must include criteria to determine whether an investigation is needed in accordance with 21 CFR 211.192.[27]

The established procedures also should include provisions to determine whether the complaint represents a serious and unexpected ADE. A serious and unexpected ADE is required to be reported to FDA in accordance with 21 CFR 310.305 and 314.80.[28]

The sponsor also is required to maintain a written record of each complaint in a designated drug product complaint file. The file should be maintained in a location where it can be accessed easily for review during a regulatory inspection. Written records on a drug product complaint should be maintained until at least one year after the drug product's expiration date or one year after the date the complaint was received, whichever is longer. In the case of certain over-the-counter (OTC) drug products that lack expiration dating because they meet exemption criteria under 21 CFR 211.137, written records should be maintained for three years after distribution.[29]

Product Recalls

A recall is a voluntary action taken by manufacturers and distributors to remove products from the market that are in violation of laws or may present a risk of injury to the public. Recall actions may be taken on the manufacturer or distributor's initiative or FDA may request a firm to recall a product. While FDA can take other formal administrative or civil actions to remove products from the market, recalls are more effective in removing products from the market quickly, particularly when a product has been distributed widely.[30] Industry responsibilities in conducting recalls are delineated in 21 CFR 7.40–7.59. Additionally, recall guidance is provided in *Guidance for Industry: Product Recalls, Including Removals and Corrections* (November 2003).

Recalls are classified as Class I, II or III as follows:

- Class I Recall—when there is a reasonable probability the use of or exposure to a suspected product will cause serious adverse health consequences or death
- Class II Recall—when the use of or exposure to a suspected product may cause temporary or medically reversible adverse health consequences, or where the probability of serious adverse health consequences is remote
- Class III Recall—when use of or exposure to a suspected product is not likely to cause adverse health consequences, but the product violates FDA labeling or manufacturing laws

The agency will review a firm's proposed recall strategy and recommend changes if necessary. The firm will conduct the recall in accordance with the approved recall strategy but should not delay initiation of a recall pending review of its recall strategy.[31]

Under 21 CFR 7.42(b), the product recall strategy should address the following elements:[32]

- recall depth—depending on the product's degree of hazard and extent of distribution, the recall strategy should specify the level in the distribution chain to which the recall is to be extended, (i.e. consumer/user level, retail level or the wholesale level).
- public warnings—to alert the public a product poses a serious hazard (Public warnings are reserved for urgent situations. Whether or not a public warning is warranted will be specified in the recall strategy.)
- effectiveness checks—to ensure all affected parties have received the recall notification and have taken appropriate action

Changes to Drug Master Files Affecting Approved Applications

Drug master files (DMFs) serve to provide the agency with information about various drug product components (e.g., drug substance proprietary formula, packaging component, manufacturing procedure, etc.) without compromising the confidentiality of a third party, the DMF holder. DMFs allow FDA to review this confidential information in support of an NDA, ANDA, supplement or amendment to an NDA or ANDA, or another DMF.[33] Changes to DMFs are submitted in the form of DMF amendments, and the firms authorized to reference the DMF are notified of any change. Similar to changes made to an approved drug application, the impact of changes to a DMF referenced in the drug file also must be evaluated to determine the appropriate reporting category (PAS, CBE-30, CBE-0, Annual Report) and, thus, the timing for distributing product manufactured using the change. The sponsor reports change to the marketing application as appropriate and references the DMF amendment.

Drug Establishment Registration and Drug Listing

Owners or operators of all drug establishments involved in the manufacture, preparation, propagation, compounding, processing, packaging, repackaging or relabeling of a human or veterinary drug, including blood and blood products and biologics, must register the establishment electronically within five days after beginning to manufacture commercial products or within five days of submitting a marketing application.[34] In addition, each product in commercial distribution must be listed with FDA. The regulations permit submission registration and listing by the parent, subsidiary or affiliate company for operations conducted at more than one establishment, and those with joint ownership and control among all the establishments. The drug listing also must include bulk drugs for commercial distribution, whether or not they are involved in interstate commerce. FDA requires all drug establishment registration and drug listing information to be submitted electronically in Structured Product Labeling (SPL) format.

After the initial registration, establishments are required to renew their registration annually. An establishment registration annual renewal schedule is provided in 21 CFR 207.21, based on the first letter of the company's name. Establishments also are required to update drug listings, including information on drugs not previously submitted, drugs for which commercial distribution has been discontinued and products previously discontinued and distribution has been resumed. Additionally, owners and operators of all registered establishments must update their drug listing information every June and December or at the registrant's discretion when a change occurs. Foreign drug establishments whose drugs are imported or offered for import into the US also must comply with establishment registration and drug listing requirements. However, if the drug products enter a foreign trade zone and are re-exported from that foreign trade zone without having entered US commerce, compliance is not required.[35] Each foreign drug establishment must submit its US agent's name, address and phone number as part of its initial and updated registration information. US agents representing foreign firms must reside or maintain a place of business in the US. Only one US agent is allowed per foreign drug establishment. The foreign drug establishment or the US agent should report changes in the agent's name, address or telephone number to FDA within 10 business days of the change. The information required for each establishment, foreign or domestic, includes:

- drug establishment name and full address
- all trade names used by the establishment
- type of ownership or operation (e.g., individually owned, partnership or corporation)
- name(s) of the establishment's owner, operator, partners or officers

For each drug substance (bulk API) and finished dosage form in commercial distribution, the drug listing information must include:

- trade name
- NDA or ANDA number or OTC monograph number
- business type and product type
- packaging type and size
- manufacturing site
- copies of all current labeling and representative sampling of advertising
- quantitative listing of the active ingredients
- National Drug Code (NDC) number
- for each listed drug product subject to the imprinting requirements of 21 CFR 206, a document providing the product name; its active ingredient(s); dosage strength; NDC number; manufacturer or distributor name; product's size, shape, color and code imprint (if any); and any other characteristic that identifies the product as unique

FDUFA requires sponsors with approved drug products to pay annual maintenance fees to FDA related to each approved product (product fees), and owners of establishments where approved products are manufactured also must pay annual fees (establishment fees) to remain in compliance. These fees are set on an annual basis and communicated through a notice in the *Federal Register*.

Approved Application Inactivation or Withdrawal

Under 21 CFR 314.150, FDA may withdraw approval of an application or abbreviated application. When the agency intends to withdraw approval of an application, it will notify the sponsor and, if appropriate, all other persons who manufacture or distribute identical, related or similar drug products, of its intent to withdraw approval, and the application holders will be afforded the opportunity for a hearing.[36] FDA may propose to withdraw an approved application for the following reasons:

- The agency finds clinical data, tests or other scientific evidence showing the drug is unsafe for use under the conditions of use on the basis of which the application or abbreviated application was approved (21 CFR 314.150(a)(2)(i)).

- New clinical data, not contained in the application or not available to FDA until after the application or abbreviated application was approved, indicate the drug is not safe under the conditions of use (21 CFR 314.150(a)(2)(ii)).
- New information indicates there is insufficient evidence from adequate and well-controlled studies as defined in 21 CFR 314.126, to support the efficacy claims under the conditions of use prescribed, recommended or suggested in its labeling (21 CFR 314.150(a)(2)(iii)).
- The agency determines the application or abbreviated application contains any untrue statement of a material fact (21 CFR 314.150(a)(2)(iv)).

Additionally, approval may be summarily suspended if FDA determines the product poses an imminent hazard to the public health (21 CFR 314.150(a)(1)). In this case, FDA will provide the application holder an opportunity for an expedited hearing on this finding.

The regulations also allow the sponsor to voluntarily request withdrawal of an approved application. A drug sponsor may choose to withdraw an application if the product is no longer being marketed (21 CFR 314.150(c)). Voluntary withdrawal of an approved marketing application by the application holder is permissible if the product does not fall into any of the categories previously discussed under involuntary withdrawal. The drug sponsor must continue to maintain postapproval activities such as submitting Annual Reports and other postapproval reporting until the agency publishes notification of the withdrawal in the *Federal Register.*

If the agency believes a product or class of products poses a significant risk to public health, it may contact holders of approved applications and request applicants to waive the opportunity for a hearing and allow FDA to withdraw approval of the application. If the application holders agree, the agency will not make an official finding as to the reason for withdrawal but will withdraw approval of the applications in a notice published in the *Federal Register* containing a brief summary of the agency's and the application holders' reasons for withdrawal. For example, in 2011 FDA announced it was requesting holders of approved applications for combination prescription products containing greater than 325 mg of acetaminophen to withdraw these products voluntarily.[37] In this case, FDA concerns about the incidence of liver damage associated with high-dose acetaminophen prompted the voluntary withdrawal of these products.

Change in Sponsor (Transfer of Ownership) of an Approved Application

21 CFR 314.72 covers the transfer of ownership of an approved application. The application holder must submit a letter or other documentation to FDA indicating all rights to the application have been transferred to the new owner as of the transfer date.

When ownership of an approved application is transferred, the new owner assumes all commitments to agreements, promises and conditions in the application made by the former owner. The new owner must submit a signed application and a letter stating acceptance of such commitments. The new application holder also must provide FDA with the effective date for the change in ownership and a statement that either the new owner has a complete copy of the approved application, including supplements and records, or has requested a copy of the application from FDA's files.

Additionally, the new application holder assumes regulatory responsibility for the application. As such, the new application holder must inform FDA of any change to the approved application under 21 CFR 314.70. Changes to the drug product's label or labeling to change the product's brand or the name of its manufacturer, packer or distributor can be submitted in the next annual report.

Summary

- Postmarketing requirements and commitments are studies and clinical trials conducted after a product is approved. The purpose of these studies is to collect additional safety, efficacy or optimal use data on the approved product.
- Sponsors of approved marketing applications are required to report almost all changes to FDA under the *FD&C Act*. The agency has provided numerous guidance documents to aid application holders in determining the appropriate reporting category for postapproval changes to components and composition, manufacturing sites, analytical testing sites, manufacturing process, specifications, container closure systems and labeling. These guidance documents also provide advice on handling multiple related changes.
- Postapproval changes to CMC or labeling sections of an application must be assessed for the appropriate reporting category (major, moderate or minor) and submitted in a supplement corresponding to that level of change (i.e., PAS, CBE-30, CBE-0) or Annual Report.
- Sponsors of approved marketing applications are required to review ADE information obtained from all potential sources. They are required to

report postmarketing safety information to FDA in 15-Day Alert Reports and periodic ADE reports.

- A REMS may be proposed by application holders or required by FDA when deemed necessary to ensure a drug or biological product's benefits outweigh its risks. Modification of an approved REMS must be submitted in a PAS and requires the sponsor to perform a REMS assessment.
- Sponsors of approved applications are required to submit an Annual Report. Each copy of the report must be accompanied by a completed Form FDA 2252 (Transmittal of Periodic Reports for Drugs for Human Use). The period covered in the report is defined as one full year from the approval anniversary date of the preceding year. The report should include a summary; distribution data; status of labeling; chemistry, manufacturing and controls information; nonclinical laboratory studies; clinical data; status of postmarketing study requirements and commitments; status of other postmarketing studies; and a log of outstanding regulatory business.
- DMFs are voluntary submissions to FDA containing detailed, confidential CMC information about drug substances, intermediates, drug products, excipients or packaging materials that may be used for human drugs. DMFs are not 'approved' by the agency; these files are retained by the agency and accessed when referenced in support of an application, supplement to an application or another DMF. Changes to DMFs are submitted in DMF amendments. The DMF holder will notify companies authorized to reference the file so they can assess the impact of the change on associated drug products.
- Manufacturers are required to register drug establishments on an annual basis and provide a current drug product list to FDA on a semi-annual basis. Drug Establishment registration must be submitted in electronic format.

References

1. Postmarketing Requirements and Commitments: Introduction. FDA website. http://www.fda.gov/Drugs/GuidanceComplianceRegulatoryInformation/Post-marketingPhaseIVCommitments/default.htm, Accessed 2 February 2015.
2. 21 CFR 314.71.
3. *Guidance for Industry: Changes to an Approved NDA or ANDA* (April 2004).
4. *Draft Guidance for Industry: Comparability Protocols—Chemistry, Manufacturing, and Controls Information* (February 2003).
5. *Draft Guidance for Industry: Postmarketing Safety Reporting for Human Drug and Biological Products Including Vaccines* (March 2001).
6. 21 CFR 314.70(a)(6).
7. 21 CFR 314.81(b)(2)(i).
8. 21 CFR 314.70(a)(1).
9. 21 CFR 314.80(b).
10. 21 CFR 314.80(c)(1)(iii)
11. FDA website. http://www.fda.gov/downloads/aboutfda/transparency/basics/ucm328784.pdf. Accessed 15 March 2015.
12. *Draft Guidance for Industry: Format and Content of Proposed Risk Evaluation and Mitigation Strategies (REMS), REMS Assessments, and Proposed REMS Modifications* (September 2009).
13. 21 CFR 314.81(b)(1).
14. New Drug Application (NDA) and Abbreviated New Drug Application (ANDA) Field Alert Reports. FDA website. http://www.fda.gov/aboutfda/centersoffices/officeofmedicalproductsandtobacco/cder/ucm082083.htm. Accessed 27 February 2015.
15. 21 CFR 314.81(b)(2).
16. 21 CFR 314.81(b)(2)(i)).
17. 21 CFR 314.81(b)(2)(ii)a.
18. 21 CFR 314.81(b)(2)(iii).
19. 21 CFR 314.81(b)(2)(iv).
20. 21 CFR 314.81(b)(2)(v).
21. 21 CFR 314.81(b)(2)(vi).
22. 21 CFR 314.81(b)(2)(vii).
23. 21 CFR 314.81(b)(2)(viii).
24. 21 CFR 314.81(b)(2)(ix).
25. 21 CFR 314.81(b)(3)(i).
26. 21 CFR 211.198.
27. Ibid.
28. Ibid.
29. Ibid.
30. 21 CFR 7.40(a).
31. 21 CFR 7.42(a)(2).
32. 21 CFR 7.42(b).
33. Drug Master Files: Guidelines. FDA website. http://www.fda.gov/Drugs/GuidanceComplianceRegulatoryInformation/Guidances/ucm122886.htm. Accessed 9 March 2015.
34. 21 CFR 207.40(a).
35. Ibid.
36. 21 CFR 314.150
37. FDA Drug Safety Communication: Prescription Acetaminophen Products to be Limited to 325 mg Per Dosage Unit; Boxed Warning Will Highlight Potential for Severe Liver Failure. FDA website. http://www.fda.gov/Drugs/DrugSafety/ucm239821.htm. Accessed 2 February 2015.

Chapter 15

Generic Drug Submissions

Updated by Samrat Sisodia, MS, MBA, MRSC, RAC

OBJECTIVES

- To gain an understanding of the history of generic drug development in the US
- To gain an understanding of FDA's generic drug approval process and requirements, including various paths to approval
- To gain an understanding of the concepts of bioequivalence and therapeutic equivalence

LAWS, REGULATIONS AND GUIDELINES COVERED IN THIS CHAPTER

- *Federal Food, Drug, and Cosmetic Act* of 1938
- *Drug Efficacy Amendments* of 1962
- *Drug Regulation Reform Act* of 1978
- *Drug Price Competition and Patent Term Restoration Act* of 1984 *(Hatch-Waxman Act)*
- *Medicare Prescription Drug, Improvement, and Modernization Act* of 2003
- *Prescription Drug User Fee Act* of 1992
- *Pediatric Research Equity Act* of 2003
- *Generic Drug User Fee Amendments* of 2012
- 21 CFR 314 Applications for FDA Approval to Market a New Drug
- 21 CFR 320 Bioavailability and Bioequivalence Requirements
- 43 *Fed. Reg.* 39,126 (1 September 1978), Abbreviated New Drug Applications; Proposed Related Drug Amendments
- 44 *Fed. Reg.* 2932 (12 January 1979), Therapeutically Equivalent Drugs; Availability of List
- 45 *Fed. Reg.* 72,582 (31 October 1980), Therapeutically Equivalent Drugs; Availability of List
- 45 *Fed. Reg.* 82,052 (12 December 1980), Response to Petition Seeking Withdrawal of the Policy Described in the Agency's "Paper" NDA Memorandum of 31 July 1978
- 46 *Fed. Reg.* 27,396 (19 May 1981), Publication of "Paper NDA" Memorandum
- 54 *Fed. Reg.* 28,872 (10 July 1989), Proposed ANDA Regulations
- 74 *Fed. Reg.* 2849 (16 January 2009) Requirements for submission of bioequivalence data

- ❑ Manual of Policies and Procedures 5240.3, "Review Order of Original ANDAs, Amendments, and Supplements" (October 2006)
- ❑ *Guidance for Industry: Bioavailability and Bioequivalence Studies for Orally Administered Drug Products—General Considerations (March 2003)*
- ❑ *Draft Guidance for Industry: Applications Covered by Section 505(b)(2) (October 1999)*
- ❑ Generic Drug User Fee Act Program Performance Goals and Procedures

Introduction

The term "generic drug" is not defined in the *Federal Food, Drug, and Cosmetic Act* of 1938 (*FD&C Act*) or in US Food and Drug Administration (FDA) regulations. It generally is used, however, to refer to a drug product with the same active ingredient, dosage form, strength and route of administration as a brand-name drug and for which FDA has concluded the generic can be substituted for the brand-name drug. Generic drugs cost less because the brand-name drug company already has done the work necessary to develop the active ingredient and show its safety and efficacy.

The first generic drugs were marketed during the period between the enactment of the *FD&C Act* (Pub. L. No. 75-717, 52 Stat 1040 (1938)) and the enactment of the *Drug Efficacy Amendments* of 1962 (Pub. L. No. 87-781, 76 Stat. 780 (1962)). These products were marketed without FDA approval, on the theory the agency's approval of the brand-name drug under a New Drug Application (NDA) (based only on safety) made the next version an "old" drug.[1] After the 1962 *Drug Efficacy Amendments*, FDA required submission of an Abbreviated New Drug Application (ANDA) for each generic version of a "pre-62" brand-name drug FDA had found to be effective under the Drug Efficacy Study Implementation (DESI) program. However, the agency did not permit ANDAs to be submitted for brand-name drugs approved after 1962.[2] This meant a second version of a post-1962 brand-name drug had to obtain full NDA approval. A full NDA typically was economically prohibitive.

Competitive pressure drove some generic drug companies to market both pre- and post-1962 drugs without FDA approval, arguing that an active ingredient became available as an "old" drug after initial FDA approval. FDA's attempts to suppress this practice culminated in the 1983 Supreme Court decision in *United States v. Generix Drug Corp.*, 460 U.S. 453 (1983). The court accepted FDA's position that "old drug" status applied not to the active ingredient, but to the individual finished product. Hence, each new version of a drug was a "new drug"[3] requiring FDA approval, no matter how many times FDA had approved its active ingredient.

Aware that its own policies and interpretations were preventing generic competition for post-1962 drugs, FDA took two steps during the 1970s to address the need for an ANDA program for post-1962 drugs:

1. development of the so-called "paper NDA" policy
2. development of ANDA regulations for post-1962 drug products

In 1978, FDA adopted the paper NDA policy, under which the agency accepted a combination of product-specific data and published literature about an active ingredient to satisfy the approval requirements for a full NDA.[4] FDA's paper NDA policy essentially permitted the sponsor of an application for a "duplicate" of a post-1962 drug product (i.e., a drug product containing the same active ingredients as an already marketed product, in a similar or identical dosage form and for the same indications) to submit published studies and bridging data to support its application.[5] However, because the paper NDA approach required published literature rather than information not publicly available, it had limited utility for most drugs.[6]

In 1978, FDA issued proposed regulations announcing its intent to extend its pre-1962 ANDA regulations to post-1962 drugs.[7] FDA began to develop these regulations in the early 1980s. The agency's initiative was controversial because it reportedly would have required a substantial waiting period after initial approval of the brand-name drug before any ANDA could be approved for a generic version. Congressional interest in FDA's initiative, however, coincided with a broader effort to develop legislation promoting both competition and innovation in the drug industry.[8]

As pressure was building for an ANDA program for post-1962 brand drugs, the innovative industry had grown frustrated with the impact of FDA's lengthening approval process for branded drugs, asserting longer approval times undercut the value of drug patents, which are granted early in the development process and whose then 17-year (now 20-year) term was spent in large part before marketing approval was granted. Congress engineered a compromise in which brand-name drug companies could obtain a patent term extension, and generic drug companies could obtain ANDA approval for pre- and post-1962 drugs. The compromise was enacted in the *Drug Price Competition and Patent Term Restoration Act* of 1984 (*Hatch-Waxman Act*).

The *Hatch-Waxman Act* amended the new drug approval provisions of the *FD&C Act* to add Section 505(j). Section 505(j) formalized the legal structure for generic drugs, under which an ANDA containing bioequivalence data to a brand drug—the Reference Listed Drug (RLD)—among other data and information, was sufficient for FDA to consider approval. As explained in Chapter 16 Patents and Exclusivity, the *Hatch-Waxman Act* also amended the patent laws to authorize a patent term extension that could be as long as five years for time lost during the regulatory review period.[9] The new law also required brand-name drug firms to "list" patents with FDA that they asserted claimed the branded drug (ingredient or product) or a method for using the branded product. FDA lists these patents—and all drug approvals—in a publication known as the *Orange Book* (after its cover's original color), the formal name of which is "Approved Drug Products With Therapeutic Equivalence Evaluations."

Under the *FD&C Act* (as amended by the *Hatch-Waxman Act*), ANDA approval is subject to several restrictions. First, non-patent market exclusivity provisions of three or five years were added by the *Hatch-Waxman Act* to compensate brand-name drug companies for allowing reliance on their proprietary research. Second, an ANDA applicant must notify the NDA holder and patent owner (if different) if an *Orange Book*-listed patent claims the RLD; if the NDA owner files a patent infringement suit, approval of the ANDA is deferred. Third, an ANDA drug product must contain the "same" active ingredient as the brand-name drug and have essentially the same labeling, including indications, warnings, contraindications, etc.

ANDA Approval Process

The premise of *FD&C Act* Section 505(j) is an ANDA drug is the "same as" the brand-name drug—i.e., the RLD, defined as "the listed drug identified by FDA as the drug product upon which an applicant relies in seeking approval of its abbreviated application" (21 CFR 314.3(b)).[10] However, "same" does not mean "identical." Differences may be allowed in route of administration, dosage form and strength as well as in a single active ingredient in a combination drug product if those differences are first approved by FDA under a suitability petition as not requiring clinical investigations.[11] *FD&C Act* Section 505(j)(2)(A) states an ANDA (not the subject of an approved suitability petition) must contain information to show the active ingredient, "the route of administration, the dosage form, and the strength of the new drug are the same as those of the [RLD]."[12]

An ANDA must contain, among other things identified in the *FD&C Act* and FDA's ANDA format and content regulations at 21 CFR 314.94, information demonstrating the generic version is bioequivalent to the RLD.[13] This information may come from *in vivo* (human) and/or *in vitro* (test tube) studies (21 CFR 320). Bioequivalence testing determines whether the inherent changes from the brand-name product presented by the proposed generic drug product's formulation or manufacturing affect the rate or extent to which the active ingredient reaches the primary site of action. Although data and information demonstrating *in vivo* bioequivalence often are required, FDA may waive this requirement if *in vivo* bioequivalence is considered self-evident (e.g., in the case of many injectable drugs) or for other reasons (21 CFR 320.22).[14]

A drug product is considered bioequivalent to the RLD if:

1. the rate and extent of the drug's absorption do not show a significant difference from the RLD's rate and extent of absorption when administered at the same molar dose of the therapeutic ingredient under similar experimental conditions in either a single dose or multiple doses or
2. the extent of the drug's absorption does not show a significant difference from the extent of the RLD's absorption when administered at the same molar dose of the therapeutic ingredient under similar experimental conditions in either a single dose or multiple doses and the difference from the listed drug in the rate of absorption of the drug is intentional, reflected in its proposed labeling, not essential to the attainment of effective body drug concentrations on chronic use and considered medically insignificant for the drug. (*FD&C Act* Section 505(j)(8)(B); 21 CFR 320.1(e))

The choice of which *in vivo* bioequivalence study design to use is based on the design's ability to compare the drug delivered by the test (generic) and reference (brand-name) drug products at the drug's particular site of action. In a standard *in vivo* bioequivalence study, single doses of the test and reference drug products are administered to volunteers (usually 24–36 healthy adults), and the rate and extent the drug's absorption is determined from measured plasma concentrations over time for each subject participating in the study. The extent of absorption (i.e., how much of the drug in the given dose was absorbed) is reflected through various measurements. The preferred study design for oral dosage forms is a single-dose, fasting, two-treatment, two sequence crossover design with a washout period between treatments.[15] In a crossover study, the subjects receive the test and reference drug products in separate sequences (either test before reference or reference before test), with a period between treatments of no drug administration (the washout period) to ensure the previous dose is cleared from the body before the second dose is administered. To demonstrate *in vitro* bioequivalence, FDA recommends an applicant use an *in vitro* test (e.g., a dissolution rate test) correlating with *in vivo* data.[16] Over the past few years, FDA has begun to publish individual product bioequivalence recommendations on its website. FDA has published almost 850 product-specific bioequivalence recommendations already, and the agency's website is updated regularly with new recommendations.

An ANDA for a generic version of an RLD also must contain one of four possible certifications "with respect to each patent which claims the [brand-name] drug...or which claims a use for such listed drug...and for which information is required to be filed" by the NDA holder and is listed in the *Orange Book* (*FD&C Act* Section 505(j)(2)(A)(vii)).

Figure 15-1. Pending ANDAs

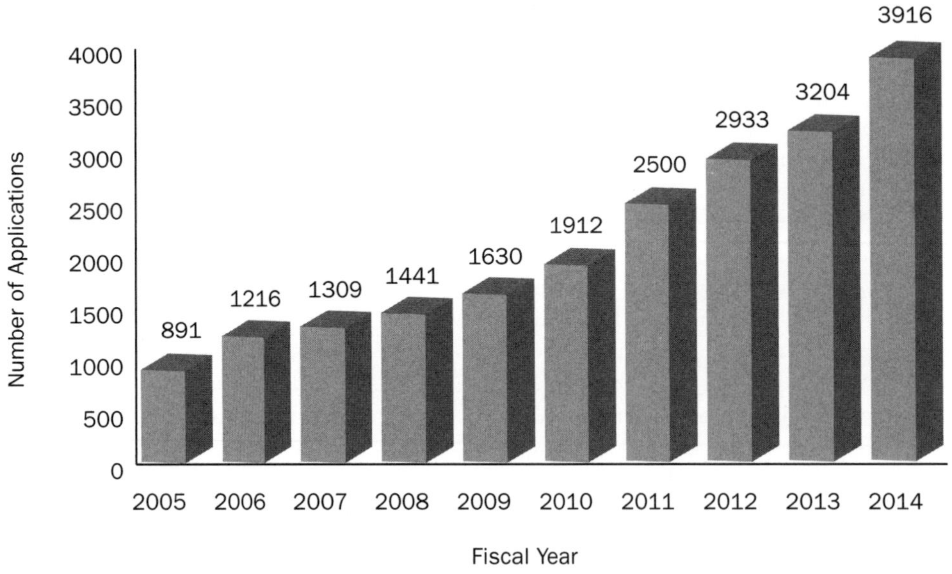

The consequences of the various types of patent certifications are discussed in Chapter 16.

Once an applicant submits an ANDA to FDA, it is reviewed to determine it is sufficiently complete to permit receipt (21 CFR 314.101). FDA generally reviews ANDA submissions within 60 days of receipt; however, the agency's decision on whether to receive an ANDA may take longer. If FDA receives an ANDA, it performs an in-depth review to determine whether to approve the application. In the past, this review typically took 15–18 months; however, due to a significant backlog of pending ANDAs at FDA—which has increased steadily since 2006 (**Figure 15-1**) and currently stands at about approximately 4,000 original ANDAs—in recent years, the review process has taken longer. For example, in Fiscal 2013, the median approval time for an original ANDA was 36 months (**Figure 15-2**) and is projected to be about 43 months for Fiscal 2014. At the end of its review, the agency either approves or refuses to approve the ANDA (21 CFR 314.127 identifies the reasons for refusing to approve an ANDA). If approved, the generic drug product is listed in the *Orange Book* and may be identified as a "therapeutic equivalent" to the RLD.

Although FDA generally reviews ANDA submissions on a "first in, first reviewed" basis to ensure fair and even-handed treatment of applicants, there are exceptions. For example, an ANDA applicant may qualify for FDA's expedited review policy:

Certain applications may be identified at the time of submission for expedited review. These include products to respond to current and anticipated public health emergencies, products under special review programs such as the President's Emergency Plan for AIDS Relief (PEPFAR),[17] products for which a nationwide shortage has been identified, and first generic products for which there are no blocking patents or exclusivities on the reference listed drug.[18]

FDA's ANDA approval process is illustrated in **Figure 15-3**.

A Few Words on GDUFA Commitments Letter

With the enactment of the *Generic Drug User Fee Amendments* of 2012 (*GDUFA*) on 9 July 2012, as part of the *Food and Drug Administration Safety and Innovation Act* (*FDASIA*, Public Law 112-144), FDA, for the first time, will accept user fees from the generic drug industry to assure prompt access to safe, high-quality and effective generic drugs.

This law comes at a decisive time, since the public health achievement of generic medicines also has caused a notable challenge. Due to inadequate resources, FDA has not been able to maintain pace with a rising number of ANDAs submitted for review. Approximately 4,000 generic drug applications are pending. Nonetheless, *GDUFA* will give FDA the required resources and personnel to eliminate the current backlog and bring generic drugs to the market and to patients more promptly.

GDUFA had some challenging goals when introduced in September 2012. By 30 September 2017, *GDUFA* requires FDA to:

- review and act on 90% of complete electronic original generic applications within 10 months after the date of submission
- facilitate industry self-identification efforts, enabling fee calculation and improving the quality of generic industry supply chain information

Figure 15-2. Median ANDA Approval Times

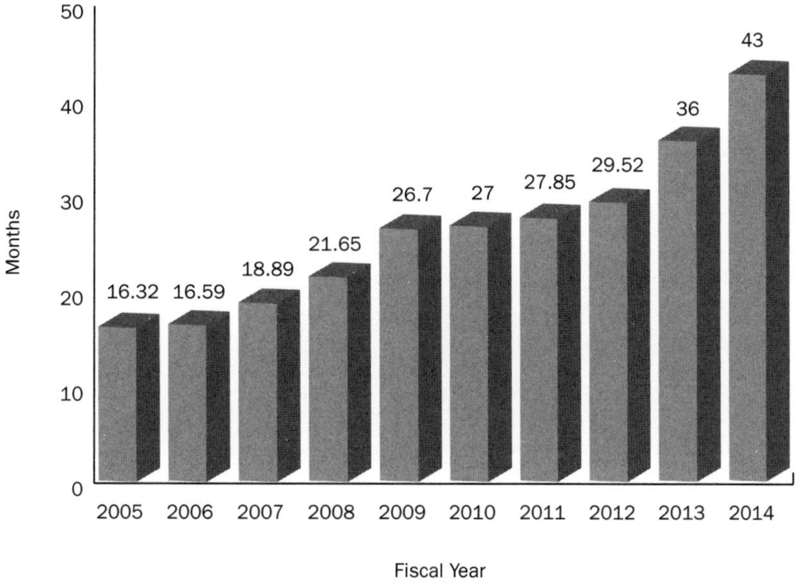

- engage in outreach efforts to educate and inform industry participants and other stakeholders about *GDUFA*
- build new information technology systems and expand on existing systems and technology investments to promote efficiency, monitor human generic drug safety and efficacy and streamline the human generic drug approval process

Table 15-1 presents *GDUFA* performance goals and targets for Fiscal 2013–17. Performance goals are met when the specified percentage of submissions are reviewed within the review-time goal shown. Goals are phased in incrementally over the five-year authorization, with most beginning in Fiscal 2015.

A Few Words About Organizational and Procedural Changes at OGD

FDA made several organizational and procedural changes to meet *GDUFA* commitments. Indeed, organizational changes also have been implemented at FDA, including elevating the Office of Generic Drugs (OGD) to "super office" status, reporting directly to the Center for Drug Evaluation and Research (CDER) Director Janet Woodcock, which will affect how ANDAs are handled, and the formation of the new Office of Pharmaceutical Quality (OPQ), responsible for chemistry, manufacturing and controls (CMC) and microbiology review. With the creation of OPQ, both ANDA and NDA CMC and microbiology reviews are consolidated under one office to improve review efficiencies among several therapeutic areas and dosage formulations. The Division of Bioequivalence (DBE) and its Regulatory Program and Labeling Support within OGD still are responsible for bioequivalence and labeling reviews respectively.

A few procedural changes also were made to enhance communication with sponsors and improve ANDA review efficiencies. As part of the *GDUFA* commitments, at the end of the ANDA review, OGD could either approve the application or issue a complete response (CR) letter. A CR letter comprises all review divisions' comments regarding the ANDA approval. Although OGD can issue Easily Correctable Deficiencies (ECDs) to allow sponsors 10 business days to address minor review deficiencies. OPQ, on the other hand, can issue up to two real-time information requests allowing 30 business days for a sponsor to respond to minor CMC and microbiology review deficiencies. If a sponsor does not respond to ECDs and real-time information requests in a timely manner, all deficiencies are rolled up into a CR letter. Major CMC, microbiology, labeling and bioequivalence deficiencies in an ANDA are conveyed only through a CR letter.

Recent ANDA review experience suggests, in addition to ECDs, bioequivalence and labeling review deficiencies also were communicated through Information Requests, even though this review process was not communicated clearly to industry. OPQ in some instances has issued more than two real-time information requests during ANDA review. These review practices clearly show a lag in communication between OGD and industry, and indicate a lack of clear review practices in the early part of *GDUFA* implementation.

Figure 15-3. FDA's ANDA Approval Process

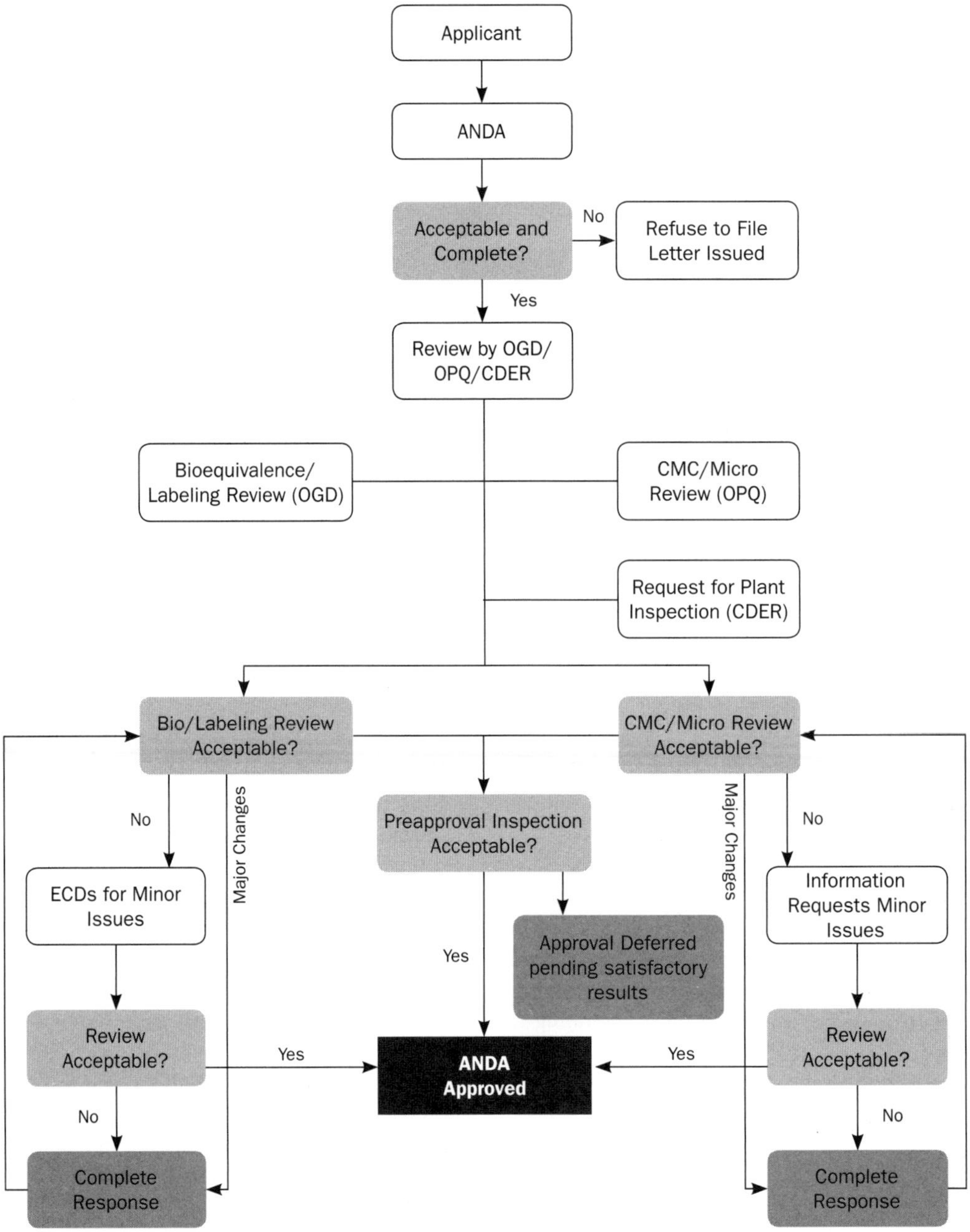

A Few Words on ANDA Suitability Petitions

Two laws enacted over the past several years have affected suitability petitions with respect to both their availability and their utility.

First, the *Pediatric Research Equity Act* (*PREA*), which was signed into law on 3 December 2003 and amended the *FD&C Act* to add new Section 505B, significantly impacts the economic attractiveness of securing a change to an RLD via an ANDA suitability petition.[19] Under *PREA* and *FD&C Act* Section 505B, Congress granted FDA the statutory authority to require pediatric studies in certain defined circumstances retroactive to 1 April 1999. Specifically, *FD&C Act* Section 505B states an applicant "that submits an application (or supplement to an application) under section 505 [of the *FD&C Act*] for a new active ingredient, new indication, new dosage form, new dosing regimen, or new route of administration…shall submit with the application" the results of pediatric studies assessing "the safety and effectiveness of the drug…for the claimed indications in all relevant pediatric subpopulations; and to support dosing and administration for each pediatric subpopulation for which the drug...is safe and effective, [unless FDA] concludes that pediatric effectiveness can be extrapolated from adequate and well-controlled studies in adults, usually supplemented with other information obtained in pediatric patients," or unless FDA defers or partially or fully waives this requirement.[20]

An ANDA requiring an approved suitability petition for a change in the RLD with respect to an active ingredient (in a combination drug), route of administration or dosage form meets the criteria of *FD&C Act* Section 505B(1)(A), because it is an application submitted under *FD&C Act* Section 505. The only change permitted by a suitability petition that does not trigger the requirements of *FD&C Act* Section 505B is a change in strength from that of the RLD.

FD&C Act Section 505(j)(2)(C)(i) requires FDA to deny a suitability petition if "investigations must be conducted to show the safety and effectiveness of the drug or of any of its active ingredients, the route of administration, the dosage form, or strength which differ from the listed drug." Thus, unless FDA fully waives the *PREA* pediatric studies requirement, the requirement to conduct (or even a deferral from conducting) pediatric studies triggers the statutory requirement to deny a suitability petition.

Second, the *Medicare Prescription Drug, Improvement, and Modernization Act* of 2003 (*MMA*) (Pub. L. No. 108173, 117 Stat. 2066 (2003)), amended the *FD&C Act* to preclude a generic applicant with a pending ANDA from amending its application to change the RLD. Specifically, *FD&C Act* Section 505(j)(2)(D)(i), the 505(b)(2) application counterpart for which is at *FD&C Act* Section 505(b)(4)(A), states, "[A]n applicant may not amend or supplement an [ANDA] to seek approval of a drug referring to a different listed drug from the listed drug identified in the application as submitted to [FDA]."[21]

FDA recently addressed *FD&C Act* Section 505(j)(2)(D)(i) in a Citizen Petition response. The agency determined an applicant with a pending ANDA subject to an approved suitability petition must submit a new application to the agency as the result of the approval of another applicant's NDA for a drug product that is the pharmaceutical equivalent of the drug product described in the pending ANDA and, which is therefore, the appropriate RLD that should be cited by the applicant.[22] Thus, if at any time before approval of an ANDA subject to an approved suitability petition (or a 505(b)(2) application), another drug product is approved that is the pharmaceutical equivalent—or is more pharmaceutically similar to the product in a pending 505(b)(2) application—FDA could require the applicant to cite a new RLD to support its petition. As a result of the statutory prohibition on amending an ANDA to change the RLD, FDA could require the applicant to submit a new application containing a certification or statement to any relevant *Orange Book*-listed patents (as well as required bioequivalence/bioavailability information).

A Few Words on Inactive Ingredients

FD&C Act Section 505(j)(4)(H) states FDA must approve an ANDA unless, among other things:

> (I)nformation submitted in the application or any other information available to [FDA] shows that (i) the inactive ingredients of the drug are unsafe for use under the conditions prescribed, recommended, or suggested in the labeling proposed for the drug or (ii) the composition of the drug is unsafe under such conditions because of the type or quantity of inactive ingredients included or the manner in which the inactive ingredients are included. FDA's regulations implementing *FD&C Act* Section 505(j)(4)(H) generally are found in the agency's ANDA content and format regulations at 21 CFR 314.94. Pertinent regulations on inactive ingredient changes for certain types of generic drug products are set forth in 21 CFR 314.94(a)(9). For example, FDA's regulations for parenteral drug products at 21 CFR 314.94(a)(9)(iii) state:
>
> Generally, a drug product intended for parenteral use shall contain the same inactive ingredients and in the same concentration as the [RLD] identified by the applicant under paragraph (a)(3) of this section. However, an applicant may seek approval of a drug product that differs from the reference listed drug in preservative, buffer, or antioxidant provided that the applicant identifies and characterizes the differences and provides information demonstrating the differences do not affect the safety or efficacy of the proposed drug product.

Preservative, buffer and antioxidant changes in generic parenteral drug products are referred to as "exception excipients," which may differ qualitatively or quantitatively from the RLD formulation. Other regulations under 21 CFR 314.94(a)(9)(iv) identify exception excipients for generic ophthalmic and otic drug products (i.e., preservative, buffer, substance to adjust tonicity and thickening agent). Excipients not identified in these regulations are referred to as "non-exception excipients."

FDA's exception excipient regulations under 21 CFR 314.94(a)(9) find their parallel in 21 CFR 314.127(a)(8)(ii), which addresses the grounds for an FDA refusal to approve an ANDA for a parenteral, ophthalmic or otic drug product. For example, one regulation states: "FDA will consider an inactive ingredient in, or the composition of, a drug product intended for parenteral use to be unsafe and will refuse to approve the [ANDA] unless it contains the same inactive ingredients, other than preservatives, buffers, and antioxidants, in the same concentration as the listed drug."[23] Thus, it is important a company understands the possible implications of changing certain drug product formulations. If such a change is for a non-exception excipient, FDA would, unless under a narrow exception discussed below, refuse to receive or approve an ANDA. Instead, a company would need to submit a 505(b)(2) application for the proposed drug product, which, like other NDAs, is subject to much higher user fees under the *Prescription Drug User Fee Act* (*PDUFA*) than those applying with to generic drugs under the *Generic Drug User Fee Amendments* of 2012, which were passed as part of *FDASIA*. For Fiscal 2015, the one-time, full NDA user fee is $2,335,200, and annual product and establishment user fees are $110,370 and $569,200, respectively. In contrast, the ANDA user fee is $58,730, and the establishment fee is $247,717, and no separate product fee exists for generic drugs. For more information on user fees, see Chapter 11.

Notwithstanding FDA's exception excipient regulations, the agency has in very limited circumstances waived these regulations to permit the receipt and approval of an ANDA for a drug product containing a non-exception excipient change from the RLD.

FDA's regulations at 21 CFR 314.99(b) state a generic applicant "may ask FDA to waive…any requirement that applies to the applicant under 21 CFR 314.92–314.99. The applicant shall comply with the requirements for a waiver under 21 CFR 314.90." 21 CFR 314.90, the parallel waiver regulation for 505(b) applicants, describes the information an applicant must submit to support a waiver request, and states FDA may grant a waiver if the agency finds: "(1) the applicant's compliance with the requirement is unnecessary for the agency to evaluate the application or compliance cannot be achieved; (2) the applicant's alternative submission satisfies the requirement; or (3) the applicant's submission otherwise justifies a waiver."[24] Pursuant to this regulation, FDA may waive its ANDA exception excipient regulations under 21 CFR 314.99(b), so the agency can receive and approve an ANDA.

FDA has granted a 21 CFR 314.99(b) waiver when an ANDA applicant seeks approval to market a drug product containing a non-exception excipient used in a discontinued RLD formulation not used in the currently marketed RLD formulation. For example, FDA has allowed applicants seeking approval to market generic Sandostatin (octreotide acetate) injection to substitute a different tonicity agent (a non-exception excipient change) and buffer system because "the inactive ingredients (including the buffer system and tonicity agent) used in the discontinued formulation of Sandostatin do not make that formulation unsafe…[and because] the discontinued formulation of Sandostatin is no less safe and effective than the new formulation."[25]

A Few Words on Inactive Ingredients Database (IID)

During ANDA development, it is common for sponsors to consult FDA's Inactive Ingredient Database (IID) to gather data on "acceptable levels" of excipients utilized in previously approved products. The reason behind this practice is the belief FDA will allow experience associated with earlier use of a particular ingredient at the level designated in the IID as satisfactory qualification of an inactive ingredient. It is essential, though, to recognize FDA's examination of the adequacy of IID's confirmation goes beyond just verifying a particular amount of the ingredient has been utilized in a given dosage form. FDA also weighs whether the conditions of the excipient's use in the prior approved product are equivalent to (or greater than) those of the proposed new product. Additional factors FDA considers in this analysis are the route of administration, exposure duration, patient population and exposure level.

FDA has not updated the IID since 2013, which has brought significant hardship in developing generic formulations with acceptable excipient levels. IPEC-Americas and OGD's Inactive Ingredient Database (IID) Excipient Working Group have been in discussions since December 2011 about enhancing FDA's IID database. One of the team's principal goals is to help resolve existing issues with the FDA IID that are impacting ANDA submissions.

New Substance Registration System (SRS) nomenclature has been used for specific grades and has resulted in several references disappearing from the IID, which has caused many commonly used excipients to be treated like new excipients that require significant safety assessment. As a result, industry has wasted significant resources, and FDA has had to re-assess the safety of well-known excipients that have no significant safety risks associated with their traditional uses. Appropriate ICH Q9 risk management concepts do not appear to be used for acceptance for filing reviews.

Therapeutic Equivalence

The term "therapeutic equivalence" is not defined in the *FD&C Act* or in FDA's ANDA regulations. However, "[d] rug products are considered to be therapeutic equivalents only if they are pharmaceutical equivalents and if they can be expected to have the same clinical effect and safety profile when administered to patients under the conditions specified in the labeling" (i.e., are bioequivalent).[26] "FDA believes that products classified as therapeutically equivalent can be substituted with the full expectation that the substituted product will produce the same clinical effect and safety profile as the prescribed product."[27]

FDA's regulations define the term "pharmaceutical equivalents" to mean:

> (D)rug products in identical dosage forms that contain identical amounts of the identical active drug ingredient, i.e., the same salt or ester of the same therapeutic moiety, or, in the case of modified release dosage forms that

Table 15-1. Median ANDA Approval Times

GDUFA Goals/Commitment Types	Review-Time Goals	Fiscal 13	Fiscal 14	Fiscal 15	Fiscal 16	Fiscal 17
Original ANDA Review						
Original ANDA submissions	15 months	–	–	60%	75%	–
Original ANDA submissions	10 months	–	–	–	–	90%
Amendment Review*						
Tier 1 - First major amendment	10 months	–	–	60%	75%	90%
Tier 1 - First through third minor amendment	3 months	–	–	60%	75%	90%
Tier 1 - First through third minor amendment requiring an inspection	10 months	–	–	60%	75%	90%
Tier 1 - Fourth through fifth minor amendment	6 months	–	–	60%	75%	90%
Tier 1 - Fourth through fifth minor amendment requiring an inspection	10 months	–	–	60%	75%	90%
Tier 2 Amendments	12 months	–	–	60%	75%	90%
PAS						
PASs not requiring inspections	6 months	–	–	60%	75%	90%
PASs requiring inspections	10 months	–	–	60%	75%	90%
Controlled Correspondence						
Controlled correspondence	4 months	–	–	70%	–	–
Controlled correspondence	2 months				70%	90%
Controlled correspondence requiring input from clinical division	5 months	–	–	70%	–	–
Controlled correspondence requiring input from clinical division	3 months	–	–	–	70%	90%
ANDA Review Efficiency						
30-minute teleconference	10 business day	–†	–†	200	250	300
Drug Master File (DMF) Review Efficiency						
30-minute teleconference	10 business day	–	–	‡	‡	‡
Backlog						
Review and act on ANDAs, ANDA amendments and ANDA PASs that are pending on 1 Oct 2012	60 months	–	–	–	–	90%
Human Resources						
Incremental staffing§	Staff/Train	25%	50%	100%	–	–

* Amendments may be submitted to either original ANDAs or PASs.
† FDA aspires to hold teleconferences in Fiscal 2013 and Fiscal 2014 at a level similar to pre-*GDUFA* levels.
‡ One teleconference per DMF holder per month. Total number of teleconferences should not exceed the number of teleconferences for ANDAs.
§ Incremental staffing goals are shown as a percentage of the final program hiring goal.

require a reservoir or overage or such forms as prefilled syringes where residual volume may vary, that deliver identical amounts of the active drug ingredient over the identical dosing period; do not necessarily contain the same inactive ingredients; and meet the identical compendial or other applicable standard of identity, strength, quality, and purity, including potency and, where applicable, content uniformity, disintegration times, and/or dissolution rates.[28]

As explained above, the term "bioequivalence" is defined in the *FD&C Act* and FDA regulations.[29] Because therapeutic equivalence requires two drug products to be pharmaceutically equivalent and bioequivalent in order to be substitutable, "pharmaceutical alternatives" are not therapeutic equivalents and are not substitutable for the RLD relied upon for approval. FDA's regulations define "pharmaceutical alternatives" as:

> (D)rug products that contain the identical therapeutic moiety, or its precursor, but not necessarily in the same amount or dosage form or as the same salt or ester. Each such drug product individually meets either the identical or its own respective compendial or other applicable standard of identity, strength, quality, and purity, including potency and, where applicable, content uniformity, disintegration times and/or dissolution rates.[30]

Thus, products approved pursuant to an approved suitability petition (i.e., a change in strength, route of administration, dosage form or active ingredient in a combination drug) are pharmaceutical alternatives and are not listed in the *Orange Book* as therapeutically equivalent to the RLD. To give one common example, tablets and capsules are considered different dosage forms. Therefore, they are pharmaceutical alternatives, not pharmaceutical equivalents. Consequently, they will not be "A-rated" in the *Orange Book* (described below), even if they are bioequivalent.

Pharmaceutically equivalent prescription drug products (i.e., multisource drug products approved under *FD&C Act* Section 505) usually are identified in the *Orange Book* with either an "A" or "B" therapeutic equivalence code designation, which is further defined by a one-character subcode.[31] (There are six "A" subcodes and 10 "B" subcodes.[32]) The *Orange Book* coding system for therapeutic equivalence evaluations allows users to determine whether FDA has evaluated a particular approved drug product as therapeutically equivalent to other pharmaceutically equivalent drug products (the first character in a code) and provides additional information on the basis of FDA's evaluations (the second character in a code). "A-rated" drug products are considered to be therapeutically equivalent to other pharmaceutically equivalent products because there are no known or suspected bioequivalence problems, or such problems have been resolved with adequate evidence supporting bioequivalence. "B-rated" drug products are not considered to be therapeutically equivalent to other pharmaceutically equivalent drug products because actual or potential bioequivalence problems identified by FDA have not been resolved by adequate bioequivalence evidence.

Drug products assigned an "A" rating fall under one of two categories:

- those active ingredients or dosage forms for which no *in vivo* bioequivalence issue is known or suspected, and for which bioequivalence to the RLD is presumed and considered self-evident based on other data in an application or by a showing an acceptable *in vitro* dissolution standard is met
- those active ingredients or dosage forms presenting a potential bioequivalence problem, but the applicant's approved application contains adequate scientific evidence establishing (through *in vivo* and/or *in vitro* studies) bioequivalence of the product to a selected RLD

Drug products falling under the first category are assigned a therapeutic equivalence code depending on the dosage form. These codes include AA, AN, AO, AP or AT.[33] Drug products falling under the second category are coded AB, the most common code assignment.

Drug products assigned a "B" rating fall under one of three categories:

- FDA has documented bioequivalence problems or a significant potential for such problems (and no adequate studies demonstrating bioequivalence have been submitted to the agency)
- FDA has an insufficient basis to determine therapeutic equivalence (e.g., quality standards are inadequate)
- the drug products are under regulatory review

Drug products falling under these categories are assigned a therapeutic equivalence code largely based on dosage form. These codes are B*, BC, BD, BE, BN, BP, BR, BS, BT or BX.[34] FDA's assignment of a "B" rating does not mean a particular drug product is not safe and effective. (Indeed, the applicant has provided sufficient data to meet the statutory and regulatory approval criteria.) Rather, a "B" rating means FDA has identified unresolved actual or potential bioequivalence problems, and because of those problems, a particular drug product cannot be considered therapeutically equivalent to other pharmaceutically equivalent drug products.

A generic drug that is a pharmaceutical alternative to an RLD (e.g., tablet versus capsule) is not assigned a therapeutic equivalence code (such drug products are, by definition, not therapeutic equivalents). Instead, they are listed separately in the *Orange Book* as single-source drug products. However, because each *Orange Book*-listed drug product may be designated as an RLD (pursuant to a request to FDA to assign RLD status), a generic applicant could cite the approved drug as the RLD and obtain approval of an ANDA for a pharmaceutically equivalent drug product. In such a case, if the drug also is shown to be bioequivalent to the RLD, FDA could assign both drug products an "A" therapeutic equivalence code appropriate for such a multisource drug product.

Therapeutic equivalence codes are assigned by FDA based on the agency's scientific and medical evaluations of a marketing application for a generic version of a listed drug. The assignment of a particular therapeutic equivalence code reflects the agency's application of specific criteria to multisource drug products (i.e., those criteria identified in reference 15). As FDA explained in the preamble to the proposal establishing the *Orange Book*:

> The term "therapeutically equivalent drug products" simply means that two such drug products can be expected, in the judgment of FDA, to have equivalent therapeutic effect and equivalent potential for adverse effects when used under the conditions set forth in their labeling. Drug products that are therapeutically equivalent may still vary in certain respects: color, shape, taste, or packaging for example. As a result, patients may not perceive them as identical or equally acceptable. For this reason, it cannot be stated that such drug products are substitutable or interchangeable in all cases. The judgment is not FDA's as to whether different drug products are substitutable or interchangeable for use by a particular patient; rather, it rests with practitioners who, in prescribing and dispensing drug products, can take into consideration the unique characteristics, needs or problems of individual patients. It is the agency's position, however, that if one therapeutically equivalent drug product is substituted for another under State law, with due professional regard for the individual patient, there is no substantial reason to believe that the patient will receive a drug product that is different in terms of the therapeutic effect intended.[35]

As to the legal status of the *Orange Book*, FDA has commented it "contain[s] only public information and advice" and "[imposes] no requirement or restriction upon any person; it [does] not interpret or apply the [*FD&C Act*] in a manner that creates any obligation on any person; it [makes] no recommendation as to which products persons should purchase, prescribe, or dispense, or conversely, which products should be avoided."[36] However, FDA's criteria for assigning therapeutic equivalence codes "are regulatory determinations which FDA is statutorily authorized to make."[37]

As to the clinical appropriateness of (and risks associated with) substituting drug products FDA does not consider to be therapeutically equivalent (e.g., a drug product with a two-character "B" therapeutic equivalence code), such issues generally are a matter of state law.[38] FDA emphasized this point in the preamble to the 1979 *Orange Book* proposal: "[A] primary purpose of [the *Orange Book*] is to provide State agencies and officials with information relating to drug products that may be selected for dispensing under applicable State law."[39]

Drug product substitutions must be made in accordance with each individual state's pharmacy practice act. There are, in general, four different approaches taken by such laws:

- the positive formulary approach (requiring substitution to be limited to drugs on a specific list, often the *Orange Book*)
- the negative formulary approach (permitting substitution for all drugs except those prohibited by a particular list—usually drugs for which there are no "A-rated" products listed in the *Orange Book*)
- the combined positive and negative formulary approach
- the "non-formulary" approach (i.e., there is not a clearly defined positive or negative formulary)[40]

In addition, state pharmacy laws may extend the prescribing authority granted to pharmacists beyond substituting a generic drug. For example, pharmacists may be permitted to substitute a product from the same class of drug, even though the drug is not identified in the *Orange Book* as therapeutically equivalent to the prescribed drug product. This procedure is known as "therapeutic interchange." The laws covering therapeutic interchange vary widely from state to state.[41] Thus, the "clinical appropriateness" of substituting drug products FDA does not consider to be therapeutically equivalent is handled on a state-by-state basis. The consequences for violating a particular state substitution law are governed by the laws of that state.

User Fees

With the backlog of unapproved ANDAs reaching over 2,900 by the end of Fiscal 2011 and reportedly not reduced since (see **Figure 15-2**), FDA, Congress and the generic industry realized historic industry resistance to user fees had to yield to the vital need to markedly increase human resources within OGD to tackle the backlog. Thus, in 2012, Congress—in addition to addressing the need to re-authorize user fees for innovative drugs, biologics and medical device every five years—enacted, as Title III of *FDASIA*, *GDUFA*.

For more details on user fees, see Chapter 11.

Summary

The term "generic drug" is not defined in the *FD&C Act* or in FDA regulations. It generally is used, however, to refer to a drug product that is the same as a brand-name drug in these key aspects: active ingredient, dosage form, route of administration and strength, and for which FDA has determined the generic version is therapeutically equivalent to the branded drug. As a result of these "sameness" aspects, state law typically allows a pharmacist to substitute the generic for a branded drug in filling a prescription. When combined with the lower costs of a generic drug—because the brand-name drug company already has done the work necessary to develop the active ingredient and show it is safe and effective for its indications—the generic can be sold for a fraction of the brand-name price. The approval of generic drugs in the US is governed by a tapestry of laws, regulations and FDA policies developed over the past few decades. While a complex regime, the generic drug approval process has allowed the use of generic drugs to rise to a level of more than 80% of all prescriptions filled in the US and is estimated to have saved Americans close to a billion dollars over the past 10 years.

References

1. Karst KR. "Marketed Unapproved Drugs–Past, Present and Future?" *Regulatory Affairs Focus*, Vol. 12, No. 2, pp 37–42 (February 2007).
2. ANDAs were permitted under FDA regulations for duplicates (i.e., generic versions). The term "duplicate" applied to a drug product that was the same as an already approved drug product in dosage form, route of administration, kind and amount of active ingredient, indication(s) and any other conditions of use. FDA regulations permitted ANDAs for "similar" and "related" products only if the agency had made a separate finding (following a firm's petition) that an ANDA was appropriate for that drug product.
3. A product that is a "new drug" within the meaning of *FD&C Act* Section 201(p) may not be introduced into interstate commerce unless there is an approved marketing application (e.g., an NDA), or unless an exemption has been granted permitting the introduction of the drug into interstate commerce (e.g., an effective Investigational New Drug Application (IND)).
4. The "paper NDA" policy is described in a 31 July 1978 FDA staff memorandum. The policy was not originally published in the *Federal Register* because FDA determined rulemaking procedures were not required because "the policy is a lawful exercise of FDA's statutory authority…" 45 *Fed. Reg.* 82,052 (12 December 1980). FDA was challenged on this issue in court and won. See *Burroughs Wellcome Co. v. Schweiker*, 649 F.2d 221, 225 (4th Cir. 1981). Subsequently, in separate litigation, the US District Court for the Northern District of Illinois ruled that upon publication of FDA's policy in the *Federal Register*, the agency could implement it without rulemaking procedures. See *American Critical Care v. Schweiker*, Food, Drug, Cosm. L. Rep. (CCH) 1980-81 Transfer Binder ¶ 38, 110 (N.D. Ill. 1981).
5. The published studies requirement could be met by referencing data available in published literature, laboratory reports, physician evaluation forms and even unpublished reports when available and necessary. However, the underlying data did not have to be included or referenced, as was required under FDA's old interpretation of "full reports" in *FD&C Act* Section 505(b)(1). Reference to information not publicly available was not permitted, including information in the brand-name product's NDA. The "bridging" data requirement could be met by submitting data from a bioavailability/bioequivalence study comparing the drug that was the subject of the "paper NDA" to the approved drug "to show that the drug is comparable in blood levels (or dissolution rate, as required) to the innovator's product." 46 *Fed. Reg.* at 27,397.
6. FDA revoked the "paper NDA" policy in 1989 when the agency proposed regulations implementing the *Drug Price Competition and Patent Term Restoration Act*, Pub. L. No. 98-417, 98 Stat. 1585 (1984) (*Hatch-Waxman Act*). See FDA, Proposed Rule, ANDA Regulations, 54 *Fed. Reg.* 28,872, 28, 890 (10 July 1989).
7. 43 *Fed. Reg.* 39126, 39128 (1 September 1978).
8. *Drug Regulation Reform Act*, 95th Cong., 2d Sess. (1978); *Drug Regulation Reform Act*, 96th Cong., 1st Sess. (1979).
9. The *Hatch-Waxman Act* also replaced the "paper NDA" with the 505(b)(2) application. The *FD&C Act* describes a 505(b)(2) application as an application "for a drug for which the investigations… relied upon by the applicant for approval of the application were not conducted by or for the applicant and for which the applicant has not obtained a right of reference or use from the person by or for whom the investigations were conducted." *FD&C Act* Section 505(b)(2). A 505(b)(2) application differs from a "paper NDA" in that it permits the sponsor of a drug that may differ substantially from a drug listed in FDA's *Approved Drug Products with Therapeutic Equivalence Evaluations* (commonly referred to as the *Orange Book* because of its bright orange cover) to rely on FDA's determination of the safety and effectiveness of a referenced drug and/or on published studies or studies in an NDA (or NDAs) sponsored by another person, together with studies generated on its own drug product, as a way to satisfy the requirement of "full reports" of safety and effectiveness. As with the old "paper NDA" policy, "bridging" studies to the referenced drug are necessary. An application for a duplicate of a drug listed in the *Orange Book* and eligible for approval as a generic drug under the ANDA provisions of *FD&C Act* Section 505(j) may not be submitted as a 505(b)(2) application.
10. While an ANDA applicant must identify an RLD in its application, a 505(b)(2) applicant must identify a "listed drug" (or drugs) in its application if the applicant seeks to rely on FDA's previous finding of safety or efficacy for that listed drug(s). While there are no FDA regulations governing how a 505(b)(2) applicant should choose a listed drug when various options are present, FDA has spoken to the issue in guidance and in citizen petition responses. FDA has stated that "[i]f there is a listed drug that is the pharmaceutical equivalent of the drug proposed in the 505(b)(2) application, the 505(b)(2) applicant should provide patent certifications for the patents listed for the pharmaceutically equivalent drug." FDA, *Draft Guidance for Industry: Applications Covered by Section 505(b)(2)*, at 8 (October 1999). This serves to "ensure that the 505(b)(2) applicant does not use the 505(b)(2) process to end-run patent protections that would have applied had an ANDA been permitted." FDA, Citizen Petition Response, Docket No. FDA-2004-P-0089 (formerly 2004P-0386), at 9 (30 November 2004) (hereinafter "RLD Choice Petition Response"). Additionally, these provisions "further ensure that the 505(b)(2) applicant (and FDA) can rely, to the maximum extent possible, on what is already known about a drug without having to re-prove (or re-review) what has already been demonstrated." Id.

   "When there is no listed drug that is a pharmaceutical equivalent to the drug product proposed in the 505(b)(2) NDA, neither the statute, the regulations, nor the Draft Guidance directly addresses how to identify the listed drug or drugs on which a 505(b)(2) applicant is to rely." Id. In FDA's RLD Choice Petition Response, however, the agency stated:

   it follows that the more similar a proposed drug is to the listed drug cited, the smaller the quantity of data that will be needed to support the proposed change. Accordingly, to avoid unnecessary duplication of research and review, when a section 505(b)(2) application has been submitted and no pharmaceutically equivalent drug product has previously been approved, the 505(b)(2) applicant should choose the listed drug or drugs that are most similar to the drug for which approval is sought. Similarly, if all the information relied on by FDA for approval…is contained in a single previously approved application and that application is a pharmaceutical equivalent or the most similar alternative to the product for which approval is sought, the 505(b)(2) applicant should certify only to the patents for that application. This is the case even when another application also contains some or all of the same information. Id.

   FDA has not defined the factors that should be taken into account when determining "similarity" of drug products; however, FDA likely considers factors, such as active ingredient, dosage form, route of administration and strength. See 21 CFR 320.1(c).
11. See *FD&C Act* Section 505(j)(2)(C); 21 CFR 314.93. As discussed later in this chapter, the *Pediatric Research Equity Act* (*PREA*), Pub. L. No. 108-155, 117 Stat. 1936 (2003), which amended the *FD&C Act* to require most applications submitted under *FD&C Act* Section 505 include a pediatric assessment (unless otherwise waived or deferred), has significantly restricted FDA's ability to approve suitability petitions. See generally *FD&C Act* Section 505B.
12. FDA has interpreted the term *same as* to mean identical in the context of dosage forms, see 21 CFR 314.92(a)(1), and has used its discretion to interpret the term *identical* to mean products having the same dosage form identified in the *Orange Book* at Appendix C ("Uniform Terms—Dosage Forms"). See FDA, Citizen Petition Response, Docket No. 1993P-0421, at 3 (12 August 1997) ("[A] proposed drug product has the same dosage form if it falls within the identical dosage form category, as listed in the *Orange Book*, Appendix C.").
13. See *FD&C Act* Section 505(j)(2)(A)(iv).
14. The *FD&C Act* states that an ANDA must include, among other things, "information to show the new drug is bioequivalent to the

[RLD]...," *FD&C Act* Section 505(j)(2)(A)(iv), and that FDA must approve an ANDA unless, among other things, "information submitted in the application is insufficient to show that the drug is bioequivalent to the [RLD] . . . ." Id. at Section 505(j)(4)(F). However, FDA has discretion to determine how the bioequivalence requirement is met. See *FD&C Act* Section 505(j)(7)(A)(i)(III). FDA's discretion need only be based on a "reasonable and scientifically supported criterion, whether [the agency] chooses to do so on a case-by-case basis or through more general inferences about a category of drugs...." *Bristol-Myers Squibb Co. v. Shalala*, 923 F. Supp. 212, 218 (D.D.C. 1996) (quoting *Schering Corp. v. Sullivan*, 782 F. Supp. 645, 651 (D.D.C. 1992), vacated as moot sub nom, *Schering Corp. v. Shalala*, 995 F.2d 1103 (D.C. Cir. 1993)); see also *Fisons Corp. v. Shalala*, 860 F. Supp. 859, 865 (D.D.C. 1994) (upholding FDA's authority to grant waivers of the requirement for submission of *in vivo* evidence of bioequivalence where bioequivalence can be determined by other available science.).

15. *Guidance for Industry: Bioavailability and Bioequivalence Studies for Orally Administered Drug Products—General Considerations* (March 2003). Although *in vivo* testing is FDA's preferred method for an ANDA applicant to demonstrate bioequivalence, agency regulations state "bioequivalence may be demonstrated by several in vivo and in vitro methods," which are described at 21 CFR 320.24 in descending order of accuracy, sensitivity and reproducibility.
16. See 21 CFR 320.24(b)(5). FDA recently amended its ANDA bioequivalence regulations to require applicants to submit data from all bioequivalence studies the applicant conducts on the "same drug product formulation" submitted for approval. See 21 CFR 314.94(a)(7), 320.21(b)(1); see also FDA, Final Rule, Requirements for Submission of Bioequivalence Data, 74 *Fed. Reg.* 2849 (16 January 2009).
17. The purpose of PEPFAR is to make antiretroviral drug products available to developing countries. The PEPFAR program applies to both NDA and ANDA drug products. In addition to expedited review for PEPFAR ANDAs, the PEPFAR program permits FDA to grant tentative ANDA approval for such applications (if there are *Orange Book*-listed patents covering the RLD) so such products can be purchased from ANDA applicants with PEPFAR funding.
18. FDA, Manual of Policies and Procedures 5240.3, "Review Order of Original ANDAs, Amendments, and Supplements," at 2 (18 October 2006).
19. Karst KR. "Is the ANDA Suitability Petition Process Dead?" *Regulatory Affairs Focus*, Vol. 10, No. 5, pp 35-6 (May 2005).
20. *FD&C Act* Sections 505B(1)(A), (2)–(4).
21. *FD&C Act* Section 505(b)(4)(A) states "[a]n applicant may not amend or supplement an application referred to in [*FD&C Act* Section 505(b)(2)] to seek approval of a drug that is a different drug than the drug identified in the application as submitted to [FDA]."
22. FDA, Citizen Petition Response, Docket No. FDA-2008-P-0329, at 16 n. 30 (25 November 2008). FDA also noted the agency's: interpretation of § 505(b)(4)(A) of the Act for 505(b)(2) applications is influenced by and intended to be consistent with section 505(j)(2)(D)(i) regarding ANDAs. Accordingly, a 505(b)(2) applicant may not amend or supplement a 505(b)(2) application to seek approval of a drug that relies on the Agency's finding of safety and/or effectiveness for a drug that is different from the drug identified in a previous submission of the application.
23. 21 CFR 314.127(a)(8)(ii)(B).
24. 21 CFR 314.90(b).
25. FDA, Citizen Petition Response, Docket No. FDA-2005-P-0370, at 6 (25 March 2005).
26. *Orange Book* Preface, 29th ed. (2009), at vii. The *Orange Book* Preface further states:

    FDA classifies as therapeutically equivalent those products meeting the following general criteria: (1) they are approved as safe and effective; (2) they are pharmaceutical equivalents in that they (a) contain identical amounts of the same active drug ingredient in the same dosage form and route of administration and (b) meet compendial or other applicable standards of strength, quality, purity, and identity; (3) they are bioequivalent in that (a) they do not present a known or potential bioequivalence problem, and they meet an acceptable *in vitro* standard or (b) if they do present such a known or potential problem, they are shown to meet an appropriate bioequivalence standard; (4) they are adequately labeled; [and] (5) they are manufactured in compliance with current Good Manufacturing Practice regulations.
27. Ibid.
29. 21 CFR 320.1(c).
30. *FD&C Act* Section 505(j)(8)(B); 21 CFR 320.1(e).
31. 21 CFR 320.1(d).
32. The *Orange Book*, which is published annually and updated monthly, only identifies therapeutic equivalence codes for multisource prescription drug products. Therefore, neither single-source prescription drugs—e.g., a brand-name drug product without generic competition—nor over-the-counter drug products are assigned a therapeutic equivalence code. Once a therapeutically equivalent generic drug is approved, it is listed in the *Orange Book* with a particular therapeutic equivalence code. The RLD and generic equivalent are differentiated from one another by a "+" sign, which denotes the RLD. FDA assigns RLD status to single-source prescription drugs.
33. In certain instances, a number is added to the end of an AB code to make a three character code (e.g., AB1, AB2, etc.). Three-character codes are assigned only in situations when more than one [RLD] of the same strength has been designated under the same heading. For example, Adalat® CC (Miles) and Procardia XL® (Pfizer), extended-release tablets, are listed under the active ingredient nifedipine. These drug products, listed under the same heading, are not bioequivalent to each other. Generic drug products deemed by FDA to be bioequivalent to Adalat® CC and Procardia XL® have been approved, Adalat® CC and Procardia XL® have been assigned ratings of AB1 and AB2, respectively. The generic drug products bioequivalent to Adalat® CC would be assigned a rating of AB1, and those bioequivalent to Procardia XL® would be assigned a rating of AB2. *Orange Book* Preface at xv.
34. For example, AO refers to injectable oil solutions, and AT refers to topical products. Some drug products are assigned more than one therapeutic equivalence code. For example, FDA has assigned both AB1 and AB2 codes to several approved levothyroxine sodium drug products because the sponsors conducted studies to establish their drugs' therapeutic equivalence to other RLDs.
35. For example, BT refers to "topical products with bioequivalence issues," and BX refers to "drug products for which the data are insufficient to determine therapeutic equivalence."
36. 44 *Fed. Reg.* 2932, 2937 (12 January 1979); see also *Orange Book* Preface at x–xi.
37. 44 *Fed. Reg.* at 2937; see also *Orange Book* Preface at x.
38. 45 *Fed. Reg.* 72,582, 72,584 (31 October 1980) (*Orange Book* final rule). When Congress amended the *FD&C Act* in 1984, it incorporated the *Orange Book* into the statute as a means of facilitating the approval of generic drugs. See *FD&C Act* Section 505(j)(7). The *Orange Book*'s therapeutic equivalence ratings have been accepted and recognized by the courts. See e.g., *Geneva Pharms. Tech. Corp. v. Barr Labs., Inc.*, 201 F. Supp.2d (S.D.N.Y. 2002) ("The *Orange Book* gives an AB rating to all generic warfarin sodium product[s] available today. Consequently, generic warfarin sodium is eligible for unrestricted substitution for Coumadin under most state pharmacy regulations.").
39. The designation of a drug as "A-rated" to another drug also has been incorporated into the federal Medicaid program. See 42 U.S.C. 1396r-8(e)(4) (setting the standard for upper limits on payment for multi-source drug products based on FDA's therapeutic equivalence evaluations).
40. 44 *Fed. Reg.* at 2938. FDA also commented in the preamble to the agency's final *Orange Book* proposal: one reason FDA is publishing the [*Orange Book*] is in response to requests from several States for assistance in developing their drug product selection legislation.

Pharmacies, hospitals, States, and private and public institutions and organizations continue to ask FDA to share its broad knowledge of the safety and effectiveness and quality of drug products, so they can continue to carry out their duties to protect and promote the public health, both in providing health care services safely and with efficiency and cost-effectiveness, and in advising physicians and pharmacists on drug product selection. 45 *Fed. Reg.* at 72,589.

41. State laws also vary regarding how the final product selection is determined. In the majority of states, prescribers must expressly indicate substitution is not permitted by writing "Brand Necessary," "Do Not Substitute," "Dispense as Written," "Medically Necessary" or other approved wording on the prescription form. Some states include lines on the prescription form with the phrases "Product Selection Permitted" (or similar wording) and "Do Not Substitute." The prescriber can prevent product substitution by signing on the line. See generally National Association of Boards of Pharmacy, Survey of Pharmacy Law, 2003–2004.
42. Vivian JC. "Legal Aspects of Therapeutic Interchange Programs," *U.S. Pharmacist* (2003).

Helpful References and Resources

- FDA's Office of Generic Drugs – Directory Information. FDA website. www.fda.gov/AboutFDA/CentersOffices/OfficeofMedicalProductsandTobacco/CDER/ucm119100.htm. Accessed 22 April 2015.
- *Federal Food, Drug, and Cosmetic Act.* FDA website. www.fda.gov/RegulatoryInformation/Legislation/default.htm. Accessed 22 April 2015.
- Generic Drugs: Information for Industry. FDA website. http://www.fda.gov/Drugs/DevelopmentApprovalProcess/HowDrugsareDevelopedandApproved/ApprovalApplications/AbbreviatedNewDrugApplicationANDAGenerics/ucm142112.htm. Accessed 22 April 2015.
- Abbreviated New Drug Application (ANDA): Generics. FDA website. http://www.fda.gov/Drugs/DevelopmentApprovalProcess/HowDrugsareDevelopedandApproved/ApprovalApplications/AbbreviatedNewDrugApplicationANDAGenerics/default.htm. Accessed 22 April 2015.
- The Electronic *Orange Book*. FDA website. www.accessdata.fda.gov/scripts/cder/ob/default.cfm. Accessed 22 April 2015.
- Generic Drug User Fee Amendments of 2012. FDA website. http://www.fda.gov/ForIndustry/UserFees/GenericDrugUserFees/default.htm. Accessed 22 April 2015.
- FDA's Paragraph IV Patent Certification List. FDA website. http://www.fda.gov/Drugs/DevelopmentApprovalProcess/HowDrugsareDevelopedandApproved/ApprovalApplications/AbbreviatedNewDrugApplicationANDAGenerics/ucm047676. Accessed 22 April 2015.
- ANDA Suitability Petition Tracking Reports. FDA website. www.fda.gov/Drugs/DevelopmentApprovalProcess/HowDrugsareDevelopedandApproved/ApprovalApplications/AbbreviatedNewDrugApplicationANDAGenerics/ucm120944.htm. Accessed 22 April 2015.
- CTD Modules/Sections Corresponding to Summary Data Tables in Bioequivalence Submissions to ANDAs. FDA website. www.fda.gov/Drugs/DevelopmentApprovalProcess/HowDrugsareDevelopedandApproved/ApprovalApplications/AbbreviatedNewDrugApplicationANDAGenerics/ucm120962.htm. Accessed 22 April 2015.
- FDA's Individual Product Bioequivalence Recommendations. FDA website. www.fda.gov/Drugs/GuidanceComplianceRegulatoryInformation/Guidances/ucm075207.htm. Accessed 22 April 2015.
- FDA Generic Drug Guidance Documents. FDA website. www.fda.gov/Drugs/GuidanceComplianceRegulatoryInformation/Guidances/ucm064995.htm. Accessed 22 April 2015.
- FDA's Dissolution Methods Database. FDA website.
- www.fda.gov/Drugs/InformationOnDrugs/ucm135742.htm. Accessed 22 April 2015.
- FDA's Inactive Ingredients Database. FDA website. www.fda.gov/Drugs/InformationOnDrugs/ucm080123.htm. Accessed 22 April 2015.

Acknowledgements

We acknowledge and thank the contribution of Michael A. Swit, Esq. of Illumina's Legal Department, whose prior version of this chapter formed the core for this current iteration.

Chapter 16

Patents and Exclusivity

Updated by Clark G. Sullivan, JD

OBJECTIVES

- ❑ Understand the laws and regulations governing patent and non-patent market exclusivity available to sponsors of brand-name drugs and their effects on generic drug approval
- ❑ Understand how FDA interprets many of these laws and regulations
- ❑ Understand the patent certification process for generic drugs and the 180-day marketing exclusivity available to certain generic drug sponsors

LAWS, REGULATIONS AND GUIDELINES COVERED IN THIS CHAPTER

- ❑ *Federal Food, Drug, and Cosmetic Act* of 1938
- ❑ *Drug Price Competition and Patent Term Restoration Act* of 1984 (*Hatch-Waxman Act*)
- ❑ *Food and Drug Administration Modernization Act* of 1997
- ❑ *Orphan Drug Act* of 1983
- ❑ *Uruguay Rounds Agreements Act* of 1994
- ❑ *Leahy-Smith America Invents Act* of 2011
- ❑ *Generating Antibiotics Incentives Now Act* (*GAIN Act*), *Food and Drug Administration Safety and Innovation Act* (*FDASIA*) Section VIII
- ❑ Humane Use Device Provisions, *FDASIA* Title VI, Part L
- ❑ *PDUFA V*, *FDASIA* Title I
- ❑ 21 CFR 314 Applications for FDA Approval to Market a New Drug
- ❑ 21 CFR 320 Bioavailability and Bioequivalence Requirements
- ❑ 21 CFR 316 Orphan Drugs
- ❑ 54 *Federal Register* 28,872 (10 July 1989), Proposed ANDA Regulations
- ❑ 59 *Federal Register* 50,338 (3 October 1994), ANDA regulations; patent and exclusivity provisions
- ❑ 68 *Federal Register* 36,676 (18 June 2003), Applications for FDA approval to market a new drug: patent submission and listing requirements and application of 30-month stays on approval of Abbreviated New Drug Applications certifying that a patent claiming a drug is invalid or will not be infringed

- ❑ *Guidance for Industry: Qualifying for Pediatric Exclusivity Under Section 505A of the Federal Food, Drug, and Cosmetic Act* (September 1999)
- ❑ *Manual of Policies and Procedures* 5240.3, "Review Order of Original ANDAs, Amendments and Supplements" (October 2006)
- ❑ *Draft Guidance for Industry: Applications Covered by Section 505(b)(2)* (October 1978)

Introduction

As discussed in Chapter 13, the *Drug Price Competition and Patent Term Restoration Act* of 1984 (*Hatch-Waxman Act*) amended the *Federal Food, Drug, and Cosmetic Act* of 1938 (*FD&C Act*) to create the Abbreviated New Drug Application (ANDA) generic drug approval pathway under Section 505(j), as well as a hybrid approval pathway under Section 505(b)(2). The ANDA applicant relies entirely on the clinical data of the third party (the Reference Listed Drug or RLD), and its product is approved solely on the basis of its sameness to the RLD, while the 505(b)(2) applicant conducts some clinical trials of its own and relies on a third party's clinical data to fill in any gaps needed to prove its drug is safe and effective under the *FD&C Act*. The *Hatch Waxman Act* also put mechanisms into place to protect the RLD's patent rights from companies relying on the RLD's clinical data, while allowing drug developers (innovators and generics alike) to conduct the work necessary to secure approval without infringing the RLD owner's patents, and ensuring these drugs come to market as early as possible after an RLD's patents have expired.

The *Hatch-Waxman Act* also gave drug companies performing clinical studies several things in return for these allowances, including the opportunity to obtain a patent term extension for time lost during a patent's early life while its product was undergoing regulatory development. In addition, 505(b)(1) and (b)(2) applicants can submit certain types of patents to FDA to list in the *Orange Book* and also may be eligible for several periods of non-patent exclusivity. Certain ANDA sponsors may be eligible for a period of 180-day marketing exclusivity for challenging patents listed in FDA's *Orange Book* for the RLD. Under the current law, an ANDA sponsor's eligibility for a period of 180-day market exclusivity can be forfeited under various scenarios.

Various other laws have been enacted since the *Hatch Waxman Act* to incentivize the development of certain drug types. These laws include the *Orphan Drug Act*, which rewards sponsors for developing products to treat rare diseases and conditions; the *Best Pharmaceuticals for Children Act* (*BPCA*), which rewards sponsors for developing products for children; and the *Generating Antibiotic Incentives Now Act* (*GAIN Act*), which rewards companies for developing antibiotics against difficult-to-treat microorganisms. Each of these non-patent exclusivities is discussed in this chapter.

Patent-Related Market Exclusivity

Patent Term Extensions

Under Title II of the *Hatch-Waxman Act*, a patent related to an FDA-regulated product is eligible for extension if patent life was lost during a period when the product was being reviewed for FDA approval.[1] This extension is known as a patent term extension (PTE). Only one patent can be extended for each drug product, and that patent can be extended only once, even if it covers more than one drug product.[2] The extended patent protects all subsequently approved drug product uses and formulations, as long as the uses and formulations are covered by the underlying patent.[3] However, the PTE does not apply to any drug product uses or formulations that do not share the same active ingredient, or salt or ester thereof.[4]

The period of regulatory review for which the PTE is intended to compensate is composed of a "testing phase" and a "review phase." For a drug product, the testing phase begins on the effective date of an Investigational New Drug (IND) Application and ends on the date a New Drug Application (NDA) is submitted to FDA.[5] The review phase is the period between NDA submission and approval.[6] A patent term may be extended for a period of time that is the sum of one-half of the time in the testing phase, plus all the time in the review phase.[7] The regulatory review period must be reduced by any amount of time the applicant "did not act with due diligence."[8] The total (calculated) extension of the patent term may not exceed five years, and the extended patent term may not exceed 14 years from the date of NDA approval.[9]

Over the years, questions have cropped up as to when the review phase begins—i.e., when is an application considered initially submitted to FDA—in the context of "rolling" or modular submissions? Insofar as NDA and Biologics License Application (BLA) "fast track" submissions are concerned, FDA has determined receipt of the last module (or application component) makes the application complete and, thus, "initially submitted" for PTE purposes.[10] Similarly, the review phase for a New Animal Drug Application (NADA) reviewed under FDA's Phased Data Review Policy and Administrative Applications for NADA begins when the company submits the final technical section to its application.[11]

As applied to drugs, the patent term extension law provides the term of a patent claiming the drug (or a use of the drug or a method of manufacturing a drug) to be extended from the original patent expiration date if:

1. the patent term has not expired
2. the patent has not previously been extended

3. the extension application is submitted by the patent owner of record within 60 days of NDA approval
4. the product, use or method of manufacturing claimed has been subject to a "regulatory review period" before it is marketed commercially
5. the NDA is the drug product's first permitted commercial use[12]

Criterion 5, the first permitted commercial use of a drug product, has been the most controversial. The law defines drug product as a new drug's active ingredient, including any salt or ester of the active ingredient.[13] The question becomes whether the term refers to the ingredient's "active moiety" or the active ingredient itself. The definition chosen can have interesting implications when, for example, one is determining whether a new ester of an old active moiety is entitled to a PTE when the active moiety was approved previously as a different ester.

Until recently, the US Patent and Trademark Office (PTO) relied on decisions by the US Court of Appeals for the Federal Circuit in *Fisons v. Quigg*, 8 U.S.P.Q.2d 1491 (D.D.C.1988), affirmed 876 F.2d 99 U.S.P.Q.2d 1869 (Fed. Cir. 1989), and *Pfizer Inc. v. Dr. Reddy's Labs.*, 359 F.3d 1361 (Fed. Cir. 2004) to support the office's interpretation of the term "product" in 35 U.S.C. §156(a)(5)(A) to mean "active moiety" (i.e., the molecule in a drug product responsible for pharmacological action, regardless of whether the active moiety is formulated as a salt, ester or other non-covalent derivative) rather than "active ingredient" (i.e., the active ingredient physically found in the drug product, which would include any salt, ester or other non-covalent derivative of the active ingredient physically found in the drug product). In contrast, the Federal Circuit's 1990 decision in *Glaxo Operations UK Ltd. v. Quigg*, 894 F.2d 392, 13 USPQ2d 1628 (Fed. Cir. 1990), construed the term "product" in 35 U.S.C. §156(a) (5)(A) to mean "active ingredient." In 2010, the US Court of Appeals for the Federal Circuit ruled in *Photocure ASA v. Kappos*, 603 F.3d 1372, 1375 (Fed. Cir. 2010) that the term "product" in 35 U.S.C. §156(a)(5)(A) means "active ingredient" rather than "active moiety."

In some cases, a patent scheduled to expire before an application for extension can be submitted to the PTO may be granted an interim patent extension.[14] This can occur, for example, if the patent will expire before the NDA is approved. Two types of interim patent extensions are available:

1. interim patent extensions available during the review phase of the statutory regulatory review period[15]
2. interim patent extensions available during the PTO's review of an application for patent term extension[16]

The cumulative patent time granted under either type of interim patent extension cannot exceed the patent term extension a company could obtain under regular patent extension provisions. The PTO reviews each application for an interim patent extension to ensure a patent will not be extended longer than its eligibility under the law.

Orange Book Patent Listing

The *FD&C Act* and FDA regulations require each NDA sponsor to submit with its application "the patent number and the expiration date of any patent which claims the drug for which the applicant submitted the [NDA] or which claims a method of using[17] such drug and with respect to which a claim of patent infringement could reasonably be asserted if a person not licensed by the owner engaged in the manufacture, use, or sale of the drug."[18] FDA regulations clarify "such patents consist of drug substance (active ingredient) patents, drug product (formulation and composition) patents, and method-of-use patents."[19] Patents covering the drug's manufacturing method cannot be listed.

Thus, to list a patent in the *Orange Book*, the patent must claim the drug or a method of using the drug that is the subject of the NDA; and a claim of patent infringement must reasonably be capable of assertion by the NDA holder or patent owner for the unauthorized manufacture, use or sale of the drug that is the subject of the NDA.[20] Once an NDA is approved, FDA is required to publish information in the *Orange Book* on the patents claiming the drug or its method of use.[21] If a new patent meeting the requirements of *FD&C Act* Section 505(b)(1) and FDA patent listing regulations is issued while an NDA is pending FDA review or has received NDA approval, the NDA sponsor must submit information on the patent to FDA within 30 days of issuance.[22]

An ANDA or 505(b)(2) application citing an RLD for approval must contain one of four possible certifications "with respect to each patent which claims the [listed] drug...or which claims a use for such listed drug...and for which information is required to be filed" by the RLD/NDA holder and listed in the *Orange Book*.[23] If there are patents on the drug, and the ANDA or 505(b)(2) applicant decides not to challenge them, the applicant submits a Paragraph III certification, and FDA cannot approve the application until the patents have expired.[24] If the patents have expired already, or the required patent information has not been filed, the ANDA or 505(b)(2) applicant submits a Paragraph II or Paragraph I certification, respectively, and FDA can approve the application.[25] If the ANDA or 505(b)(2) applicant decides to challenge a patent listed in the *Orange Book*, the applicant submits a Paragraph IV certification claiming the patent is "invalid or will not be infringed by the manufacture, use, or sale of the new drug for which the [ANDA or 505(b)(2) application] is submitted."[26]

ANDA applications also have an alternative to these four certifications if the patent is a "method of use patent which does not claim a use for which the applicant is seeking approval." In this case, the application instead may contain "a statement that the method of use patent does not claim such a use."[27] This often is referred to as a "section viii statement" and permits a generic applicant to "carve out" a patent-protected use from its proposed labeling, provided the omission of such protected information does not "render the proposed drug product less safe or effective than the listed drug for all remaining, non-protected conditions of use."[28] An ANDA applicant that submits a section viii statement is not entitled to the 180-day exclusivity period discussed below based on that statement, although it still might be entitled to the exclusivity based on a paragraph IV certification for another patent.[29] Similarly, an ANDA is not barred from approval by the 180-day exclusivity period of another ANDA applicant, based on the ANDA containing a section viii statement, although the ANDA still might be barred if it contains a paragraph IV certification for a different patent.[30]

An NDA or patent owner may choose to sue a generic applicant that submits a Paragraph IV certification. If suit is brought, FDA is statutorily proscribed from approving the ANDA for 30 months, with certain limited exceptions (i.e., the so-called "30-month stay").[31] If a patent infringement suit is not brought by the NDA or patent owner, FDA can approve the ANDA once it has determined all conditions required for approval have been met.

FDA has developed various procedural tools to carry out its obligations under the *Hatch-Waxman Act*, including its use code system for evaluating a section viii statement's propriety. Under this system, the RLD owner submits to FDA a use code for any method of use patents listed in the *Orange Book* that describes what the patent covers.[32] When evaluating a section viii statement's propriety, FDA will compare the labeling in the ANDA to the use code and determine whether the label describes a use claimed in the patent. If the patent covers a use described in the label, FDA will deny the section viii statement and require the ANDA holder to include an appropriate patent certification.[33] In 2011, in *Caraco Pharm. Labs., Ltd. v. Novo Nordisk A/S*, 132 S. Ct. 1670 (U.S. 2012), the US Supreme Court held an ANDA applicant who objects to the use code could bring a lawsuit against the patent owner for a declaration the use code is written too broadly.

Until recently, questions also have arisen regarding FDA's RLD policies, with some believing FDA would require an application submitted under Section 505(b)(2) to cite the closest RLD as its supporting drug, and to furnish patent certifications for any patents listed in the *Orange Book* for the RLD. In January 2015, a district court affirmed FDA's determination that a 505(b)(2) application for colchicine capsules that did not rely on any clinical data from an earlier approval for colchicine tablets, did not need to provide patent certifications for patents listed in the *Orange Book* for the colchicine tablets.[34]

Non-Patent Statutory Market Exclusivity

Five-Year Exclusivity

Under the *FD&C Act* (as amended by Title I of the *Hatch-Waxman Act*), five-year exclusivity is available to the sponsor of an application (either a full 505(b)(1) NDA or a 505(b)(2) application) for a drug product not containing an active moiety previously approved under Section 505(b) of the *FD&C Act* (i.e., an NDA for a New Chemical Entity (NCE)). Five-year exclusivity prevents the submission of an ANDA (and a 505(b)(2) application) that "refers to the drug for which the [approved Section 505(b) NCE NDA] was submitted before the expiration of five years from the date of the approval" of the NCE NDA.[35] Thus, five-year exclusivity sometimes is called "NCE exclusivity." NCE exclusivity prevents the approval of a generic application for the approved active ingredient or any salt or ester of the approved active ingredient for five years. However, five-year exclusivity does not prevent FDA from approving, or a company from submitting, a full Section 505(b)(1) NDA for the same drug.[36]

As with the PTE provisions for new molecules approved under the *FD&C Act*, the statutory provisions governing the term "drug," and whether a drug is new for purposes of NCE exclusivity under Sections 505(c)(3)(E)(ii) and 505(j)(5)(F)(ii), are ambiguous.[37] Neither provision addresses whether drug means the particular drug product that is the subject of a previously approved NDA with five-year exclusivity or, more generally, the approved active moiety. FDA identified this ambiguity in the preamble to its proposed rule implementing the exclusivity provisions of the *Hatch-Waxman Act*:

> The language of sections 505(c)(3)(E) and 505(j)(5)(F)[38] of the act is ambiguous as to which ANDAs or 505(b)(2) applications are affected by an innovator's exclusivity. The statutory language allows at least two interpretations. The narrower interpretation of the protection offered by exclusivity is that exclusivity covers only specific drug products and therefore protects from generic competition only the first approved version of a drug... The broader interpretation of the coverage of exclusivity is that it covers the active moieties in new chemical entities...FDA has concluded that the broader interpretation of the scope of exclusivity should be applied to all types of exclusivity conferred by sections 505(c)(3)[(E)] and 505(j)[(5)(F)] of the act. Therefore, when exclusivity attaches to an active moiety or to an innovative change in an already approved drug, the submission or effective date of approval of ANDAs and 505(b)(2) applications for a drug with that active moiety or innovative change will be delayed until the innovator's exclusivity has expired, whether or not FDA has approved subsequent versions of the drugs entitled to exclusivity, and

> regardless of the specific listed drug product to which the ANDA or 505(b)(2) application refers.[39]

This policy, known as FDA's Umbrella Policy, effectively replaces the term "drug" in the statutory text with the term "active moiety."[40] However, this should not be taken to mean a drug cannot qualify for NCE exclusivity simply because it yields the same active moiety as a previously approved drug. If the molecule has structural differences from a previously approved molecule, other than a difference in salt or ester form, it still might qualify for NCE exclusivity, even though it yields the same active moiety *in vivo.*

Combination products also have presented interesting issues of statutory interpretation for FDA. Until 2014, FDA required all the active ingredients in a new drug product not to have been previously approved in order to qualify for NCE exclusivity. FDA changed its policy in 2014 in response to several industry-sponsored Citizen Petitions and now will grant NCE exclusivity for a combination product as long as one of the active ingredients satisfies its requirements for a new chemical entity.[41]

Three-Year Exclusivity

Under the *FD&C Act* (as amended by Title I of the *Hatch-Waxman Act*), a sponsor may qualify for a three-year period of exclusivity for an application (a full 505(b)(1) NDA, a 505(b)(2) application or a supplement to either) if the application contains "reports of new clinical investigations (other than bioavailability studies)" that were "essential to approval" of the application and were "conducted or sponsored by" the applicant.[42] All three of these criteria must be satisfied to qualify for three-year exclusivity.[43] Three-year exclusivity often is referred to as "new clinical investigation" or "new use" exclusivity.

Each criterion is defined in FDA's implementing regulations. A "new clinical investigation" is:

> an investigation in humans the results of which have not been relied on by FDA to demonstrate substantial evidence of effectiveness of a previously approved drug product for any indication or of safety for a new patient population and do not duplicate the results of another investigation that was relied on by the agency to demonstrate the effectiveness or safety in a new patient population of a previously approved drug product.[44]

An investigation is "essential to approval" of an application if "there are no other data available that could support approval of the application."[45] FDA explained, if the agency were aware of "published reports of studies other than those conducted or sponsored by the applicant, or other information...sufficient for FDA to conclude that a proposed drug product or change to an already approved drug product is safe and effective," exclusivity would not be appropriate.[46] The applicant must submit a list of all publicly available reports of clinical investigations "that are relevant to the conditions for which the applicant is seeking approval" and explain why these studies or reports do not provide a sufficient basis for approval.[47]

Finally, an investigation is "conducted or sponsored by the applicant" if:

> (B)efore or during the investigation, the applicant was named...as the sponsor of the [IND]...under which the investigation was conducted, or the applicant or the applicant's predecessor in interest, provided substantial support for the investigation. To demonstrate "substantial support," an applicant must either provide a certified statement from a certified public accountant that the applicant provided 50 percent or more of the cost of conducting the study or provide an explanation why FDA should consider the applicant to have conducted or sponsored the study if the applicant's financial contribution to the study is less than 50 percent or the applicant did not sponsor the investigational new drug. A predecessor in interest is an entity, e.g., a corporation, that the applicant has taken over, merged with, or purchased, or from which the applicant has purchased all rights to the drug. Purchase of nonexclusive rights to a clinical investigation after it is completed is not sufficient to satisfy this definition.[48]

Three-year exclusivity prevents FDA from approving[49] an ANDA or a 505(b)(2) application "that relies on the information supporting a change approved in the [NDA or NDA supplement]" until three years after the date FDA approved the application.[50]

Although the general rule is the labeling of a generic drug product approved under an ANDA must have the "same" labeling as the RLD,[51] in order to prevent NDA holders from continually supplementing their labels with new data that could repeatedly extend the three-year exclusivity period, and thereby bar FDA from approving the ANDA indefinitely, FDA regulations permit the ANDA labeling to omit "an indication or other aspect of labeling protected by patent or accorded exclusivity under [505(j)(5)(F)] of the [*FD&C Act*]."[52] FDA can approve an ANDA with labeling "carve outs" if a particular use of the innovator drug is protected by a patent or period of exclusivity, and other uses are not protected. Before approving such a drug, FDA must first determine the "carve out" of the protected information does not "render the proposed drug product less safe or effective than the listed drug for all remaining, non-protected conditions of use."[53]

One particular issue that has arisen in the 505(b)(2) context is whether a 505(b)(2) applicant can be subject to the three-year exclusivity of an earlier approved NDA involving the same active moiety, even though the 505(b)(2) applicant does not rely on any clinical data supporting the earlier approved NDA. In December 2014, Veloxis Pharmaceuticals sued FDA for delaying its approval of tacrolimus for organ transplant rejection until another company's three-year exclusivity for another tacrolimus product expired.[54] According to Veloxis, FDA delayed its approval based on this period of exclusivity even though the Veloxis NDA did not rely on any of the clinical data that supported the grant of exclusivity.

Pediatric Exclusivity

The *BPCA* amended the *FD&C Act* to create Section 505A, which provides an additional six months of exclusivity to pharmaceutical manufacturers that conduct acceptable pediatric studies[55] of new and currently marketed drug products identified by FDA in a Pediatric Written Request (PWR) for which pediatric information would be beneficial. A grant of pediatric exclusivity extends to all *Orange Book*-listed patents[56] and non-patent market exclusivity periods granted to an application holder under the *FD&C Act*. The exclusivity does not extend the term of a patent, but it does extend for six months the date until which FDA cannot approve an ANDA that contains a Paragraph III certification.[57] The *Food and Drug Administration Safety and Innovation Act* of 2012 (*FDASIA*) made the *BPCA* amendments permanent, and they are not required to be reauthorized by future user fee negotiations.

An important aspect of an initial grant of pediatric exclusivity is it provides additional market exclusivity not just for the pediatric indications or formulations, but for all protected indications and formulations of that sponsor's drug. Thus, an initial grant of pediatric exclusivity attaches to the patent and non-patent market exclusivities for any of the sponsor's approved drug products (including certain combination products) containing the active moiety for which pediatric exclusivity was granted, and not to a specific drug product.[58]

While an initial period of pediatric exclusivity is broad, a second exclusivity period is narrow. Specifically, a second period of pediatric exclusivity attaches only to any period of three-year new clinical investigation exclusivity granted by FDA with respect to a pediatric use supplement containing studies submitted in response to a second PWR issued by FDA.[59] A second period of pediatric exclusivity does not apply to any existing *Orange Book*-listed patent exclusivity or any existing periods of five-year NCE exclusivity or orphan drug exclusivity. FDA's September 1999 guidance document further explains the scope of a second period of pediatric exclusivity:

> Pediatric studies submitted in a supplemental application for a drug that has already received one period of pediatric exclusivity may qualify the drug to receive a different 6-month period of pediatric exclusivity if submitted in response to a [PWR]. The different 6-month period of pediatric exclusivity will attach only to any exclusivity period under sections 505(c)(3)(D)(iv) and 505(j)(5)(D)(iv) [(i.e., three-year exclusivity)] granted to the supplemental application for which the studies were completed.[60]

An important exception to the applicability of pediatric exclusivity relative to new PWRs was added to the law in 2007. Under the exception, FDA will not apply a period of pediatric exclusivity to an unexpired period of patent or non-patent exclusivity if the agency's decision to grant pediatric exclusivity "is made later than 9 months prior to the expiration of such period."[61]

Orphan Drug Exclusivity

Under the *Orphan Drug Act* of 1983 (Pub. L. No. 97-414, 96 Stat. 2049 (1983)), as amended, a manufacturer or sponsor may submit a written request for FDA to designate a drug as a drug for a rare disease or condition (i.e., an "orphan drug"). A "rare disease or condition" is one that affects fewer than 200,000 people in the US, or affects more than 200,000 people, but for which the sponsor can show it will be unable to recover its development and marketing costs from sales of the product in the US.[62]

Once FDA approves a marketing application for a drug designated as an orphan drug, the agency may not approve another company's version of the "same drug" for the same disease or condition for seven years, unless the subsequent drug is "different" from the approved orphan drug.[63] In addition, the *FD&C Act* and FDA's orphan drug regulations identify circumstances under which the agency can approve another version of the "same drug" for the same orphan disease or condition during the term of another sponsor's orphan drug exclusivity (e.g., failure to assure a sufficient quantity of the drug).[64]

A drug is "different" from an approved orphan drug if it is chemically or structurally distinct. The degree of chemical or structural similarity allowing FDA to determine whether two drugs are "the same" depends on whether the drugs are small molecules or macromolecules.[65] However, even a drug structurally "the same" as an approved orphan drug may be approved for the same condition if it is "clinically superior" to the approved orphan drug. FDA's orphan drug regulations define a "clinically superior" drug as "a drug... shown to provide a significant therapeutic advantage over and above that provided by an approved orphan drug (that is otherwise the same drug)" in one of three ways:

1. greater effectiveness as assessed by effect on a clinically meaningful endpoint in adequate and well-controlled trials
2. greater safety in a substantial portion of the target populations
3. a demonstration the drug makes a major contribution to patient care[66]

Paragraph IV Litigation and 180-Day Exclusivity

An ANDA or 505(b)(2) applicant making a Paragraph IV certification must notify the NDA holder and patent owner of its application once FDA determines the application is substantially complete. The applicant must give notice to the NDA holder and patent owner "not later than 20 days after the date of the postmark on the notice with which [FDA] informs the applicant that the application has been filed."[67] If the patent certification is in an amendment or supplement to the ANDA, the applicant must give notice to the NDA holder and patent owner "at the time at which the applicant submits the amendment or supplement, regardless of whether the applicant has already given notice with respect to another such certification contained in the application or in an amendment or supplement to the application."[68] The notice to the NDA owner and patent owner must include a "detailed statement of the factual and legal basis of the applicant's opinion that the patent is not valid or will not be infringed" and must "state that an application that contains data from bioavailability or bioequivalence studies has been submitted for the drug with respect to which the certification is made to obtain approval to engage in the commercial manufacture, use, or sale of the drug before the expiration of the patent referred to in the certification."[69]

The NDA holder or patent owner has 45 days from the date of receipt of such notice to file a suit for patent infringement, to benefit from the 30-month stay provided by the *Hatch-Waxman Act*.[70] If a patent infringement suit is brought within this 45-day period, FDA cannot approve the ANDA or 505(b)(2) application until the earlier of:

- the expiration of a single 30-month stay of approval, which may be shortened or lengthened by the court if "either party to the action fail[s] to reasonably cooperate in expediting the action"[71]
- the date on which a district court enters judgment in favor of the defendant (i.e., the ANDA or 505(b)(2) applicant) that the patent is invalid or not infringed (or on the date of a settlement order or consent decree signed and entered by the court stating the patent that is the subject of the certification is invalid or not infringed)
- if the district court enters judgment in favor of the plaintiff (i.e., the NDA holder or patent owner) and that decision is appealed by the ANDA or 505(b)(2) applicant, the date on which the court of appeals enters judgment in favor of the ANDA or 505(b)(2) applicant that the patent is invalid or not infringed (or on the date of a settlement order or consent decree signed and entered by the court of appeals stating that the patent that is the subject of the certification is invalid or not infringed)

If the judgment of the district court is not appealed or is affirmed by the court of appeals, an ANDA or 505(b)(2) approval can be made effective immediately. An ANDA or 505(b)(2) applicant also may assert a counterclaim "seeking an order requiring the [NDA] holder to correct or delete the patent information submitted by the [NDA] holder on the grounds that the patent does not claim either the drug for which the application was approved or an approved method of using the drug."[72] A counterclaimant is not entitled to damages resulting from inappropriate listing of patent information.[73]

If a patent infringement suit is not brought by the NDA holder or the patent owner within the 45-day period, FDA can approve the ANDA or 505(b)(2) application as soon as it is satisfied the application satisfies its requirements. In addition, an applicant whose application contains a Paragraph IV certification may bring an action for declaratory judgment on patent infringement or invalidity if it is not sued within the 45-day period.[74] To file a declaratory judgment on non-infringement grounds, an applicant must provide an offer of confidential access to its application to allow the NDA holder or patent owner the opportunity "of evaluating possible infringement of the patent that is the subject of the [Paragraph IV] certification."[75] An applicant is not entitled to damages in such an action even if it obtains a declaratory judgment in its favor.[76]

FD&C Act Section 505(j)(5)(B)(iv) establishes an incentive for generic manufacturers to submit Paragraph IV certifications and to challenge *Orange Book*-listed patents as invalid or not infringed by providing a 180-day period of market exclusivity.[77] This means, in certain circumstances, the applicant submitting an ANDA containing the first Paragraph IV certification to an *Orange Book*-listed patent is protected from competition from other generic versions of the same drug product for 180 days.

Prior to the enactment of the *Medicare Prescription Drug, Improvement and Modernization Act* of 2003 (*MMA*), 180-day exclusivity was patent-based, such that a period of 180-day exclusivity could arise from each *Orange Book*-listed patent. Pre-*MMA*, 180-day exclusivity (which applies to a dwindling number of pending ANDAs) began on the date FDA "receives notice from the applicant of the first commercial marketing of the drug" under the first ANDA or "the date of a decision of a court in [a patent infringement action] holding the patent which is the subject of the certification to be invalid or not infringed," whichever is earlier. Post-*MMA*, 180-day exclusivity generally is drug-based, providing a single 180-day exclusivity period (that can be shared by multiple first applicants) with respect to each listed drug. Also post-*MMA*, there is a single trigger to 180-day exclusivity—first commercial marketing.

Under changes made to the *FD&C Act* by the *MMA*, the first applicant that qualifies for 180-day exclusivity can forfeit exclusivity under various circumstances. While some of the statutory forfeiture provisions are straightforward— e.g., 180-day exclusivity is forfeited if the ANDA sponsor withdraws its exclusivity-qualifying Paragraph IV certification—others

Table 16-1. 180-Day Exclusivity Forfeiture Snapshot

- **"Failure to Market:"** A first applicant forfeits exclusivity if it fails to market the drug by the ***later of*** –
  (1) The ***earlier of*** 75 days after ANDA ***approval*** or 30 months after ANDA ***submission***; and
  (2) Either:
    - 75 days after favorable court decision on all qualifying patents (***appeals*** court, or unappealed district court, decision); or
    - 75 days after favorable court settlement or consent decree on all qualifying patents; or
    - 75 days after all qualifying patents are delisted from the Orange Book.

- **Immediate Forfeiture:**
    - If the ANDA applicant withdraws the ANDA or the application is withdrawn because the applicant failed to meet approval requirements;
    - If the ANDA applicant amends or withdraws its Paragraph IV certification;
    - If the ANDA applicant fails to obtain tentative approval within 30 months after filing the application (unless the failure is caused by a review of or change in approval requirements imposed after the ANDA is filed or because of a related Citizen Petition);
    - If the ANDA applicant enters into an agreement with another generic applicant, the NDA holder, or patent owner, and the Federal Trade Commission (FTC) files a complaint, and either the FTC or an appeals court rules that the agreement violates antitrust laws; or
    - If all of the patents certified to in the generic applicant's Paragraph IV certification have expired.

are more complex. In particular, the so-called "failure to market" forfeiture provisions under *FD&C Act* Section 505(j)(5)(D)(i)(I) require FDA to calculate a forfeiture date based on the later of two events. Although FDA has not issued formal regulations yet implementing the 180-day exclusivity forfeiture provisions added to the *FD&C Act* by the *MMA*, the agency has applied them on a case-by-case basis and has issued several letter decisions describing its interpretation of these provisions. Those letters are posted on FDA's website at www.fda.gov/Drugs/DevelopmentApprovalProcess/HowDrugsareDevelopedandApproved/ApprovalApplications/AbbreviatedNewDrugApplicationANDAGenerics/ucm142112.htm. Congress enacted the forfeiture provisions to "ensure that the 180-day exclusivity period enjoyed by the first generic to challenge a patent cannot be used as a bottleneck to prevent additional generic competition."[78]

Of the six 180-day exclusivity forfeiture provisions created by the *MMA*, the provision invoked by FDA most often is *FD&C Act* Section 505(j)(5)(D)(i)(IV), which states that 180-day exclusivity eligibility is forfeited if:

The first applicant fails to obtain tentative approval of the application within 30 months after the date on which the application is filed, unless the failure is caused by a change in or review of the requirements for approval of the application imposed after the date on which the application is filed.

The *Food and Drug Administration Amendments Act* of 2007 (*FDAAA*) clarified *FD&C Act* Section 505(j)(5)(D)(i)(IV) such that if "approval of the [ANDA] was delayed because of a [citizen] petition, the 30-month period under such subsection is deemed to be extended by a period of time equal to the period beginning on the date on which the Secretary received the petition and ending on the date of final agency action on the petition (inclusive of such beginning and ending dates) . . ."[79] The growing number of 180-day exclusivity forfeitures under *FD&C Act* Section 505(j)(5)(D)(i)(IV) likely is due, in part, to the increasing time it takes FDA's Office of Generic Drugs to review and act on ANDAs. *FDASIA* further clarified and modified the timeframe within which an ANDA must receive tentative approval to avoid forfeiting the 180-day marketing exclusivity. *FDASIA* shortened the time for FDA to respond to certain Citizen Petitions related to generic drugs and biologics from 180 to 150 days (see **Table 16-1**).

Exclusivity for Antibiotic Drugs

Until 1997, antibiotic drugs were approved under *FD&C Act* Section 507 and were not entitled to any *Hatch-Waxman* benefits.[80] In 1997, the *Food and Drug Administration Modernization Act* (*FDAMA*) (Pub. L. No. 105-115, 111 Stat. 2295 (1997)), among other things, repealed *FD&C Act* Section 507 and required all NDAs for antibiotic drugs to be submitted under *FD&C Act* Section 505.

FDAMA included a transition provision declaring an antibiotic application approved under Section 507 before the enactment of *FDAMA* would be considered an application submitted, filed and approved under *FD&C Act* Section 505.[81] Congress created an exception to this transition provision. *FDAMA* Section 125(d)(2) exempted certain applications for antibiotic drugs from those provisions of *FD&C Act* Section 505 providing patent listing, patent certification and market exclusivity. Specifically, *FDAMA* Section 125(d)(2) exempted an antibiotic application from *Hatch-Waxman* benefits when "the drug that is the subject of the application contains an antibiotic drug and the antibiotic drug was the subject of an application" received by FDA under *FD&C Act* Section 507 before the

Table 16-2. Differences Among Applications Submitted and Approved Under FD&C Act Section 505

	505(b)(1) NDA	505(b)(2) Application	ANDA
Patient and Exclusivity Information	Submit information on patents claiming the drug or a method of use; exclusivity request claiming exclusivity	Submit information on patents claiming the drug or a method of use (if any); generally, a patent certification (Paragraph I, II, III or IV) or "section viii" statement is required; exclusivity request claiming exclusivity and exclusivity statement the listed drug is subject to exclusivity (if any exists)	Patent certification (Paragraph I, II, III or IV) or a "section viii" statement is required; exclusivity statement the RLD is subject to exclusivity (if any exists)
Five-Year Exclusivity	Prevents the submission of an ANDA or 505(b)(2) application for five years after NDA approval, except an ANDA or 505(b)(2) application with a Paragraph IV certification to an Orange Book-listed patent may be submitted after four years	Only for applications for NCEs; prevents the submission of an ANDA or another 505(b)(2) application for five years after application approval, except an ANDA or other 505(b)(2) application with a Paragraph IV certification to an Orange Book-listed patent may be submitted after four years; also subject to NDA holder's exclusivity	No exclusivity; subject to five-year exclusivity of NDA or 505(b)(2) applicant
Three-Year Exclusivity	Only if one or more of the clinical studies, other than BA/BE studies, was essential to the product's approval; prevents FDA from making effective an ANDA or 505(b)(2) application for the conditions of approval of the NDA	Only if one or more of the clinical studies, other than BA/BE studies, was essential to the product's approval; prevents FDA from making an ANDA or other 505(b)(2) application effective for the conditions of approval of the 505(b)(2) application; also subject to NDA holder's exclusivity	Subject to three-year exclusivity of NDA or 505(b)(2) applicant
Orphan Drug Exclusivity	Prevents FDA from approving an application for the same condition for seven years	Prevents FDA from approving an application for the same drug for the same condition for seven years; also subject to NDA holder's exclusivity	Subject to seven-year exclusivity of NDA or 505(b)(2) applicant
Antibiotic Exclusivity	Provides an additional five-year exclusivity for qualified infectious disease products	Not applicable	Not applicable
Pediatric Exclusivity	Extends by six months all other types of patent and non-patent market exclusivity an NDA holder may have under the *FD&C Act* for a particular active moiety	Extends by six months all other types of patent and non-patent market exclusivity an NDA holder may have under the *FD&C Act* for a particular active moiety; also subject to NDA holder's exclusivity	Subject to exclusivity of NDA or 505(b)(2) applicant
180-Day Exclusivity	Not applicable	Not applicable	Available to any "first applicant" that files an ANDA with a Paragraph IV certification; prevents FDA from approving other ANDAs submitted by applicants that are not "first applicants"
Orange Book Listing	Included in the Orange Book as a listed drug; may be identified as an RLD	Included in the Orange Book as a listed drug; can be identified as a therapeutic equivalent (e.g., "AB-rated") to the list d drug if BE is demonstrated and also is a pharmaceutical equivalent	Included in the Orange Book as a listed drug; can be identified as a therapeutic equivalent (e.g., "AB-rated") to RLD if BE is demonstrated and also is a pharmaceutical equivalent; listed in the Orange Book as a "pharmaceutical alternative" without a therapeutic equivalence evaluation code if approved under an approved suitability petition

enactment of *FDAMA* (i.e., 21 November 1997). Thus, applications for antibiotic drugs received by FDA prior to 21 November 1997, and applications submitted to FDA subsequent to that date for drugs containing an antibiotic drug that was the subject of an application received by FDA prior to 21 November 1997 are within the *FDAMA* Section 125(d)(2) exemption and not eligible for *Hatch-Waxman* benefits. These drugs are referred to as "old antibiotics." Applications for antibiotic drugs not subject to the *FDAMA* Section 125(d)(2) exemption (i.e., so-called "new antibiotics") are eligible for *Hatch-Waxman* benefits.

In October 2008, Congress effectively repealed *FDAMA* Section 125(d)(2) so old antibiotic drugs now are eligible for some *Hatch-Waxman* benefits. Specifically, Section 4 of the *Qualifying Individual (QI) Program Supplemental Funding Act* of 2008 (*QI Act*) amended the *FD&C Act* to add new Section 505(v) "Antibiotic Drugs Submitted Before November 21, 1997," to create certain *Hatch-Waxman* benefits for old antibiotics. The *Generating Antibiotic Incentives Now Act* (*GAIN Act*), which was a part of *FDASIA* Title VIII, adds a new Section 505E (21 U.S.C. 355E), which grants an additional five years of market protection at the end of the existing exclusivity for Qualified Infectious Disease Products (QIDP). This adds to any applicable *Hatch-Waxman* five-year NCE exclusivity, *Hatch-Waxman* three-year new clinical studies exclusivity or seven-year orphan drug exclusivity. The five-year extension also is in addition to any six-month pediatric exclusivity. Under Section 505E(d) of the *FD&C Act*, Section 505E(a) provides an five-year market exclusivity extension to the exclusivity periods provided by Sections 505(c)(3)(E) (ii)–(c)(3)(E)(iv) (21 U.S.C. 355(c)(3)(E) (ii)–(c)(3)(E)(iv)), 505(j)(5)(F)(ii)–(j)(5)(F)(iv) (21 U.S.C. 355(j)(5)(F)(ii)–(j) (5)(F)(iv)), 505A (21 U.S.C. 355a) and 527 (21 U.S.C. 360cc) of the *FD&C Act*. However, as Section 505E(c) of the *FD&C Act* states, not all QIDP applications are eligible for the additional market exclusivity. In addition, an application for a drug designated as a QIDP is eligible for Priority Review and Fast Track designation (*FD&C Act* Sections 524A and 506(a)(1) (21 U.S.C. 356(a) (1))), respectively. The *GAIN Act* also grants an additional six months of exclusivity for drugs for which a companion diagnostic test is cleared or approved beyond the cumulative total of other applicable exclusivities.

Exclusivity for Enantiomers of Previously Approved Racemates

For decades, FDA has treated single enantiomers of approved racemates as previously approved active moieties not eligible for five-year NCE exclusivity (but eligible for three-year exclusivity).[82] (In chemistry, enantiomers are stereoisomers that are non-superimposable complete mirror images of one another. Enantiomers may be either "right-handed" or "left-handed." A racemic mixture is one with equal amounts of "left- and right-handed" enantiomers of a particular chiral molecule.) *FDAAA*, however, amended the *FD&C Act* to add Section 505(u), which permits a 505(b)(1) NDA applicant for an enantiomer (contained in a previously approved racemic mixture) containing full reports of clinical investigations conducted or sponsored by the applicant to "elect to have the single enantiomer not be considered the same active ingredient contained in the approved racemic drug," and thus be eligible for five-year NCE exclusivity.[83] The enantiomer NDA applicant cannot "rely on any investigations that are part of an application submitted under [*FD&C Act* Section 505(b)] for approval of the approved racemic drug."[84]

There are certain limitations under the new *FD&C Act* §505(u). The enantiomer 505(b)(1) NDA must not be for a condition of use "(i) in a therapeutic category in which the approved racemic drug has been approved or (ii) for which any other enantiomer of the racemic drug has been approved."[85] In addition, if the enantiomer NDA applicant elects to receive exclusivity, FDA may not approve the enantiomer drug for any condition of use in the "therapeutic category" in which the racemic drug is approved until 10 years after approving the enantiomer.[86] The term "therapeutic category" is defined in *FD&C Act* Section 505(u) to mean "a therapeutic category identified in the list developed by the United States Pharmacopeia pursuant to section 1860D-4(b)(3)(C)(ii) of the *Social Security Act* and as in effect on [27 September 2007]," which FDA must publish and may be amended by regulation.[87]

Summary

Brand-name drug sponsors may qualify for various periods of patent and non-patent exclusivities, which could delay the submission or final approval of a marketing application for a generic version of the brand-name drug. In addition, certain generic drug sponsors also may qualify for their own 180-day period of market exclusivity. Each type of exclusivity is different in scope and subject to different rules and interpretations (**Table 16-2**).

References

1. Before 8 June 1995, patents typically had 17 years of patent life from the date the patent was issued by the US Patent and Trademark Office (PTO). The *Uruguay Rounds Agreements Act* (*URAA*), Pub. L. No. 103-465, 108 Stat. 4809 (1994), changed the patent term in the US so that patents granted after 8 June 1995 (the effective date of *URAA*) have a 20-year patent life from the date of the first filing of the patent application with PTO. Under a transition provision in *URAA*, a patent in effect on 8 June 1995 was awarded a term of the greater of 20 years from the filing of the patent or 17 years from the date of patent issuance. See 35 U.S.C. §154(c)(1).
2. 35 U.S.C. §156(a).
3. 35 U.S.C. §156(b).
4. 35 U.S.C. §156(b)(1).
5. 35 U.S.C. §156(g)(1)(B)(i).
6. 35 U.S.C. §156(g)(1)(B)(ii).
7. 35 U.S.C. §§156(c)(2) and 156(g)(1)(B).

8. 35 U.S.C. §156(c)(1).
9. 35 U.S.C. §§156(g)(6)(A) and 156(c)(3).
10. This has been the topic of several letter decisions, including in Docket No. FDA-2005-E-0310 concerning KEPIVANCE, in Docket No. FDA-2009-E-0237 concerning DEXILANT and in Docket No. FDA-2007-E-0278 concerning ZOLINZA.
11. Wyeth Holdings Corp. v. Sebelius, 603 F.3d 1291 (Fed. Cir. 2010).
12. 35 U.S.C. §156(a)(1)-(5). The patent term extension law defines the term "drug product" to mean "the active ingredient of a new drug [as defined in §201(p) of the FD&C Act]...including any salt or ester of the active ingredient, as a single entity or in combination with another active ingredient." Id. §156(f)(2). With respect to the applicability of patent term extensions to combination drugs, the US Court of Appeals for the Federal Circuit ruled in 2004 "the statute places a drug product with two active ingredients, A and B, in the same category as a drug product with a single ingredient.... To extend the term of a patent claiming a composition comprising A and B, either A or B must not have been previously marketed." Arnold Partnership v. Dudas, 362 F.3d 1338, 1341 (Fed. Cir. 2004).
13. 35 U.S.C. §156(f).
14. 35 U.S.C. §§156(a)(1), 156 (d)(5) and 156 (e)(2).
15. 35 U.S.C. §156(d)(5).
16. 35 U.S.C. §156(e)(2).
17. Method-of-use patents listed in the *Orange Book* are typically assigned a "patent use code." The *Orange Book* contains hundreds of such use codes.
18. *FD&C Act* §505(b)(1).
19. FDA regulations at 21 CFR 314.53(b)(1) further state:
For patents that claim the drug substance, the applicant shall submit information only on those patents that claim the drug substance that is the subject of the pending or approved application or that claim a drug substance that is the same as the active ingredient that is the subject of the approved or pending application... For patents that claim a drug product, the applicant shall submit information only on those patents that claim a drug product, as is defined in [21 CFR 314.3 (i.e., a finished dosage form that contains a drug substance)], that is described in the pending or approved application. For patents that claim a method of use, the applicant shall submit information only on those patents that claim indications or other conditions of use that are described in the pending or approved application.... Process patents, patents claiming packaging, patents claiming metabolites and patents claiming intermediates are not covered by this section, and information on these patents must not be submitted to FDA.
20. FDA, Final Rule; Applications for FDA Approval to Market a New Drug: Patent Submission and Listing Requirements and Application of 30-Month Stays on Approval of Abbreviated New Drug Applications Certifying That a Patent Claiming a Drug Is Invalid or Will Not Be Infringed, 68 Fed. Reg. 36,676 (18 June 2003).
21. *FD&C Act* Sections 505(b)(1) & 505(c)(2).
22. `Ibid Section 505(c)(2); see also 21 CFR 314.53(c)(2)(ii).
23. *FD&C Act* Section 505(j)(2)(A)(vii).
24. Ibid Section 505(j)(2)(A)(vii)(III) and Section 505(j)(5)(B)(ii).
25. Ibid Sections 505(j)(2)(A)(vii)(I)-(II) & (j)(5)(B)(i).
26. Ibid Sections 505(j)(2)(A)(vii)(IV) & 505(j)(5)(B)(iii).
27. Ibid Section 505(j)(2)(A)(viii). For a listed drug covered by a period of five-year NCE exclusivity, generally an ANDA and 505(b)(2) applicant may not reference the listed drug until such exclusivity (described in the next sections) applicable to that listed drug has expired. For this reason, the information in the NDA for the listed drug is sometimes said to be under "data exclusivity."
28. 21 CFR 314.127(a)(7). An ANDA applicant must make an additional certification (or submit an additional "section viii statement") as to any new patent listed in the *Orange Book* while its application is pending if the NDA holder submits the new patent to FDA for *Orange Book* listing within 30 days of patent issuance. See 21 CFR 314.94(a)(12)(vi). A Paragraph IV certification to a later-listed patent will not result in an additional 30-month stay of ANDA approval.
29. *FD&C Act* Section 505(j)(5)(A)(iv)(I) states that "Subject to subparagraph (D), if the application contains a certification described in paragraph (2)(A)(vii)(IV) and is for a drug for which a first applicant has submitted an application containing such a certification, the application shall be made effective on the date that is 180 days after the date of the first commercial marketing of the drug (including the commercial marketing of the listed drug) by any first applicant." Section 8 does not yield exclusivity.
30. Ibid.
31. *FD&C Act* Section 505(j)(5)(B).
32. 21 CFR 314.53(c)(2)(ii)(P)(3) requires the NDA owner to submit "[t]he description of the patented method of use as required for publication." This description is the use code.
33. Caraco Pharm. Labs., Ltd. v. Novo Nordisk A/S, 132 S. Ct. 1670 (U.S. 2012).
34. Takeda Pharms., U.S.A., Inc. v. Burwell, 2015 U.S. Dist. LEXIS 5908 (D.D.C. Jan. 13, 2015).
35. Specifically, five-year exclusivity prevents the submission of an ANDA or 505(b)(2) application for five years unless the applicant submits a Paragraph IV patent certification. See *FD&C Act* Sections 505(b)(2)(A) and 505(j)(2)(A)(vii). In this case, the ANDA or 505(b)(2) application can be submitted after four years; however, "if an action for patent infringement is commenced during the one-year period beginning [four years] after the date of the approval of the [NCE NDA], the thirty-month [stay] period...shall be extended by such amount of time which is required for seven and one-half years to have elapsed from the date of approval of the [NCE NDA]." *FD&C Act* Sections 505(c)(3)(E)(ii) & 505(j)(5)(F)(ii).
36. In addition, it is FDA's policy that five-year exclusivity is not granted for a combination drug containing a previously approved drug. Thus, an application for a two-drug combination containing two previously approved drugs, or even an NCE plus a previously approved drug, is not eligible for five-year exclusivity.
37. A similar ambiguity exists with regard to the scope of three-year exclusivity in Sections 505(c)(3)(E)(iii) and 505(j)(5)(F)(iii) of the *FD&C Act.*
38. The original citations are to Sections 505(c)(3)(D) and 505(j)(4)(D) of the *FD&C Act.* These sections were recodified in the *MMA.*
39. 54 Fed. Reg. at 28,897.
40. FDA's regulations define the term "active moiety" to mean "the molecule or ion, excluding those appended portions of the molecule that cause the drug to be an ester, salt (including a salt with hydrogen or coordination bonds), or other noncovalent derivative (such as a complex, chelate or clathrate) of the molecule, responsible for the physiological or pharmacological action of the drug substance." 21 CFR 314.108(a).
41. Combination PTE CP response
42. 21 CFR 314.108(b)(4), (5); see also *FD&C Act* Sections 505(j)(5)(F)(iii) and (iv).
43. 21 CFR 314.50(j)(4).
44. 21 CFR 314.108(a).
45. Ibid.
46. FDA, Final Rule, ANDA Regulations; Patent and Exclusivity Provisions, 59 Fed. Reg. at 50,338, 50,357 (3 October 1994).
47. 21 CFR 314.50(j)(4)(ii).
48. 59 Fed. Reg. at 50,368-69; see also 21 CFR 314.50(j)(4)(iii).
49. This is an important difference compared to five-year exclusivity, which prevents the submission of a generic application.
50. 21 CFR 314.108(b)(4), (5).
51. *FD&C Act* Section 505(j)(2)(A)(v).
52. 21 CFR 314.94(a)(8)(iv).
53. 21 CFR 314.127(a)(7).
54. Veloxis Pharmaceuticals, Inc. v. United States Food and Drug Administration et al., Civil Action No. 1:14-cv-02126-RBW (District of Columbia filed 16 December 2014).
55. The term "pediatric studies" is defined as "at least one clinical investigation (that, at [FDA's] discretion, may include pharmacokinetic

studies) in pediatric age groups (including neonates in appropriate cases) in which a drug is anticipated to be used." *FD&C Act* Section 505A(a).

56. *FD&C Act* Section 505A does not extend the term of the patent itself, but only the period during which FDA cannot approve (or accept for review) an ANDA or 505(b)(2) application that includes a Paragraph II or Paragraph III certification, or a Paragraph IV certification that concerns a patent that a court has determined is valid and would be infringed. See *FD&C Act* Section 505A(c)(2).
57. Exclusivity does not extend term of patent.
58. See National Pharmaceutical Alliance v. Henney, 47 F. Supp. 2d 37 (D.D.C. 1999); and *Guidance for Industry: Qualifying for Pediatric Exclusivity Under Section 505A of the Food, Drug, and Cosmetic Act* (September 1999).
59. *FD&C Act* Section 505A(g).
60. *Guidance for Industry: Qualifying for Pediatric Exclusivity Under Section 505A of the Food, Drug, and Cosmetic Act*, at 14.
61. *FD&C Act* Sections 505A(b)(2), 505A(c)(2).
62. *FD&C Act* Section 526(a)(2).
63. Orphan drug exclusivity operates independently of patent protection and independently of five- and three-year exclusivity (and therefore, pediatric exclusivity as well).
64. *FD&C Act* Sections 527(b)(1) and (2); see also 21 CFR 316.31(a).
65. 21 CFR 316.3(13).
66. 21 CFR 316.3(b)(3)(i)-(iii).
67. *FD&C Act* Section 505(j)(2)(B)(ii)(I).
68. *FD&C Act* Section 505(j)(2)(B)(ii)(II).
69. *FD&C Act* Sections 505(j)(2)(B)(iv)(I)–(II).
70. *FD&C Act* Section 505(j)(5)(B)(iii).
71. *FD&C Act* Section 505(j)(5)(B)(iii).
72. *FD&C Act* Section 505(j)(5)(C)(ii).
73. *FD&C Act* Section 505(j)(5)(C)(iii).
74. *FD&C Act* Section 505(j)(5)(C)(i).
75. Ibid.
76. *FD&C Act* Section 505(j)(5)(C)(iii).
77. A 505(b)(2) application is not eligible for 180-day exclusivity.
78. 149 Cong. Rec. S15746 (daily ed. Nov. 24, 2003) (statement of Sen. Schumer).
79. *FD&C Act* Section 505(q)(1)(G)
80. Glaxo, Inc. v. Heckler, 623 F. Supp. 69 (E.D.N.C. 1985).
81. *FDAMA* Section 125(d)(1).
82. See 54 Fed. Reg. at 28,898. "FDA will consider whether a drug contains a previously approved active moiety on a case-by-case basis. FDA notes that a single enantiomer of a previously approved racemate contains a previously approved active moiety and is therefore not considered a new chemical entity."
83. *FD&C Act* Section 505(u)(1).
84. *FD&C Act* Section 505(u)(1)(A)(ii)(II).
85. *FD&C Act* Section 505(u)(1)(B).
86. *FD&C Act* Section 505(u)(2)(A).
87. *FD&C Act* Section 505(u)(3).

Helpful References and Resources

- FDA's Office of Generic Drugs, including exclusivity decisions. FDA website. www.fda.gov/Drugs/DevelopmentApprovalProcess/HowDrugsareDevelopedandApproved/ApprovalApplications/AbbreviatedNewDrugApplicationANDAGenerics/ucm142112.htm.
- *Federal Food, Drug, and Cosmetic Act.* FDA website. www.fda.gov/RegulatoryInformation/Legislation/default.htmThe Electronic *Orange Book* www.accessdata.fda.gov/scripts/cder/ob/default.cfm.
- FDA's Paragraph IV Patent Certification List. FDA website. www.fda.gov/Drugs/DevelopmentApprovalProcess/HowDrugsareDevelopedandApproved/ApprovalApplications/AbbreviatedNewDrugApplicationANDAGenerics/ucm047676.htm.

Chapter 17

Over-the-Counter (Nonprescription) Drug Products

Updated by Shekhar Natarajan, MSc, MRSC

OBJECTIVES

- ❑ Definition and characteristics of OTC drug products
- ❑ Understand OTC drug development and regulation
- ❑ Understand OTC drug development through the NDA and OTC drug monograph processes
- ❑ Regulatory pathways available for industry to request an OTC drug monograph be reopened and/or amended
- ❑ Understand Rx-to-OTC switch
- ❑ Understand OTC "Drug Facts" label
- ❑ Packaging requirement for OTC drugs, tamper-evident packaging

LAWS, REGULATIONS AND GUIDELINES COVERED IN THIS CHAPTER

- ❑ *Federal Food, Drug, and Cosmetic Act (FD&C Act)*
- ❑ 1951 *Durham-Humphrey Amendment*
- ❑ *Kefauver-Harris Amendments* of 1962
- ❑ 21 CFR Part 330.10
- ❑ 21 CFR 343
- ❑ 21 CFR Part 330.14
- ❑ 21 CFR 10.30
- ❑ 21 CFR 201.66
- ❑ 21 CFR 211.132
- ❑ 21 CFR 343
- ❑ *Poison Prevention Packaging Act* of 1970 (*PPPA*)
- ❑ *Dietary Supplement and Nonprescription Drug Consumer Protection Act* of 2006

Introduction

Over-the-counter (OTC) drugs are defined as drugs safe and effective for use by the general public without a prescription. More than 300,000 OTC drug products are marketed in the US, encompassing about 800 significant active ingredients. These include more than 80 classes (therapeutic categories) of OTC drugs, ranging from acne drug products to weight control drug products. As with prescription drugs, the Center for Drug Evaluation and Research (CDER) oversees OTC drugs to ensure they are labeled properly and their benefits outweigh their risks. These drugs often are located on pharmacy shelves easily accessible by patients, but also may be located in non-pharmacy outlets, such as grocery and convenience stores and large discount retailers.

Prior to 1951, there was no legal basis for the designation of what was acceptable as an OTC drug product. The 1951 *Durham-Humphrey Amendment* to the *Federal Food, Drug, and Cosmetic Act (FD&C Act)* established three criteria that would limit a drug to prescription status:

- habit-forming drugs
- not safe for use unless supervised by a healthcare professional
- limited to prescription use under a New Drug Application (NDA)

OTC drugs generally have the following characteristics:

- their benefits outweigh their risks
- the potential for misuse and abuse is low
- consumers can use them for self-diagnosed conditions
- they can be labeled adequately
- healthcare practitioners are not needed for the products' safe and effective use

A restricted class of OTC drugs also exists in the US that includes drugs such as pseudoephedrine, emergency contraception and some Schedule V controlled substances. These products, while considered OTC, are kept behind the pharmacy counter and must be dispensed by a pharmacist pursuant to proper identification, age verification and patient education. In March 2012, FDA considered expanding the definition of nonprescription drugs to include cholesterol, blood pressure, asthma and birth control medications. This new Rx-to-OTC switch ruling currently is in an FDA public review and comment process.

OTC medications can carry risks, including the possibility of side effects, drug or food interactions, or harm due to excessive doses. Patients should read the "Drug Facts" label found on all OTC products. All consumers, including older patients, pregnant women and parents of young children, always should consult with a pharmacist or other healthcare provider if they have additional questions concerning OTC drug use.

OTC Drug Development and Regulation

OTC drugs are developed under either the OTC Monograph or OTC New Drug Application (NDA) process. FDA's review of OTC drugs is handled primarily by CDER's Office of Drug Evaluation IV (ODE-IV).

Regulations relating to all aspects of drug manufacture and testing (current Good Manufacturing Practices (CGMPs)), facility listing and inspection, drug registration, clinical trials and safety oversight apply equally to prescription and OTC drug products.

In addition, the use of OTC drug products requires consumers to:

- self-diagnose
- self-treat
- self-manage

These can be assessed through label comprehension studies and actual use studies.

OTC Drugs Developed Through the NDA Process

A sponsor seeking to market an OTC product, either as a new NDA or as a switch from a prescription product, can submit an application to the Division of Nonprescription Clinical Evaluation (DNCE) in ODE-IV. DNCE will oversee drug development, including review and regulatory action on Investigational New Drugs (INDs), and may obtain input from the specific subject matter review division (SSMRD) during the development process. After a sponsor submits an NDA, DNCE reviews the consumer studies, postmarketing safety data, OTC labeling and any regulatory issues. SSMRD collaborates with DNCE and typically reviews the efficacy and safety data related to controlled clinical trials. Additional input is obtained as needed from other disciplines outside DNCE, including clinical pharmacology, statistics and chemistry.

Products not covered by the OTC drug monographs are subject to FDA preapproval through the NDA process prior to marketing. Four NDA routes are available for OTC products:

- RX-to-OTC switches
  - Full switch (NDA supplement)
  - Partial switch (new NDA)
- Direct-to-OTC NDA
- NDA Monograph deviation (§330.11)
- Generic (ANDA)

OTC Drugs Developed Under the OTC Drug Monograph Process

The Division of Nonprescription Regulation Development (DNRD) in ODE-IV is responsible for OTC drug monograph development. Supporting data for the safety and efficacy of different active ingredients in a particular drug monograph are reviewed by appropriate scientific personnel. Efficacy data may require the input of a medical officer and/or statistician from a prescription review division. Carcinogenicity or other animal toxicology data may require input from a CDER pharmacologist. While DNRD is considered the lead division in development of an OTC drug monograph, reviewers from multiple divisions within the Office of New Drugs (OND) also are involved in this process.

How is an OTC Monograph Established?

Currently, more than 300,000 OTC drug products are on the market, and many of these products were approved by the OTC monograph route. FDA reviews the active ingredients and labeling of more than 80 therapeutic classes of drugs, rather than reviewing individual drug products. For each category, an OTC drug monograph is developed and published in the *Federal Register*. In 1972, FDA initiated the OTC drug review process as part of the implementation of the *Kefauver-Harris Amendments* of 1962. The OTC

Table 17-1. NDA vs. OTC Drug Monograph

NDA Route	OTC Monograph Route
Premarket approval	No premarket approval (conditions of marketing are codified) • The onus is on the manufacturer/distributor to assure compliance
Confidential filing	Public process
Drug product-specific	Active ingredient-specific • OTC drug therapeutic category
May require a user fee	No user fees
Potential for marketing exclusivity	No marketing exclusivity
Mandated FDA review timelines	No mandated FDA review timelines
May require clinical studies for application • Safety and efficacy • Label comprehension • Actual use • Demonstration of appropriate consumer	May require clinical studies • Label comprehension and actual use studies not required

drug review process encompassed review of the safety and efficacy of products already on the market. The OTC drug monograph provides specific guidance covering generally recognized as safe and effective (GRASE) active ingredients (strength and dosage form) and label requirements (indications, warnings and directions for use). By grouping products into therapeutic drug categories and evaluating active ingredients rather than assessing each product, FDA was able to make the process more efficient. **Table 17-2** details more than 80 therapeutic categories that are reviewed by an expert Advisory Panel and undergo a three-step public rulemaking process (call for information, proposed rules and a codified final rule) followed by publication in the *Federal Register*.

Under 21 CFR Part 330.10, data regarding OTC monographs can be submitted by anyone, including a drug company, health professional, consumer or citizen's group.

A request to amend an existing drug monograph or an opinion regarding a drug monograph must be submitted in the form of a Citizen Petition or as correspondence to an established monograph docket. However, if no monograph exists, data must be submitted in the format outlined in 21 CFR Section 330.1. The review process commences with the creation of therapeutic category-specific Advisory Panels composed of subject matter experts.

A call for information is published in the *Federal Register* for the public (i.e., industry, healthcare professionals and consumers) to submit data within a defined time period. Open Advisory Panel meetings are held to review the data and provide recommendations, including categorizing active ingredients into one of three categories:

- Category I: generally recognized as safe and effective for the claimed therapeutic indication
- Category II: not generally recognized as safe and effective or unacceptable indications
- Category III: insufficient data available to permit final classification

Advisory Panel recommendations are published as an Advance Notice of Proposed Rulemaking (ANPR) for public review and comment within a defined time period. After collecting public comments, FDA publishes its conclusions in the form of Tentative Final Monograph (TFM) (Proposed Rule). The TFM also is published for public review and comment. FDA reviews any additional information submitted prior to publishing a Final Monograph (FM) (Final Rule). Once the FM is published, manufacturers of products not complying with FM requirements are given a defined timeframe to withdraw their products from the market, bring the products into compliance with the monograph or submit an NDA. FMs are codified in the CFR. Products complying with monographs can be marketed without FDA preapproval, provided they are appropriately drug listed, compliant with CGMPs and manufactured in a registered facility.

The monograph process can be very lengthy, as FDA timelines for moving a TFM to an FM have not been defined. Hence, there still are a number of monographs that have not been finalized. For example, the monograph for oral healthcare drug products is not final, even though the original Advisory Panel provided its expert opinion in 1979. Products meeting the conditions of in-process TFMs can be marketed. FDA can amend FMs as new information becomes available. For example, the *OTC Internal Analgesic Drug Products* monograph (21 CFR 343) was amended in 2009 to include an organ-specific warning statement for acetaminophen and NSAIDs. Two regulatory pathways are

Table 17-2. OTC monograph therapeutic category subtopics evaluated* as part of the OTC review process. (Therapeutic category subtopics in BOLD are codified in the final monographs)

Acne	**Callus Remover**	**Nighttime Sleep Aid**
Allergy	**Corn Remover**	**Ophthalmic**
Analgesic, External	**Dandruff**	Oral Health Care
Analgesic, Internal	Daytime Sedative	Oral Wound Healing
Anorectal	**Decongestant, Nasal**	**Otic**
Antacid	**Dental Care**	Overindulgence, Food & Drink
Anthelmintic	**Deodorant, Internal**	Pancreatic Insufficiency
Antibiotic, First Aid	**Diaper Rash**	**Pediculicide**
Anticaries	Digestive Aid	**Poison Oak/Ivy**
Anticholinergic	Drink Overindulgence	Poison Treatment
Antidiarrheal	Exocrine Pancreatic Insufficiency	Prostatic Hypertrophy
Antiemetic	**Expectorant**	**Psoriasis**
Antiflatulent	**External Analgesic**	**Seborrheic Dermatitis**
Antifungal	Fever Blister	Sedative, Daytime
Antihistamine	**First Aid Antibiotic**	Skin Bleaching
Antimalarial	Food Overindulgence	**Skin Protectant**
Antimicrobial	Hair Growth & Loss	**Sleep Aid, Nighttime**
Antiperspirant	Hormone	
Antipyretic	Hypophosphatemia/ Hyperphosphatemia	Smoking Deterrent
Antirheumatic	**Ingrown Toenail**	**Stimulant**
Antitussive	Insect Bite & Sting	Stomach Acidifier
Aphrodisiac	Insect Repellent, Oral	**Sunscreen**
Astringent	**Internal Analgesic**	Thumbsucking
Benign Prostatic Hypertrophy	**Internal Deodorant**	**Topical Analgesic**
Boil Treatment	Laxative	Vaginal Contraceptive
Bronchodilator	Leg Muscle Cramps	Vaginal Drug Products
Camphorated Oil	**Male Genital Desensitizers**	Vitamins & Minerals
Cholecystokinetic	Menstrual	**Wart Remover**
Cold & Cough	Nailbiting	Weight Control
Colloidal Silver	**Nasal Decongestant**	

*Therapeutic category subtopic active ingredients have been implemented as part of therapeutic category Final Monograph, are part of a proposed rule or have been designated by FDA as not GRASE and/or misbranded.

available for industry to request an OTC drug monograph be reopened and/or amended:

1. Citizen Petition
2. Time and Extent Application (TEA)

The Citizen Petition process, codified in 21 CFR 10.30, can be used to amend an OTC drug monograph at any stage of the process. The TEA process, codified in 21 CFR 330.14, can be used to add an ingredient to an OTC monograph that has been approved under an NDA or has been marketed in another country. This process can be utilized only when the ingredient has been used for a significant time (five or more continuous years in the same country) with a significant marketing distribution (tens of millions of dosage units sold).

Table 17-1 summarizes the differences between the NDA/ANDA and OTC drug monograph marketing pathways.

Direct-to-OTC NDA

A product can be approved by the OTC route even if it never was available as a prescription. The same requirements apply for direct-to-OTC NDA products as for new prescription drug products, with the exception that the applicant also must prove the product can be used safely by the wide consumer population without healthcare professional oversight. Colgate Total toothpaste (active ingredients: Sodium Fluoride and Triclosan) and Abreva (active ingredient: docosanol) are examples of direct-to-OTC NDAs.

Rx-to-OTC Switch

This route is used when it can be demonstrated a prescription product can be used by the wide consumer population without healthcare professional oversight. FDA evaluates the product's toxicity and safe consumer use as well as whether the condition can be self-diagnosed and recognized without a healthcare professional's intervention. This route has gained popularity because it can be timed to coincide with patent expiry, allowing an innovator company to market a product for a longer period of time, without generic competition and to a wider consumer base.

One of the challenges in the switch process is transcribing information from the prescription drug product label to the "Drug Facts" OTC label, which has a limited amount of space, and ensuring the information is presented in a format consumers can comprehend and apply. Some examples of product switches are Prilosec OTC (proton pump inhibitor for frequent heartburn), Nicorette (smoking cessation aid), Zyrtec (antihistamine) and Plan B (emergency contraceptive). Several attempts to switch cholesterol-lowering medication have failed to date to meet FDA's criteria for appropriate self-selection.

An Rx-to-OTC switch that creates a new OTC product category is referred to as a first-in-class switch and often is subject to FDA Advisory Panel review (composed of applicable prescription drug Advisory Committee members and members of the Nonprescription Drug Advisory Committee). Examples of first-in-class switches are Prilosec OTC, Alli (weight loss aid) and Claritin (a non-sedating antihistamine). Rx-to-OTC switches also can be partial or complete. For a complete switch (e.g., Claritin, Nicorette), the full product range and indications are switched. For a partial switch, either the product strength or the indication remains prescription (e.g., Prilosec OTC). To address rules for a partial switch, an ANPR was published in the *Federal Register* in 2005 to elicit comments on whether clarification was necessary in circumstances when an active substance can be marketed simultaneously as OTC and prescription. While rulemaking for this issue has not been finalized, FDA indicated it will not allow the same active substance to be marketed with a prescription in a certain population and as an OTC for a subset of that population.

NDA Monograph Deviation

This route can be used when the drug product deviates in any aspect from the OTC drug monograph. The applicant submits an NDA referencing the monograph, with data to support the drug product's safety and efficacy with the deviation. This route was utilized for approval of a head lice aerosol foam product, Rid Mousse. This drug product met all the conditions of the Pediculicide Final Monograph with the exception of dosage form.

Generic (ANDA)

The ANDA (505)(j) route can be used when a company intends to market an equivalent OTC drug product to one already on the market. The same regulations apply here as for prescription products; however, a company must submit bioequivalence data in lieu of safety and efficacy studies. In addition, the product's labeling must be the same as that of the original product.

OTC NDA Products and Specific Studies

As with prescription products, OTC product manufacturers conduct preclinical studies to assess safety and efficacy. However, three additional studies are required for OTC products:

- label comprehension
- self-selection
- actual use or OTC simulation trials

Label comprehension studies are used to evaluate the extent to which a consumer can understand the information on the proposed OTC drug label and then apply the information when making drug product use decisions in a hypothetical situation. Label comprehension studies are open label and uncontrolled. No drug product is used in these studies, and they do not have to be conducted under an IND; however, it is recommended manufacturers submit these studies under an IND to obtain CDER advice on the protocol. FDA issued a guidance document on design aspects of label comprehension testing in August 2010, which describes test standards, hurdle rates and test population literacy demographics. Identification of a suitable label may take several iterations and should achieve a satisfactory comprehension level prior to running self-selection and actual use trials (AUT). Self-selection studies are used to evaluate whether a consumer can make a correct decision about using a drug product based on the drug product label information and knowledge of the customer's personal medical history. No drug product is used in these studies, although a self-selection measure can be incorporated into AUT design. AUTs are used to evaluate consumer behavior—whether a consumer actually will use the product safely without healthcare practitioner supervision and as per label instructions. These trials typically are designed as "all comers" studies, to measure consumer behavior against product usage intent described in the product labeling, and conducted under an IND. The product label tested in AUTs should have been evaluated previously in the label comprehension study. The sponsor must follow the same process when selecting the proprietary name for an OTC product as for a prescription drug when using submitting an NDA. Ideally, a primary and alternate proposed proprietary name should be submitted to the Division of Medication Error Prevention and Analysis (DMEPA) for review and approval.

OTC "Drug Facts" Label

The label of an OTC product must include specific information that will help the consumer understand the product's usage and safety information without the oversight of a healthcare professional. The final rule on the use of "Drug Facts" became effective in 1999. The rule standardized the format, content, headings, graphics and minimum type size required to be used on all OTC drug products.

All OTC medicine labels have detailed usage and warning information to help consumers determine whether the product is appropriate to treat their condition and how to take the product correctly.

Specific information on the OTC label must include:

- active ingredient
- uses
- warnings
- inactive ingredients
- purpose
- directions
- other information

An example of a "Drug Facts" label is provided in **Figure 17-1**. All OTC drug products must bear the "Drug Facts" label in accordance with 21 CFR 201.66, and it must be visible to consumers at the time of purchase.

FDA regulations require OTC labeling to be written and tested for use by ordinary people, including those with low comprehension skills, to ensure product information is easy to find and understand, including:

- product's intended uses and results
- active and inactive ingredients
- adequate directions for proper use
- warnings against unsafe use, side effects and adverse reactions

Some OTC drug monographs also provide professional labeling information including specific information for healthcare professionals on uses outside the scope permitted by OTC consumer drug labeling.

Packaging Requirements

Tamper-evident packaging, as required by 21 CFR 211.132, is becoming the standard for most OTC drug products. Statements must be included on both outer and inner cartons clearly describing the tamper-evident features utilized. In addition, OTC drugs must comply with child-resistant packaging requirements as defined in the *Poison Prevention Packaging Act* of 1970 *(PPPA)*. The US Consumer Product Safety Commission (CPSC) enforces child-resistant packaging requirements. A provision is in place for one container size to be marketed in non-child resistant packaging as long as it is adequately labeled and child-resistant packages also are supplied.

Figure 17-1. Example of an OTC Drug Facts Label

Drug Facts

Active ingredient(s) ***Purpose***
Calcium carbonate USP 750mg................Antacid

Use(s) relieves ▪acid indigestion ▪heartburn ▪sour stomach

Warnings
Ask a doctor or pharmacist before use if you are taking a prescription drug. Antacids may interact with certain prescription drugs.

When using this product
▪do not take more than 10 tablets in 24 hours
▪do not use the maximum dosage for more than 2 weeks

Keep out of reach of children. In case of overdose, get medical help or contact a Poison Control Center right away.

Directions
chew 2-4 tablets as symptoms occur, or as directed by a doctor

Other information store at room temperature

Inactive ingredients sucrose, corn starch, talc, mineral oil, natural and artificial flavors, adipic acid, sodium polyphosphate, red 40 lake, yellow 6 lake, yellow 5 lake, blue 1 lake

Questions or comments? 1-800-xxx-xxxx

FDA Oversight of OTC Drug Products

Two divisions within ODE-IV have oversight responsibility for OTC drugs. DNCE is responsible for managing INDs and the associated NDAs for those products approved under the NDA route. The Division of Non-prescription Regulation Development is responsible for the OTC drug monograph process and the products marketed under the respective monograph. OTC and prescription drugs generally adhere to the same regulatory requirements. All OTC drug manufacturing activities must comply with 21 CFR 210 and 211, current Good Manufacturing Practices for Pharmaceuticals. Drug substance and drug product manufacturing sites are required to be registered with FDA and are subject to Prior Approval Inspections (PAIs) for NDA products and routine FDA inspections. All OTC drug products are required to be drug listed; the National Drug Code (NDC) is suggested, but not required, to be displayed on the product label. Medical oversight activities for OTC drug products also mimic those required for prescription products. The *Dietary Supplement and Nonprescription Drug Consumer Protection Act* of 2006 mandated safety reporting requirements for OTC drug products marketed without an NDA. Prior to this, only NDA products were subject to adverse event reporting requirements. NDA lifecycle management and maintenance activities are identical to those of their prescription counterparts.

Challenges in Assigning a Product Class

Products are classified as drugs based on their intended use as defined by the *FD&C Act*. Intended use can be determined through the product indications or claims, consumer perception or drug ingredients. Because product positioning can define product classification, some cosmetics can be considered unapproved drugs. This is why some cosmetics manufacturers making drug claims either on product labeling or through advertising and promotion, have been subject to FDA regulatory actions. Some OTC drug products containing cosmetic-like claims (cleaning)—such as toothpastes—are considered drugs based on the presence of the anti-caries drug ingredient, fluoride. In fact, many OTC products meet the definition within the *FD&C Act* of both a cosmetic and a drug because they have two intended uses. Examples of such products include antidandruff shampoo, deodorants containing antiperspirant actives and moisturizers and makeup with sun-protection ingredients. These products must comply with requirements for both cosmetics and drugs, e.g., drugs that are also cosmetics are required to list inactive ingredients in descending order of predominance as required by the cosmetic regulations, rather than in alphabetical order as required by drug regulations.

Advertising

OTC drug product advertising is regulated by the Federal Trade Commission (FTC). In 1971, a Memorandum of Understanding between FDA and FTC gave FTC primary responsibility for OTC drug advertising and gave FDA primary responsibility for OTC drug labeling. Unlike prescription products, there is no fair balance requirement for OTC drugs, and promotional material is not required to be submitted to FTC prior to distribution. FTC has a number of policy guides on advertising. The National Advertising Division (NAD) of the Council of Better Business Bureaus also oversees advertising, either by challenging the advertisement directly or resolving the advertisement challenge submitted by a competitor.

In addition, the Consumer Healthcare Product Association (CHPA), a not-for-profit trade association representing the OTC drug industry, established an advertising code of practice.

The regulatory professional should ensure advertising standards are followed, including quality claim support data, prior to initiation advertising.

Summary

OTC drug manufacturers must comply with the same quality standards and regulatory requirements as those for prescription product manufacturers. However, unlike prescription products, OTC products must be proven to be safe and effective for use without healthcare professional supervision. Hence, the information on an OTC drug product label is critical. A number of regulatory pathways are available to market OTC drug products in the US. The regulatory professional's role in creating a strategy for product innovation and product differentiation through claims and/or promotion and advertising, while ensuring compliance with the applicable rules and regulations, is essential in the dynamic and challenging arena of OTC drugs.

References

- Over the Counter Medications. Drugs.com website. www.drugs.com/otc. Accessed 31 May 2015.
- Status of OTC Rulemakings. FDA website. http://www.fda.gov/Drugs/DevelopmentApprovalProcess/DevelopmentResources/Over-the-CounterOTCDrugs/StatusofOTCRulemakings/. Accessed 31 May 2015.
- OTC Ingredient list, FDA website. http://www.fda.gov/downloads/AboutFDA/CentersOffices/CDER/UCM135691.pdf. Accessed 31 May 2015.
- FTC, Bureau of Consumer Protection, Business Center. Health Claims. FTC website. https://www.ftc.gov/tips-advice/business-center/advertising-and-marketing/health-claims. Accessed 31 May 2015.
- FTC, Bureau of Consumer Protection, Business Center. Advertising FAQ's: A Guide for Small Business. FTC website. https://www.ftc.gov/tips-advice/business-center/guidance/advertising-faqs-guide-small-business. Accessed 31 May 2015.
- ODE-IV Presentation of Regulation of Nonprescription Drug Products. FDA website.
- Is It a Cosmetic, a Drug, or Both? (Or Is It Soap?). FDA website. http://www.fda.gov/cosmetics/guidanceregulation/lawsregulations/ucm074201.htm. . Accessed 7 April 2015.
- Drug Applications for Over-the-Counter (OTC) Drugs. FDA website. www.fda.gov/Drugs/DevelopmentApprovalProcess/HowDrugsareDevelopedandApproved/ApprovalApplications/Over-the-CounterDrugs/default.htm. Accessed 7 April 2015.
- FAQs About CDER. FDA website. www.fda.gov/AboutFDA/CentersOffices/OfficeofMedicalProductsandTobacco/CDER/FAQsaboutCDER/default.htm. Accessed 7 April 2015.
- Development and Approval Process (Drugs) FDA website. www.fda.gov/drugs/developmentapprovalprocess/default.htm. Accessed 07 April 2015.
- FDA MAPP 6020.5R Good Review Practice: OND Review Management of INDs and NDAs for Nonprescription Drug Products. FDA website. http://www.fda.gov/downloads/aboutfda/centersoffices/cder/manualofpoliciesprocedures/ucm082003.pdf.. Accessed 7 April 2015.
- *Guidance for Industry: Label Comprehension Studies for Nonprescription Drug Products* (August 2010). FDA website. http://www.fda.gov/downloads/drugs/guidancecomplianceregulatoryinformation/guidances/ucm143834.pdf. Accessed 7 April 2015.
- *Guidance for Industry: Postmarketing Adverse Event Reporting for Nonprescription Human Drug Products Marketed Without an Approved Application* (July 2009). FDA website. http://www.fda.gov/downloads/Drugs/.../Guidances/ucm171672.pdf. Accessed 7 April 2015.
- *Guidance for Industry: Time and Extent Applications for Nonprescription Drug Products* (September 2011). FDA website. http://www.fda.gov/downloads/Drugs/Guidances/ucm078902.pdf. Accessed 7 April 2015.
- *Guidance for Industry: Labeling OTC Human DrugProducts—Questions and Answers* (December 2008). FDA website. http://www.fda.gov/

downloads/drugs/guidancecomplianceregulatoryinformation/guidances/ucm078792.pdf. Accessed 7 April 2015.

- *Guidance for Industry: Contents of a Complete Submission for the Evaluation of Proprietary Names* (February 2010). FDA website. http://www.fda.gov/downloads/drugs/guidancecomplianceregulatoryinformation/guidances/ucm075068.pdf. Accessed 7 April 2015.

Chapter 18

Prescription Drug Labeling, Advertising and Promotion

Updated by Mitchell E. Parrish, JD, CIP, RAC

OBJECTIVES

- ❑ Understand the scope of FDA's regulatory authority over prescription drug labeling and advertising
- ❑ Learn general FDA requirements for prescription drug labeling, advertising and promotion
- ❑ Recognize the importance of agency enforcement actions pertaining to prescription drug labeling, advertising and promotion

LAWS, REGULATIONS AND GUIDELINES COVERED IN THIS CHAPTER

- ❑ *Federal Food, Drug, and Cosmetic Act* of 1938
- ❑ *Federal Trade Commission Act* of 1914
- ❑ *Kefauver-Harris Drug Amendments* of 1962
- ❑ 21 CFR 99 Dissemination of information on unapproved/new uses for marketed drugs, biologics and devices
- ❑ 21 CFR 200.5 General; mailing of important information about drugs
- ❑ 21 CFR 201 Labeling
- ❑ 21 CFR 201.56 Labeling; requirements on content and format of labeling for human prescription drug and biological products
- ❑ 21 CFR 201.57 Labeling; specific requirements on content and format of labeling for human prescription drug and biological products described in 201.56(b)(1)
- ❑ 21 CFR 202 Prescription drug advertising
- ❑ 21 CFR 203 Prescription drug marketing
- ❑ 21 CFR 208 Medication Guides for prescription drug products
- ❑ 21 CFR 312.7 Investigational new drug application; promotion of investigational drugs
- ❑ 21 CFR 314.50(l)(i) Applications for FDA approval to market a new drug; content and format; labeling
- ❑ 21 CFR 314.70 Applications for FDA approval to market a new drug; supplements and other changes to an approved application
- ❑ 21 CFR 314.81(b)(2)(iii) Applications for FDA approval to market a new drug; reporting requirements; annual report; labeling

- ❑ 21 CFR 314.81(b)(3)(i) Applications for FDA approval to market a new drug; reporting requirements; other reporting; advertisements and promotional labeling
- ❑ 21 CFR 314.126 Applications for FDA approval to market a new drug; adequate and well-controlled studies
- ❑ 21 CFR 314.550 Applications for FDA approval to market a new drug; promotional materials
- ❑ 21 CFR 601.12(f)(4) Licensing; changes to an approved application; labeling changes; advertisements and promotional labeling
- ❑ 21 CFR 601.45 Licensing; promotional materials
- ❑ *Guidance for Industry: Dosage and Administration Section of Labeling for Human Prescription Drug and Biological Products—*Content and Format (March 2010)
- ❑ *Guidance for Industry: Warnings and Precautions, Contraindications, and Boxed Warnings Sections of Labeling for Human Prescription Drug and Biological Products—Content and Format* (October 2011)
- ❑ *Guidance for Industry: Adverse Reactions Section of Labeling for Human Prescription Drug and Biological Products—Content and Format* (January 2006)
- ❑ *Draft Guidance for Industry: Clinical Pharmacology Labeling for Human Prescription Drug and Biological Products—Considerations, Content, and Format* (August 2014)
- ❑ *Guidance for Industry: Clinical Studies Section of Labeling for Human Prescription Drug and Biological Products—Content and Format* (January 2006)
- ❑ *Guidance for Industry: Content and Format for Geriatric Labeling* (October 2001)
- ❑ *Guidance for Industry: Warnings and Precautions, Contraindications, and Boxed Warning Sections of Labeling for Human Prescription Drug and Biological Products—Content and Format* (October 2011)
- ❑ *Guidance for Industry and Review Staff: Labeling for Human Prescription Drug and Biological Products—Determining Established Pharmacologic Class for Use in the Highlights of Prescribing Information* (October 2009)
- ❑ *Guidance for Industry: Labeling for Human Prescription Drug and Biological Products—Implementing the PLR Content and Format Requirements* (February 2013)
- ❑ *Draft Guidance for Industry and Review Staff: Pediatric Information Incorporated Into Human Prescription Drug and Biological Products Labeling* (February 2013)
- ❑ *Guidance for Industry: Providing Regulatory Submissions in Electronic Format—Content of Labeling* (April 2005)
- ❑ *Guidance: Medication Guides—Distribution Requirements and Inclusion in Risk Evaluation and Mitigation Strategies (REMS)* (November 2011)
- ❑ *Draft Guidance for Industry: Public Availability of Labeling Changes in "Changes Being Effected" Supplements* (September 2006)
- ❑ *Guidance for Industry: Patient-Reported Outcome Measures: Use in Medical Product Development to Support Labeling Claims* (December 2009)
- ❑ *Guidance for Industry: Indexing Structured Product Labeling* (June 2008)
- ❑ *Draft Guidance for Industry: SPL Standard for Content of Labeling Technical Qs & As* (October 2009)
- ❑ *Guidance for Industry: Providing Regulatory Submissions in Electronic Format—Drug Establishment Registration and Drug Listing* (May 2009)
- ❑ *Draft Guidance for Industry: Accelerated Approval Products—Submission of Promotional Materials* (March 1999)
- ❑ *Guidance for Industry: Aerosol Steroid Product Safety Information in Prescription Drug Advertising and Promotional Labeling* (December 1997)

- ❑ *Revised Draft Guidance for Industry: Brief Summary and Adequate Directions for Use: Disclosing Risk Information in Consumer-Directed Print Advertisements and Promotional Labeling for Human Prescription Drugs* (February 2015)
- ❑ *Guidance for Industry: Consumer-Directed Broadcast Advertisements* (August 1999)
- ❑ *Guidance for Industry and FDA Staff: Dear Health Care Provider Letters: Improving Communication of Important Safety Information* (January 2014)
- ❑ *Draft Guidance for Industry: "Help-Seeking" and Other Disease Awareness Communications by or on Behalf of Drug and Device Firms* (January 2004)
- ❑ *Guidance for Industry: Industry-Supported Scientific and Educational Activities* (November 1997)
- ❑ *Guidance for Industry: Product Name Placement, Size, and Prominence in Advertising and Promotional Labeling* (January 2012)
- ❑ *Draft Guidance for Industry: Product Name Placement, Size, and Prominence in Advertising and Promotional Labeling—Revision 1* (November 2013)
- ❑ *Draft Guidance for Industry: Promoting Medical Products in a Changing Healthcare Environment; I. Medical Product Promotion by Healthcare Organizations or Pharmacy Management Companies (PBMs)* (December 1997)
- ❑ *Draft Guidance for Industry: Providing Regulatory Submissions in Electronic Format—Prescription Drug Advertising and Promotional Labeling* (January 2001)
- ❑ *Draft Guidance for Industry: Using FDA-Approved Patient Labeling in Consumer-Directed Print Advertisements* (April 2001)
- ❑ *Guidance for Industry: Good Reprint Practices for the Distribution of Medical Journal Articles and Medical or Scientific Reference Publications on Unapproved New Uses of Approved Drugs and Approved or Cleared Medical Devices* (January 2009)
- ❑ *Draft Guidance for Industry: Presenting Risk Information in Prescription Drug and Medical Device Promotion* (May 2009)
- ❑ *Draft Guidance for Industry: Direct-to-Consumer Television Advertisements—FDAAA DTC Television Ad Pre-Dissemination Review Program* (March 2012)
- ❑ *PhRMA Code on Interactions with Healthcare Professionals* (July 2008, effective January 2009)
- ❑ *PhRMA Guiding Principles: Direct to Consumer Advertisements About Prescription Medicines* (December 2008)
- ❑ *Draft Guidance for Industry: Labeling for Human Prescription Drug and Biological Products Approved Under the Accelerated Approval Regulatory Pathway* (March 2014)
- ❑ *Draft Guidance for Industry: Fulfilling Regulatory Requirements for Postmarketing Submissions of Interactive Promotional Media for Prescription Human and Animal Drugs and Biologics* (January 2014)
- ❑ *Draft Guidance for Industry: Internet/Social Media Platforms with Character Space Limitations—Presenting Risk and Benefit Information for Prescription Drugs and Medical Devices* (June 2014)
- ❑ *Draft Guidance for Industry: Internet/Social Media Platforms: Correcting Independent Third-Party Misinformation About Prescription Drugs and Medical Devices* (June 2014)
- ❑ *Draft Guidance for Industry: Distributing Scientific and Medical Publications on risk Information for Approved Prescription Drugs and Biological Products—Recommended Practices* (June 2014)
- ❑ *Guidance for Industry: Patient Counseling Information Section of Labeling for Human Prescription Drug and Biological Products* (December 2014)
- ❑ *Draft Guidance for Industry: Abuse-Deterrent Opioids – Evaluation and Labeling* (January 2013)

- ❑ *Guidance for Industry: Consumer-Directed Broadcast Advertisements* (April 2002)
- ❑ *Guidance for Industry: Toll-Free Number Labeling and Related Requirements for Over-the-Counter and Prescription Drugs Marketed With Approved Applications* (June 2012)
- ❑ *Draft Guidance for Industry: Responding to Unsolicited Requests for Off-Label Information About Prescription Drugs and Medical Devices* (December 2011)
- ❑ *Draft Guidance for Industry: Drug Interaction Studies—Study Design, Data Analysis, Implications for Dosing, and Labeling Recommendations* (February 2012)
- ❑ *Draft Guidance for Industry: Safety Considerations for Container Labels and Carton Labeling Design to Minimize Medication Errors* (April 2013)
- ❑ *Draft Guidance for Industry: Pregnancy, Lactation, and Reproductive Potential: Labeling for Human Prescription Drug and Biologics Products* (December 2014)

Introduction

The *Federal Food, Drug, and Cosmetic Act* of 1938 (*FD&C Act*) grants the US Food and Drug Administration (FDA) broad authority over prescription drug labeling and advertising. Labeling includes the product's actual "label" affixed to its container, as well as the broader term "labeling" encompassing any words or graphics on the drug product, on its containers or wrappers, or any material issued in association with the drug. Advertising includes advertisements intended to overtly sell a drug product to consumers, as well as promotional material called "promotional labeling." Such labeling is any material intended to promote the use of a drug and typically is directed at physicians through various media such as product detail aids, displays at professional conventions, booklets, videotapes and even oral statements by sales representatives.

FDA is responsible for protecting and advancing public health and upholds its responsibility on both fronts by ensuring prescription drug information is truthful, balanced and communicated accurately. A misinformed consumer and physician create the potential for serious injury, while a well-informed consumer and physician are empowered to make better informed health decisions.

Summary of Labeling Requirements

There are specific requirements for labels and labeling. Explicit container label requirements are discussed below as well as labeling requirements for professional and patient labeling. No matter the requirements, FDA requires submission of labeling content in a predetermined electronic format.

Electronic Labeling, Including Structured Product Labeling (SPL)

FDA requires the submission of "content of labeling" in electronic format for initial New Drug Application (NDA) submissions (21 CFR 314.50(l)), labeling supplements and Annual Reports for approved NDAs (21 CFR 314.81(b)). "Content of labeling" is defined as the complete professional labeling, including all text, tables and figures.

SPL is the electronic document markup standard adopted by FDA as the mechanism for electronic submission of the content of labeling. The SPL standard uses the extensible markup language (XML) file format with specifications (schema and controlled terminology) as defined by FDA's Data Standards Council. Additional information on SPL, including both technical and nontechnical guidance, can be found on FDA's Structured Product Labeling Resources website (www.fda.gov/ForIndustry/DataStandards/StructuredProductLabeling/default.htm).

General Label Requirements (21 CFR 201 Subparts A and B)

Some of the most broadly applicable label requirements are:

- manufacturer, packager or distributor's name and address (21 CFR 201.1)
- location of National Drug Code (NDC) number (requested but not required) (21 CFR 201.2) (note: the determination of NDC numbers is included in 21 CFR 207.35)
- statement of ingredients (21 CFR 201.10), including required warning statements for specific ingredients (e.g., FD&C Yellow No. 5 (21 CFR 201.20))
- location of expiration date (21 CFR 201.17) and significance of control numbers (21 CFR 201.18)
- bar code label requirements (21 CFR 201.25)
- statement of identity (21 CFR 201.50)
- declaration of net quantity of contents (21 CFR 201.51)
- statement of dosage (21 CFR 201.55)

The appropriate label content placement and prominence also are key concerns in FDA's regulation of drug labeling (21 CFR 201.10). Apart from FDA, the US Pharmacopeia sets voluntary standards for prescription container labels and the Institute for Safe Medicine Practices recommends the following for labels:

- words typed in easy-to-read 12-point type

- the patient's name, drug name and drug instructions in the largest letters, prominently displayed at the top of the label
- warnings typed directly onto labels
- images or physical descriptions of the pills in the container
- no extra zeroes (5.0 mg could be misread as 50 mg)
- the dispensing pharmacy's information

Package Insert and the *Physician Labeling Rule*

The drug product's professional labeling, or package insert, is a compilation of product information based on FDA's comprehensive review of the sponsor's approved NDA or Biologics License Application (BLA). The package insert is considered "adequate directions for use," written to direct healthcare professionals in their use of a drug product.

Requirements intended to assist healthcare professionals' ability to access, read and use the package insert are known as the *Physician Labeling Rule* (*PLR*) (21 CFR 201.56 and 201.57) The *PLR* format includes three main sections:

- Highlights of Prescribing Information—intended to provide the prescriber with one location to find the information they most commonly refer to and consider most important
- Full Prescribing Information: Contents—a "table of contents" for the Full Prescribing Information (FPI)
- FPI—in fixed numbered sections

The *PLR* format also requires inclusion of contact information to help make reporting adverse events easier.

FDA has issued several guidance documents articulating standards for the content of professional labeling. As with the rest of the *PLR* initiatives, the goal of these guidance documents is to provide standards for the development of clear, concise and useful prescribing information. In February 2013, FDA published the final *Guidance for Industry: Labeling for Human Prescription Drug and Biological Products—Implementing the PLR Content and Format Requirements*. An overview of the *PLR* format, associated regulations and available guidance documents are provided in **Table 18-1**.

Also notable is the *PLR* regulations establish minimum requirements for font size and certain other graphic elements (21 CFR 201.57(d)). These requirements vary depending on the intended use of the labeling (e.g., whether labeling is to accompany the drug product or is for use in accompanying promotional materials). See *Guidance for Industry: Labeling for Human Prescription Drug and Biological Products—Implementing the New Content and Format Requirements* (February 2013) for additional information. The guidance also sets forth requirements for labeling format, including the Package Insert highlights section, to address changes or updates to labeling. For example, major changes within the past 12 months to boxed warnings, indications and usage, dosage and administration, contraindications and warnings must be listed in the highlights section as well as within the body of the FPI.

Professional labeling for all drugs approved after June 2001 (or for which an efficacy supplement was approved after June 2001) must be converted to the new *PLR* format (21 CFR 201.56(c)). In addition, for drug products approved in June 2006 or later, efficacy supplements may necessitate revisions of the labeling to the *PLR* format; however, as a general rule, bioequivalence or CMC supplements would not trigger a revision. See the February 2013 guidance for a complete list of the types of supplements that require conversion to the *PLR* format.

Since converting a product's professional labeling from the old format to *PLR* format is a difficult and time-consuming process, FDA suggests manufacturers develop new sections; assess whether new information warrants a re-analysis of data or new studies to avoid being misleading; and systematically evaluate labeling information to identify and revise and/or remove unsubstantiated claims and outdated information.

FDA has instituted a staggered implementation schedule, prioritizing label revision from the most recently approved products to older products. The deadline for submitting revised labeling to meet the new requirement is based on the date of the most recent NDA efficacy supplement (or the original approval, if no approved efficacy supplements have been submitted). However, manufacturers are encouraged to convert product labeling into the *PLR* format voluntarily. In any case, all label conversions must be submitted as Prior Approval Supplements. A table outlining FDA's implementation schedule is provided in Appendix A of the above-mentioned February 2013 guidance.

Patient Labeling, Including Medication Guides

Patient labeling is product information derived from professional labeling, written in consumer-friendly language. Patient labeling usually focuses on directions for use and risks associated with the product. For certain products determined by FDA to pose serious and significant risks, the agency may require a patient Medication Guide (21 CFR 208).

All Medication Guides must comply with specific content and format requirements (21 CFR 208.20), including a type size no smaller than 10 point. In addition, Medication Guides must be distributed to patients each time the prescription drug product is dispensed (21 CFR 208.24). Because a manufacturer cannot be present when each prescription is distributed, the manufacturer is required to ensure adequate means exist for dispensers

Table 18-1. *PLR* Format, Associated Regulations and Guidance Documents

PLR Format	Associated Regulations/Guidance (if any)
Overall	21 CFR 201.56 and 21 CFR 201.57 *Guidance for Industry: Labeling for Human Prescription Drug and Biological Products—Implementing the PLR Content and Format Requirements* (February 2013)
Highlights of Prescribing Information Product Names, Other Required Information Boxed Warning Recent Major Changes Indications and Usage Dosage and Administration Dosage Forms and Strengths Contraindications Warnings and Precautions Adverse Reactions Drug Interactions Use in Specific Populations	21 CFR 201.57(a) *Guidance for Industry: Labeling for Human Prescription Drug and Biological Products—Implementing the PLR Content and Format Requirements* (February 2013) *Guidance for Industry and Review Staff: Labeling for Human Prescription Drug and Biological Products—Determining Established Pharmacologic Class for Use in the Highlights of Prescribing Information* (October 2009)
Full Prescribing Information: Contents	21 CFR 201.57(b)
Full Prescribing Information	21 CFR 201.57(c)
Boxed Warning (if applicable)	21 CFR 201.57(c)(1) *Guidance for Industry: Warnings and Precautions, Contraindications, and Boxed Warning Sections of Labeling for Human Prescription Drug and Biological Products—Content and Format* (October 2011) *Guidance for Industry: Labeling for Human Prescription Drug and Biological Products—Implementing the PLR Content and Format Requirements* (February 2013)
Indications and Usage	21 CFR 201.57(c)(2) *Guidance for Industry: Labeling for Human Prescription Drug and Biological Products—Implementing the PLR Content and Format Requirements* (February 2013)
Dosage and Administration	21 CFR 201.57(c)(3) *Guidance for Industry: Dosage and Administration Section of Labeling for Human Prescription Drug and Biological Products—Content and Format* (March 2010) *Guidance for Industry: Labeling for Human Prescription Drug and Biological Products—Implementing the PLR Content and Format Requirements* (February 2013)
Dosage Forms and Strengths	21 CFR 201.57(c)(4) *Guidance for Industry: Labeling for Human Prescription Drug and Biological Products—Implementing the PLR Content and Format Requirements* (February 2013)
Contraindications	21 CFR 201.57(c)(5) *Guidance for Industry: Warnings and Precautions, Contraindications, and Boxed Warning Sections of Labeling for Human Prescription Drug and Biological Products—Content and Format* (October 2011) *Guidance for Industry: Labeling for Human Prescription Drug and Biological Products—Implementing the PLR Content and Format Requirements* (February 2013)
Warnings and Precautions	21 CFR 201.57(c)(6) *Guidance for Industry: Warnings and Precautions, Contraindications, and Boxed Warning Sections of Labeling for Human Prescription Drug and Biological Products—Content and Format* (October 2011) *Guidance for Industry: Labeling for Human Prescription Drug and Biological Products—Implementing the PLR Content and Format Requirements* (February 2013)
Adverse Reactions	21 CFR 201.57(c)(7) *Guidance for Industry: Adverse Reactions Section of Labeling for Human Prescription Drug and Biological Products—Content and Format* (January 2006) *Guidance for Industry: Labeling for Human Prescription Drug and Biological Products—Implementing the PLR Content and Format Requirements* (February 2013)
Drug Interactions	21 CFR 201.57(c)(8) *Guidance for Industry: Labeling for Human Prescription Drug and Biological Products—Implementing the PLR Content and Format Requirements* (February 2013)
Use in Specific Populations	21 CFR 201.57(c)(9) *Guidance for Industry: Content and Format for Geriatric Labeling* (October 2001) *Guidance for Industry: Labeling for Human Prescription Drug and Biological Products—Implementing the PLR Content and Format Requirements* (February 2013) *Draft Guidance for Industry and Review Staff: Pediatric Information Incorporated Into Human Prescription Drug and Biological Products Labeling* (February 2013)

PLR Format	Associated Regulations/Guidance (if any)
Drug Abuse and Dependence	21 CFR 201.57(c)(10)
Overdosage	21 CFR 201.57(c)(11)
Description	21 CFR 201.57(c)(12)
Clinical Pharmacology	21 CFR 201.57(c)(13) *Draft Guidance for Industry: Clinical Pharmacology Labeling for Human Prescription Drug and Biological Products—Considerations, Content, and Format* (August 2014)
Nonclinical Toxicology	21 CFR 201.57(c)(14)
Clinical Studies	21 CFR 201.57(c)(15) *Guidance for Industry: Clinical Studies Section of Labeling for Human Prescription Drug and Biological Products—Content and Format* (January 2009)
References	21 CFR 201.57(c)(16)
How Supplied/Storage and Handling	21 CFR 201.57(c)(17)
Patient Counseling Information	21 CFR 201.57(c)(18) *Guidance for Industry: Labeling for Human Prescription Drug and Biological Products—Implementing the PLR Content and Format Requirements* (February 2013)
Medication Guide (if applicable)	21 CFR 208 *Guidance: Medication Guides—Distribution Requirements and Inclusion in Risk Evaluation and Mitigation Strategies (REMS)* (November 2011)

themselves to comply with the requirement. (This usually is achieved by providing sufficient numbers of printed Medication Guides with each unit of drug product.) FDA clarifies its expectations for the distribution of Medication Guides in its *Guidance for Industry: Medication Guides—Distribution Requirements and Inclusion in Risk Evaluation and Minimization Strategies (REMS)* (November 2011).

Labeling Changes

Any changes to approved drug product labeling are considered a change to the NDA or BLA and are required to be reported to FDA according to the regulations governing supplements to an approved application (21 CFR 314.70). FDA has the authority to require approved NDA holders to make safety-related labeling changes based on new safety information that becomes available after a drug's approval. NDA holders have a limited time to respond and implement these FDA-requested labeling changes (see Section 505(o)(4) of the *FD&C Act* for details).

Summary of Prescription Drug Promotion and Advertising

No Preapproval Promotion

According to 21 CFR 312.7, sponsors or investigators "shall not represent in a promotional context that an investigational new drug is safe or effective for the purposes for which it is under investigation."

The only exceptions to the prohibition on preapproval promotion are disease-state-only promotion, institutional promotion (which links the name of the drug manufacturer with a field of research), and "Coming Soon" promotions. "Coming Soon" advertisements reveal only the name of a product that will be available soon, without any written, verbal or graphic suggestions of potential indications or safety or effectiveness claims. During the preapproval period, a company may choose one of these types of promotional campaigns but may not switch back and forth between them. The reason is if a disease awareness campaign is underway for a time (e.g., "Company X is involved in research in the field of diabetes" followed by a "Coming Soon from Company X: Product Y" campaign), the audience could link the name of the drug with the disease state, which is considered tantamount to preapproval promotion. FDA's *Draft Guidance for Industry: "Help-Seeking" and Other Disease Awareness Communications by or on Behalf of Drug and Device Firms* provides clarification on FDA's thinking about preapproval promotion.

Submission and Preclearance of Promotional Materials

With only one exception, all promotional materials must be submitted to the Office of Prescription Drug Promotion (OPDP) at the time of their initial publication or dissemination using Form FDA 2253 (21 CFR 314.81).

Manufacturers of products approved under Subpart H (Accelerated Approval of New Drugs for Serious or Life- Threatening Illnesses) are required to submit drafts of all promotional labeling for advisory comment at least 30 days prior to dissemination (21 CFR 314.550 and 601.45). Additionally, for products anticipated to receive accelerated approval during the NDA preapproval review period, all promotional materials intended to be used in the first 120 days following marketing approval must be submitted to OPDP for advisory review prior to the drug's approval. For additional details about the submission of promotional materials for accelerated approval products, see *Draft Guidance for Industry: Accelerated Approval Products—Submission of Promotional Materials* (March 1999).

For drugs approved under standard conditions, common industry practice (although not required) is to submit a drug's launch materials to OPDP for advisory comment. OPDP pays careful attention to launch materials during the first year after a drug's approval. For example, OPDP has issued a letter to a company for violations found in a promotional launch journal advertisement, taking issue with claims such as "novel," "next generation" and "unique." The company was asked to pull the advertisement and run a corrective advertising campaign. Another company received an Untitled Letter from OPDP for a branded story that was part of the launch campaign. The branded story included a patient testimonial that overstated efficacy, omitted key information and minimized important risk information. Although a company spokeswoman told the press the patient testimonial was never circulated to the public, this did not stop the FDA letter.

Additionally, while not required, it is common industry practice to send direct-to-consumer television advertisements to OPDP for preclearance prior to dissemination. OPDP's website explains the submission process for preclearance of TV ads and other materials.

Substantial Evidence Standard

Promotional materials may not suggest a use of the product that is not approved or otherwise permitted for use in FDA-approved labeling (i.e., FPI). This is referred to as "off-label" use of a product.

In addition to the "on label" requirement, promotional materials may not suggest a drug is better, safer or more effective than has been demonstrated by "substantial evidence." Generally, FDA's standard for "substantial evidence" in support of a drug product claim is two adequate and well-controlled clinical trials (21 CFR 314.126). Although certain claims may be allowable based on a single study, OPDP has on numerous occasions articulated the requirement for two studies for claims of product superiority.

Even if product claims are "on-label," if the claims (either overt or implied) are not supported by substantial evidence, FDA will consider the materials to be misleading and therefore violative. Although the regulations in 21 CFR 202.1(e)(6) and (7) detail the general principles by which FDA will evaluate whether or not promotional materials are misleading (e.g., failure to reveal material facts or improper use of graphics or statistics), reviewing OPDP enforcement letters is the best way to learn the agency's expectations in this area.

Fair Balance

All effectiveness claims in prescription drug advertising and promotion must be accompanied by information about the product's risks, and the risk information must have comparable prominence to the promotional claims (21 CFR 202.1(e)(5)). This commonly is known as "fair balance." The omission or minimization of risk information is the most commonly cited concern in OPDP's enforcement letters.

OPDP considers many factors when determining fair balance, including whether the safety and efficacy messages have equal prominence, typography and layout, contrast and white space or other methods used to achieve emphasis (21 CFR 202.1(e)(7)(viii)). In addition, if promotional material is directed to a consumer audience, the fair balance information should be written in consumer-friendly language.

FDA's 2009 draft guidance, *Guidance for Industry: Presenting Risk Information in Prescription Drug and Medical Device Promotion*, sheds more light on factors the agency considers when evaluating the presentation of risk information in advertisements and promotional labeling. This draft guidance includes many helpful, concrete examples to illustrate FDA's thinking on this important topic.

Product Name Placement, Size and Prominence

Promotional labeling must include a reference to the established (generic) name of the drug, per 21 CFR 202.1(b)(1). The regulations require the most prominent mention of the brand name to be accompanied by the generic name "in letters at least half as large as the letters comprising the proprietary name or designation with which it is joined." In January 2012, FDA issued *Guidance for Industry: Product Name Placement, Size, and Prominence in Advertising and Promotional Labeling* to clarify issues in this area.

Advertising

Brief Summary Requirement

The 21 CFR 202(l) regulations differentiate materials constituting advertising from other forms of promotional labeling. The regulations require prescription drug advertising to contain a "[t]rue statement of information in brief summary relating to side effects, contraindications, and effectiveness" (21 CFR 202.1(e)). Promotional labeling that is not an advertisement must be disseminated with a copy of the FPI.

In February 2015, FDA issued *Revised Draft Guidance for Industry: Brief Summary and Adequate Directions for Use: Disclosing Risk Information in Consumer-Directed Print Advertisements and Promotional Labeling for Human Prescription Drugs* to explain the agency's expectations regarding the brief summary in print advertisements directed to consumers. Like "fair balance," FDA encourages sponsors to write a brief summary for consumer pieces in easily understandable language. FDA also recommends sponsors include a statement in the advertisement reminding consumers the risk information is not comprehensive, and sponsors should provide a toll-free telephone number or website where more information can be found.

Direct-To-Consumer (DTC) Advertising

Consumer-directed broadcast advertisements (i.e., television and radio) must include a "major statement" of the product's primary risks, in the audio portion and, for television, in the video portion of the advertisement. In addition, the advertisement should make "adequate provision...for dissemination of the approved or permitted package labeling in connection with the broadcast presentation" (21CFR 202.1(e)(1)). This sometimes is referred to as the "adequate provision" requirement and, in August 1999, FDA issued *Draft Guidance for Industry: Consumer-Directed Broadcast Advertisements* to clarify the approach manufacturers may take to fulfill the requirement. As noted previously, most companies submit their television advertisements to FDA for advisory comment prior to broadcast. To learn more about submitting DTC television advertisements for pre-dissemination review, consult the March 2012 *Draft Guidance for Industry: Direct-to-Consumer Television Advertisements—FDAAA DTC Television Ad Pre-Dissemination Review Program.*

In addition to other requirements, *FDAAA* requires published DTC advertisements to include the following statement printed in conspicuous text: "You are encouraged to report negative side effects of prescription drugs to the FDA. Visit www.fda.gov/Safety/MedWatch/default.htm, or call 1-800-FDA-1088."

Reminder Advertisements and Items

An exception to the brief summary requirement and certain other advertisement requirements is reminder labeling (commonly known as "reminder advertisements"), which according to 21 CFR 201.100(f), "calls attention to the name of the drug product but does not include indications or dosage recommendations for use... containing no representation or suggestion relating to the drug product." Reminder advertisements are not permitted for products carrying a boxed warning in their labeling. Reminder advertisements are exempt from risk disclosure requirements because they historically were designed to remind healthcare professionals of a product's availability. Healthcare professionals presumably know the name of a product, its use and its risks.

In the past, it was common practice for pharmaceutical companies to give away reminder items. In July 2008, the Pharmaceutical Research and Manufacturers of America (PhRMA) issued an updated PhRMA Code on Interactions with Healthcare Professionals (PhRMA Code) addressing the topic of reminder items. The Advanced Medical Technology Association (AdvaMed) issued similar guidelines to medical device manufacturers.

The PhRMA Code, which is a voluntary non-regulatory standard, prohibits distribution of non-educational and practice-related promotional materials, including such reminder items as pens, notepads and mugs with product logos on them, even if the item is of minimal value and related to the healthcare professional's work or for the benefit of the patient. Most manufacturers have adopted the PhRMA Code voluntarily and no longer give away reminder items.

Help-Seeking, Bulk Sale and Compounding Drug Advertising

Another exception to the brief summary requirement and certain advertisement requirements includes "help-seeking advertisements," bulk-sale and compounding drug advertisements. A help-seeking advertisement is intended to inform consumers about a specific medical condition and encourage them to talk to their healthcare professionals about the condition. These advertisements must not mention any product name or imply a certain prescription drug is intended to treat the medical condition. In January 2004, FDA issued *Draft Guidance for Industry: "Help-Seeking" and Other Disease Awareness Communications by or on Behalf of Drug and Device Firms.* The draft guidance indicates FDA does not regulate help-seeking advertisements because no drug product is mentioned or implied and hence, no FDA-regulated product is involved.

Bulk-sale drugs intended to be used for further processing or manufacturing also are exempt from the Brief Summary requirement, as are drugs sold to pharmacies for the purpose of compounding. As with help-seeking advertisements, neither bulk-sale drugs nor compounding drugs are permitted to make safety or efficacy claims (21 CFR 202.1(e)(2)(ii) and (iii)).

Promotion

Pharmacoeconomic Claims and Promotion to Formulary Decision Makers

Pharmaceutical companies may promote their drug products to formularies or other related entities primarily responsible for managed care coverage and reimbursement decisions. This kind of promotion often focuses on healthcare economic information (pharmacoeconomic claims).

Section 114 of *FDAAA* provides for a legal mechanism to allow the promotion of pharmacoeconomic claims using a less-stringent standard than the "substantial evidence" standard described above. The law states pharmacoeconomic claims may be made based on "competent and reliable" evidence, as long as the information relates directly to an approved indication and is provided only to formularies or other similar managed care decision makers.

Press Releases

Press releases often cause confusion over where the appropriate regulatory jurisdiction lies. Typically, the Securities and Exchange Commission (SEC) regulates how information is communicated to the investment community. Nevertheless, FDA believes product-specific press releases fall under its promotional regulations, thus requiring fair balance and avoiding false or misleading content or preapproval promotion. Many companies have received Warning Letters and Untitled Letters from OPDP for violative statements in their press releases. In February 2013, a company received an Untitled Letter for a video press release. The release was cited for omission of risk information, an unsubstantiated superiority claim and inadequate communication of indication.

Product Detailing

Product detailing, including oral statements company representatives make about their firm's prescription drug products, is considered promotional labeling. While it is difficult for FDA to monitor conversations, OPDP has issued Warning Letters and Untitled Letters to companies for presentations made to healthcare professionals by sales representatives. FDA also has issued letters to companies for professional telephone scripts. In July 2014, a company received an Untitled Letter citing its script as omitting risk information and material facts and inadequately disclosing the product's name in direct conjunction with the proprietary name.

Historically, many conversations resulting in enforcement letters have occurred and been overheard at exhibit halls at major medical meetings. This is an enforcement area for OPDP, and FDA representatives may attend major medical meetings and pay close attention to activities in the exhibit halls, including collecting materials passed out at the meetings.

Reprints

FDA-cleared or approved prescription drugs, biologics and medical devices frequently are the subject of medical research, with study results typically published in medical journals, textbooks and other scientific reference publications. Often these studies describe or suggest product uses that go beyond the PI to include "off-label" use. Since manufacturers must limit product promotion to only approved, labeled uses, the promotional use of reprints can be challenging.

FDA helped address the appropriate use of reprints by publishing *Guidance for Industry on Good Reprint Practices for the Distribution of Medical Journal Articles and Medical or Scientific Reference Publications on Unapproved New Uses of Approved Drugs and Approved or Cleared Medical Devices (Good Reprint Practices Guidance)* (January 2009). This guidance describes the kind of material FDA considers a true reprint (e.g., one that is peer-reviewed versus a publication funded by the manufacturer), what information should accompany a reprint and appropriate dissemination of reprints.

Internet and Social Media

The Internet—from specific drug websites, to sponsored links, to social media sites—commonly is used for prescription drug promotion. OPDP's predecessor, the Division of Drug Marketing, Advertising and Communication (DDMAC), issued its first letter regarding a promotional website in 1996. FDA has never issued formal regulations, citing rapidly changing technology as the reason. However, FDA took its first step in addressing social media in June 2014 with the release of two draft guidances.

The first draft, *Guidance for Industry: Internet/Social Media Platforms with Character Space Limitations—Presenting Risk and Benefit Information for Prescription Drugs and Medical Devices,* provides recommendations for presenting benefit-risk information for prescription drugs or medical devices using media sources with character space limitations, such as Twitter and paid search results links on Google, Yahoo and Bing. The takeaway is, even if there are character space limitations, the promotion must satisfy FDA's fair balance requirement. Moreover, these character space-limited promotions should link consumers to a website containing a complete discussion of product risks.

The second draft, *Guidance for Industry: Internet/Social Media Platforms: Correcting Independent Third-Party Misinformation About Prescription Drugs and Medical Devices,* provides recommendations to companies that choose to correct third-party misinformation related to their own prescription drugs and medical devices (e.g., a manufacturer that chooses to correct inaccurate information about its product on a highly trafficked blog or Facebook page). The takeaway is manufacturers are not required to correct misinformation controlled by independent third parties. However, if manufacturers choose to correct such misinformation, they should follow FDA's recommendations to be relevant and responsive to the misinformation; be limited and tailored to the misinformation; be nonpromotional in nature, tone and presentation; and be consistent with the FDA-required product labeling.

While FDA's guidances are groundbreaking as the first two to enter the Internet/social media realm, the recommendations contained therein are limited in scope—a scope that does not communicate FDA's standards for online promotion. To determine such standards, regulatory professionals must continue to review the many examples of improper Internet promotion cited in OPDP enforcement letters to develop their own best judgment and practices for online promotion. Some notable examples include a letter for a video posted on YouTube (25 September 2008), a letter for a Facebook widget placed on a product site (29 July 2010), a letter for a video posted on WebMD (20 June 2012) and a letter for an online banner advertisement (31 July 2013). Even an FDA district office issued a Warning Letter in December 2012 to a company over Facebook "likes" of off-label content.

Product Promotion versus Scientific Exchange

FDA does distinguish between drug promotion and the exchange of scientific information. Truly independent and nonpromotional industry-supported activities serving as an exchange of scientific information, if done properly, may not be deemed promotional labeling, even if the information being exchanged is considered "off-label." Historically, manufacturers were involved in setting up continuing medical education (CME) programs to facilitate an exchange of scientific information. These events and the manufacturers organizing them fell under harsh scrutiny, however, when it was alleged the CME events were merely "dressed up product promotion."

In December 1997, FDA issued *Guidance for Industry: Industry-Supported Scientific and Educational Activities* to explain its thinking on this topic. This guidance still defines what is considered "nonpromotional" and "educational" and places great importance on keeping the scientific activity independent of influence from manufacturers.

Enforcement of Prescription Drug Promotion and Advertising

FDA has regulatory authority over the advertising and promotion for prescription drugs via the *FD&C Act* and monitors company promotional activity through OPDP. While the language in *FD&C Act* Section 502 is relatively brief and does not specifically define "advertising" or "promotion," FDA has interpreted the act broadly in its regulations and guidances covering drug advertising and promotion. With the passage of the 1962 *Kefauver-Harris Amendments*, the agency gained greater authority over prescription drug marketing. Regulations covering prescription drug promotion are found in 21 CFR 202 and are cross-referenced to 21 CFR 201.

If OPDP finds advertising or promotion to be violative, the agency has both administrative and judicial tools at its disposal for dealing with violations. FDA's administrative tools include issuing Notice of Violation (NOV) letters, often referred to as "Untitled Letters;" issuing Warning Letters; ordering a recall; and calling for the delay, suspension or withdrawal of a product approval. Of these, the most common administrative actions taken by FDA are NOVs and Warning Letters.

NOVs are different from Warning Letters in that they typically require the company to stop using the materials that make the claim(s) FDA finds violative. Warning Letters typically are addressed to the company CEO, with a warning FDA will take further action if the matter is not immediately addressed and corrected by the company. If the subject of the letter is a product advertisement, this correction typically is a remedial advertisement in each of the same venues where the violative advertisement was run. Warning Letters also may require the company to issue a "Dear Doctor" letter to physicians as described in both 21 CFR 200.5(c)(3) and the *Draft Guidance for Industry and FDA Staff: Dear Health Care Provider Letters: Improving Communication of Important Safety Information* (November 2010). All letters issued by OPDP are posted publicly on FDA's "Enforcement Activities" webpage and often include a copy of the violative promotion; this also serves as one of the most important tools in understanding OPDP's position on certain topics.

As in other areas of FDA enforcement, judicial tools at FDA's disposal include injunction, seizure or criminal prosecution. However, OPDP rarely seeks judicial action on its own for promotional violations. FDA is more likely to work with the Office of the Inspector General (OIG), Department of Justice (DOJ) or individual state's attorneys general in pursuing companies for significant promotional violations.

To supplement its enforcement activities, OPDP administers a program, started in 2010, called Truthful Prescription Drug Advertising and Promotion (or more commonly, the "Bad Ad" program). The stated goal of the Bad Ad program is to educate prescribers about their role in reporting false or misleading detailing by sales representatives and other forms of drug promotion to FDA. Since the inception of the Bad Ad Program, OPDP has attended a number of major medical meetings each year and continues to educate attendees about the Bad Ad Program. FDA distributes materials encouraging prescribers to recognize and report any activities and promotional messages they believe are false or misleading.

Enforcement by Agencies Beyond FDA

FDA is not the only agency closely tracking prescription drug advertising and related activities. Many other government agencies, including DOJ, the OIG in the Department of Health and Human Services (DHHS), states' attorneys general, the Federal Trade Commission (FTC) and Congress, closely monitor drug companies' activities.

Government enforcement efforts against the pharmaceutical industry in the US were enhanced greatly beginning in 2001. The original focus was suspected kickbacks and violations of the pricing statutes (the *Anti-Kickback Statute*).

This act makes it illegal for any person—e.g., healthcare provider, office manager or sales agent—to knowingly and willfully solicit, offer, pay or receive "remuneration" (including kickbacks, bribes, rebates or anything of value) directly or indirectly in cash or in kind to any person to induce or cause that person to prescribe a product for which payment may be made in whole or in part under a federal healthcare program (42 USC 1320a-7b).

More recently, government agencies have focused on off-label promotion by pharmaceutical and medical device manufacturers in connection with the *False Claims Act* (*FCA*). The *FCA* was born out of the Civil War when fraud was pervasive, particularly by defense contractors who unscrupulously sold bad goods (defective guns, putrid rations, etc.) to the US government and then sought payment for such goods. Under the *FCA*, an individual not affiliated with the government can bring a suit claiming fraud. In such cases, the person filing the claim is known as a "whistleblower."

While this legislation has undergone some changes over the years, the tenets remain the same: it is unlawful to knowingly present or cause to be presented to the US government a false claim for payment. Modern-day changes to the laws impose treble (triple) damages and civil fines of $5,000–$10,000 per false claim, among other things. In practical application today, whistleblowers, working with DOJ and states' attorneys general, have investigated and brought many high-profile claims against companies for off-label drug promotion, resulting in false claims for payment submitted to federal insurance programs, such as Medicare and Medicaid, which do not provide coverage for off-label uses. In these cases, each off-label prescription is considered one false claim. Many healthcare product manufacturers that settle FCA claims also agree to enter into Corporate Integrity Agreements (CIA) with DHHS, placing strict requirements on corporate compliance for a number of years.

In recent years, settlements have reached the billion dollar figure. In July 2012, the largest settlement in history was reached with a manufacturer over allegations the company engaged in unlawful promotion of some of its drugs, failed to report certain safety data and engaged in false price reporting practices. The company agreed to pay $3 billion and plead guilty to charges, which included introducing misbranded drugs into interstate commerce. The company also agreed to enter into a strict five-year CIA with DHHS. The CIA requires individual accountability of the company's executives and board of directors.

More recently, in February 2014, a DOJ settlement was reached with a manufacturer over a prescription drug's labeling and promotion. The allegations included lack of adequate directions for use and that certain sales representatives were instructed how to expand sales conversations with healthcare providers beyond the product's approved indication. While not in the billions, this approximately $192.7 million settlement was the largest in 2014.

Finally, manufacturers must consider their competition as they develop advertising and promotional materials. Competitors have brought suit against manufacturers for violations of the *Lanham Act*. While this legislation often is thought of in terms of trademark protection, it also allows manufacturers to sue competitors for false advertising. Manufacturers have used courts' interpretations of the act to bring suits charging comparative claims in advertising are false and misleading, they deceive a substantial part of the audience viewing the ads and the deception could influence purchasing decisions. If a plaintiff prevails on a *Lanham Act* false advertising claim, the court can not only bar the advertising but also can order corrective advertising or a product recall.

Summary

- Drug labeling includes the drug product's affixed container label as well as any material issued in association with the drug, including package inserts, patient labeling and Medication Guides.
- FDA requires the submission of labeling content in electronic format using Structured Product Labeling (SPL). SPL uses the extensible markup language (XML) file format that permits a standardized mechanism for exchanging drug information.
- Container labels must contain the specific content outlined in 21 CFR 201 and must display such content with appropriate placement and prominence.
- The package insert is for healthcare professionals and is intended to direct their use of a drug product. The *Physician Labeling Rule* guides the required format and content of package inserts for new drug products.
- Patient labeling is product information, usually taken from the package insert, but written in consumer-friendly language. A Medication Guide is a type of patient labeling for drugs with serious risks and is required to be distributed to the consumer each time a prescription is filled or refilled.
- Advertising includes advertisements and promotional material called "promotional labeling."
- FDA monitors prescription drug advertising and promotion through OPDP. No drug can be promoted until FDA has approved the NDA.
- All advertising and promotional labeling must be submitted at the time of first use with Form FDA 2253, except that for products receiving accelerated approval, which must be submitted for advisory opinion 30 days prior to initial dissemination. Although generally not required, it is strongly recommended launch materials and new television

advertisements be submitted to OPDP for advisory comment prior to dissemination.

- Promotional materials may not suggest a use for a drug that is not approved or otherwise permitted in FDA-approved labeling. Such use is "off-label" use. Additionally, materials cannot claim a product is safer or more effective than has been established by "substantial evidence." Such evidence typically is obtained through two adequate and well-controlled clinical trials. *FDAMA* Section 114 allows the distribution of pharmacoeconomic data using a less-stringent standard as long as certain requirements are met.
- All promotional materials must include a "fair balance" of efficacy and risk information, with the exception of reminder labeling (not allowed for products with a Boxed Warning).
- Prescription drug advertisements must contain a "brief summary" of the FPI, and broadcast advertisements must include a "major statement" of risk and make "adequate provision" for disseminating the drug's permitted labeling.
- Promotional labeling that is not an advertisement must be disseminated with a copy of the full FPI.
- Beyond traditional advertising, there are many ways to promote a prescription drug product, including press releases, oral statements by drug company representatives, reprints in medical journals and, more commonly, through the Internet and social media. In June 2014, FDA entered the social media space by issuing two draft guidances, one covering social media with character space limitations and the other addressing the correction of online drug product misinformation.
- FDA takes strict action to enforce its labeling and advertising regulations. Typical FDA enforcement actions include NOVs and Warning Letters. Although rarely used, the agency has other tools at its disposal to deal with violative advertising and promotional materials.
- FDA works with other agencies, such as the US Attorney's Office and OIG in prosecuting companies alleged to be in violation of the *FCA* or *Anti-Kickback Statute* through off-label promotion. Companies found in violation of the *FD&C Act, Anti-Kickback Statute* and/or *FCA* risk disbarment from participation in federal programs (e.g., Medicare), Corporate Integrity Agreements and large monetary fines.

Chapter 19

Pharmacovigilance and Risk Management

Updated By Treena Jackson, MS, CQA, CSSGB, RAC (US)

OBJECTIVES

- ❑ Understand reporting requirements for Investigational New Drug (IND) safety data
- ❑ Understand postmarketing requirements for safety data for drugs and biologics
- ❑ Understand postmarketing requirements for safety data for medical devices
- ❑ Understand requirements for Risk Evaluation and Mitigation Strategies (REMS)
- ❑ Understand requirements for proprietary name review of drugs and biologics

LAWS, REGULATIONS AND GUIDELINES COVERED IN THIS CHAPTER

- ❑ Center for Drug Evaluation and Research (CDER) Manual of Policies and Procedures (MAPP) 4151.3R3: Drug Safety Oversight Board (DSB)
- ❑ CDER MAPP 5240.8: Handling of Adverse Experience Reports and Other Generic Drug Postmarketing Reports
- ❑ CDER MAPP 6004.2R: Procedures for Completing and Processing the Form "Annual Status Report Review Form: PMR and PMC Summary"
- ❑ CDER MAPP 6010.R: Responsibilities for Tracking and Communicating the Status of Postmarketing Requirements and Commitments
- ❑ CDER MAPP 6010.9: Procedures and Responsibilities for Developing Postmarketing Requirements and Commitments
- ❑ CDER MAPP 6700.1: Risk Management Plan Activities in OND and ODS
- ❑ CDER MAPP 6700.9: FDA Posting of Potential Signals of Serious Risks Identified by the Adverse Event Reporting System
- ❑ CDER MAPP 6720.2: Procedures for Handling Requests for Proprietary Name Review
- ❑ Center for Biologics Evaluation and Research (CBER) Manual of Regulatory Standard Operating Policies and Procedures (SOPP) 8401.6: The Responsibilities of the Division of Epidemiology (DE/OBE) in the BLA Review Process
- ❑ CBER SOPP 8413: Postmarketing Commitment Annual Reports, Final Reports, and Related Submissions—Administrative Handling, Review and CBER Reporting CBER SOPP 8415: Procedures for Developing Postmarketing Requirements and Commitments
- ❑ CBER SOPP 8420: FDAAA Section 921: Posting of Potential Signals of Serious Risk

- ❑ CBER SOPP 8508: Procedures for Handling Adverse Reaction Reports Related to "361" Human Cells, Tissues, and Cellular and Tissue-Based Products (HCT/Ps)
- ❑ Compliance Program Guidance Manual 7353.001: Enforcement of the Postmarketing Adverse Drug Experience Reporting Regulations
- ❑ *Guidance for Industry Good Pharmacovigilance Practices and Pharmacoepidemiologic Assessment* (March 2005)
- ❑ *Guidance for Industry: Postmarketing Adverse Event Reporting for Nonprescription Human Drug Products Marketed Without an Approved Application* (July 2009)
- ❑ *Guidance for Industry: Postmarketing Adverse Event Reporting for Medical Products and Dietary Supplements During an Influenza Pandemic* (February 2012)
- ❑ *Guidance for Industry: Reports on the Status of Postmarketing Study Commitments—Implementation of Section 130 of the Food and Drug Administration Modernization Act of 1997* (February 2006)
- ❑ *Guidance for Industry: Format and Content of Proposed Risk Evaluation and Mitigation Strategies (REMS), REMS Assessments and Proposed REMS Modifications* (September 2009)
- ❑ *Guidance for Industry and Investigators: Safety Reporting Requirements for INDs and BA/BE Studies* (December 2012)
- ❑ *Guidance for Industry and Investigators: Enforcement of Safety Reporting Requirements for Investigational New Drug Applications and Bioavailability/Bioequivalence Studies* (June 2011)
- ❑ *Guidance for Industry: Development and Use of Risk Minimization Action Plans* (March 2005)
- ❑ *Guidance: Medication Guides—Distribution Requirements and Inclusion in Risk Evaluation and Mitigation Strategies (REMS)* (November 2011)
- ❑ *Draft Guidance: Drug Safety Information—FDA's Communication to the Public* (March 2012)

Final Rule: Postmarketing Safety Reports for Human Drug and Biological Products; Electronic Submission Requirement (effective June 2015)

- ❑ *Draft Guidance: Classifying Significant Postmarketing Drug Safety Issues* (March 2012)
- ❑ International Conference on Harmonisation (ICH) *Clinical Safety Data Management: Definitions and Standards for Expedited Reporting E2A* (Final) (1 March 1995)
- ❑ ICH, *Pharmacovigilance Planning E2E* (Final) (April 2005)
- ❑ ICH, *Electronic Transmission of Individual Case Safety Reports E2B (R2)*
- ❑ ICH, *Periodic Benefit-Risk Evaluation Report E2C (R2)* (17 December 2012)

Introduction

Safety is a key component of investigating and marketing drugs, biologics and medical devices in the US. Reporting requirements are rigorous, and compliance with these requirements is extremely important. When a drug is first approved, not everything is known about it. Additional information is continuously learned about a drug as it is used by more and more individuals. Postmarketing safety data monitoring is required by both industry and the US Food and Drug Administration (FDA). Other regulatory agencies also require postmarketing follow-up, and safety databases are maintained globally. The International Conference on Harmonisation (ICH) defines safety reporting standards and requirements globally, and US legislation is consistent with these requirements. As new safety signals are detected and validated, labeling is revised or other health communications are forwarded to healthcare professionals. Regulatory and pharmacovigilance professionals serve key functions in monitoring the safety of the products used by patients and consumers.

Clinical Trials

Definitions of adverse events or suspected adverse reactions are slightly different when used in a clinical trial setting. Definitions given below are consistent with ICH definitions used worldwide.

Definitions of Adverse Events in Clinical Studies

- adverse event—An adverse event is any untoward medical occurrence associated with the use of a drug in humans whether or not considered drug-related.

- life-threatening adverse event or life-threatening suspected adverse reaction—An adverse event or suspected adverse reaction is considered "life-threatening" if, in the view of either the investigator or sponsor, its occurrence places the patient or subject at immediate risk of death. It does not include an adverse event or suspected adverse reaction that, had it occurred in a more severe form, might have caused death.
- serious adverse event or serious suspected adverse reaction—An adverse event or suspected adverse reaction is considered "serious" if, in the view of either the investigator or sponsor, it results in any of the following outcomes: death, a life-threatening adverse event, inpatient hospitalization or prolongation of existing hospitalization, a persistent or significant incapacity or substantial disruption of the ability to conduct normal life functions, or a congenital anomaly or birth defect. Important medical events that may not result in death, be life-threatening or require hospitalization may be considered serious when, based on appropriate medical judgment, they may jeopardize the patient or subject and may require medical or surgical intervention to prevent one of the outcomes listed in this definition. Examples of such medical events include allergic bronchospasm requiring intensive treatment in an emergency room or at home, blood dyscrasias or convulsions not resulting in inpatient hospitalization or development of drug dependency or drug abuse.
- suspected adverse reaction—A suspected adverse reaction is any adverse event for which there is a reasonable possibility the drug caused the adverse event. For the purposes of Investigational New Drug (IND) application safety reporting, "reasonable possibility" means there is evidence to suggest a causal relationship between the drug and the adverse event. Suspected adverse reaction implies a lesser degree of certainty about causality than adverse reaction, which means any adverse event caused by a drug.
- unexpected adverse event or unexpected suspected adverse reaction—An adverse event or suspected adverse reaction is considered "unexpected" if it is not listed in the Investigator's Brochure (IB) or is not listed at the specificity or severity observed; or if an IB is not required or available, is not consistent with the risk information described in the general investigational plan or elsewhere in the current application, as amended. For example, under this definition, hepatic necrosis would be unexpected (by virtue of greater severity) if the IB referred only to elevated hepatic enzymes or hepatitis. Similarly, cerebral thromboembolism and cerebral vasculitis would be unexpected (by virtue of greater specificity) if the investigator brochure listed only cerebral vascular accidents. "Unexpected," as used in this definition, also refers to adverse events or suspected adverse reactions mentioned in the IB as occurring with a class of drugs or as anticipated from the pharmacological properties of the drug, but are not specifically mentioned as occurring with the particular drug under investigation.

Reporting Requirements for Clinical Trials

The clinical trial investigator is required to report all adverse events encountered with the drug to the sponsor promptly.[1] The sponsor is responsible for reviewing all information relevant to the drug's safety obtained or otherwise received by the sponsor from any source, foreign or domestic, including information derived from any clinical or epidemiological investigations, animal investigations, commercial marketing experience, reports in the scientific literature and unpublished scientific papers, as well as reports from foreign regulatory authorities the sponsor has not reported to the agency already.[2] The sponsor must notify FDA and all participating investigators promptly in a written IND safety report of:

- any adverse experience associated with the drug's use that is both serious and unexpected

or

- any laboratory animal test finding that suggests a significant risk for human subjects, including reports of mutagenicity, teratogenicity or carcinogenicity

As a result of the Drug Safety Reporting Requirements for Human Drug and Biological Products and Safety Reporting Requirements for Bioavailability and Bioequivalence studies in Humans,[3] the following information must be reported to the agency within 15 days of the sponsor becoming aware of an occurrence:

- findings from clinical or epidemiological studies suggesting a significant risk to study participants
- serious suspected adverse reactions occurring at a rate higher than expected
- serious adverse events from bioavailability studies and bioequivalence studies conducted without an IND

For clinical studies, an adverse experience or fatal outcome need not be submitted to FDA unless the applicant concludes there is a reasonable possibility the product caused the adverse experience or fatal outcome (See 21 CFR 310.305(c)(1)(ii), 314.80(e)(1) and 600.80(e)(1)). Each written notification may be submitted on Form FDA 3500A or in a narrative format (foreign events may be submitted either on a Form FDA 3500A or, if preferred, on a Council for International Organizations of Medical

Sciences (CIOMS) I form). Reports from animal or epidemiological studies should be submitted in a narrative format. All reports should be labeled prominently as "IND Safety Report." Each written notification to FDA should be transmitted to the Center for Drug Evaluation and Research's (CDER) New Drug Review Division or Center for Biologics Evaluation and Research's (CBER) product review division responsible for the IND.

The sponsor is required to notify FDA by telephone or by facsimile transmission of any unexpected fatal or life-threatening experience associated with the drug's use as soon as possible, but in no event later than seven calendar days after the sponsor's initial receipt of the information. Each telephone call or facsimile transmission to FDA shall be transmitted to the new drug review division in CDER or product review division in CBER responsible for review of the drug.

The sponsor must provide follow-up information for each IND safety report submitted. The follow-up information should be submitted as soon as all available information has been gathered. If, upon further investigation into an adverse event, a sponsor establishes an event not initially determined to be reportable is now reportable, the sponsor shall then report this event as soon as possible, but no later than 15 calendar days after the event has been made clear. FDA may require a sponsor to submit IND safety reports in a format or frequency different than those established in the regulations. The sponsor shall provide all additional safety information it has obtained regarding the drug in an information amendment or an annual report.[4]

For bioavailability (BA) and bioequivalence (BE) studies conducted without an IND, the person conducting the study, including any contract research organization (CRO), is required to notify FDA of any serious adverse event within 15 days of its occurrence, and of any fatal or life-threatening adverse event from the study within seven days of its occurrence. Each notification under this paragraph must be submitted to the director, Office of Generic Drugs in CDER. Relevant follow-up information to a BA/BE safety report must be submitted as soon as the information is available and must be identified as such, i.e., "Follow-up BA/BE safety report." Upon FDA's request, the person conducting the study, including any CRO, must submit to FDA any additional data or information the agency deems necessary within 15 days after receiving the request.

The sponsor's submission of an IND safety report for a drug product under a clinical study does not constitute the sponsor's or FDA's admission that the drug caused or contributed to the adverse event.

Postmarketing Surveillance of Drugs and Biologics

Postmarketing surveillance is the systematic collection, analysis, interpretation and dissemination of health-related data to improve public health and reduce morbidity and mortality. FDA requires manufacturers, packagers and distributors of marketed prescription and nonprescription drug products to establish and maintain records and make reports to the agency of all serious, unexpected adverse drug experiences associated with the use of their drug products. Reporting by healthcare professionals outside industry is voluntary.

Definitions

The following definitions apply to postmarketing adverse drug experience reporting:[5]

- adverse drug experience—An adverse drug experience is any adverse event associated with the use of a drug, whether or not considered drug related, including:
    - o an adverse event occurring in the course of the drug product's use in professional practice
    - o an adverse event occurring from drug overdose, whether accidental or intentional
    - o an adverse event occurring from drug abuse
    - o an adverse event occurring from drug withdrawal
    - o any failure of expected pharmacological action
- associated with the use of the drug—There is a reasonable possibility the experience may have been caused by the drug.
- disability—An adverse event resulting in a substantial disruption of a person's ability to conduct normal life functions.
- FDA Adverse Event Reporting System (FAERS)—A computerized information database designed to support FDA's postmarketing safety surveillance program for drug and nonvaccine biological products.
- Individual Case Safety Report (ICSR)—A description of an adverse experience related to an individual patient or subject.
- life-threatening adverse drug experience—Any adverse drug experience placing the patient, in the view of the initial reporter, at immediate risk of death from the adverse drug experience as it occurred, i.e., does not include an adverse drug experience that, had it occurred in a more severe form, might have caused death.
- serious adverse drug experience—Any adverse drug experience occurring at any dose resulting in any of the following outcomes: death, a life-threatening adverse drug experience, inpatient hospitalization or prolongation of existing hospitalization, a persistent or significant disability or incapacity, or a congenital

anomaly or birth defect. Important medical events that may not result in death, be life-threatening or require hospitalization may be considered a serious adverse drug experience when, based on appropriate medical judgment, they may jeopardize the patient or subject and may require medical or surgical intervention to prevent one of the outcomes listed in this definition. Examples of such medical events include allergic bronchospasm requiring intensive treatment in an emergency room or at home, blood dyscrasias or convulsions not resulting in inpatient hospitalization or the development of drug dependency or drug abuse.

- unexpected adverse drug experience—An unexpected adverse drug experience is any adverse drug experience not listed in the drug product's current labeling. This includes events that may be symptomatically and pathophysiologically related to an event listed in the labeling but differ from the event because of greater severity or specificity. For example, under this definition, hepatic necrosis would be unexpected (by virtue of greater severity) if the labeling only referred to elevated hepatic enzymes or hepatitis. Similarly, cerebral (of greater specificity) if the labeling only listed cerebral vascular accidents. "Unexpected," as used in this definition, refers to an adverse drug experience that has not been observed previously (i.e., included in the labeling) rather than from the perspective of such experience not being anticipated from the pharmaceutical product's pharmacological properties

Authorities

CDER's Office of Surveillance and Epidemiology Divisions consists of three divisions:

- Division of Drug Risk Evaluation (DDRE)
- Division of Medication Errors and Technical Support (DMETS)
- Division of Surveillance, Research, and Communication Support (SRCS)

The DDRE staff includes safety evaluators whose primary role is to detect and assess safety signals for all marketed drug products. They work closely with medical reviewers in the Office of New Drugs so potential safety signals are placed in the context of existing preclinical, clinical or pharmacologic knowledge of the drugs in question. The DDRE staff reviews study protocols required of manufacturers as Phase 4 commitments. They evaluate various postmarketing surveillance tools that may be incorporated into risk management strategies, such as patient registries and restricted distribution systems. They estimate the public health impact of safety signals by evaluating computerized databases and the published literature.

The DMETS staff primarily provides premarketing reviews of all proprietary names, labels and labeling in CDER to reduce a proposed product's medication error potential. DMETS also provides postmarketing review and analysis of all medication errors CDER receives.

SRCS staff handle data resources, risk communication and outcomes and effectiveness research components of drug safety risk management programs. This division oversees MedWatch, risk communication research and activities such as Medication Guides, Patient Package Inserts and pharmacy information surveys, and international regulatory liaison activities for all drug and biologic postmarketing safety issues. SRCS also manages expansion in the use and number of safety and epidemiologic data resources.

CDER's Drug Safety and Risk Management Advisory Committee advises the FDA commissioner on risk management, risk communication and quantitative evaluation of spontaneous reports for drugs for human use and any other product for which FDA has regulatory responsibility. The committee also advises regarding the scientific and medical evaluation of all information gathered by the Department of Health and Human Services (DHHS) and the Department of Justice with regard to safety, efficacy and abuse potential of drugs or other substances, and recommends actions to be taken by DHHS with regard to the marketing, investigation and control of such drugs or other substances.

CDER's Drug Safety Oversight Board provides oversight and advice to CDER leadership on managing important drug safety issues and the flow of emerging safety information to healthcare professionals and patients.

Postmarketing Drug/Biologic Surveillance: Individual Case Safety Reports (ICSRs)

Applicants of approved New Drug Applications (NDAs), Abbreviated New Drug Applications (ANDAs) and antibiotic applications, manufacturers of marketed prescription drugs for human use without approved NDAs or ANDAs, and licensed manufacturers of approved biologic product license applications are required to report adverse experiences to FDA under 21 CFR 310.305, 314.80, 314.98, and 600.80. Before considering any clinical incident for submission to FDA in an Individual Case Safety Report (ICSR), applicants should, at a minimum, have knowledge of the five categories applicable to all products, including vaccines. Examples of some of the types of information in each category are:

- patient information (e.g., age, gender)
- information about the adverse experience (e.g., date and description of the adverse drug experience)

- information about the suspect medical product (e.g., drug name, dose, indication, National Drug Code (NDC) number)
- information about the initial reporter (e.g., name and contact information)
- information about the applicant or manufacturer or responsible person (e.g., name and contact information)

In addition, the following two categories of information apply to vaccine products only:

- information about other vaccine(s) administered in the previous four weeks
- information on the facility and personnel where the vaccine was administered (e.g., name of person who administered vaccine, name of responsible physician and facility where the vaccine was administered)

If any one of these basic elements remains unknown after being actively sought by the applicant, the applicant should maintain records of its efforts to obtain the basic elements for an individual case in its corporate drug or biological safety files.

It is notable FDA has moved to an electronic requirement for submission of ICSRs. Electronic ICSR submission enhances global pharmacovigilance by facilitating electronic transmission and exchange of appropriate information from ICSRs among regulatory bodies and regulated entities through use of common data elements and transmission standards.

An applicant actively seeking information on an adverse experience should use direct verbal contact with the initial adverse experience reporter (e.g., in person, by telephone or other interactive means, such as a videoconference). The applicant should not merely send the initial reporter a letter requesting information concerning the adverse experience. Applicants should use a healthcare professional (e.g., physician, physician assistant, dentist, pharmacist, nurse) for initial contact with reporters to be able to understand the medical consequences of the case and ask appropriate questions to acquire relevant information rapidly to determine the case's significance.

With regard to an "identifiable" patient, reports stating "some patients got anaphylaxis" should be excluded until further patient information is obtained. However, a report stating "an elderly woman had anaphylaxis" or a "young man experienced anaphylaxis" should be included because there is enough information to suspect specific patients were involved. Patients should not be identified by name or address. Instead, the applicant should assign a unique code as the patient identifier for reporting purposes. The exception to using the unique code is if the patient is the reporter. FDA has determined it is important for the reporter's name to be included, even when the reporter is the patient, to allow follow-up as needed by FDA. Names of patients, healthcare professionals, hospitals and geographical identifiers in adverse drug experience reports are not releasable to the public under FDA's public information regulations.

For spontaneous reports, the applicant should assume an adverse experience or fatal outcome was thought to be due to the suspect drug or biological product (implied causality). An adverse experience should, at minimum, consist of signs (including abnormal laboratory findings, if appropriate), symptoms or disease diagnosis (including any colloquial descriptions) obtained for purposes of reporting. Thus, a report stating a patient "experienced unspecified injury" or a "suffered irreparable damages" should not be included until more specific information about the adverse experience can be determined.

Current regulations dealing with postmarketing reporting of adverse drug experiences (ADEs) include 21 CFR 314.80 and 310.305. US regulations are consistent with ICH and CIOMS standards.

Under 21 CFR 314.80, the sponsor is required to review ADE information obtained from all potential sources (foreign and domestic), including:

- marketing experience
- scientific literature (peer-reviewed and non-peer-reviewed)
- unpublished reports
- postmarketing clinical investigations
- postmarketing epidemiological or surveillance studies

Further, the sponsor is required to develop written procedures for the surveillance, receipt, evaluation and reporting of postapproval ADE reports to FDA and maintain records of all ADEs known to the applicant for a period of 10 years, including raw data and any correspondence relating to ADEs. Any company (sponsor, manufacturer, distributor or packer) listed on the approved product labeling is held to these ADE reporting requirements. Obligations of a non-sponsor may be met by submitting all reports of serious ADEs to the sponsor. If a non-sponsor elects to submit ADE reports to the sponsor rather than to FDA, the non-sponsor shall submit and report to the sponsor within five calendar days of receipt of the report, and the sponsor would be responsible for submitting ADEs to FDA. The non-sponsor should maintain a record of the submission to the sponsor.

Serious and unexpected adverse experiences from all sources, whether domestic or foreign, must be submitted to FDA. Possible sources include, for example, scientific literature, postmarketing studies or commercial marketing experience. Scientific literature reports include published and unpublished scientific papers known to the applicant. All adverse events (domestic and foreign) that are both serious and unexpected must be submitted within 15 calendar days of initial receipt by anyone in the employ of the applicant.

For marketed products with an approved application, manufacturers, packers, or distributors that do not hold the application continue to have the option of submitting 15-day Alert reports directly to FDA or to the application holder under Sections 314.80(c)(1)(iii) and 600.80(c)(1)(iii). If they opt to submit reports directly to FDA, they are required to do so in electronic format. If they choose to report to the applicant, they may submit the report in any format acceptable to the reporter and applicant. The applicant, however, is required to use electronic reporting when it subsequently reports the information to FDA.

Unlike IND Safety Reports, causality does not enter into the decision for postmarketing reports, with the exception of postmarketing clinical investigations or studies (whether or not conducted under an IND). In these instances, if the reporter concludes there is a reasonable possibility the drug caused the adverse experience, the report is subject to a 15-Day Alert if serious and unexpected. This is the one exception in reporting postmarketing adverse drug experiences where an assessment of causality is required. Reports from postmarketing studies should be separate and identified as coming from postmarketing studies to differentiate them from spontaneous reports.

It should be noted reports from the scientific literature, i.e., from medical journals, are required to be submitted as either case reports or the result of a formal clinical trial. Reports based on the scientific literature also should be reported and accompanied by a copy of the published article.

The sponsor is required to investigate all adverse drug experiences that are the subject of postmarketing 15-Day Alert reports and submit follow-up reports. If additional information is not obtainable, records should be maintained of the number of unsuccessful steps taken to seek additional information. Postmarketing 15-Day Alert Reports and follow-ups to them shall be submitted under separate cover. The mailing label should prominently say "15-Day Alert Report" or "15-Day Alert Report Follow-up."

A sponsor should protect the patient's privacy with an ADE by assigning a unique code instead of using the patient's name and address in the reports. A sponsor can include a disclaimer statement in the report indicating it is not admitting or denying the ADE report submitted constitutes an admission the drug caused or contributed to an adverse effect.

The *Dietary Supplement and Nonprescription Drug Consumer Protection Act* (*DSNDCA*) (PL 109-462) was signed into law in 2006. The *DSNDCA* amended the *Federal Food, Drug, and Cosmetic Act* (*FD&C Act*) to add safety reporting requirements for nonprescription drug products marketed without an approved application. Section 760(b) states the manufacturer, packager or distributor whose name appears on the label of a nonprescription drug marketed in the US without an approved application (referred to as the responsible person) must submit to FDA any report of a serious adverse event associated with such drug when used in the US, accompanied by a copy of the label on or within the retail package of such drug. In addition, the responsible person must submit follow-up reports of new medical information related to a submitted serious adverse event report received within one year of the initial report.

Postmarketing Drug/Biologic Surveillance: Periodic Reporting

The sponsor is required to submit the following periodic reports to FDA, for the first three years following approval, on a quarterly, basis. Unless otherwise requested by FDA, after three years, the sponsor shall submit the periodic ADE report at annual intervals. Quarterly reports are required to be filed within 30 days of the close of the quarter, with the first quarter beginning on the date of the application's approval. Annual Reports are required to be submitted within 60 days of the close of the year. FDA may extend or re-establish the requirement for an applicant to submit quarterly reports after the approval of a major supplement. Applicants have the option of submitting ICSRs at any time up until the periodic report due date to allow flexibility with electronic reporting.

The regulations require a postmarketing periodic report to contain:

- a narrative summary and analysis of the information in the report and an analysis of the 15-day Alert Reports submitted during the reporting interval
- ICSRs for serious, expected and nonserious adverse experiences
- a history of actions taken since the last report because of adverse experiences

An applicant may request a waiver of the requirement to submit postmarketing periodic safety reports in the format described in the regulations. Instead, applicants can prepare these reports using the Periodic Safety Update Report (PSUR) or Periodic Benefit Risk Evaluation Report (PBRER) formats described in ICH E2C. Even if a waiver has been obtained to submit in PSUR format, a separate waiver must be requested to submit in PBRER format.

Postmarketing Drug/Biologic Surveillance: Safety Monitoring by FDA

FDA tracks adverse drug reaction reports by entering all safety reports for approved drugs and therapeutic biologic products into the computerized FAERS database, which uses standardized international terminology from the *Medical Dictionary for Regulatory Activities.* FDA uses FAERS to facilitate postmarketing drug surveillance and compliance activities. The goal of FAERS is to improve the public health by providing the best available tools for storing and analyzing safety data and reports. Data and trends from

FAERS may lead to FDA action on products, such as "Dear Health Care Professional" letters or requests to a sponsor for additional safety studies. This is part of an FDA initiative to rapidly collect, analyze and disseminate drug safety information. This initiative is highlighted by FDA's *Draft Guidance: Drug Safety Information—FDA's Communication to the Public* (March 2012).

FDA also posts potential signals of serious risks or new safety information identified from FAERS on its website on a quarterly basis. The appearance of a drug on this list does not mean FDA has concluded the drug has this listed risk. It means FDA has identified a potential safety concern, but does not mean the agency has identified a causal relationship between the drug and the listed risk. If, after further evaluation, FDA determines the drug is associated with the risk, it may take a variety of actions, including requiring changes to the drug's labeling, requiring development of Risk Evaluation and Mitigation Strategies (REMS) or gathering additional data to better characterize the risk. FDA posts these quarterly reports in accordance with Title IX, Section 921 of the *Food and Drug Administration Amendments Act* of 2007 (*FDAAA*). This section in *FDAAA*, among other things, directs FDA to "conduct regular, biweekly screening of the Adverse Event Reporting System (AERS) database and post a quarterly report of new safety information or potential signal of a serious risk identified in the last quarter." FDA staff in CDER and CBER regularly examine the FAERS database as part of routine safety monitoring. When a potential serious risk signal is identified from FAERS data, it is entered as a safety issue into CDER's Document Archiving, Reporting and Regulatory Tracking System (DARRTS) or into CBER's Therapeutics and Blood Safety Branch Safety Signal Tracking (SST) system. The table in each quarterly report lists the names of products and potential safety issues entered into the above tracking systems where the FAERS database identified (or contributed to identification of) the potential safety issues. Additional information on each issue, such as an FDA Drug Safety Communication, also is provided.

Proprietary Name Review

FDA has considered the role of names and naming processes in medication errors as part of its focus on the safe use of medical products. FDA has developed internal procedures and processes as part of its marketing application review process for evaluating the potential for a proposed product name (submitted as part of an NDA, Biologics License Application (BLA) or ANDA) to cause or contribute to medication errors. *Guidance for Industry: Contents of a Complete Submission for the Evaluation of Proprietary Names* is intended to assist industry in submitting a complete package of information for FDA to use in assessing safety aspects of a proposed proprietary name (to reduce medication errors) and promotional implications of a proposed name (to ensure compliance with other requirements for labeling and promotion).

Risk Management and REMS

FDAAA created Section 505-1 of the *FD&C Act*, which authorizes FDA to require sponsors of certain applications to submit and implement a REMS. Risk management is defined in FDA's *Guidance for Industry: Good Pharmacovigilance Practices and Pharmacoepidemiologic Assessment* as an iterative process of:

- assessing a product's benefit-risk balance
- developing and implementing tools to minimize a product's risks while preserving its benefits
- evaluating tool effectiveness and reassessing the benefit-risk balance
- making adjustments, as appropriate, to the risk minimization tools to further improve the benefit: risk balance

FDA's *Draft Guidance for Industry: Format and Content of Proposed Risk Evaluation and Mitigation Strategies (REMS), REMS Assessments, and Proposed REMS Modifications* provides guidance to industry on:

- format and content of a proposed REMS, including REMS supporting documentation
- content of assessments and proposed modifications of approved REMS
- what identifiers to use on REMS documents
- how to communicate with FDA about REMS

Guidance for Industry: Medication Guides—Distribution Requirements and in Risk Evaluation and Mitigation Strategies (REMS) outlines the use of a Medication Guide if required as part of a REMS. The guidance also provides information on enforcement discretion regarding Medication Guide dispensing requirements.

The *Food and Drug Administration Safety Innovation Act* of 2012 (*FDASIA*) requires an assessment strategy to determine whether a REMS is effective. Under the law, the assessment will determine whether a modification is necessary to maintain an acceptable benefit-risk balance and keep the burden on the healthcare system at an acceptable level. Applicants may propose a modification to a REMS at any time, FDA may propose a modification to a REMS at any time or FDA may request an applicant to submit a modification. If such a request is made by the agency, the applicant must respond within 120 days (or another timeframe agreed upon by FDA and applicant), and the agency must review and act on the submitted strategy within 180 days of the request or within 60 days for minor modifications or modifications based on safety label changes. FDA is required to provide guidance on this process.

Postmarketing Device Surveillance

Medical device postmarketing surveillance presents unique challenges compared to drugs and biologics due to the great diversity and complexity of medical devices, the iterative nature of medical device product development, the learning curve associated with technology adoption and the relatively short product lifecycle. Proper medical device operation depends on optimal device design, the use environment, user training and adherence to directions for use and maintenance. In some cases, these features limit the utility of relying on systems designed for identifying of drug-related adverse events.

The primary regulations governing postmarketing reporting requirements are included in the following:

- 21 CFR 803 Medical device reporting:
  - Device user facilities must report deaths and serious injuries a device has or may have caused or contributed to, establish and maintain adverse event files and submit summary Annual Reports.
  - Manufacturers or importers must report deaths and serious injuries their device has or may have caused or contributed to. In addition, they must report certain device malfunctions. They also must establish and maintain adverse event files. In addition, manufacturers must submit specified follow-up information.
  - Medical device distributors must maintain records of incidents but are not required to file these incidents.
- 21 CFR 806 Medical devices; reports of corrections and removals
- 21 CFR 822 Postmarket surveillance

In 2012, *FDASIA* expanded the Sentinel network to apply to devices. FDA is required to establish procedures for tracking device risk and analyzing public health trends. FDA also was given the ability to require postmarketing studies at any time in the product's marketed lifecycle.

The current US medical device postmarket surveillance system depends primarily on the following:

- Medical Device Reporting (MDR)—See above
- Medical Product Safety Network (MedSun)—MedSun is an enhanced surveillance network comprised of approximately 280 hospitals nation wide working interactively with FDA to better understand and report on device use and adverse outcomes in the real-world clinical environment. The overall quality of the approximately 5,000 reports received annually via MedSun is significantly higher than those received via MDR. Specialty networks within MedSun focus on device-specific areas such as cardiovascular devices (HeartNet) and pediatric intensive care unit devices (KidNet). In addition, the network can be used for targeted surveys and focused clinical research.
- Postapproval Studies—FDA may order a postapproval study as a condition of approval for a device approved under a Premarket Approval (PMA) application. Typically, postapproval studies are used to assess device safety, effectiveness and/or reliability, including longer-term, real-world device performance. Status updates for more than 160 ongoing postapproval studies may be found on FDA's website (www.accessdata.fda.gov/scripts/cdrh/cfdocs/cfpma/pma_pas.cfm).
- Postmarket Surveillance Studies—FDA may order a manufacturer of certain Class II or Class III devices to conduct postmarket surveillance studies (often referred to as "522 studies"). Study approaches vary widely and may include nonclinical device testing, analysis of existing clinical databases, observational studies and, rarely, randomized controlled trials. Status updates for ongoing postmarket surveillance studies covering approximately a dozen device types may be found on FDA's website (www.accessdata.fda.gov/scripts/cdrh/cfdocs/cfPMA/pss.cfm).
- FDA Discretionary Studies—In addition to medical device adverse event reports, postapproval and postmarket surveillance studies, FDA also conducts its own research to monitor device performance, investigate adverse event signals and characterize device-associated benefits and risks to patient sub-populations A variety of privacy-protected data sources are used, including national registries, Medicare and Medicaid administrative and claims data, data from integrated health systems, electronic health records and the published scientific literature.
- Other Tools—FDA has other tools it may use in the postmarket setting to track devices, restrict or ban device use and remove unsafe, adulterated or misbranded products from the market.

The Sentinel Initiative in Drug, Biologic and Device Postmarket Surveillance

FDAAA required FDA to collaborate with public, academic and private entities to develop methods for obtaining access to disparate healthcare data sources and to analyze healthcare safety data. In May 2008, the secretary of DHHS and the FDA commissioner announced the Sentinel Initiative, a long-term effort to create a national electronic system for monitoring FDA-regulated medical product safety. The Sentinel System ultimately will expand FDA's existing postmarket safety surveillance systems by enabling the agency to conduct active surveillance and related observational studies on the safety and performance of its regulated medical products once they reach the market.

The Mini-Sentinel is a pilot project sponsored by FDA to create an active surveillance system, the Sentinel System, to monitor the safety of FDA-regulated medical products. It uses pre-existing electronic healthcare data from multiple sources. Collaborating institutions provide access to data as well as scientific and organizational expertise. Mini-Sentinel is exploring a variety of approaches for improving the agency's ability to quickly identify and assess safety issues. The Mini-Sentinel program currently includes data on 126 million individuals.

Conclusion

This chapter has reviewed both clinical trial and postmarketing reporting requirements for manufacturers and distributors of drugs, biologics and medical devices, including reporting requirements under INDs.

Periodic update reports also have been discussed. In addition, FDA's activities in monitoring postmarketing safety of healthcare products through the Sentinel and Mini-Sentinel programs and through other safety monitoring have been addressed. A review of proprietary nomenclature for pharmaceutical products and the need for a REMS have been discussed. Safety is one of FDA's highest priorities and one of pharmaceutical companies developing products for the benefit of patients and consumers. For regulatory and pharmacovigilance professionals, vigilant attention to product safety is of paramount importance.

References

1. 21 CFR Part 312.64(b) Investigator reports. FDA website. http://www.accessdata.fda.gov/SCRIPTs/cdrh/cfdocs/cfcfr/CFRSearch.cfm?fr=312.64. Accessed 1 April 2015.
2. 21 CFR Part 312.32(b) IND safety reporting. FDA website. http://www.accessdata.fda.gov/scripts/cdrh/cfdocs/cfcfr/cfrsearch.cfm?fr=312.32. Accessed 1 April 2015.
3. Investigational New Drug Safety Reporting Requirements for Human Drug and Biological Products and Safety Reporting Requirements for Bioavailability and Bioequivalence Studies in Humans, 21 CFR Parts 312 and 320 (Final Rule). *Federal Register*, 29 September 2010. Federal Register website. https://www.federalregister.gov/articles/2010/09/29/2010-24296/investigational-new-drug-safety-reporting-requirements-for-human-drug-and-biological-products-and. Accessed 1 April 2015.
4. Postmarketing Safety Reports for Human Drug and Biological Products; Electronic Submission Requirements (Final Rule). *Federal Register*, https://www.federalregister.gov/articles/2014/06/10/2014-13480/postmarketing-safety-reports-for-human-drug-and-biological-products-electronic-submission. Accessed 1 April 2015.
5. 21 CFR Part 312.32(d) IND safety reporting. FDA website. www.accessdata.fda.gov/scripts/cdrh/cfdocs/cfcfr/cfrsearch.cfm?fr=312.32. Accessed 1 April 2015.
6. 21 CFR Part 314.80 Postmarketing reporting of adverse drug experiences. FDA website. www.accessdata.fda.gov/scripts/cdrh/cfdocs/cfcfr/cfrsearch.cfm?fr=314.80. Accessed 1 April 2015.

Chapter 20

Medical Device Submissions

Updated by Sharad Mi. Shukla, RAC (US and EU) and Rajaram Balasubramanian, RAC (US and EU)

OBJECTIVES

- ❑ Understand medical device classification and how it affects submission requirements
- ❑ Learn the types of submissions made to the Center for Devices and Radiological Health (CDRH), including Investigational Device Exemption (IDE) requirements for clinical device studies
- ❑ Understand Premarket Approval (PMA) submission requirements
- ❑ Review Humanitarian Device Exemption (HDE) requirements
- ❑ Discuss the types of FDA communications during review of medical device submissions and when Expedited Review should be requested
- ❑ Provide an overview of the Unique Device Identification (UDI)

LAWS, REGULATIONS AND GUIDELINES COVERED IN THIS CHAPTER

- ❑ *Federal Food, Drug, and Cosmetic Act* of 1938
- ❑ *FD&C Act* as amended by the *Food and Drug Administration Modernization Act* of 1997
- ❑ 21 CFR 807 Establishment Registration and Device Listing, Premarket Notification
- ❑ 21 CFR 812 Investigational Device Exemptions
- ❑ 21 CFR 814 Premarket Approval
- ❑ 21 CFR 860 Medical Device Classification Procedures

Introduction

The 1906 *Pure Food and Drugs Act*[1] act was the true beginning of US federal food and drug legislation. Medical devices were not represented in the act, in large part because contemporary devices, such as stethoscopes and scalpels, were relatively simple, and their corresponding risks, if any, were conspicuous. In 1938, the act was modernized by passage of the *Federal Food, Drug and Cosmetic Act* (*FD&C Act*), in part due to the recognized need to introduce a definition of medical devices into federal law. The *FD&C Act* gave the US Food and Drug Administration (FDA) authority to mandate requirements for exporting unapproved devices. Under the act, devices were examined for adulteration and misbranding, but no provision was made for review of their safety or effectiveness prior to marketing. In the late 1960s, FDA started to concentrate on issuing recalls and replacements for devices with safety and effectiveness problems.

In the early 1960s, President John F. Kennedy advocated changes to how medical devices enter the US market; however, the changes he sought were not realized until the mid-1970s. New legislation was enacted in 1976 establishing the ground rules and standards to which all US medical device manufacturers and importers now must adhere: the *Medical Device Amendments*. This new law applied safety and effectiveness safeguards to new devices and required FDA to establish, for the first time, regulations concerning establishment registration and device listing; Good Manufacturing Practices (GMPs) for medical devices; medical device reporting (MDR); and guidelines on policy, procedures and industry responsibilities for field corrections and removals. Under the act's amendments, FDA was authorized to set standards, to grant premarket clearance for some devices and premarket approval for others. Devices posing little or no risk to users or patients were exempted from standards and premarket clearance but were not necessarily exempt from complying with parts of the GMP requirements for devices under 21 CFR 820, the Quality System Regulation (QSR).

FDA, primarily through the Center for Devices and Radiological Health (CDRH), is responsible for ensuring medical devices are safe and effective. Per the FDA Intercenter Agreement (31 October 1991), the Center for Biologics Evaluation and Research (CBER) has responsibility for devices related to blood and cellular products (see Chapter 3 Overview of Drug, Biologic and Device Regulatory Pathways and Chapter 24 Biologics Submissions). The agency's authority is granted by the *FD&C Act* and carried out in accordance with the regulations found in Title 21 of the Code of Federal Regulations (CFR). Medical devices, referred to as "devices," are defined in Section 201(h) of the *FD&C Act*:

> "The term 'device' means an instrument, apparatus, implement, machine, contrivance, implant, in vitro reagent, or other similar or related article, including any component, part, or accessory, which is:
> (1) recognized in the official National Formulary, or the United States Pharmacopeia, or any supplement to them,
> (2) intended for use in the diagnosis of disease or other conditions, or in the cure, mitigation, treatment, or prevention of disease, in man or other animals, or
> (3) intended to affect the structure or any function of the body of man or other animals, and which does not achieve its primary intended purposes through chemical action within or on the body of man or other animals and which is not dependent upon being metabolized for the achievement of its primary intended purposes."

Numerous changes to device laws and regulations have been implemented over the years via various amendments to the *FD&C Act*. Four of the most notable changes, mandated by the *Safe Medical Devices Act* of 1990 (*SMDA*) and the *Medical Device Amendments* of 1992, were:

- introduction of the Humanitarian Device Exemption (HDE), the medical device equivalent of orphan drug designation, providing limited exemptions from the law for devices intended to treat or diagnose rare diseases or conditions affecting fewer than 4,000 persons in the US
- promulgation of the QSR, resulting in substantial revisions that essentially harmonized US GMPs for medical devices with the EU's quality system regulations in EN 46001 and ISO 9001, and added design controls to the GMP regulation, bringing product development under FDA scrutiny for the first time
- establishment of a regulatory requirement (previously an FDA request) for manufacturers and distributors to report field corrections and removals to FDA within 10 days after their initiation
- promulgation of the first device tracking regulation

The *FD&C Act* underwent additional change and reform as a result of the *Food and Drug Administration Modernization Act* of 1997 (*FDAMA*). *FDAMA* empowered FDA to restrict the marketing of products for which the manufacturing processes are so deficient the use of the products could present a serious health hazard. The agency was given authority to take appropriate action if a device manufacturer advocates an off-label use that may be potentially harmful. *FDAMA* further enhanced FDA's risk-based approach to medical device regulation, allocating FDA resources and diligence to the oversight of medical devices presenting the greatest patient risks. For example, the law exempts Class I devices not intended for a use of substantial importance in preventing impairment of human health or not presenting a potential unreasonable risk of illness or injury from premarket notification. The law also directs FDA to focus its postmarket surveillance on higher-risk devices and implement a reporting system that concentrates on a representative sample of user facilities, such as hospitals and nursing homes, where patients may experience device-related deaths and serious illnesses or injuries.

In addition, *FDAMA* expanded an ongoing pilot program to accredit outside (third-party) experts to conduct the initial review of all Class I and low-to-intermediate-risk Class II device applications. The act, however, prohibits any accredited person from reviewing devices that are permanently implantable, life-supporting, life-sustaining or for which clinical data are required. The *Medical Device User Fee and Modernization Act* of 2002 (*MDUFMA*), signed into law 26 October 2002, further amended the *FD&C Act* to include provisions that affect compliance regulations. Under *MDUFMA*:

- Establishment inspections may be conducted by accredited persons (third parties) under carefully prescribed conditions.
- New labeling requirements were established for reprocessed single-use devices.
- The submission of validation data for some reprocessed single-use devices is required. On 30 April

2003, FDA identified the types of devices subject to this requirement (see 68 FR 23139).[4]

MDUFMA made several other significant changes to the law involving FDA postmarket surveillance appropriations, combination product review, electronic labeling, electronic registration, devices intended for pediatric use and breast implant reports. Additionally, it requires manufacturer identification on the device itself, with certain exceptions.

Background information, reference materials and additional information about *MDUFMA* can be found on the CDRH website.[5] *MDUFMA* also imposed various user fees. On 28 September 2007, as part of the *Food and Drug Administration Amendments Act* (*FDAAA*), user fees were reauthorized through Fiscal 2012.

The *Food and Drug Administration Safety and Innovation Act* (*FDASIA*) (Public Law 112-144) included the *Medical Device User Fee Amendments* of 2012, or *MDUFA III*. *MDUFA III* took effect 1 October 2012 and reauthorized user fees through Fiscal 2017. It added additional performance goals for FDA, and several guidance documents tied to *MDUFA III* provisions were issued, including guidance on review actions taken on 510(k) and premarket approval applications.

New fees include:

- a fee for each 30-day notice submitted to FDA
- a fee for each 513(g) request for classification information submitted to FDA
- an annual fee for periodic reporting made under a condition of approval for a Class III device
- an annual fee for the registration of each medical device establishment

Small businesses may qualify for reduced fees through an application process. However, this discount does not apply to the annual establishment registration fee.

Premarket Requirements

Medical devices marketed in the US are subject to the regulatory controls in the *FD&C Act* and the regulations in 21 CFR Parts 1-58, 800-1299.

Radiation-emitting also are subject to regulations for radiation-emitting electronic products cited in 21 CFR Parts 1000-1050.

Some requirements apply to medical devices before they are marketed (premarket requirements), and others apply to medical devices after they are marketed (postmarket requirements). Postmarket requirements are discussed in detail in Chapter 21 Medical Device Compliance and Postmarketing Activities.

Prior to marketing a medical device in the US, a manufacturer must perform the following steps:

- Step One—classify the device
- Step Two—choose the correct premarket submission
- Step Three—prepare the appropriate information for the FDA premarket submission
- Step Four:—send the premarket submission to FDA and interact with FDA staff during review
- Step Five—complete the establishment registration and device listing

Medical Device Classification (21 CFR 860)

Federal law (*FD&C Act*, Section 513), established the risk-based classification system for medical devices. Medical devices are regulated based on a classification system that evaluates the risk posed by the product and the level of control needed to assure adequate safety. The device classification system has been modified by subsequent amendments but generally remains as originally intended. The act defines three classes of medical devices according to increasing complexity and regulatory control:

- Class I—general controls (with or without exemptions)
- Class II—general controls and special controls (with or without exemptions)
- Class III—general controls and premarket approval

Device classification depends on the device's intended use and its indications for use. For example, a scalpel's intended use is to cut tissue. A subset of intended use arises when a more specialized indication is added to the device's labeling such as "for making incisions in the cornea." In addition, classification is risk-based, that is, the risk the device poses to the patient and/or user is a major factor in the class to which it is assigned. Class I includes devices with the lowest risk and Class III includes those with the greatest risk.

Class I devices generally are low-risk devices, such as nonprescription sunglasses or examination gloves, for which safety and effectiveness are well established and can be ensured by adherence to a set of guidelines or "general controls." General controls include:

- Establishment Registration (Form FDA 2891) of companies are required to register under 21 CFR Part 807.20, such as manufacturers, distributors, repackagers and relabelers. Foreign establishments, however, are not required to register their establishments with FDA.
- Medical Device Listing (Form FDA 2892) of devices to be marketed
- manufacturing devices in accordance with the QSR (21 CFR Part 820)
- device labeling in accordance with labeling regulations in 21 CFR Part 801 or 809
- premarket notification (510(k)) submission before marketing a device

Most Class I devices are exempt from premarket notification and/or GMP regulation. In rare circumstances, some Class I devices also require premarket clearance by FDA through the 510(k) process.

Class II devices are intermediate-risk, such as blood glucose test systems and infusion pumps, where general controls are not sufficient to ensure their safety and effectiveness. Class II devices are subject to special controls in addition to general controls. Special controls may include special labeling requirements, mandatory performance standards and postmarket surveillance. Most Class II devices are subject to FDA premarket review and clearance through the 510(k) premarket notification process. At times, the review and requirements are just as rigorous as those for a Class III device.

FDA considers Class III devices, such as life-sustaining, life-supporting or implantable devices, to pose the greatest risk. Devices with a new intended use or employing a unique, new technology not substantially equivalent to a legally marketed predicate device also are categorized as Class III. Class III devices are subject to the most rigorous controls, including general controls (like Class I and Class II devices), any relevant special controls (like Class II devices) and, in most cases, premarket approval, which requires evidence to establish reasonable assurance of the device's safety and effectiveness. Detailed manufacturing information also may be required. FDA may request a panel of outside experts to recommend the action to be taken on the Class III device. However, the agency is not compelled to take the panel's advice. Not all Class III devices require an approved PMA to be marketed. Class III devices equivalent to devices legally marketed before 28 May 1976 may be marketed through the 510(k) process until FDA has published a requirement for manufacturers of that generic device type to submit premarket approval data.

Class III devices that require an approved PMA before marketing are those:

- regulated as new drugs prior to 28 May 1976, also called transitional devices
- devices found not substantially equivalent to devices marketed prior to 28 May 1976
- Class III preamendment devices required by 21 CFR to have a PMA

FDA uses procedures described in 21 CFR 860 to determine medical device classifications. 21 CFR 862–892 contain classification regulations. A device may be classified by its regulation and by a product code. Product codes may provide more specific designations within a classification regulation. Occasionally, FDA assigns a product code to a category of devices prior to the formal assignment of a regulatory classification. CDRH's Product Classification database can be used to help determine classifications.

Classification product codes are a method of internally classifying and tracking medical devices. CDRH and a subset of CBER-regulated medical device product codes consist of a three-letter combination that associates a device's type with a product classification designated for the application. Classification product codes and information associated with these devices, e.g., names and attributes, are assigned by CDRH to support their regulation.

Reclassification

As experience and knowledge about a device increase, the original classification can be adjusted via the reclassification process. Reclassification is based on FDA's receipt of new information about a device. FDA, on its own or in response to an outside petition, may change a device's classification by regulation. A manufacturer wishing to have a device reclassified to a lower class must convince FDA the less stringent class requirements will be sufficient to provide reasonable safety and effectiveness assurance.

The rules and procedures for establishing a device's classification and requesting a change in classification are contained in 21 CFR 860. Advantages of reclassifying a device from the PMA to a 510(k) route to marketing include reduced user fees for FDA's submission review; often, reduced information requirements; and reduced requirements for submissions for changes.

Since 1976, the primary reclassification activity has been geared toward down-classifying Class III devices into Class II or I. Generating reclassification data requires considerable effort and resources. If successful, the reclassified device and any substantially equivalent device can be cleared for marketing through the less-burdensome 510(k) process. It was the intent of Congress that reclassification play a potentially significant role in the medical device clearance process, although CDRH's interpretation of its mandate has not permitted the reclassification process to be utilized to a meaningful extent. A primary obstacle has been the high level of scientific information CDRH requires to support a device's reclassification. A second obstacle has been the difficulty in obtaining agreement among manufacturers whose products have been cleared already via PMAs. Removal of the PMA requirement may be seen as loss of a barrier to entry that limits competitors. In 2009, FDA initiated the 515 Program Initiative[11] to facilitate reclassifications.

FDA must complete five tasks before finalizing the classification process for each device type:

- Task A—collect existing scientific information in the public domain and/or from scientific experts in the medical community and assess the risks versus benefits of the medical device type subject to the classification

- Task B—convene a meeting of the Medical Device Advisory Committee (panel) to request input on the classification of the device type
- Task C—issue a proposed order (proposed classification) reclassifying the device type into Class I or II or, if retaining the device in Class III, calling for PMAs
- Task D—review and consider comments submitted by the public
- Task E—issue a final order (final classification) reclassifying the device type into Class I or II or, if retaining the device in Class III, calling for PMAs

513(g) Request for Information

The classification into which a device falls sometimes is unclear. A provision in Section 513(g) of the *FD&C Act* allows the device sponsor to request a classification determination and regulatory information from FDA. This requires a letter with a device description and a fee payment.[13] The agency usually responds within 60 days with a classification assignment based on the material presented. More information is provided in a guidance document on Procedure for Section 513(g) Request for Information[12] and in the CDRHLearn presentation on 513(g).[14]

Upon receipt of the 513(g) Request for Information and the necessary user fee, the Document Control Center (DCC) will assign a submission number to the 513(g) Request for Information and forward the request to a review branch in the Office of Device Evaluation (ODE) or Office of In Vitro Diagnostics Evaluation and Safety (OIVD) for consideration. The DCC will send an "acknowledgement of receipt" letter to the 513(g) submitter The 513(g) Request for Information generally will be accepted for review by staff from ODE or OIVD, and other offices within CDRH with appropriate scientific and regulatory expertise, to review the information provided, meet as necessary and draft a response for signature by the ODE or OIVD director. The response should address the regulatory question(s) asked in the 513(g) Request for Information.

De Novo Classification

FDAMA created a process for the classification of certain low-risk devices for which there is no predicate. Before *FDAMA*, such a device would automatically be designated Class III. Reclassification would be required to move the device to Class I or II. However, under this process, the sponsor of a low- or a moderate-risk device had to go through a 510(k) review process and receive a Not Substantially Equivalent (NSE) determination before applying for a risk-based determination. This process was proving to be unwieldy and redundant. *FDASIA* amended, among others, Section 513(f) of the *FD&C Act*. It eliminates the 510(k) review requirement and allows sponsors to directly request a *de novo* classification.

In accordance with Section 513(f)(2) of the *FD&C Act*, sponsors of devices determined to be not substantially equivalent (NSE) through the 510(k) program may be eligible to submit a *de novo* petition requesting FDA to make a risk-based classification determination for the device under Section 513(a)(1) of the *FD&C Act*. Because devices classified under this pathway (*de novo* devices) are low- to moderate-risk, they may not need to confer as substantial a benefit to patients to have a favorable benefit-risk profile. Devices granted marketing authority under *de novo* petitions should be understood sufficiently to explain all the device's risks and benefits so all risks can be mitigated appropriately through the application of general and/or special controls to provide reasonable assurance of safety and effectiveness. Further, devices classified under *de novo* petitions may serve as predicates for future devices that can be appropriately regulated through the 510(k) program; therefore, FDA carefully considers the benefit-risk profile of these devices in determining reasonable assurance of safety and effectiveness.

However, because factors may change over time—such as a device no longer being a first-of-a-kind or the only available treatment as new therapies are approved—the benefit-risk determination for a specific device at one point in time may no longer represent the proper weighting of the factors for the same or similar type of device in the future.[15,16]

CDRH issued *De novo Classification Process (Evaluation of Automatic Class III Designation) —Draft Guidance for Industry and Food and Drug Administration Staff* on 14 August 2014, which, when finalized, will represent FDA's current thinking on this topic.[17]

Medical Device Submissions

The term "preamendment device" refers to devices legally marketed in the US by a firm before 28 May 1976, which have not been changed or modified significantly since then and for which FDA has not issued a regulation requiring a PMA application. Devices meeting the above criteria are considered "grandfathered" devices and do not require 510(k)s. The device must have the same intended use as was marketed before 28 May 1976. If the device is labeled for a new intended use, it is considered a new device, and a 510(k) must be submitted to FDA for marketing clearance. The sponsor must be the owner of the device on the market before 28 May 1976, for the device to be grandfathered. If the subject device is similar to a grandfathered device and marketed after 28 May1976, the subject device does not meet the requirements to be grandfathered, and the sponsor must submit a 510(k). For a firm to claim it has a preamendment device, it must demonstrate its device was labeled, promoted and distributed in interstate commerce for a specific intended use and its intended use has not changed. Preamendment device determination requests should be submitted using Form FDA 3752.

The most common types of premarket submissions include:

- 510(k) (Premarket Notification)
- PMA (Premarket Approval)
- *De Novo* (Evaluation of automatic Class III designation)
- HDE (Humanitarian Device Exemption)

Investigational Device Exemption (IDE) (21 CFR 812)

PMAs, HDEs and some 510(k)s and *de novos* require clinical evidence. Prior to initiating a clinical study, the sponsor may need to obtain IDE approval from FDA. The study also will need to be approved by the appropriate Institutional Review Board (IRB). Clinical studies must comply with all applicable IDE regulations and Good Clinical Practices (GCPs).

The IDE regulations provide a means of distributing devices not cleared or approved to be marketed (i.e., by 510(k), PMA or Class I exemption) for the purposes of clinical research or to gather clinical evidence of safety and effectiveness. Guidance is provided at Device Advice: Investigational Device Exemption (IDE).[18]

Quoting the Regulations (21 CFR 812.1):

> "An IDE approved under 812.30 or considered approved under 812.2(b) exempts a device from the requirements of the following sections of the Federal Food, Drug, and Cosmetic Act and regulations issued thereunder: Misbranding under section 502 of the act, registration, listing, and premarket notification under section 510, performance standards under section 514, premarket approval under section 515, a banned device regulation under section 516, records and reports under section 519, restricted device requirements under section 520(e), good manufacturing practice requirements under section 520(f) except for the requirements found in 820.30, if applicable (unless the sponsor states an intention to comply with these requirements under 812.20(b)(3) or 812.140(b)(4)(v)) and color additive requirements under section 721."

FDA regulations and guidances often use the terms "significant risk" device and "non-significant risk" (NSR) device. In practice, FDA considers the study's risk, not that of the device. For example, a Class III device, depending on the nature of the study, may be the focus of a significant risk study or a non-significant risk study, or one that is exempt from IDE requirements. The rest of this section uses FDA's terminology, e.g., "significant risk device."

A "significant risk device" must comply with full IDE requirements, including FDA approval of an IDE submission. NSR devices must comply with abbreviated IDE requirements as described in 21 CFR 812.2(b). Abbreviated IDEs do not require FDA approval but do require IRB approval. Abbreviated requirements also include informed consent and some reporting and recordkeeping. FDA IDE approval is presumed for NSR devices.

As per 21 CFR 812.3(m), A "significant risk" device means an investigational device:

- intended as an implant and presents a potential for serious risk to a subject's health, safety or welfare
- purported or represented to be for a use in supporting or sustaining human life and presents a potential for serious risk to a subject's health, safety or welfare
- for a use of substantial importance in diagnosing, curing, mitigating or treating disease, or otherwise preventing impairment of human health and presents a potential for serious risk to a subject's health, safety or welfare
- otherwise presenting a potential for serious risk to a subject's health, safety or welfare

A device is exempt from IDE requirements if it is:[19]

- a device in commercial distribution prior to 28 May 1976
- a device, other than a transitional device, "introduced into commercial distribution on or after May 28, 1976, that FDA has determined to be substantially equivalent to a device in commercial distribution immediately before May 28, 1976, and that is used or investigated in accordance with the indications in the labeling FDA reviewed under subpart E of part 807 in determining substantial equivalence" (Note a "transitional device" is one FDA considered to be a new drug before 28 May 1976)
- a diagnostic device that:
    - o is noninvasive
    - o does not require a significant risk invasive sampling procedure
    - o does not intentionally introduce energy into a subject
    - o is not used for a diagnostic procedure without confirmation by another established procedure
- a device undergoing consumer preference testing, if the testing is not for determining safety and effectiveness or puts the subject at risk
- a device for veterinary use or research on animals
- a custom device unless it is being used to establish safety and efficacy for commercial distribution

An IDE application includes:

1. sponsor name and address
2. a complete report of prior investigations of the device and an accurate summary of those sections of the investigational plan described in 812.25(a)-(e) or, in lieu of the summary, the complete plan; a complete investigational plan and a complete report

of prior investigations of the device if no IRB has reviewed them, if FDA has found an IRB's review inadequate or if FDA requests them

3. a description of the methods, facilities and controls used for the manufacture, processing, packing, storage and, where appropriate, installation of the device, in sufficient detail that a person generally familiar with GMPs can make a knowledgeable judgment about the quality control used in the device's manufacture
4. an example of the agreements to be signed by all investigators to comply with investigator obligations, and a list of the names and addresses of all investigators who have signed the agreement
5. a certification that all investigators who will participate in the investigation have signed the agreement, the list of investigators includes all who are participating in the investigation and no investigators will be added to the investigation until they sign the agreement
6. a list of the name, address and chairperson of each IRB that has been or will be asked to review the investigation, and a certification of the action concerning the investigation taken by each such IRB
7. name and address of any institution at which a part of the investigation may be conducted not identified in accordance with the regulations
8. if the device is to be sold, the amount to be charged and an explanation of why sale does not constitute device commercialization; the submitter also will need to demonstrate cost recovery if sale is approved
9. a claim for categorical exclusion under 21 CFR 25.30 or 25.34 or an environmental assessment under 25.40
10. copies of all device labeling, forms and informational materials to be provided to subjects to obtain informed consent
11. any other relevant information FDA requests for review of the application
    a. Additional information—FDA may request additional information concerning an investigation or revision in the investigational plan. This constitutes a clinical hold. The sponsor may treat such a request as a disapproval of the application for purposes of requesting a hearing.
    b. Information previously submitted—Information previously submitted to CDRH need not be resubmitted but may be incorporated by reference.

FDA requires a risk analysis under 21 CFR 812.25 investigational plan. This is a description and analysis of increased risks to which subjects will be exposed by the investigation; the manner in which these risks are minimized; a justification for the investigation; and a description of the patient population, including the number of patients and each patient's age, sex and condition. When considering an IDE application, FDA reviews background information, such as animal testing, bench testing and the clinical protocol, to determine whether the product is safe for testing in humans and whether efficacy can be shown based on the protocol requirements.

Supplemental IDE Submissions

Supplemental submissions are required for changes in the investigational plan, informed consent or other substantive information. Supplemental IDE submissions include:

- an IDE supplement, which is any additional submission to an IDE after approval
- an IDE amendment, which is any additional submission to an IDE before approval of the IRB (Per 21 CFR 812.42, IRB approval is necessary before an investigation begins. For further information on IRB regulations and consent forms, see 21 CFR 50 and 56, respectively.)

Pre-IDE Meeting

Sponsors are encouraged to contact FDA to obtain further guidance prior to submitting an IDE application. (Pre-IDE Meetings also may be used to obtain guidance on 510(k) submissions even though no clinical data are required.) Early interaction with the agency helps the sponsor understand FDA requirements, regulations and guidance documents and allows FDA personnel to familiarize themselves with the new technologies. Communication with FDA may take the form of a Pre-IDE Meeting and/or a Pre-IDE Submission.

Informal Guidance Meeting

Sponsors are encouraged to meet with the ODE reviewing division to obtain advice to be used to develop supporting preclinical data or the investigational plan. These meetings may take the form of telephone conference calls, video conferences or face-to-face discussions. The sponsor should contact the reviewing division directly or may contact the IDE staff for assistance.

Formal Guidance Meetings

There are two types of formal guidance meetings—a Determination Meeting and an Agreement Meeting.

A sponsor anticipating the submission of a PMA submits a written request for a Determination Meeting to discuss the types of valid scientific evidence necessary to demonstrate the device is effective for its intended use. This meeting focuses on the broad outline of clinical trial design. The request and summary information for a meeting should be submitted as a Pre-IDE Submission and identified as a Determination Meeting request. FDA's determination is provided to the applicant in writing within 30 days following the meeting.

For an Agreement Meeting, a sponsor submits a written meeting request to reach an agreement with FDA regarding its review of an investigational plan (including a clinical protocol). The request and summary information should be submitted as a pre-IDE submission and identified as an Agreement Meeting request. This meeting should take place no later than 30 days after receipt of the request. The written request should include detailed descriptions of the device and its proposed conditions of use, a proposed plan (including a clinical protocol) for determining whether there is a reasonable assurance of effectiveness, and, if available, information regarding the device's expected performance. If an agreement is reached between FDA and the sponsor or applicant regarding the investigational plan (including a clinical protocol), the terms of the agreement are put into writing and made part of FDA's administrative record.

It is important to establish a good working relationship with the FDA project officer. The project officer may expedite meeting requests and also can provide clarification, ideas and suggestions.

Presubmission Program

In 1995, FDA established a pre-IDE program to allow sponsors to submit preliminary information as a "pre-IDE" submission. Sponsors are encouraged to submit pre-IDE submissions while they are preparing the formal IDE submission to obtain informal FDA guidance on troublesome parts of the IDE application, e.g., clinical protocol design, preclinical testing proposal, preclinical test results and protocols for foreign studies when the studies will be used to support future marketing applications to be submitted to FDA.

Upon completing its review of the pre-IDE submission, the reviewing division will issue a response to the sponsor in a timely manner, usually within 60 days of receipt. The response may take the form of a letter or comments provided during a meeting or conference call. FDA will prepare a memo of the meeting if responding via meeting or conference call.

Originally, the pre-IDE program was designed to provide applicants a mechanism to obtain FDA feedback on future IDE applications. Over time, the pre-IDE program has evolved to include feedback on other device submissions, such as PMA applications, HDE applications and 510(k) submissions, as well as to address questions related to whether a clinical study requires submission of an IDE. To reflect this broader scope of the pre-IDE program, FDA issued *Request for feedback on Medical Device Submissions: The Pre- Submission Program and Meetings with FDA Staff—Guidance for Industry and Food and Drug Administration Staff* on 18 February 2014.[20] This guidance also broadens the program to include devices regulated by CBER and renames the pre-IDE program the Presubmission (Pre-Sub) program.

In this final guidance, FDA provides examples of when a Pre-Sub may be particularly helpful; for example, before conducting a clinical study for a device involving a novel technology or prior to submitting a marketing application to gain insight into potential hurdles for approval or clearance. FDA also provides recommendations for what information should be included in specific types of Pre-Subs. One of industry's primary concerns about the pre-IDE program has been that FDA often provides advice and guidance in a pre-IDE meeting and subsequently changes its position. The sponsor then must decide whether it has sufficient resources to address FDA's newly stated concerns or if it must abandon its efforts due to FDA's new approach. Although the guidance clearly states the advice provided in a Pre-Sub is "not decisional or binding on the agency or the applicant," it also states "it is FDA's intent to provide the best advice possible based on the information provided in the Pre-Sub and to remain consistent in our approach to regulating similar products."

510(k) Premarket Notification

A 510(k) is a premarket submission made to FDA to demonstrate the device to be marketed is at least as safe and effective, i.e., substantially equivalent, to a legally marketed device (21 CFR 807.92(a)(3)) not subject to a PMA.

Each sponsor that wants to market a Class I, II or III device intended for human use, for which a PMA is not required, must submit a 510(k) to FDA unless the device is exempt from the *FD&C Act*'s 510(k) requirements and does not exceed the exemption limitations in xxx.9 of the device classification regulation (e.g., 21 CFR 862.9, 21 CFR 864.9). There is no 510(k) form; however, 21 CFR 807 Subpart E describes 510(k) submission requirements.

A 510(k) submission is required for some Class I products, most Class II products and a small number of Class III products. Product families, such as catheters of various sizes or patient monitor systems of varying configurations, can be cleared on a single 510(k) if the intended uses, technological characteristics and issues of safety and effectiveness are essentially the same within the family.

The purpose of a 510(k) is to demonstrate a new or modified device is "substantially equivalent" in its intended use, safety and effectiveness as a "predicate device." A predicate device is a legally marketed device cleared onto the market by a 510(k). A preamendment device also can be used as a predicate device, but the sponsor may need to provide documentation that it meets the preamendment status criteria. Because medical science has advanced greatly since 1976, it is recommended a device recently cleared under a 510(k) be used as a predicate device.

The content of 510(k) premarket notifications, described in 21 CFR 807.87, includes: the device name and class, an establishment registration number, an "Indications for

Use Statement," a 510(k) summary, proposed labeling, substantial equivalence comparison with the predicate device, supporting performance data and a statement that all data and information submitted are truthful and accurate and no material fact has been omitted. In particular, the Indications for Use Statement provides the specific indications, clinical settings, target population, anatomical sites, device configuration and other information critical to how the device is intended to be used clinically.

The format and amount of information in a 510(k) varies depending on the device's intended use, technology, issues of safety and effectiveness, reliance on standards and special controls and, for modified devices, the nature of the modification.

For more detail, see Device Advice: Premarket Notification.[21] This webpage provides links to guidance and required forms.

Often, clinical studies are not required for 510(k) devices. However, clinical studies may be necessary if the device cannot be shown to be as safe and effective as the predicate device using laboratory tests, such as biocompatibility, engineering, bench performance, design verification and voluntary standards tests.

It is important to note FDA does not perform 510(k) pre-clearance facility inspections. The submitter may market the device immediately after 510(k) clearance is granted. The manufacturer should be prepared for an FDA quality system (21 CFR 820) inspection at any time after 510(k) clearance.

The act and the 510(k) regulation (21 CFR 807) do not specify who must apply for a 510(k). Instead, they specify which actions, such as introducing a device to the US market, require a 510(k) submission. The following four categories of parties must submit a 510(k) to FDA:

1. Domestic finished device manufacturers must submit a 510(k) if they manufacture a device according to their own specifications and market it in the US. Accessories to finished devices sold to the end user also are considered finished devices. However, device component manufacturers are not required to submit a 510(k) unless such components are promoted for sale to an end user as replacement parts. Contract manufacturers, firms that manufacture devices under contract according to someone else's specifications, are not required to submit a 510(k).
2. A specification developer develops the specifications for a finished device but the device is manufactured under contract by another firm or entity. The specification developer submits the 510(k), not the contract manufacturer.
3. Repackagers or relabelers may be required to submit 510(k)s if they change the labeling significantly or otherwise affect any device condition. Significant labeling changes may include modification of manuals, such as adding a new intended use, deleting or adding warnings, contraindications, etc. Operations, such as sterilization, could alter the device's condition; however, most repackagers or relabelers are not required to submit 510(k)s.
4. Foreign manufacturers or exporters or US representatives of foreign manufacturers or exporters introducing a device to the US market are required to submit 510(k)s.

All manufacturers (including specification developers) of Class II and III devices and select Class I devices are required to follow design controls (21 CFR 820.30) during the development of their device. A 510(k) holder must have design control documentation available for FDA review during a site inspection. In addition, any changes to the device specifications or manufacturing processes must be made in accordance with the QSR and may be subject to a new 510(k).

As described in 21 CFR 807.81(a)(3), a new complete 510(k) application is required for changes or modifications to an existing device, where the modifications could affect the device's safety or effectiveness significantly, or the device is to be marketed for a new or different indication.[22] Examples of modifications that may require a 510(k) submission include, but are not limited to, the following:

- sterilization method
- structural material
- manufacturing method
- operating parameters or conditions for use
- patient or user safety features
- sterile barrier packaging material
- stability or expiration claims
- design

More detail is provided in *Deciding When to Submit a 510(k) for a Change to an Existing Device (K97-1)*.[24] There are no provisions for a 510(k) amendment or supplement to an existing 510(k); a new 510(k) must be submitted. However, FDA developed a streamlined 510(k) process for modifications to a device cleared under 510(k), called the Special 510(k).

Three types of Premarket Notification 510(k) submissions for marketing clearance are available: traditional, special and abbreviated. The Traditional 510(k) is the original complete submission as provided in 21 CFR 807. In 1998, FDA developed "The New 510(k) Paradigm" to streamline the evaluation of Premarket Notifications, providing two optional approaches for obtaining 510(k) marketing clearance under certain instances: Special 510(k) and Abbreviated 510(k).

Traditional 510(k)

A Traditional 510(k) is the most common. The submitter provides descriptive information about the indications for use and technology and, if not identical to the predicate, results of performance testing to demonstrate substantial equivalence.

The Traditional 510(k) may be used for any original 510(k) or for a modification to a previously cleared device under 510(k). The traditional method is the original complete submission as provided in 21 CFR 807 and is the default format. The Traditional 510(k) method may be used under any circumstances.

Additional information is provided in Device Advice: How to Prepare a Traditional 510(k).[25]

A Traditional 510(k) submission must include the required elements identified in 21 CFR 807.87 (Information required in a premarket notification submission).[26] CDRH recommends the applicant follow the Traditional 510(k) format provided in *Guidance for Industry and FDA Staff: Format for Traditional and Abbreviated 510(k)s.*[27]

Special 510(k)

The Special 510(k) is used for device modifications and utilizes the QSR design controls (21 CFR 820.30). Special 510(k)s may be submitted for a modification to a device cleared under the 510(k) process. If a 510(k) is needed for a device's modification, and if the modification does not affect the device's intended use or alter its fundamental scientific technology, summary information resulting from the design control process can serve as the basis for clearing the application along with the required elements of a 510(k). See Device Advice: How to Prepare a Special 510(k).[28]

Modifications to the Indications for Use or any labeling change affecting the device's intended use are not accepted as Special 510(k)s. Special 510(k) sponsors should highlight or otherwise prominently identify proposed labeling changes that may result from modifications to the legally marketed device. The Special 510(k) submission should state clearly the device's intended use has not changed as a result of the modification(s). Note that a labeling change from prescription to over-the-counter use, or vice versa, is considered a change in intended use and is not eligible for a Special 510(k) submission.

Special 510(k)s are not accepted for modifications that alter the device's fundamental scientific technology. Such changes include modifications to the device's operating principle(s) or mechanism of action. Specific examples of changes that alter the fundamental scientific technology and should not be submitted as Special 510(k)s include:

- a change in a surgical instrument that uses a sharpened metal blade to one that cuts with a laser
- a change in an in vitro diagnostic device (IVD) that uses immunoassay technology to one that uses nucleic acid hybridization or amplification technology
- incorporation of a sensing mechanism in a device to allow it to function "on demand" rather than continuously

Device modifications that should be appropriate for review as Special 510(k)s include:

- energy type
- environmental specifications
- performance specifications
- ergonomics of the patient-user interface
- dimensional specifications
- software or firmware
- packaging or expiration dating
- sterilization

It is important for manufacturers to incorporate FDA guidance, special controls or recognized standards addressing issues such as device testing or performance when implementing design control requirements. For example, if a manufacturer is modifying a contact lens, the manufacturer's design control inputs should include the special controls FDA has established for the device. Further, if a manufacturer modifies an IVD, the manufacturer's design inputs should include any recognized clinical standards such as those developed by NCCLS (formerly known as National Committee of Clinical Laboratory Standards) or a reasonable alternative.

A sponsor may make changes to the device that do not change the intended use or alter the technology and may not require a 510(k) submission. These changes may be minor but do require appropriate change control in the Device Master Record (DMR) and Device History File (DHF).

A Special 510(k) should be well organized and formatted in paginated sections and include the required elements suggested in Device Advice: How to prepare a special 510(k).[29]

The most frequently observed problem with Special 510(k)s has been related to the design control information submitted in support of device modification. In several instances, submissions did not include a complete declaration of conformity to design controls. Other submissions were cited for containing a statement the firm would comply with the design control requirements rather than a statement the firm was in conformance. In a few 510(k)s, it was determined the firm had not performed a complete risk analysis for the device modification. One of the other problems observed with Special 510(k)s has been related to the device modifications that are the subjects of the submissions. As discussed in FDA guidance, changes to the intended use and fundamental scientific technology should be submitted as Abbreviated or Traditional 510(k)s rather than Special 510(k)s.

Abbreviated 510(k)

An Abbreviated 510(k) relies on the use of FDA guidance documents and special controls established by regulations and standards (particularly FDA-recognized consensus standards). Typically, an Abbreviated 510(k) includes one or more declarations of conformity to an FDA-recognized consensus standard or part of a standard.[30] An Abbreviated 510(k) submission must include required elements. Under certain conditions, the submitter may not need to include test data. See Device Advice: How to Prepare an Abbreviated 510(k).[31]

Device sponsors may choose to submit an Abbreviated 510(k) when:

- a guidance documents already exists
- a special control already has been established
- FDA has recognized a relevant consensus standard

In an Abbreviated 510(k) submission, sponsors provide summary reports on the use of guidance documents and/or special controls or Declarations of Conformity to recognized consensus standards to expedite submission review.

An Abbreviated 510(k) that relies on a guidance document should include a summary report describing how the relevant guidance document was employed. It also should note how the guidance was used during device development and testing. The summary report should include information regarding the sponsor's efforts to conform to the guidance and outline any deviations.

Special controls are defined as those controls (such as performance standards, postmarket surveillance, patient registries, development and dissemination of guidelines, recommendations and other appropriate actions) that establish reasonable assurance of a Class II device's safety and effectiveness. The device classification regulations list special controls for the device, if any.

An Abbreviated 510(k) that relies on a special control(s) must include a summary report describing adherence to the special control(s). It also must describe how the special control(s) was used during device development and testing, including how it was used to address a specific risk or issue. The summary report includes information regarding the sponsor's efforts to conform to the special control(s) and should outline any deviations.

Recognized consensus standards may be cited in guidance documents or individual policy statements or established as special controls that address specific risks associated with a type of device. FDA has recognized more than 1,000 standards to which 510(k) submitters can declare conformity. The current list of FDA-recognized consensus standards is available in CDRH's standards database.[32]

A submitter may suggest a standard not yet recognized by FDA. The submitter should discuss such a strategy with the agency prior to submitting an Abbreviated 510(k) based on an unrecognized standard.

An Abbreviated 510(k) that relies on a standard must include a Declaration of Conformity to that standard. If FDA determines an Abbreviated 510(k) does not meet eligibility requirements, the reviewer notifies the sponsor and offers the option of having the document converted to a traditional 510(k) or withdrawing it for future submission. If the 510(k) is withdrawn, and a new one submitted, a new user fee applies. If the 510(k) is converted, the original receipt date remains as the start of the review period. Sponsors should be aware, in most cases, additional information is necessary for converted submissions.

In the Abbreviated 510(k) process, a sponsor must assess the device's conformance to a recognized consensus standard. Once the assessment is completed satisfactorily, the sponsor may submit the Abbreviated 510(k). Under certain conditions, conformance test data are not required to be submitted in the 510(k). For clarification on this issue, consult with the reviewing branch.

The sponsor may use a third party to perform a conformance assessment with the standard and provide a statement to this effect. For example, a third party may be used to assess conformance to the standard for electromagnetic interference testing and shock hazards, IEC 60601-1-2.

The Abbreviated 510(k) should include a Declaration of Conformity signed by the sponsor, while the third party's statement should be maintained in the DMR and DHF (21 CFR 820.30).

Declarations of Conformity to recognized consensus standards should include the following:

- identification of applicable recognized consensus standards met
- statement, for each consensus standard, all requirements were met except inapplicable requirements or deviations
- identification, for each consensus standard, of any way(s) in which it may have been adapted for application to the device under review (e.g., identification of an alternative series of tests performed)
- identification, for each consensus standard, of any requirements not applicable to the device
- specification of any deviations from each applicable standard applied
- specification of the differences that may exist, if any, between the tested device and the device to be marketed and a justification of the test results in these areas of difference
- name and address of any test laboratory and/or certification body involved in determining the device's conformance with applicable consensus standards and a reference to any of those organizations' accreditations

eCopy Program for Medical Device Submissions

An electronic copy (eCopy) is defined as an exact duplicate of the paper submission, created and submitted on a compact disc (CD), digital video disc (DVD) or a flash drive. An eCopy is accompanied by a paper copy of the signed cover letter and the complete paper submission. Including an eCopy with a submission has been required since 1 January 2013. A submission with an eCopy not meeting the technical standards, outlined in the eCopy guidance, will be placed on eCopy hold until a valid eCopy is received.

Inclusion of an eCopy is expected to improve review process efficiency by allowing the immediate availability of an electronic version for review rather than relying solely on the paper version. FDA issued a guidance document 10 October 2013 on FDA's interpretation of the statutory eCopy requirement and the agency's current thinking on the best means for implementing other aspects of the eCopy program.[33]

The eCopy program is not intended to impact (reduce or increase) the type or amount of data the applicant includes in a submission to support clearance or approval.

Section 745A(b) of the *FD&C Act*, as added by Section 1136 of *FDASIA*, requires an eCopy for the following submission types:

- 510(k) submissions, including third party 510(k)s
- evaluation of automatic Class III designation petitions (*de novos*)
- PMA applications, including Transitional PMAs
- Modular PMAs
- product development protocols (PDPs)
- IDEs
- HDEs
- Emergency Use Authorizations (EUAs)
- certain investigational new drug applications (INDs)
- certain biologics license applications (BLAs)
- presubmissions

All subsequent submissions to the types identified above would require eCopy format, including amendments (amendments include add-to-files), supplements and reports (reports include annual, periodic and postapproval reports) even if the original was submitted to FDA prior to implementation of the eCopy requirements.

The submission size is irrelevant; eCopy requirements apply to a single-page submission (i.e., the company cover letter is the only content) or a multi-volume submission.

Refuse to Accept Policy for 510(k)s

FDA issued a guidance document, *Refuse to Accept Policy for 510(k)s*, on 31 December 2012, which supersedes CDRH's Premarket Notification (510(k)) Refuse to Accept Policy, dated 30 June 1993, and 510(k) Refuse to Accept Procedures (K94-1) blue book memo, dated 20 May 1994.[34]

The new guidance's purpose is to explain the procedures and criteria FDA intends to use in assessing whether a 510(k) submission meets a minimum threshold of acceptability and is accepted for substantive review. This will enable FDA to focus its resources on completed submissions to provide a more efficient review, resulting in faster clearance of new devices. The guidance appendix includes checklists that clarify the necessary elements and contents of a complete 510(k) submission to help the sponsor understand the information FDA needs to conduct a substantive review.

Once the sponsor submits a 510(k), the acceptance review clock begins, and FDA has 15 days to complete its review and notify the sponsor whether the 510(k) is administratively complete. If one or more items are missing in the 510(k), FDA notifies the sponsor the submission is not being accepted and provides a completed checklist indicating which item(s) is the basis for the Refuse to Accept (RTA) designation. The sponsor may respond by submitting the missing information, and FDA then will have another 15 days to perform the acceptance review.

The FDA (substantive) review clock for the 510(k) begins on the receipt date of the most recent submission or additional information resulting in the 510(k) acceptance designation. For example, if the submission is accepted for substantive review on the first acceptance review, FDA's review clock start date is the receipt date of the submission. However, if the submission is designated RTA, the FDA review clock start date is not yet known. In such cases, the clock start date will be the receipt date of the submission including the additional information resulting in an acceptance designation (even if FDA later requests information that should have been requested during acceptance review). In the event the acceptance review is not completed within 15 calendar days, the submission will be considered to be under substantive review, and FDA's review clock start date will be the receipt date of the most recently received information for the submission. For more information on the RTA policy, refer to the guidance on FDA's website (http://www.fda.gov/downloads/MedicalDevices/DeviceRegulationandGuidance/GuidanceDocuments/ucm315014.pdf).

Third-Party Review

FDAMA established the Accredited Persons Program for third-party reviews. Accredited Persons, which may be companies or individuals, are authorized to perform 510(k) reviews for certain Class II devices. The product classification database includes the Accredited Persons, if any, authorized to perform third-party reviews for the device classification. Third-party reviews are not subject to an FDA user fee. However, the fee paid to the third-party reviewer usually is higher than the FDA 510(k) user fee. Advantages of third-party reviews typically include:

- shorter review times
- responsiveness to questions
- expertise in testing, standards and international requirements
- local service, depending on the location of the third-party reviewer's office

See the "Device Advice" guidance on Third Party Review.[35]

PMAs

PMA is FDA's process of scientific and regulatory review to evaluate Class III medical device safety and effectiveness. A PMA is the most stringent device marketing application required by FDA. PMA approval is based on an FDA determination the PMA contains sufficient "valid scientific evidence" to assure the device is safe and effective for its intended use(s).

Essentially, there are two types of PMA applications:

- Traditional PMA
- product development process

FDAMA introduced other PMA options:

- Modular PMA
- Streamlined PMA
- Humanitarian Device Exemption

See the Device Advice guidance on PMA Application Methods.[36]

Traditional PMA

The information required in a PMA is detailed in 21 CFR 814.20(b). In addition to voluntary completion of the applicable sections of a cover sheet, other required information includes:

1. table of contents showing the volume and page number for each item
2. summary of information in the submission, including:
   a. general description of the Indications for Use
   b. explanation of how the device functions, scientific concepts upon which the device is based, general physical and performance characteristics and a brief description of the manufacturing process, if it aids understanding
   c. device generic, proprietary and trade names
   d. description of existing alternative practices and procedures for which the device is intended
   e. brief description of the device's foreign and US marketing history by the applicant and/or any other person, including a list of the countries in which it has been marketed and from which marketing was withdrawn because of adverse safety and effectiveness experiences
   f. summary of studies and reports submitted with the PMA, including:
      I. nonclinical laboratory studies
      II. human clinical investigations, other data, information or reports relevant to an evaluation of the device's safety and effectiveness from any source, known or that reasonably should be known to the applicant
      III. discussion demonstrating the data and information in the submission constitute valid scientific evidence providing reasonable assurance of the device's safety and effectiveness, and conclusions drawn from the studies with a discussion of benefit-risk considerations and adverse effects
3. complete description of:
   a. device, including photos, drawings and schematics
   b. each functional component and/or ingredient
   c. device properties relative to its specific indications for use
   d. principles of operation
   e. methods, facilities and controls used to manufacture, process, package, store and, if appropriate, install the device
4. references to any performance standard in effect or proposed at the time of submission and any voluntary standard relevant to the device's safety or effectiveness, including adequate information to demonstrate compliance with the applicable standards and an explanation of any deviation from the standards
5. technical sections containing data and information in sufficient detail to enable approval or disapproval of the application, including results of:
   a. nonclinical laboratory studies in a separate section, including a statement that each study was conducted in accordance with Good Laboratory Practices (21 CFR 58)
   b. clinical investigations in a separate section, including a statement that each study was conducted in accordance with IRB rules (21 CFR 56), informed consent rules (21 CFR 50) and IDE rules (21 CFR 812)
6. bibliography of all published reports known or reasonably should be known concerning the device's safety or effectiveness not submitted under number 5 above:
   a. identification, analysis and discussion of any other data, information and reports relevant to evaluation of the device's safety and effectiveness from any sources known or reasonably should be known

   b. copies of all reasonably obtainable published and unpublished reports described in 3d and 3e, if requested by FDA or an FDA Advisory Committee
7. samples of the device and its components, if requested by FDA, submitted or available at a named location if impractical to submit
8. copies of all proposed labeling, including labels, Instructions for Use, installation, maintenance and servicing, and any information, literature and/or advertising that constitutes labeling (Section 201(m) of the *FD&C Act* and 21 CFR 801 or 809)
9. environmental assessment in accordance with 21 CFR 25.20(n) or justification for categorical exclusion under 21 CFR 25.30 and 25.34
10. disclosure of any financial arrangements between the sponsor and clinical investigators who performed studies included in the submission, or a certification on Form FDA 3454 attesting to the absence of any financial arrangements (21 CFR 54)
11. any other information requested by FDA

Omission of any required information must be identified and justified in a statement attached as a separate section of the PMA. A DHF or other applicable information in FDA files may be incorporated by reference. However, if this information was not submitted by the PMA applicant, the applicant must receive permission from the filer of the information for it to be reviewed by FDA.

The sponsor is required to update a pending PMA periodically with new or newly learned safety and effectiveness information that reasonably could affect the device's evaluation and labeling (21 CFR 814.20(e)). To ensure adherence to all content and format requirements, manufacturers should review the regulations in 21 CFR 814.20(a)–(h) carefully, as well as FDA's guideline on the arrangement and format of a PMA.

Acceptance and Filing Reviews for PMAs

FDA issued a guidance document on Acceptance and Filing Reviews for Premarket Approval Applications (PMAs) on 31 December 2012 that identifies the criteria for PMA filing and supersedes the 2003 PMA filing guidance.[37]

This guidance divides PMA filing criteria into two steps: acceptance criteria and filing criteria. The PMA's acceptance and filing review's purpose is to make a threshold determination about whether an application is administratively complete enough for the agency to undertake a substantive review. FDA has 15 days to complete the acceptance review and 45 days to complete the filing review. To enhance the consistency of FDA's acceptance and filing decisions and help applicants better understand the types of information FDA needs to conduct a substantive PMA review, this guidance and its associated checklist clarify the necessary elements and contents of a complete PMA application. For more information, see the guidance document.

An FDA team generally consisting of a medical officer, engineer, biologist, statistician, labeling expert and manufacturing expert performs the PMA review. A decision to approve or not approve must be made by FDA within 180 calendar days following receipt of a complete PMA, although, in reality, reviews take much longer. During the review process, FDA will order an inspection of the sponsor's manufacturing facility to provide evidence the manufacturer complies with QSR requirements.

Often, PMAs for important or new technologies also will be reviewed by FDA Advisory Panels consisting of experts in particular medical specialties (e.g., MDs, PhDs, engineers) and consumer and industry representatives. Advisory personnel are not FDA employees but are paid as "special government employees" for the days they participate as members of a panel. The panel members' recommendation is not binding; however, FDA generally follows their advice.

FDA issued *Guidance for Industry and Food and Drug Administration Staff: Factors to Consider When Making Benefit-Risk Determinations in Medical Device Premarket Approval and De Novo Classifications* on 28 March 2012, providing greater clarity for FDA reviewers and industry regarding the principal factors FDA considers when making benefit-risk determinations during the premarket review process for certain medical devices. While reviewing PMA or *de novo* applications, FDA will consider whether the application provides a reasonable assurance of safety and effectiveness by weighing any probable benefit to health from a device's use against any probable risk of injury or illness from such use.[38] FDA's review process can result in the following outcomes:

- Approval—The PMA substantially meets the requirements of the applicable part of the regulations and the device is safe and effective for its intended use(s).
- Not Approvable—The PMA has major deficiencies, and remaining review issues are preventing approval (specifically identified in a letter to the applicant). This requires submission of a PMA amendment(s) to respond to issues, and results in an additional review cycle.
- Denial—The PMA does not meet the requirements of the applicable part of the regulations and the device is not safe and effective for its intended use(s).

PMA Amendments 21 CFR 814.37

Changes or revisions to the original PMA submission are submitted to FDA in the form of amendments. Amendments also are submitted to FDA for changes to PMA supplements.

Modular PMA

MDUFMA amended Section 515(c) of the *FD&C Act* to allow early FDA review of PMA information submitted in separate modules. Although the Modular PMA has the same content requirements as the Traditional PMA, the sponsor must meet with FDA to reach agreement on the content of the PMA "Shell," a framework of modules identifying the information necessary to support filing and approval. Generally, this occurs during a Pre-IDE Submission meeting.

In a Modular PMA, the complete PMA contents are broken down into well-delineated components (or modules), and each is submitted to FDA as soon as the applicant has completed it, compiling a complete PMA over time. The PMA is viewed as a compilation of sections or "modules," such as preclinical, clinical and manufacturing, which combine to form a complete application. The Modular PMA is useful particularly for devices at an early development stage, rather than for devices far along in the development process.

Each module is submitted to FDA as it is completed. The target FDA review period is 90 days for each module or amendment submitted in response to an agency deficiency letter. Upon receipt of the final module, a PMA number is assigned, and a 180-day review clock will start. The entire PMA user fee is due with the submission of the first module.

Advantages of the Modular PMA may include:

- more efficient use of resources
- potential reduction of PMA application review time
- ongoing open dialogue between FDA and the sponsor

Disadvantages may include:

- can be more expensive and lengthen time to approval
- the need to establish a plan prior to approaching FDA about utilizing the modular approach

Advice on filing a Modular PMA can be found in *Guidance for Industry and FDA Staff: Premarket Approval Application Modular Review* (3 November 2003).[39]

Streamlined PMA

A Streamlined PMA is designed for devices using well-known technologies for well-known disease processes. A PMA may qualify as streamlined if: the device has a review guidance; two or more previous PMAs have been approved for the same type of device; or the device has a study protocol jointly developed by the manufacturer and FDA. The Manufacturing Facility Inspection may be deferred if FDA completed a GMP inspection within the past two years. The review time is the same as for Traditional PMAs (180 days).

Humanitarian Device Exemption (HDE) (21 CFR 814 Subpart H)

The Humanitarian Use Device (HUD) program was established in 1990 with passage of the *Safe Medical Devices Act* and creates an alternative pathway for market approval for medical devices that may help people with rare diseases or conditions. As defined by 21 CFR 814.3(n), an HUD is a "medical device intended to benefit patients in the treatment or diagnosis of a disease or condition that affects or is manifested in fewer than 4,000 individuals in the United States per year."[40]

The number of patient contacts with a device may exceed one per patient, but the total number of patients treated or diagnosed with the device is fewer than 4,000 per year.

The HUD regulation provides a financial incentive for the development of devices for these small populations because manufacturers' research and development costs far exceed market returns for diseases or conditions affecting small patient populations.

To obtain approval for an HUD, a humanitarian device exemption (HDE) application is submitted to FDA. An HDE is similar in both form and content to a PMA application but is exempt from the PMA effectiveness requirements. An HDE application is not required to contain the results of scientifically valid clinical investigations demonstrating the device is effective for its intended purpose. The application, however, must contain sufficient information for FDA to determine the device does not pose an unreasonable or significant risk of illness or injury and the probable benefit to health outweighs the risk of injury or illness from its use, taking into account the probable benefits and risks of currently available devices or alternative forms of treatment. Additionally, the applicant must demonstrate no comparable devices are available to treat or diagnose the disease or condition, and they could not otherwise bring the device to market.

A sponsor must receive Humanitarian Use status by submitting a Request for HUD Designation to FDA's Office of Orphan Products Development (OOPD).

The request should include:

- a statement the applicant is requesting a HUD designation for a rare disease or condition
- the applicant's name and address
- a description of the rare disease or condition for which the device is to be used
- a description of the device
- documentation, with appended authoritative references, to demonstrate the device is designed to treat or diagnose a disease or condition affecting or is manifested in fewer than 4,000 people in the US per year.

FDA issued *Guidance for Industry and Food and Drug Administration Staff: Humanitarian Use Device (HUD) Designations* on 24 January 2013 to help sponsors demonstrate their devices qualify for HUD designation.[41]

The agency has 75 days from the date of receipt to review an HDE, including a 30-day filing period during which the agency determines whether the HDE is sufficiently complete to permit substantive review. If FDA notifies the sponsor the HDE is incomplete and cannot be filed, the 75-day clock resets upon receipt of any additional information.

When approved by FDA, an HUD may be used only in facilities that have an established local IRB to supervise clinical testing of devices and have obtained IRB approval for the device's use to treat or diagnose the specific disease. HDE amendments and supplements are subject to the same regulations as those for Traditional PMAs; however, the HDE amendment and supplement review timeframe is 75 days, the same as for HDE originals.

The Product Development Protocol (PDP) (21 CFR 814.19)

The PDP was authorized several years ago as an alternative to the IDE and PMA in *FD&C Act* Section 515(f). For Class III devices subject to premarket approval, the successful completion of a PDP results in market clearance and essentially is a PMA approval.

One intent of the *Medical Device Amendments* of 1976 was to create an alternate pathway for device approval and marketing by having the sponsor and FDA agree early in the development process on items needed for the successful analysis of a Class III device's safety and efficacy. Once agreement is reached, the PDP contains all the information about design and development activities and acceptance criteria. A project timeline is established, and information is provided to FDA sequentially.

The PDP includes:

- a description of the device and any changes that may be made to it
- a description of the preclinical trials, if any
- a description of the clinical trials, if any
- a description of the manufacturing methods, facilities and controls
- a description of any applicable performance standards
- samples of proposed labeling
- any other information "relevant to the subject matter of the protocol"

Upon completion of clinical studies, reports are furnished to FDA, which has 120 days to act on a PDP. This approach rarely is utilized.

PMA Supplements

When a significant change to the device approved under a PMA affects the device's safety or effectiveness, a supplement to the original PMA is required. This became law when the *FD&C Act* was amended by Section 515(d)(6).

PMA supplements are required in the following situations:

- new indication for use of the device
- labeling changes
- the use of a different facility or establishment to manufacture, process, sterilize or package the device
- changes in manufacturing facilities, methods or quality control procedures
- changes in sterilization procedures
- changes in packaging
- changes in the device's performance or design specifications, circuits, components, ingredients, principles of operation or physical layout
- extension of the device's expiration date based on data obtained under a new or revised stability or sterility testing protocol not approved previously by FDA (If the protocol has been approved by FDA, a supplement is not submitted but the change must be reported to FDA in the postapproval periodic reports as described in the Section 814.39(b).)

An applicant may make a change in a device after FDA's approval of the PMA without submitting a PMA supplement if:

1. the change does not affect the device's safety or effectiveness, and
2. the change is reported to FDA in a postapproval periodic report (Annual Report) required as a condition of approval of the device, e.g., an editorial change in labeling that does not affect the device's safety or effectiveness (Trivial changes, such as changes in the color of a label, would not have to be included in the postapproval periodic report.)

Pending supplements also can be amended with more information. There are several ways to file a PMA supplement:

PMA Supplement (180 days) (21 CFR 814.39(a))

The PMA Supplement is for significant changes that affect the device's safety and effectiveness and will require an in-depth review and approval by FDA before implementing the change. This also may require review by an Advisory Panel.

Some 180-day PMA supplements may be reviewed using the Real-Time Review process. In this process, the supplement is reviewed during a meeting or conference call with the applicant. FDA will fax its decision to the applicant within five working days after the meeting or call. The change must meet certain criteria to be eligible for this type of review. Supplements with detailed clinical data generally are not considered for this program. The criteria and process for the Real-Time Review program are outlined in *Device Advice: Real-Time Premarket Approval Application (PMA) Supplements*.[42]

Special PMA Supplement—Changes Being Effected (CBE) (21 CFR 814.39(d))

The CBE generally is used when the change enhances or increases the device's safety. It does not require FDA approval before making the change. The following changes are permitted:

- labeling changes adding or strengthening a contraindication, warning, precaution or information about an adverse reaction
- labeling changes adding or strengthening an instruction is intended to enhance the device's safe use
- labeling changes deleting misleading, false or unsupported indications
- changes in quality controls or the manufacturing process adding a new specification or test method, or otherwise providing additional assurance of device purity, identity, strength or reliability

30-Day Notice and 135-Day PMA Supplement (21 CFR 814.39(f))

A 30-Day Notice is used for modifications to manufacturing procedures or methods that affect the device's safety and effectiveness. If FDA does not respond within 30 days after notification, the change can be made to the device, and it can be marketed accordingly. If FDA finds the 30-Day Notice is not adequate but contains data meeting appropriate content requirements for a PMA supplement, the 30-Day Notice will become a 135-Day PMA Supplement. For more information, see *Guidance for Industry and FDA Staff: 30-Day Notices, 135-Day Premarket Approval (PMA) Supplements and 75-Day Humanitarian Device Exemption (HDE) Supplements for Manufacturing Method or Process Changes*.[43]

PMA Manufacturing Site Change Supplement

When the manufacturing site is changed, a supplement needs to be filed. The site must have received a Quality System/GMP inspection within the last two years. If requirements are not met, a 180-Day PMA Supplement must be submitted.

Annual (Periodic) Report or 30-Day Supplements (21 CFR 814.39(e))

Changes also can be reported in the Annual Report instead of in a formal supplement. However, to use this approach, a sponsor should seek an advisory opinion from FDA. In April 1996, ODE implemented a pilot program for "Real-Time" reviews of PMA supplements, where the sponsor and the FDA review team meet to discuss any concerns FDA may have. Results of the pilot program demonstrated faster review times for manufacturers and more efficient use of FDA staff time. Because this type of review is not available for all supplements, a sponsor is advised to contact its FDA reviewer to understand the criteria established for the "Real-Time" review program within a particular ODE branch and division.

Document to File

For changes not affecting the device's safety or effectiveness, the document to file process is used. FDA has very limited or no involvement prior to implementation of the change. Minor manufacturing changes and minor quality control changes can be documented to file, e.g., editorial changes to a Standard Operating Procedure (SOP) to make instructions clearer or combining two SOPs into one.

PMA Amendments (21 CFR 814.37)

An applicant may amend a pending PMA or PMA supplement to revise existing information or provide additional information. FDA may ask the applicant to amend its PMA or PMA supplement with any necessary information about the device the agency considers necessary to complete the review of the PMA or PMA supplement. If the applicant submits a major PMA amendment on its own initiative or at FDA's request, the review period may be extended up to 180 days. A major amendment is one containing significant new data from a previously unreported study, significant updated data from a previously reported study, detailed new analyses of previously submitted data or significant required information previously omitted.

A PMA amendment must include the PMA or PMA supplement number assigned to the original submission and the reason for the amendment.

Withdrawal and Resubmission (21 CFR 814.37)

Applicants may voluntarily withdraw their PMAs or PMA supplements. If FDA requests an applicant to submit a PMA amendment, and a written response is not received within 180 days, FDA will consider the pending PMA supplement to be withdrawn voluntarily by the applicant (abandoned).

An applicant may resubmit a PMA or PMA supplement that was withdrawn, FDA has refused to accept for filing or FDA has disapproved. A resubmitted PMA or PMA supplement must comply with the requirements of 21 CFR 814.20 or 814.39, respectively, and must include the PMA number assigned to the original submission as well as the applicant's reason for resubmission.

PMA Acceptance and Filing Review Process

During the administrative and limited scientific review, FDA determines whether a PMA is suitable for filing by reviewing the PMA submission for information required by the *FD&C Act*, the PMA regulations (21 CFR 814) and the PMA Acceptance and Filing Review Policy.[44]

Filing an application means FDA has made a threshold determination the application is sufficiently complete to begin an in-depth review. Within 45 days after a PMA is received by FDA, the agency will notify the applicant whether the application has been filed. The letter will include the PMA reference number and the date FDA filed the PMA. Expedited review status, if appropriate, may be communicated at this time. The date of filing is the date a PMA accepted for filing was received by the agency. The 180-day period for review of a PMA starts on the date of filing.

FDA will refuse to file the application for substantive review if a PMA does not meet a minimum threshold of acceptability. If the information or data are presented unclearly or incompletely or cannot withstand rigorous scientific review, FDA may consider the PMA incomplete and not file it. If FDA refuses to file a PMA, it will notify the applicant of the reasons for the refusal. This notice will identify the deficiencies in the application that prevent filing and will include the PMA reference number. FDA will advise the manufacturer what information must be provided, or steps to be taken, to make the application fileable.

For more information, see *Acceptance and Filling Reviews for Premarket Approval Applications (PMAs)—Guidance for Industry and Food and Drug Administration Staff*.[45]

Expedited Review

Devices Appropriate for Expedited Review

FDA considers a device or combination product containing a device appropriate for expedited review if the device or combination product:

1. is intended to treat or diagnose a life-threatening or irreversibly debilitating disease or condition
2. addresses an unmet medical need, as demonstrated by one of the following:
   a. The device represents a breakthrough technology that provides a clinically meaningful advantage over existing technology. Breakthrough technologies should be demonstrated to lead to a clinical improvement in the treatment or diagnosis of the life-threatening or irreversibly debilitating condition.
   b. No approved alternative treatment or means of diagnosis exists.
   c. The device offers significant, clinically meaningful advantages over existing approved alternative treatments. The device should provide a clinically important earlier or more accurate diagnosis, or offer important therapeutic advantages in safety and/or effectiveness over existing alternatives. Such advantages may include demonstrated superiority over current treatments for effects on serious outcomes, the ability to provide clinical benefit for those patients unable to tolerate current treatments, or the ability to provide a clinical benefit without the serious side effects associated with current treatments.
   d. The availability of the device is in the best interest of patients. That is, the device provides a specific public health benefit or meets the need of a well-defined patient population. This also may apply to a device designed or modified to address an unanticipated serious failure occurring in a critical component of an approved device for which there are no alternatives, or for which alternative treatment would entail substantial risk of morbidity for the patient.

For more information, see *Guidance for Industry and Food and Drug Administration Staff: Priority Review of Premarket Submissions for Devices*.[46]

Expedited Access Pathway (EAP) is a new voluntary program for certain medical devices demonstrating the potential to address unmet medical needs for life-threatening or irreversibly debilitating diseases or conditions and are subject to PMAs or *de novo* requests. FDA believes the EAP program will help patients have more-timely access to these medical devices by expediting their development, assessment and review, while preserving FDA's statutory standard for PMA approval (reasonable assurance of safety and effectiveness) and the statutory standards for granting *de novo* requests.

Through the EAP program, FDA intends to engage with sponsors of EAP devices earlier and more interactively during the device's development, assessment and review. As part of this program, FDA intends to provide, as resources permit, more interactive communications during device development and more interactive review of IDEs, PMA applications and *de novo* requests. In addition, FDA intends to work interactively with the sponsor to create a Data Development Plan (DDP) specific to the device. The DDP should outline all data the sponsor intends to collect in support of device approval, including what data will be collected premarket and postmarket.

Included below are the criteria FDA considers when determining whether a device qualifies for the EAP program. This program includes a four-step process:

1. request for designation as an EAP Device (EAP Designation)
2. agreement on a DDP
3. PMA or *de novo* request for an EAP Device review
4. if approved and appropriate, postmarket data collection and evaluation

FDA issued a final guidance document 13 April 2015. For more information, see *Expedited Access for Premarket*

Approval and De Novo Medical Devices Intended for Unmet Medical Need for Life Threatening or Irreversibly Debilitating Diseases or Conditions—Guidance for Industry and Food and Drug Administration Staff.[47]

Combination Products

Until 1990 and the introduction of the *Safe Medical Devices Act*, no formal process was available to determine which FDA center would regulate combination products, such as drug-device, device-biologic or biologic-drug products. Regulations since have established FDA makes a determination based on the combination product's primary mode of action. By making this determination, the agency in effect decides whether the item is a drug, a device or a biologic. Then, FDA determines which center (Center for Drug Evaluation and Research (CDER), CBER or CDRH) is the primary reviewer. However, representatives of other appropriate centers are included on the review committee.

If it is not clear whether the combination product is a device or drug, the manufacturer may file a Request for Designation with FDA. This compels the agency to classify the combination product and indicate which center is the primary review group. The agency must respond within 60 days. For more information on combination products, see Chapter 27.

Type of Communication During Review of Medical Device Submissions

During the review of a premarket submission, FDA's practice has been to communicate with applicants through either a formal communication (such as a Major Deficiency Letter or an additional information request issued through a letter, or through phone, fax or email, with a follow-up letter confirming the hold) or through the process of Interactive Review.

The four types of communication (Acceptance Review, Substantive Interaction, Interactive Review, Missed *MDUFA* Decision Communication) and the submissions to which they apply are defined in detail in *Types of Communication During the Review of Medical Device Submissions—Guidance for Industry and Food and Drug Administration Staff* and discussed in Chapter 4.

Establishment Registration and Product Listing

Registration and listing information provides FDA with the locations of medical device establishments and what devices are manufactured at each site and increases FDA's ability to prepare for and respond to public health emergencies. A US establishment owner or operator initiating or developing medical device specifications; manufactures, assembles, processes, repackages or relabels medical devices for domestic human use; or is an initial importer of medical devices (distributor for a foreign manufacturer), must register the establishment annually with FDA and submit medical device listing information, including activities performed on those devices, for all such devices in commercial distribution. Note if a device requires a premarket submission (e.g., 510(k), PMA, PDP or HDE) for clearance, the owner or operator also should submit the FDA premarket submission number.

There is a fee for annual registration for some establishment types. On 1 October 2008, FDA instituted a new payment process for those establishments required to pay the device establishment user fee. This process involves first visiting the Device Facility User Fee website (DFUF) to pay the user fee and obtain a Payment Identification Number (PIN). Once the payment has been received and processed, the owner or operator will be notified by email. The email will include directions to return to the DFUF website to obtain the Payment Confirmation Number (PCN) for the order. The PIN and PCN are required as proof of payment before the facility can be registered using the FDA Unified Registration and Listing System (FURLS).[48]

Changes brought about by *FDAMA* require foreign manufacturers of devices intended for US commercial distribution to register and list their products with FDA. Additionally, foreign manufacturers are required to designate a US agent to act as the official correspondent responsible for, among other things, submitting establishment registration, device listing and medical device reports (MDRs). This requirement had been stayed indefinitely in July of 1996 but was reinstated effective 11 February 2002.

FDA changed the requirements for medical device registration and listing as a result of the enactment of *FDASIA* and the publication of the revised Title 21 CFR, Part 807 on 2 August 2012.

Since Fiscal 2013, all registered medical device establishments have been required to pay the annual registration fee, regardless of establishment type or activities conducted there. In addition, certain establishments must comply with additional registration and listing requirements.

The initial registration and listing must be submitted 30 days prior to starting any operations at the establishment for the production and/or commercial distribution of finished devices. A device family with variations in physical characteristics should be considered a single device for listing purposes, provided the function or intended use does not differ within the family. All subsequent establishment registration and product listing information must be updated annually between 1 October and 31 December, even if no changes have occurred. Failure of an establishment to register or maintain its registration can render its commercial medical device products misbranded and subject to regulatory actions.

After 30 September 2007, *FDAAA* mandated that all registration and listing information be submitted electronically via the FURLS Device Registration and Listing

Module (DRLM), unless a waiver had been granted. This electronic registration and listing process replaced the previously used Forms FDA 2891 and 2891a, "Registration of Device Establishment," and Form FDA 2892 "Medical Device Listing." All owners or operators can access FURLS at any time throughout the year to update their registration and listing information as changes occur. Examples of changes to listings include:

- another device being introduced into commercial distribution
- a change to a previously listed device, such as place of manufacture
- a previously listed device is removed from commercial distribution, or commercial distribution is resumed

The information required for registering an establishment and listing medical device products is provided in 21 CFR 807.25 and is clearly cued during the electronic registration process. A permanent establishment registration number will be assigned to each registered establishment. FDA requires any person or entity initiating and developing device specifications and commercially distributing that device to register and list any such medical device products (21 CFR 807.20(a)). A person or entity that only manufactures devices according to another's specifications and does not commercially distribute the devices is not required to register. Registration and listing also are not required of contract sterilizers that do not commercially distribute the devices (21 CFR 807.20 (c)(2)). *FDAMA* repealed the previous requirement in 21 CFR 807.20(c) to eliminate the registration and listing requirements for distributors who are not importers, effective 19 February 1998.

As amended by *FDAMA*, 21 CFR 807 asserts entities that reprocess single-use devices for reuse in human patients are considered manufacturers; therefore, owners and operators of such establishments also must comply with registration and listing requirements. *Guidance for Industry: Enforcement Priorities for Single Use Devices Reprocessed by Third Parties and Hospitals*[49] provides additional information about this requirement.

Unique Device Identification (UDI)

Section 226 of *FDAAA* and Section 614 of *FDASIA* amended the *FD&C Act* to add Section 519(f), which directs FDA to publish regulations establishing a unique device identification system for medical devices. The Unique Device Identifier (UDI) Proposed Rule was published 10 July 2012, followed by an amendment, published 19 November 2012, modifying the implementation timeframe for certain devices. The UDI Final Rule was published 24 September 2013. UDI initiatives also are underway globally—the European Commission released a framework for a UDI System in April 2013, and the International Medical Device Regulators Forum (IMDRF) UDI Work Group issued a guidance document on UDI in December 2013.

FDA issued a guidance document, primarily intended for device labelers, on submitting data to the Global Unique Device Identification Database (GUDID).

The UDI should be created and maintained by device labelers based on global device identification standards managed by FDA-accredited issuing agencies. A UDI is required to appear on the label of every medical device and every device package, unless an exception is granted by FDA. This includes combination products containing a device constituent part; convenience kits; IVDs; human cells, tissues and cellular and tissue-based products (HCT/Ps) regulated as devices; and standalone software. For further details, please refer to *Global Unique Device Identification Database (GUDID)—Guidance for Industry and Food and Drug Administration Staff.*

FDA-CMS Parallel Review

FDA and the Centers for Medicare & Medicaid Services (CMS) (the agencies) have established a pilot program for concurrent review of certain FDA premarket review submissions for medical devices and CMS national coverage determinations. This process will reduce the interval between FDA marketing approval and medical coverage and will facilitate the development of innovative products and shorten the time it takes to bring these important products to patients.

During its pilot phase, the agencies will offer to perform parallel review for up to five innovative devices per year. Appropriate candidates for the parallel review pilot are medical devices meeting one of the following criteria:

- new technologies for which the sponsor or requester has a pre-investigational device IDE or an approved IDE application designation
- new technologies that would require an original or supplemental PMA or a petition for *de novo* review
- new technologies falling within the scope of a Part A or Part B Medicare benefit category and are not subject to a national coverage decision (NCD)

The pilot program is voluntary and will not change the existing separate and distinct review standards for FDA device approval and CMS coverage determination. It is only available for medical device technologies that meet the above criteria.[51]

Patient Preference Information

FDA believes patients can and should bring their own experiences to bear in helping the agency evaluate the benefit-risk profile of certain devices. This kind of input can raise important considerations during regulatory decision making for certain devices.

FDA's *Factors to Consider When Making Benefit-Risk Determinations in Medical Device Premarket Approval and De Novo Classifications* (*Benefit-Risk Guidance*) explains reviewers may consider certain data measuring patient perspectives during the premarket review process for PMAs and *de novo* classification requests, when such information is available. Specifically, patient tolerance for risks and perspective on benefits, in addition to several other factors, may be considered in FDA's assessment of the benefit-risk profile when the information meets FDA's standards for valid scientific evidence.

FDA issued *Draft Guidance for Industry and Food and Drug Administration Staff: Patient Preference Information—Submission, Review in PMAs, HDE Applications, and De Novo Requests, and Inclusion in Device Labeling* [51] on 18 May 2015, which takes the next step and provides guidance on patient preference information (PPI) FDA staff may use in decision making relating to these applications.

PPI submission to FDA is voluntary. Such information may not be relevant or appropriate for all device types. Further, not all benefit-risk scenarios are "preference-sensitive." PPI can be useful during FDA's benefit-risk assessment for devices in several major ways:

- help identify the most important benefits and risks of a technology from a patient's perspective
- assess the relative importance to patients of different benefit and risk attributes and clarify patients' thinking about the tradeoffs of these benefits and risks for a given technology
- help understand the heterogeneity or distribution of patient preferences regarding benefits and risks of various treatment or diagnostic options.

Summary

- FDA's device regulations comprise sets of classification rules for devices requiring agency clearance or approval. Devices may be classified as Class I, II or III. Reclassification, or the *de novo* process, allows classifications to be changed, but is complex. Classes I and II may require 510(k) Notification or be 510(k)-exempt. Except for a small and decreasing number, Class III devices require a PMA. The exceptions require a 510(k).
- Significant-risk clinical studies require FDA approval of an IDE.
- Pre-IDE meetings are mechanisms for sponsors to discuss proposals for submission strategies and clinical trials with FDA.
- Both domestic and foreign medical device manufacturers are required to register their establishments with FDA and list the devices they distribute.
- The unique device identifier (UDI) should be created and maintained by device labelers based on global device identification standards managed by FDA-accredited issuing agencies.

References

1. When and why was FDA formed? FDA website. http://www.fda.gov/AboutFDA/Transparency/Basics/ucm214403.htm. Accessed 3 May 2015.
2. How to Study and Market Your Device. FDA Website. http://www.fda.gov/MedicalDevices/DeviceRegulationandGuidance/HowtoMarketYourDevice/default.htm. Accessed 3 May 2015.
3. Medical Device and Radiological Health Regulations Come of Age. *FDA Consumer magazine*. The Centennial Edition/January-February 2006. FDA website. www.fda.gov/aboutfda/whatwedo/history/productregulation/medicaldeviceandradiologicalhealthregulationscomeofage/default.htm. Accessed 3 May 2015.
4. Federal Register/Vol. 68, No. 83/Wednesday, April 30, 2003/Notices.
5. Background on *MDUFMA*. FDA website. http://www.fda.gov/MedicalDevices/DeviceRegulationandGuidance/Overview/MedicalDeviceUserFeeandModernizationActMDUFMA/ucm109149.htm. Accessed 3 May 2015.
6. Medical Device User Fee and Modernization Act (*MDUFMA*). FDA website. http://www.fda.gov/MedicalDevices/DeviceRegulationandGuidance/Overview/MedicalDeviceUserFeeandModernizationActMDUFMA/default.htm. Accessed 3 May 2015.
7. Regulating Cosmetics, Devices, and Veterinary Medicine After 1938. FDA website http://www.fda.gov/AboutFDA/WhatWeDo/History/Origin/ucm055137.htm. Accessed 3 May 2015.
8. *Medical Device Classification Product Codes—Guidance for Industry and Food and Drug Administration Staff.* FDA website. http://www.fda.gov/MedicalDevices/DeviceRegulationandGuidance/Overview/ClassifyYourDevice/ucm285317.htm. Accessed 3 May 2015.
9. Product Classification. FDA website. http://www.accessdata.fda.gov/scripts/cdrh/cfdocs/cfPCD/classification.cfm. Accessed 3 May 2015.
10. 515 Program Initiative. FDA website. http://www.fda.gov/AboutFDA/CentersOffices/OfficeofMedicalProductsandTobacco/CDRH/CDRHTransparency/ucm240310.htm. Accessed 3 May 2015.
11. FDA and Industry Procedures for Section 513(g) Requests for Information under the *Federal Food, Drug, and Cosmetic Act*. FDA website. http://www.fda.gov/RegulatoryInformation/Guidances/ucm209841.htm. Accessed 3 May 2015.
12. User Fees for 513(g) Requests for Information. FDA website. http://www.fda.gov/medicaldevices/deviceregulationandguidance/guidancedocuments/ucm209852.htm. Accessed 3 May 2015.
13. 513(g) including 513(g) user fees. FDA website. http://www.fda.gov/downloads/Training/CDRHLearn/UCM400791.pdf. Accessed 3 May 2015.
14. Factors to Consider When Making Benefit-Risk Determinations in Medical Device Premarket Approvals and *De Novo* Classifications. FDA website. http://www.fda.gov/medicaldevices/deviceregulationandguidance/guidancedocuments/ucm267829.htm. Accessed 3 May 2015.
15. *De Novo Classification Process (Evaluation of Automatic Class III Designation)—Draft Guidance for Industry and Food and Drug Administration Staff.* FDA website. http://www.fda.gov/downloads/MedicalDevices/DeviceRegulationandGuidance/GuidanceDocuments/UCM273903.pdf. Accessed 3 May 2015.
16. Device Advice: Investigational Device Exemption (IDE). FDA website. http://www.fda.gov/MedicalDevices/DeviceRegulationandGuidance/HowtoMarketYourDevice/InvestigationalDeviceExemptionIDE/ucm2005715.htm. Accessed 3 May 2015.
17. Medical Device Classification Product Codes. FDA website. http://www.fda.gov/MedicalDevices/DeviceRegulationandGuidance/Overview/ClassifyYourDevice/ucm285317.htm. Accessed 3 May 2015.

18. 21 CFR 812, Investigation Device Exemptions. FDA website. http://www.accessdata.fda.gov/scripts/cdrh/cfdocs/cfcfr/CFRSearch.cfm?CFRPart=812&showFR=1. Accessed 3 May 2015.
19. Request for feedback on Medical Device Submissions: The Pre-Submission Program and Meetings with FDA Staff. FDA website. http://www.fda.gov/ucm/groups/fdagov-public/@fdagov-meddev-gen/documents/document/ucm311176.pdf. Accessed 10 May 2015.
20. Device Advice: Premarket Notification 510(k). FDA website. www.fda.gov/MedicalDevices/DeviceRegulationandGuidance/HowtoMarketYourDevice/PremarketSubmissions/PremarketNotification510k/default.htm. Accessed 10 May 2015.
21. Device Advice: Is a new 510(k) required for a modification to the device. FDA website. http://www.fda.gov/MedicalDevices/DeviceRegulationandGuidance/HowtoMarketYourDevice/PremarketSubmissions/PremarketNotification510k/ucm134575.htm. Accessed 10 May 2015.
22. Device Advice: Preamendment Status. FDA website. http://www.fda.gov/MedicalDevices/DeviceRegulationandGuidance/MedicalDeviceQualityandCompliance/ucm379552.htm. Accessed 10 May 2015.
23. Device Advice: Deciding When to Submit a 510(k) for a Change to an Existing Device (K97-1). FDA website. http://www.fda.gov/MedicalDevices/DeviceRegulationandGuidance/GuidanceDocuments/ucm080235.htm. Accessed 10 May 2015.
24. Device Advice: How to prepare a traditional 510(k). FDA Website. http://www.fda.gov/MedicalDevices/DeviceRegulationandGuidance/HowtoMarketYourDevice/PremarketSubmissions/PremarketNotification510k/ucm134572.htm. Accessed 10 May 2015.
25. 21 CFR 807.87. FDA website. http://www.accessdata.fda.gov/scripts/cdrh/cfdocs/cfcfr/CFRSearch.cfm?FR=807.87. Accessed 10 May 2015.
26. *Guidance for Industry and FDA Staff: Format for Traditional and Abbreviated 510(k)s*. FDA website. http://www.fda.gov/MedicalDevices/DeviceRegulationandGuidance/GuidanceDocuments/ucm084365.htm. Accessed 10 May 2015.
27. Device Advice: How to prepare a special 510(k). FDA website. http://www.fda.gov/MedicalDevices/DeviceRegulationandGuidance/HowtoMarketYourDevice/PremarketSubmissions/PremarketNotification510k/ucm134573.htm. Accessed 10 May 2015.
28. Ibid.
29. Op cit. 27.
30. Device Advice: How to prepare an Abbreviated 510(k). FDA website. http://www.fda.gov/MedicalDevices/DeviceRegulationandGuidance/HowtoMarketYourDevice/PremarketSubmissions/PremarketNotification510k/ucm134574.htm. Accessed 10 May 2015.
31. Database: Recognized Consensus Standards. FDA website. http://www.accessdata.fda.gov/scripts/cdrh/cfdocs/cfStandards/search.cfm. Accessed 10 May 2015.
32. *Guidance for Industry and Food and Drug Administration Staff: eCopy Program for Medical Device Submissions*, issued on October 10, 2013. FDA website. http://www.fda.gov/ucm/groups/fdagov-public/@fdagov-meddev-gen/documents/document/ucm313794.pdf. Accessed 10 May 2015.
33. *Guidance for Industry and Food and Drug Administration Staff: Refuse to Accept Policy for 510(k)s*. FDA website. http://www.fda.gov/downloads/MedicalDevices/DeviceRegulationandGuidance/GuidanceDocuments/ucm315014.pdf. Accessed 10 May 2015.
34. Device Advice: Third Party Review. FDA website. http://www.fda.gov/medicaldevices/deviceregulationandguidance/howtomarketyourdevice/premarketsubmissions/thirdparyreview/default.htm. Accessed 10 May 2015.
35. Device Advice: PMA Application Methods. FDA website. http://www.fda.gov/MedicalDevices/DeviceRegulationandGuidance/HowtoMarketYourDevice/PremarketSubmissions/PremarketApprovalPMA/ucm048168.htm. Accessed 10 May 2015.
36. *Guidance for Industry and Food and Drug Administration Staff: Acceptance and Filing Reviews for Premarket Approval Applications (PMAs)*. FDA website. http://www.fda.gov/ucm/groups/fdagov-public/@fdagov-meddev-gen/documents/document/ucm313368.pdf. Accessed 10 May 2015.
37. *Guidance for Industry and Food and Drug Administration Staff: Factors to Consider When Making Benefit-Risk Determinations in Medical Device Premarket Approval and De Novo Classifications*. FDA website. http://www.fda.gov/ucm/groups/fdagov-public/@fdagov-meddev-gen/documents/document/ucm296379.pdf. Accessed 10 May 2015.
38. Premarket Approval Application Modular Review. FDA website. www.fda.gov/MedicalDevices/DeviceRegulationandGuidance/GuidanceDocuments/ucm089764.htm. Accessed 10 May 2015.
39. Designating Humanitarian Use Device (HUD). FDA website. http://www.fda.gov/ForIndustry/DevelopingProductsforRareDiseasesConditions/DesignatingHumanitarianUseDevicesHUDS/default.htm. Accessed 10 May 2015.
40. *Guidance for Industry and Food and Drug Administration Staff: Humanitarian Use Device (HUD) Designations*. FDA website. http://www.fda.gov/ucm/groups/fdagov-public/@fdagov-afda-fda4you/documents/document/ucm336515.pdf. Accessed 10 May 2015.
41. Device Advice: Real-Time Premarket Approval Application (PMA) Supplements. FDA website. http://www.fda.gov/MedicalDevices/DeviceRegulationandGuidance/GuidanceDocuments/ucm089602.htm. Accessed 10 May 2015.
42. *Guidance for Industry and FDA Staff: 30-Day Notices, 135-Day Premarket Approval (PMA) Supplements and 75-Day Humanitarian Device Exemption (HDE) Supplements for Manufacturing Method or Process Changes*. FDA website. http://www.fda.gov/MedicalDevices/DeviceRegulationandGuidance/GuidanceDocuments/ucm080192.htm. Accessed 10 May 2015.
43. *Acceptance and Filling Reviews for Premarket Approval Applications (PMAs)—Guidance for Industry and Food and Drug Administration Staff*. FDA website. http://www.fda.gov/downloads/MedicalDevices/DeviceRegulationandGuidance/GuidanceDocuments/UCM313368.pdf. Accessed 10 May 2015.
44. Ibid.
45. *Guidance for Industry and Food and Drug Administration Staff: Priority Review of Premarket Submissions for Devices*. FDA website. http://www.fda.gov/MedicalDevices/DeviceRegulationandGuidance/GuidanceDocuments/ucm089643.htm. Accessed 10 May 2015.
46. *Expedited Access for Premarket Approval and De Novo Medical Devices Intended for Unmet Medical Need for Life Threatening or Irreversibly Debilitating Diseases or Conditions)—Guidance for Industry and Food and Drug Administration Staff*. FDA website. http://www.fda.gov/ucm/groups/fdagov-public/@fdagov-meddev-gen/documents/document/ucm393978.pdf. Accessed 10 May 2015.
47. Device Advice: Device Registrations and Listings. FDA website. http://www.fda.gov/medicaldevices/deviceregulationandguidance/howtomarketyourdevice/registrationandlisting/default.htm Accessed 10 May 2015.
48. *FDA Guidance: Enforcement Priorities for Single Use Devices Reprocessed by Third Parties and Hospitals*. FDA website. http://www.fda.gov/MedicalDevices/DeviceRegulationandGuidance/GuidanceDocuments/ucm107164.htm. Accessed 10 May 2015.
49. *Global Unique Device Identification Database (GUDID)—Guidance for Industry and Food and Drug Administration Staff. FDA* website. http://www.fda.gov/ucm/groups/fdagov-public/@fdagov-meddev-gen/documents/document/ucm369248.pdf. Accessed 10 May 2015.
50. Device Advice: FDA-CMS Parallel Review. FDA website. http://www.fda.gov/MedicalDevices/DeviceRegulationandGuidance/HowtoMarketYourDevice/PremarketSubmissions/ucm255678.htm. Accessed 10 May 2015.

51. *Draft Guidance for Industry and Food and Drug Administration Staff: Patient Preference Information—Submission, Review in PMAs, HDE Applications, and De Novo Requests, and Inclusion in Device Labeling.* FDA website. http://www.fda.gov/downloads/MedicalDevices/DeviceRegulationandGuidance/GuidanceDocuments/UCM446680.pdf. Accessed 26 June 2015.

Chapter 21

Medical Device Compliance and Postmarketing Activities

Updated by Andrew P. Zeltwanger, MS and Anthony P. Schiavone

OBJECTIVES

- ❑ Understand basic requirements for compliance with FDA regulations for medical devices
- ❑ Understand medical device postmarketing requirements for devices marketed within the US
- ❑ Understand US postmarketing requirements for medical devices, particularly Medical Device Reports (MDR and eMDR), corrections and removals (recalls) and medical device tracking
- ❑ Review US requirements for importing and exporting medical devices

LAWS, REGULATIONS AND GUIDELINES COVERED IN THIS CHAPTER

- ❑ *Pure Food and Drugs Act* of 1906
- ❑ *Federal Food, Drug, and Cosmetic Act* of 1938 (*FD&C Act*)
- ❑ *FD&C Act* as amended by the *Food and Drug Administration Modernization Act* of 1997
    - o Chapter III—Prohibited Acts and Penalties
    - o Chapter V—Drugs and Devices
        - ▪ Section 501—Adulterated Drugs and Devices
        - ▪ Section 502—Misbranded Drugs and Devices
        - ▪ Section 506A—Manufacturing Changes
        - ▪ Section 506B—Reports of Postmarket Studies
        - ▪ Section 518(e)—Recall Authority
        - ▪ Section 519(e)—Device Tracking
        - ▪ Section 522—Postmarket Surveillance
    - o Chapter VIII—Imports and Exports
        - ▪ Section 801—Imports and exports
        - ▪ Section 802—Exports of certain unapproved products
- ❑ 21 CFR Part 7—Enforcement Policy
- ❑ 21 CFR Part 803—Medical Device Reporting
- ❑ 21 CFR Part 806—Medical Devices; Reports of Corrections and Removals
- ❑ 21 CFR Part 807—Establishment Registration and Device Listing for Manufacturers and Initial Importers of Devices
- ❑ 21 CFR Part 810—Medical Device Recall Authority

- ❑ 21 CFR Part 814(e)—Postapproval Requirements
- ❑ 21 CFR Part 822—Postmarket Surveillance
- ❑ *Questions and Answers about eMDR—Electronic Medical Device Reporting—Guidance for Industry, User Facilities and FDA Staff* (February 2014)
- ❑ *Balancing Premarket and Postmarket Data Collection for Devices Subject to Premarket Approval—Guidance for Industry and Food and Drug Administration Staff* (April 2015)
- ❑ *Distinguishing Medical Device Recalls from Medical Device Enhancements—Guidance for Industry and Food and Drug Administration Staff* (October 2014)
- ❑ *Unique Device Identifier System: Frequently Asked Questions, Vol. 1 Guidance for Industry and Food and Drug Administration Staff* (August 2014)
- ❑ *Unique Device Identification System: Small Entity Compliance Guide Guidance for Industry and Food and Drug Administration Staff* (August 2014)
- ❑ *Medical Device Tracking—Guidance for Industry and Food and Drug Administration Staff* (March 2014)
- ❑ *Compliance Program Guidance Manual 7382.845: Inspection of Medical Device Manufacturers* (February 2011)
- ❑ *Design Control Guidance for Medical Device Manufacturers* (March 1997)
- ❑ *Guidance for Industry and FDA Staff: Recognition and Use of Consensus Standards* (September 2007)
- ❑ *Global Unique Device Identification Database (GUDID)—Guidance for Industry and Food and Drug Administration Staff* (June 2014)
- ❑ *Draft Guidance for Industry and Food and Drug Administration Staff: Medical Device Reporting for Manufacturers* (July 2013)
- ❑ Procedures for Handling Post-Approval Studies Imposed by PMA Order (June 2009)
- ❑ Postmarket Surveillance Under Section 522 of the Federal Food, Drug and Cosmetic Act (April 2006)
- ❑ *Medical Device Reporting—Remedial Action Exemption: Guidance for FDA and Industry* (September 2001)
- ❑ MEDWATCH Medical Device Reporting Code Instructions (April 2001)

Introduction

As discussed in Chapter 10, the core of US medical device regulations is contained in 21 CFR Parts 800–899, which provide the framework of requirements for the US medical device industry. This chapter is intended to meet the objectives above by providing a brief overview of how the Quality System Regulation (QSR) applies to medical devices, while focusing more deeply on postmarketing requirements, which serve to make medical device quality and design living processes that readily can be adapted to challenges and changes arising following a medical device's market launch. This system of requirements, from postapproval study results to complaint and adverse event analyses leading to actions taken on marketed products, exists as a sentinel for the safety of millions of medical device users in the US today.

The first section of this chapter is a detailed overview of the registration and listing requirements for medical devices. This is followed by a general restatement of the QSR as applied to medical devices, which will help lay the framework for further discussion on postmarketing activities and actions. This chapter then focuses on various postmarket activities, including medical device reporting, and importing and exporting medical device finished goods.

Establishment Registration and Product Listing

The ability to identify responsible parties is fundamental to any compliance system. Time spent struggling to find a medical device's source, especially as the result of a required field action, only serves to increase public health risk by delaying corrective actions for adulterated or dangerous products. Such delays are unacceptable from both an ethical and regulatory standpoint and are the basis for FDA's requirements for registration and listing of both medical device establishments and medical device manufacturing locations. As a result, facilities that produce or distribute medical devices for commercial sale and distribution within the US are required to register with FDA and update that registration annually. Depending on the individual activities at each registered location, many facilities also will be required to list the devices and associated activities in addition to their facility registrations. **Table 21-1** Domestic

Table 21-1. Domestic Establishments

Activity	Register	List	Pay Fee
Contract manufacturer (including contract packagers)	**YES** 807.20(a)(2)	**YES** 807.20(a)(2)	**YES**
Contract sterilizer	**YES** 807.20(a)(2)	**YES** 807.20(a)(2)	**YES**
Device under IDE investigation	**NO**	**NO** 807.40(c)	**NO**
Domestic distributor that does not import devices	**NO** 807.20(c)(3)	**NO**	**NO**
Any establishment located in a foreign trade zone involved with the manufacture, preparation, propagation, compounding, assembly or processing of a device intended for commercial distribution in the US	**YES**	**YES**	**YES**
Import agent, broker and other parties who do not take first possession of a device imported into the US	**NO**	**NO**	**NO**
Initial importer	**YES** 807.40(a)	**NO** Identify manufacturers per 807.20(a)(5)	**YES**
Maintains complaint files as required under 21 CFR 820.198	**YES**	**YES**	**YES**
Manufacturer of accessories or components packaged or labeled for commercial distribution for health-related purposes to an end user	**YES** 807.20(a)(6)	**YES** 807.20(a)(6)	**YES**
Manufacturer of components, not otherwise classified as a finished device, distributed only to a finished device manufacturer	**NO** 807.65(a)	**NO**	**NO**
Manufacturer (including kit assemblers)	**YES** 807.20(a)	**YES** 807.20(a)	**YES**
Custom device manufacturer	**YES** 807.20(a)(2)	**YES** 807.20(a)(2)	**YES**
Refurbishers or remarketers of used devices already in commercial distribution in the US	**NO**	**NO**	**NO**
Relabeler or repackager	**YES** 807.20(a)(3)	**YES** 807.20(a)(3)	**YES**
Remanufacturer	**YES**	**YES**	**YES**
Reprocessor of single-use devices	**YES** 807.20	**YES** 807.20	**YES**
Specification consultant only	**NO**	**NO**	**NO**
Specification developer	**YES** 807.20(a)(1)	**YES** 807.20(a)(1)	**YES**
US manufacturer of export only devices	**YES** 807.20(a)(2)	**YES** 807.20(a)(2)	**YES**
Wholesale distributor that is not a manufacturer or importer	**NO**	**NO**	**NO**

Establishments and **Table 21-2** Foreign Establishments, from FDA's Device Advice website (http://www.fda.gov/MedicalDevices/DeviceRegulationandGuidance/HowtoMarketYourDevice/RegistrationandListing/ucm053165.htm), show the registration, listing and fee responsibilities of both foreign and domestic establishments, based on the activities they undertake.

FDA requires establishments to complete their registration and listing activities electronically, unless the facility requests and receives a written waiver from the agency. As part of this process, Congress has authorized FDA to collect fees for device establishment registration. Congress sets the fee structure each August, prior to the registration period. For Fiscal 2015, the fee is $3,646. The electronic payment and registration process requires the registrant to first pay its annual registration user fee through the Device Facility User Fee (DFUF) website and then use the payment confirmation to register the facility through FDA's Unified Registration and Listing System (FURLS). The steps for completing registration are summarized in **Table 21-3** Annual Registration Process.

Table 21-2. Foreign Establishments

Activity	Register	List	Pay Fee
Contract manufacturer (including contract packagers)	**YES** 807.40(a)	**YES** 807.40(a)	**YES**
Contract sterilizer	**YES** 807.40(a)	**YES** 807.40(a)	**YES**
Custom device manufacturer	**YES** 807.20(a)(2)	**YES** 807.20(a)(2)	**YES**
Device under IDE investigation	**NO** 812.1 (a)	**NO** 812.1(a), 807.40(c)	**NO**
Foreign exporter of devices located in a foreign country	**YES** 807.40 (a)	**YES** 807.40 (a)	**YES**
Foreign manufacturers (including kit assemblers)	**YES** 807.40(a)	**YES** 807.40(a)	**YES**
Maintains complaint files as required under 21 CFR 820.198	**YES**	**YES**	**YES**
Manufacturer of accessories or components are packaged or labeled for commercial distribution for health-related purposes to an end user	**YES** 807.20(a)(5)	**YES** 807.20(a)(5)	**YES**
Manufacturer of components distributed only to a finished device manufacturer	**NO** 807.65(a)	**NO**	**NO**
Relabeler or repackager	**YES** 807.20(a)(3)	**YES** 807.20(a)(3)	**YES**
Remanufacturer	**YES**	**YES**	**YES**
Reprocessor of single-use device	**YES** 807.20(a)	**YES** 807.20(a)	**YES**
Specification developer	**YES**	**YES**	**YES**

Annual registration must be submitted each year between 1 October and 31 December, whether or not there have been any changes to the establishment's status or activities. Device listing information must be reviewed and updated at the same time.

Initial facility registration and device listing must occur within 30 days of the start of a facility's regulated activity or device introduction into commercial distribution in the US.

QSR Compliance

The QSR applies to finished device manufacturers that introduce those devices into commercial distribution. The legal definition of a "finished device" is found in the QSR under 21 CFR 820.3(l) and reads,

> "Finished device" means any device or accessory to any device that is suitable for use or capable of functioning, whether or not it is packaged, labeled, or sterilized."

The key to this definition, and one worth restating, is any functioning device or accessory, at the moment it becomes capable of functioning, is subject to the QSR. A small list of specifically exempted devices can be found in the *Federal Register*.

A detailed history of the QSR's development and its applicability to manufacturers can be found in Chapter 10 of this book. This section briefly highlights some key points relevant to medical devices. Quality systems, as they apply to medical devices and other FDA-regulated products, are known as current Good Manufacturing Practices (CGMPs). The scope of CGMPs for medical devices is contained in 21 CFR 820 and has grown and evolved greatly since its inception in 1978. Milestones in the evolution and development of quality systems and CGMPs can be found in Chapter 10.

One of the most important and elegant aspects of the QSR is its adaptability across the medical device industry. By providing the framework of general requirements for all device manufacturers, the QSR creates a system of requirements for procedures and processes individual manufacturers must develop for their particular devices. By placing the responsibility for detailing device-specific procedures and processes on the manufacturer, the QSR remains a living document applicable to current, state-of-the-art manufacturing and technology advances. This adaptability allows medical devices to advance with technology, rather than lag behind waiting for regulatory updates and changes. It is important to restate this flexibility represents an incredible manufacturer responsibility. The manufacturer must select specific QSR sections applicable to its business and develop the specific procedures necessary to meet them. This activity and the resulting objective evidence of its completion cannot be delegated to another party even though specific manufacturing, design, fulfillment and other activities can be. Meeting the QSR requirements and having objective evidence as proof is a core responsibility of the registered establishment.

The remainder of this chapter focuses on postmarket requirements that take effect once a device is released for commercial distribution and details these requirements and regulations.

Postmarket Activities

Following market clearance or approval and release into commercial distribution, medical devices move into a postmarketing phase under additional regulations and specific requirements, many focused on safety and the public health. Key features of the postmarketing regulations include, but are not limited to: medical device tracking; reporting serious malfunctions, injuries or deaths; managing recalls, corrections and removals; postmarket surveillance, including customer service and complaint handling; postapproval studies; and continuous product improvement.

Additionally, there are compliance activities spanning the total product lifecycle, including some postmarket actions. These include FDA inspections and enforcement activities, covered in Chapter 39; facility registrations, discussed above; and quality system maintenance, covered in Chapter 10. These activities, while not solely postmarket in nature, nonetheless are vital to maintaining the safety and effectiveness of commercially distributed medical devices within the US.

Medical Device Reporting

The Medical Device Reporting (MDR) regulation (21 CFR 803) provides the requirements for reporting device-related adverse events to FDA. The MDR regulation is far broader in application than the QSR and includes reporting requirements for manufacturers, importers and device user facilities. The expansion of responsible parties subject to reporting requirements developed, as is often the case with postmarket regulations, as an additional safeguard to the public health. By including direct reporting requirements for importers and device user facilities, FDA is able to react quickly to potential threats to the public health. FDA defines the responsible parties under 21 CFR 803.3 as:

1. "Device user facility" means a hospital, ambulatory surgical facility, nursing home, outpatient diagnostic facility or outpatient treatment facility as defined in this section, which is not a physician's office, as defined in this section. School nurse offices and employee health units are not device user facilities.
2. "Importer" means any person who imports a device into the US and who furthers the marketing of a device from the original place of manufacture to the person who makes final delivery or sale to the ultimate user, but who does not repackage or otherwise change the container, wrapper or labeling of the device or device package. Any person who repackages or otherwise changes the container, wrapper or labeling is considered a manufacturer as defined in this section.
3. "Manufacturer" means any person who manufactures, prepares, propagates, compounds, assembles or processes a device by chemical, physical, biological or other procedure. The term includes any person who:
    a. repackages or otherwise changes a device's container, wrapper or labeling in furtherance of the device's distribution from the original place of manufacture
    b. initiates specifications for devices manufactured by a second party for subsequent distribution by the person initiating the specifications
    c. manufactures components or accessories that are devices ready to be used and intended to be distributed commercially and intended to be used as is, or processed by a licensed practitioner or other qualified person to meet the needs of a particular patient
    d. is the US agent of a foreign manufacturer

Three key players are required to report to FDA as follows:

1. Device User Facilities:
    a. Report a suspected medical device-related death to FDA and the manufacturer. Report within 10 working days of becoming aware.
    b. Report a medical device-related serious injury to the manufacturer or to FDA if the manufacturer is unknown. Report within 10 working days of becoming aware.
    c. Submit a Form 3419 Annual User Facility Report to FDA no later than 1 January of each year.
    d. Additionally, the device user facility has a pathway for optional reporting of medical device malfunctions through MedWatch (https://www.accessdata.fda.gov/scripts/medwatch/index.cfm?action=reporting.home), the FDA Safety Information and Adverse Event Reporting Program.
2. Importers:
    a. Report to FDA and the manufacturer upon learning one of its devices may have contributed to a death or serious injury. Report within 30 days of becoming aware of the event.
    b. Report to the manufacturer if an imported device malfunctions and likely would cause a death or serious injury if the malfunction were

to recur. Report within 30 days of becoming aware of the event.

3. Manufacturers:
   a. Report to FDA if they learn one of their devices has contributed to a death or serious injury. Report within 30 days of becoming aware of the event.
   b. Report to FDA if one of their devices malfunctions and likely would cause a death or serious injury if the malfunction were to recur. Report within 30 days of becoming aware of the event.
   c. Report to FDA within five days of becoming aware of any instance or event requiring immediate remedial action to prevent unreasonable risk of substantial harm to the public health.

Mandatory reports for manufacturers and importers are, in accordance with FDA's published final rule in the *Federal Register* on 14 February 2014 (https://www.federalregister.gov/articles/2014/02/14/2014-03279/medical-device-reporting-electronic-submission-requirements), required to be submitted electronically through a system now known as eMDR. This change is effective as of 14 August 2015. Device user facilities are authorized to submit required reports electronically under this rule but are not required to do so. User facilities will retain the ability to submit written reports to FDA utilizing Form FDA 3500A, which has been updated to match the eMDR and *Medical Device User Fee and Modernization Act* of 2002 (*MDUFMA*) requirements. In conjunction with the final rule requiring use of electronic reporting for manufacturers and importers, FDA released a guidance document, *Questions and Answers about eMDR—Electronic Medical Device Reporting: Guidance for Industry, User Facilities and FDA Staff* (http://www.fda.gov/MedicalDevices/DeviceRegulationandGuidance/GuidanceDocuments/ucm175805.htm), detailing common questions and answers as well as instructions for completing the required eMDR process. Voluntary Reports, User Facility Reports, Manufacturer Reports and Distributor Reports of adverse events involving medical devices all can be found in the Manufacturer and User Facility Device Experience (MAUDE) Database. Searchable data for non-exempted reports stretches back for the previous 10 years and can be found at http://www.accessdata.fda.gov/scripts/cdrh/cfdocs/cfMAUDE/search.CFM.

How does a manufacturer "become aware" of a reportable event? The QSR, 21 CFR 820.198, defines in detail a manufacturer's responsibility to create complaint files and conduct investigations in a timely fashion. Further, the newly released Q&A guidance mentioned above defines "becoming aware:"

> "As a manufacturer, you are considered to have "become aware" of an event whenever [21 CFR 803.3]:
>
> - Any of your employees becomes aware of information that reasonably suggests that an event is required to be reported in a 30-day report or in a 5-day report that we have requested from you; or
> - Any of your employees with management or supervisory responsibilities over persons with regulatory, scientific or technical responsibilities, or whose duties relate to the collection and reporting of adverse events, becomes aware from any information (including any trend analysis) that an MDR reportable event(s) necessitates remedial action to prevent an unreasonable risk of substantial harm to the public health. In this case, you must submit a report no later than 5 work days after the day that you become aware."

Based on this definition, it is very important for manufacturers and importers to put proactive systems in place to rapidly collect, forward and analyze complaint data from all available sources. In recent years, this has grown to include social media. As manufacturers, distributors and importers increasingly use direct-to-customer social media advertising to market devices, the sources of complaint data multiply as well. It is critical to train customer service and general employees in the basics of complaint handling, so appropriate data are forwarded to the responsible departments in a timely fashion. Additionally, as telemedicine becomes more prevalent, user facility reporting requirements can expand into the "virtual facility." Regulation and guidance for this rapidly developing area will continue to expand to address communication technology advances.

MDR's fundamental purpose is rapidly gathering and analyzing medical devices' performance in the field and how that performance may impact both device users and the public health negatively. This analysis can result in a device recall, correction or removal.

Medical Device Recalls, Corrections and Removals

According to 21 CFR 7.3(g):

> "Recall means a firm's removal or correction of a marketed product that the Food and Drug Administration considers to be in violation of the laws it administers and against which the agency would initiate legal action, e.g., seizure. Recall does not include a market withdrawal or a stock recovery."

A recall is a voluntary action by a manufacturer or distributor as part of its overall responsibility, as defined the establishment's policies and procedures developed to conform to the QSR, to protect the public health from products presenting a risk of injury, are defective or are deceptive in nature. Recall actions can be requested directly by FDA, but this

Table 21-3. Annual Registration Process

Step	Registration Action
1	Log in to DFUF User Fee System (https://userfees.fda.gov/OA_HTML/furls.jsp)
2	Make the payment (acceptable methods include electronic payments (credit cards or automated clearing house electronic checks), wire transfers or submitting a paper check via the mail)
3	Obtain the Payment Identification Number (PIN) and Payment Confirmation Number (PCN)
4	Log in to the FURLS facility registration system (https://www.access.fda.gov/oaa/)
5	Select the Device Registration and Listing Module (DRLM)
6	Review and update the establishment information
7	Review and update the listing information
8	Certify all the information is correct and select "Submit"
9	Enter the PIN and PCN numbers as proof of registration fee payment
10	Once the above steps are completed and the confirmation screen is displayed, the establishment is registered with FDA
11	Updates to listings are possible throughout the year through the main menu of the FURLS site

typically is reserved for high-risk situations where, as a result of device user facility report of deaths or serious injuries with no follow-up report from the manufacturer, for example, FDA initiates the request as a direct intervention to protect the public health under the authority of 21 CFR 810.

Relevant recall regulations fall under several parts of Title 21 and include:

- 21 CFR 7—Enforcement Policy, particularly Subpart C—contains FDA's guidance on recalls and product corrections and is particularly useful for voluntary recalls
- 21 CFR 806—Medical Device Corrections and Removals—details the notification requirements for medical device corrections and removals
- 21 CFR 810—Mandatory Device Recall Authority—details the procedures FDA will follow in exercising its medical device recall authority under Section 518(e) of the *FD&C Act*

Recalls are classified into three designations, based on the evaluated degree of health hazard the product subject to recall presents. Health hazard evaluation is a critical element in the recall decision-making process and a key component in FDA's recall classification. Contributing factors to the evaluation can include, but are not limited to:

1. diseases or injuries that have occurred already
2. health hazard severity
3. likelihood of health hazard to occur
4. assessments of population segments at risk from the product

Using this information from the firm and the agency's separate subjective evaluation, FDA will classify the recall using one of three designations, which are, in ascending order of severity:

- Class III—use of or exposure to the product is not likely to cause adverse health consequences
- Class II—use of or exposure to the product may cause temporary or medically reversible adverse health consequences; the probability of serious adverse consequences is remote
- Class I—use of or exposure to the product can or will cause serious adverse health consequences or death

Once the decision is made to initiate a recall, a detailed recall strategy is necessary. This strategy will include particulars on identifying the devices in question; health hazard evaluation results; analyzing the device's market penetration and saturation; a communication plan for distributors, vendors or users; public warning plans; and effectiveness checks for the recall's communication and execution. FDA will review the strategy and make suggestions for changes as it sees fit.

FDA assesses recall activities' effectiveness through the initial and periodic recall reports from the recalling firm. Subpart B of 21 CFR 806 defines recall and removal reporting responsibilities. Part 806 requires a firm to report any recall that reduces a risk to health posed by the device, or remedies a violation of the *FD&C Act* that may present a risk to health, unless such information already has been provided in a correction or removal report submitted under Part 803 Medical Device Reporting or Part 1004 Repurchase, Repairs, or Replacement of Electronic Products, or is exempt from reporting. The health risk is the basis of defining the three recall classes, and reportable recalls generally are Class I or II. Reporting sometimes is dictated on a district-by-district basis, and the firm should establish a dialog with its district recall coordinator to determine its reporting requirements.

The initial report to the appropriate FDA District Office for a Class I or Class II recall must occur within 10 working days of the recall decision. The initial report should include the following, at a minimum, so FDA can conduct its own analysis of risk to health. The initial report requirements are found in 21 CFR 810(c):

1. seven-digit registration number of the entity responsible for submitting the corrective or removal action report (if applicable); the month, day and year the report is made; and a sequence number (i.e., 001 for the first report, 002 for the second report, 003, etc.), and the report type designation "C" or "R"
2. manufacturer or importer name, address and telephone number; and the name, title, address and telephone number of the manufacturer or importer representative responsible for conducting the device correction or removal
3. device's brand name, common name, classification name or usual name and its intended use
4. device's marketing status, i.e., any applicable premarket notification number, premarket approval number, indication it is a preamendments device and the device listing number (A manufacturer or importer that does not have an FDA establishment registration number shall indicate in the report whether it has ever registered with FDA.)
5. unique device identifier (UDI) that appears on the device label or package, or the device identifier, universal product code (UPC), model, catalog or code number and the manufacturing lot or serial number or other identification number
6. manufacturer name, address, telephone number and contact person if different from the person submitting the report
7. description of the event(s) giving rise to the information reported and the corrective or removal actions that have been and are expected to be taken
8. any illness or injuries that have occurred with the device's use; if applicable, medical device report numbers should be included
9. total number of devices subject to correction or removal manufactured or distributed and the number in the same batch, lot or equivalent production unit subject to the correction or removal
10. device manufacture or distribution date and its expiration date or expected life
11. names, addresses and telephone numbers of all domestic and foreign consignees of the device and the dates and number of devices distributed to each such consignee
12. copy of all communications regarding the correction or removal and the names and addresses of all communication recipients not provided in accordance with Section 810 paragraph (c)(11)
13. a statement as to why any required information is not available and when it will be submitted

Each recall is different, and FDA will set reporting frequencies based on the specifics of the case at hand. Reports will include such data as the number of affected people notified and methods of notification; number of affected people who failed to respond; amount of product returned; effectiveness check results; and recall completion timeframes. Reporting will continue until FDA terminates the recall.

Class III recalls and removals, since they are unlikely to cause a risk to health, have FDA recordkeeping, but not reporting, requirements. Recordkeeping requirements for recalls or corrections not subject to FDA reporting include: product name(s), model numbers, catalog numbers, classification, product codes, affected serial or lot numbers, description of initiating event, decision tree to justify non-reporting and all communications concerning the correction or removal. These records should be maintained in accordance with the manufacturer or importer's document retention policy for a minimum of two years beyond the affected device's expected life.

Not all incidents with a commercially distributed medical device are subject to recall reporting. Actions that can be exempted from reporting requirements include routine servicing and stock recoveries. However, these exemptions are contingent on their underlying root causes. If a manufacturer or importer conducts a stock rotation because the distributed devices are approaching the end of their labeled shelf life, that is not subject to reporting. If the same product were being replaced because it was in violation of the *FD&C Act* or poses a risk to health, it would not be exempted. Another example is device recovery for routine servicing and calibration versus recovery to repair a known defect that prevents the device from meeting its intended use. Proper complaint investigation and data trending will help a firm determine whether servicing can be considered routine or represents remedying a systemic defect.

Medical Device Tracking

To support its authority to order mandatory recalls and public health notifications, FDA also is empowered to require manufacturers of certain devices to track all such devices from manufacture through distribution and use. Use of this regulatory control allows the rapid identification of specific device populations by such information as user identity, serial number or batch information and manufacture date. This is found most commonly with devices that, while benefit outweighs risk in proper use, may present serious health risks in the event of a required recall action, such as implantables. Medical device tracking helps facilitate rapid and proper notifications and reduce risk.

While the regulations implementing tracking can be found in 21 CFR 821, the current list of tracked devices and the current guidance on implementing medical device tracking regulations has gone through several evolutions and can be found in the 2014 guidance document, *Medical Device Tracking: Guidance for Industry and Food and Drug Administration Staff* (http://www.fda.gov/MedicalDevices/DeviceRegulationandGuidance/GuidanceDocuments/ucm071756.htm).

No manufacturer or distributor tracking requirement exists without first receiving an FDA tracking order. This typically is done as part of the premarket approval or premarket clearance process.

Unique Device Identification (UDI)

On 24 September 2013, FDA published a final rule in the *Federal Register* to implement a US Unique Device Identification System for medical devices (https://www.federalregister.gov/articles/2013/09/24/2013-23059/unique-device-identification-system#h-7). This effort matches a worldwide regulatory effort to institute a medical device identification system to improve several key postmarket activities:

1. reduce medical errors resulting from device misidentification
2. more accurate adverse event reporting by making device identification easier
3. allow FDA, healthcare providers and industry to extract useful adverse event report information more rapidly to take appropriate, better-focused, corrective action
4. standardize medical device label dates to be understood clearly by device users
5. help establish a secure global supply chain and prevent counterfeiting

UDI implementation is ongoing and will continue over the next several years, resulting in a rapidly searchable database and tracking system with global significance. **Table 21-4**, taken from the FDA Device Advice site for UDI, shows the key UDI implementation milestones.

For more information about the UDI program, see:

1. Unique Device Identification System—Final Rule https://www.federalregister.gov/articles/2013/09/24/2013-23059/unique-device-identification-system#h-7
2. Chapter 22 Advertising, Promotion, and Labeling of Medical Devices and In Vitro Diagnostics, in this publication
3. *Global Unique Device Identification Database (GUDID): Guidance for Industry and Food and Drug Administration Staff* http://www.fda.gov/downloads/MedicalDevices/DeviceRegulationandGuidance/GuidanceDocuments/UCM369248.pdf
4. *Unique Device Identification System: Small Entity Compliance Guide: Guidance for Industry and Food and Drug Administration Staff* http://www.fda.gov/downloads/MedicalDevices/DeviceRegulationandGuidance/GuidanceDocuments/UCM409401.pdf
5. *Unique Device Identifier System: Frequently Asked Questions, Vol. 1—Guidance for Industry and Food and Drug Administration Staff* http://www.fda.gov/downloads/MedicalDevices/DeviceRegulationandGuidance/GuidanceDocuments/UCM410439.pdf

Postapproval Studies

Postapproval Studies (PAS) are directed by FDA to help ensure and study an approved and marketed device's continued safety and effectiveness. PAS requirements, similar to those for device tracking, are directed as part of the Premarket Approval (PMA) order, Protocol Development Product (PDP) or Humanitarian Device Exemption (HDE). Such orders will include the reason for the requirement, required reports and the number of patients or users to be evaluated as part of the PAS. PAS program and development responsibility and oversight are controlled by FDA's Center for Devices and Radiological Health's (CDRH) Office of Surveillance and Biometrics' (OSB) Division of Epidemiology's (DEPI) medical device epidemiology program. Further information on postapproval studies can be found in Chapter 9 Clinical Trials: GCPs, Regulations and Compliance.

Importing Medical Devices

Foreign manufacturers and/or importers of medical devices or radiation-emitting products wishing to import those products into the US must conform to applicable US federal regulations at all product development and lifecycle points.

As noted in the previous establishment registration and listing section, foreign manufacturers, regardless of their products' market authorization status in other countries, must meet applicable US device regulations to import devices. This includes registration, device listing, QSR compliance, reporting (as discussed above) and premarket authorization or clearance (as required). **Table 21-2** displays registration, listing and fee requirements by facility activity. In addition to meeting those requirements, foreign establishments must designate a US agent to represent the company within the US.

In addition to importing directly into the US, foreign manufacturers may contract an initial importer to further marketing of the manufacturer's device by acting as a go-between for the device's manufacturer and purchaser. Like foreign manufacturers, initial importers have several regulatory requirements to import medical devices into the US successfully. These include both the establishment registration and MDR requirements outlined earlier in this chapter.

Table 21-4. UDI Implementation Compliance Dates

Compliance Date	Requirement
One year after publication of the final rule (24 September 2014)	The labels and packages of Class III medical devices and devices licensed under the *Public Health Service Act (PHS Act)* must bear a UDI. (21 CFR 801.20) Dates on the labels of these devices must be formatted as required by 21 CFR 801.18. Data for these devices must be submitted to the GUDID database. (21 CFR 830.300) A one-year extension of this compliance date may be requested under 21 CFR 801.55; such a request must be submitted no later than 23 June 2014. Class III standalone software must provide its UDI as required by 21 CFR 801.50(b).
Two years after publication of the final rule (24 September 2015)	The labels and packages of implantable, life-supporting and life-sustaining devices must bear a UDI. (21 CFR 801.20) Dates on the labels of these devices must be formatted as required by 21 CFR 801.18.
	A life-supporting or life-sustaining device required to be labeled with a UDI must bear a UDI as a permanent marking on the device itself if the device is intended to be used more than once and intended to be reprocessed before each use. (21 CFR 801.45) Standalone software that is a life-supporting or life-sustaining device must provide its UDI as required by 21 CFR 801.50(b).
	Data for implantable, life-supporting and life-sustaining devices required to be labeled with a UDI must be submitted to the GUDID database. (21 CFR 830.300)
Three years after publication of the final rule (24 September 2016)	Class III devices required to be labeled with a UDI must bear a UDI as a permanent marking on the device itself if the device is intended to be used more than once and intended to be reprocessed before each use. (21 CFR 801.45)
	The labels and packages of Class II medical devices must bear a UDI. (21 CFR 801.20) Dates on the labels of these devices must be formatted as required by 21 CFR 801.18. Class II standalone software must provide its UDI as required by 21 CFR 801.50(b).
	Data for Class II devices required to be labeled with a UDI must be submitted to the GUDID database. (21 CFR 830.300)
Five years after publication of the final rule (24 September 2018)	A Class II device required to be labeled with a UDI must bear a UDI as a permanent marking on the device itself if the device is intended to be used more than once and is intended to be reprocessed before each use. (21 CFR 801.45)
	The labels and packages of Class I medical devices and devices that have not been classified into Class I, Class II or Class III must bear a UDI. (21 CFR 801.20) Dates on the labels of all devices, including devices that have been excepted from UDI labeling requirements, must be formatted as required by 21 CFR 801.18.
	Data for Class I devices and devices that have not been classified into Class I, Class II or Class III required to be labeled with a UDI must be submitted to the GUDID database. (21 CFR 830.300) Class I standalone software must provide its UDI as required by 21 CFR 801.50(b).
Seven years after publication of the final rule (24 September 2020)	Class I devices and devices that have not been classified into Class I, Class II or Class III required to be labeled with a UDI must bear a UDI as a permanent marking on the device itself if the device is intended to be used more than once and intended to be reprocessed before each use. (21 CFR 801.45)
Compliance dates for all other final rule provisions. Except for the provisions listed above, FDA requires full compliance with the final rule as of the effective date that applies to the provision.	

Additional responsibilities can be designated by contract and may include acting as an official correspondent or a liaison between FDA and a foreign manufacturer.

Finally, any product imported into the US also must, in addition to meeting any product-specific regulation, meet US Bureau of Customs and Border Production (CBP) requirements. CBP requirement violations, such as inappropriate declarations or failing to use only treated lumber or synthetic pallets for shipments, can result in product seizure or forfeiture at the port of entry.

Exporting Approved or Cleared Medical Devices

No additional requirements or restrictions apply for exporting medical devices approved or cleared for marketing within the US. Any approved or cleared device may be exported anywhere in the world without prior FDA export approval. The exception to this rule is nations currently embargoed by the US government (Department of State website: http://www.pmddtc.state.gov/embargoed_countries/). In most instances, trade embargoes have humanitarian exemptions in place for medical products, but export to a country subject to an embargo should be confirmed through the Department of State and may have additional documentation and inspection requirements. To support worldwide medical device distribution, FDA will provide, upon request and for a small fee, a Certificate for Foreign Government (CFG), a certification that the requesting establishment is in compliance with US law, and the device subject to the export was cleared or approved by FDA.

Exporting Unapproved or Uncleared Medical Devices

By definition, a medical device that has not been approved or cleared for market by FDA is adulterated and/or misbranded, creating a very complex regulatory quandary. How does a US manufacturer specifically design and develop a medical device for a foreign market? There is no straightforward, direct answer that can apply to all situations. The rules are quite complex and can vary from situation to situation, so the following general options are provided for manufacturers seeking export approval under *FD&C Act* Section 801(e)(1).

Class I and/or II Devices

The manufacturer and exporter of an unapproved or uncleared Class I or II medical device has to meet the following basic requirements to apply for 801(e)(1) approval to export:

1. The device must meet the foreign purchaser's specifications.
2. The device must not be in conflict with the importing country's laws.
3. The device shipping package must be labeled "For Export Only."
4. The device must not be sold or offered domestically.
5. The manufacturer must reasonably believe the device, if submitted for approval or clearance on the US market, would receive that approval or clearance.

Manufacturers sign an attestation their devices meet the above requirements as part of their application for a Certificate of Exportability (COE). The COE process also requires the exporting manufacturer to maintain records demonstrating evidence of meeting the above requirements; records are retained as Quality Records within the manufacturer's quality system. By meeting these provisions and obtaining a COE, manufacturers may export unapproved or uncleared Class I or Class II devices.

Class III/Banned Devices

In addition to the requirements above, manufacturers wishing to export unapproved Class III or banned devices also must meet the requirements of *FD&C Act* Section 802. To accomplish this, the exporting manufacturer must apply for FDA approval to export and submit the following:

1. device description
2. statement of the device's US status (unapproved, banned, etc.)
3. evidence from the importing government's regulatory agency or authority the device is not in conflict with that nation's laws; the device's US status is known to the importing country; and the import is acceptable
4. device safety data

Recordkeeping requirements are the same as those for Section 801(e)(1), and the manufacturer must maintain records associated with this application as quality records. Additional options available for Section 802 do not necessarily require FDA approval but have several other device-specific regulatory pathways contingent on the manufacturer's QSR compliance records. For more information, consult *FD&C Act* Sections 801 and 802.

Summary: Postmarket and the Total Product Lifecycle

This chapter showed that the medical device development pathway to marketing approval or clearance is actually only one of the first steps in complying with the QSR and continuing to provide cutting edge medical technology to the US and the world. Postmarket requirements, from registration and listing, to complaint handling and medical device reporting, serve to create an endless feedback loop, constantly providing design and process improvement inputs to the device while also acting as a sentinel to protect the public health. Key elements of this process detailed throughout the chapter included:

- registration and listing for both foreign and domestic establishments involved in manufacturing, distribution or importing medical devices
- complaint handling and Medical Device Reporting of adverse events through FDA's new eMDR system
- classification and responsibilities for manufacturers and importers with regard to recalls, corrections and removals
- when to implement medical device tracking and the new Unique Device Identification process currently being implemented by FDA

- import and export requirements for both approved/cleared and unapproved/uncleared medical devices

Recommended Reading for Additional Study:

- FDA Regulatory Procedures Manual (http://www.fda.gov/iceci/compliancemanuals/regulatoryproceduresmanual/default.htm).
- ISO 9001:2008 *Quality Management Systems—Requirements.*
- ISO 13485:2003 *Medical Devices—Quality Management Systems—Requirements for Regulatory Purposes.*
- Harnack G. *Mastering and Managing the FDA Maze.* ASQ Quality Press (2014).
- Kahan JS. *Medical Device Development: Regulation and Law.* Parexel International Corporation (2009).

Chapter 22

Advertising, Promotion and Labeling for Medical Devices and In Vitro Diagnostics

Updated by Rajaram Balasubramanian, RAC (US and EU) and Sharad Mi. Shukla, RAC (US and EU)

OBJECTIVES

- ❑ Understand the difference between "labels" and "labeling"
- ❑ Understand the basic regulatory requirements for labels and labeling for medical devices and in vitro diagnostics (IVDs)
- ❑ Understand the basic regulatory promotion and advertising requirements
- ❑ Explain the jurisdiction for promotion and advertising
- ❑ Understand advertising and promotional material submission requirements
- ❑ Explain possible enforcement actions for violations of relevant laws and regulations
- ❑ Understand medical device misbranding
- ❑ Understand use of Consensus Standards and future of graphics and symbols in medical device and IVD labeling

LAWS, REGULATIONS AND GUIDELINES COVERED IN THIS CHAPTER

- ❑ *Federal Food, Drug, and Cosmetic Act*
- ❑ 21 CFR 801 (Subpart A) General Labeling Provisions
- ❑ 21 CFR 801 (Subpart C) Labeling Requirements for Over-the-Counter (OTC) Devices
- ❑ 21 CFR 801.119 In vitro diagnostic products
- ❑ 21 CFR 809 In vitro diagnostic products for human use
- ❑ 21 CFR 809.10 General labeling requirements on content of labeling for in vitro diagnostic products
- ❑ 21 CFR 809.20 General requirements for manufacturers and producers of in vitro diagnostic products
- ❑ 21 CFR 809.30 Restrictions on the sale, distribution and use of analyte-specific reagents
- ❑ 21 CFR 809.40 Restrictions on the sale, distribution, and use of OTC test sample collection systems for drugs of abuse testing
- ❑ 21 CFR 99 Dissemination of information on unapproved/new uses for marketed drugs, biologics, and devices
- ❑ 21 CFR 99.103 Mandatory statements and information
- ❑ *Guidance for Industry and FDA Staff: Use of Symbols on Labels and in Labeling of In Vitro Diagnostic Devices Intended for Professional Use* (November 2004)

- ❑ *Guidance for Industry: Alternative to Certain Prescription Device Labeling Requirements* (January 2000)
- ❑ *Guidance for Industry: User Labeling for Devices that Contain Natural Rubber (21 CFR §801.437); Small Entity Compliance Guide* (April 2003)
- ❑ *Guidance on Medical Device Patient Labeling; Final Guidance for Industry and FDA Reviewers* (April 2001)
- ❑ *Guidance for Industry: Designation of Special Controls for Male Condoms Made of Natural Rubber Latex (21 CFR 884.5300); Small Entity Compliance Guide* (January 2009)
- ❑ *Human Factors Principles for Medical Device Labeling* (September 1993)
- ❑ *Labeling Regulatory Requirements for Medical Devices* (August 1989)
- ❑ *Device Labeling Guidance #G91-1* (Blue Book Memo) (March 1991)
- ❑ *Write it Right: Recommendations for Developing User Instruction Manuals for Medical Devices Used in Home Health Care* (August 1993)
- ❑ *Draft Guidance for Industry: Product Name Placement, Size, and Prominence in Advertising and promotional Labeling* (January 1999)
- ❑ *Draft Guidance for Industry: "Help-Seeking" and other Disease Awareness Communications by or on Behalf of Drug and Device Firms* (January 2004)
- ❑ *Draft Guidance for Industry and FDA: Consumer-Directed Broadcast Advertising of Restricted Devices* (February 2004)
- ❑ *Guidance for Industry: Good Reprint Practices for the Distribution of Medical Journal Articles and Medical or Scientific Reference Publications on Unapproved New Uses of Approved Drugs and Approved or Cleared Medical Devices* (January 2009)
- ❑ *Guidance for Industry: Accelerated Approval Products—Submission of Promotional Materials* (March 1999)
- ❑ *Labelling Recommendations for Single-Use Devices Reprocessed by Third Parties and Hospitals; Final Guidance for Industry and FDA* (September 2001)

Definition of Label and Labeling

As described in Chapter 18, a "label," as defined under the *Federal Food, Drug, and Cosmetic Act* (*FD&C Act*),[1] is a display of written, printed or graphic material on the immediate container of any article (for the purposes of this chapter, "article" refers to a medical device or IVD).

Label Outline

FD&C Act Sections 502(f)(1) and (2) require medical device labeling to bear adequate directions for use, proper operating and servicing instructions, warnings where a device's use may be dangerous to health, or any information necessary to protect the user(s). All devices require directions for use unless specifically exempted by regulation.[2]

The basic outline for labels and/or labeling specific to medical devices includes, but is not limited to:

- manufacturer, packer or distributor name and principal place of business
- device name, other required information
- description
- indications and usage
- contraindications
- warnings
- precautions
- use in specific patient populations (if applicable)
- adverse reactions (if applicable)
- prescription device statement or symbol[3]
- date of issue or latest revision of labeling bearing information for use

Additional Labeling Requirements for Over-the-Counter Devices

Regulations for over-the-counter (OTC) devices are found in 21 CFR 801.60. Label and labeling requirements for Investigational Device Exemption (IDE) medical devices are located in 21 CFR 812.[4]

IVD Label

In vitro diagnostic (IVD) products, according to 21CFR 809.3, are "reagents, instruments and systems intended for use in the diagnosis of diseases or other conditions, including a determination of the state of health, in order to cure, mitigate, treat or prevent disease or its sequelae."

IVDs are intended for use in the collection, preparation and examination of specimens taken from the human body. They are considered devices, as defined in *FD&C Act* Section 201(h). IVDs also are covered under a separate

FDA regulation (21 CFR 809). These devices have their own labels and labeling regulations within Part (809.10).

In addition to some basic items outlined above, specific requirements are determined by IVD type:

- proprietary name and established (common or usual) name, if applicable
- indications and usage
- manufacturer, packer or distributor name and place of business
- warnings/precautions per 16 CFR 1500
- IVD use statement and/or reagent use statement lot or control number

Reagent Label

- quantity of contents (i.e., weight or volume, numerical count or any combination of these or accurate indication of the package contents)
- proportion or concentration of each reactive ingredient
- storage conditions such as:
  - o temperature
  - o light
  - o humidity
  - o other pertinent factors as applicable
- statement of reagent purity and quality
- if reagent is derived from biological material, the source and a measure of its activity
- expiration date
- statement in reference to any observable indication of product alteration

Labeling

"Labeling" is a broader term and refers to any written, printed or graphic material on any article, on any of its containers or wrappers or on any material accompanying it. It includes any information such as posters, tags, pamphlets, circulars, booklets, brochures, instruction or direction sheets, fillers, etc., as well as labeling intended to be used in promotional activities, which sometimes is referred to as promotional labeling or marketing literature, for example, on a company's website.

The phrase, "or any material accompanying it," was defined further by the Supreme Court in *Kordel v United States*, 335 U.S. 345 (1948).[5] In this landmark case for the *FD&C Act*, the Supreme Court ruled the phrase, "accompanying such article" is not restricted or limited to labels on or in the article or package that is transported. This more-liberal interpretation meant a physical association with the device was not necessary. Thus, labeling is considered a wide variety of written, printed or graphic matter such as pamphlets, circulars, booklets, brochures, sales sheets, etc., bearing a textual relationship with the device.

Medical Device Labeling

The US Food and Drug Administration (FDA), therefore, recognizes three types of device labeling. The first two are FDA-approved labeling and promotional labeling. FDA-approved labeling is part of the submission process for a New Drug Application (NDA), a Biologics License Application (BLA) or a Premarket Approval (PMA) application. For prescription medical device products, the FDA-approved labeling must be included in or within the package from which the device is to be dispensed; otherwise, the product is considered misbranded since it lacks adequate directions for use (*FD&C Act* Section 502(f) and 21 CFR 801.109(c)).

The third type of recognized labeling falls under the Premarket Notification or 510(k) process. The 510(k) submission process provides draft labeling to the agency, but since this submission type receives "clearance," the labeling is not classified as FDA-approved. FDA does provide comment and request revisions to package insert labeling, thereby implying the labeling is cleared during the submission process. Industry practice refers to this labeling category as "FDA-cleared." In much the same manner as FDA-approved labeling, prescription medical device products cleared under the 510(k) process must be accompanied by appropriate FDA-cleared labeling, or the product is considered misbranded. FDA-cleared labeling is subject to change by manufacturers but, under guidance provided by FDA for the 510(k) process, significant labeling changes can require submission of a new 510(k) application for FDA review.

IVD Labeling (i.e., Package Insert, Instruction Manual)

- proprietary name and established (common or usual) name, if any
- indication and usage
- procedure type (qualitative or quantitative)
- warnings/precautions (per 16 CFR 1500)
- IVD use statement and/or reagent use statement
- test summary and explanation (methodology history)
- procedure's chemical, physical, physiological or biological principles

Reagent Labeling Requirements

- declaration of reagent ingredient quantity, proportion or concentration
- statement indicating presence of and characterizing any catalytic or nonreactive ingredients (i.e., buffers, preservatives, stabilizers)
- instructions for reconstitution, mixing, dilution, etc., of reagent, if any
- storage conditions:
  - o temperature
  - o light
  - o humidity

    - o other pertinent factors as applicable
- statement of any purification or treatment required for use
- physical, biological or chemical indications of instability or deterioration

IVD Instrument Labeling Requirements

A labeling outline for an IVD instrument can be found in 21 CFR 809.10(b)(6). Following is an abbreviated list of the basic requirements for instrument labeling:

- use or function
- installation procedures
- principles of operation
- performance characteristics and specifications
- operating instructions
- calibration procedures, including materials and/or equipment to be used
- operational precautions and any limitations
- hazards
- storage, handling or shipping instructions
- list of all materials provided as well as those materials required but not provided
- calibration details
- details of quality control procedures and materials required (i.e., state if there are both positive and negative controls)
- expected values
- specific performance characteristics (i.e., accuracy, precision, specificity and sensitivity)
- bibliography

Additional labeling requirements for OTC IVDs may be found in 21 CFR 801.60. Analyte-specific reagents (ASRs) are considered restricted devices under *FD&C Act* Section 520(e) and are defined and classified in 21 CFR 864.4020. The associated labeling is regulated by 21 CFR 809.10(e) and 809.30. ASRs are defined as antibodies, both polyclonal and monoclonal; specific receptor proteins; ligands; nucleic acid sequences; and similar reagents that, through specific binding or chemical reaction with substances in a specimen, are intended for use in diagnostic application for identification and quantification of an individual chemical substance or ligand in biological specimens.[6] Although most are Class I devices, some more-complex ASRs require submission as Class II or III medical devices.

Use of Symbols in Labeling

Unlike drug labels or labeling, there are no specific regulations establishing minimum requirements for key graphic elements such as bold type, bullet points, type size, spacing or use of vertical and horizontal lines for medical devices and IVDs. Within the labeling requirements, it is recommended instructions or any specific user-related information be clear, concise and understandable by the user—either a healthcare professional or lay person. Although there are no regulations for key graphic elements in medical device labeling, 21 CFR 801.15 does, in fact, reference some specific labeling format requirements for prescription medical devices. Of particular note is the requirement "[a]ll words, statements, and other information required by or under authority of the act to appear on the label or labeling shall appear thereon in the English language." This particular requirement has led to the interpretation that the use of any graphics, pictures or symbols in labeling that represent required information must be accompanied by explanatory English text adjacent to the symbol in order to "appear thereon in the English language." This has created no small challenge for manufacturers who utilize internationally recognized standards, such as (AAMI)/ANSI/ISO 15223-1:2012, *Medical Devices—Symbols to be Used With Medical Device Labels, Labeling and Information to be Supplied, Part 1, General Requirements*, for the development of their devices, requiring them to develop vastly different labels and labeling for devices to be marketed in the US and on international markets.

In response to industry complaints about this issue, FDA published a proposed rule in the *Federal Register* (Vol.78, No. 76, Friday, 19 April 2013) concerning the use of symbols and graphic representations. Under this proposal, the regulations (21 CFR 660, 801, and 809) will be amended explicitly to allow the use of symbols under the following conditions:

- the symbol was developed and approved by a nationally or internationally recognized standards development organization
- the symbol is part of a standard recognized by FDA for use in the labeling of medical devices
- the symbol is explained in a glossary accompanying the device
- additionally, the symbol, "Rx Only" would be officially authorized for medical devices

This standard was recognized on 17 October 2014 by all CDRH offices and divisions.

Guidance Documents

The labeling format for OTC medical devices is described in 21 CFR 801.60 and 801.61. Additionally, guidance documents are available to assist in developing such labels and labeling:

- *Guidance for Industry: Alternative to Certain Prescription Device Labeling Requirements* (January 2000)
- *Guidance on Medical Device Patient Labeling; Final Guidance for Industry and FDA Reviewers* (April 2001)
- *Device Labeling Guidance #G91-1* (Blue Book Memo) (March 1991)

- *Write it Right: Recommendations for Developing User Instruction Manuals for Medical Devices Used in Home Health Care* (August 1993)
- *Human Factors Principles for Medical Device Labeling* (September 1993)
- *Guidance for Industry: User Labeling for Devices that Contain Natural Rubber* (21 CFR 801.437); *Small Entity Compliance Guide* (April 2003)

The following guidance documents are specific to IVD labels and labeling:

- *Guidance for Industry and FDA Staff: Use of Symbols on Labels and in Labeling of In Vitro Diagnostic Devices Intended for Professional Use* (November 2004)
- *Guidance for Industry and FDA Staff. Commercially Distributed Analyte-Specific Reagents (ASRs): Frequently Asked Questions* (September 2007)

Human Factors and Label Design

Since most medical device labeling consists of instructions for using the device properly and safely and, where necessary, any care instructions for the device, it would be appropriate to evaluate and include human factors when developing, writing and validating instructional labeling. "Human factors" in this context is the study or evaluation of how people use technology, specifically the interaction of human abilities, expectations and limitations with work environments and system design. FDA's Center for Devices and Radiological Health (CDRH) has a webpage dedicated to human factors (http://www.fda.gov/medicaldevices/deviceregulationandguidance/humanfactors/default.htm), which includes links to specific FDA guidance documents.

It is important for all medical devices to contain complete and accurate labeling, as it is essential for the device's safe and reliable operation, whether used by a customer in a home or by a professional in a hospital.[7] In addition to reviewing labeling requirements per 21 CFR 801 (medical devices) and 809 (ASRs and IVDs), two FDA guidance documents are available to manufacturers containing examples of medical device labeling presentation, format and content: *Human Factors Principles for Medical Device Labeling* (September 1993) and *Write It Right, Recommendations for Developing User Instruction Manuals for Medical Devices Used in Home Health Care* (August 1993). These two guidance documents are important reference tools when developing and creating medical device labeling for both home and professional use.

With the increased FDA emphasis on risk management and human factors, as evidenced by guidance documents previously referenced and the issuance of recent draft guidance documents such as, *Applying Human Factors and Usability Engineering to Optimize Medical Device Design*, it is clear integrating label and labeling development into a manufacturer's design control verification and validation process is essential for FDA approval or clearance of medical devices and IVDs. Further, manufacturers must be aware if they modify any of their medical devices, the labels and labeling also should be reviewed to ensure they reflect all current revisions and/or specifications. Therefore, a manufacturer's internal change control process should include a means to capture such label and labeling reviews.

Jurisdiction for Promotional Labeling and Advertising

As noted in Chapter 18, the same agencies have jurisdiction over promotional labeling and advertising of medical devices, including IVDs, as over those for drug products. Healthcare product advertising is regulated by two federal agencies. First, the Federal Trade Commission (FTC), under the *Federal Trade Commission Act* (*FTC Act*),[8] utilizes three legal standards (represented as policy statements) in the regulation of all advertising: substantiation, deception and fairness. The *FTC Act* prohibits advertising that makes deceptive claims, fails to reveal material information, is unfair or makes objective claims for which there is no reasonable basis. FTC has primary responsibility for the advertising of foods, cosmetics, OTC drugs, non-restricted medical devices and other products whose safety, efficacy and labeling are regulated by FDA.

A Memorandum of Understanding (MOU) between FDA and FTC establishing the division of responsibility between the two agencies with regard to advertising has been in effect since 1971. Although FTC retains legal authority over some aspects of advertising, it generally defers to FDA's more specific authority. Under the MOU, FDA has primary responsibility for the labeling of foods, drugs, devices and cosmetics.

Each FDA center has its own division responsible for enforcing those regulations. Within the Center for Drug Evaluation and Research (CDER), the Office of Prescription Drug Promotion (OPDP) (formerly DDMAC—the Division of Drug Marketing, Advertising and Communication) is responsible for the regulation of prescription drug promotion (see Chapter 18). In 1993, the Center for Biologics Evaluation and Research (CBER) formed the Advertising and Promotional Labeling Staff (APLS) within the Office of Compliance and Biologics Quality to review and monitor the promotion of biologic products. Because some of the regulations are open to interpretation, this can result in the application of different standards to drug and biologic products competing in the same therapeutic class. In 2003, CDRH's Office of Compliance (OC) assumed responsibility for the review and enforcement of restricted medical device advertising and promotional materials. CDRH has a webpage with links to all guidance documents covering medical devices and radiation-emitting products (http://www.fda.gov/MedicalDevices/DeviceRegulationandGuidance/GuidanceDocuments/default.htm).

The 1976 *Medical Device Amendments* to the *FD&C Act* gave FDA authority over the promotion of restricted medical devices.[9] As defined in Section 520(e) of the act, "restricted medical devices" have the potential for harmful effect or require collateral measures for use. They have no implementing regulation. However, the approval order for a PMA or FDA's recommendations for many devices cleared for marketing via the 510(k) process, may restrict the device's sale, distribution and use as a condition of approval. Under 21 CFR 801(D)(b)(1), labeling must bear the statement: "Caution: Federal law restricts this device to sale by or on the order of a (indicate type of practitioner and, if applicable, required training/experience, and facilities to which use is restricted)." Promotional labeling cannot make claims beyond the intended use for which the device was cleared.

FTC retains authority for nonrestricted medical devices. It is important to note, while FDA governs the promotion of restricted medical devices, it also maintains authority over unapproved and uncleared devices used in investigational settings (i.e., clinical trials). Within the scope of 21 CFR 812.1, FDA allows the shipment of devices that otherwise would be required to conform with a performance standard or to have received premarket approval for the purpose of device investigation. Of importance in this section are the labeling requirements set forth in 21 CFR 812.5(a), which mandate the statement: "CAUTION—Investigational device. Limited by Federal (or United States) law to investigational use." Also required on the label or other labeling are descriptions of relevant contraindications, hazards, adverse effects, interfering substances or devices, warnings and precautions. Those shipping investigational devices also must refrain from including any false or misleading statements, including those that would lead a user to believe the device is safe or effective for its investigational purpose.

Promotional Labeling and Advertising

The terms "advertising," "marketing literature," "marketing communications" and the regulations surrounding them, are somewhat vague with respect to medical devices and IVDs. Generally, advertising is differentiated from promotional labeling simply by the practicality of supplying a copy of the complete prescribing information versus providing only a brief summary. Even though FDA does not specifically define advertising, the agency's interpretation of labeling, as noted above, is broad enough to cover most printed materials regardless of media, which include most advertising. FDA's view of advertising also includes virtually all promotional activities including, but not limited to, written pamphlets, letters, websites, social media pages, video content (television, Internet, hard disk, etc.), magazine ads, etc.

Unlike FDA regulations for prescription drug advertising and promotional materials (21 CFR 202.1), the agency currently has no specific advertising and promotional regulations for medical devices. However, the medical device labeling regulation (21 CFR 801.109(a)(2)) does discuss "other labeling," which FDA considers to be promotional labeling, and Section 502(r) of the *FD&C Act* addresses advertising for restricted devices.

Three applicable guidance documents provide FDA's current thinking on promotional materials and activities:

- *"Help-Seeking" and Other Disease Awareness Communications by or on Behalf of Drug and Device Firms (Draft)* (January 2004)
- *Consumer-Directed Broadcast Advertising of Restricted Devices (Draft)* (February 2004)
- *Good Reprint Practices for the Distribution of Medical Journal Articles and Medical or Scientific Reference Publications on Unapproved New Uses of Approved Drugs and Approved or Cleared Medical Devices (Final)* (January 2009)

FDA treats press releases, investor relations materials and exhibits as advertising and, therefore, considers them to be labeling by definition. Additionally, information posted on the Internet is considered promotional labeling rather than advertising.

Misbranding

Section 502 of the *FD&C Act* (21 U.S.C. 352) contains misbranding provisions for prescription devices. A device is misbranded and considered in violation of the law if the device labeling:

1. is false or misleading in any way
2. does not contain "adequate directions for use"

In the case of a restricted device, the labeling also must contain:

1. the device's established name printed in type at least half as large as the trade or brand name
2. a brief statement of the intended uses, relevant warnings, precautions, side effects and contraindications

21 CFR 801.125 does provide an exemption from labeling requirements in 502(f)(1) (21 U.S.C. 352). Under this exemption, medical devices for use in research, analysis, law enforcement and instruction (in pharmacy, chemistry or medicine) need not be shipped with "adequate directions for use." The devices must not, however, be for clinical use. In the case of sale for instruction, these devices must be sold to persons regularly and lawfully engaged in that endeavor.

The *Medical Device Amendments* expanded the authority of the *FD&C Act* over misbranded medical devices. The amendments contain further conditions under which a device is considered misbranded:

- The device's established name (if applicable), name in an official compendium or common or usual name is not printed prominently in type at least half as large as used for any proprietary name.
- The device is subject to a performance standard and does not bear labeling requirements prescribed in that standard.
- There is a failure to comply with any requirement prescribed under the *FD&C Act* (Section 518, 21 U.S.C. 36h) on notification and other remedies; failure to furnish material or information requested by or under Section 518; or failure to furnish any materials or information requested by or under Section 519 of the act on records and reports.
- The device is distributed commercially without FDA clearance on a 510(k) premarket notification submission.

Scientific Dissemination of Information

In parallel with the rules for drugs outlined in Chapter 18, FDA traditionally has objected to the dissemination of information not supported by the approved product labeling, typically referred to as "off-label" information. FDA does not prohibit physicians from prescribing drugs or devices off label, allowing the appropriate exchange of scientific information. However, the agency historically has had a restrictive policy on off-label information dissemination, which has been challenged repeatedly. In response to the provisions outlined in the *Food and Drug Administration Modernization Act* of 1997 (*FDAMA*) regarding dissemination of information, FDA codified regulations under 21 CFR 99 entitled, "Dissemination of Information on Unapproved/New Uses for Marketed Drugs, Biologics, and Devices." These regulations do not apply to a manufacturer's lawful dissemination of information responding to a healthcare practitioner's unsolicited request for information. The regulations state off-label information concerning the safety, efficacy or benefit of a use not included in the approved labeling for a drug or device approved/cleared by FDA may, conditionally, be disseminated to applicable individuals or institutions (healthcare practitioner, pharmacy benefit manager, health insurance issuer, group health plan or federal or state governmental agency).

The information disseminated must:

- be about a drug or device approved, licensed or cleared for marketing by FDA
- be in the form of an unabridged, peer-reviewed journal reprint (does not include letters to the editor or abstracts) or reference publication
- not pose a significant risk to public health
- not be false or misleading
- not be derived from clinical research conducted by another manufacturer without permission

The regulations (21 CFR 99.103) also require the disseminated off-label information to display prominently:

- the statement "This information concerns a use that has not been approved (additionally "or cleared" for devices) by the Food and Drug Administration"
- information on the research funding and the association of the authors and investigators with the manufacturer, and a statement, if applicable, if products or treatments approved or cleared for the use are presented in the off-label information
- a copy of the approved labeling
- a bibliography of other relevant articles (supporting and not supporting the off-label information)
- any other information that will provide objectivity and balance to the information being presented

The regulations also require the manufacturer to submit the information 60 days before dissemination and eventually submit a supplemental application for the new use that is the subject of the disseminated information.

The requirements in these regulations have been challenged legally by claiming protection under the First Amendment's provisions for freedom of speech. In response to such challenges, FDA clarified that rather than defining the requirements, these regulations provide sponsors with a "safe harbor" to disseminate information on unapproved new uses for marketed drugs, biologics and devices under specific conditions without threat of enforcement action. This safe harbor allows for the dissemination of information regarding the safety, effectiveness or benefits of new uses of approved or cleared products, but does not provide for statements about approved uses FDA otherwise would find misleading.

FDA reserves the right, on a case-by-case basis, to prosecute a manufacturer for misbranding its product if it can be shown the company was promoting an unapproved use. At least one court has sided with industry, opining FDA permits physicians to practice medicine and use pharmaceuticals and devices off-label, but "prohibits the free flow of information [from industry] that would inform that outcome" (United States v. Caronia, 703 F.3d 149 (2d Cir. 2012). While not the law of the land, this ruling protects this dissemination of information under the auspices of free speech.

In January 2009, the guidance entitled, *Good Reprint Practices for the Distribution of Medical Journal Articles and Medical or Scientific Reference Publications on Unapproved New Uses of Approved Drugs and Approved or Cleared Medical Devices* was issued. Much of this draft guidance originates from the regulations found in 21 CFR 99. It discusses the:

- various types of reprints, articles and reference publications permitted to be distributed
- manner in which scientific and medical information is disseminated

Enforcement

FDA can enforce violations of the *FD&C Act* or agency regulations through a variety of mechanisms, including Notices of Violations (NOV), Untitled Letters or Warning Letters and, if the violation warrants, referring the issue for judicial action. With regard to devices, FDA will look at such things as a company's website, videos, brochures, flyers/promotional flyers, advertisements in journals, bulk mailings, press releases and newsletters. FDA usually sends an NOV for the least violative practices that, in the agency's opinion, do not greatly jeopardize the public health. An NOV usually requires only that the company stop using materials containing the claim the agency found to be violative. FDA also may issue a Warning Letter with or without a prior NOV letter. Warning Letters contain stronger language and generally are addressed to the company's CEO. In addition to requiring the company to cease using the violative materials, Warning Letters may require the company to perform corrective actions. For example, a company may be required to run a remedial advertisement to reach the same audience as the original violative advertisement or disseminate corrective information through the issue of a "Dear Healthcare Professional" letter as described in 21 CFR 200.5(c)(3). Warning Letters also frequently direct the sponsor to provide FDA with information on any other promotional items that contain similar messages. All FDA Warning Letters, regardless of issuing center or office, are available at http://www.fda.gov/ICECI/EnforcementActions/WarningLetters/default.htm.

With the advent of social media, a new frontier of advertisement has sprung up within the medical device and pharmaceutical industries. FDA has delayed providing guidance to industry on this topic; therefore, there is no clear direction on proper use of these newer tools. Regardless of its lack of direction, FDA still is taking enforcement actions against companies it deems are breaking the rules in the use of social media. FDA has cited "liking" consumer comments on Facebook in a Warning Letter. The agency's apparent rationale is the "like" by the company is an endorsement of uncleared or unapproved claims (See Amarc Enterprises Warning Letter http://www.fda.gov/ICECI/EnforcementActions/WarningLetters/2012/ucm340266.htm).

While this example is for a drug, it shows the agency's thinking with regard to social media, and the care a company must take with its online presence. If FDA is not satisfied by the sponsor's response to the actions, it may choose to recommend enforcement action, carried out by the Department of Justice, in the form of injunctions, seizures and/or criminal prosecution. One possible outcome is the company agrees to enter into an arrangement with the government, called a consent decree. A consent decree places severe restrictions on company operations to ensure the firm comes into compliance.

Actions That May be Brought by Competitors

The *Lanham Act*[10] of 1946 (*US Trademark Act*) allows private parties a course of action against false and misleading advertising. Trademarks, themselves, identify a product's source. The *Lanham Act* prohibits use of another's mark and prohibits false or unfair advertising and is administered by the Patent and Trademark Office (PTO). This act has been amended several times under the *Trademark Law Revision Act* of 1988, which made it easier to register trademarks, and the *Trademark Dilution Act* of 1995, which prohibited the use of terms that would dilute a trademark (e.g., Buick aspirin).

Although not invoked often in these cases, state laws covering false advertising, defamation and disparagement also can be applied to comparative advertising. FTC brings cases, primarily before administrative judges, against those companies it believes are making misleading statements in their promotions. In cases of fraud, FTC brings these into federal court. Many companies will settle out of court, agreeing to "cease and desist" while not admitting guilt.

Summary

- Labeling subject to FDA regulations includes the container label, package insert used by the physician, patient labeling/medication guide and promotional labeling.
- FDA and FTC regulate healthcare product advertising. FDA regulates advertising for drugs (CDER, OPDP) and restricted medical devices (CDRH, OC) under the *FD&C Act* and regulates biologics (CBER, APLS) under the *PHS Act.* FTC regulates food, cosmetics, OTC drugs and nonrestricted medical devices under the *FTC Act.*
- Advertising and promotional materials must not be false or misleading, must present fair balance and must reveal material facts.
- Advertising and promotional labeling are not allowed for unapproved products or unapproved uses of an approved product.
- FDA does, conditionally, allow for the appropriate exchange of scientific materials (unsolicited requests, scientific exhibits).
- FDA can enforce violations through NOVs, Warning Letters or judicial action (consent decrees, injunctions and seizures).

References

1. *Food, Drug, and Cosmetic Act* of 1938 (under Title 21 of the United States Code (U.S.C.)).
2. 21 CFR Part 801 Labeling. FDA website. http://www.accessdata.fda.gov/scripts/cdrh/cfdocs/cfcfr/cfrsearch.cfm?cfrpart=801 . Accessed 16 June 2015.
3. *Guidance for Industry: Alternative to Certain Prescription Device Labeling Requirements* (January 2000). FDA website. http://www.

fda.gov/downloads/MedicalDevices/DeviceRegulationandGuidance/GuidanceDocuments/ucm072748.pdf . Accessed 16 June 2015.
4. 21 CFR Part 812 Investigational Device Exemptions. FDA website. http://www.accessdata.fda.gov/scripts/cdrh/cfdocs/cfcfr/cfrsearch.cfm?cfrpart=812. Accessed 12 June 2015.
5. Kordel v United States, 335 U.S. 345 (1948). US Supreme Court website. http://supreme.justia.com/us/335/345/. Accessed 16 June 2015.
6. 21 CFR 864.4020(a) Analyte specific reagents, Identification. FDA website. http://www.accessdata.fda.gov/scripts/cdrh/cfdocs/cfcfr/cfrsearch.cfm?fr=864.4020. Accessed 12 June 2015.
7. *Human Factors Principles for Medical Device Labeling* (September 1993). FDA website. http://www.fda.gov/downloads/MedicalDevices/.../UCM095300.pdf. Accessed 12 June 2015.
8. *Federal Trade Commission Act* of 1914 (*FTC Act*).
9. *Public Health Service Act* of 1944 (*PHS Act*), 42 USC Section 351 [262].
10. *Trademark Act* of 1946 (*Lanham Act*), 15 USC Chapter 22.

Chapter 23

In Vitro Diagnostics Submissions and Compliance

Updated by Jocelyn Jennings, MS, RAC

OBJECTIVES

- ❑ Know the FDA centers with oversight of in vitro diagnostic devices (IVD)
- ❑ Know the definition of an in vitro diagnostic device
- ❑ Understand the risk-based classification of IVDs
- ❑ Understand *CLIA* categorization
- ❑ Understand the presubmission process, regulatory submission types and their requirements
- ❑ Understand the *de novo* classification process
- ❑ Understand the framework for oversight of LDTs

LAWS, REGULATIONS AND GUIDELINES COVERED IN THIS CHAPTER

- ❑ 21 CFR 50, Protection of human subjects
- ❑ 21 CFR 54, Financial Disclosure
- ❑ 21 CFR 56, Institutional review boards
- ❑ 21 CFR 801, Labeling
- ❑ 21 CFR 807, Subpart E, Premarket Notification procedures
- ❑ 21 CFR 809, In vitro diagnostic products for human use
- ❑ 21 CFR 812, Investigational device exemptions
- ❑ 21 CFR 814, Premarket approval of medical devices
- ❑ 21 CFR 820, Quality system regulation
- ❑ 21 CFR 862, Clinical chemistry and clinical toxicology devices
- ❑ 21 CFR 864, Hematology and pathology devices
- ❑ 21 CFR 866, Immunology and microbiology devices
- ❑ 42 CFR 493, Laboratory Requirements
- ❑ *Guidance for Industry and FDA Staff: In Vitro Diagnostic (IVD) Device Studies—Frequently Asked Questions* (June 2010)
- ❑ *Guidance for Industry and FDA Staff: Administrative Procedures for CLIA Categorization* (March 2014)
- ❑ *Draft Guidance for Industry and FDA Staff: De Novo Classification Process (Evaluation of Automatic Class III Designation* (August 2014)

- ❑ *Draft Guidance for Industry and FDA Staff: eCopy Program for Medical Device Submissions* (October 2013)
- ❑ *Guidance for the Content of Premarket Submissions for Software Contained in Medical Devices* (May 2005)
- ❑ *Guidance for Industry and FDA Staff: Commercially Distributed Analyte Specific Reagents (ASRs): Frequently Asked Questions* (September 2007)
- ❑ *Draft Guidance for Industry and FDA Staff: Requests for Feedback on Medical Device Submissions: The Pre-Submission Program and Meetings with Food and Drug Administration Staff* (February 2014)
- ❑ *Guidance for Industry and FDA Staff: Content of Premarket Submissions for Management of Cybersecurity in Medical Devices* (October 2014)
- ❑ *Draft Guidance for Industry, FDA Staff and Clinical Laboratories: Framework for Regulatory Oversight of Laboratory Developed Tests (LDTs)* (October 2014)

Introduction

The Center for Devices and Radiological Health (CDRH) and the Center for Biologics Evaluation and Research (CBER), under a 1991 intercenter agreement, both have oversight of in vitro diagnostic devices (IVDs). CDRH was assigned the lead role for policy development, procedural regulations, regulating all IVDs not assigned to CBER, small business assistance programs, registration and listing, GMP advisory activities and medical device reporting. CBER was assigned the lead role in regulating all IVDs for screening or confirmatory laboratory tests associated with blood banking operations, as well as those medical devices intended for use in collecting, processing, storing and administering blood products and their components. CBER's Office of Blood Research and Review (OBRR) is responsible for these activities. Each center retains authority for surveillance activities and compliance actions, issuing special controls guidance documents and performance standards and reviewing Investigational Device Exemption (IDE), 510(k) and Premarket Approval (PMA) submissions.

The Office of In Vitro Diagnostics and Radiological Health (OIR) (formerly Office of In Vitro Diagnostic Device Evaluation and Safety (OIVD)) consolidates all regulatory activities for IVDs and radiological medical devices, along with electronic product radiation control responsibilities and leadership of the Mammography Quality Program. OIR is comprised of the Office of the Director (OD), which includes personalized medicine staff and six divisions. Of the six divisions, four are the main review divisions for IVDs: Division of Chemistry and Toxicology (DCTD), Division of Immunology and Hematology (DIHD), Division of Microbiology Devices (DMD) and Division of Molecular Genetics and Pathology (DMGP).

OIR also administers complexity categorization and waiver determination under the *Clinical Laboratory Improvement Amendments* of 1988 (*CLIA*). *CLIA* sets standards and certification requirements for clinical laboratory tests.

Definitions

The US Food and Drug Administration (FDA) defines IVDs in Title 21 of the Code of Federal Regulations (CFR) Part 809.3 as "products that are those reagents, instruments, and systems intended for use in diagnosis of disease or other conditions, including a determination of the state of health, in order to cure, mitigate, treat, or prevent disease or its sequelae." Such products are intended for use in the collection, preparation and examination of specimens taken from the human body. These products are "devices" as defined in Section 210(h) of the *Federal Food, Drug, and Cosmetic Act* (*FD&C Act*) and also may be "biological products" subject to Section 351 of the *Public Health Service Act* (*PHS Act*). IVD products are labeled "For In vitro diagnostic use" (21 CFR 809.10(a)(4)) or will carry the IVD symbol.

Additionally, the regulations in 21 CFR 809.10 and 21 CFR 864 define four other types of IVDs: Research Use Only (RUO), Investigational Use Only (IUO), General Purpose Reagent (GPR) and Analyte Specific Reagent (ASR). Neither RUO nor IUO products are considered to be effective IVDs and can be shipped or delivered for an investigation not subject to 21 CFR 812 (IDEs).

RUOs are IVD products in the laboratory research phase of development and not represented as effective IVDs (21 CFR 809.10(c)(2)(i)). Such products must be labeled prominently with the following statement: "For Research Use Only. Not for use in diagnostic procedures." RUO products are reagents, instruments or systems under development and the focus of manufacturer-initiated studies to evaluate design, limited-scale performance and such issues as test usability. They are being evaluated for their potential use as IVDs. Alternatively, some RUO products are used in conducting nonclinical laboratory research with goals other than commercial IVD product development (i.e., these RUOs are used to carry out research and are not, themselves, the object of the research) and are used in basic life science research and not intended for further clinical diagnostic use development.

IUO products are those being shipped or delivered for product testing prior to full commercial marketing (e.g., for use on specimens derived from humans to compare usefulness of the product with other products or procedures currently in use or recognized as useful) (21 CFR 809.10(c)(2)(ii)). IUO products are reagents, instruments or test systems being used in a clinical investigation or research involving one or more subjects to determine a device's safety and effectiveness (21 CFR 812.3(h)). Such products must be labeled prominently with the following statement: "For Investigational Use Only. The performance characteristics of this product have not been established."

GPR products are chemical reagents with a general laboratory application, used to collect, prepare and examine specimens from the human body for diagnostic purposes, and not labeled or otherwise intended for specific diagnostic application (21 CFR 864.4010(a)). They may be either individual substances or multiple substances reformulated that, when combined with or used in conjunction with an appropriate ASR and other GPR products, are part of a diagnostic test procedure or system constituting a finished IVD test. GPRs do not include laboratory machinery, automated or powered systems. Examples of GPRs are cytological preservatives, isotonic solutions and pH buffers. Importantly, GPRs are classified as Class I (general controls) and exempt from premarket notification, subject to the limitations described in 21 CFR 864.9. Such products must be labeled in accordance with 21 CFR 809.10(d) with basic identifying information, storage conditions, warnings and precautions and the statement: "For Laboratory Use."

ASR products are antibodies, both polyclonal and monoclonal, specific receptor proteins, ligands, nucleic acid sequences and similar reagents that, through specific binding or chemical reaction with substances in a specimen, are intended for use in a diagnostic application for identifying and quantifying an individual chemical substance or ligand in biological specimens (21 CFR 864.4020(a)). Information on ASR classifications is in 21 CFR 864.4020(b). ASRs are Class I and exempt from premarket notification except when they are used in blood banking tests that have been classified as Class II (e.g., cytomegalovirus serological reagents) and when they are intended to be used as components in Class III tests used in screening for contagious fatal diseases (e.g., tuberculosis) or blood donor screening (e.g., blood group typing or hepatitis). ASRs must be labeled in accordance with 21 CFR 809.10(e)(1). Class I ASRs must bear the statement: "Analyte Specific Reagent. Analytical and performance characteristics are not established." Class II and III ASRs must bear the statement: "Analyte Specific Reagent. Except as a component of the approved/cleared test (Name of approved/cleared test), analytical and performance characteristics of this ASR are not established."

Risk-Based Classification

IVDs are regulated according to a risk-based classification scheme based on their intended uses and indications for use. Intended use is the device's general purpose or function, and encompasses the indications for use, meaning whether the device will be used for diagnosis, aid in diagnosis, monitoring or screening. Per 21 CFR 814.20(b)(3)(i), indications for use describe the disease or condition the device will diagnosis, treat, prevent, cure or mitigate, including a description of the patient population for which the device is intended. Additional factors that determine IVD classification are the types of specimens to be tested and the consequence of a false test result.

FDA classifies all medical devices, including IVDs, into three product classes: Class I, Class II and Class III. The level of control required to ensure devices are reasonably safe and effective when they are placed on the market determines the IVD class. IVD classification will determine the regulatory pathway (510(k) or Premarket Approval (PMA)) to market. The CFR lists the device classification panels for medical devices and IVDs. The majority of IVDs are in three classification panels: 21 CFR 862 (clinical chemistry and toxicology devices), 864 (hematology and pathology devices) and 866 (immunology and microbiology devices).

Class I: General Controls

General controls apply to all medical devices, regardless of class, and include establishment registration as a manufacturer, distributor, repackager or relabeler; listing the devices intended to be marketed with FDA; manufacturing in accordance with Good Manufacturing Practices (GMPs) (21 CFR 820), including maintenance of records and providing reports to FDA; and labeling in accordance with 21 CFR 801 and 809. Class I IVDs are the lowest risk category. Most, but not all, Class I IVDs are exempt from 510(k) provisions. Class I IVDs must comply with General Controls.

Examples of Class I IVDs include clinical chemistry tests for urine pH and osmolality, reagents and kits for immunohistochemistry stains and serological reagents for immunology and microbiology and blood culture systems.

Class II: Special Controls

Special controls include certain mandatory performance standards, special labeling requirements and postmarket surveillance requirements. Most Class II products require a 510(k) submission including evidence for a determination of "substantial equivalence" to a similar product already on the market (predicate device). Class II IVDs pose a moderate risk of harm; they are devices for which general controls alone are insufficient to assure safety and effectiveness, and existing methods are available to provide assurance.

Examples of Class II IVDs include clinical chemistry tests for newborn screening for metabolic disorders, drugs of abuse tests, hematology tests for sickle cell hemoglobin, antimicrobial susceptibility tests and microbiology tests for pathogenic organisms that cause such diseases as meningitis.

Class III: Premarket Approval (PMA)

Class III products require PMA submission, including a complete description of the manufacturing process and clinical evidence (diagnostic sensitivity and specificity) of safety and effectiveness in the intended use population. Class III IVDs present a potential high risk of harm. They typically employ complex methodologies and algorithms for calculating a result and may be intended for diagnosis of serious infectious diseases. Class III is the most stringent classification category. These products are those for which general controls and special controls alone are insufficient to provide assurances of safety and effectiveness. They are subject to the most rigorous premarket scrutiny, often requiring extensive clinical data.

Examples of Class III IVDs include tests for screening for various cancers (e.g., breast, prostate) and tests for screening the blood supply for infectious agents, such as Hepatitis B and C.

CLIA Categorization

In 1992, the Department of Health and Human Services (DHHS) published laboratory standards regulations that implemented the *Clinical Laboratory Improvement Amendments*. *CLIA* regulations are codified in 42 CFR 493. *CLIA* regulates laboratory testing and requires clinical laboratories to obtain a certificate before accepting materials derived from the human body for the purpose of providing information for the diagnosis, prevention or treatment of any disease, or the impairment of, or assessment of the health of human beings. The *CLIA* certificate type depends on the complexity of the laboratory tests. There are three test complexity levels: waived tests, moderate complexity tests and high complexity tests (42 CFR 493.5(a)).

For IVDs, the Centers for Disease Control and Prevention had responsibility for *CLIA*. That changed in 2000, when the responsibility was transferred to CDRH. This transfer allowed IVD manufacturers to submit 510(k) s or applications for tests and requests for complexity categorization to one agency.

CDRH uses a scorecard methodology to determine the complexity categorization. The scorecard assigns a score of 1 (lowest complexity level), 2 (moderate complexity level) or 3 (high complexity level) in each of seven criteria, which are:

- knowledge
- training and experience
- reagents and materials preparation
- characteristics of operational steps
- calibration, quality control and proficiency testing materials
- test system troubleshooting and equipment maintenance
- interpretation and judgment

Scores are totaled, and tests receiving scores of 12 or less are assigned moderate complexity; tests receiving scores of 12 or higher are assigned high complexity.

An IVD manufacturer can obtain a waiver for its test. To qualify for a waiver, the device must be simple to use, and studies conducted at intended use sites must demonstrate the test is accurate and poses an insignificant risk of erroneous results.

CLIA categorization is determined at the time a 510(k) or PMA is submitted. Once FDA receives the application, a *CLIA* Record (CR) number will be assigned to the submission along with the 510(k) or PMA number. The primary document FDA uses to determine the product's complexity is the package insert or instructions for use. Once FDA reaches a positive marketing decision (clearance or approval), it will notify the IVD manufacturer within two weeks of the *CLIA* categorization. The *CLIA* categorization is effective as of the date of the written notification to the IVD manufacturer.

Presubmission

A Presubmission is defined as a formal written request from an applicant or sponsor for FDA to provide feedback in the form of a formal written response or, if the manufacturer chooses, a meeting or teleconference after which feedback is documented in meeting minutes. A Presubmission is appropriate when FDA's feedback on specific questions is necessary to guide product development and/or application preparation.

In 2012, FDA acknowledged the pre-IDE program had evolved to include review of a larger scope of submissions than originally had been intended. Due to the increase in scope, FDA decided to rename the Pre-IDE program to Presubmission (Pre-Sub) program.

When the Pre-Sub program was first introduced in 1995 through a memorandum, it was used as a mechanism for IDE application sponsors under 21 CFR 812 to submit preliminary information to FDA prior to submitting an IDE. Since most IVDs are exempted from IDE regulations, the Pre-IDE became an informal method for manufacturers to obtain FDA advice and comment on the regulatory pathway and proposed studies prior to submission of a 510(k) or PMA. In fact, OIR routinely requested manufacturers to submit a Pre-Sub when a new device had novel performance characteristics or a new intended use. It was designed specifically for those devices likely to require a *de novo* petition, *CLIA* waiver application or complexity categorization, 510(k) or PMA submission for multiplex tests or companion diagnostics.

A Pre-Sub should be submitted when the intended use (including the target patient population) has been defined, and the manufacturer is ready to discuss analytical and clinical performance studies that may be required for clearance or approval. The *Food and Drug Administration Safety and Innovation Act* of 2012 (*FDASIA*) expanded the Pre-Sub concept to include submissions to CBER. The Pre-Sub process begins with submitting a written request to the Document Control Center. An important consideration regarding the Pre-Sub is it is nonbinding on both the manufacturer and FDA.

The Pre-Sub package consists of a cover letter with contact information, a brief device description, proposed intended use, predicate device (if known), previous submissions or discussions, overview of product development (should include planned analytical and clinical trial testing plans or protocols) and any specific questions the manufacturer has regarding the proposed preclinical studies' analytical and clinical data requirements or regulatory pathway. Typically, FDA will respond to a Pre-Sub submission within 90 days by returning a Pre-Sub review memo to the submitter. This document will contain FDA's current thinking regarding how the device likely will be regulated, and the data likely to be required in a 510(k) or PMA submission.

As part of the Pre-Sub, the IVD manufacturer or sponsor can specify how it would like to receive FDA feedback. The manufacturer or sponsor can request an in-person meeting, teleconference, facsimile or email. FDA ultimately will decide how to provide feedback, taking into consideration the Pre-Sub request. If a meeting is requested, FDA will try to provide feedback within 75 days and no later than 90 days after receiving the Pre-Sub. An agenda with meeting materials, manufacturer or sponsor attendees, requested FDA attendees and specific questions or topics to discuss must be provided to the agency prior to the face-to-face meeting or teleconference. Meeting minutes with agreed upon decisions will be provided to the manufacturer or sponsor for review and comments following the meeting.

IVD Premarket Submissions

Premarket Notifications (510(k))

There are two types of premarket submissions for IVD products: 510(k)s and PMAs. A 510(k) is a premarketing submission made to FDA at least 90 days prior to placing a device on the market, to demonstrate the device to be marketed is as safe and effective (substantially equivalent (SE)) to a legally marketed device (predicate device) not subject to a PMA. A predicate device is one with a similar intended use and similar technological characteristics. Once FDA has determined the new device is SE to the predicate device, the new device is cleared for marketing in the US. If FDA determines the new device has no predicate, or its performance is not equivalent to the predicate, a not substantially equivalent (NSE) decision is rendered.

Class I IVDs not exempt from premarket notification requirements and Class II IVDs will require 510(k) application submissions to FDA.

The content and format of a 510(k) are detailed in 21 CFR 807.87. The nonclinical and clinical performance data constitute the evidence establishing substantial equivalence to the predicate. This could include analytical sensitivity and specificity, precision, limit of detection, reproducibility and reagent and sample stability. FDA recommends the use of standards published by the Clinical Laboratory Standards Institute (CLSI) to guide analytical performance evaluation. Additionally, a method comparison study showing performance similar to the predicate device can be required. In some cases, a prospective clinical trial using both the predicate and new devices, or the new device against a known reference method, is required for Class I and Class II IVDs. Clinical studies must be conducted in accordance with Good Clinical Practice guidelines (while these guidelines apply mainly to drug and biologic studies, the principles also apply to medical device or IVD clinical trials), including the Informed Consent regulations in 21 CFR 50, the Institutional Review Board regulations in 21 CFR 56 and Financial Disclosure regulations in 21 CFR 54.

Manufacturers have a choice between submitting a 510(k) summary or 510(k) Statement in a 510(k). The 510(k) summary provides a synopsis of performance data, predicate information and other pertinent information in the 510(k). This document, along with other information in the 510(k), is used by FDA to craft its decision summary. OIR will post a decision summary of the 510(k) review on FDA's website, detailing the basis for SE determination. These summaries can provide valuable information to manufacturers of similar IVDs on the choice of likely predicates or reference methods and data requirements for establishing SE for their IVDs.

Premarket Approval

A PMA is any Premarket Approval Application for a Class III medical device, including all information submitted with or incorporated by reference therein. Required PMA contents are found in 21 CFR 814.20. PMAs are reviewed under a 180-day timeline. For most PMAs, a clinical study using prospectively collected samples is required to establish the device's safety and effectiveness. These studies also must be conducted in accordance with Informed Consent, Institutional Review Board regulations and Financial Disclosure regulations. If the device is the first of its kind, or if FDA's PMA review raises significant questions regarding safety and effectiveness, the agency may seek advice or a determination of PMA approvability from an Advisory Panel comprised of external experts. In most cases, an FDA inspection of the manufacturer's facility is required prior to PMA approval. Additionally, a bioresearch monitoring audit of clinical study sites is conducted prior to PMA approval. FDA often will add postapproval requirements for manufacturers of Class III devices as a condition of approval. These may include additional studies of safety and effectiveness and periodic reporting of the results of such studies. Once a formal approval order is issued, FDA posts a Summary of Safety and Effectiveness Data (SSED) on its website.

Investigational Device Exemption (IDE)

For significant risk IVDs, clinical trials must be conducted under an IDE. Significant risk refers to an investigational device that:

- is intended as an implant and presents a potential for serious risk to the subject's health, safety and welfare
- is purported or represented to be for use in supporting or sustaining human life and presents a potential for serious risk to the subject's health, safety or welfare
- is for a use of substantial importance in diagnosing, curing, mitigating or treating disease, or otherwise preventing impairment of human health and presents a potential for serious risk to the subject's health, safety or welfare
- otherwise presents a potential for serious risk to the subject's health, safety or welfare

IDE regulations and content requirements are in 21 CFR 812.20. The IDE application must be submitted to FDA prior to initiation of the clinical trial. Within 30 days of receiving the IDE application, FDA will issue a written order either approving the investigation as purposed, approving it with modifications or disapproving it.

De Novo Classification

De novo classification can be used for Class III IVDs; it was created by the *Food and Drug Administration Modernization Act* of 1997 (*FDAMA*) as a way of classifying new, lower-risk devices placed in Class III automatically when the original classification rules were established. These devices have no predicate but are devices for which Special Controls would be an appropriate means of controlling risks and ensuring devices are reasonably safe and effective. *De novo* allows a manufacturer of an IVD that has been found NSE due to the lack of a predicate device to submit a petition to have a risk-based classification made for the device (often Class II) without submitting a PMA.

The *Food and Drug Administration Safety and Innovation Act* of 2012 (*FDASIA*) created an alternative *de novo* pathway that does not require a device to be reviewed first under a 510(k) and found NSE prior to submission of a *de novo* request. Under the *de novo* pathway, if a sponsor believes its device is appropriate for classification into Class I or Class II and determines there is no legally marketed predicate device, it may submit a *de novo* request without a preceding 510(k) and NSE. FDA will provide written notification of the device's class within 120 days of receipt of the *de novo* request.

eCopy Submission Process

FDASIA created the requirement for eCopy submissions of certain FDA applications. An electronic copy (eCopy) is defined as an exact duplicate of the paper submission, created and submitted on a compact disc (CD), digital video disc (DVD) or flash drive. An eCopy is accompanied by a paper copy of the signed cover letter and the complete paper submission. If the paper copy accompanying the eCopy is not an exact duplicate, that information must be noted in the cover letter with an explanation of the differences. Currently, all major FDA medical device and IVD submissions must be submitted via eCopy. The specific submissions and number of copies to submit are included in a table in the eCopy guidance document.

There are two types of eCopy submissions: volume-based and non-volume-based. The manufacturer or sponsor determines which type to submit to FDA. Whichever type the manufacturer or sponsor choose must comply with the specific format. The eCopy also must meet specific technical standards and will go through an FDA review prior to acceptance. If the eCopy does not meet the required technical standards, an eCopy deficiency letter will be sent to the applicant. The deficiencies must be corrected and the eCopy resubmitted. FDA has an eSubmitter tool sponsors can use to ensure there are no technical issues with their eCopy submissions. The eSubmitter eCopies tool provides the formatted eCopy content to be downloaded onto the sponsor's computer and used to burn the information onto a CD, DVD or flash drive. The eCopy content is saved in a folder with a long alpha-numeric name. No other folders or documents should be submitted with this eSubmitter formatted eCopy. The eSubmitter software is a free download available on FDA's website. A guide for the operation of the eSubmitter software is also available on FDA's website.

Software

Many IVDs employ software or firmware to control instrumentation and calculate complex algorithms prior to providing test result. As with other medical devices, FDA regulates the software and firmware integral to the diagnostic test systems' operation and safety. Therefore, a certain amount of information related to the software's design and development must be included in premarket submissions. The extent of the documentation to be included in a 510(k) or PMA is based on the software's level of concern.

- Major—The level of concern is major if a failure or latent flaw could result directly in patient or operator death or serious injury. The level of concern also is major if a failure or latent flaw could result indirectly in patient or operator death or serious injury through incorrect or delayed information or through a care provider's action.
- Moderate—The level of concern is moderate if a failure or latent design flaw could result directly

in minor patient or operator injury. The level of concern also is moderate if a failure or latent flaw could result indirectly in minor patient or operator injury through incorrect or delayed information or through a care provider's action.

- Minor—The level of concern is minor if failures or latent design flaws are unlikely to cause any injury to the patient or operator.

The amount of documentation required for software or firmware in a 510(k) or PMA is determined by the level of concern. The FDA guidance document includes a series of questions to assist the manufacturer or sponsor in determining the software or firmware's level of concern. Also included in the guidance is a table listing the documentation to be included in the 510(k) or PMA once the level of concern has been determined. One of the most important pieces of software documentation required to be submitted in a premarket application is a device hazard analysis. This must include the hardware and software hazards identified during design and development, an assessment of their severity and the mitigations implemented to control them. To the extent software plays a role in mitigating hazards associated with laboratory examination of clinical specimens (e.g., user errors, incorrect or delayed diagnostic results), the hazard analysis must address the severity of the harm resulting from software failures.

Additionally, FDA has become concerned in recent years with medical device cybersecurity, including IVDs. It specifically is concerned about devices that are Internet-connected or networked with clinical laboratory or hospital networks. This puts device-related health information at risk. Effective cybersecurity management is intended to reduce patient risk by decreasing the likelihood device functionality is intentionally or unintentionally compromised by inadequate cybersecurity. Manufacturers should develop a set of cybersecurity controls to ensure IVD cybersecurity and maintain IVD functionality and safety. The manufacturer should be developing these controls during its IVDs design and development. FDA recognizes medical device security is a shared responsibility among stakeholders, including healthcare facilities, patients, providers and IVD manufacturers. Failure to maintain cybersecurity can result in compromised device functionality, loss of data availability or integrity (medical or personal) or exposure of other connected devices or networks to security threats. This, in turn, potentially may result in patient illness, injury or death.

Laboratory Developed Tests (LDTs)

A laboratory developed test is an IVD intended for clinical use and designed, manufactured and used within a single laboratory. Single laboratory refers to a facility with a single *CLIA* certificate (42 CFR 493.43(a)-(b)). Since the *CLIA* regulations were passed in 1988, diagnostic tests have reached the market in one of two ways: FDA clearance or approval of a premarket application submitted by a commercial manufacturer, or the offering of such tests directly to clinicians by *CLIA*-licensed laboratories. In a regulatory practice known as "enforcement discretion," FDA allowed the commercialization of LDTs without premarket review. Over the past decade, FDA increasingly has become concerned with the lack of oversight of such tests, particularly a subset of molecular diagnostic tests purported to predict the genetic risk of developing clinical diseases, marketed on direct-to-consumer (DTC) websites. Specifically, FDA cited concerns over the apparent lack of clinical validity, absence of premarket review of diagnostic claims and lack of postmarket surveillance and reporting.

FDA has decided to close the LDT oversight gap and has issued new guidance documents to alert clinical laboratories and IVD manufacturers of its general intent to no longer exercise enforcement discretion toward all LDTs. FDA believes LDT oversight will provide for independent review and evaluation of LDT clinical and analytical performance and claims, assurances of consistent manufacturing, and postmarket controls. FDA will be applying a risk-based approach to LDT oversight as it does with all IVDs and medical devices. FDA will be issuing additional draft guidance to describe Class I, Class II and Class III LDTs.

Postmarket Surveillance

IVDs have the same postmarket surveillance requirements as other medical devices, such as establishment registration, device listing, medical device reporting, recalls, corrections and removals and postapproval studies. Chapter 21 Medical Device Compliance and Postmarketing Activities provides details on the requirements listed above.

Summary

IVDs are a subset of medical devices defined in 21 CFR 809.3. There are four types of IVDs: RUOs, IUOs, GPRs and ASRs. RUO and IUO products are pre-commercial and, under specific circumstances, may be shipped without complying fully with the labeling requirements that apply to commercial IVDs.

IVDs are regulated according to a risk-based classification scheme as Class I, II or III, based on their intended uses and indications for use. Factors that determine the classification of IVDs include: whether the device is intended for diagnosis, monitoring or screening of a specific disease or condition; the patient population in which it will be used; the type of specimen to be tested; and the consequence of a false test result.

Most, but not all, Class I IVDs are exempt from premarket review and subject to General Controls only. Class I IVDs not exempt from premarket notification and Class II IVDs (Special Controls) require submission of a premarket notification (510(k)) at least 90 days prior to placing the device on the market. The 510(k) must contain evidence the device to be marketed is SE to another (predicate) device already marketed legally (i.e., safe and effective). A predicate device is one with a similar intended use and similar technological characteristics. Class III IVDs require PMA submission. For most PMAs, a clinical study using prospectively collected samples is required to establish the device's safety and effectiveness. Such studies must be conducted in accordance with Good Clinical Practices, including informed consent regulations, Institutional Review Board regulations and financial disclosure regulations. Submission of 510(k)s, PMAs and other applications now are required via the eCopy process. The eCopy submission must contain an accompanying cover letter and an exact duplicate paper copy of the eCopy. The eCopy application must pass certain technical standards before it will be accepted by FDA for review.

A laboratory developed test is an IVD intended for clinical use and designed, manufactured and used within a single laboratory. FDA is providing guidance on the framework for its oversight of these tests and no longer will have general enforcement discretion for LDTs. FDA will provide additional guidance on the classification (risk-based) of LDTs.

Chapter 24

Biologics Submissions

Updated by Irina Kulinets, PhD, CQE, RAC

OBJECTIVES

- ❑ Learn basic concepts of biologics submissions
- ❑ Understand the organizational structure and responsibilities of the Center for Biologics Evaluation and Research (CBER) and Center for Drug Evaluation and Research (CDER) in review of premarket biologics submissions
- ❑ Understand the changes to biologics regulations
- ❑ Understand CBER's Investigational New Drug (IND) process
- ❑ Review US Food and Drug Administration (FDA) recommendations for development of biologics, including requirements for clinical, manufacturing and preclinical development to support regulatory submissions
- ❑ Understand Biologic License Application (BLA) contents and the BLA review process
- ❑ Become familiar with FDA and sponsor meeting procedures and requirements
- ❑ Become familiar with FDA postapproval and compliance regulations for biologics
- ❑ Review special situations

LAWS, REGULATIONS AND GUIDELINES COVERED IN THIS CHAPTER

- ❑ *Public Health Service Act*, Section 351, including new section (k) Licensure of Biological Products as Biosimilar or Interchangeable
- ❑ *Federal Food, Drug, and Cosmetic Act* of 1938
- ❑ 21 CFR 210 Current Good Manufacturing Practice in Manufacturing, Processing, Packing, or Holding of Drugs, General
- ❑ 21 CFR 211 Good Manufacturing Practice for Finished Pharmaceuticals
- ❑ 21 CFR 600 Biological Products: General
- ❑ 21 CFR 601 Biologics Licensing
- ❑ 21 CFR 610 General Biological Products Standards
- ❑ 21 CFR 312 Investigational New Drug Application
- ❑ 21 CFR 314 Applications for FDA Approval to Market a New Drug
- ❑ 21 CFR 25 Environmental Impact Considerations
- ❑ ICH M4: The Common Technical Document
- ❑ Administrative Processing of Biologics License Applications (BLA), SOPP 8401

- ❑ Guidance for Sponsors, Industry, Researchers, Investigators, and Food and Drug Administration Staff: Certifications To Accompany Drug, Biological Product, and Device Applications Submissions: Compliance with Section 402(j) of The Public Health Service Act, Added By Title VIII of The Food and Drug Administration Amendments Act of 2007
- ❑ *Draft Guidance for the Public and the Food and Drug Administration Staff on Convening Advisory Committee Meetings* (August 2008)
- ❑ *Guidance for Industry: Formal Dispute Resolution: Appeals Above the Division Level* (February 2000)
- ❑ "Intercenter Consultative/Collaborative Review Process" (August 2002), SOPP 8001.5
- ❑ *Guidance for Industry: Cooperative Manufacturing Arrangements for Licensed Biologics* (November 2008)
- ❑ *Guidance for Industry: Submitting Type V Drug Master Files to the Center for Biologics Evaluation and Research* (August 2001)
- ❑ SOPP 8110, "Investigational and Marketable Applications: Submission of Regulatory Documents to CBER" (October 2014)
- ❑ *Draft Guidance for Industry: Investigational New Drugs (INDs)—Determining whether Human Research Studies can be Conducted without an IND* (October 2010)
- ❑ *Guidance for Industry Preclinical Assessment of Investigational Cellular and Gene Therapy Products* (November 2013)
- ❑ *Draft Guidance for Industry: Investigating and Reporting Adverse Reactions Related to Human Cells, Tissues, and Cellular and Tissue-Based Products (HCT/Ps) Regulated Solely under Section 361 of the Public Health Service Act and 21 CFR Part 1271* (February 2015)
- ❑ *Draft Guidance for Industry: Current Good Manufacturing Practice Requirements for Combination Products* (January 2015)
- ❑ *Guidance for Industry: Providing Regulatory Submissions in Electronic Format—Submissions Under Section 745A(a) of the Federal Food, Drug, and Cosmetic Act* (December 2014)
- ❑ *Draft Guidance for Industry: The Effect of Section 585 of the FD&C Act on Drug Product Tracing and Wholesale Drug Distributor and Third-Party Logistics Provider Licensing Standards and Requirements: Questions and Answers* (October 2014)
- ❑ *Draft Guidance for Industry, Food and Drug Administration Staff, and Clinical Laboratories—Framework for Regulatory Oversight of Laboratory Developed Tests (LDTs)* (September 2014)
- ❑ *Guidance for Industry: Immunogenicity Assessment for Therapeutic Protein Products* (August 2014)
- ❑ *Draft Guidance for Industry and Food and Drug Administration Staff—De Novo Classification Process (Evaluation of Automatic Class III Designation)* (August 2014)
- ❑ *Draft Guidance for Industry: Reference Product Exclusivity for Biological Products Filed Under Section 351(a) of the PHS Act* (August 2014)
- ❑ *Guidance for Industry: Expedited Programs for Serious Conditions—Drugs and Biologics* (May 2014)
- ❑ *Draft Guidance for Industry: Product Development Under the Animal Rule* (May 2014)
- ❑ *Draft Guidance for Industry: Clinical Pharmacology Data to Support a Demonstration of Biosimilarity to a Reference Product* (May 2014)
- ❑ *Draft Guidance for Industry: Best Practices in Developing Proprietary Names for Drugs* (May 2014)
- ❑ *Draft Guidance for Industry and Food and Drug Administration Staff: Balancing Premarket and Postmarket Data Collection for Devices Subject to Premarket Approval* (April 2014)
- ❑ *Draft Guidance for Industry and Food and Drug Administration Staff: Expedited Access for Premarket Approval Medical Devices Intended for Unmet Medical Need for Life Threatening or Irreversibly Debilitating Diseases or Conditions* (April 2014)

- ❑ *Draft Guidance for Industry: Fulfilling Regulatory Requirements for Postmarketing Submissions of Interactive Promotional Media for Prescription Human and Animal Drugs and Biologics* (January 2014)

- ❑ *Guidance for Industry: Providing Regulatory Submissions to the Center for Biologics Evaluation and Research (CBER) in Electronic Format—Biologics Marketing Applications [Biologics License Application (BLA), Product License Application (PLA)/Establishment License Application (ELA) and New Drug Applications (NDA)]* (November 1999)

Introduction

FDA's Definition of 'Biologic' and Implications of Product Application Review and Postmarket Surveillance Process

Biotechnology has led to the development of many of today's most important medicines, including: monoclonal antibodies for treating cancer; human insulin for treating diabetes; cloning the naturally occurring protein, erythropoietin, to stimulate the production of red blood cells in the treatment of chronic anemia; and products used for tissue regeneration (e.g., cartilage and skin). Biological products can be made of sugars, proteins, nucleic acids or complex combinations of these substances, or may be living entities such as cells and tissues.

Classification of a product as a drug, biologic, medical device or combination product depends primarily on that product's intended use and principal mode of action. Biological products, or biologics, are medical products. Biologics are made from a variety of natural sources (human, animal or microorganism). Like drugs, some biologics are intended to treat diseases and medical conditions. Other biologics are used to prevent or diagnose diseases. Examples of biologics regulated by FDA include:

- vaccines (bacterial and viral)
- blood and blood products for transfusion and/or manufacturing into other products
- allergenic extracts, used for both diagnosis and treatment (e.g., allergy shots)
- human cells and tissues used for transplantation (e.g., tendons, ligaments and bone)
- gene therapies
- cellular therapies, including somatic cells
- tests to screen potential blood donors for infectious agents such as HIV
- toxin, antitoxin, growth factors and monoclonal antibodies

The *Public Health Service Act* (*PHS Act*), Section 351(i) defines a biological product as "any virus, therapeutic serum, toxin, antitoxin, vaccine, blood, blood component or derivative, allergenic product, protein (except any chemically modified synthetic polypeptide), or analogous product...that is intended for use in the diagnosis, cure, mitigation, treatment, or prevention of disease." Biological products are approved for marketing under the *PHS Act*, but because most biological products also meet the definition of "drugs" under the *Federal Food, Drug, and Cosmetic Act* of 1938 (*FD&C Act*), they also are regulated under this law.

Pursuant to Section 351(a) of the *PHS Act*, a biologics license must be in place for any biological product introduced or delivered into interstate commerce. Biological products subject to the *PHS Act* also meet the definition of "drugs" under Section 201(g) of the *FD&C Act* and must comply with Title 21 of the Code of Federal Regulations (CFR) Parts 210 and 211, current Good Manufacturing Practices (CGMP). A submission for a biological product approval might be accomplished through a Biologics License Application (BLA); however, biological products meeting the definition of a drug are submitted through a New Drug Application (NDA).

Biological medicines are proteins made in living organisms, often by genetically modifying cell constructs or cell lines. Biologic medical products also might be made using processed allogenic or autologous cells (e.g., stem cells, mononucleous cells) or tissues to stimulate the regeneration of patient tissues or bones.

Biologic products are known for complex manufacturing processes and require product testing and an evaluation of their safety and efficacy. DNA technology often is used to insert desirable genes or to remove undesirable ones within a living cell or via a vector such as a virus, prompting a specific function, such as production of a protein to treat disease. The DNA sequence of a chosen protein, such as human insulin or an immune system antibody, is identified and introduced into a vector suitable for introduction into the genetic material of the bacterial, yeast or mammalian cell line that will produce it. Genetically modified cell lines are carefully selected and cultured in bioreactors before the biologic medicine is extracted through complex and lengthy purification processes. During selection, the cell line that can produce the biologic most effectively is identified and expanded to manufacture the medicine. This cell line is unique to each manufacturer and is the source of all future product. Each of the thousands of steps in the manufacturing process is intricate, sensitive and often specific to a particular medicine, requiring robust quality systems and significant experience, expertise and financial investment. Even minor alterations to the cell line or process may lead to changes in cell behavior and differences in the end product's structure, stability or other quality aspects. Any of these differences has the potential to affect the treatment's safety, efficacy and/or shelf life, and can increase the risk of an unwanted immune response.

Like drugs, biologics are eligible for postmarket safety evaluations. In that respect, FDA assesses several data sources including:

- the product's preapproval safety profile
- the product's current FDA-approved label
- reports made to the FDA Adverse Event Reporting System (FAERS), previously known as AERS
- reports made to the Vaccine Adverse Event Reporting System (VAERS)
- manufacturer-submitted periodic safety reports
- medical literature
- drug utilization databases
- data from postapproval clinical trials and other studies, when applicable

Beginning no later than 18 months after approval, a safety review and evaluation is conducted by scientists from CBER's Office of Biostatistics and Epidemiology and the relevant product office (Office of Blood Research and Review, Office of Vaccine Research and Review, or Office of Cellular, Tissue and Gene Therapies). FDA compiles the postmarket safety evaluations and posts summary reports on its website periodically.

History of Biologics Regulation

In 1902, Congress passed the *Biologics Control Act*, which applied to "any virus, therapeutic serum, toxin, antitoxin, or analogous product applicable to the prevention and cure of diseases of man" and required licensure of facilities making these products. Over the next hundred-plus years, Congress expanded this list of covered products to include, among other things, the following products and those "analogous" to them: vaccines, blood, blood products, allergenic products and proteins (except chemically synthesized polypeptides).

The overlapping definition of "drug" added to this complexity. The *Food and Drugs Act* of 1906 and *FD&C Act* defined "drug" broadly to include, among other things, substances intended for use in the cure, mitigation, or prevention of disease, and the latter statute mandated submission of an NDA before marketing a drug. Although these "drug" definitions encompassed many biologics, the statutes did not provide concrete parameters for distinguishing nonbiological drugs from biological products. In 1944, when Congress revised and recodified the 1902 act in the *PHS Act*, it clarified the NDA requirement did not apply to biologics, but it did not define the scope of the biological product. Regulators attempted to fill this gap by promulgating regulatory definitions of virus, therapeutic serum, toxin, antitoxin and analogous product. For example, the 1947 regulations, which are essentially similar to current regulations, defined products "analogous" to a toxin or antitoxin as those intended for preventing, treating or curing diseases or injuries "through specific immunization." The 1947 definition of products analogous to therapeutic serums excluded hormones. Hormones, such as insulin and human growth hormone, were approved under the *FD&C Act*, not the *PHS Act*. Despite the 1947 regulations, differentiating biologics from drugs remained challenging at the margins.

Since the 1970s, a revolution in biotechnology has resulted in a new class of medicine: the biologic. The advent of biotechnology, along with agency organizational disputes, brought this issue to the forefront of FDA's focus. In 1986, FDA issued a policy stating it would determine whether biotechnology products constituted biologics "based on the intended use of each product on a case-by-case basis." Thus, FDA continued to make product-specific determinations informed by history and precedent, and different FDA offices had to agree on a given product's approval pathway. This proved to be difficult, with press reports of "turf battles" between CDER and CBER for jurisdiction over blockbuster biotechnology products and claims the decisions were inconsistent. For example, epidermal growth factors were regulated as drugs because their first approved indications traditionally were drug indications. Most monoclonal antibodies (mAbs) were licensed as biologics because of their biological source material and immunologic function. Recombinant insulin and human growth hormone, similar to their naturally derived counterparts, were approved pursuant to NDAs.

CDER and CBER subsequently executed an Intercenter Agreement (ICA) to attempt to clarify the governing authorities for products derived from living material. The agreement provided the following products, among others, were subject to licensure under the *PHS Act*: vaccines, proteins, peptides and carbohydrates produced by cell culture (other than hormones and products previously derived from human or animal tissue and approved as drugs), proteins made in transgenic animals, blood and blood products and allergenic products. NDAs were required for, among other things, hormones (regardless of method of manufacture), synthetic mononucleotide and polynucleotide products and naturally derived products other than vaccines or allergenics.

Twelve years later, FDA consolidated review of most therapeutic proteins in CDER, but this transfer did not include any modification to the governing statutory scheme for any ICA product, and FDA continued to decide whether new products were biological products or nonbiologic drugs on a case-by-case basis using ICA principles and historical precedent.

In February 2012, FDA issued draft guidance aimed at implementing recent legislation that added "protein (except any chemically synthesized polypeptide)" to the biological product definition. In this draft guidance, FDA proposed a bright-line rule distinguishing proteins from "peptides" and "chemically synthesized polypeptide[s]" approved by

FDA under the *FD&C Act*. The agency proposed defining "protein" as "any alpha amino acid polymer with a specific defined sequence that is greater than 40 amino acids in size." According to the draft guidance, "peptides" have 40 or fewer amino acids and are not "proteins." The agency also proposed defining "chemically synthesized polypeptide" as an alpha amino acid polymer made entirely by chemical synthesis and with fewer than 100 amino acids.

Types of US Premarket Submissions Applicable to Biologics: BLA, NDA or PMA?

Several types of FDA submissions are needed for the approval of biologics. Choosing the correct regulatory approval pathway affects product development phases (including clinical research) and has to be defined early. Depending on the applicable FDA center, a biologic product's approval might require a BLA or an NDA or, in some cases of biologic/device combination products, a Premarket Approval Application (PMA).

As discussed earlier, the responsibility for reviewing biologics submissions is divided primarily between CBER and CDER.

The following sections review FDA's review responsibilities for biologic products.

CBER and its Function

CBER is the primary FDA center for the review of a biological products.

Effective 30 June 2003, oversight responsibility for "well-characterized" or "therapeutic" biological products was transferred from CBER to CDER. The review of these therapeutic proteins is conducted by the appropriate therapeutic review division within CDER's Office of New Drugs (OND). These products continue to be regulated as licensed biologics (i.e., BLA) per 21 CFR 601.2(a). CDER also has responsibility for hormone protein products, e.g., insulin, growth hormone and pituitary hormones, as part of an October 1991 ICA between CBER and CDER; these products have been regulated as NDAs. However, under the *Biologics Price Competition and Innovation Act (BPCI Act)*, proteins (with the exception of synthetic polypeptides) that have been approved as NDAs will be considered licensed biologics and will be required to comply with Section 351 of the *PHS Act* by March 2020, 10 years after the date of the *BPCI Act*'s enactment.

CBER's regulatory authority is derived from the *PHS Act*, Section 351(a). The first biologics regulation, the *Biologics Control Act*, was approved in 1902. The Division of Biologics Standards (DBS) within the National Institutes of Health (NIH) was responsible for the control and release of biologics until 1972. The DBS was transferred from NIH to FDA and renamed the Bureau of Biologics, which ultimately became CBER. **Table 24-1** lists key milestones in the regulatory oversight of biologics. CBER regulates a wide range of biological products, including:

- allergenic extracts (e.g., for allergy shots and tests)
- blood and blood components
- plasma derivatives
- gene therapy products
- devices and test kits
- human tissue and cellular products used in transplantation
- vaccines

The responsibility for reviewing the wide range of biological product submissions is divided among three main review offices within CBER: the Office of Blood Research and Review (OBRR), the Office of Cellular, Tissue and Gene Therapies (OCTGT) and the Office of Vaccine Research and Review (OVRR).

CBER also regulates all medical devices associated with the collection and testing of licensed blood and cellular products, through the FDA ICA. The devices also must comply with all appropriate medical device laws and regulations.

CDER and its Function in Review of Biologic Products

Both CDER and CBER have regulatory responsibility for therapeutic biological products, including premarket review and oversight.

On 30 June 2003, FDA transferred some therapeutic biological products previously reviewed and regulated by CBER to CDER. CDER now has regulatory responsibility, including premarket review and continuing oversight, over the transferred products. CBER and CDER consult with each other regularly and whenever necessary in regulating products assigned to them.

On 1 October 2003, the staff comprising CBER's Office of Therapeutics Research and Review also transferred to CDER. CDER created two new offices to accommodate the former CBER staff:

- Office of Drug Evaluation VI, within CDER's OND
- Office of Biotechnology Products, within CDER's Office of Pharmaceutical Science

When developing a great and much needed biologic product, where to start to prove it safe and efficacious?

Preclinical Development for Biologics

Successful and efficient development of new biological medicines requires planning an integrated development program that coordinates the trilogy of product manufacture—chemistry, manufacturing, and controls (CMC),

Table 24-1. Key Milestones in the Regulatory Oversight of Biologics

Year	Regulatory Action
1902	• *Biologics Control Act* (*Virus-Toxin Law*) later called the *Public Health Service Act (PHS Act)*—required regulation of vaccine and antitoxin producers, including licensing and inspections of manufacturers and the interstate sale of serum, vaccines and related products
1903	• First biologics regulations by Public Health Service Hygienic Laboratory—"Poison Squad," effect of food preservatives and artificial colors on public health
1906	• *Pure Food and Drug Act*—prohibited "misbranding and adulteration"
1930	• PHS Hygienic Lab became National Institutes of Health (NIH)
1937	• NIH reorganized, Hygienic Lab became Division of Biologics Standardization
1938	• *Food, Drug and Cosmetics Act (FD&C Act)*—products must be shown to be "safe;" authorized factory inspections
1944	• *PHS Act*—required Product License Application/Establishment License Application (PLA/ELA, precursor to the BLA); gave seizure power
1955	• The Division of Biologics Control became an independent entity within NIH after polio vaccine thought to have been inactivated is associated with about 260 cases of polio
1972	• Division of Biologics Standardization, which was responsible for regulation of biologics, including serums, vaccines and blood products transferred from NIH to FDA; became what is now called CBER
1982	• Bureau of Drugs and Bureau of Biologics combined to form National Center for Drugs and Biologics (ODRR and OBRR)
1988	• FDA becomes part of Department of Health and Human Services (DHHS); Center for Drug Evaluation and Research (CDER) and Center for Biologics Evaluation and Research (CBER) established
1995	• Regulatory Initiative REGO IIb—eliminated ELA requirement and lot release requirement for specified biotechnology products
1997	• *Food and Drug Administration Modernization Act (FDAMA)*—Revised *PHS Act* and eliminated the ELA for all biologics
2003	• Review of "well-characterized" proteins transferred to CDER
2009	• *Biologics Price Competition and Innovation Act* of 2009 *(BPCI Act)* created an abbreviated approval pathway for biosimilars
2010	• *BPCI Act* Contained in *Affordable Care Act* signed into law
2014	• United States Government Policy for Institutional Oversight of Life Sciences Dual Use Research of Concern
2014	• FDA released a new draft guidance document explaining how biological products approved under Section 351(a) of the *PHS Act* are given periods of market exclusivity

preclinical studies (distribution, metabolism and pharmacokinetics [DMPK], pharmacology and toxicology) and clinical trials—within the framework of the regulatory development strategy. Preclinical safety studies must support each successive phase of clinical development, as well as any significant changes to product manufacturing, formulating or administering methods. The preclinical safety package for biologics (large molecules) can be different from the toxicology package for small molecule drugs. Special considerations for toxicological assessment types for biologics are described in ICH S6 *Preclinical Safety Evaluation of Biotechnology-Derived Pharmaceuticals*. The important points of S6 are:

- biological activity—Biological activity may be evaluated using *in vitro* assays to determine which product effects may be related to clinical activity. The use of cell lines and/or primary cell cultures can be useful to examine the direct effects on cellular phenotype and proliferation.
- animal model selection—Due to the species-specificity of many biotechnology-derived pharmaceuticals, it is important to select relevant animal species for toxicity testing. The biological activity, together with species and/or tissue specificity of many biotechnology-derived products, often preclude standard toxicity testing designs in commonly used species (e.g., rats and dogs).
- safety evaluation—Safety evaluation normally requires data from two relevant species. However, in certain justified cases, one relevant species may suffice (e.g., when only one relevant species can be identified or where the biological activity of the biopharmaceutical is well understood). In addition, even where two species may be necessary to

characterize toxicity in short-term studies, it may be possible to justify the use of only one species for subsequent long-term toxicity studies when the toxicity profile in the two species is comparable in the short-term.

- analogous products—Where there is no animal in which the biologic can function, due to either lack of specificity or anti-drug antibodies, preparing an analogous product, such as an animal homologue of the product intended for humans (e.g., a mouse monoclonal antibody that binds to the same intended target in mice), can be used to assess potential safety issues.
- Maximum Tolerated Dose (MTD)—Because biologics typically are not inherently toxic, it is difficult to provide drug concentrations at high enough levels to induce overt toxicity. Consequently, clinical dosing may be based on the biologically effective dose rather than the MTD. However, an attempt to cover the planned maximum human dose (preferably with up to a 10-fold safety margin) should be assessed in the safety studies.
- safety pharmacology and acute toxicity studies—Safety pharmacology endpoints normally are incorporated into multiple-dose toxicity testing rather than conducted as separate studies.
- immunogenicity—Many biotechnology-derived pharmaceuticals intended for humans are immunogenic in animals. Therefore, measurement of antibodies associated with the administration of these products should be performed when conducting repeated-dose toxicity studies to aid in study interpretation. Antibody responses should be characterized, and their appearance should be correlated with any pharmacological and/or toxicological changes.
- metabolism—The expected consequence of biotechnology-derived pharmaceutical metabolism is degradation to small peptides and individual amino acids. Therefore, the metabolic pathways generally are understood. Classic biotransformation studies for pharmaceuticals are not needed. Instead, understanding the biopharmaceutical's behavior in the biologic matrix and the possible influence of binding proteins is important.
- immunotoxicity—Many biotechnology-derived pharmaceuticals are intended to stimulate or suppress the immune system and, therefore, may affect not only humoral but also cell-mediated immunity. Inflammatory reactions at the injection site may be indicative of a stimulatory response. Immunotoxicological testing strategies may require screening studies followed by mechanistic studies to clarify such issues. Routine tiered testing approaches or standard testing batteries are not recommended for biotechnology-derived pharmaceuticals.
- genotoxicity studies—The range and type of genotoxicity studies routinely conducted for pharmaceuticals are not applicable to biotechnology-derived pharmaceuticals and, therefore, are not needed. Moreover, the administration of large quantities of peptides or proteins may yield uninterpretable results. Studies should be conducted in available and relevant systems.
- carcinogenicity studies—Standard carcinogenicity bioassays generally are inappropriate for biotechnology-derived pharmaceuticals. However, product-specific assessment of carcinogenic potential still may be needed, depending on the duration of clinical dosing, patient population and/or the product's biological activity. When there is concern about carcinogenic potential, a variety of approaches may be taken to evaluate risk.
- local tolerance studies—Local tolerance should be evaluated using the formulation intended for marketing. The product's potential adverse effects an be evaluated in single- or repeated-dose toxicity studies, obviating the need for a separate local tolerance study.

IND Process for Biologics

FDA regulates US clinical research involving drugs, biological products and medical devices regardless of funding source. Clinical investigations with an unapproved drug or biologic must be conducted under an Investigational New Drug Application (IND).

An IND is a formal submission with defined structure and content providing an exemption from restrictions on interstate commerce of shipment of an unapproved new drug or biologic (21 USC 355).

IND requirements are outlined in 21 CFR 312:

- §312.23 IND Content and Format
- §312.42 Clinical Holds
- §312.50 – 312.69 Responsibilities of Sponsors/Investigators

An IND is a "living document," updated by the sponsor over time to include protocol amendments, study data, safety reports, manufacturing changes, preclinical reports and Annual Reports.

IND Submission Process

- Step 1: Pre-IND teleconference with OCTGT
- highly recommended for new products
- Step 2: Submission of complete IND package
- all forms, all sections
- Step 3: IND Review

- o FDA will notify the sponsor within 30 calendar days of receipt of the IND whether the study may proceed or is placed on clinical hold
- o studies may not begin until the 30-day review is complete or FDA notifies the sponsor studies may proceed

21 CFR Part 312 describes three clinical investigation categories exempt from IND requirements: 1) clinical research involving marketed drug products; 2) bioavailability or bioequivalence studies in humans; and 3) radioactive drugs for certain research uses. Clinical investigations that do not meet these three criteria, by regulation, must be conducted under an IND. Most IND regulations for small molecular drugs also apply to biologics, including IND format and content, financial disclosure, special INDs, orphan products, clinical hold and pediatric studies.

An IND for a biologic may be submitted electronically or on paper/DVD following the Common Technical Document (CTD) format. The IND application must contain:

- administrative information—a cover letter and forms, such as Forms FDA 1571, 1572 and 3674 (Certificate of Compliance), should be included in the IND (Form FDA 3674 is an FDA requirement to include clinical trial registration and results on ClinicalTrials.gov)
- preclinical (animal pharmacology and toxicology) studies—preclinical data to permit an assessment as to whether the product is reasonably safe for initial testing in humans
- previous human experience—any previous experience with the drug in humans, such as results from clinical trials conducted outside the US
- chemistry, manufacturing and control—information pertaining to the composition, manufacturer, testing, stability and controls for the drug substance and the drug product
- clinical protocols and investigator information—protocols for proposed clinical studies to assess whether the initial clinical trials will expose subjects to unnecessary risks; information on clinical investigators' qualifications to assess their qualifications to fulfill their clinical trial duties; the clinical development plan for the next 12 months, Investigator's Brochure (IB) and commitments to obtain informed consent from the research subjects, to obtain study approval from an Institutional Review Board (IRB), and to adhere to the investigational new drug regulations and study protocols

Regulatory Basis of IND Application Elements

- Form FDA 1571—21 CFR 312.23(a)(1)
- Table of Contents—21 CFR 312.23(a)(2)
- Introductory Statement—21 CFR 312.23(a)(3)
- Investigator's Brochure—21 CFR 312.23(a)(5)
- Protocols—21 CFR 312.23(a)(6)
- Product/CMC Information—21 CFR 312.23(a)(7)
- Pharmacology/Toxicology Information—21 CFR 312.23(a)(8)
- Previous Human Experience—21 CFR 312.23(a)(9)
- Additional Information—21 CFR 312.23(a)(10)

Recommended Preclinical Information:

- scientific basis for conducting the clinical study
- data from animal or *in vitro* studies to establish an initial safe dose in humans
- proof-of-concept animal models, if appropriate
- toxicology studies in relevant animal model
- submission of complete study reports

Once the IND is submitted, the sponsor must wait 30 calendar days before initiating any clinical trials. During this time, FDA has an opportunity to review the IND for safety to ensure research subjects will not be subjected to unreasonable risk.

To accommodate the issues related to biologics, both CDER and CBER have developed a number of guidance documents, including those entitled "Points to Consider," representing FDA's current thinking on a variety of topics. In addition, guidance from the International Conference on Harmonisation (ICH) is applicable to biologics.

Processes FDA Uses to Review a Biological Product IND Submission

FDA's primary objectives in reviewing an IND are, in all phases of the investigation, to ensure subjects' safety and rights, and in Phases 2 and 3, ensure the scientific evaluation's quality is adequate to permit an evaluation of the product's effectiveness and safety (21 CFR 312.22).

FDA takes a team approach to IND Review. The FDA review team typically consists of:

- regulatory project manager
- product/CMC reviewer
- pharmacology/toxicology reviewer
- clinical reviewer
- statistical reviewer
- consults as needed (e.g., from CDRH for review of a device component)

Within 30 days, FDA determines whether the file is active or on hold, and issues outstanding hold and non-hold orders by telephone, email or in a detailed letter. All hold issues must be satisfactorily resolved to proceed.

IND Review Status Stages

- pending—within the initial 30-day review period

- active—study may proceed
- hold—an order issued by FDA to delay a proposed clinical investigation or suspend an ongoing investigation (21 CFR 312.42)
- partial hold—a delay or suspension of part of the clinical work under an IND (e.g., IND with two protocols where one can proceed and one is on clinical hold)

Clinical Development Considerations for Biologics

Clinical study designs and requirements are similar for biological drugs/products and small molecule drugs; however, there may be additional safety concerns related to immunogenicity with biological products. Thus, additional testing may be required during clinical trials to assess immunogenicity and the potential development of autoimmunity. As is the case for NDA drugs, clinical trials for biologics are conducted in phases. The initial safety of biologics is evaluated in Phase 1 trials. Phase 2 trials are performed to assess how well the biologic works in patients and to evaluate safety and dosing assessments in a larger group of subjects. Phase 2 studies sometimes are divided into Phase 2A and Phase 2B. Phase 2A is designed to assess dosing requirements and also can include combination dosing studies if the biologic is to be administered in combination with another therapy. Phase 2B is designed to study efficacy and can include exploratory endpoints to assess other pharmacodynamic markers, safety and efficacy endpoints and patient populations to better design the Phase 3 trial(s). Phase 3 studies typically are randomized controlled studies in larger patient groups, intended to be the definitive assessment of how effective the drug is, sometimes compared to the current standard of care. Certain Phase 3 trials (Phase 3B) continue while the regulatory submission is being reviewed. This allows patients to continue to receive potentially life-saving drugs until the drug is approved, and allows additional safety and efficacy data to be collected. While not required in all cases, two successful Phase 3 trials demonstrating a drug's safety and efficacy normally are recommended to obtain approval from the appropriate regulatory agencies.

ICH Efficacy Guidelines (E1–E18) and multidisciplinary (M3) guidelines cover topics relevant to biologics' clinical development. In addition, FDA has issued a number of guidance documents that provide general guidelines on clinical trial designs. Selected guidances are listed below:

- *Guidance for Industry: Clinical Pharmacogenomics: Premarket Evaluation in Early-Phase Clinical Studies and Recommendations for Labeling*—This guidance focuses on evaluating how variations in the human genome, specific DNA sequence variants, could affect a drug's pharmacokinetics (PK), pharmacodynamics (PD), efficacy and/or safety. The guidance provides recommendations on when and how genomic information should be considered to address questions arising during drug development and regulatory review.
- *Draft Guidance for Industry: Enrichment Strategies for Clinical Trials to Support Approval of Human Drugs and Biological Products*—This document focuses on enrichment strategies that can be used in clinical trials to support effectiveness and safety claims for NDAs and BLAs, including strategies to decrease heterogeneity, prognostic enrichment strategies and predictive enrichment strategies.
- *Draft Guidance for Industry Premarketing Evaluation in Early Phase Clinical Studies*—This draft focuses particularly on use and evaluation of genomic strategies in early drug development and highlights identification of enrichment options for later trials.
- *Draft Guidance for Industry and Food and Drug Administration Staff: In Vitro Companion Diagnostic Devices*—This draft guidance describes FDA's policies for approval of companion diagnostics concurrently with the therapeutic product's approval and labeling.
- *Draft Guidance for Industry: Adaptive Design Clinical Trials for Drugs and Biologics*—This document considers enrichment approaches introduced only after randomization and based on interim evaluations. It discusses how to design clinical trials with adaptive features (i.e., design or analytical changes guided by examining the accumulated data at an interim point in the trial). These adaptive trial designs may make the studies more efficient (e.g., shorter duration, fewer patients), more likely to demonstrate a drug efficacy if one exists, or more informative (e.g., by providing broader dose-response information). Such retrospective findings would have to be implemented carefully.
- *Guidance for Industry: Providing Clinical Evidence of Effectiveness for Human Drug and Biological Product*—This guidance describes the amount and type of evidence needed to demonstrate effectiveness.
- *Draft Guidance for Industry: Determining the Extent of Safety Data Collection Needed in Late Stage Premarket and Post approval Clinical Investigations*—This draft provides advice on how and when to simplify data collection to maintain a balance between eliminating the collection of data that will not be useful and collecting sufficient data to allow adequate characterization of a drug's safety profile given the potential benefits. The amount and types of safety data collected during clinical trials and safety evaluations vary based on a range of factors, including the disease, patient population, subgroup of interest, preclinical results, prior experience with the drug,

experience with the drug class, phase of development and study design.

- *Draft Guidance for Industry: Non-Inferiority Clinical Trials*—This draft guidance describes the underlying principles involved in the use of noninferiority (NI) study designs to provide evidence of a drug or biologic's effectiveness. It provides advice on when NI studies can be interpretable, how to choose the NI margin and how to analyze the results.
- *Guidance for Industry: Postmarketing Studies and Clinical Trials—Implementation of Section 505(o)(3) of the Federal Food, Drug, and Cosmetic Act*—The *FD&C Act* was amended in September 2007, adding a new Section 505(o). Section 505(o)(3) authorizes FDA to require certain postmarketing studies and clinical trials for prescription drugs and biological products approved under Section 351 of the *PHS Act*. This guidance provides information about requirements for postmarketing studies and describes the types of postmarketing studies generally required under the new legislation.
- *Guidance for Industry: Population Pharmacokinetics*—This document makes recommendations on the use of population pharmacokinetics in the drug development process to help identify differences in drug safety and efficacy among population subgroups. It summarizes scientific and regulatory issues that should be addressed using population pharmacokinetics.
- *Draft Guidance for Industry: General Considerations for Pediatric Pharmacokinetic Studies for Drugs and Biological Products*—This draft guidance addresses general considerations for conducting such studies to enable drug and biological products to be labeled for pediatric use.
- *Guidance for Industry: Providing Clinical Evidence of Effectiveness for Human Drug and Biological Products*—This guidance provides FDA's current thinking concerning the quantitative and qualitative standards for demonstrating effectiveness of drugs and biologics.
- *Guidance for Industry: Pharmacokinetics in Patients with Impaired Renal Function—Study Design, Data Analysis, and Impact on Dosing and Labeling*—This document focuses on how to conduct studies to assess the influence of renal impairment on an investigational drug's pharmacokinetics, when PK studies should be conducted with patients with impaired renal function and the design. It also covers the conduct of PK studies in patients with end-stage renal disease.

FDA has issued several guidances on the use of pharmacogenomics (PGx) in the drug development process. PGx studies can contribute to a greater understanding of inter-individual differences in an investigational biologic's efficacy and safety. Across the drug development continuum, genomic data may be used for understanding PK variations and variability in clinical response; elucidating the molecular basis for lack of efficacy or adverse events; and designing clinical trials to test for effects in identified subgroups, possibly for use in study enrichment strategies.

FDA also provides guidance on key safety issues relevant to drug development, such as understanding risks of a prolonged QT interval related to drug treatment or considerations for monitoring a drug's ability to cause drug-induced liver injury. FDA published two guidances particularly relevant for biologics: *Draft Guidance for Industry: Immunogenicity, Assay Development for Immunogenicity Testing of Therapeutic Proteins* (December 2009); and *Draft Guidance for Industry: Immunogenicity Assessment for Therapeutic Protein Products* (February 2013). These two guidances are particularly relevant for biologics because treatments with therapeutic proteins frequently stimulate immune responses. The clinical efficacy of these immune responses to therapeutic proteins, however, have ranged from none to extremely harmful. Such varied immune responses can affect product safety, efficacy and immunogenicity rates observed during clinical trials, which are included in the product labeling. Thus, the development of a valid, sensitive immune assay is a key product development aspect. Because immunogenicity poses a high risk, real-time data concerning patient responses are needed. Generally, a preliminary validated assay should be used during clinical studies. Even though immunogenicity in animal models is not predictive of immunogenicity in humans, it may reveal potential antibody-related toxicities that should be monitored in clinical trials. Multiple approaches may be appropriate for immunogenicity testing during clinical trials; however, testing strategies should address sensitivity, interference, functional or physiological consequences and risk-based application. The rationale for the immunogenicity testing paradigm should be provided in the IND.

Chemistry, Manufacturing and Controls for Biologics

Investigational biological products are subject to Section 501(a)(2)(B) of the *FD&C Act* (21 U.S.C. 351(a)(2)(B)) and the IND regulations at 21 CFR Part 312. During Phase 1 studies, emphasis generally should be placed on elements to assure subjects' safety. This should include identification, control and stability of raw materials, drug substances and drug products. In each investigational phase, sufficient information is required to ensure the proper investigational drug identification, quality, purity and strength. The amount of information necessary for that assurance will vary with the investigation phase, proposed duration, dosage form and amount of information known.

In 2008, FDA issued *Guidance for Industry: CGMP for Phase 1 Investigational Drugs*. This guidance recognizes both manufacturing controls and the extent of such manufacturing controls needed to achieve appropriate product quality differ not only between investigational and commercial manufacture, but also among the various phases of clinical trials.

CBER issued *Guidance for Industry: Chemistry, Manufacturing, and Control Information* in 2012, with recommendations regarding IND submissions for early clinical trials with live biotherapeutic products (LBPs) in the US. An LBP is a biological product containing live organisms such as bacteria; is applicable to the prevention, treatment or cure of a disease or condition of humans; and is not a vaccine. The guidance describes the CMC information requirements in the IND. The unique requirements for biologics include:

- biological name and strain—original source of cells from which the drug substance was derived, product strains with special attention to biological activity and modifications
- characterization—description of the acceptable limits and analytical methods used to ensure drug substance and drug product identity, strength, quality and purity
- master cell bank (MCB)—complete MCB history and characterization, including the original source of cells used in the establishment of cell banks, the culture/passage history of the cells, the method used to derive the cell bank, phenotypic and genotypic characterization, purity of culture and a description of all media components
- working cell banks (WCBs)—description of the cell banking procedures used, including banking system; cell banks' size; methods, reagents and media used for cell bank preparation; conditions employed for cryopreservation and storage; in-process controls; storage conditions and procedures used to avoid extraneous microbial contamination
- cell growth and harvesting—step-by-step description from cell bank retrieval to culture harvest; media used at each step, with details of their preparation and sterilization; inoculation and growth of initial and sub-cultures; incubation(s) time and temperature; how transfers are performed; in-process testing conducted to control contamination; the nature of the main culture system, including operating conditions and control parameters
- purification and downstream processing—step-by-step description of the methods and materials in the concentrate intermediate and the final bulk forms (The description of each step in downstream processing also should include the accompanying analytical tests developed or adopted by the manufacturer to show identity, purity and concentration and the levels of impurities.)

The presence of adventitious agents is of particular concern with biological products, especially vaccines that contain animal materials and/or cellular substrates. An adventitious agent is an infectious agent extraneous to the product; potential agents include Transmissible Spongiform Encephalopathy (TSE), viruses and oncogenic agents. Testing and clearance of known agents must be demonstrated to be sufficiently sensitive; testing also should be capable of detecting unsuspected agents. Suitable tests may include such techniques as cell culture, polymerase chain reaction (PCR), electron microscopy and egg or animal inoculation. In addition, sourcing of materials to avoid animal-derived materials can help reduce material and substrate exposure to specified TSE risk materials.

Information amendments are required during the IND stage for significant changes and any changes likely to affect safety and efficacy prior to the revised process material's use in clinical studies. During development through Phase 3, testing specifications will evolve and become more defined; critical assays will need to be validated and determined to be reproducible, quantitative, sensitive, specific and biologically relevant; and the manufacturing process will be optimized.

Unique requirements for biologics are found in 21 CFR 610, General Biological Product Standards. Under these standards, for FDA to receive the BLA or NDA, the product must be shown to be "safe, pure, and potent." In addition, an inspection must confirm the production facility can manufacture the product to meet these standards. The biological standards provide specific tests to be performed on each lot prior to release:

- potency—ideally via a product-specific bioassay that correlates with the *in vivo* mechanism of action or is predictive of function
- sterility—similar to *United States Pharmacopeia* (*USP*) Chapter 71
- purity—essentially free of extraneous materials, such as residual solvents, antibiotics, animal products, contaminating cell populations and co-purifying proteins; also includes residual moisture and pyrogenic substances (e.g., endotoxin)
- identity—if product comprises multiple components (e.g., cell lines and proteins), the test method should identify all components
- constituent materials—all ingredients should meet general standards of purity and quality
- mycoplasma—if applicable

Alternative methods are permitted if they are equal to or greater than the assurances provided by the specified tests and must be validated by the end of Phase 3 to show equivalency to the established tests. The standards also include

Table 24-2. Key CMC Guidance for Biological Product Development

ICH Guidelines Specifically Targeted at Biotech Products
• *Q5C: Quality of Biotechnological Products: Stability Testing of Biotechnological/Biological Products (November 1995)*
• *Q5B Quality of Biotechnological Products: Analysis of the Expression Construct in Cells Used for Production of r-DNA Derived Protein Products* (February 1996)
• *Q5D: Derivation and Characterisation of Cell Substrates Used for Production of Biotechnological/Biological Products* (July 1997)
• *Q5A Viral Safety Evaluation of Biotechnology Products Derived From Cell Lines of Human or Animal Origin* (September 1998)
• *Q6B: Specifications: Test Procedures and Acceptance Criteria for Biotechnological/Biological Products* (August 1999)
• *Q5E: Comparability of Biotechnological/Biological Products Subject to Changes in Their Manufacturing Process* (June 2005)
• *Q4B Annex 14: Bacterial Endotoxins Test General Chapter* (July 2010)
• *S6(R1) Preclinical Safety Evaluation of Biotechnology-Derived Pharmaceuticals* (May 2012)
FDA Points to Consider and Other Applicable CMC Guidance Documents
• *Points to Consider in the Production and Testing of New Drugs and Biologicals Produced by Recombinant DNA Technology* (April 1985)
• *Guideline on Validation of the Limulus Amebocyte Lysate Test as an End-Product Endotoxin Test for Human and Animal Parenteral Drugs, Biological Products, and Medical Devices* (December 1987)
• *Points to Consider in the Collection, Processing, and Testing of Ex-Vivo Activated Mononuclear Leukocytes for Administering to Humans* (August 1989)
• *Guidance for Industry: Content and Format of Investigational New Drug Applications (INDs) for Phase 1 Studies of Drugs, Including Well-Characterized, Therapeutic, Biotechnology-Derived Products* (November 1995).
• *Guidance for Industry: Content and Format of INDs for Phase 1 Studies of Drugs, Including Well-Characterized, Therapeutic, Biotechnology-Derived Products. Questions and Answers* (November 1995)
• *Demonstration of Comparability of Human Biological Products, Including Therapeutic Biotechnology-derived Products* (April 1996)
• *Guidance on Applications for Products Comprised of Living Autologous Cells Manipulated ex Vivo and Intended for Structural Repair or Reconstruction* (May 1996)
• *Guidance for Industry for the Submission of Chemistry, Manufacturing, and Controls Information for a Therapeutic Recombinant DNA-Derived Product or a Monoclonal Antibody Product for In Vivo Use* (August 1996)
• *Proposed Approach to Regulation of Cellular and Tissue-Based Products* (February 1997)
• *Points to Consider in the Manufacture and Testing of Monoclonal Antibody Products for Human Use* (February 1997)
• *Guidance for Industry: Changes to an Approved Application for Specified Biotechnology and Specified Synthetic Biological Products* (July 1997)
• *Guidance for Industry: Guidance for Human Somatic Cell Therapy and Gene Therapy* (March 1998)
• *Guidance for Industry: Environmental Assessment of Human Drug and Biologics Applications* (July 1998)
• *Guidance for Industry: Monoclonal Antibodies Used as Reagents in Drug Manufacturing* (March 2001)
• *Guidance for Industry: IND Meetings for Human Drugs and Biologics Chemistry, Manufacturing, and Controls Information* (May 2001)
• *Guidance for Industry: Container Closure Systems for Packaging Human Drugs and Biologics—Questions and Answers* (May 2002)
• *Draft Guidance for Industry: Drugs, Biologics, and Medical Devices Derived from Bioengineered Plants for Use in Humans and Animals* (September 2002)
• *Draft Guidance for Industry: Comparability Protocols—Protein Drug Products and Biological Products—Chemistry, Manufacturing, and Controls Information* (September 2003)
• *Draft Guidance for Industry: Labeling for Human Prescription Drug and Biological Products—Implementing the New Content and Format Requirements* (January 2006)
• *Draft Guidance for Industry: Characterization and Qualification of Cell Substrates and Other Biological Starting Materials Used in the Production of Viral Vaccines for the Prevention and Treatment of Infectious Diseases* (September 2006)
• *Draft Guidance for Industry: Validation of Growth-Based Rapid Microbiological Methods for Sterility Testing of Cellular and Gene Therapy Products* (February 2008)
• *Guidance for Food and Drug Administration Reviewers and Sponsors: Content and Review of Chemistry, Manufacturing, and Control (CMC) Information for Human Somatic Cell Therapy Investigational New Drug Applications (INDs)* (April 2008)

•	*Guidance for Food and Drug Administration Reviewers and Sponsors: Content and Review of Chemistry, Manufacturing, and Control (CMC) Information for Human Gene Therapy Investigational New Drug Applications (INDs)* (April 2008)
•	*Guidance for Industry: CGMP for Phase 1 Investigational Drugs* (July 2008)
•	*Draft Guidance for Industry: Potency Tests for Cellular and Gene Therapy Products* (October 2008)
•	*Guidance for Industry: Labeling for Human Prescription Drug and Biological Products—Determining Established Pharmacologic Class for Use in the Highlights of Prescribing Information* (October 2009)
•	*Draft Guidance for Industry: Assay Development for Immunogenicity Testing of Therapeutic Proteins* (December 2009)
•	*Draft Guidance for Industry: CMC Post approval Manufacturing Changes Reportable in Annual Reports* (June 2010)
•	*Draft Guidance for Industry: Early Clinical Trials with Live Biotherapeutic Products: Chemistry, Manufacturing, and Control Information* (December 2010)
•	*Guidance for Industry: Process Validation: General Principles and Practices* (January 2011)
•	*Draft Guidance for Industry: Guidance for Industry on Biosimilars: Q&As Regarding Implementation of the BPCI Act of 2009* (February 2012)
•	*Draft Guidance for Industry: Scientific Considerations in Demonstrating Biosimilarity to a Reference Product* (February 2012)
•	*Draft Guidance for Industry: Quality Considerations in Demonstrating Biosimilarity to a Reference Protein Product* (February 2012)
•	*Guidance for Industry: Limiting the Use of Certain Phthalates as Excipients in CDER-Regulated Products* (December 2012)
•	*Draft Guidance for Industry: Immunogenicity Assessment for Therapeutic Protein Products* (February 2013)
•	*Draft Guidance for Industry: Allowable Excess Volume and Labeled Vial Fill Size in Injectable Drug and Biological Products* (March 2014)
•	*Draft Guidance for Industry: Current Good Manufacturing Practice Requirements for Combination Products* (January 2015)

Source: http://www.fda.gov/Drugs/GuidanceComplianceRegulatoryInformation/Guidances/ucm065005.htm

testing requirements for communicable disease agents, product dating periods and product labeling requirements (i.e., the product package to be labeled with the biologic's proper name; the manufacturer's name, address and applicable license number; and the expiration date).

The amount of information on analytical procedures and methods validation necessary for submissions will vary with the investigation phase (21 CFR 312.23(a)(7)). For general guidance on analytical procedures and validation methods to be submitted for Phase 1 studies, sponsors can refer to FDA's *Guidance for Industry: Content and Format of Investigational New Drug Applications (INDs) for Phase 1 Studies of Drugs, Including Well-Characterized, Therapeutic, Biotechnology-Derived Products* (November 1995). And for Phase 2 or Phase 3 studies, FDA's *Guidance for Industry: INDs for Phase 2 and 3 Studies of Drugs, Including Specified Therapeutic Biotechnology-Derived Products, Chemistry, Manufacturing, and Controls Content and Format* (draft guidance published in April 1999). All analytical procedures should be fully developed and validated when the BLA is submitted. The requested BLA analytical procedure format and content are the same as for an NDA.

A number of guidances for appropriate CMC development are available, including ICH guidelines, CBER Points to Consider and other FDA guidances. Key CMC-related guidances are listed in **Table 24-2**. In addition, several general and specific *USP* chapters are relevant to biologics, including testing methods and viral safety evaluation.

Drug Master Files

A Drug Master File (DMF) is a submission to FDA, usually concerning confidential CMC information of a drug substance, intermediates, container closures and excipients, which permits FDA to review the confidential information in support of a third party's submission. DMFs are optional and are categorized in 21 CFR 314.420 as follows:

- Type I: reserved, no longer applicable
- Type II: drug substance, drug substance intermediate and material used in their preparation
- Type III: packaging material
- Type IV: excipient, colorant, flavor, essence
- Type V: FDA-accepted reference material

Submitted DMFs are reviewed only in conjunction with a sponsor's IND, NDA or BLA when that DMF is referenced, and there is a letter of authorization granting FDA permission to access the DMF in support of the submission. If there are deficiencies in the DMF, the DMF holder will be notified to provide additional information. The sponsor also will be notified in either an Information Request (IR) or Complete Response (CR) letter; however, no confidential details about the deficiency will be included in this communication. If there are no deficiencies, the DMF holder will not receive any communication. DMFs should be updated annually, although FDA does not send reminders. After three years' inactivity (i.e., no annual updates), FDA will notify the holder the DMF is considered inactive; the holder has 90 days to either close the DMF or provide an annual update to keep it open.

A DMF's content should be based on applicable guidance, and the submission should follow the M4Q CTD-Quality format. The submission also must contain a statement of commitment to CGMP compliance. One commonly used DMF submission for CBER is the Type V DMF, under which CBER accepts:

- facility information in support of gene- and cell-based therapies (which may be used to support clinical trials and to facilitate IND review)
- production information for a contract manufacturer providing a list of other products manufactured in the facility (this information was formerly filed as a Type I DMF)
- submissions from contract testing facilities, such as cell bank testing and viral clearance studies

Before submitting any Type V DMF, a letter of intent should be submitted to FDA to determine the suitability of the DMF submission.

Animal Rule

FDA's regulations concerning when human efficacy studies are not ethical or feasible for biological products are codified in 21 CFR 601.90. Approval under the Animal Rule can be pursued only if definitive human efficacy studies cannot be conducted because it would be unethical, and field trials are not feasible. The Animal Rule states for products developed to ameliorate or prevent serious or life-threatening conditions caused by exposure to lethal or permanently disabling toxic substances, when performing human challenge studies would be unethical, and field trials to study effectiveness after accidental or intentional human exposure are not feasible, FDA may grant marketing approval based on adequate and well-controlled animal efficacy studies when the results of those studies establish the drug is reasonably likely to produce clinical benefit. Products evaluated for efficacy under the Animal Rule should be evaluated for safety under the existing requirements for establishing new drugs' safety. The Animal Rule states FDA will rely on evidence from animal studies to provide substantial evidence of effectiveness only when all of the following four criteria are met:

1. There is a reasonably well-understood pathophysiological mechanism of the substance's toxicity and its prevention or substantial reduction by the product.
2. The effect is demonstrated in more than one animal species and is expected to react with a response predictive for humans, unless the effect is demonstrated in a single animal species that represents a sufficiently well-characterized animal model for predicting the response in humans.
3. The animal study endpoint clearly is related to the desired benefit in humans, generally the enhancement of survival or prevention of major morbidity.
4. Data or information on the product's kinetics and pharmacodynamics or other relevant data or information, in animals and humans, allows selection of an effective dose in humans.

Submitting the BLA

BLA Submission and Review Process

BLA Format and Content

The BLA is a request for permission to introduce or deliver for introduction a biologic product into interstate commerce (21 CFR 601.2). BLAs are required for all biological products submitted to CBER or, for well-characterized proteins to CDER. The BLA may be submitted in paper or DVD CTD format or in eCTD format following ICH CTD requirements. Major NDA and BLA sections are the same, with a few exceptions. For instance, biologics typically are excluded categorically from requiring an environmental assessment under 21 CFR 25.5(c). In addition, the process needs to be validated for biologics prior to submitting the BLA, which is reviewed as part of the Preapproval Inspection (PAI) requirements for small molecule drugs.

A BLA, similar to an NDA, must provide the multidisciplinary FDA review team (medical officers, microbiologists, chemists, biostatisticians, etc.) with the efficacy and safety information necessary to make a benefit-risk assessment and to recommend or oppose a drug product's approval.

BLAs are regulated under 21 CFR Parts 600–680. A BLA can be submitted by any legal person or entity taking responsibility for compliance with product and establishment standards. Form FDA 356h specifies a BLA's requirements, including:

- administrative information, including applicant information
- product and manufacturing (CMC) information, including facilities information
- preclinical studies
- clinical studies
- labeling

Timetable for BLA Review

The NDA/BLA review process is divided into five phases:

1. filing determination and review planning
2. review
3. Advisory Committee meeting preparation and conduct
4. action
5. post-action

Table 24-3 is a representative timetable of the NDA/BLA review process.

Table 24-3. BLA Review Timetable

	Activity	Responsibility
Day 0		Central Document Room (CDER) or Document Control Center (CBER)
Day 1–14		
By Day 14	Acknowledge application receipt in writing	Review Discipline Team Leaders (CDER) Review Division Management (CBER)
Day 0-45	Conduct filing review/convey potential RTF issues to applicant	Review Team
By Day 45	Make filing decision/plan and schedule for filing meeting	Review Division Director Office Director (consulted for RTFs)/ Review Team
By Day 60		RPM/Review Division Director
By Day 74	Communicate filing review issues to applicant	RPM
By the end of Month 5	Mid-cycle Meeting	Review Team
Variable	Issue Discipline Review Letters	Review Team
2 months and 12 days prior to the approval date	Late-cycle Meeting	Review Team
By end of Month 8 (per PDUFA IV, additional 2 months per PDUFA V)	Complete primary review/conduct Advisory Committee Meeting	Review Team
4 weeks before approval action	Initiate compliance check request (BLAs)	RPM
3 weeks before approval	Labeling discussions (for Approval and Approvable Actions)	Review Team/ODS/DDMAC Labeling Team
By PDUFA goal date	Send official copy to applicant	RPM
After PDUFA goal date		Review Team

Per 21 CFR 601.2, an application for licensure is not considered filed until CBER has received all pertinent information and data from the applicant. A refuse to file (RTF) decision may be made on applications containing incomplete or inadequate information required under Section 351 of the *PHS Act*, the *FD&C Act* or in FDA regulations (e.g., 21 CFR 601.2). RTF decisions can be based on:

- an application's administrative incompleteness
- an application's scientific incompleteness (i.e., omission of critical data, information or analyses needed to evaluate safety, purity and potency or provide adequate directions for use (21 CFR 601.2))
- an application's inadequate information content or organization, precluding a substantive and meaningful review
- a technically deficient electronic submission

In summary, CBER's initial decision on whether to file a BLA will be based on a threshold determination of whether the information submitted to support the license application is sufficiently complete to permit a substantive and meaningful review. An RTF may apply if the application contains uncorrected deficiencies (e.g., manufacturing or product specifications) clearly communicated to the applicant before application submission or, for electronic submissions, technical deficiencies sufficient to require resolution before a meaningful review can occur. An RTF is not a final determination concerning potential approvability; it can be an early opportunity for the applicant to develop a complete application but will delay a full review of the application.

Applicants may receive additional information requests as a result of ongoing reviews and are encouraged to respond promptly and completely to such requests. During the first cycle, the FDA division ordinarily reviews all amendments solicited by the agency during the review and any amendments to the application previously agreed upon during the pre-NDA/BLA meeting. Substantial amendments submitted late in the review cycle may be reviewed in a subsequent cycle, depending on other identified application deficiencies. Following FDA's review of a license application, the applicant and FDA may present their findings to FDA's Related Biological Products Advisory Committee. This non-FDA expert committee (scientists, physicians, biostatisticians and a consumer representative) provides advice to the agency regarding the product's safety and efficacy for the proposed indication. Based on Advisory Committee discussions and committee recommendations, FDA may ask an applicant to submit additional data or analyses for review.

A CR Letter after a complete review can be issued based on either critical omissions of data or analyses or an adverse judgment about the data, conclusions, rationale, etc., presented in the application. For example, a CR Letter could be issued if CBER concludes effectiveness has not been demonstrated, an analysis was carried out incorrectly, clinical trials were poorly designed or conducted, safety has not been adequately demonstrated and/or outstanding compliance issues remain. These judgments would not serve as the basis for an RTF unless the deficiencies were so severe as to render the application incomplete.

Other action letters include the IR Letter and the Discipline Review (DR) Letter. An IR Letter requests further information or clarification necessary to complete the discipline review. A DR Letter is sent to convey early thoughts on possible deficiencies found by a discipline review team at the conclusion of its review. A single DR letter may contain comments from multiple discipline reviews.

A PAI will be conducted for the proposed manufacturing facilities during the late stage of the application review.

Approval to market a biologic is granted by issuance of a biologics license (including US license number) as part of the approval letter. A license represents a determination that the product, the manufacturing process and the manufacturing facilities meet applicable requirements to ensure the product's continued safety, purity and potency. Among other things, safety and purity assessments must consider the storage and testing of cell substrates often used to manufacture biologics. A potency assay is required due to biologics' complexity and heterogeneity.

Product approval also requires product labeling adequate to allow healthcare providers to understand the product's proper use, including its potential benefits and risks, to communicate with patients and parents, and to safely deliver the product to the public.

On 9 July 2012, the *Food and Drug Administration Safety and Innovation Act* of 2012 *(FDASIA)* was signed into law. This new law includes the reauthorization of the *Prescription Drug User Fee Act (PDUFA),* which provides FDA with the necessary resources to maintain a predictable and efficient review process for human drug and biologic products. Under *PDUFA V*, FDA promotes innovation through enhanced communication between FDA and sponsors during drug development. As part of its commitments in *PDUFA V*, FDA has established a new review program to promote greater transparency and increased communication between the FDA review team and the applicant on the most innovative products reviewed by the agency. The program applies to all New Medical Entity (NME) NDAs and original BLAs received from 1 October 2012 through 30 September 2017.

PDUFA V increases the review timeline from six to eight months for priority reviews and 10 to 12 months for standard reviews. The increase in the duration of reviews is intended to increase the likelihood of an on-time approval (first-cycle approval).

Under *PDUFA* provisions, submission of a major amendment during the last three months of a review may trigger a three-month extension of the review clock. *PDUFA V* modifies this, as a major amendment can extend the review clock by three months at any time during the review.

The key time points for FDA communication defined by *PDUFA V* are:

- Day 60 Filing Letter—application accepted for filing
- Day 74 Letter (74 days after FDA receives the application)—The letter will identify substantive review issues identified during the first 14 days of the review and will include FDA's preliminary plans on whether to hold an Advisory Committee meeting.
- Mid-cycle Communication—For a priority review, this is three months after the filing date, i.e., five months after FDA receipt of the application for priority review, or nine months for standard review. The letter may include any significant issues identified to date and an update on the status of the review.
- Late-cycle Meeting—For priority applications, it is two months and 12 days prior to the approval date. The meeting will discuss the status of the review and issues that will be raised at the Advisory Committee.

Biologics Advertising and Promotional Labeling and Proprietary Name

CBER reviews draft and final professional and direct-to-consumer (DTC) advertising and promotional labeling materials submitted for licensed biological products. CBER also reviews promotional materials to ensure information about the product's risks and benefits is communicated in a truthful, non-misleading and balanced manner, and the materials are in compliance with pertinent federal laws and regulations. Final advertising and promotional labeling materials may be submitted in paper or electronic format by applicants. Submissions must contain:

- Form FDA-2253: Transmittal of Advertisements and Promotional Labeling for Drugs and Biologics for Human Use
- two copies of final advertisements and promotional labeling materials
- two copies of the product's current professional labeling (e.g., approved Package Labeling (PI), Patient Package Insert (PPI), Medication Guide and Instructions for Use)

Draft DTC television advertising and promotional labeling materials also may be submitted in paper or electronic format. For products approved under accelerated approval, all advertising and promotional materials intended for dissemination or publication within 120 days following marketing approval must be submitted using Form FDA 2253 for agency review during the preapproval review period. Furthermore, after 120 days following marketing approval, all advertising and promotional materials must be submitted at least 30 days prior to the intended time of initial dissemination or publication.

CBER's Advertising and Promotional Labeling Branch (APLB) reviews and evaluates proposed proprietary names for biological products in accordance with SOPP 8001.4: Review of Proprietary Names for CBER Regulated Products. Proposed proprietary names are evaluated to avoid potential medication errors related to look-alike and sound-alike proprietary names and to avoid names that are fanciful or misleading.

APLB also evaluates other factors that could contribute to medication errors, such as unclear label abbreviations, acronyms, dose designations and error-prone label and packaging design.

Biosimilars—Long Awaited Development

The *Biologics Price Competition and Innovation Act (BPCI Act)* passed as part of health reform (*Affordable Care Act*) was signed into law 23 March 2010. The *BPCI Act* creates an abbreviated licensure pathway for biological products shown to be biosimilar to or interchangeable with an FDA-licensed reference product. Objectives are similar to those of the *Drug Price Competition and Patent Term Restoration Act* of 1984 (*Hatch-Waxman Act*), which established abbreviated approval pathways for drug products under Sections 505(b)(2) and 505(j) of the *FD&C Act*. The *BPCI Act* amended the *PHS Act* and created a licensure pathway in Section 351(k) of the *PHS Act*. The *BPCI Act* aligns with FDA's policy of permitting appropriate reliance on what is already known about a drug, thereby saving time and resources and avoiding unnecessary duplication of human or animal testing.

A biological product may be demonstrated to be "biosimilar" if data show it is "highly similar" to the reference product, notwithstanding minor differences in clinically inactive components, and there are no clinically meaningful differences between the biological product and the reference product in terms of safety, purity and potency. In order to meet the higher standard of interchangeability, a sponsor must demonstrate the biosimilar product can be expected to produce the same clinical result as the reference product in any given patient and, for a biological product administered more than once, the risk of alternating or switching from the reference product to the biosimilar product is not greater than the risk of maintaining the patient on the reference product. Interchangeable products may be substituted for the reference product by a pharmacist without the prescribing healthcare provider's intervention. To be approved as a biosimilar, the following criteria must be met:

- The biological product and reference product utilize the same mechanism or mechanisms of action for the condition(s) of use prescribed, recommended or suggested in the proposed labeling.
- The condition(s) of use prescribed, recommended or suggested in the labeling proposed for the biological product has been previously approved for the reference product.
- The route of administration, dosage form and strength of the biological product are the same as those of the reference product.
- The facility in which the biological product is manufactured, processed, packed or held meets standards designed to ensure the product continues to be safe, pure and potent.

FDA has established three committees to ensure consistency in regulatory approach and guidance to sponsors regarding development programs for proposed biosimilar biological products intended for submission under new Section 351(k) of the *PHS Act* and related issues. The committees charged with discussing and coordinating issues include:

- CDER/CBER Biosimilar Implementation Committee
- CDER Biosimilar Review Committee
- CBER Biosimilar Review Committee

At this time, FDA is continuing to consider the type of information sufficient to enable it to determine a biological product is interchangeable with the reference product.

FDA developed several guidance documents to implement and comply with the *BPCI Act* (**Table 24-4**). Three major documents were developed in February 2012 to address a broad range of issues, including:

- *Draft Guidance for Industry: Scientific Considerations in Demonstrating Biosimilarity to a Reference Product*—This guidance discusses important scientific considerations in demonstrating biosimilarity, including: a stepwise approach to demonstrating biosimilarity, which can include a comparison of the proposed product and the reference product with respect to structure, function, animal toxicity, human PK and PD, clinical immunogenicity and clinical safety and effectiveness; the "totality-of-the-evidence" approach FDA will use to review applications for biosimilar products; general scientific principles in conducting comparative structural and functional analysis, animal testing, human PK and PD studies, clinical immunogenicity assessment, and clinical safety and effectiveness studies. Additional factors to be considered include the complexities of the therapeutic protein; use of data

Table 24-4. Biosimilarity Guidance Documents

Category	Title	Type	Date
Biosimilarity; Procedural	*Formal Meetings Between the FDA and Biosimilar Biological Product Sponsors or Applicants*	Draft Guidance	29 March 2013
Biosimilarity	*Guidance for Industry on Biosimilars: QAs Regarding Implementation of the BPCI Act of 2009*	Draft Guidance updated for 508 compliance	9 February 2012
Biosimilarity	*Scientific Considerations in Demonstrating Biosimilarity to a Reference Product*	Draft Guidance	9 February 2012
Biosimilarity	*Quality Considerations in Demonstrating Biosimilarity to a Reference Protein Product*	Draft Guidance	9 February 2012
Biosimilarity	*Clinical Pharmacology Data to Support a Demonstration of Biosimilarity to a Reference Product*	Draft Guidance	13 May 2014
Procedural; Biosimilarity	*Reference Product Exclusivity for Biological Products Filed Under Section 351(a) of the PHS Act*	Draft Guidance	4 August 2014

derived from studies comparing a proposed product with a non-US-licensed product and postmarketing safety monitoring considerations.

- *Draft Guidance for Industry: Biosimilars: Questions and Answers Regarding Implementation of the Biologics Price Competition and Innovation Act of 2009*—This draft provides answers to common questions from sponsors interested in developing proposed biosimilar products, including: biosimilarity or interchangeability; provisions related to the requirement to submit a BLA for a "biological product;" and exclusivity. The guidance recommends sponsors of proposed biosimilar products request an initial meeting with FDA as soon as the sponsor can provide a proposed plan for its biosimilar development program, manufacturing process information and preliminary comparative analytical data with the reference product. Comparative analytical data provide the foundation for a biosimilar development program and can influence decisions about the type and amount of animal and clinical data needed.
- *Draft Guidance for Industry: Quality Considerations in Demonstrating Biosimilarity to a Reference Protein Product*—This guidance focuses on analytical studies that may be relevant to assessing whether the proposed biosimilar product and a reference product are highly similar, which is an important part of the biosimilarity assessment.

The approval of a biosimilar application under Subsection 351(k) of the *PHS Act* may not occur until 12 years after the date on which the reference product was first licensed. In addition, an application under Subsection 351(k) may not be accepted for review until four years after the date on which the reference product was first licensed.

FDA is evaluating the extent to which nonclinical data from animal studies and clinical data comparing a proposed biosimilar product with a non-US-licensed product can be used to support a demonstration of biosimilarity to a US-licensed reference product and the type of bridging data needed to provide adequate scientific justification for this approach. FDA also is considering acceptable types of scientific justification for use of a non-US-licensed biological product as an active control in a clinical trial in a "stand-alone" 351(a) BLA.

Preapproval Inspections

The pre-license inspection is performed as part of the "Biologics License Application" review process. There are circumstances when a pre-license inspection can be waived, but an inspection generally is necessary. An applicant can be either a non-FDA-licensed firm applying for its first license, in which case it will definitely get an inspection, or, an already FDA-licensed firm with a new product. A licensed firm would submit a new BLA, but its facility could be licensed for other products already. The pre-license inspection may become more complicated if it involves several sites at different locations. A pre-license inspection is necessary for licensure under the CFR, which requires a BLA to be approved only after inspection of the establishments listed in the application and upon determination the establishments comply with the application's standards and the requirements prescribed in the applicable regulations.

Preapproval inspection is slightly different from a pre-license inspection.

The preapproval inspection may be completed for a new manufacturing facility, a new contract manufacturing facility or because of significant changes to the manufacturing process. With pre-license and preapproval inspections, the sponsor is supposed to be ready for an inspection at the time of its submission; CBER wants the investigator to see all the facility's pertinent operations. With respect to pre-license and preapproval inspections, as per the CFR, CBER will make a determination of compliance with the application and applicable standards, including GMP standards, to approve the application or supplement. The product to be introduced into interstate commerce has to be available for inspection during all phases of manufacturing.

Inspections occur about halfway through the review cycle. For a new BLA, that would be about five months after the application was received, since there is a 10-month review timeframe. For a prior approval supplement, the inspection would occur at about two months, because that submission type has a four-month review timeframe. There are times when CBER determines an inspection in support of an application or supplement is not necessary (e.g., if it is a production or processing area CBER recently has inspected, and the sponsor has a good compliance history, the inspection might be waived). FDA Standard Operating Procedure 8410, also called SOP 8410, is used as a guide in determining when pre-license or preapproval inspections are necessary. The Division of Manufacturing and Product Quality in CBER's Office of Compliance and Biologics Quality (OCBQ) serves as the lead on pre-license or preapproval inspections of biologic drugs and devices. For blood and blood products, the Division of Blood Applications in CBER's OBRR acts as the lead for the inspection.

There are also preapproval inspections performed for a prior approval supplement. This inspection is for changes to an approved application, which is defined in CFR, and covers the general regulation for changes to an approved application.

BIMO Process to Assess the Validity of the Scientific Evidence Submitted to Support a BLA

The BIMO inspection is part of the investigational stage of product development and falls within the IND process.

The term "clinical" refers to studies in human subjects. The requirements for conducting clinical research are also referred to as Good Clinical Practices (GCPs). The term "nonclinical" refers to studies in animals or tissue cultures used to evaluate safety before the products are tested in humans. The regulations for nonclinical laboratories are referred to as Good Laboratory Practices (GLPs).

The BIMO Program has three purposes: to ensure human research subjects' rights, safety and welfare are protected; to determine the clinical trial data accuracy and reliability; and to assess compliance with FDA regulations during inspections.

For marketing applications, CBER usually inspects from three to five clinical investigator sites to evaluate whether the sites followed the study protocol. During the inspection, FDA verifies the critical safety and efficacy endpoint data the sponsor submitted in the marketing application.

Communications With FDA

Meetings With FDA

Three types of meetings occur between sponsors or applicants and FDA staff: Type A, Type B and Type C. Each meeting type is subject to different procedures:

- Type A—to resolve a clinical hold or RTF or to resolve a dispute or discuss a special protocol assessment (SPA)
- Type B—key milestone meetings to include Pre-IND, End-of-Phase 1 (for products developed under 21 CFR 601 Subpart E), End-of-Phase 2/Pre-Phase 3 and Pre- BLA
- Type C—for any other purpose

If applicants are considering a request for a Type A meeting, before submitting the request, they should contact the review division in either CBER or CDER to discuss appropriateness of the request. Type A meetings should be scheduled to occur within 30 days of FDA receipt of a written meeting request.

Type B meetings should be scheduled to occur within 60 days of FDA receipt of the written meeting request. FDA, in general, will not grant more than one of each Type B meeting for each potential application.

A Type C meeting is any meeting other than a Type A or Type B meeting between CBER or CDER and a sponsor regarding a product's development and review. Type C meetings should be scheduled to occur within 75 days of FDA receipt of the written meeting request.

A meeting background package should be submitted to the appropriate review division so it is received in accordance with the following timeframes:

- Type A meeting—at least two weeks before the formal meeting
- Type B meeting—at least four weeks before the formal meeting
- Type C meeting—at least four weeks before the formal meeting

Advisory Committee Meetings

The *Federal Advisory Committee Act* became law in 1972 and is the legal foundation defining how these committees operate. The law places special emphasis on open meetings, chartering, public involvement and reporting. Advisory Committees are groups of experts from outside the agency FDA sometimes turns to for advice on complex scientific, technical and policy issues. Advisory Committees provide independent, professional expertise related to the development and evaluation of FDA-regulated products, such as allergenic products; blood products; cellular, tissue and gene therapies; transmissible spongiform encephalopathies; and vaccines and related biological products. In general, Advisory Committees include a chairman, several members, plus representatives of consumer groups, industry and, sometimes, patients. Additional experts with special knowledge may be added for individual meetings, as needed. Although the committees provide advice to the agency, FDA makes the final decisions. In some cases, FDA is required by law to refer an issue to an Advisory Committee. In others, it has discretion to consider whether to refer a matter to an Advisory Committee. For all first-of-a-kind or first-in-class products for human use, FDA either refers the product to an Advisory Committee or summarizes the reasons it does not do so before approval in the action letter.

Once the review has progressed within the reviewing division, CBER will notify the sponsor 55 days in advance if it has determined an Advisory Committee meeting is required. The sponsor prepares materials for Advisory Committee review and designates which materials are publically releasable under the *Freedom of Information Act* (*FOIA*) and which are to be treated as proprietary, non-public materials. FDA may disagree with the sponsor's designations and request that additional information be made public. In general, product information not in the labeling, such as manufacturing processes, formulation information and quality control testing, as well as the raw data from preclinical and clinical studies, can be considered exempt from *FOIA*. Advisory Committee members will receive both public and proprietary materials. During the meeting, sponsors may be permitted to make presentations, but they are not allowed to approach committee members without the consent of a federal officer.

Market Exclusivity

Biologics are allowed a 12-year market exclusivity instead of the five years allowed for NDA drugs (seven years for orphan products). With the passage of the *BPCI Act*, the additional six months of market exclusivity for pediatric indications now applies to biologics as well.

Once a product is licensed, what needs to be considered?

Post-Licensure Changes and Continuous Compliance

Under 21 CFR 601.12, a change in the approved product, labeling, production process, quality control, equipment or facility must be reported to FDA. The change can be reported in a supplement requiring approval prior to distribution, a supplement submitted at least 30 days prior to distribution of the product made using the change, a supplement submitted prior to distribution of the product made using the change, or an annual report, depending on its potential to have an adverse effect on the biological product's "identity, strength, quality, purity, or potency" as it may relate to the product's safety or effectiveness. Before distributing a licensed product manufactured using a change, the manufacturer is required to demonstrate, through appropriate validation and/or clinical or nonclinical laboratory studies, the lack of adverse effect of the change on the product's safety or effectiveness.

Due to the sometimes limited ability to identify clinically active component(s) of complex biological products, such products often are defined by their manufacturing processes. In 1996, FDA provided recommendations in its *Guidance Concerning Demonstration of Comparability of Human Biological Products, Including Therapeutic Biotechnology Products*, which explains how an applicant may demonstrate—through a combination of analytical testing, functional assay, assessment of PK, pharmacodynamics (PD) and toxicity in animals and clinical studies—a manufacturing change does not adversely affect its FDA-approved product's identity, purity or potency. Since 1996, FDA has approved many manufacturing process changes for licensed biological products, based on a demonstration of product comparability before and after the process change, as supported by quality criteria and analytical testing without the need for additional nonclinical data and clinical safety and/or efficacy studies. In cases where the change's effects are uncertain, additional data may be required, including nonclinical and/or clinical studies, to demonstrate product comparability. In July 1997, CBER issued *Guidance for Industry: Changes to an Approved Application for Specified Biotechnology and Specified Synthetic Biological Products* to assist applicants in determining which reporting mechanism is appropriate for a change to an approved license application. These concepts were developed further by ICH and resulted in Q6E *Comparability of Biotechnological/Biological Products subject to Changes in their Manufacturing Process* (June 2005).

Applicable Types of Submissions

The three reporting categories for changes to an approved application are defined in 21 CFR 601.12:

- Prior Approval Supplement (PAS)—changes with a substantial potential to have an adverse effect on the product's safety or effectiveness, which require submission of a supplement and approval by FDA prior to distribution of the product made using the change (major changes)
- Changes Being Effected (CBE) 30 or CBE—changes with a moderate potential to have an adverse effect on the product's safety or effectiveness, which require submission of a supplement to FDA at least 30 days prior to distribution of the product made using the change or, for some changes, the 30 days may be waived (moderate changes)
- Annual Report—changes with minimal potential to have an adverse effect on the product's safety or

effectiveness reported by the applicant in an Annual Report (minor changes)

Monitor the Safety and Stability of Approved Biological Products

Manufacturers must report certain problems to FDA's Biological Product Deviation Reporting System. Manufacturers also must report and correct product problems within established timeframes. If a significant problem is detected, a manufacturer may need to recall or even stop manufacturing a product.

GMP Inspections

CBER inspects manufacturing facilities on a regular basis. The purpose of these inspections is to assess whether biological products are made in compliance with appropriate laws and regulations and to assist in identifying any changes needed to help ensure product quality.

GMP inspections are mandated by 21 CFR Part 600 requirements that each licensed establishment, and any of its additional locations, shall be inspected at least every two years. These facility inspections determine whether the establishment is meeting the regulation's minimal requirements for licensed biologics. They also determine whehther the facility is in compliance with the *PHS Act*, the *FD&C Act*, and any particular requirements approved in the BLA. If the biologics license is for a device regulated by CBER, 21 CFR Part 600 and /or Part 1271 (as applicable) regulations establish the minimal requirements, and the facility also must comply with the *PHS Act*, *FD&C Act*, and the BLA. If the device is approved under a PMA, it would be subject to the *FD&C Act* and specific provisions in the PMA.

For CBER products, per 21 CFR Part 600.21 each licensed establishment shall be inspected biannually. For human cell and tissue establishments, there is a risk-based approach in prioritizing inspections. There is no statutory or regulatory requirement regarding inspectional frequency for human cells, tissues and cellular-based products, known as HCT/Ps. For flu vaccine manufacturers, inspections occur annually and early in the manufacturing cycle, so problems or issues can be detected and resolved in a timely fashion, ensuring an adequate supply of vaccine for the upcoming flu season.

GMP inspections of biological drugs and devices, are conducted by "Team Biologics," a core group of investigators from various districts in the Office of Regulatory Affairs (ORA).

For routine GMP inspections, the coverage is of CGMPs, for all products or of the high-risk products manufactured at the location. Again, for flu vaccine manufacturers, this occurs every year. Production processes are inspected for all high-risk products manufactured at that location. Additionally, a review is performed of any complaints the firm has received; any adverse event reports the firm has received; any trends they see, for example, in their environmental monitoring; all Biological Product Deviation Reports the firm has submitted to CBER; medical device reports, which are similar to the Adverse Event Reporting System, or AERS, but specific to devices; recalls; and any changes made since the last inspection. If the manufacturer has had to change its process, it is important to make sure it has submitted appropriate supporting documentation, as outlined in the CFR.

Biologics Establishment Registration and Listing

Manufacturers of biological drug products are required to update registration and listing information with CDER or CBER in the proper electronic format. FDA has adopted Structured Product Labeling (SPL) as the electronic means for submission of registration and listing information to the agency. As of 1 June 2009, FDA no longer accepts paper registration and listing submissions, unless a waiver is granted. Under Section 510 of the *FD&C Act* and regulations in 21 CFR Part 207, manufacturers of biological drug products must:

- register their establishments annually on or before 31 December of each year
- list all of their products in commercial distribution at the time of initial registration, with bi-annual updates to their listings in June and December, as necessary

Special Circumstances—Commercial Biologics Manufacturing and Supply

Lot Release

After a BLA is approved, some products may be subject to official lot release. As part of the manufacturing process, the manufacturer is required to perform certain tests on each lot of the product before it is released for distribution. If the product is subject to official release by CBER, the manufacturer submits samples of each lot of product to CBER together with a release protocol showing a summary of the lot's manufacturing history and the results of lot testing performed by the manufacturer. CBER also may perform certain confirmatory tests on lots of some products, such as viral vaccines, before releasing the lots for manufacturer distribution.

Short Supply

When a licensed biologic is in short supply, the manufacturer may obtain an initial or partially manufactured version of the product from an unlicensed, but registered facility, when the product is shipped solely to the licensee and when the licensee can ensure the product made at the unlicensed facility will be manufactured in full compliance with applicable regulations. The license holder must update its license with FDA to explain this arrangement. This provision is used most commonly to obtain source materials, such as those used in producing allergenic extracts; specific types of human plasma containing rare antibodies; venoms used in producing antitoxins and antivenins; and recovered plasma.

Divided Manufacturing

Divided manufacturing is an arrangement in which two or more manufacturers, each registered with FDA and licensed to manufacture a specific biological product in its entirety, participate jointly in the manufacture of that product by only performing part of the approved process. BLAs should be updated to describe the role of each manufacturer and may need to demonstrate the intermediate products' equivalency and stability during shipment. The intermediate also should be labeled "for further manufacturing use" as part of the proper name. Each licensed manufacturer must notify the other licensee(s) and the appropriate FDA center regarding proposed changes in its product's manufacture, testing or specifications, in accordance with 21 CFR 601.12.

Shared Manufacturing

Shared manufacturing is an arrangement in which two or more manufacturers are registered and licensed for specific aspects of a product's manufacture, but neither is licensed for the product's total manufacturing process. A common shared manufacturing arrangement makes one manufacturer responsible for an intermediate product and another for the final product. All license applications or supplements under a shared manufacturing arrangement should be submitted concurrently to FDA for BLA review. Lack of one or more related applications may result in an RTF.

Contract Manufacturing

When a sponsor holds the BLA license, it must establish, maintain and follow procedures for receiving information from the contract manufacturing facility on all deviations, complaints and adverse events that may affect product quality. Specific identification of the contractor in the product labeling is not required since it does not hold the license.

Summary

- Biologics are drug products or live cells derived from living sources, e.g., humans, animals and microorganisms, which are approved for licensure under the *PHS Act*, unlike small molecule drugs, which are approved under the *FD&C Act*. CBER is the primary reviewing center for biologics and is organized into three offices for the review of blood products; vaccines; and cell, tissue and gene therapy products.
- The review of "well-characterized" biological products was moved from CBER to CDER in 2003. This category comprises biotechnology products and naturally- and synthetically-derived proteins and includes such products as monoclonal antibodies, cytokines, growth factors, enzymes, immunomodulators and thrombolytics.
- The IND process for biologics is much the same as for drugs. A number of preclinical, clinical and manufacturing guidance documents have been published to assist sponsors with issues unique to the development of biological products.
- The BLA format and general review process also is similar to that for NDAs, including the utilization of the eCTD format for submissions.
- It now is possible for a sponsor to seek approval of a "biosimilar" product under new Section 351(k) of the *PHS Act*. The sponsor must show the product is highly similar to the reference product and there are no clinically meaningful differences between the biological product and the reference product in terms of safety, purity and potency. However, to meet the higher standard of interchangeability, a sponsor must demonstrate the risk of alternating or switching between use of the biosimilar product and the reference product is no greater than the risk of maintaining the patient on the reference product.

Chapter 25

Biologics Compliance

Updated by Nisha Pandya, MS, RAC

OBJECTIVES

- ❑ Understand and learn general regulatory compliance principles for biologics preapproval, including chemistry, manufacturing and controls (CMC); change control; Investigational New Drug (IND) safety reports; role of bioresearch monitoring; product naming; and pre-license inspections
- ❑ Understand and learn general regulatory postapproval compliance principles for biologics, including inspections, postapproval commitments, change control, biologic deviations reporting and import/export
- ❑ Understand the organization, roles and responsibilities of the Office of Compliance and Biologics Quality at the US Food and Drug Administration's Center for Biologics Evaluation and Review
- ❑ Understand risk management plans for biologics, including setting up Risk Evaluation and Mitigation Strategies (REMS)
- ❑ Understand FDA enforcement activities for biologics

LAWS, REGULATIONS AND GUIDANCE DOCUMENTS COVERED IN THIS CHAPTER

- ❑ *Public Health Service Act* of 1946, Sections 351 and 361
- ❑ *Federal Food, Drug, and Cosmetic Act* of 1938
- ❑ *Food and Drug Administration Amendments Act* of 2007 (*FDAAA*)
- ❑ 21 CFR 600 Biologics General
- ❑ 21 CFR 601 Biologics Licensing
- ❑ 21 CFR 610 General Biological Products Standards
- ❑ Compliance Program Guidance Manual—Inspection of Biological Drug Products—7345.848
- ❑ Regulatory Procedures Manual, Chapter 9, Subchapter 9.3, "Importation of Biological Products," Office of Regulatory Affairs, US Food and Drug Administration
- ❑ *Guidance for Industry: Comparability Protocols—Chemistry, Manufacturing, and Controls Information* (February 2003)
- ❑ *Guidance for Industry: Comparability Protocols—Protein Drug Products and Biological Products—Chemistry, Manufacturing, and Controls Information* (September 2003)
- ❑ ICH, *Comparability of Biotechnological/ Biological Products Subject to Changes in Their Manufacturing Process Q5E* (June 2005)

- ❑ *Guidance For Industry: Changes to an Approved Application for Specified Biotechnology and Specified Synthetic Biological Products* (July 1997)
- ❑ SOPP 8410: Determining When Prelicense/ Preapproval Inspections are Necessary (December 2001)
- ❑ SOPP 8001.4: Review of CBER Regulated Product Proprietary Names (November 2008)
- ❑ *Draft Guidance for Industry: Contents of a Complete Submission for the Evaluation of Proprietary Names* (November 2008)
- ❑ *Guidance for Industry: Regulation of Human Cells, Tissues, and Cellular and Tissue-Based Products (HCT/Ps)—Small Entity Compliance Guide* (August 2007)
- ❑ Exports Under the FDA *Export Reform and Enhancement Act* of 1996 (July 2007)
- ❑ *Draft Guidance for Industry: Postmarketing Safety Reporting for Human Drug and Biological Products Including Vaccines* (March 2001)
- ❑ *Guidance for Industry: Biological Product Deviation Reporting for Licensed Manufacturers of Biological Products Other than Blood and Blood Components* (October 2006)
- ❑ SOPP 8404: Refusal to File Procedures for Biologics License Applications (August 2007)
- ❑ *Guidance for Industry: Good Pharmacovigilance Practices and Pharmacoepidemiologic Assessment* (March 2005)
- ❑ *Guidance for Industry: Premarketing Risk Assessment* (March 2005)
- ❑ *Guidance for Industry: Changes to an Approved Application: Biological Products* (July 1997)
- ❑ *Guidance for Industry: Format and Content of Proposed Risk Evaluation and Mitigation Strategies (REMS), REMS Assessments, and Proposed REMS Modifications* (September 2009)
- ❑ *Draft Guidance for Industry: Safety Reporting requirements for INDs and BA/BE Studies* (September 2010)
- ❑ *Guidance for Industry: Postmarketing Studies and Clinical Trials—Implementation of Section 505(o)(3) of the Federal Food, Drug, and Cosmetic Act* (April 2011)
- ❑ Medication Guides—Distribution Requirements and Inclusion in Risk Evaluation and Mitigation Strategies (REMS) (February 2011)
- ❑ *Guidance for Industry and Investigators: Safety Reporting Requirements for INDs and BA/BE Studies* (December 2012)
- ❑ *Guidance for Industry: Electronic Submission of Lot Distribution Reports* (March 2015)

Introduction

Compliance is a key part of ensuring a robust product lifecycle, starting with successful development and approval of a product to commercialization and postapproval monitoring. Biologics compliance follows a risk-based approach and specifically focuses on FDA requirements (Code of Federal Regulations (CFR), US Food and Drug Administration (FDA) guidance and International Conference on Harmonisation (ICH) guidelines). Biologics encompasses many products, such as fractionated blood and its recombinant analogues; antitoxins; allergenic products; vaccines; products of manipulated, cultured or expanded human cells, and gene therapy products that introduce genetic material into the body to replace faulty or missing genetic material.[1]

Regulations

FDA's Center for Biologics Evaluation and Research (CBER) is responsible for ensuring biological drug products are safe and effective and in compliance with applicable laws and regulations. Biological drug products are licensed under Section 351 of the *Public Health Service Act* (*PHS Act*) (42 U.S.C.) and fall within the definition of a drug, found in Section 201(g)(1) of the *Food, Drug, and Cosmetic Act* (*FD&C Act*). Biological drug products are subject to inspection under the provisions of both the *PHS Act* and the *FD&C Act*.

Biological drug products are subject to the applicable regulations promulgated under both acts, including the current Good Manufacturing Practice (CGMP) regulations, found in 21 CFR, Parts 210 and 211, and the biologics regulations, 21 CFR Parts 600–680. In addition, human cells, tissues and cellular and tissue-based products regulated as biological drug products also are subject to the registration and listing, donor eligibility and Current Good Tissue Practice (CGTP) regulations in 21 CFR Part 1271. CGMP regulations apply to the manufacture of biological drug products under Section 501(a)(2)(b) of the *FD&C Act*, and CGMP principles apply to the manufacture of biological intermediates and drug substances, and the biologics regulations under 21 CFR Part 600.

Establishments also must comply with their FDA-approved Biologics License Application (BLA) commitments and applicable standards. Biological drug products include a wide variety of indications, dosage forms and manufacturing processes, all of critical importance in promoting and protecting the public health. To help ensure manufacturers consistently produce safe, pure, potent and effective biological products, FDA conducts CGMP inspections of each establishment at least biennially. Pre-license inspections (PLI) for new biological products and preapproval inspections (PAI) for significant changes to a biologics license application are performed to ensure compliance with the regulations prior to approval of a new license or significant change to the license.[2]

To provide more effective and efficient regulation of biological drug products, the Office of Regulatory Affairs (ORA) and CBER established Team Biologics in 1997 to conduct routine and compliance follow-up CGMP inspections of biological drug product manufacturers, including blood establishments.[3] Team Biologics uses the investigative skills of ORA and the medical, scientific and product expertise of CBER, to promote and protect the public health through coordinated, integrated assessments of biological drug manufacturers' compliance status. CBER conducts PLIs and PAIs utilizing the CGMP requirements and CBER reviewers' scientific expertise.[4]

This compliance program builds on knowledge gained during previous FDA inspections of biological drug and tissue industries. It reflects the objectives identified in FDA's Strategic Action Plan for developing and implementing new inspection approaches using a resource-efficient, risk-based approach to provide high-quality, cost-effective oversight of biological drug products' manufacturing, processing and distribution to reduce risk.[5]

This systems-based, risk management approach identifies key systems and three critical elements common to biological drug product establishments. Most biological drug products covered under this compliance program were identified as critical to public health, and are processed aseptically. These factors help form the basis for establishing appropriate inspection coverage levels under this program.

The program also establishes two inspection levels to evaluate an establishment's compliance with applicable CGMP regulations: Level I (Full)—a comprehensive evaluation of at least four systems; and Level II (Abbreviated)—an evaluation of one mandatory system, plus one additional system on a rotating basis. This approach is similar in concept to that set forth in CBER's CPG 7342.001—Inspection of Licensed and Unlicensed Blood Banks, Brokers, Reference Laboratories, and Contractors, which incorporates a systems-based approach covering critical elements within each system, and a Level I/II inspection option.[6]

This quality management approach focuses on the facilities' key operating systems, and the two-tiered inspection option provides a method to focus the inspectional coverage and resources appropriate for each inspection, with appropriate advisory, administrative or regulatory action taken, when necessary.

Continued biennial inspections under this compliance program will:[7]

- safeguard the public health by reducing the risk of adulterated or misbranded biological drug products reaching the marketplace
- increase communication between industry and the agency
- provide timely feedback during inspections to improve industry compliance with CGMPs

Subsequent to implementation, CBER will evaluate this inspection program annually to determine its effectiveness and assess and improve its quality.

FDA requirements for the biologics licensing standards and 21 CFR 600.3 state biologics must be "safe, pure, and potent."

Under 21 CFR 601.20, upon inspection, the production facility must demonstrate assurance the product meets these standards and complies with the applicable regulations. Therefore, during the Investigational New Drug (IND) application stage, the manufacturer must develop processes and methods to ensure these attributes are in place before the product is licensed. These attributes are defined as follows:

- safety—relative freedom from harmful effect to persons affected, directly or indirectly, by a product when it is administered prudently, taking into consideration the product's character in relation to the recipient's condition at the time
- purity—relative freedom from extraneous matter in the finished product, whether or not harmful to the recipient or deleterious to the product; purity includes, but is not limited to, relative freedom from residual moisture or other volatile and pyrogenic substances
- potency—specific product ability or capacity, as indicated by appropriate laboratory tests or adequately controlled clinical data obtained through the product's administration in the manner intended, to effect a given result

Upon BLA approval, a manufacturer receives a license to market its product in interstate commerce. The compliance and surveillance activities related to biologics licenses during the product's lifecycle are overseen by the Office of Compliance and Biologics Quality (OCBQ). OCBQ comprises four divisions, plus additional staff within the Immediate Office of the Director (IOD) of OCBQ:

- Division of Case Management (DCM)
- Division of Inspections and Surveillance (DIS)
- Division of Manufacturing and Product Quality (DMPQ)
- Division of Biological Standards and Quality Control (DBSQC)
- Immediate Office of the Director (IOD)

OCBQ performs the following tasks and activities to ensure pre- and postapproval compliance:[8]

- ensures the quality of products regulated by CBER over their entire lifecycle, from premarket review and inspection to postmarket review, surveillance, inspection, outreach and compliance
- monitors the quality of marketed biological products through surveillance, inspections and compliance programs; reviews, evaluates and takes appropriate compliance action, in coordination with other agency components
- reviews and evaluates all administrative action recommendations, including suspension, revocation, denial of license, disqualification of investigators and recommended civil and criminal actions, including seizures, injunctions and prosecution based on findings of inspections and investigations
- directs the biologic product shortages program for CBER-regulated products
- directs the recall program for CBER-regulated products
- directs CBER's bioresearch monitoring program, and takes appropriate compliance actions, in coordination with other agency components
- directs CBER's program for Biological Product Deviations Reports (BPDRs) and reports of complications of blood collection and transfusion confirmed to be fatal
- reviews, evaluates and takes appropriate action on manufacturing supplements submitted by manufacturers (except blood and plasma establishments), and leads preapproval and prelicense inspections supporting BLA submissions and supplements as part of the CBER managed review process
- assesses the compliance status of regulated establishments within CBER's purview (compliance status checks)
- evaluates proposed proprietary names to avoid potential medication errors related to look-alike and sound-alike proprietary names and other mitigating factors that contribute to medication errors, such as unclear label abbreviations, acronyms, dose designations and error-prone label and packaging design
- provides consultative reviews of proposed product labeling
- plans and conducts tests on biological products and conducts research to develop and improve procedures to evaluate biological products' safety, efficacy and purity
- in cooperation with other center components, tests biological products submitted for release by manufacturers, as appropriate
- advises the center director and other agency officials on emerging and significant compliance issues for biological products and serves as CBER's focal point for surveillance and enforcement policy
- develops, with other CBER and agency components, biological products' policies and compliance standards, including CGMP regulations; ensures the uniform interpretation of standards and evaluates industry's conformance with CGMPs in manufacturing biological products.

Preapproval Compliance

CMC Change Control

During the IND stage, CMC change control includes filing information amendments to the IND to substantiate the comparability or improvements related to manufacturing changes, prior to making the change. During product development, multiple changes are likely to arise in the manufacturing process that could impact drug product quality, safety and efficacy. Comparability studies generally are performed to demonstrate nonclinical and clinical data generated with pre-change product are applicable to post-change product, to facilitate further development and, ultimately, support marketing approval. Comparability studies conducted during product development are influenced by factors such as the availability of validated analytical procedures and the extent of product and process knowledge, which can vary based on manufacturer experience. Due to analytical tools' limitations in early clinical development, physicochemical and biological tests alone might not be adequate to determine comparability, and it may be necessary to bridge nonclinical and/or clinical studies.

When process changes are introduced in later stages of development, and no additional clinical studies are planned to support the marketing authorization, the comparability study should be as comprehensive as that for an approved product. However, some comparability study outcomes on quality attributes still may require additional nonclinical or clinical studies.

IND Safety Reporting

During premarketing, expedited safety reports are required for serious and unexpected adverse experiences associated with the biologic's use, as is the case for drugs (21 CFR 312.32). These requirements were amended recently to update the definitions for safety reporting and to clarify when to submit expedited safety reports. In summary, expedited safety reporting applies to suspected adverse reactions that are both serious and unexpected and where there is a reasonable possibility of a causal relationship between the drug and the adverse event. For other adverse events, the sponsor should collect the information and develop a process for ongoing evaluation of accumulating safety data. The new ICH Development Safety Update Report, not yet adopted in the US, is consistent with this safety reporting framework.

FDA has issued final regulations addressing IND safety reporting requirements in 21 CFR Part 312. *Guidance for Industry and Investigators: Safety Reporting Requirements for INDs and BA/BE Studies* (December 2012) is aimed at improving the quality of safety reports submitted to FDA, thereby enhancing patient safety in clinical trials. The guidance lays out clear definitions and standards to ensure critical safety information on investigational new drugs is reported to FDA quickly and accurately, minimizing uninformative reports and enhancing reporting of meaningful, interpretable information.

Additional safety reporting guidance is available for specific biological products, such as those used in gene therapy clinical trials. In gene therapy trials, where there is heightened concern about the potential for delayed adverse events as a consequence of persistent biological activity of the transferred genetic material, long-term follow-up safety studies are recommended. Adverse events associated with gene therapy trials also may need to be reported to the National Institutes of Health (NIH) if the trial includes NIH-funded sites.

Bioresearch Monitoring (BIMO)

BIMO refers to FDA's compliance program for Good Clinical Practice (GCP) and Good Laboratory Practice (GLP) inspections during development. BIMO covers clinical investigators, Institutional Review Boards (IRBs), sponsors, contract research organization (CRO) monitors, in vivo bioequivalence laboratories and facilities and GLP facilities. The emphasis in clinical inspections is on how sponsors ensure the validity of clinical data submitted to FDA, and the adherence of sponsors, CROs and monitors to applicable regulations, such as adverse event reporting and article integrity from the time of manufacture until receipt by the investigator. To carry out these responsibilities, BIMO staff conduct preapproval data audit inspections, investigate complaints, answer questions about GCP and help evaluate data integrity concerns.

Biological Product Naming

The nonproprietary/proper name for a new biological product, as for a drug, is determined by submitting an application and fee to the United States Adopted Names Council (USANC), which is part of the American Medical Association (see www.ama-assn.org/). Sponsors should provide several selections and the naming rationale to USANC. When submitting suggested names, consideration should be given to the naming conventions used by USANC to assess submissions (i.e., use of common stems and/or syllables for existing products or product classes). For biologics, CBER has developed naming conventions for certain product categories, e.g., cellular therapies, which must be followed to the extent possible. Thus, sponsors may want to discuss nonproprietary name selection with CBER prior to submission to USANC, to assist in the naming process. For well-characterized proteins, certain suffixes are standard and must be included in the nonproprietary name, e.g., monoclonal antibodies use -mab as the final syllable.

The proprietary name for a new biological is approved by CBER and reviewed by OCBQ's Advertising and Promotional Labeling Branch (APLB). Two names may be submitted, with a clear indication of the sponsor's preference. The rationale for the choice, with summaries from marketing research studies, should be included. These studies should assess similar sounding names and how names may be interpreted, including foreign language translations. The application also should include full descriptions of the product, therapeutic category and/or indication and the setting for use (e.g., doctor's office, hospital or home). Proprietary name submissions can be made any time after Phase 2, but a recommendation made prior to product approval will be reevaluated within 90 days of approval to ensure no new products have entered the marketplace that could give rise to confusion because of similarity in spelling or pronunciation.

Prelicense Inspection

This is an inspection of an establishment that has not yet been licensed or approved by CBER for the product under review and may include all facilities involved in the biologic's manufacture (drug substance and drug product manufacturing, packaging and testing). These inspections apply to the company itself and any contract sites. The inspection also can include establishments that already have one or more biologics license(s) or approvals for other products. *PHS Act* Section 351 and Section 704 of the *FD&C Act* provide the regulatory authority to conduct inspections at any biological product manufacturing establishment.

CBER's policy is a prelicense or preapproval inspection generally will be necessary for a BLA or supplement if any of the following criteria are met:

- The manufacturer does not hold an active US license or, in the case of a contract manufacturer, the facility is not approved for use in manufacturing a licensed product.
- FDA has not inspected the establishment in the last two years.

- The previous inspection revealed significant GMP deficiencies in areas related to the processes in the submission (similar processes), or systemic problems, such as quality control or quality assurance oversight.
- The establishment is performing a significant manufacturing step(s) in new (unlicensed) areas using different equipment (representing a process change). This would include currently dedicated areas not approved as multiproduct facilities, buildings or areas.
- The manufacturing process is sufficiently different (new production methods, specialized equipment or facilities) from that of other approved products produced by the establishment.

In some cases, CBER relies on inspections to obtain validation and facility information that previously may have been submitted in the BLA; thus, greater coordination and efficiency are required in planning and conducting inspections. However, some BLAs and supplements include manufacturing establishments use production areas common to other licensed products, so conducting a prelicense or preapproval inspection may not be necessary. In such cases, both the director of the division with product responsibility and the director of DMPQ within OCBQ must agree to waive an inspection, or the inspection should be scheduled according to established procedures.

Inspections for biologics are much the same as those for drugs. Systems-based inspections include review of:

- quality systems (e.g., change controls, deviations/investigations, training, etc.)
- buildings and facilities
- equipment cleaning and maintenance
- laboratory controls

In addition, the BLA's CMC section will be compared to manufacturing site documents to establish the submission's accuracy and integrity. Because of the manufacturing process complexity of biologics, the investigator is likely to spend considerably more time observing the process than is typical for small-molecule inspections. The investigator usually works with the manufacturer to schedule an appropriate time to conduct the inspection so the entire manufacturing process can be observed; any delay by the sponsor in this activity may delay the BLA review. Another difference is the BLA review CMC product specialist generally will participate in a biologics inspection.

The regulations require Annual Reports, provided within 60 days after the application approval anniversary date, for products marketed under a BLA for certain situations, such as: making changes to the application (21 CFR 601.12(d)); providing information related to pediatric studies (21 CFR 601.28); and providing status reports on postmarket study requirements related to clinical safety, clinical efficacy, clinical pharmacology or nonclinical toxicology (21 CFR 601.70).

The *Food and Drug Administration Amendments Act* of 2007 (*FDAAA*) authorizes FDA to require additional postmarketing studies related to assessing known safety risks, including both serious risk signals and potential serious risks associated with the drug's use. *FDAAA* also gave FDA authority to require labeling changes based on such studies' results. *FD&C Act* Section 505(o)(3)(E)(ii), enacted under *FDAAA*, stipulates the following information be provided in the Annual Report for required postmarketing studies: a timetable for the completion of each study; periodic reports on required studies' status, including whether enrollment has begun, the number of participants enrolled and whether any difficulties in completing the study have been encountered; and registration information with respect to clinical trial certification. In addition, *FDAAA* requires applicants to report on each study "otherwise undertaken by the applicant to investigate a safety issue." The status of other types of postmarketing commitments (e.g., those concerning chemistry, manufacturing, production controls and studies conducted on an applicant's own initiative) are not required to be reported under Sections 314.81(b)(2)(vii) and 601.70.

Once a required postmarketing study commitment has been made, an Annual Report is due each year within 60 days after the anniversary date and must be accompanied by a completed transmittal Form FDA 2252. Sponsors must continue to report on the commitment's progress until the postmarketing study is completed or terminated, unless the postmarketing study commitment is either no longer feasible or no longer would provide useful information (as agreed with FDA). Failure to comply with the timetable, the periodic reporting submissions or other requirements of Section 505(o)(3)(E)(ii) will be considered a violation unless the applicant demonstrates good cause for the noncompliance (only as agreed with FDA). Violations could result in civil penalties of up to $250,000 per violation and the penalties can be increased (i.e., doubled) if the violation continues for more than 30 days, and can continue to double for subsequent 30-day periods.

Inspections[10]

After approval, two other types of inspections may take place: routine, periodic inspections that should occur every two years (biennial) and directed (for cause) inspections. CBER and ORA have built a partnership to focus resources on inspectional and compliance issues in the biologics area. To accomplish this, Team Biologics, as mentioned earlier, inspects licensed biological drug and device product facilities regulated by CBER. The goal of Team Biologics is to assure biological products' quality and safety and resolve inconsistencies quickly.

Import/Export

CBER oversees biologic products' import and export to determine whether imported products, drugs and devices regulated by the center comply with the requirements of the *FD&C Act*, the *PHS Act* and the regulations promulgated under these statutes. Imported products regulated by FDA are subject to inspection at the time of entry by the US Customs and Border Protection (CBP) (see www.cbp.gov/). Shipments found not to comply with the law are subject to detention. For imports, FDA works with CBP to verify licensure; FDA may perform random sampling and will issue import alerts for noncompliant products. A foreign manufacturer must have a US license to import a biological product into the US. Per FDA's Regulatory Procedures Manual, Chapter 9, Subchapter 9.3, "Importation of Biological Products," licensed biologics lot-released (or exempt) by CBER may be imported into the US and may proceed through CBP without FDA examination. Entry documents for IND biologics must declare a valid, active IND number. Products in short supply also may be imported under 21 CFR 601.22; however, these products must be registered with CBER, which CBP will verify. Under 7 CFR Chapter III, overseen by the US Department of Agriculture (USDA), biological products also may require an Animal and Plant Health Inspection Service (APHIS) permit to enter the country if the product contains certain microbial, plant- or animal-derived materials or is otherwise a regulated product, such as a genetically engineered organism.

A licensed biologic may be exported without FDA authorization (*Guidance for Industry: FDA Export Certificates* (August 2002)) and in accordance with Section 801(e) Exports or 802 Export of Certain Unapproved Products of the *FD&C Act* or Section 351(h) of the *PHS Act*, which states a biologic is not adulterated or misbranded if it:

- accords to the specifications of the foreign purchaser
- is not in conflict with the laws of the country to which it is intended for export
- is labeled on the outside of the shipping package that it is intended for export
- is not sold or offered for sale in domestic commerce

FDA supplies a Certificate to Foreign Government, if requested, for the export of products that can be legally marketed in the US. It also supplies a Certificate of Exportability for the export of products that cannot be legally marketed in the US but meet *FD&C Act* requirements.

Import for export, per the *FDA Export Reform and Enhancement Act* of 1996, allows the importation of drug and device components for incorporation into a finished product that can then be exported in accordance with 801, 802 and *PHS Act* 351(h).

Postapproval Changes

In accordance with *FD&C Act* Section 506A(b), the effect of any postapproval CMC changes on a product's identity, strength, quality, purity or potency, as they may relate to the product's safety or efficacy, must be assessed.

Before distributing a product made following a change, sponsors are required to demonstrate, through appropriate validation and/or other clinical or nonclinical laboratory studies, the lack of the change's adverse effect on identity, strength, quality, purity or potency as they may relate to the product's safety or effectiveness.

Sponsors should assess the change to determine the correct product reporting category:

- Prior Approval Supplement (PAS)—major changes requiring supplement submission and approval prior to distribution of the product made using the change (21 CFR 601.12(b)). A PAS is used to report changes with substantial potential to adversely affect a product's identity, strength, quality, purity or potency as they may relate to the product's safety or effectiveness. Examples include: a change in manufacturing processes or analytical methods resulting in change of specification limits; a change to larger-scale production; major construction; a change in the stability protocol or acceptance criteria; and extension of the expiration dating period.
- Changes Being Effected in 30 Days (CBE-30)—moderate changes (CBE-30) require a supplement to FDA 30 days prior to distribution (21 CFR 601.12(c)(3)). A CBE-30 is used to report changes with moderate potential to adversely affect a product's identity, strength, quality, purity or potency as they may relate to the product's safety or effectiveness. Examples include: addition of a duplicated process chain or unit process; change in the testing site from one facility to another (e.g., from a contract laboratory to the sponsor; from an existing contract laboratory to a new contract laboratory; from the sponsor to a new contract laboratory).
- Changes Being Effected in 0 Day (CBE-0)—these changes have minimal potential to adversely affect a product's identity, strength, quality, purity or potency as they may relate to the product's safety or effectiveness. A CBE-0 supplement would be received by FDA before, or concurrently with, distribution of the product made using the change. CBE-0's typically are filed when a manufacturer wants to inform FDA immediately, even though the change does not require FDA approval.
- Annual Report—minor changes can be included in the Annual Report, which is submitted within 60 days of the product's anniversary date. These are changes with minimal potential to affect a product's identity, strength, quality, purity or potency

adversely as they may relate to the product's safety or effectiveness. Examples include: an increase in the scale of aseptic manufacturing for finished product without a change in equipment, e.g., increased number of vials filled; modifications in analytical procedures with no change in the basic test methodology or existing release specifications, provided the change is supported by validation data; and establishment of a new working cell bank derived from a previously approved master cell bank according to an SOP on file in the approved license application.

By using a comparability protocol previously reviewed by FDA, the sponsor may be able to file certain CMC changes under a less-restrictive reporting category, e.g., a change that normally would be a PAS may be allowed as a CBE-30 if it has been approved already as a comparability protocol. While submitting a comparability protocol is not required for changes, in many cases, it will facilitate the subsequent CMC change implementation and reporting requirements, which could result in moving a product into distribution more quickly.

A comparability protocol is a well-defined, detailed, written plan for assessing the effect of specific CMC changes on a particular drug product's identity, strength, quality, purity and potency as they may relate to the product's safety and effectiveness. A comparability protocol describes the changes it covers and specifies the tests and studies to be performed, including establishing analytical procedures and acceptance criteria to demonstrate specified CMC changes do not affect the product adversely. However, it is important to note comparability protocols are not recommended for CMC changes that cannot be evaluated definitively, require a new IND or require efficacy, safety (clinical or nonclinical) or pharmacokinetic/pharmacodynamic data to evaluate the change's effect (e.g., certain formulation changes or clinical or nonclinical studies to qualify new impurities).

An FDA review committee will determine whether the changes reported in the supplement require on-site review. If the review committee determines an inspection is necessary for one or more establishments included in the supplement, the inspection(s) will be performed prior to sending the action letter for the supplement. Failure to comply with the reporting requirements outlined in 21 CFR 601.12 could result in an FDA request that every change be submitted as a PAS. Two examples of failure to comply are the constant downgrading of changes (e.g., from a PAS to a CBE) and failing to supply sufficient information to support the changes.

Similarly, under 21 CFR 601.12(f), changes to a product package label, container label and package insert require one of the following:

- submission of a supplement with FDA approval needed prior to product distribution, e.g., the addition of superiority claims or changes based on additional preclinical and/or postmarketing clinical studies
- submission of a supplement with product distribution allowed at the time of supplement submission (does not require a 30-day waiting period), e.g., strengthening cautionary statements or instructions
- submission of the final printed label in an Annual Report, e.g., editorial changes and changes in how the product is supplied, provided there is no change in dosage strength or form

Additionally, under 21 CFR 601.12(f)(4), changes to advertising and promotional labeling must comply with the provisions of 21 CFR 314.81(b)(3)(i), which requires sponsors to submit specimens of mailing pieces and any other labeling or advertising devised for promotion of a drug product to FDA at the time of initial dissemination of the labeling, and at the time of initial publication of the advertisement for a prescription drug product. Mailing pieces and labeling designed to contain samples of a drug product are required for the submission to be considered complete, with the exception of the sample of the drug product itself (see Chapter 26 Biologics Labeling, Advertising and Promotion for more on labeling).

Postmarketing Reporting Requirements

Postmarketing expedited reporting requirements for serious and unexpected adverse experiences from all sources (domestic and foreign) related to biologics are similar to those for drugs and are stated in 21 CFR 600.80 and 600.81. Reporting requirements include: Postmarketing 15-day "Alert Reports," which include reports based on scientific literature; Postmarketing 15-day Alert Report follow-ups, which also are required to be reported within 15 days of receiving new information; and periodic adverse experience reports. The reporting format for individual case study reports is the MedWatch mandatory Form FDA 3500A. However, adverse events related to vaccines must be reported on a separate form under the Vaccine Adverse Event Reporting System (VAERS). Foreign adverse experience may be reported using either the 3500A or, if preferred, a CIOMS I form. Sponsors may request waivers of the requirement to file Form FDA 3500A for nonserious, expected adverse experiences; however, FDA does not intend to grant waivers within one year of licensure for new biological molecular entities, blood products, plasma derivatives or vaccines. For biological combination products, reports must be filed with both relevant centers. Adverse events related to vaccines also are monitored by the Centers for Disease Control and Prevention (CDC). The VAERS reporting system is not linked to the vaccine injury compensation program.

Periodic adverse experience reports (PADERs) include serious and unexpected adverse experience summaries as well as reports of nonserious expected adverse experiences. Periodic reports are made at quarterly intervals for three years from the date of issuance of the biologics license, and then annually. The licensed manufacturer is required to submit each quarterly report within 30 days of the close of the quarter (the first quarter beginning on the date of the biologics license's issuance) and each Annual Report within 60 days of the anniversary date.

Distribution reports for biological products, including vaccines, also are required under 21 CFR 600.81; this requirement is unique for biologics with approved BLAs. The distribution report includes the bulk, fill and label lot numbers for the total number of dosage units of each strength or potency distributed, expiration date, distribution date and quantity returned. The licensed manufacturer submits this report every six months to either CBER or CDER, as applicable. *Guidance for Industry: Electronic Submission of Lot Distribution Reports*, issued March 2015, outlines the electronic submission requirements for the Lot Distribution Reports. The information required for the distribution reports is the same, but electronic submission requirements now are formalized.[11]

Risk Assessment[12]

Risk assessment should occur throughout a product's lifecycle, from early potential product identification and preclinical testing, through the premarketing development process, and postapproval during marketing. Premarketing risk assessment is a key step in this process, and product approval requires adequate assessment of the product's underlying risks and benefits. The adequacy of this risk assessment is a matter of both quantity (ensuring enough patients are studied) and quality (the appropriateness of the assessments performed, appropriateness and breadth of the patient populations studied and how results are analyzed). In reaching a final approvability decision, both existing risk information and any outstanding safety questions are considered in a product's risk assessment and weighed against its demonstrated benefits. The fewer a product's demonstrated benefits, the less acceptable its higher levels of demonstrated risks.

For postapproval risk assessment, labeling and routine reporting requirements are sufficient to mitigate risks and preserve benefits for the majority of approved products. However, in other cases, FDA has requested additional risk minimization strategies, originally called Risk Minimization Action Plans, or RiskMAPs. *FDAAA* created Risk Evaluation and Mitigation Strategies (REMS). A REMS is a strategy to manage a serious drug or biological product's safety risk while preserving the product's benefits. FDA also has the authority to apply a REMS retroactively and require sponsors to submit a REMS for an already approved product.

A REMS can include a Medication Guide, a Patient Package Insert, a communication plan for healthcare professionals, various Elements to Assure Safe Use (ETASU) and an implementation system. The Medication Guide is the most common REMS component, now required for more than 150 approved drugs. Medication Guides are utilized when specific information is necessary to prevent serious adverse effects, when patient decision making should include knowledge about a serious side effect, or if patient adherence to directions for use is essential for the product's effectiveness. The responsibility for ensuring Medication Guides are available to patients lies with the sponsor, not the pharmacist.

ETASU may include one or more of the following requirements:

- Healthcare providers who prescribe the drug must have particular training or experience or be specially certified.
- Pharmacies, practitioners or healthcare settings dispensing the drug must be specially certified.
- The drug is dispensed to patients only in certain healthcare settings, such as hospitals.
- The drug is dispensed to patients with evidence or other documentation of safe use conditions, such as laboratory test results.
- Each patient using the drug is subject to certain monitoring requirements.
- Each patient using the drug is enrolled in a registry.

The REMS also must include a timetable for assessment; the minimum assessment timeframe is 18 months, three years and seven years after approval.

Biological Product Deviation Reporting (BPDR)

Licensed biological product manufacturers are required to report events representing unexpected or unforeseeable events or deviations from CGMPs, applicable regulations, applicable standards or established specifications that may affect a product's safety, purity or potency per 21 CFR 600.14. Prior to 2001, this was termed "error and accident" reporting. The BPDR is reported on Form FDA 3486—Biological Product Deviation Report Form—and must include the appropriate event type deviation code. The report must not be dated more than 45 calendar days from the date the information reasonably suggests a reportable event has occurred is discovered. Reportable events are those occuring at the sponsor's facility or a facility under the sponsor's control, e.g., a contract manufacturer, and include events for products distributed and no longer under the sponsor's control. Therefore, investigation procedures for an unexplained discrepancy or failure of a lot to meet any of its specifications should include provisions for timely investigation; an appropriate corrective action plan to prevent recurrence; procedures to gain control of unsuitable products in a timely manner; and appropriate disposition of all affected products (in-date and expired). All BPDRs should be submitted to OCBQ, except in the case of biological products transferred to CDER in 2003.

FDA Enforcement Actions

Regulatory Action Letters

CBER may issue several types of regulatory action letters. These letters ordinarily are issued to biological product manufacturers in an effort to stop practices in violation of the regulations and to promote corrective action. Examples of regulatory action letters issued by CBER include:

- Warning Letters
- Notice of Initiation of Disqualification Proceedings and Opportunity to Explain (NIDPOE) Letters
- Untitled Letters
- Administrative License Action Letters
- Orders of Retention, Recall, Destruction and Cessation of Manufacturing Related to Human Cell, Tissue, and Cellular and Tissue-Based Products (HCT/Ps)

Warning Letters are issued for violations considered to be of regulatory significance to achieve voluntary compliance. Significant violations are those that may lead to enforcement action if not corrected promptly and adequately. A Warning Letter is issued to a responsible individual or firm to establish prior notice the agency considers one or more products, practices, processes or other activities to be in violation of the *FD&C Act*, its implementing regulations and other federal statutes. A Warning Letter is one of FDA's principal means of achieving prompt voluntary *FD&C Act* compliance.

A NIDPOE Letter informs the recipient clinical investigator the agency is initiating an administrative proceeding to determine whether the investigator should be disqualified from receiving investigational products pursuant to FDA regulations. Generally, the agency issues a NIDPOE letter when it believes it has evidence the clinical investigator repeatedly or deliberately violated FDA's regulations governing proper clinical study conduct involving investigational products or submitted false information to the sponsor.

An Untitled Letter is an initial correspondence with a sponsor citing violations that do not meet the regulatory significance threshold for a Warning Letter. CBER has issued Untitled Letters, for example, after review of a manufacturer's advertising and promotional labeling, after an inspection under CBER's Bioresearch Monitoring program or by Team Biologics, and as a result of Internet website surveillance.

Administrative License Action Letters include license revocation and suspension. License revocation is the cancellation of a license and withdrawal of the authorization to introduce biological products into interstate commerce. Examples of revocation grounds include: FDA inability to gain access for inspection; manufacturer failure to report a change as required; product or establishment failure to conform to standards in the license or comply with CGMPs; or the product not being safe or effective, or being misbranded. Except in the case of license suspension or willful violations, CBER will issue a Notice of Intent to Revoke License Letter and provide the sponsor an opportunity to demonstrate or achieve compliance before initiating revocation proceedings and issuing a license revocation letter. The licensee has 10 days to notify FDA of its commitment to, and plans for, achieving compliance, and then has 30 days to submit a comprehensive report with rigid timetables.

License Suspension is a summary action providing for immediate withdrawal, without prior notice or a hearing, of the authorization to introduce biological products into interstate commerce when there are reasonable grounds to believe the product is a danger to public health (*PHS Act* Section 351). The Department of Justice does not need to concur. All product shipping and manufacturing activities must cease until the license is reactivated.

Recalls

Recalls generally are voluntary sponsor acts because FDA has limited statutory authority to prescribe a recall. However, the *National Childhood Vaccine Injury Act* of 1986 amended the *PHS Act* to provide recall authority for biological products (42 U.S. 262). Therefore, FDA can order a recall if the biological product constitutes an imminent or substantial hazard to public health per *PHS Act* Section 351(a), or if it is considered a "dangerous" medical device per the *FD&C Act*. Recalls can be ordered for any reason, but if a recall is due to misbranding or adulteration, FDA should be notified to prevent further action. Companies should work closely with the agency during a recall. There are four key stages in the recall process: discovery, planning, implementation and termination of the recall event. Final disposition of the recalled product should be discussed with FDA and typically involves destruction.

Judicial Enforcement

FDA's civil and criminal enforcement actions include:

- Seizure—an action taken to remove a product from commerce because it is in violation of the law. FDA initiates a seizure by filing a complaint with the US District Court where the product is located. A US Marshal then is directed by the court to take possession, i.e., seize the goods where they are found, until the matter is resolved.

- Injunction—a civil action taken against an individual or firm seeking to stop continued production or distribution of a violative product until the firm complies with FDA requirements.
- Prosecution—a criminal action taken as the result of acts prohibited in the *FD&C Act* that can be directed at the responsible persons in management

Conclusion

The compliance and surveillance activities related to biologics licenses during the product lifecycle are overseen by CBER's Office of Compliance and Biologics Quality. Manufacturers are required to comply with FDA's preapproval and postapproval requirements. If CBER identifies areas of noncompliance, it may issue one of several types of regulatory action letters, up to and including license revocation, to stop practices found to be in violation of the regulations and to promote corrective action. CBER also has options for judicial enforcement, including seizure, injunction and prosecution, if warranted.

References

1. 21 CFR 600.3
2. FDA. Office of Compliance and Biologics Quality (OCBQ) FDA website. http://www.fda.gov/BiologicsBloodVaccines/GuidanceComplianceRegulatoryInformation/ucm331317.htm Accessed 17 March 2015.
3. Compliance—Program Guidance Manual—Inspection of Biological Drug Products—7345.848
4. Ibid.
5. Op cit 2.
6. SOPP 8410: Determining When Prelicense/Preapproval Inspections are Necessary (December 2001).
7. Ibid.
8. Op cit 2.
9. Ibid.
10. Op cit 3.
11. *Guidance for Industry: Electronic Submission of Lot Distribution Reports* (March 2015).
12. *Guidance for Industry: Format and Content of Proposed Risk Evaluation and Mitigation Strategies (REMS), REMS Assessments, and Proposed REMS Modifications* (September 2009).

Chapter 26

Biologics Labeling, Advertising and Promotion

Updated by Jennifer Wilhelm, MSc, MBA, RAC

OBJECTIVES

- ❑ Understand FDA requirements for labeling of biological drugs under the jurisdiction of CBER or CDER
- ❑ Review FDA requirements for advertising and promotion of biological drugs under the jurisdiction of CBER or CDER
- ❑ Understand the application of these regulations through FDA compliance and enforcement

LAWS, REGULATIONS AND GUIDELINES COVERED IN THIS CHAPTER

- ❑ *Federal Food, Drug, and Cosmetic Act* of 1938
- ❑ 21 CFR 99 Dissemination of information on unapproved/new uses for marketed drugs, biologics and devices
- ❑ 21 CFR 201 Labeling
- ❑ 21 CFR 202.1 Prescription drug advertisements
- ❑ 21 CFR 203 Prescription drug marketing
- ❑ 21 CFR 208 Medication guides for prescription drug products
- ❑ 21 CFR 312.6–7 Labeling and promotion for investigational new drugs
- ❑ 21 CFR 314.70 Supplements and other changes to an approved application
- ❑ 21 CFR 314.81 Other postmarketing reports
- ❑ 21 CFR 601.2 Applications for biologics licenses; procedures for filing
- ❑ 21 CFR 601.12 Changes to an approved application
- ❑ 21 CFR 601.25 Review procedures to determine that licensed biological products are safe, effective, and not misbranded under prescribed, recommended, or suggested conditions of use
- ❑ 21 CFR 601.45 Promotional materials
- ❑ 21 CFR 610 Subpart G Labeling standards
- ❑ 21 CFR 606.120–122 Labeling, general requirements
- ❑ 21 CFR 660 Additional standards for diagnostic substances for laboratory tests
- ❑ 21 CFR 660.2(c) General requirements, labeling
- ❑ 21 CFR 660.28 Blood grouping reagent labeling
- ❑ 21 CFR 660.35 Reagent red blood cells labeling

- ❑ 21 CFR 660.45 Hepatitis B surface antigen labeling
- ❑ 21 CFR 660.55 Anti-human globulin labeling
- ❑ *Draft Guidance for Industry: Brief Summary and Adequate Directions for Use: Disclosing Risk Information in Consumer-Directed Print Advertisements and Promotional Labeling for Human Prescription Drugs* (February 2015)
- ❑ Patient Counseling Information Section of Labeling for Human Prescription Drug and Biological Products—Content and Format (December 2014)
- ❑ Pregnancy, Lactation, and Reproductive Potential: Labeling for Human Prescription Drug and Biological Products-Content and Format (December 2014)
- ❑ Structured Product Labeling (SPL) Implementation Guide with Validation Procedures (December 2014)
- ❑ *Guidance for Industry: Clinical Pharmacology Labeling for Human Prescription Drug and Biological Products—Considerations, Content and Format* (August 2014)
- ❑ *Draft Guidance for Industry: Labeling for Human Prescription Drug and Biological Products Approved Under the Accelerated Approval Regulatory Pathway* (March 2014)
- ❑ *Draft Guidance for Industry: Labeling Naming of Drug Products Containing Salt Drug Substances* (December 2013)
- ❑ *Draft Guidance for Industry: Product Name Placement, Size, and Prominence in Advertising and Promotional Labeling* (November 2013)
- ❑ *Guidance for Industry: Labeling for Human Prescription Drug and Biological Products—Implementing the PLR Content and Format Requirements* (February 2013)
- ❑ *Draft Guidance for Industry: Pediatric Information Incorporated Into Human Prescription Drug and Biological Products Labeling Good Review Practice* (February 2013)
- ❑ *Draft Guidance for Industry: Guidance for Industry Providing Regulatory Submissions in Electronic Format—Certain Human Pharmaceutical Product Applications and Related Submissions Using the eCTD Specifications* (January 2013)
- ❑ *Draft Guidance for Industry: Direct-to-Consumer Television Advertisements—FDAAA DTC Television Ad Pre-Dissemination Review Program* (March 2012)
- ❑ *Guidance: Medication Guides—Distribution Requirements and Inclusion in Risk Evaluation and Mitigation Strategies (REMS)* (November 2011)
- ❑ *Guidance for Industry: Warnings and Precautions, Contraindications, and Boxed Warning Sections of Labeling for Human Prescription Drug and Biological Products—Content and Format* (October 2011)
- ❑ *Guidance for Industry: Bar Code Label Requirements* (August 2011)
- ❑ *Guidance for Industry: Content and Format of the Dosage and Administration Section of Labeling for Human Prescription Drug and Biological Products* (March 2010)
- ❑ *Guidance for Industry: Contents of a Complete Submission for the Evaluation of Proprietary Names* (February 2010)
- ❑ *Guidance for Industry: Patient-Reported Outcome Measures: Use in Medical Product Development to Support Labeling Claims* (December 2009)
- ❑ *Draft Guidance for Industry: SPL Standard for Content of Labeling Technical Qs & As* (October 2009)
- ❑ *Guidance for Industry: Labeling for Human Prescription Drug and Biological Products—Determining Established Pharmacologic Class for Use in the Highlights of Prescribing Information* (October 2009)
- ❑ *Draft Guidance for Industry: Presenting Risk Information in Prescription Drug and Medical Device Promotion* (May 2009)

- *Guidance for Industry: Indexing Structured Product Labeling* (June 2008)
- *Guidance for Industry: Adverse Reactions Section of Labeling for Human Prescription Drug and Biological Products—Content and Format* (January 2006)
- *Guidance for Industry: Clinical Studies Section of Labeling for Human Prescription Drug and Biological Products—Content and Format* (January 2006)
- *Draft Guidance for Industry: Public Availability of Labeling Changes in "Changes Being Effected" Supplements* (September 2006)
- *Guidance for Industry: Providing Regulatory Submissions in Electronic Format—Content of Labeling* (April 2005)
- *Draft Guidance for Industry: "Help-Seeking" and Other Disease Awareness Communications by or on Behalf of Drug and Device Firms* (January 2004)
- *Draft Guidance for Industry: Providing Regulatory Submissions in Electronic Format—Prescription Drug Advertising and Promotional Labeling* (January 2001)
- *Guidance for Industry: Consumer-Directed Broadcast Advertisements* (August 1999)
- *Final Guidance on Industry-Supported Scientific and Educational Activities* (November 1997)
- *Guidance for Industry: Changes to an Approved Application: Biological Products* (July 1997)

Introduction

The *Federal Food, Drug, and Cosmetic Act* of 1938 (*FD&C Act*) grants the US Food and Drug Administration (FDA) authority over prescription drug "labeling" for drug and biological products. The *FD&C Act* defines a "label" as a display of written, printed or graphic material on the immediate container of a drug, and Section 201(m) of the *FD&C Act* defines "labeling" to mean "all labels and other written, printed, or graphic matter (1) upon any article or any of its containers or wrappers, or (2) accompanying such article." Therefore, it includes container labels, professional labeling (generally referred to as the package insert or prescribing information (PI)), patient labeling (Patient Package Insert (PPI)), Medication Guides, instructions for use and risk management materials.

The umbrella term "labeling" also is used to describe promotional materials. The US Supreme Court has explained the language "accompanying such article" in the "labeling" definition is interpreted broadly, and no physical attachment between the materials and the article is necessary. As such, FDA generally recognizes two types of labeling for drugs, including biologics: 1) FDA-approved labeling and 2) promotional labeling. Promotional labeling is any product material (other than FDA-required labeling as defined above) intended to promote the use of a product.

Labelling Regulations and Requirements

The *FD&C Act* provides the legal basis for labeling drugs, devices and biologic products. 21 CFR Part 201 provides general label provisions, labeling requirements for prescription and over-the-counter drugs, exemptions and specific labeling claims; 21 CFR Part 601 also provides general label provisions for biologic products.

Labeling Filed With Original BLA Submissions

The initial labelling for biological products begins when the first BLA is filed. The BLA is a request for permission to introduce or deliver for introduction a biologic product into interstate commerce, and labeling information is required in the BLA submissions to FDA (21 CFR 601.2), with review and approval by FDA's Center for Biologics Evaluation and Review (CBER) or Center for Drug Evaluation and Review (CDER). This information is the sponsor's proposed labeling for postapproval marketing. The content and format are regulated by 21 CFR 201.56–57 and 21 CFR 610.60–68 and further explained in various guidance documents. Typically, four types of prescription drug labeling information are submitted in the original BLA:

1. professional labelling with annotated draft labeling text
2. patient labeling
3. draft container and carton labels
4. Structured Product Labelling (SPL)

1. Prescribing Information/Professional Labeling

"Prescribing information," commonly referred to as "professional labeling," "content of labeling," "package insert," "physician labeling," "direction circular," "circular of information" or "package circular," is a component of prescription drug labeling and contains the information necessary for safe and effective product use by the healthcare professional. The sponsor's proposed labeling is submitted as part of the BLA and should conform to the format required by regulations and guidance.

In 2006, FDA issued final regulations governing the content and format of prescribing information for human drug and biological products, commonly referred to as the "Physician Labeling Rule" (PLR) since it applies to labeling used by prescribers and healthcare providers. The goal of the requirements in 21 CFR 201.56–57 is to enhance the safe and effective use of prescription drug products with a clear and concise PI that is easier to access, read and use, facilitating practitioners' use of labeling to make prescribing decisions.

Labeling includes three sections including:

1. Full Prescribing Information (FPI) containing the detailed information necessary for safe and effective use of the drug
2. Highlights of Prescribing Information (Highlights), containing selected information from the FPI healthcare practitioners most commonly reference and consider most important
3. Table of Content (Contents) listing FPI sections and subsections

Several guidelines are available describing the necessary content and format of prescription drug and biological product labeling sections.

An annotated version of the draft labeling text needs to be included in the BLA submission to substantiate each labeling claim. This is a separate file from the draft labeling text required in the initial submission and is called "annotated labeling."

PI submitted with BLAs and postapproval submissions must conform to the labeling content and format regulations, and the Labeling Team works with review divisions to ensure PI conforms with the PLR as described in 21 CFR 201.56–57.

2. Patient Labelling/Medication Guides

"Patient labeling" is another component of FDA-approved labeling for some prescription drugs and biological products that is intended for patient use, and includes PPIs and Medication Guides. FDA requires a Medication Guides for prescription drugs and biological products (21 CFR Part 208.1(a)) when:

- patient labeling could help prevent serious adverse effects
- the patient should be informed by information about a known serious side effect for decision making
- patient adherence to directions for use is crucial to the drug's effectiveness

Medication Guides are approved by FDA and distributed to patients when the agency determines such a guide is necessary safe and effective patient use of a drug product (21 CFR 208.1 (b)), and patient labeling must be reprinted in the prescribing information or must accompany the prescribing information (21 CFR 201.57(c)(18) and 201.80(f)(2)). Medications Guides also may be required as an element to assure safe use as part of a drug's Risk Evaluation and Mitigation Strategies (REMS). The majority of biologic products (66.7%) approved 2008–12 have had a REMS,[1] with the most common element being a Medication Guide.

3. Container and Carton Labels

Based on the *FD&C Act* definitions of the "label" and "labeling," any outer container, carton or package is "labeling." Biological product labeling regulations further distinguish between a "container label" and "package label" (21 CFR 610.60 and 610.61). Per 21 CFR 610.60, the container label for biological products should bear the following information:

1. proper name of the product
2. manufacturer name, address and license number
3. lot number or other lot identification
4. expiration date
5. recommended individual dose, for multiple dose containers
6. the statement, "Rx only," for prescription biologics
7. Medication Guide, if required

In special cases, certain information may be expanded or omitted. For example, expansion may be needed if the container is not inserted in any package, or text can be omitted if the container is too small to affix a label containing all the information listed above (see 21 CFR 610.60(b), (c) and (d)). To allow visual inspection of the contents, the label should not cover the container completely.

Per 21 CFR 610.61, the package label for biological products should contain:

1. proper name of the product
2. manufacturer name, address and license number
3. lot number or other lot identification
4. expiration date
5. preservatives, if any
6. number of containers, if more than one
7. amount of product in the container
8. recommended storage temperature
9. the words "shake well" or "do not freeze," as required
10. recommended individual dose, for multi-dose container
11. type and calculated amount of antibiotics added during manufacture
12. adjuvant, if present
13. product source, when it is a factor in safe administration
14. minimum potency of product or the statement: "No US standard of potency"
15. the statement: "Rx only" for prescription biologics
16. reference statement to PI inside the package for any other pertinent information

The container and package label font size, type, color, position and legibility should meet the requirements in 21 CFR 610.62. Divided manufacturing responsibility also should be shown on either the package or the container label. Bar code label requirements under 21 CFR 201.25 apply to all biologics except biological devices or blood and blood components intended for transfusion, which follow the requirements in 21 CFR 606.121(c)(13). *Guidance for Industry: Bar Code Label Requirements Questions and Answers* (August 2011), covers requirements for machine-readable label requirements for blood and blood components.

4. Structured Product Labeling (SPL)

Labeling changes submitted electronically as part of a regulatory submission must be filed in a specific format FDA can process, review and archive. Structured Product Labeling (SPL) is a key component for making regulated product information publicly available on FDA's Online Label Repository at http://labels.fda.gov/ and on the National Library of Medicine's DailyMed Website (http://dailymed.nlm.nih.gov/dailymed/index.cfm). The SPL standard is based on extensible markup language (XML). Instructions for preparing SPL are detailed in *Guidance for Industry: Providing Regulatory Submissions in Electronic Format—Content of Labeling* (April 2005) and *Guidance for Industry: Indexing Structured Product Labeling* (June 2008). The SPL standard should be used when submitting content of labeling for biological products to CBER or to CDER in XML with original submissions, supplements and annual reports.

Labelling is expected to move toward fully electronic distribution rather than paper format based on a published proposed rule.[2] The proposed rule would require sponsors to submit labeling in SPL format for each content change, and labeling would be distributed via FDA's publicly accessible labeling repository (labels.fda.gov). The aim is to ensure the most current prescribing information is available at a single, comprehensive website, so healthcare professionals could access the information readily and be better informed at the time of clinical decision making and dispensing.

Lifecycle Management and Postapproval Labeling Changes

The labeling lifecycle begins when draft labeling is submitted to FDA. During the BLA review phase, labeling content may be revised by the sponsor or at the agency's request. Once the labeling is modified and approved by FDA, the sponsor can begin to commercialize the product by promoting and advertising the approved labeling information through various marketing channels such as television, newspapers, magazines, radio or Internet. However, changes to the initially approved labeling may be required, to add new information or to delete or clarify specific information to prevent misunderstanding in the marketplace.

Postapproval labeling changes are managed per *Guidance for Industry: Changes to an Approved Application—Biological Products* (July 1997). Any postapproval labeling changes to a BLA must comply with 21 CFR 314.70, 314.97 or 601.12, as applicable, to notify FDA about changes to approved applications (21 CFR 314.70(a) and 601.12(a)). Depending their type, changes may be submitted through a supplement for prior approval ("prior approval supplements") before distribution, as a Changes Being Effected (CBE) supplement or by including the information in the Annual Report (21 CFR 314.70(b), (c) and (d); 314.81(b)(2); 601.12(b), (c) and (d)). Depending on the category into which a change falls, the sponsor needs to develop a strategy, collect necessary information and submit the relevant regulatory documents to FDA.

Advertising and Promotion

Overview of Nonpromotional and Promotional Materials

FDA traditionally has recognized important reasons not to regulate all industry-supported scientific and educational activities as advertising, since this can restrict participants' freedom to discuss data or express views. To permit industry support for scientific and educational discussions, including unapproved uses, FDA has distinguished between nonpromotional and promotional activities and materials. Those activities the agency has deemed to be independent from influence by the supporting company and nonpromotional have neither been treated as advertising or labeling nor been subjected to the agency's regulatory scrutiny.

Nonpromotional Scientific and Educational Activities

Scientific media include journal publications and scientific abstracts and presentations at purely scientific forums. To determine whether a communication truly is a scientific exchange, FDA looks at who the communicator is, disclosures and the program's focus, as described in *Final Guidance on Industry-Supported Scientific and Educational Activities* (November 1997). If a promotional individual (e.g., pharmaceutical sales representative) provides the communication in a promotional venue (e.g., promotional presentation), this is unlikely to be considered nonpromotional. However, if a clinical researcher from the company, in response to a request from a medical society, provides a presentation on current findings in a purely scientific forum, this may qualify as a scientific exchange.

The nuances are slight and sometimes difficult to discern; therefore, this is an area of much discussion. Consequently, in one-on-one communications, sponsors generally do not allow any proactive communication of information that may be deemed inconsistent with the label and restrict any sharing of additional information to reactive responses to unsolicited requests from medical customers.

Nonpromotional Disease Awareness and "Help-Seeking" Communications

"Help-seeking" communications or advertisements are disease-awareness communications directed at consumers or healthcare practitioners discussing a particular disease or health condition, to encourage consumers to seek and healthcare practitioners to provide appropriate treatment. As outlined in the draft guidance, *Draft Guidance for Industry: "Help-Seeking" and Other Disease Awareness Communications by or on Behalf of Drug and Device Firms* (January 2004), FDA believes this is particularly important for underdiagnosed and undertreated conditions (such as osteoporosis and diabetes). To qualify as a disease awareness and help-seeking communication, a piece must meet the following requirements:

- discuss a disease or health condition
- if directed toward consumers, advise the consumer to "see your doctor"
- if directed at healthcare practitioners, encourage awareness of the signs of the disease or condition to assist in diagnosis
- not mention or identify a particular drug
- not contain any representation or suggestion relating to the drug

This type of communication is not considered a product advertisement because no drug is mentioned or implied and, therefore, is not subject to *FD&C Act* or FDA requirements or regulations.

Preapproval Product Communications

FDA generally prohibits any promotional activity and claims of safety and efficacy for investigational products, including biologics, prior to approval. Specifically, 21 CFR 312.7(a) states: "A sponsor or investigator, or any person acting on behalf of a sponsor or investigator, shall not represent in a promotional context that an investigational new drug is safe or effective for the purposes for which it is under investigation or otherwise promote the drug." However, companies often need to provide product information to the public prior to approval (e.g., clinical trial recruitment, press releases, etc.). In these instances, the following recommendations can help ensure product information is not linked to promotional safety and efficacy claims:

- when presenting efficacy information, provide an objective presentation of data; state all endpoints and provide data without bias
- when presenting safety information, include all adverse event grades with material percentages and/or incidences
- avoid characterizing data as well- tolerated, revolutionary or robust
- always clarify the product is not yet approved by using descriptions such as "investigational" or "study medication"

Promotional Materials

The *FD&C Act* does not define what constitutes an "advertisement," but per 21 CFR 202.1(l)(2), regulated promotional materials include advertisements in published journals, magazines, other periodicals and newspapers, and advertisements broadcast through such media as radio, television and telephone communication systems. Promotional labelling generally is any labelling, other than the FDA-required labelling is devised to promote the product.

Regulatory Oversight of Biologic Advertising and Promotion Labelling

FDA has primary jurisdiction over prescription advertising under the 1962 *Kefauver-Harris Drug Amendments* to the *FD&C Act* and over biologics advertising under the *Public Health Service Act* (*PHS Act*). Both CDER and CBER have regulatory responsibility for therapeutic biological products, including premarket review and oversight.[3] In some cases, guidance differs between CDER to CBER because of differences in the centers' procedures and computer infrastructure.

At CBER, the Advertising and Promotional Labeling Branch (APLB) within the Office of Compliance and Biologics Quality is responsible for reviewing and monitoring biologic product promotion. Specific oversight activities include reviews of final and draft advertising and promotional labeling of licensed biological products to ensure product communications are fairly balanced (with risks and benefits), truthful, non-misleading and in compliance with federal laws and regulations.

At CDER, the Office of Prescription Drug Promotion (OPDP) is responsible for promotional materials for biological products including monoclonal antibodies and recombinant proteins. OPDP consists of the Division of Direct-to-Consumer Promotion and the Division of Professional Promotion. OPDP's primary roles include establishing policy for regulating prescription drug promotion, including advertisements and promotion labeling, and planning and supervising research studies.

FDA does not pre-approve or "clear" drug advertising prior to its dissemination except in certain instances, such as accelerated approval applications. Regulatory oversight of promotion serves to ensure the following advertising and promotional labeling overarching principles:

- Drug promotion must be consistent with approved product labeling or PI.
- Claims must be supported by substantial evidence.
- Promotion must not be false or misleading.
- Promotion must be fairly balanced.
- Promotion must reveal all material information.

General Content and Format Requirements

The requirements for the information to be included in advertisements for prescription drug products, including biologics, are described in detail in 21 CFR 202.1(e)(1)–(5), as well as in such relevant guidance documents such *Draft Guidance for Industry: Brief Summary and Adequate Directions for Use: Disclosing Risk Information in Consumer-Directed Print Advertisements and Promotional Labeling for Human Prescription Drugs* (February 2015) and *Draft Guidance for Industry: Product Name Placement, Size, and Prominence in Advertising and Promotional Labeling* (November 2013).

Presentation of Product Name

As is the case for prescription drug products in 21 CFR 202.1 and draft guidance documents, product names in advertising and promotional labeling for biologics should be presented as follows:

- The entire proprietary (brand or trade) name should be presented together, without any intervening written or graphic matter.
- The established (generic) name must be printed in letters at least half as large as the letters comprising the proprietary name, and the prominence of the established name must be comparable with the prominence of the proprietary name.
- The order of ingredients and respective quantities should be listed in the same manner as they are listed in the product's label, and the quantity of each ingredient also should correspond to the product label.

Product Claims

As per 21 CFR 202.1, all biologics advertising and promotional labeling only may recommend or suggest the product's approved use as indicated in the PI. Any suggestions or recommendations inconsistent with the specific product use or indication presented in the label could constitute off-label promotion or broadening of the indication.

To determine whether a product claim is consistent with the product's approved use, FDA looks not just at the product indication, but also at the PI's clinical trials section. The PI's clinical trials section provides study background, patient populations included and study results. Generally, if a product is promoted for use in a patient population broader than was tested in the clinical trials used for product approval, this may be construed as broadening of the indication and be considered a violation of the regulations. Consistent with these requirements, FDA issued a Warning Letter in 2013 for a mailer for a biologic product, stating it "suggests that the drug is useful in a broader range of patients or conditions than has been substantiated, makes unsubstantiated efficacy claims, and omits material facts."[4]

Product claims held to this standard include not just verbal and textual communications, but also graphics. Advertising and promotional labeling graphics must be consistent with the FDA-approved product label and be supported by substantial evidence. For instance, a patient depicted in an advertisement should represent the average patient in the clinical trials conducted for product approval. An example of an inconsistent advertising claim would contain a graphic of a patient climbing a mountain when the product is indicated for a seriously physically disabling disease; if the majority of patients in the clinical trial had seriously debilitating physical disabilities, this depiction could constitute overstating the product's efficacy.

Fair Balance and Presentation of Risk Information

The presentation of a product's risks in advertising and promotional labeling in comparison to the efficacy information is of utmost importance. Essentially, safety and effectiveness claims in advertising and promotional labeling must be fairly balanced with risk information. In addition, the risk information must be presented with equal prominence to the promotional claims (21 CFR 202.1(e)(5)). Material facts about the product being promoted also must be communicated, including facts about possible consequences from using the product as suggested in the promotional piece (21 CFR 202.1 (e)(5)(iii)). *Revised Draft Guidance for Industry: Brief Summary and Adequate Directions for Use, Disclosing Risk Information in Consumer-Directed Print Advertisements and Promotional Labeling for Human Prescription Drugs* (February 2015) provides insight into FDA's thinking on appropriate risk presentation and the various factors used to evaluate adequate risk disclosure. In the past, there may have been a general misconception that merely providing a statement of the serious and most common risks in any piece, regardless of the number of benefits or effectiveness claims provided, would be sufficient risk disclosure. This statement of risks often was referred to as the "Fair Balance Statement." Through the revised draft guidance, it has become clear FDA believes the brief summary should focus on the most important risk information rather than an exhaustive list of risks and information should be presented in the way most likely to be understood by consumers. When FDA evaluates risk communication in promotional pieces, it does not look only at specific risk statements, but rather at the net impression. The net impression is the message communicated by the promotional piece in its entirety; the piece as a whole should convey an accurate and non-misleading impression of the product's benefits and risks. Furthermore, even if individual claims are not misleading, if the piece as a whole provides a misleading impression (e.g., the drug is safer than has been proven by substantial evidence), the piece may be deemed to be violative.

Consistent with these guidelines, FDA issued an enforcement letter in May 2014 for a sales aid for a radiotherapeutic antibody in which the imagery misleadingly suggested that the product "can precisely target lymphoma cells without targeting healthy cells" and "minimize[s] the serious risks that [the product] presents to patients as a result of its destruction of healthy cells and tissues." The Warning letter stated the "sales aid is false or misleading because it minimizes important risk information, overstates the efficacy."[5]

Advertising Requirements for Specific Media

Content and format requirements apply to any promotional piece for prescription drug and biological products, regardless of the medium by which it is communicated—including broadcast advertising (on television or radio), print media and Internet or social media. Generally, advertising and promotional labeling are treated in the same manner, with the following distinctions.

Broadcast Advertising

There are requirements specific to broadcast advertising (television and radio) for prescription drugs, including biologics. First, the advertisement must include a statement of risk-related information relating to the major side effects and contraindications in the audio or audio/video parts of the advertisement, referred to as the "Major Statement" (21 CFR 202.1(e)(1)). Second, FDA recognizes the medium's inherent limitations by allowing broadcast advertising to include only the most important risk information if the advertisement makes "adequate provision" and directs viewers and/or listeners to a source where they can obtain the full FDA-approved prescribing information. Broadcast advertisements can meet the "adequate provision" requirement as described in *Guidance for Industry Consumer-Directed Broadcast Advertisements* (August 1999) by communicating the location of a drug's prescribing information such as a website address or toll-free telephone number or referring to a healthcare provider (e.g., a doctor or pharmacist).

Print Advertising

Print advertisements for prescription drugs, including biologics, must contain the product's established, quantitative composition, a 'brief summary" relating to side effects, contraindications and effectiveness, and, for direct-to-consumer advertisements, a statement encouraging adverse event reporting to FDA (21 CFR 202.1(e)). As consumers are unlikely to understand the traditional approach of including the PI's risk-related sections verbatim and in small font, FDA believes the brief summary in consumer-directed prescription drug advertisements, referred to as the consumer brief summary, should focus on the most important risk information, excluding certain information from the PI or FDA-approved patient labeling. Since the consumer brief summary's risk information is not complete, statements must be included to advise consumers the information is not comprehensive, to speak with their healthcare provider or pharmacist, and of a toll-free number or website address where FDA-approved labeling can be obtained.

Internet/Social Media Platforms

FDA has issued draft guidances to describe its thinking on promotion of FDA-regulated medical products, including prescription drugs and biologics, on electronic/digital platforms such as the Internet and through social media or other technological venues (Internet and social media). Internet and social media platforms, such as online microblogs, messaging services (e.g., Twitter) and online paid search (e.g., "sponsored links" on search engines such as Google and Yahoo) can limit character spaces, as discussed in the *Draft Guidance for Industry Internet/Social Media Platforms with Character Space Limitations— Presenting Risk and Benefit Information for Prescription Drugs and Medical Devices* (June 2014). FDA's policy, regardless of character space constraints, is if a firm chooses to make a product benefit claim, it also should incorporate risk information within the same character-space-limited communication. A mechanism to allow direct access to a more complete discussion of the risks also must be provided. With respect to user-generated content and misinformation, FDA has determined it may benefit public health for firms to correct misinformation about medicinal products, and recommendations have been provided for when a firm chooses to correct misinformation for third-party user-generated content.

Requirement: Reminder Labeling

"Reminder labeling," per 21 CFR 201.100(f), calls attention to the drug product's name but does not include indications or dosage recommendations for use. Reminder labeling must contain the drug product's proprietary name and, optionally, established name of each active ingredient and descriptive information relating to quantitative ingredients statements, dosage form, quantity of package contents or price. The assumption behind reminder advertisements is that the audience knows what the drug is for and does not need to be told. Reminder advertisements must not include indication(s), dosage recommendation(s) or claims, and they are not considered appropriate for drugs whose labelling contains a "black box" warning.

Note that merely indicating a patient population in the material, either through text or a graphic, would violate this exemption and would require the sponsor to provide risk disclosure. For instance, if along with the name, Product X, there was a graphic of a child in the background, this would provide a representation that the product is appropriate for use in a pediatric population; therefore, the sponsor would have to include the appropriate risk disclosure.

Submitting Advertising and Promotional Labelling for Biologics

First Use

Sponsors are required to submit all biologic advertisements and promotional labeling at the time of dissemination, also referred to as "time of first use" on Form FDA 2253 (21 CFR 314.81(b)(i)). The form requires sponsors to indicate the type of advertising or promotional labeling being submitted, using the specific coding provided on the form, and the initial date of dissemination. While CDER's OPDP and CBER's APLB require the same form for these submissions, each center provides slightly different directions the sponsor should be careful to note when completing it. Failure to submit advertising and promotional labeling on Form FDA 2253 constitutes a violation of 21 CFR 314.81(b)(i)).

A common misconception in industry is if FDA does not comment on an item when submitted at first use on Form FDA 2253, it is deemed to be "approved." This misconception can wrongly encourage the continued use of inappropriate or violative materials. In general, the submission on Form FDA 2253 is for documentation purposes and does not constitute any type of "approval."

Advisory Comments

While not a requirement, sponsors have the option of requesting advisory comments on draft advertising and promotional materials. Advisory comments can be requested only for draft materials not yet published or disseminated and currently not in use or in the public domain. When sponsors are uncertain about promotional campaigns or language, this can be a very valuable option. APLB strongly encourages this option's use when launching a new product or indication. Specific directions on how to submit draft materials for advisory comments can be found on FDA's website.[6] Requests for advisory comments on promotional materials for prescription drug and biologics, other than DTC ads, can be submitted to OPDP.[7]

Note, even after submitting material for advisory comments or withdrawing a submission for advisory comments, the sponsor still is required to submit the items on Form FDA 2253 at time of dissemination/first use.

Accelerated Approval Products

While most products' materials initially can be submitted to FDA at the time of dissemination, there is an exception that requires prior submission for products approved under the Accelerated Approval program (21 CFR 601.45) and for those that may cause fatalities or serious damage but for which the information has not been widely publicized (as described in 21 CFR 202.1(j)(1). In these cases, approval by FDA prior to dissemination is required.

The sponsor of an Accelerated Approval product must submit all advertisements and promotional materials intended to be published within 120 days after approval, during the preapproval review period. After 120 days post-approval, the applicant must submit materials at least 30 days prior to publication. Once submitted, the sponsor must wait the minimum 30 days to receive advisory comments (often referred to as "pre-clearance") from FDA. If no comments are received at 30 days, the sponsor can choose to withdraw the submission and move ahead with the use of the piece.

Compliance and Enforcement

FDA can enforce violations of the *FD&C Act* or agency regulations through a variety of mechanisms, including: Notices of Violations (NOVs), also known as Untitled Letters; Warning Letters; and, if the violation warrants, referral for judicial action. All three mechanisms are intended to induce compliance with regulations. CBER's APLB reviews complaints about promotional activities or materials related to CBER-regulated products, and OPDP reviews complaints for prescription drugs. It should be noted OPDP is responsible for the review and oversight of all prescription drug advertising and promotional labeling, including many therapeutic biological products. OPDP's mission is to protect public health by assuring prescription drug information is truthful, balanced and accurately communicated. The majority of advertising and promotion NOVs are issued by OPDP and can be found on FDA's website.[8]

NOVs generally are reserved for less-serious violations and do not greatly jeopardize public health but still are significant concerns. An NOV usually requires the sponsor only to discontinue use of the violative materials along with any other pieces that may contain a similar violation.

Warning Letters usually are reserved for more serious violations that may pose a risk to public safety. They typically contain stronger language and commonly are addressed to the company's CEO. In addition to ceasing use of the violative materials, Warning Letters also may require the company to conduct corrective actions. For example, a company may be required to run a remedial advertisement to reach the same audience as the original violative advertisement, or disseminate corrective information through a "Dear Healthcare Professional" letter as described in 21 CFR 200.5(c)(3). Generally, the corrective action is meant to be communicated in the same medium as the original violative piece. Warning Letters frequently direct the sponsor to provide FDA with information on any other promotional items that contain similar messages. All FDA Warning Letters, regardless of issuing center or office, are available on FDA's website.[9]

In determining whether a sponsor should be issued an enforcement letter and, if so, which grade, FDA often looks at the following elements:

- Do the product materials have recurrent violations?
- Is there a pattern and/or consistency of these violations through different forms of media?
- Is there a risk to public health?

If FDA is not satisfied by the sponsor's response to the Warning Letter, it may recommend such enforcement actions as injunctions, seizures and/or criminal prosecution. The Department of Justice carries out these activities. One possible outcome is the company agreeing to enter into an arrangement with the government, called a consent decree, which places severe restrictions on the company's operations to ensure it comes into compliance.

Corrective actions that can be taken by FDA on inadequate dissemination of medical and scientific information relating to an unapproved use of an approved biologics are outlined in 21 CFR 99.401–405.

Conclusion (Summary)

- The umbrella term "labeling" generally is used to describe two types of labeling for drugs, including biologics: 1) FDA-approved labeling and 2) promotional labeling.
- Typically, four prescription drug labeling information types are submitted in the original BLA: 1) professional labelling with annotated draft labeling text; 2) patient labeling; 3) draft container and carton labels; and 4) Structured Product Labelling (SPL). Upon approval, the labeling content can be applied appropriately to promotional and advertising activities.
- Labeling information content and format for biologics are subject to FDA regulations commonly referred to as the "Physician Labeling Rule" (PLR).
- Postapproval changes to the original labeling, promotional labeling and advertising content need to be reported to FDA. Depending on the nature of the change, changes are reported via one of three mechanisms: Prior Approval Supplement, Changes Being Effected or Annual Report.
- FDA has distinguished between promotional and non-promotional activities, such as scientific and educational activities and disease awareness communications. However, product communications intended to be "non-promotional" in nature can be subject to FDA regulations if they make product claims.
- Regulated promotional materials include advertisements in published journals, magazines, other periodicals and newspapers, and advertisements broadcast through such media as radio, television and telephone communication systems.
- FDA has jurisdiction over prescription advertising, and both CDER and CBER have regulatory responsibility for promotional labeling for biologics. In CDER, OPDP is responsible for promotional materials, while in CBER, APLB oversees all labeling activities.
- Advertising and promotional labeling must be consistent with the FDA-approved product labeling, must be supported by substantial evidence, must not be false or misleading and must reveal all material information.
- Generally, advertising and promotional labeling are treated in the same manner; however there are some specific requirements for broadcast, print and Internet or social media platforms.
- Sponsors are required to submit all advertisements and promotional labeling for biologics at the time of dissemination, also referred to as "time of first use," and advisory comments can be requested. An exception requires prior submission for products approved under the Accelerated Approval program and for products that may cause fatalities or serious damage but for which the information has not been widely publicized.
- FDA uses a variety of enforcement tools, such as Notices of Violations, Warning Letters and other corrective actions to ensure industry compliance with the *FD&C Act* and safe and effective use of biologics in patients. Most NOVs related to prescription drug advertising, including many therapeutic biologicals, are issued by OPDP.

References

1. Rodriguez-Monguio R, Spielberger K and Seoane-Vazquez E. "Examination of risk evaluation and mitigation strategies and drug safety in the US." *Research in Social and Administrative Pharmacy* Vol. 10; pp. 232–238. (2014)
2. *Federal Register*: "Electronic Distribution of Prescribing Information for Human Prescription Drugs, Including Biological Products. (Proposed Rule)" Vol 79, No. 243. https://www.federalregister.gov/articles/2014/12/18/2014-29522/electronic-distribution-of-prescribing-information-for-human-prescription-drugs-including-biological. Accessed 18 April 2015.
3. FDA. *Frequently Asked Questions About Therapeutic Biological Products*. FDA website. http://www.fda.gov/Drugs/DevelopmentApprovalProcess/%20HowDrugsareDevelopedandApproved/ApprovalApplications/TherapeuticBiologicApplications/ucm113522.htm. Accessed 18 April 2015.
4. FDA. Untitled Letter: BLA 103951. FDA Website. http://www.fda.gov/Drugs/GuidanceComplianceRegulatoryInformation/EnforcementActivitiesbyFDA/WarningLettersandNoticeofViolationLetterstoPharmaceuticalCompanies/ucm339597.htm Accessed 18 April 2015.
5. FDA. Untitled Letter: BLA 125019. FDA Website. http://www.fda.gov/Drugs/GuidanceComplianceRegulatoryInformation/EnforcementActivitiesbyFDA/WarningLettersandNoticeofViolation

LetterstoPharmaceuticalCompanies/ucm339597.htm Accessed 18 April 2015.
6. Submitting Biologics Advertising & Promotional LabelingFrequently Asked Questions About Therapeutic Biological Products. FDA website. www.fda.gov/BiologicsBloodVaccines/DevelopmentApprovalProcess/AdvertisingLabelingPromotionalMaterials/ucm118171.htm Accessed 18 April 2015.
7. FDA. Requests for Advisory Comment on Promotional Materials Other than Proposed Direct-To-Consumer (DTC) TV Ads. FDA Website. http://www.fda.gov/AboutFDA/CentersOffices/OfficeofMedicalProductsandTobacco/CDER/ucm090168.htm Accessed 18 April 2015.
8. FDA. Warning Letters and Notice of Violation Letters to Pharmaceutical Companies. FDA Website. http://www.fda.gov/Drugs/GuidanceComplianceRegulatoryInformation/EnforcementActivitiesbyFDA/WarningLettersandNoticeofViolationLetterstoPharmaceuticalCompanies/default.htm Accessed 18 April 2015.
9. FDA. Inspections, Compliance, Enforcement, and Criminal Investigations. FDA Website. http://www.fda.gov/ICECI/EnforcementActions/WarningLetters/default.htm. Accessed 18 April 2015.

Recommended Reading

- Federal Register: Requirements on Content and Format of Labeling for Human Prescription Drug and Biological Products - 21 CFR Parts 201, 314, and 601 (Final rule), 24-Jan-2006. http://www.fda.gov/OHRMS/DOCKETS/98fr/06-545.pdf. Accessed 27 April 2015.
- https://www.federalregister.gov/articles/2014/12/04/2014-28241/content-and-format-of-labeling-for-human-prescription-drug-and-biological-products-requirements-for. Accessed 18 April 2015.

Chapter 27

Combination Products

Updated by Michael D'Amico

OBJECTIVES

- ❑ Review the regulatory definition of a combination product
- ❑ Understand the overall regulatory scheme for combination products
- ❑ Explain how combination product jurisdictional determinations are made
- ❑ Discuss the premarket review process for combination products
- ❑ Describe proposed combination product postmarket safety reporting regulation
- ❑ Describe proposed CGMP requirements for combination products
- ❑ Discuss relevant combination product guidance documents
- ❑ Discuss how user fees are applied for combination products

LAWS, REGULATIONS AND GUIDELINES COVERED IN THIS CHAPTER

- ❑ 21 CFR 3 Product Jurisdiction
- ❑ Proposed 21 CFR 4 Regulation of Combination Products
- ❑ 21 CFR 210 Current Good Manufacturing Practice in Manufacturing, Processing, Packing, or Holding of Drugs; General
- ❑ 21 CFR 211 Current Good Manufacturing Practice for Finished Pharmaceuticals
- ❑ 21 CFR 820 Quality System Regulation
- ❑ *Federal Food, Drug, and Cosmetic Act* of 1938
- ❑ *Safe Medical Devices Act* of 1990
- ❑ *Medical Device User Fee and Modernization Act* of 2002
- ❑ *Public Health Service Act* of 1944

Introduction

Combination products raise a variety of regulatory and review challenges. Although the US regulatory frameworks for drugs, devices and biological products share many of the same basic features, each is also somewhat unique. Drugs, devices and biological products each have their own types of marketing applications, Good Manufacturing Practice (GMP) regulations and adverse event reporting requirements. When drugs and devices, drugs and biologics or devices and biologics are combined to create a new product, consideration must be given to how the combination product as a whole will be regulated.

Until 1990, there was no clear process or mandate for the US Food and Drug Administration (FDA) to determine the regulatory pathway of "borderline" products, or products comprised of more than one type of regulated article. The

Safe Medical Devices Act of 1990 (*SMDA*) introduced the concept of a combination product in Section 503(g) of the *Federal Food, Drug, and Cosmetic Act* of 1938 *(FD&C Act)*, adding a provision requiring a combination product to be assigned to a lead agency center based on its "primary mode of action" (PMOA). In 1991, FDA implemented the *SMDA* provision in Title 21 of the Code of Federal Regulations (CFR) Part 3. This regulation vested jurisdictional authority for both combination and non-combination products in FDA's Product Jurisdiction Office (originally FDA's Office of the Ombudsman, and reassigned in 2003 to FDA's newly established Office of Combination Products (OCP)).

21 CFR Part 3 also established a "Request for Designation" (RFD) process to determine which FDA center would be assigned review responsibilities for combination products, or for any product for which jurisdiction is unclear or in dispute. This regulation was intended to eliminate in most cases, but did not preclude, the need for separate approvals for each individual component of a combination product.

Despite *SMDA*, the perception persisted that combination products were still vulnerable to "falling through the cracks" between FDA medical product centers. To address these issues, in the *Medical Device User Fee and Modernization Act* of 2002 (*MDUFMA*), Congress amended Section 503(g) of the *FD&C Act* to mandate FDA to establish OCP with the following responsibilities for combination product assignment, premarket review and postmarket regulation:

- prompt assignment of the center with primary jurisdiction ("lead center") for a combination product's review and regulation
- ensure timely and effective premarket review by overseeing the timeliness of and coordinating reviews involving more than one center
- ensure consistent and appropriate postmarket regulation
- resolve disputes regarding review timeliness
- review and/or revise agreements, guidance and practices specific to the assignment of combination products
- report to Congress on OCP's activities and impact

While not part of its statutory mandates, OCP also works with FDA centers to develop guidance and regulations to clarify combination product regulation and serves as a focal point for combination product issues for internal and external stakeholders. Note, OCP itself does not review combination products, but assigns the product to the lead reviewing center and oversees the intercenter consultation process.

Definition of a Combination Product

A "combination product" is defined in 21 CFR 3.2(e) as a combination of two or more different types of regulated products, i.e.:

- a product comprised of two or more regulated components, i.e., drug and device, biologic and device, drug and biologic or drug and device or biologic, physically, chemically or otherwise combined or mixed and produced as a single entity
- two or more separate products packaged together in a single package or as a unit and comprised of drug and device products, device and biological products or biological and drug products
- a drug, device or biological product packaged separately that, according to its investigational plan or proposed labeling, is intended for use only with an approved, individually specified drug, device or biological product where both are required to achieve the intended use, indication or effect and, following the proposed product's approval, its labeling would need to be changed, e.g., to reflect a change in intended use, dosage form, strength, route of administration or significant change in dose
- any investigational drug, device or biological product packaged separately that, according to its proposed labeling, is for use only with another individually specified investigational drug, device or biological product where both are required to achieve the intended use, indication or effect

A combination product's individual components ("constituent parts") can be:

- physically or chemically combined (21 CFR 3.2 (e)(1)[1])
- co-packaged (21 CFR 3.2 (e)(2)[2])
- separate, cross-labeled products (21 CFR 3.2(e)(3)[3])

Examples of combination products where the components are physically, chemically or otherwise combined include (21 CFR 3.2(e (1)):

- drug-coated or drug-eluting device (e.g., drug-eluting stent)
- drug packaged with a syringe, pre-filled syringe or injector pen
- controlled-release drug delivery device (e.g., transdermal patch)
- orthopedic implant coated or packaged with biologic growth factor
- chemotherapy drug and monoclonal antibody (biologic) conjugate
- scaffold (device) seeded with autologous cells (biologic)
- cross-labeled drug or in vitro pharmacogenomic test (A list of recent FDA

examples of combination approvals can be found at www.fda.gov/CombinationProducts/AboutCombinationProducts/ucm101598.htm.)

Examples of combination products where the components are packaged together (21 CFR 3.2(e)(2)):

- drug or biological product packaged with a delivery device
- surgical tray with surgical instruments, drapes and lidocaine or alcohol swabs

Examples of combination products where the components are provided separately but labeled for use together (21 CFR 3.2(e)(3) or (e)(4)):

- photosensitizing drug and activating laser/light source
- iontophoretic drug delivery patch and controller

Recent examples of combination product approvals may be found on the OCP website: http://www.fda.gov/CombinationProducts/.

Determining Combination Product Jurisdiction and Regulatory Path

FDA is required to assign a combination product to a lead center based on its PMOA. In the 25 August 2005 *Federal Register*, FDA promulgated a final regulation (PMOA Rule) to describe the principles of how combination products will be assigned to an agency center. The regulation defined "mode of action" (MOA) and PMOA and set forth an algorithm for how FDA would assign combination products for which the PMOA cannot be determined with "reasonable certainty."

FDA defined MOA as the means by which a product achieves an intended therapeutic effect or action. For purposes of this definition, "therapeutic" action or effect includes any effect or action of the combination product intended to diagnose, cure, mitigate, treat or prevent disease, or affect the structure or any function of the body. Because combination products are comprised of more than one type of regulated article (biological product, device or drug), and each constituent part contributes a biological product, device or drug mode of action, combination products typically will have more than one identifiable mode of action. The definitions of biological product, device and drug mode of actions are related closely to the statutory definitions of a biological product, device and drug, respectively:

1. A constituent part has a biological product MOA if it acts by means of a virus, therapeutic serum, toxin, antitoxin, vaccine, blood, blood component or derivative, allergenic product or analogous product applicable to the prevention, treatment or cure of a disease or condition of human beings, as described in section 351(i) of the *Public Health Service Act* (*PHS Act*). (Note, while not currently reflected in the biological product MOA definition, the statutory definition of a biological product was amended in 2010 to include proteins (except any chemically synthesized polypeptide).
2. A constituent part has a device MOA if it meets the definition of device contained in *FD&C Act* Section 201(h)(1)–3, does not have a biological product MOA and does not achieve its primary intended purposes through chemical action within or on the body of man or other animals and is not dependent upon being metabolized for the achievement of its primary intended purposes.
3. A constituent part has a drug mode of action if it meets the definition of drug contained in *FD&C Act* Section 201(g)(1) and does not have a biological product or device MOA.

PMOA is defined as "the single mode of action of a combination product that provides the most important therapeutic action of the combination product." The regulation further clarifies PMOA as the "mode of action expected to make the greatest contribution to the overall intended therapeutic effects of the combination product." For example, if a drug-device combination product's PMOA is attributable to its device constituent part, the Center for Devices and Radiological Health (CDRH) would have primary jurisdiction for the combination product, whereas if a drug-device combination product's PMOA is attributable to its drug constituent part, the Center for Drug Evaluation and Research (CDER) would have primary jurisdiction.

When FDA is unable to determine the most important therapeutic action with reasonable certainty, 21 CFR 3.4 defines an "assignment algorithm," describing the assignment process. First, FDA would look at historical precedents to assign the combination product to the agency component that regulates other combination products presenting similar safety and effectiveness questions regarding the combination product as a whole. When no other combination products present similar safety and effectiveness questions regarding the combination product as a whole, FDA would decide the most appropriate assignment based on the new combination product's safety and effectiveness questions. FDA assigns the product to the center with the most expertise related to the combination product's most significant safety and effectiveness questions. For example, if the most significant safety and effectiveness issues a drug-device combination product presents in this scenario were attributable to the drug constituent part, the combination product likely would be assigned to CDER.

Understanding the regulatory pathway early in a combination product's development phase often is essential for the sponsor to establish a realistic regulatory strategy. There are two ways in which a manufacturer can seek FDA's feedback for determining product jurisdiction: informal or formal processes. Informal processes involve seeking advice from center or OCP staff, typically by telephone, email or meeting. Informal procedures generally are appropriate where the most important therapeutic action of the combination product is clear, or when FDA has experience and has determined jurisdiction for similar combination products. However, one disadvantage of the informal approach is the advice is not binding on FDA and may be subject to change.

Formal designation of a product, whether a single entity (i.e., non-combination drug, device or biologic) or a combination product, is achieved by submitting a Request for Designation (RFD). An RFD is a written submission to OCP requesting designation of the center with primary jurisdiction for a product. An RFD submission is not necessary for every product but generally is indicated when the jurisdiction of a single entity or combination product is unclear or in dispute.

FDA action on an RFD is a binding jurisdictional determination with respect to center assignment and is subject to change only under conditions specified in 21 CFR 3.9 and Section 563 of the *FD&C Act*. However, while a designation is binding for a particular product's assignment, such assignment pertains only to the product described in the RFD. For example, if the product's configuration, composition, modes of action, intended use or any other key aspect changes after the designation letter is issued, it may be necessary to submit a new RFD to determine the modified product's appropriate assignment.

An RFD is limited by regulation to 15 pages, including attachments. Under the regulation, if FDA does not provide an answer within 60 days of the RFD filing date, the sponsor's request for classification or assignment is granted. As described in 21 CFR 3.7(c), the following information is required in an RFD submission. FDA has issued *Guidance for Industry: How to Write a Request for Designation*, which further elaborates on these requirements:[5]

- sponsor identity, including company name and address, establishment registration number, company contact person and telephone number
- product description, including:
  - classification, name of the product and all component products, if applicable
  - common, generic or usual name of the product and all component products
  - proprietary product name
  - identification of any product component that has received premarket approval already, is marketed as not being subject to premarket approval, or has received an investigational exemption
  - status of any discussions or agreements between sponsors regarding the product's use as a component of a new combination product
  - chemical, physical or biological composition
  - status and brief reports of developmental work results, including animal testing
  - manufacturing process description, including all component sources
  - proposed use or indications
  - description of all known MOAs, sponsor's identification of the PMOA and the basis for that determination
  - schedule and duration of use
  - drug or biologic dose and route of administration
  - description of related products, including the regulatory status of those related products
  - any other relevant information
- sponsor's recommendation on which agency component should have primary jurisdiction, with accompanying statement of reasons

FDA generally reviews an RFD for completeness within five working days of receipt. An incomplete RFD is "not filed," and the applicant is notified of the information necessary to permit OCP to undertake a substantive review. If an RFD is filed, the sponsor is notified of the filing date, as well as the date by which OCP will respond. Within 60 days after the RFD is filed, OCP issues a letter specifying the agency component with primary jurisdiction for the product's premarket review and regulation. The designation letter also usually identifies any consulting agency components and sometimes describes the regulatory authorities (e.g., device or drug provisions of the *FD&C Act*) to which the product will be subject.

If the sponsor disagrees with the designation, it may request OCP to reconsider the decision. The Request for Reconsideration (RFR) must be submitted within 15 days of receipt of the designation letter, may not include new information and must not exceed five pages. OCP, in turn, will respond in writing to the RFR within 15 days.

Many resources are available to help sponsors understand a combination product's jurisdiction. The original resources were the three inter-center agreements (ICAs) between the Center for Biologics Evaluation and Research (CBER) and CDER, CDER and CDRH, and CBER and CDRH, established in 1991. The ICAs' usefulness has decreased over time due to agency organizational realignments, the development of new products not envisioned in the original ICAs, new uses of existing products and laws enacted since 1991. In 2006 (71 FR 56988[6]), the agency announced it had reviewed these agreements and preliminarily proposed to continue using the CBER-CDRH and CDER-CDRH ICAs, as they provide helpful, nonbinding guidance, with the understanding they should not be relied upon as the agency's most current, complete jurisdictional statements. Due to the transfer of many therapeutic biologic products from CBER to CDER in 2003, the agency stated the CBER-CDER ICA was out of date.

The 2006 notice also explained that while FDA does not plan to update the existing ICAs, it believes transparency in jurisdictional decision making should result in greater predictability and reduce ambiguity about FDA perspectives. The agency has implemented a number of mechanisms to provide this transparency. For example, it has used its website to disseminate information concerning product jurisdiction. Some examples of these are:

- jurisdictional determinations—approximately 250 capsular descriptions of selected RFD decisions have been posted on OCP's website: www.fda.gov/CombinationProducts/JurisdictionalInformation/RFDJurisdictionalDecisions/CapsularDescriptions"One-Liners"/default.htm
- jurisdictional updates—detailed statements on updated classification and assignment of specific product classes are available on OCP's website: www.fda.gov/CombinationProducts/JurisdictionalInformation/JurisdictionalUpdates/default.htm
- RFD decision letters—for approximately 50 approved or cleared products covered by an RFD, the OCP website includes the written jurisdictional determination for the RFD, redacted to remove trade secret and confidential commercial information in accordance with the *Freedom of Information Act*: www.fda.gov/CombinationProducts/JurisdictionalInformation/RFDJurisdictionalDecisions/RedactedDecisionLetters/default.htm

Premarket Review

The assigned lead center has primary responsibility for a combination product's review and regulation; however, a second center often is involved in the review process, especially to provide input regarding the "secondary" component. In some cases, secondary center involvement may be extensive, depending on the issues a particular product or submission raises.

To make the combination product review process more efficient, FDA established a Standard Operating Procedure (SOP), the *Intercenter Consultative and Collaborative Review Process*.[7] This SOP outlines procedures for FDA staff to follow when requesting, receiving, handling, processing and tracking formal consultative and collaborative reviews of combination products, devices, drugs and biologics. The SOP's objectives are to improve inter-center communication on combination products as well as inter-center consultative and collaborative timeliness and consistency.

While a combination product's PMOA dictates the lead center assignment, it does not dictate the regulatory authorities that may be applied. In most cases, the lead center applies its usual regulatory pathway. For example, a drug-device combination product assigned to CDRH typically is reviewed under the 510(k) or Premarket Approval Application (PMA) process, while a drug-device combination product assigned to CDER typically will be reviewed under a New Drug Application (NDA). In most cases, a single marketing application is sufficient to review a combination product, but in some cases, particularly where the two components are themselves separate products, two applications (e.g., a PMA and an NDA) may be desirable or required.

FDA published the concept paper "Number of Marketing Applications for a Combination Product" for stakeholder comment.[8] This document describes FDA's thinking about when single or separate marketing applications may be appropriate for the constituent parts of a combination product. Separate marketing applications sometimes are appropriate. Normally, only one investigational application (Investigational New Drug (IND) or Investigational Device Exemption (IDE) is submitted to authorize a combination product's clinical investigation. It is recommended the sponsor contact the agency, ideally during early product development, to determine the nature of technical and scientific information that may be necessary for investigational and marketing applications for a combination product. In September 2006, FDA published *Guidance for Industry and Staff: Early Development Considerations for Innovative Combination Products*,[9] which provides helpful perspectives on combination product development.

Special consideration also should be given to intellectual property when more than one manufacturer is co-developing a combination product. For example, the sponsor of an IDE or PMA for a device-drug combination product may not be given access by the drug manufacturer to confidential or trade secret drug information, such as drug synthesis, formulation, purification or manufacturing processes, yet such information may be required for regulatory purposes.

Confidentiality of such information usually can be maintained while providing FDA the necessary information to support the investigational or marketing application in one of two ways. One is through a Letter of Authorization (LOA), which allows the applicant to cross-reference an existing application and allows FDA to consider this information in the application review used for the combination product. The second alternative is the use of master files. Drug Master Files (DMFs) or Device Master Files (DMFs) are voluntary submissions to FDA to provide confidential information about a product or process (e.g., manufacturing processes or toxicology data) that one sponsor wishes to keep confidential but is necessary for the other sponsor to support the premarket review process. It should be noted FDA does not approve information or data in a master file, but rather accesses and reviews the information in context of the referring application.

Additional information on DMFs can be found in 21 CFR 314.420 and on FDA's website.

New Regulations Proposed in 2009 for Combination Products

In late 2009, FDA published two proposed rules that would amend the combination product regulations by creating a new 21 CFR 4. Subpart A would address current GMP (CGMP) requirements for combination products, while Subpart B would promulgate postmarketing safety reporting requirements for combination products. A similar legal framework underlies both proposed rules and sets forth FDA's view that drugs, devices and biological products do not lose their individual regulatory identities when they become constituent parts of a combination product. Under this framework, in general, the CGMP and postmarket safety reporting requirements specific to each combination product's constituent part also apply to the combination product itself. However, rather than impose duplicative requirements for manufacturers to fully comply with both sets of requirements, the proposed rules set out a streamlined framework whereby a manufacturer would comply with one set of requirements, as well as specific, additional provisions to ensure any unique requirements attributable to the "other" component are not lost if the product were to comply with only one set of requirements. Application of this general approach is further described below for both postmarket safety reporting and CGMP requirements.

Good Manufacturing Practice Requirements

In 2004, FDA published *Draft Guidance for Industry and FDA: Current Good Manufacturing Practice for Combination Products on the applicability of GMP requirements to combination products.* In the 23 September 2009, *Federal Register,*[10] FDA proposed codifying an approach similar to the one taken in the draft guidance, by establishing a new 21 CFR 4, Subpart A. The proposed rule embodied the legal framework that, in FDA's view, drugs, devices and biological products do not lose their individual regulatory identities when they become constituent parts of a combination product. In other words, a drug-device combination product is both a drug and a device, and both sets of CGMP requirements (21 CFR 210 and 211 for drugs and 21 CFR 820 for devices) apply to the combination product. FDA published the final rule on GMP requirements for combination products 22 January 2013 in the *Federal Register.*[11] The rule became effective 22 July 2013.

The final rule recognizes that 21 CFR 210 and 211 and 820 are similar in most respects. In this context, for single entity and co-packaged combination products, the rule provides a streamlined approach as an alternative to fully implementing and complying with both sets of CGMP requirements. Under this streamlined approach, a manufacturer could choose to operate under and comply with either 21 CFR 210 and 211 or 21 CFR 820, rather than both, provided additional specific aspects of the other CGMP framework also are incorporated.

Specifically, under the final rule, a manufacturer choosing to operate under and comply with drug CGMP regulations under 21 CFR 210 and 211 for its single-entity or co-packaged drug-device combination product, also would be considered to have complied with all provisions of the device Quality System Regulation (QSR) at 21 CFR 820, if it complies with the following specific provisions from 21 CFR 820:

1. 820.20 Management responsibility
2. 820.30 Design controls
3. 820.50 Purchasing controls
4. 820.100 Corrective and preventive action
5 820.170 Installation
6. 820.200 Servicing

In an analogous manner, a manufacturer choosing to operate under and comply with device QSR requirements under 21 CFR 820 for its single-entity or co-packaged drug-device combination product, would be considered to have complied with all provisions of the drug CGMP requirements in 21 CFR 210 and 211, if it complies with the following specific provisions from 21 CFR 210 and 211:

1. 211.84 Testing and approval or rejection of components, drug product containers, and closures
2. 211.103 Calculation of yield
3. 211.132 Tamper-evident packaging for over-the counter (OTC) human drug products
4. 211.137 Expiration dating
5. 211.165 Testing and release for distribution
6. 211.166 Stability testing
7. 211.167 Special testing requirements
8. 211.170 Reserve samples

The streamlined approach may be used when two or more types of constituents are manufactured in the same facility. When constituent part manufacture occurs at a separate facility from all other constituent parts, the manufacture of that part would be required to follow the CGMP regulations applicable to that part. For example, the manufacture of a drug constituent part at a facility separate from all other combination product constituent parts would be subject to 21 CFR 210 and 211, while the facility where that drug constituent part is manufactured with the device into a single-entity or co-packaged constituent part could implement the streamlined approach.

For a combination product that includes a biological product constituent part, in addition to demonstrating compliance with either the drug CGMPs or the device QSR, the CGMP operating system also would have to comply with additional CGMP requirements that apply to that constituent part as a biological product (see 21 CFR 600–680). Similarly, if the combination product includes a

Table 27-1. Unique Proposed Postmarket Safety Reporting Provisions for Combination Products

Type of Requirement	Name of Requirement	Regulatory Citation
Device	5-Day Report	21 CFR 803.53(a)
Device	30-Day Device Malfunction Report	21 CFR 803.20(b)(3)(ii)
Drug/Biological Product	15-Day Alert Report	21 CFR 314.80(c)(1) and (e) 21 CFR 600.80(c)(1) and (e)
Drug	3-Day Field Alert Report	21 CFR 314.81(b)(1)
Biological Product	Expedited Blood Fatality Report	21 CFR 606.170

human cellular or tissue (HCT/P) constituent part, it also would have to be shown to comply with the requirements of 21 CFR 1271.

Finally, for combination products with separately packaged constituent parts (21 CFR 3.2(e)(3) and (e)(4)), each constituent part would remain separate for CGMP purposes. For example, for a combination product comprised of a drug and a cross-labeled but separately packaged delivery device, the drug constituent part would be subject to 21 CFR 210 and 211, while the delivery device would be subject to 21 CFR 820.

Postmarket Safety Reporting for Combination Products

The rule[12] (http://www.fda.gov/Drugs/DrugSafety/ucm400526.htm), finalized 10 June 2014, recognizes there are many similarities and an underlying purpose among the individual reporting requirements for drugs (21 CFR 310 and 314), devices (21 CFR 803) and biological products (21 CFR 600 and 606), i.e., to protect the public health by ensuring a product's continued safety and effectiveness. For example, each set of regulations requires reports of death and serious adverse events; provides for periodic and follow-up reports; and provides a method to signal certain types of safety events that warrant expedited reporting. Despite these similarities, each set of regulations also has certain unique reporting standards and timeframes based on product characteristics for which the regulations were designed. For example, the drug reporting provisions have no requirement analogous to device malfunction reporting, while the device reporting provisions have no requirement analogous to drug 3-Day Field Alert Reporting. The proposed rule's intent is to consolidate the requirements, so a combination product is subject primarily to the reporting requirements of the marketing application type under which it is approved or cleared, while ensuring the public health benefit of the alternative marketing application's specific unique provisions is not lost.

FDA has identified five such provisions, described in **Table 27-1**, unique to drugs, devices and biological products the agency believes need to be preserved to appropriately reflect the product's combination nature and ensure consistent and appropriate combination product postmarketing safety reporting.

Under the proposed rule, a drug-device combination product approved or cleared under the device provisions of the *FD&C Act* would be subject to Medical Device Reporting under 21 CFR 803 and, in addition, would be subject to 15-Day Alert Reporting under 21 CFR 314.80(c)(1) and 3-Day Field Alert Reporting under 21 CFR 314.81(b)(1). A drug-device combination product approved under the *FD&C Act*'s drug provisions would be subject to the drug reporting provisions under 21 CFR 314.80 and 314.81, as well as 5-Day Reporting under 21 CFR 803.53(a) and 30-Day Malfunction Reporting under 21 CFR 803.20(b)(3)(ii). Expedited blood fatality reporting under 21 CFR 606.170 would apply to combination products with a blood constituent part.

The proposed rule also describes how reporting would work in less frequent situations, e.g., where there are separate marketing applications for the combination product's constituent parts or where there are multiple reporters (i.e., one application holder for one constituent part and a second application holder for another).

When there are multiple reporters, each reporter would be subject to the applicable requirements for its constituent report. The device constituent part application holder would submit in accordance with 21 CFR 803, while the drug constituent part application holder would submit in accordance with 21 CFR 314. In addition, to ensure each reporter is aware of and can investigate and follow-up on events about which the other may learn that may impact a constituent part, the proposed rule would require each application holder to submit any information learned about any component to the other manufacturer for investigation or follow-up, or to FDA.

The proposed requirements currently are not in effect and may be revised to incorporate stakeholder comments, but the final rule is expected to be similar in overall approach.

User Fees for Combination Products

FDA published *Guidance for Industry and Staff: Application User Fees for Combination Products*[13] in April 2005 to clarify the application of user fees for combination products. The guidance explains a combination product, as defined in 21

CFR 3.2(e), is subject to the appropriate fee for the application type submitted for premarket approval or clearance. For example, a biologic-device or a drug-device combination product for which a PMA is submitted is subject to the PMA fee under *MDUFMA*. Likewise, a combination product for which an NDA is submitted is subject to the NDA fee under *PDUFA*.

In specific situations, a sponsor may opt to submit separate marketing applications for each combination product constituent part, even though one application (covering the entire combination product) would suffice. Usually, this is done to pursue some type of benefit, such as new drug product exclusivity, orphan status or proprietary data protection when two firms are involved. Because the submission of two applications when one would suffice places an extra burden on FDA resources, a user fee for each application ordinarily would be required.

However, in cases where two marketing applications are required by FDA for the combination product (rather than at the discretion of the sponsor), an "innovative combination product waiver" might allow the dual application fee to be reduced. More information on eligibility for fee reduction provided by this waiver is available in the guidance document referenced above.

Summary

- As defined in 21 CFR 3.2(e), a combination product is any combination of a drug and a device; a biological product and a device; a drug and a biological product; or a drug, device and biological product. Four definitions within 3.2(e) explain these combinations.
- The *FD&C Act* gives OCP broad responsibilities covering a combination product's lifecycle. However, primary responsibility and oversight reside with the lead center (CDRH, CDER or CBER) to which the product is assigned.
- OCP is responsible for promptly assigning a lead center that will have primary jurisdiction for the combination product's review and regulation based on a determination of its PMOA.
- Formal designation of a single entity (i.e., drug, device or biologic) or combination product is achieved by submitting an RFD.
- In 2009, FDA proposed new postmarket safety reporting and CGMP regulations for combination products. The proposed regulations were predicated on the general legal framework that a combination product is subject to the legal authorities governing its constituent parts; however, streamlined approaches are proposed that recognize the similarities while also preserving the unique differences among the respective regulations for drugs, devices and biologics.
- A marketing application for a combination product is subject to the usual fee associated with its application type. In unique situations where two applications are required, and the eligibility criteria are met, an "innovative combination product waiver" may apply.

References

1. 21 CFR 3.2(e)(1): a product comprised of two or more regulated components, i.e., drug/device, biologic/device, drug/biologic or drug/device/biologic, that are physically, chemically or otherwise combined or mixed and produced as a single entity.
2. 21 CFR 3.2(e)(2): two or more separate products packaged together in a single package or as a unit and comprised of drug and device products, device and biological products or biological and drug products.
3. 21 CFR 3.2(e)(3): a drug, device or biological product packaged separately that, according to its investigational plan or proposed labeling, is intended for use only with an approved, individually specified drug, device or biological product where both are required to achieve the intended use, indication or effect and where, upon approval of the proposed product, the labeling of the approved product would need to be changed, e.g., to reflect a change in intended use, dosage form, strength, route of administration or significant change in dose.
4. 21 CFR 3.2(e)(4): any investigational drug, device or biological product packaged separately that, according to its proposed labeling, is for use only with another individually specified investigational drug, device or biological product where both are required to achieve the intended use, indication or effect.
5. *Guidance for Industry: How to Write a Request for Designation* (April 2011). FDA website. www.fda.gov/RegulatoryInformation/Guidances/ucm126053.htm. Accessed 20 April 2015.
6. *Federal Register*, 71:56988 (28 September 2006). "Review of Agreements, Guidances, and Practices Specific to Assignment of Combination Products in Compliance With the Medical Device User Fee and Modernization Act of 2002; Request for Comments." GPO website. http://edocket.access.gpo.gov/2006/pdf/E6-15967.pdf . Accessed 20 April 2015.
7. Manual of Standard Operating Procedures and Policies, General Information—Review, Intercenter Consultative/Collaborative Review Processes, Version 4 (18 June 2004).
8. Concepts for Comment Purposes Only—Not for Implementation; Number of Marketing Applications for a Combination Product. FDA website. www.fda.gov/downloads/CombinationProducts/RequestsforComment/UCM108197.pdf . Accessed 20 April 2015.
9. *Guidance for Industry and FDA Staff: Early Development Considerations for Innovative Combination Products* (September 2006). FDA website. www.fda.gov/downloads/RegulatoryInformation/Guidances/ucm126054.pdf. Accessed 20 April 2015.
10. *Federal Register* 74:48423 (23 September 2009). "Current Good Manufacturing Practice Requirements for Combination Products " Proposed Rule.
11. *Federal Register* 78:4307 (22 January 2013) "Current Good Manufacturing Practice Requirements for Combination Products" Final Rule. FDA website. http://www.fda.gov/downloads/CombinationProducts/UCM336194.pdf . Accessed 20 April 2015.
12. *Federal Register* 74:50744 (1 October 2009). "21 CFR Part 4, Postmarketing Safety Reporting for Combination Products." GPO website. http://edocket.access.gpo.gov/2009/pdf/E9-23519.pdf. Accessed 20 April 2015.
13. *Guidance for Industry and FDA Staff: Application User Fees for Combination Products* (April 2005).

Recommended Reading

- Product Jurisdiction, 21 CFR 3. FDA website. www.accessdata.fda.gov/scripts/cdrh/cfdocs/cfCFR/CFRSearch.cfm?CFRPart=3&showFR=1. Accessed 20 April 2015.

Chapter 28

Products for Small Patient Populations

Updated by Brian E. Harvey, MD, PhD

OBJECTIVES

- ❑ Review laws and regulations for products for small patient populations
- ❑ Recognize orphan products include not only drugs but also biological products, devices and medical foods
- ❑ Learn about US orphan product regulatory history and process, including HUD and HDE process for medical devices
- ❑ Understand differences between patent protection and exclusivity provisions under US law
- ❑ Recognize many countries or regions have their own orphan product regulations, guidelines or policies
- ❑ Learn about the joint parallel orphan product designation application process between the US (FDA) and the EU (EMA)

LAWS, REGULATIONS AND GUIDELINES COVERED IN THIS CHAPTER

- ❑ *Orphan Drug Act* of 1983, Public Law 97-414, 1983 with amendments in 1985 and 1988
- ❑ 21 U.S. Code 360bb(a)(2) Designation of drugs for rare diseases or conditions
- ❑ 21 CFR 316.3(b)(13) Definition of same drug
- ❑ 21 CFR 814.20(b)(10) Proposed labeling and 21 CFR 814.102 Designation of HUD status
- ❑ 21 CFR 814, Subpart H Humanitarian Use Devices
- ❑ 21 CFR 814.104 Original applications

Introduction

Orphan Drug Act

The *Orphan Drug Act* of 1982 (*ODA)* was signed into law (Public Law 97-414)[1] on 4 January 1983 to provide tax incentives and exclusive licensing to encourage manufacturers to develop and market drugs or biologics for diseases affecting relatively few people (fewer than 200,000 in the US). *ODA* defines an "orphan drug" as one developed for a disease or condition that occurs so infrequently in the US there is no reasonable expectation the costs of research, development and marketing would be recovered from sales revenues.[2]

The US Food and Drug Administration's (FDA) Office of Orphan Product Development (OOPD) administers *ODA*'s major provisions, including the Orphan Products Grants Program, which provides funding for clinical research on rare diseases. OOPD also works on rare disease issues with the medical and research communities, professional organizations, academia, government agencies, industry and rare disease patient groups.

Prior to this legislation, private industry had little economic incentive to invest in developing treatments for small patient populations, since the drugs were expected to be unprofitable. The law provides several incentives to promote product development for these orphan populations, including seven-year marketing exclusivity for approved orphan products; a tax credit of 50% of clinical trial costs; and the Orphan Products Grants Program. Marketing exclusivity prevents competition by denying other companies from approval to market the same drug for the same orphan indication.

The original *ODA* required a sponsor to establish a lack of commercial viability. It also expanded the definition of "orphan drugs" to include biological products, antibiotics, medical devices and medical foods.[3] It was amended to clarify the term "rare disease or condition" as any disease or condition in the US affecting:

- fewer than 200,000 people (for vaccines and blood products, the figure of 200,000 or fewer applies to patients receiving the product annually)
- more than 200,000 people and offering no reasonable expectation the drug's development and distribution costs will be recovered from sales[4]

As amended, the act changed the standard for orphan designation from profitability to prevalence. The requirement to show lack of economic viability applies only when prevalence exceeds 200,000. Only one drug has been approved for orphan status under the second criterion and manufacturers rarely attempt to use it because regulation requires FDA to verify unprofitability and examine all relevant financial and sales records.[5]

ODA further states an orphan medical device is one treating "any disease or condition that occurs so infrequently in the US that there is no reasonable expectation that a medical device for such disease or condition will be developed without the assistance" of grants and contracts from OOPD. Similar statements regarding medical foods and biologics are included.

ODA also created an Orphan Products Board within the Department of Health and Human Services (DHHS) to determine policy on orphan product development and to coordinate federal efforts and private sector activities.

ODA's impact has been far-reaching, including 490 drugs for rare diseases, in addition to 60 medical devices approved through the Humanitarian Use Device (HUD) program. A complete listing of Humanitarian Device Exemptions (HDEs) can be found at http://www.fda.gov/MedicalDevices/ProductsandMedicalProcedures/DeviceApprovalsandClearances/HDEApprovals/ucm161827.htm.

Conditions for Orphan Status

To be eligible for orphan status, a product must:

- have a sponsor (i.e., a company, individual, scientific institution or government agency)
- not have been approved previously under a New Drug Application (NDA), Biologics License Application (BLA) or Premarket Approval (PMA) application for the disease or condition for which orphan status is requested
- not be the subject of a marketing application submitted prior to the filing of an orphan designation request

Orphan Drug Designation Application Process

To receive orphan drug designation, the sponsor must first submit an orphan drug designation request to OOPD for the product proposed for a specific rare disease or condition. The request should include:

- description of the rare disease or condition and proposed indication
- description of the product and the scientific rationale (including data available) supporting its use in the disease or condition
- documentation supporting the assertion potential users number fewer than 200,000 in the US

As of April 2015, approximately 3,465 drugs had been granted orphan drug designation. Of these, 490 had received marketing approval. A sponsor may request orphan drug designation at any time during drug development prior to submitting a marketing application. An orphan drug also can have more than one orphan drug designation. Such multiple designations can include:

- same drug with different indications sponsored by the same company
- identical or different drugs with same indications sponsored by different companies

For example, Interferon has six designations for cancer or viral infections, and Interferon Alfa-2b has 10 designations. Similarly, there may be multiple designations for the same orphan indication.

Until recently, FDA decided on a case-by-case basis whether two drugs were different to determine marketing exclusivity. A case involving a human growth hormone and a slight variation of the same product resulted in regulations promulgated in 1992 to use structural similarity to create a presumption of "sameness" between two drugs.[7]

Typically, orphan designation applies to the active ingredient only. However, if superiority is expected or demonstrated, uniqueness is presumed. For example, if a product with an active ingredient has been approved for an orphan indication, another orphan designation with the same active ingredient but a different formulation still can be requested only when the different formulation is believed to be "clinically superior" to the approved product in effectiveness, safety or providing a major contribution to patient care. Therefore, to break orphan exclusivity before the first orphan drug's marketing exclusivity expires, the subsequent entry needs to demonstrate "clinical superiority" if the two products are to be considered the same.

Orphan Drug Designation Annual Reports (21 CFR 316.30)

Within 14 months after the date on which a drug was granted orphan designation and annually thereafter until marketing approval, the designated drug's sponsor shall submit a brief progress report (21 CFR 316.30) to OOPD that includes:

- short account of the drug development progress, including a review of preclinical and clinical studies initiated, ongoing and completed, and a short summary of such studies' results status or results
- description of the coming year's investigational plan, as well as any anticipated development, testing or marketing difficulties
- brief discussion of any changes that may affect the product's orphan drug status (For example, sponsors of products nearing the end of the approval process should discuss any disparity between the probable marketing indication and the designated indication as related to the need for an amendment to the orphan drug designation pursuant to 21 CFR 316.26.)

Regulatory and Financial Incentives for Orphan Drugs

The sponsor may be eligible for the following incentives for a product with US orphan drug designation:

- FDA protocol assistance
- 50% federal tax credit for qualified clinical testing expenses (Under the tax-credit provision, no credit is allowed for clinical testing conducted outside the US, unless there is an insufficient patient population available for testing within the US.)
- *Pediatric Research Equity Act* (*PREA*) requirements exemption
- *Prescription Drug User Fee Act* (*PDUFA*) fee waiver for marketing application
- research grants from OOPD to support clinical studies to develop orphan drugs

FDA Protocol Assistance

ODA Section 525 provides for formal protocol assistance when requested by orphan drug sponsors. Formal review of such a request is the direct responsibility of the Center for Drug Evaluation and Research (CDER) or the Center for Biologics Evaluation and Research (CBER), whichever has jurisdiction for the product's review. OOPD is responsible for ensuring the request qualifies for consideration under Section 525 of the *Federal Food, Drug, and Cosmetic Act* (*FD&C Act*). FDA utilizes these meetings to guide the sponsor to ensure studies are designed properly to meet regulatory requirements.

The Orphan Products Grants Program

OOPD funds the development of qualifying orphan products through its clinical study grants program, which announces fund availability in the *Federal Register*. Eligibility for grant funding is extended to drugs, medical devices and medical foods for which there are no reasonable expectation of development without such assistance. An orphan designation for a drug does not guarantee a research grant will be awarded. Grant applications, submitted in response to a Request for Application (RFA), are reviewed by panels of outside experts and funded by priority score. The grant program is very competitive and only about 30% of applicants receive funding each year. Any organization, whether domestic or foreign, public or private, or profit or nonprofit, is eligible to apply for a grant. Small businesses are encouraged to apply as well. Although rare, large pharmaceutical companies have qualified for some grants.

Applications first are reviewed by OOPD program staff for relevance and responsiveness to the RFA. Responsive applications are reviewed and evaluated for scientific and technical merit by an *ad hoc* expert panel. A national advisory council conducts a second review for concurrence with the initial review group's recommendations. Rank-ordered priority scores determine the final awards.

OOPD plans to facilitate orphan drugs further by:[6]

- developing a simplified application based entirely on the prevalence requirement and the proposed product's rationale (Is there reason to believe this is a promising drug that can be expected to be effective against the proposed rare disease or condition?) and working to revise current regulations and ways of dividing patients with a specific disease or disorder into credible subsets acceptable to OOPD (What is the acceptable medical rationale for a particular disease?)
- addressing study design for small clinical trials, which are appropriate for small patient populations
- informing policymakers of the grant program's success ($14 million awarded per year); greater awareness might lead to an increase in the grant budget, which has not changed in recent years

Common Mistakes in Requesting Orphan Drug Designation

Depending on the rare condition or disease type, applicants requesting orphan designation tend to make the following mistakes in attempting to meet orphan designation requirements:

- dividing a subset of patients with a common disease condition, which is not justified medically

- orphan requests with words such as severe, refractory, metastatic, late-stage, acute or chronic that may raise questions on subset issues
- erroneously using disease or condition incidence instead of prevalence when incidence does not apply
- inadequate scientific rationale to support the product's use for the proposed indication

Population Increase and Its Impact on Orphan Drug Status

In general, if orphan drug status was granted for treatment of a disease or condition estimated to affect fewer than 200,000 people in the US, the drug designation status holds. This can be illustrated by multiple sclerosis (MS). Although MS no longer is considered a rare disease because its prevalence now is known to exceed 250,000 in the US, orphan drug regulations regarding marketing exclusivity still apply to the beta-interferons, since they were granted orphan drug status for MS treatment at a time when the disease was estimated to affect fewer than 200,000 in the US.

Public Knowledge of Orphan Drug Designations

Once a drug or biologic receives orphan designation, the following information is available from OOPD's website (www.accessdata.fda.gov/scripts/opdlisting/oopd/index.cfm): drug chemical name, trade name, date of designation and proposed indication, sponsor name, address and contact information and, if applicable, approved indication and marketing exclusivity date (typically, the date of NDA or BLA approval). The scientific rationale used to define a medically plausible patient subset is not revealed.

After the designated orphan product receives FDA marketing approval, however, additional product and application information, including a copy of the written review conducted by the FDA OOPD officer, can be requested through the *Freedom of Information Act* (*FOIA*).

Pharmacogenomics, Disease Stratification and Potential Orphan Status

Genetic profiling techniques could benefit drug development and clinical testing, by allowing subjects to be included in or excluded from certain clinical trials. Screening subjects with pharmacogenomic approaches potentially could indicate whether the drug is effective, ineffective or unsuitable for an individual. This methodology also opens the door to including selected subjects in a clinical trial, provided they are screened for a known genetic diversity or genetic composition. This is patient stratification and could make clinical trials smaller, faster and more cost-effective. When a pharmacogenomic approach is effective, it has the potential to reduce overall drug development costs. Disease stratification consequences could create a much smaller market for an individual drug that may reach "orphan" levels. As the field expands, and the understanding of disease stratification deepens, it may be possible to stratify the patient population for a certain disease into a smaller subset reaching orphan levels, based on genetic variants.

ODA has been very successful, resulting in new drugs for more than 200 rare diseases, and FDA actively encourages drug companies to pursue pharmacogenomic approaches to more of the 7,000 remaining rare diseases identified by NIH.[7] However, continued advancements in pharmacogenomics could change current disease classification schemes drastically as well as basic assumptions about what constitutes a rare disease.[8,9] Diverse rare diseases may turn out to share molecular genetic disease processes amenable to the same drug. Additional indications for the drug driven by a common set of genes likely will be found. In the future, an increased understanding of these mechanisms could lead to a redefinition of rare disease.[10]

Exclusivity and Patents

Another amendment to the act changed the exclusivity provision and made orphan status available to both patentable and unpatentable drugs.[11] The 1985 amendment extended exclusivity to orphan drugs having either of two characteristics:

1. no use or product patent issued
2. no use patent issued and an expired product patent

The biotechnology industry, where some products have taken as long as four to six years to receive patent approval, while the approval of others are delayed by legal challenges, has benefited from the exclusivity provision. Biotechnology drugs with orphan status may use the seven-year exclusivity provision as a surrogate patent. The *Food and Drug Administration Modernization Act* of 1997 (*FDAMA*)[12] extended exclusivity an additional six months for orphan drugs for a pediatric indication.

There are, however, important differences between patent protection and *ODA*'s seven-year exclusivity provision. The seven years of marketing exclusivity for patented products run concurrently with any outstanding patent(s). Further, the protected use is for the rare disease approved only. Patent protection is broader; a product patent covers an active ingredient and all its uses. A second company cannot receive approval for any use of the active ingredient until the patent has expired. Use patents and process patents similarly provide broad protection. Exclusivity differs from patent protection, which gives the patent holder exclusive rights, regardless of whether patent rights are exercised. Exclusivity provisions, during the seven-year period that begins with the product's approval, permit a second company to receive approval to market the product for a common disease or some other rare one (provided the patent has expired).[13] The sponsor may grant other manufacturers or distributors the privilege of marketing the orphan product; however, a written request for the privilege must be submitted to FDA. A firm can lose its research and development investment while studying an orphan product because a second firm attains market approval first. To minimize these risks, companies may file cross-licensing agreements or shared exclusivity for the same or different indications. If a sponsor fails to make adequate quantities of the orphan product available, it may lose exclusivity. The sponsor also may relinquish orphan drug status, as with the AIDS drug didanosine (DDI).

Under the new biosimilar legislation, the *Biologics Price Competition and Innovation Act* of 2009 (*BPCIA*),[14] enacted on 23 March 2010, biologic orphan drugs now are granted protection for 12 years of market exclusivity concurrent with four years of market data exclusivity.

Postmarketing Approval Conditions

Once an orphan product is on the market, there are no constraints against a physician prescribing it to treat other diseases. The drug may have a market much broader than the approved orphan indication, although the sponsor must advertise the product only in compliance with the approved rare indication(s).[15] Also, the seven-year market exclusivity immunizes the sponsor from market competition and provides no price controls. Finally, a company can divide a projected market of more than 200,000 patients into several subsets and attempt to achieve orphan approvals for each indication. FDA scrutinizes orphan drug applications for evidence of "arbitrary subsets" (medically implausible) and can impose penalties, including revoking orphan drug status. Although many legislative attempts have tried to close *ODA* loopholes (e.g., by capping profits), none has become law.

In recent years, orphan drug development has become a focus not only of organizations such as the National Organization of Rare Disorders (NORD),[16] the Pharmaceutical Research and Manufacturers of America's (PhRMA) Commission on Drugs for Rare Diseases and rare disease patient advocacy groups, but also an area of interest for an increasing number of pharmaceutical companies entering due to the incentives provided and decreasing productivity in other traditional therapeutic areas.

Orphan Drugs Globally

The impact of the *Orphan Drug Act* on the international stage has been significant. Japan adopted an orphan drug regulation in 1993 (offering 10 years of data exclusivity), followed by Australia in 1997 with an orphan drug policy (offering five years of marketing exclusivity, similar to other drugs), and the EU in 2000. Even some emerging markets, such as Brazil, Mexico, Russia, Singapore, South Korea and Taiwan, have partial orphan drug policies.

European Union (EU)

In 2000, the EU passed its first legislation specifically for orphan drugs, Regulation (EC) 141/2000 of the European Parliament and the Council on orphan medicinal products.[17,18]

Under the EU *Orphan Medicinal Product Regulation*, a rare disease is defined as affecting no more than five in 10,000 people in the community. The legislation offers protocol assistance, 10 years of market exclusivity and financial incentives (fee reduction or exemptions).[19,20]

The legislation is overseen by the European Medicines Agency (EMA), which has the authority to award orphan status and also approves drugs for marketing. However, each Member State is responsible for making the drug available and dealing with reimbursement issues.

EMA's Committee for Orphan Medicinal Products examines all orphan designation applications and advises the European Commission on the establishment and development of policies on orphan medicinal products in the EU, as well as drawing up detailed guidelines and working internationally on matters relating to orphan medicinal products.

Common US-EU Orphan Drug Designation Application and Orphan Annual Report

In recent years, regulatory agencies have increased their collaborative efforts significantly in achieving global harmonization, one example being the introduction of a common US-EU orphan drug designation application. If a sponsor wishes to submit orphan drug designation applications for the same product for the same indication in both the US and the EU, it may use the "Common EMA/FDA Application Form for Orphan Medicinal Product Designation" in conjunction with other supporting documents.

Subsequently, on 26 February 2010, FDA and EMA released in the International Collaboration Announcement[21] that both agencies now allow a single orphan annual report for products designated in both the US and the EU. Orphan Annual Reports can be submitted either on World Rare Disease Day (last day of February) or the normal US or EU annual reporting date.

According to FDA's website, "there have been some changes in 21 CFR 316.20(b) Content and format of a request for orphan-drug designation. The Common EMEA/FDA Application for Orphan Medicinal Product Designation form/template has not yet been revised to reflect this change**.** Please see 21 CFR 316.20(b) for these changes" (http://www.fda.gov/ForIndustry/DevelopingProductsforRareDiseasesConditions/HowtoapplyforOrphanProductDesignation/ucm124795.htm).

Of interest, the most substantive change in the process is FDA no longer requires a statement of party of interest for an orphan drug designation (page 9 of 10). It is understood that until this change is made, sponsors can leave the Statement of Party of Interest section blank.

Humanitarian Device Exemptions

History

Although the *Orphan Drug Act* does not mention medical devices specifically, the *Safe Medical Devices Act* of 1990 (*SMDA*) includes orphan medical devices. In 1996, FDA promulgated a final rule describing the orphan devices process, subsequently codified in 21 CFR 814, Subpart H.13.22. OOPD is responsible for granting orphan designation to devices known as humanitarian use devices (HUDs), which must meet the following criteria:

- device treats or diagnoses a disease in fewer than 4,000 patients per year in the US
- no comparable FDA-approved therapy exists for the proposed indication
- evidence is provided the applicant could not otherwise bring the device to market

Incentives to manufacturers for developing HUDs are identical to those for developing orphan drugs.

Process

The Humanitarian Device Exemption (HDE) process[22,23] involves two steps:

1. The applicant must request and obtain HUD designation from OOPD. The application's required contents are outlined in 21 CFR 814.102. Among other requirements, the application must define the proposed indication for use precisely. If the applicant proposes using the device for a limited subset of a larger group of patients suffering from a more common disease or condition, the application must contain evidence the subset is medically plausible and justify the proposed limitation. The application also must document, with appended authoritative references, the rare disease affects fewer than 4,000 individuals per year in the US. Upon receipt of the application, OOPD has 75 days to approve or deny the HUD request under 21 CFR 814.114. A 30-day filing period is included in the 75 days. After initial review to determine the package's completeness, OOPD can ask the applicant to provide more information. At this time, the clock stops and resets when FDA receives the requested information.
2. Once the applicant receives HUD designation, it must submit an HDE application to the Office of Device Evaluation (ODE) at the Center for Devices and Radiological Health (CDRH). HDE application contents are set forth in 21 CFR 814.104. The application's purpose is to assist ODE reviewers in understanding why the device deserves HDE designation. One major difference between a PMA and an HDE application is the HDE is exempt from PMA effectiveness requirements, unless specifically requested by FDA. Otherwise, effectiveness would be required under *FD&C Act* Sections 514 and 515. However, the application must contain an explanation of probable device benefits and demonstrate those "probable benefits" outweigh the risk of injury or illness from use. If the device's intended price is more than $250, the HDE application must include verification the amount charged does not exceed the research, development, fabrication and distribution costs per either of two statements:
   - report by a certified public accountant
   - attestation by a responsible individual of the applicant organization

FDA makes a threshold determination as to whether the HDE application is sufficiently complete to permit substantive review. The agency can refuse to file for any of four reasons:

1. application is incomplete
2. comparable device already is available to treat or diagnose the disease or condition
3. application contains an untrue statement or omits material information
4. HDE lacks a statement of certification or disclosure, or both, as required by 21 CFR 54

ODE has 75 days to review the application and send the applicant an approval order, an approvable letter, a nonapprovable letter or an order denying approval.

Labeling

HDE labeling requirements match those for PMA-approved devices in 21 CFR 814.20(b)(10). In addition, an approved HDE's labeling must bear the following statement: "Humanitarian Device. Authorized by Federal law for use in the treatment [or diagnosis] of [specify disease or condition]. The effectiveness of this device for this use has not been demonstrated."

Distribution

The HDE holder is responsible for ensuring an HUD is administered only at hospitals or institutions with an Institutional Review Board (IRB) constituted and acting in accordance with 21 CFR 56. The HUD's initial use must be approved by the IRB, and the IRB must provide continuing oversight of the HUD's use. The IRB does not have to review and approve each individual HUD use. Instead, the IRB may approve the device's use in general for groups of patients meeting certain criteria or for devices under a treatment protocol. The IRB may specify limitations on the device's use based on any criterion it deems appropriate. Unless the data are intended for use in a clinical investigation, informed consent is not required because an HDE provides temporary marketing approval and does not constitute research or an investigation.

Additional Indication(s)

Once an HUD is approved, the applicant may seek different indications for use by requesting and obtaining HUD designation and filing a new, original HDE for the new indication. The new, original HDE may incorporate any information or data submitted to the agency by reference to the previous HDE.

Quality System

An approved HDE is subject to the same Quality System Regulation (QSR) in 21 CFR 820 and postapproval requirements as a PMA-approved product. The latter may include the following:

- restriction of the device's sale, use and distribution (prescription only)
- Phase 4 studies to evaluate the device's safety, effectiveness and reliability for its intended use; in the HDE-approval order, FDA states the study conditions, which include:
    - o reason or purpose
    - o number of patients to be evaluated
    - o reports required
- prominent display in the labeling (and advertising/promotional materials) of warnings, hazards or precautions important for the device's safe and effective use, including any patient information
- inclusion of identification codes on the device or its labeling
- records pertaining to patient tracing if such information is necessary to protect public health
- maintenance of records for specified periods of time and records organization and indexing into identifiable files to enable FDA to determine whether there is reasonable assurance of the device's safety or effectiveness
- periodic reports in accordance with the HDE approval order, the contents of which are described in 21 CFR 814.126(b)(1)
- batch testing of the device
- Medical Device Reports (MDRs) submitted to FDA in compliance with 21 CFR 803 (also should be submitted to the IRB of record)
- records of the facility names and addresses to which the HUD has been shipped and all correspondence with reviewing IRBs

Revocation

Once FDA approves a PMA or clears a 510(k) for treating (or diagnosing) the same disease or condition, the HDE can be revoked by FDA.

Misbranding

The HDE holder can promote the device only to the target patient population for the indicated HDE use. Promotion to groups other than the target population constitutes misbranding. In addition, an HDE holder cannot imply that its device is effective for the indicated use because there is no requirement to submit clinical effectiveness data in the HDE. Through 51 March 2015, 63 devices had been approved under the HDE program.

Summary

- Many regulatory agencies around the world attempt to incentivize orphan drug, biological product and humanitarian medical device development.
- Patients with rare diseases are benefiting from having access to orphan drugs, biologics and humanitarian devices.

References

1. *Orphan Drug Act*, Public Law 97-414, 4 January 1983. FDA website. www.fda.gov/regulatoryinformation/legislation/federalfooddrugand-cosmeticactfdcact/significantamendmentstothefdcact/orphandrugact/default.htm. Accessed 4 June 2015.
2. Ibid.
3. *Orphan Drug Amendments* of 1988, Public Law 100-290, 18 April 1988. GPO website. www.gpo.gov/fdsys/pkg/STATUTE-102/pdf/STATUTE-102-Pg90.pdf. Accessed 4 June 2015.
4. *Health Promotion and Disease Prevention Amendments* of 1984, Public Law No. 98–551, 30 October 1984). NIH website. http://history.nih.gov/research/downloads/PL98-551.pdf. Accessed 4 June 2015.
5. Op cit 1.
6. Tankosic T. "Orphan Drug Development: commercial strategies flourish." *SCRIP* "Drug Market Developments," 2008; 19(5)
7. The Office of Rare Diseases at the NIH maintains a list of rare diseases and conditions on its website. http://rarediseases.info.nih.gov/. Accessed 4 June 2015.
8. Maher PD and Haffner M. "Orphan Drug Designation and Pharmacogenomics: Options and Opportunities." *BioDrugs*, 20, no. 2 (2006): pp. 71–79.
9. Shah J. "Economic and regulatory considerations in pharmacogenomics for drug licensing and healthcare." *Nature Biotechnology*, 21, no. 7 (July 2003): pp. 747–753.
10. Tucker L. "Pharmacogenomics: A Primer for Policymakers" National Health Policy Forum, Background Paper, 28 January 2008.
11. *Orphan Drug Amendments* of 1985, Public Law 99-91, 99, 15 August 1985. NIH website. http://history.nih.gov/research/downloads/PL99-91.pdf . Accessed 4 June 2015.
12. *Food and Drug Administration Modernization Act* of 1997. FDA website. www.fda.gov/RegulatoryInformation/Legislation/FederalFoodDrugandCosmeticActFDCAct/SignificantAmendmentstotheFDCAct/FDAMA/. Accessed 4 June 2015.
13. Op cit 11.
14. *Biologics Price Competition and Innovation Act of* 2009. FDA website. www.fda.gov/downloads/drugs/guidancecomplianceregulatoryinformation/ucm216146.pdf. Accessed 4 June 2015.

15. 21 CFR 312.2.
16. Myers AS. "Orphan Drugs: The Current Situation in the United States, Europe and Asia." *Drug Information Journal* 31 (1997): 101–104.
17. Regulation (EC) 141/2000 of the European Parliament and of the Council of 16 December 1999 on orphan medicinal products. EUR-Lex website. http://ec.europa.eu/health/files/eudralex/vol-1/reg_2000_141_cons-2009-07/reg_2000_141_cons-2009-07_en.pdf. Accessed 4 June 2015.
18. Commission Regulation (EC) 847/2000 of 27 April 2000 laying down the provisions for implementation of the criteria for designation of a medicinal product as an orphan medicinal product and definitions of the concepts "similar medicinal product' and 'clinical superiority." EC website. http://ec.europa.eu/health/files/eudralex/vol-1/reg_2000_847/reg_2000_847_en.pdf. http://ec.europa.eu/health/files/eudralex/vol-1/reg_2000_847/reg_2000_847_en.pdf. Accessed 4 June 2015.
19. *SCRIP* "Drug Market Developments," 2008; 19(5).
20. 21 CFR 814, Subpart H Humanitarian Use Devices. FDA website. www.accessdata.fda.gov/scripts/cdrh/cfdocs/cfcfr/CFRSearch.cfm?CFRPart=814&showFR=1&subpartNode=21:8.0.1.1.11.7. Accessed 4 June 2015.
21. FDA news release: "International Collaboration: FDA and European Medicines Agency Agree to Accept a Single Orphan Drug Designation Annual Report," 26 February 2010. FDA website. www.fda.gov/NewsEvents/Newsroom/PressAnnouncements/ucm202300.htm. Accessed 4 June 2015.
22. FDA. "Final Rule: Medical Devices; Humanitarian Use of Devices," *Federal Register* 61:33232. (1996).
23. FDA. "Final Rule: Medical Devices; Humanitarian Use of Devices," *Federal Register* 63:59222 (1998).

Recommended Reading

Carter MJ and Bennett AR. "Developments in Orphan Drugs." *Food, Drug, Cosmetic Law Journal* 44 (1989): 627–632.

Clissold DB. "Prescription for the Orphan Drug Act: The Impact of the FDA's 1992 Regulations and the Latest Congressional Proposals for Reform." *Food and Drug Law Journal* 50 (1995): 125–147.

Finke MJ. "Orphan Products and the Pharmaceutical Industry." *Clinical Research Practices and Drug Regulatory Affairs* (1983): 19–25.

Grossman DB. "The Orphan Drug Act: Adoption or Foster Care." *Food, Drug, Cosmetic Law Journal* 39 (1984): 128–132.

Henkel J. "Orphan Products: New Hope for People With Rare Disorders." *FDA Consumer* (18 June 1994): 17–20.

Levitt JA and Kelsey JV. "The Orphan Drug Regulations and Related Issues." *Food and Drug Law Journal* 48 (1993): 526–530.

Sasinowski, Frank J. "Quantum of Effectiveness Evidence in FDA's Approval of Orphan Drugs." *Therapeutic Innovation and Regulatory Science* 03/2012; 46(2):238-263.

Shah J. "Economic and regulatory considerations in pharmacogenomics for drug licensing and healthcare." 2003 Nature Publishing Group, http://www.nature.com/naturebiotechnology

Shulman SR et. al. "Implementation of the Orphan Drug Act: 1983–1991." *Food and Drug Law Journal* 47 (1992): 363–401.

Tucker L. "Pharmacogenomics: A Primer for Policymakers." National Health Policy Forum, Background Paper, 28 January 2008.

Woodcock J. "The future of orphan drug development." *Clin Pharmacol Ther*. 2012;92(2):146-148.

Chapter 29

Blood and Blood Products

Updated by Jennifer Wilhelm, MSc, MBA, RAC

OBJECTIVES

- ❑ Understand FDA strategies to protect the blood supply and the "five layer approach"
- ❑ Understand licensing requirements for a new blood product and the Advisory Committees employed by FDA for blood and blood products
- ❑ Understand labeling requirements for blood and blood products, including the Circular of Information and barcode labeling
- ❑ Understand requirements for establishments with registration, inspection and "lookback" procedures

LAWS, REGULATIONS AND GUIDELINES COVERED IN THIS CHAPTER

- ❑ *Public Health Service Act* of 1944, Section 351
- ❑ *Federal Food, Drug, and Cosmetic Act* of 1938
- ❑ 21 CFR 600 Biological Products: General
- ❑ 21 CFR 601 Licensing Requirements
- ❑ 21 CFR 606 Current Good Manufacturing Practice for Blood and Blood Components
- ❑ 21 CFR 607 Establishment Registration and Product Listing For Manufacturers of Human Blood and Blood Products
- ❑ 21 CFR 630 General Requirements for Blood, Blood Components and Blood Derivatives
- ❑ 21 CFR 640 Additional Standards for Human Blood and Blood Products
- ❑ *Draft Guidance for Industry: Bacterial Detection Testing by Blood and Blood Collection Establishments and Transfusion Services to Enhance the Safety and Availability of Platelets for Transfusion* (December 2014)
- ❑ *Guidance for Industry: Changes to an Approved Application: Biological Products: Human Blood and Blood Components Intended for Transfusion or for Further Manufacture* (November 2014)
- ❑ *Guidance for Industry: Recommendations for Screening Testing, and Management of Blood Donors and Blood and Blood Components Based on Screening Test for Syphilis* (September 2014)
- ❑ *Guidance for Industry: Recommendations for Donor Questioning, Deferral, Reentry and Product Management to Reduce the Risk of Transfusion-Transmitted Malaria* (August 2014)
- ❑ *Guidance for Industry: Recognition and Use of a Standard for Uniform Blood and Blood Final Component Container Labels* (June 2014)

- ❑ *Guidance for Industry: Circular of Information for the Use of Human Blood and Blood Components* (April 2014)
- ❑ *Guidance for Industry: Implementation of an Acceptable Abbreviated Donor History Questionnaire and Accompanying Materials for Use in Screening Frequent Donors of Blood and Blood Components* (May 2013)
- ❑ *Guidance for Industry: Blood Establishment Computer System Validation in the User's Facility* (April 2013)
- ❑ *Guidance for Industry: Implementation of Acceptable Full-Length and Abbreviated Donor History Questionnaires and Accompanying Materials for Use in Screening Donors of Source Plasma* (February 2013)
- ❑ *Guidance for Industry: Use of Nucleic Acid Tests on Pooled and Individual Samples from Donors of Whole Blood and Blood Components, Including Source Plasma, to Reduce the Risk of Transmission of Hepatitis B Virus* (October 2012)
- ❑ *Guidance for Industry: Amendment to "Guidance for Industry: Revised Preventive Measures to Reduce the Possible Risk of Transmission of Creutzfeldt-Jakob Disease and Variant Creutzfeldt-Jakob Disease by Blood and Blood Products* (June 2012)
- ❑ *Guidance for Industry: Availability of FDA's eSubmitter Program for Regulatory Submissions from Licensed Blood Establishments* (August 2011)
- ❑ *Guidance for Industry: Donors of Blood and Blood Components: Notification of Donor Deferral - Small Entity Compliance Guide* (June 2011)
- ❑ *Guidance for Industry: "Lookback" for Hepatitis C Virus (HCV): Product Quarantine, Consignee Notification, Further Testing, Product Disposition, and Notification of Transfusion Recipients Based on Donor Test Results Indicating Infection with HCV* (December 2010)
- ❑ *Guidance for Industry: Use of Serological Tests to Reduce the Risk of Transmission of Trypanosoma cruzi Infection in Whole Blood and Blood Components Intended for Transfusion* (December 2010)
- ❑ *Guidance for Industry: Recommendations for Blood Establishments: Training of Back-Up Personnel, Assessment of Donor Suitability and Reporting Certain Changes to an Approved Application* (November 2010)
- ❑ *Guidance for Industry: Revised Preventative Measures to Reduce the Possible Risk of Transmission of Creutzfeldt Jakob Disease (CJD) and Variant Creutzfeldt-Jakob Disease (vCJD) by Blood and Blood Products* (May 2010)
- ❑ *Guidance for Industry: Nucleic Acid Testing (NAT) for Human Immunodeficiency Virus Type 1 (HIV-1) and Hepatitis C Virus (HCV): Testing, Product Disposition, Donor Deferral and Reentry* (May 2010)
- ❑ *Guidance for Industry: Use of Nucleic Acid Tests to Reduce the Risk of Transmission of West Nile Virus from Donors of Whole Blood and Blood Components Intended for Transfusion* (November 2009)
- ❑ *Guidance for Industry: Recommendations for Management of Donors at Increased Risk for Human Immunodeficiency Virus Type 1 (HIV-1) Group O infection* (August 2009)
- ❑ *Guidance for Industry: Adequate and Appropriate Donor Screening Tests for Hepatitis B; Hepatitis B Surface Antigen (HBsAg) Assays Used to Test Donors of Whole Blood and Blood Components, Including Source Plasma and Source Leukocytes* (November 2007)
- ❑ *Guidance for Industry: Biological Product Deviation Reporting for Blood and Plasma Establishments* (October 2006)
- ❑ *Guidance for Industry: Notifying FDA of Fatalities Related to Blood Collection or Transfusion* (September 2003)
- ❑ *Guidance for Industry: Revised Recommendations for the Assessment of Donor Suitability and Blood Product Safety in Cases of Suspected Severe Acute Respiratory Syndrome (SARS) or Exposure to SARS* (September 2003)
- ❑ *Guidance for Industry: Recommendations for Deferral of Donors and Quarantine and Retrieval of Blood and Blood Products in Recent Recipients of Smallpox Vaccine (Vaccinia Virus)*

and Certain Contacts of Smallpox Vaccine Recipients (December 2002)

- ❑ *Guidance for Industry: Recommendations for Assessment of Donor Suitability and Blood and Blood Product Safety in Cases of Possible Exposure to Anthrax* (October 2001)
- ❑ *Guidance for Industry For the Submission of Chemistry, Manufacturing and Controls and Establishment Description Information for Human Blood and Blood Components Intended for Transfusion or for Further Manufacture and For the Completion of the Form FDA 356h "Application to Market a New Drug, Biologic or an Antibiotic Drug for Human Use"* (May 1999)
- ❑ *Guidance for Industry: For the Submission of Chemistry, Manufacturing and Controls and Establishment Description Information for Human Plasma-Derived Biological Products, Animal Plasma or Serum-Derived Products* (February 1999)

Introduction

The US Food and Drug Administration (FDA) is responsible for ensuring the safety of the US blood supply. Blood and blood products are considered biological products under Section 351(a) of the *Public Health Service Act* (*PHS Act*), and blood and blood components are also drugs or devices subject to regulation under the *Federal Food, Drug, and Cosmetic Act* (*FD&C Act*). The Center for Biologics Evaluation and Research (CBER) within FDA regulates the collection of blood and blood components and establishes standards for blood products used for transfusion or for the manufacture of pharmaceuticals derived from blood components. CBER also regulates related products such as cell separation devices, blood collection containers and Human Immunodeficiency Virus (HIV) screening tests, and enforces quality standards, inspects blood establishments and monitors reports of errors, accidents and adverse clinical events.

Strategies to Protect the Blood Supply

Since the documentation of HIV infection resulting from blood transfusion beginning in 1982,[1] FDA has implemented comprehensive measures to prevent the introduction, transmission or spread of communicable disease through the blood supply. FDA has focused on ensuring the safety of blood and blood products by advocating the use of new technologies, standards, guidelines and strategies to minimize the risk of consumer exposure to unsafe products. In 1995, the Institute of Medicine released its report, "HIV and the Blood Supply," an analysis of decisions and actions on blood related to the AIDS crisis.[2] FDA responded to the criticisms contained in the report and, in 1997, initiated the Blood Action Plan.[3]

Blood Action Plan: Five Layer Approach

FDA's efforts to improve and promote the safety of blood and blood products through the Blood Action Plan, leveraging technology and science, has resulted in a key systematic program. This program has a "five layer" approach to ensure the safety of the blood supply and products derived from blood or blood components, including: 1) donor suitability standards; 2) donor deferral lists; 3) testing blood for communicable disease agents; 4) quarantining unsuitable blood and blood components; and 5) monitoring establishments for problems and deficiencies. These five layers overlap to create a seamless safety system, from the initial collection of blood from the donor center though processing and distribution to the recipient.

Donor Screening and Suitability Standards

Potential donors must answer questions about their health and risk factors because transmission of HIV and other blood-borne viruses can occur during transfusion of blood components (e.g., whole blood, packed red cells, fresh-frozen plasma, cryoprecipitate and platelets) derived from the blood of an infected individual. Donor screening establishes a donor's eligibility to donate blood and blood components by documenting the individual is free of any diseases transmissible by blood transfusion. This process must be done on the day of the donation (21 CFR 640.3(a) and 640.63(a)).

After completing the questionnaire at the donation site, potential donors are interviewed by a trained healthcare professional about their medical histories and given physical examinations. Donors may be deferred temporarily from donating blood for what may seem to be minor illnesses, such as a fever, cold, cough or sore throat, or if they are taking certain drugs. These precautions are necessary to prevent any unintentional disease transmission. Once donors have recovered and show no symptoms of the minor illness, they may donate. Donors also may be deferred permanently, either indefinitely or for a specified period of time. In addition, reasonable attempts must be made to notify donors they have been deferred.

Donor Deferral Lists

All blood donation establishments keep a current list of deferred donors and check donor names against that list each time a person offers to donate. Any person whose name appears on the list may not donate. These lists are shared among blood donation establishments to ensure an individual who has been identified as a risk for infectious disease transmission cannot avoid detection by going to another establishment.

Blood Testing

The third layer ensuring blood supply safety is testing of each unit of blood collected. Each unit or bag of donor blood must be tested for HIV 1 and 2, hepatitis B, hepatitis C, syphilis, human T-lymphotropic virus (HTLV) Types I and II and West Nile virus. In some situations, testing for CMV (cytomegalovirus) also may be performed, and testing for antibodies to *Trypanosoma cruzi* must be performed at least once for each blood donor. Any donor who is positive for one of these diagnostic tests will be placed on a deferred donor list, and the unit collected will be destroyed.

Quarantining

Blood products collected must be stored appropriately and not released for use until all testing has been completed and the information checked for accuracy. Whenever a donor has repeated reactive screening tests for HBsAg, anti-HBc, anti-HCV or anti-HTLV-I, blood establishments should identify and quarantine promptly, within 72 hours if possible, within-date blood and blood components in inventory from prior collections, extending back five years. For such a donor, where there is a record available of the donor's last negative test results from a licensed screening test, quarantine of prior collections should extend back only to 12 months before such a test. In addition, blood establishments should request consignees of such products to immediately quarantine all previously distributed products extending back five years or 12 months before the donor's last negative test results from licensed serological tests. Quarantined units should be destroyed or appropriately labeled as either 1) "biohazard" and "Not for use for transfusion or further manufacturing into injectable products," in the case of products originating from donors who subsequently have repeatedly reactive test results for HBsAg or anti-HCV, or 2) "biohazard" and "Not for use for transfusion," in the case of products originating from donors who subsequently have repeatedly reactive test results for anti-HBc or anti-HTLV-I.

Problems and Deficiencies

Finally, blood establishments must investigate any deviations where the safeguards cited in the other four layers of the five layer approach were ineffective and correct system deficiencies that allowed the failure to occur. Licensed establishments must report to FDA any manufacturing problems, errors or accidents that may affect the distributed finished product's safety, purity or potency using a Biological Product Deviation Report (BPDR). A manufacturer is required to report to CBER's Office of Compliance and Biologics Quality (OCBQ) as soon as possible, but not to exceed 45 calendar days from the date of discovery, of information reasonably suggesting a reportable event has occurred. To facilitate reporting, FDA has developed a standardized reporting format that may be used for electronic or hard copy submissions. Directions for completing and mailing the forms are provided by CBER and can be accessed at www.fda.gov/downloads/AboutFDA/ReportsManualsForms/Forms/UCM061463.pdf.

Licensing and Labeling Requirements

Registration and Licensing Applications

Under 21 CFR 607, all owners or operators of establishments engaged in manufacturing blood products are required to register, and applicants also must hold an approved license to distribute product across state lines. Blood components and associated products may be licensed under various pathways. CBER's Office of Blood Research and Review (OBRR) reviews several different types of regulatory applications for blood and blood components, including Biologics License Applications (BLAs). The Center for Drug Evaluation and Research (CDER) reviews NDA applications such as those involving solutions used for collecting blood and anticoagulants. Devices associated with blood donor testing require Premarket Approval Applications (PMAs), while devices used by the blood banking industry, including blood establishment computer software, transfer devices, collection systems, separators, culture bottles and fluid warmers, require 510(k) submissions, both to the Center for Devices and Radiological Health (CDRH).

Novel blood and biologic product licensing under the *PHS Act* is similar to the new drug approval process for prescription drugs. Following preclinical testing, a new blood product is studied in human clinical trials under an Investigational New Drug (IND) Application. If the data generated demonstrate the product is safe and effective for its intended use, a BLA may be submitted to CBER for review and marketing approval. The BLA will contain quality and establishment information specific to blood products and may be submitted electronically per *Guidance for Industry For the Submission of Chemistry, Manufacturing and Controls and Establishment Description Information for Human Blood and Blood Components Intended for Transfusion or for Further Manufacture and For the Completion of the Form FDA 356h "Application to Market a New Drug, Biologic or an Antibiotic Drug for Human Use"* and *Guidance for Industry: Availability of FDA's eSubmitter Program for Regulatory Submissions from Licensed Blood Establishments.*

Advisory Committees

Three Advisory Committees are associated with blood products. The Blood Products Advisory Committee (BPAC) reviews and evaluates available data concerning blood products' safety, effectiveness and appropriate use and advises the commissioner of food and drugs of its findings.[4] The Transmissible Spongiform Encephalopathies Advisory Committee (TSEAC) advises the commissioner in discharging responsibilities related to helping ensure safe and effective products.[5] This committee specifically focuses on the safety of products possibly at risk for transmission of spongiform encephalopathies having an impact on the public health. A third committee, the Advisory Committee on Blood and Tissue Safety and Availability (ACBTSA), is overseen by the Department of Health and Human Services (DHHS). This committee provides advice to the secretary and assistant secretary for health regarding research initiatives on diseases involving blood and blood products and on issuing and enforcing regulations concerning the collection, preparation and distribution of these products and regulations related to the transmission of communicable diseases.[6]

Circular of Information

The Circular of Information, essentially the "package insert" for blood products, provides specific labeling instructions for the administration and use of blood and blood components intended for transfusion. *Guidance for Industry: Circular of Information for the Use of Human Blood and Blood Components* recognizes the Circular of Information prepared jointly by the American Association of Blood Banks (AABB), the American Red Cross, America's Blood Centers and the Armed Services Blood Program as acceptable for use and provides the circular to assist in complying with 21 CFR 606.122. The specific product manufacturer's package insert also should be reviewed for instructions pertaining to use of transfusion devices (e.g., filters, blood administration sets).

Barcode Labeling for Blood and Blood Products

The requirement for barcodes on certain products is another step in ensuring blood safety by preventing mistakes in blood product handling. The intent of FDA's barcode rule is to reduce medication errors, including transfusion errors in the hospital setting. The regulation requiring machine-readable barcode labeling for blood and blood components intended for transfusion is 21 CFR 606.121. This requirement applies to all blood establishments that manufacture, process, repack or relabel blood and blood components, including hospital transfusion services that pool or aliquot blood components. Version 3.0.0 of the International Council for Commonality in Blood Banking Automation (ICCBBA) Standard describes a uniform container labeling system for blood and blood components intended for transfusion or for further manufacturing use, and recently has been recognized in CBER guidelines as acceptable to FDA.

Postapproval Changes

If a change is made following BLA approval, it must conform to applicable laws and regulations. Reporting categories for common types of changes are outlined in *Guidance for Industry: Changes to an Approved Application: Biological Products: Human Blood and Blood Components Intended for Transfusion or for Further Manufacture.*

Notification Process for Fatalities

21 CFR 606.170(b) requires facilities notify to CBER's OCBQ as soon as possible after confirming a fatal complication of blood collection or transfusion. The collecting facility is to report donor fatalities, and the compatibility testing facility is to report recipient fatalities. The regulation also requires the reporting facility to submit a report of the investigation within seven days after the fatality. In addition, 21 CFR 640.73 requires notification by telephone as soon as possible if a source plasma donor has a fatal reaction that, in any way, may be associated with plasmapheresis.

Establishment Requirements

Registration

All owners or operators of establishments that manufacture blood products are required to register with FDA, pursuant to Section 510 of the *FD&C Act*, unless they are exempt under 21 CFR 607.65. A list of every blood product manufactured, prepared or processed for commercial distribution must be submitted with the registration documentation. Products must be registered and listed within five days of beginning operation, and annually between 15 November and 31 December. Blood product listings must be updated in June and December each year. Form FDA 2830, Blood Establishment Registration and Product Listing, is used to submit registration and product listing information to the agency.

Computer and Software

A Blood Establishment Computer System includes: computer hardware, computer software, peripheral devices, personnel and documentation. The computer software used includes Blood Establishment Computer Software, which is a medical device. FDA considers a Blood Establishment Computer System to be equipment under 21 CFR 606.60, and automated or electronic equipment under 21 CFR 211.68.

Blood Establishment Computer Software is software designed to be used in a blood establishment and intended for use in the diagnosis of disease or other conditions in donors, or in the prevention of disease in humans by the release of unsuitable blood and blood components. CBER has issued guidance to assist blood establishments in their use of computer systems, *Guidance for Industry: Blood Establishment Computer System Validation in the User's Facility.*

"Lookback" Procedures

All licensed and registered blood establishments must implement "lookback" procedures audited by FDA to ensure they are functional at each inspection. Under a lookback procedure, blood establishments retrieve and quarantine units previously collected from a donor who originally tested negative for HIV or another infectious disease but subsequently tested positive at a later donation. As part of the investigation, the blood establishment will conduct additional testing on a current sample of the donor's blood to confirm the positive result. If the results are confirmed, previously donated units from that individual cannot be used in transfusions or the manufacture of injectable products, and anyone receiving such units must be notified. Further guidance for lookback procedures may be found on the CBER website: *Guidance for Industry: "Lookback" for Hepatitis C Virus (HCV): Product Quarantine, Consignee Notification, Further Testing, Product Disposition, and Notification of Transfusion Recipients Based on Donor Test Results Indicating Infection with HCV.*

Inspection

Under the provisions of Section 351 of the *PHS Act* and the *FD&C Act*, FDA investigators inspect blood establishments, including those that manufacture or participate in the manufacture of blood or blood products.[7,8] The inspections' purpose is to "ensure that blood establishments manufacture biological products that are safe, pure, potent and have the quality they represent and the establishment manufactures them according to Current Good Manufacturing Practice (CGMP) for Blood and Blood Component regulations and applicable standards."

FDA's compliance program takes a system-based approach to achieve the five layers of protection for the blood supply. Systems (with associated layers of protection) are:

- quality assurance system—various planned activities providing confidence all procedures or processes influencing product manufacture and overall quality are monitored to ensure they are working as expected (donor screening, donor deferral, product testing, quarantining, monitoring and investigating problems)
- donor (suitability) eligibility system—protects donor safety, determines a donor's suitability for blood collection, notifies donors of unsuitability for donation and, where acceptable to FDA, permits donor re-entry (donor screening, donor deferral)
- product testing system—tests for communicable diseases, blood grouping and typing and cross-matches blood for transfusion by direct or electronic testing (product testing)
- quarantine/inventory management system—product storage, distribution and retrieval, quarantine and distribution (quarantining)
- production and processing system—process controls in the manufacture of specific blood and blood components and equipment quality control, calibration and maintenance (product testing, quarantining, monitoring and investigating problems)

The inspection of each element should review:

- procedures' accuracy, availability and appropriateness
- adequacy of personnel qualifications, training and number for the operations
- appropriateness of the facility for operations and the adequacy of its maintenance
- equipment maintenance to ensure it will perform as intended
- record maintenance to ensure traceability of steps and that a complete history of work performed is provided

Routine inspections are required by statute and generally occur biennially. They may be conducted at two levels:

- Level 1—comprehensive evaluation of the establishment's compliance
- Level 2—streamlined evaluation of an establishment's compliance when the facility has met a defined standard of performance during past FDA inspections

Conclusion

FDA is responsible for ensuring the safety of the US blood supply and regulates the collection of blood and blood components, such as clotting factors used for transfusion or manufacture of drugs.

- FDA's authority for the review and approval of blood products resides in Section 351 of the *PHS Act*, and the regulation of these products resides under the *FD&C Act*.
- FDA has a "five layer" approach to ensure the safety of the blood supply and products derived from blood or blood components. These five layers overlap from the initial collection of blood at the donor center all the way through to the distributor of a blood product.
- There are specific licensing and labeling requirements for blood products, including the Circular of Information for blood and blood components intended for transfusion, as well as uniform container labels.
- All owners or operators of establishments that manufacture blood products are required to register with FDA, pursuant to Section 510 of the *FD&C Act*, unless they are exempt under 21 CFR 607.65, and routine inspections evaluating systems to achieve the five layers of protection generally occur biennially.

References

1. Peterman TA, Jaffe HW, Feorino PM, Getchell JP, Warfield DT, Haverkos HW, Stoneburner RL, Curran JW. "Transfusion-associated acquired immunodeficiency syndrome in the United States." JAMA. 1985 Nov 22–29;254(20):2913–7.

2. Leveton et al, 1995. HIV and the Blood Supply: An analysis of crisis decision making. Leveton LB, Sox HC and Stoto MA, eds. Institute of Medicine, National Academy Press, Washington, DC, 1995.
3. Freidman, 1997. FDA's Role in Regulating and Protecting the Nation's Blood Supply. Testimony of Lead Deputy Commissioner Michael A. Friedman before the Subcommittee on Human Resources and Intergovernmental Affairs of the House Committee on Government Reform and Oversight. 5 June 1997. FDA website. www.fda.gov/newsevents/ testimony/ucm114940.htm. Accessed 22 January 2015.
4. Blood Products Advisory Committee Charter. FDA website. www.fda.gov/AdvisoryCommittees/CommitteesMeetingMaterials/BloodVaccinesandOtherBiologics/BloodProductsAdvisoryCommittee/ucm121602.htm Accessed 22 January 2015.
5. Transmissible Spongiform Encephalopathies Advisory Committee Charter. FDA website. http://www.fda.gov/AdvisoryCommittees/CommitteesMeetingMaterials/BloodVaccinesandOtherBiologics/TransmissibleSpongiformEncephalopathiesAdvisoryCommittee/ucm129558.htm. Accessed 22 January 2015.
6. Advisory Committee on Blood and Tissue Safety and Availability Charter. FDA website. http://www.hhs.gov/ash/bloodsafety/advisorycommittee/ Accessed 22 January 2015.
7. Compliance Program Guidance Manual. Chapter 42 – Blood and Blood Products. 7342.001 - Inspection of Licensed and Unlicensed Blood Banks, Brokers, Reference Laboratories, and Contractors. FDA website. http://www.fda.gov/BiologicsBloodVaccines/GuidanceComplianceRegulatoryInformation/ComplianceActivities/Enforcement/CompliancePrograms/default.htm. Accessed 22 January 2015.
8. Compliance Program Guidance Manual. Chapter 42 – Blood and Blood Products. 7342.002 - Inspection of Source Plasma Establishments, Brokers, Testing Laboratories, and Contractors. FDA website. http://www.fda.gov/BiologicsBloodVaccines/GuidanceComplianceRegulatoryInformation/ComplianceActivities/Enforcement/CompliancePrograms/default.htm Accessed 22 January 2015.

Chapter 30

Human Cell and Tissue Products

Updated by Martha Wells, MPH, RAC

OBJECTIVES

- ❑ Review the history of human tissue regulations
- ❑ Explain the legal basis and authority for human tissue regulation under the *Public Health Service Act*
- ❑ Identify the differences between 21 CFR Part 1270 and 21 CFR Part 1271
- ❑ Differentiate between tissue-related products regulated by FDA and those that are not
- ❑ Identify those criteria that allow regulation of a cell or tissue without premarket approval
- ❑ Understand the key concepts of the cell and tissue product regulations
- ❑ Identify policies for streamlined licensure of cord blood products regulated as biological products
- ❑ Provide information on contacts for regulatory pathways

LAWS, REGULATIONS AND GUIDANCES COVERED IN THIS CHAPTER

- ❑ *Public Health Service Act*, 42 USC 264
- ❑ *Federal Food, Drug, and Cosmetic Act* of 1938
- ❑ 21 CFR Part 1270 Human Tissue Intended for Transplantation
- ❑ 21 CFR Part 1271 Human Cells, Tissues, and Cellular and Tissue-Based Product
- ❑ *Guidance for Industry: Regulation of Human Cells, Tissues, and Cellular and Tissue-Based Products (HCT/Ps)—Small Entity Compliance Guide* (August 2007)
- ❑ *Guidance for Industry: Eligibility Determination for Donors of Human Cells, Tissues, and Cellular and Tissue-Based Products (HCT/PS)* (August 2007)
- ❑ *Guidance for Industry: Minimally Manipulated, Unrelated Allogeneic Placental/Umbilical Cord Blood Intended for Hematopoietic Reconstitution for Specified Indications* (October 2009)
- ❑ *Guidance for Industry: Current Good Tissue Practice (CGTP and Additional Requirements for Manufacturers of Human Cells, Tissues, and Cellular and Tissue-Based Products* (December 2011)
- ❑ *Guidance for Industry: BLA for Minimally Manipulated, Unrelated Allogeneic Placental/Umbilical Cord Blood Intended for Hematopoietic and Immunologic Reconstitution in Patients with Disorders Affecting the Hematopoietic System* (March 2014)

- *Guidance for Industry and FDA Staff: IND Applications for Minimally Manipulated, Unrelated Allogeneic Placental/Umbilical Cord Blood Intended for Hematopoietic and Immunologic Reconstitution in Patients with Disorders Affecting the Hematopoietic System* (March 2014)

History and Background of Human Cell and Tissue Regulation

In the early 1990s, the US Centers for Disease Control and Prevention (CDC) reported the human immunodeficiency virus (HIV) had been transmitted through transplantation of human tissue. Information also was reported suggesting potentially unsafe tissue was being imported into the US for transplantation into humans. Prompted by reports potentially unsafe bone was being imported, the commissioner of food and drugs ordered an investigation, which identified an immediate need to protect the public health from the transmission of HIV and Hepatitis B and C through transplantation of unsuitable tissue. Concerns disease transmission could occur, coupled with information derived from these investigations, prompted the US Food and Drug Administration (FDA) to publish an interim final rule in December 1993 specifically requiring testing for certain communicable diseases and donor screening, as well as recordkeeping for certain human tissues intended for transplantation. This regulation (21 CFR Part 1270)1 only applied to musculoskeletal, ocular and skin products from non-living human donors. A final rule was issued in July 1997.

21 CFR 1270

Under 21 CFR Part 1270, FDA chose to regulate tissues under the legal authority of Section 361 of the *Public Health Service Act* (*PHS Act*).[2] This section authorizes the surgeon general, with the approval of the secretary of the, Department of Health and Human Services (DHHS), to make and enforce such regulations as judged necessary to prevent the introduction, transmission or spread of communicable diseases from foreign countries into the US or from state to state. Tissues and cells regulated only under the authority of Section 361 do not require premarket approval. Applicable regulations apply to these products regardless of intra- or inter-state distribution. This regulation only addressed tissues from non-living donors.

21 CFR 1271

In 1997, FDA announced its plans for a more comprehensive, risk-based approach for regulating human cells, tissues and cellular and tissue-based products (HCT/Ps).[3] FDA's new regulatory framework 's goals were to:

- prevent unwitting use of contaminated tissues with the potential for transmitting infectious disease
- prevent improper handling or processing that might contaminate or damage tissues
- ensure clinical safety and effectiveness are demonstrated for cells and tissues that are highly processed, used for purposes other than replacement or combined with non-tissue components, or have systemic effects.

In the interim, the agency has proposed and finalized three rules to implement this proposed approach. These requirements also were promulgated under *PHS Act* Section 361 and are codified as 21 CFR Part 1271.[4] They became effective in whole for cells and tissues recovered on or after 25 May 2005. General guidance has been published for establishments regulated under the new requirements.[5] Summaries of the three rules are listed in **Table 30-1**.

Scope of Oversight

Human cells or tissues intended for implantation, transplantation, infusion or transfer into a human recipient are regulated as HCT/Ps. FDA's Center for Biologics Evaluation and Research (CBER) regulates HCT/Ps under 21 CFR Parts 1270 and 1271.

CBER does not regulate the transplantation of vascularized human organ transplants such as kidney, liver, heart, lung or pancreas; the Health Resources Services Administration (HRSA) oversees those transplants. HRSA is a separate agency within DHHS.

Table 30-1. 21 CFR 1271

Final Rule	21 CFR 1271 Subpart(s)	Effective Date (Published Date)	Issues Addressed
Establishment Registration and Listing	A, B	4 April 2001 21 January 2003 (19 January 2001)	Applicability: types and uses of products that will be regulated by these rules; requirements for registering and listing HCT/Ps
Donor Eligibility	C	25 May 2005 (25 May 2004)	Requirements for donor screening and testing for relevant communicable disease agents and diseases
Current Good Tissue Practices (CGTP)	D, E, F	25 May 2005 (24 November 2004)	Manufacturing to ensure HCT/Ps do not contain communicable disease agents; reporting; labeling and compliance/inspections

Under FDA regulations, the following are considered HCT/Ps:

- bone (including demineralized bone)
- ligaments
- tendons
- fascia
- cartilage
- ocular tissue (corneas and sclera)
- skin
- arteries and veins
- pericardium
- amniotic membrane
- dura mater
- heart valves
- hematopoietic stem/progenitor cells derived from peripheral and cord blood
- semen, oocytes and embryos

Examples of articles are not considered HCT/Ps include:

- vascularized human organs for transplantation (HRSA)
- whole blood or blood components or blood derivative products (subject to 21 CFR 607 or 207)
- secreted or extracted human products such as milk, collagen and cell factors (however, semen is an HCT/P)
- minimally manipulated bone marrow for homologous use and not combined with another article (HRSA)
- products used in the manufacture of an HCT/P (ancillary products)
- cells, tissues and organs derived from animals other than humans (xenotransplantation)
- in vitro diagnostic products (defined in 21 CFR 809.3(a))
- blood vessels recovered with organs for use in organ transplantation (HRSA)

General Provisions (21 CFR Part 1271, Subpart A)

This section defines important terms in 21 CFR 1271.3. The criteria that are the foundation of FDA's tiered, risk-based approach to regulating HCT/Ps are found in 21 CFR 1271.10(a). HCT/Ps meeting all of these criteria are subject only to regulation under Section 361 of the *PHS Act* and to 21 CFR Part 1271. No premarket approval is required and compliance is determined at FDA inspection. These four criteria are:

- minimal manipulation
- intended for homologous use
- not combined with another article
- no systemic effect and not dependent on metabolic activity of living cells, except if for autologous use, use in a first-degree or second-degree blood relative or for reproductive use

21 CFR Part 1271.3 includes important definitions for understanding 21 CFR Part 1271.10:

- autologous use—use in the individual from whom the cells or tissue were recovered
- allogeneic use—use in a first- or second-degree blood relative, including parents, children, siblings, aunts, uncles, nieces, nephews, first cousins, grandparents and grandchildren (important for hematopoietic stem cell therapies)
- minimal manipulation—for structural tissue, processing that does not alter the tissue's original relevant characteristics relating to its utility for reconstruction, repair or replacement; for cells or nonstructural tissues, processing that does not alter their relevant biological characteristics
- homologous use—repair, reconstruction, replacement or supplementation of a recipient's cells or tissues with an HCT/P that performs the same basic function or functions in the recipient as in the donor

HCT/Ps not meeting all four criteria in 21 CFR 1271.10(a) are regulated as drugs, devices and/or biological products under Section 351 of the *PHS Act* and the *Federal Food, Drug, and Cosmetic Act*. Thus, these HCT/Ps are subject to the regulations specific to drugs, biological products or medical devices, in addition to applicable sections of Part 1271. In other words, the requirements in 21 CFR Part 1271 supplement the Good Manufacturing Practice (GMP) requirements for HCT/Ps regulated as biological products and the *Quality Systems Regulation (QSR)* requirements for HCT/Ps regulated as medical devices.

Examples of HCT/Ps that would be regulated under Section 351 are:

- autologous chondrocytes expanded *in vitro* for repair of cartilage defects
- allogeneic hematopoietic stem/progenitor cells, cord blood
- genetically modified cell therapy

Registration and Listing (21 CFR Part 1271, Subpart B)

Since 2001, FDA has required any establishment manufacturing HCT/Ps to register and submit a list of every HCT/P it manufactures within five days of beginning operation, and to re-register annually. All foreign establishments exporting HCT/Ps to the US also must register and list. Manufacture means any or all steps in the recovery, processing, storage, labeling or distribution of any human cell or tissue, and the screening or testing of the cell or tissue donor. Establishment registration does not mean an establishment is in compliance with all requirements. Compliance is determined at inspection. As of 2015, more than 2,000 establishments have active FDA registrations. Establishments engaged in the following activities are not required to register and list:

- HCT/Ps solely used for nonclinical scientific or educational purposes
- removal and implantation of autologous HCT/Ps in the same surgical procedure
- carriers that accept, receive, carry or deliver HCT/Ps
- establishments that receive or store HCT/Ps solely for implantation, transplantation, infusion or transfer within the same facility
- establishments that recover reproductive cells or tissue and immediately transfer them into a sexually intimate partner of the cell or tissue donor
- individuals who solely recover cells or tissue and send them to a registered establishment under contract, agreement or other arrangement with a registered establishment

Establishments may register and list by downloading and completing Form FDA 3356,[6] although FDA prefers registration to be performed electronically through a secure web server.[7]

Donor Eligibility (21 CFR Part 1271, Subpart C)

A donor eligibility determination based on donor screening and testing for relevant communicable disease agents and disease (RCDADs) is required for all HCT/P donors, with some exceptions. Examples of donors not requiring donor eligibility determinations include autologous donors and sexually intimate donors of reproductive cells and tissues. HCT/Ps must not be administered until donor eligibility has been determined, with some exceptions.

Unless exempt, all donors must be tested for these RCDADs:

- HIV, types 1 and 2
- hepatitis B and C viruses
- *Treponema pallidum*

Donors of leukocyte-rich HCT/Ps, such as hematopoietic stem/progenitor cells and semen, also must be tested for:

- cytomegalovirus
- human T-lymphotropic virus, types I and II

In addition, reproductive donors must be tested for the following sexually transmitted agents:

- Chlamydia trachomatis
- Neisseria gonorrhea

Donor testing must be performed using the appropriate FDA-licensed, -approved or -cleared donor screening tests, in accordance with the manufacturer's instructions, to reduce the risk of transmission of RCDADS adequately and appropriately. Required donor testing must be performed by a laboratory either certified to perform such testing on human specimens under the *Clinical Laboratory Improvement Amendments* of 1988 (42 U.S.C. 263a) and 42 CFR Part 493, or meeting equivalent requirements determined by the Centers for Medicare and Medicaid Services.

Donors must be screened by reviewing their relevant medical records for risk factors for and clinical evidence of the RCDADs listed above and for communicable disease risks associated with xenotransplantation (live cells, tissue or organs from a nonhuman animal source) and human transmissible spongiform encephalopathy (TSE) including Creutzfeldt-Jakob disease. In addition, they must be screened for other RCDADs such as West Nile Virus, sepsis and vaccinia (recent smallpox vaccination). Relevant medical records are defined as a collection of documents that includes a current donor medical history interview; a current cadaveric donor physical assessment report or living donor's physical examination and other available records. FDA has provided detailed guidance concerning its current thinking regarding donor testing and screening.[8]

Current Good Tissue Practices (21 CFR Part 1271, Subparts D)

Current Good Tissue Practices (CGTP) requirements address the methods, facilities and controls used for manufacturing HCT/Ps to prevent the introduction, transmission and spread of communicable disease. Communicable diseases include, but are not limited to, those transmitted by viruses, bacteria, fungi, parasites and TSE agents. The donor eligibility requirements discussed above also are considered CGTPs. These CGTP requirements are applicable to the manufacture of Section 361 HCT/Ps and, to some extent, HCT/Ps regulated as biological products and medical devices. They address all aspects of manufacture from recovery to distribution, with the focus on establishing a comprehensive quality program to oversee such manufacture. The quality program must be designed to prevent, detect and correct deficiencies that may lead to an increased risk of introduction, transmission or spread of communicable diseases. FDA determined the core CGTP requirements are those directly related to preventing communicable disease introduction, transmission or spread by HCT/Ps. The core CGTP requirements along with brief descriptions are listed in **Table 30-2**. FDA has finalized a guidance on CGTPs.[9]

Table 30-2. Overview of the Core CGTP Requirements (21 CFR 1271, Subpart D)

Facilities	• Facilities must be of suitable size, construction and location to prevent contamination of HCT/Ps with communicable disease agents and maintained in a good state of repair—kept in a clean, sanitary and orderly manner. They should be divided into separate or defined areas of adequate size for each operation that takes place in the facility, or establish and maintain other control systems to prevent improper labeling, mix-ups, contamination, cross-contamination and accidental exposure of HCT/Ps to communicable disease agents. • Establish and maintain procedures for facility cleaning and sanitation. • Document, and maintain records of (and retain for three years after their creation) all cleaning and sanitation activities performed to prevent contamination of HCT/Ps.
Environmental Controls	• Where appropriate, provide for the following control activities or systems: o temperature and humidity controls o ventilation and air filtration o cleaning and disinfecting rooms and equipment to ensure aseptic processing operations o maintenance of equipment used to control conditions necessary for aseptic processing operations • Each environmental control system should be periodically inspected and records should be maintained.
Equipment	• The equipment used in the manufacture of HCT/Ps must be of appropriate design for its use and must be suitably located and installed to facilitate operations, including cleaning and maintenance. • Any automated, mechanical, electronic or other equipment used for inspection, measuring or testing in accordance with this part must be capable of producing valid results. • The procedures and schedules, calibration of equipment, inspections and records also are addressed.
Supplies and Reagents	• Only supplies and reagents verified to meet specifications shall be used. Verification may be accomplished by the establishment that uses the supply or reagent or by the supply or reagent vendor. • Reagents used in processing and preservation of HCT/Ps must be sterile, where appropriate. • The production of in-house reagents must be validated, and records pertaining to supplies and reagents must be maintained.
Recovery	• The recovery of each HCT/P should be performed in a way that does not cause contamination or cross-contamination during recovery, or otherwise increase the risk of the introduction, transmission or spread of communicable disease.
Processing and Process Controls	• Human cells or tissues from two or more donors must not be pooled (placed in physical contact or mixed in a single receptacle) during manufacturing. • In-process control and testing requirements must be met and controlled until the required inspection and tests or other verification activities have been completed, or necessary approvals are received and documented. Sampling of in-process HCT/Ps must be representative of the material to be evaluated. • With respect to dura mater, when there is a published validated process that reduces TSE risk, such a process should be used (or an equivalent validated process), unless following this process adversely affects the dura mater's clinical utility.
Labeling Controls	• Procedures to control HCT/P labeling should be established and maintained. They must be designed to ensure proper HCT/P identification and prevent mix-ups. Procedures must include verification of label accuracy, legibility and integrity. • Procedures must be in place to ensure each HCT/P is labeled in accordance with all applicable labeling requirements, including those in 1271.55, 1271.60, 1271.65, 1271.90, 1271.290 and 1271.270, and each HCT/P made available for distribution is accompanied by documentation of the donor eligibility determination as required under 1271.55.
Storage	• Storage areas and stock rooms are to be controlled to prevent mix-ups, contamination and cross-contamination of HCT/Ps, supplies and reagents. These areas also should be designed to prevent an HCT/P from being improperly made available for distribution. • Temperature, expiration date, corrective action and acceptable temperature limits also are addressed.
Receipt, Predistribution Shipment and Distribution	• Upon receipt, each incoming HCT/P must be tested for the presence and significance of microorganisms and inspected for damage and contamination. • A determination of whether to accept, reject or place each incoming HCT/P in quarantine should be established, based on pre-established criteria designed to prevent communicable disease transmission. Pre-distribution shipment, availability for distribution, packaging and shipping, procedures and returns to inventories also are covered.
Donor Eligibility Determination	See "Donor Eligibility (21 CFR 1271, Subpart C)"

Table 30-3. FDA Regulation of Minimally Manipulated Cord Blood Products

Origin and Use of Cord Blood	Applicable FDA Requirements	Premarket Application Required
Autologous	21 CFR 1271 (exempt from donor eligibility requirements)	No, if 1271.10 criteria met
Allogeneic: first- or second-degree blood relative	21 CFR 1271 (donor eligibility required)	No, if 1271.10 criteria met
Allogeneic: unrelated	21 CFR Parts 1271, 201, 211, 600, 610	Yes, IND and/or BLA

Reporting and Labeling (21 CFR 1271, Subpart E)

The reporting and labeling requirements in 21 CFR Part 1271 currently apply only to nonreproductive HCT/Ps regulated under *PHS Act* Section 361. Those HCT/Ps regulated as biological products or medical devices must follow other requirements. Labeling requirements focus on information that must appear on the HCT/P label, including a distinct identification code and a description of the HCT/P type. Other requirements address information that may accompany the HCT/P or appear on the label, such as the name and address of the establishment that determined release criteria and made the HCT/P available for distribution.

Adverse reactions involving a communicable disease must be reported to FDA if they are fatal, life-threatening, result in permanent impairment or damage or necessitate medical or surgical intervention, including hospitalization. As required for other FDA adverse event reports, HCT/P adverse reaction reports are submitted to FDA's MedWatch system.[10,11]

In addition, establishments distributing HCT/Ps are required to report certain deviations in manufacturing related to a core CGTP requirement. These HCT/P deviations can be reported on Form FDA 3486[12] or, preferably, via FDA's Electronic Biological Product Deviation Report (eBPDR) system.[13] CBER also has implemented a Direct Recall Classification (DRC) Program[14] to expedite and streamline recall classification. This system utilizes information from the eBPDR.

Inspection and Enforcement (21 CFR Part 1271, Subpart F)

This subpart only applies to HCT/Ps regulated under *PHS Act* Section 361. For example, general inspectional provisions are described for notification, frequency and copying records. What distinguishes these Part 1271 provisions from the inspection and enforcement requirements for other FDA-regulated products is the focus of possible compliance actions on providing protection against communicable disease transmission risks. FDA investigators have been provided detailed descriptions of how to conduct HCT/P inspections and address HCT/P importation.[15,16,17] FDA is not required under regulation to inspect establishments at certain intervals. For instance, in 2013, FDA reported 671 HCT/P establishment inspections.

Regulation of Hematopoietic Progenitor Cells From Umbilical and Cord Blood Products

FDA has developed a streamlined approach to licensure of hematopoietic progenitor cells derived from cord blood (HPC-C) for allogeneic use. Although some cord blood products for autologous and family-related use are regulated only under the new requirements in 21 CFR Part 1271 and *PHS Act* Section 361, those intended for allogeneic, unrelated recipients are considered biological products (See **Table 30-3**).

FDA delayed implementation of requirements for Biologics License Applications (BLA) and Investigational New Drug (IND) application submissions for these HCT/Ps and published final guidances for each of these applications in March 2014.[18,19] For specific indications listed in the BLA guidance, applications will be streamlined to not require each establishment to demonstrate clinical efficacy; however, the sponsor can rely on clinical data submitted for FDA review in a public docket. In addition, FDA has updated a compliance program guidance for biological products[20] to include cord blood issues to assist investigators with both pre-licensure and annual investigations.

FDA has not completed its policy yet for another HCT/P, hematopoietic progenitor cells derived from peripheral blood. Because these also are life-saving therapies where access to the best human leukocyte antigen (HLA) match for a patient is crucial, FDA is being very careful to develop guidance that will ensure product safety and efficacy but not impede patient care.

Additional Updates from FDA

The following documents can be found on CBER's tissue website.[21]

- Guidance documents: Since 21 CFR 1271 became effective 25 May 2005, FDA has provided guidance to assist industry in implementing its requirements.

In addition to the final guidances noted earlier, important draft guidances issued in 2014 and 2015 include:

- o Same Surgical Procedure Exception under 21 CFR 1271.15(b) (October 2014)
- o Adipose Tissue: Regulatory Considerations (December 2014)
- o Minimal Manipulation (December 2014)
- o Investigating and Reporting Adverse Reactions (February 2015)

These draft guidances are subject to change based on FDA review of public docket comments. In addition, FDA announced in a *Federal Register* notice that a forthcoming draft guidance on homologous use of HCT/Ps will be published in 2015.

- Proposed revisions to Part 1271: FDA published a *Federal Register* notice 31 December 2014 proposing certain revisions to the 1271.90 exception regulation. According to the notice, these proposed regulation changes would provide additional flexibility to HCT/P establishments to make certain embryos available for reproductive use. Again, this is a proposed regulation that will be finalized after public comment.

Regulatory Pathways

FDA has several mechanisms to assist industry in determining the proper regulatory strategy for further developing HCT/P products.

- FDA has a well-established program for assisting industry in product development through its Pre-IND meeting and other formal meetings. FDA guidance is available for scheduling and conducting such meetings, and CBER personnel are generous in providing assistance through this mechanism.
- FDA's website contains numerous guidance documents addressing regulatory considerations for a variety of cellular products and diseases. Valuable information also can be found in the background materials provided for the Cellular, Tissue, and Gene Therapies Advisory Committee. This FDA Advisory Committee, made up of subject matter experts, evaluates available data relating to cellular therapies' safety, effectiveness and appropriate use.
- FDA formed the Tissue Reference Group (TRG) to provide a single reference point for product-specific questions concerning applicable HCT/P regulation. The TRG provides a general update of its recommendations annually that can be utilized as a point of reference but should not be considered applicable to all similar products, as they are based on specific information from a sponsor.
- FDA's Office of Combination Products (OCP), although focused on providing guidance for regulatory designations through the Request for Designation (RFD) mechanism for combination products (21 CFR Part 3), is a resource to for companies developing HCT/Ps with a cellular component or combined with another product. The OCP website has a wealth of information on previous decisions as well as contacts and guidance for preparation of an RFD.

Summary

- FDA has developed and implemented comprehensive risk-based regulations applicable to a wide range of HCT/Ps:
  - o The regulation level and type is commensurate with the risk posed by product characteristics.
  - o Like products are treated alike.
  - o FDA exercises regulatory oversight only to the degree appropriate to protect the public health.
- These requirements are broad and focus on ensuring HCT/Ps are neither contaminated nor capable of transmitting communicable diseases.
- FDA continues to publish guidance for industry to assist in interpreting these requirements.
- Unlike many other FDA-regulated products, most HCT/Ps are not required to undergo premarket review and approval before distribution.
- For certain HCT/Ps (Section 361 HCT/Ps), new regulations comprise the sole regulatory requirements.
- All establishments performing a manufacturing function must register and list with FDA.
- FDA has completed policy development for streamlined allogeneic cord blood licensure and still is in the process of formulating a policy for peripheral blood stem cell products.
- For HCT/Ps regulated as drugs, devices and/or biological products, the new tissue regulations supplement other requirements (GMP/QSR). Regulatory pathways for addressing these are described.

References

1. 21 CFR Part 1270. FDA website. http://www.accessdata.fda.gov/scripts/cdrh/cfdocs/cfcfr/CFRSearch.cfm?CFRPart=1270. Accessed 12 March 2015.
2. *Public Health Service Act.* GPO website. http://www.gpo.gov/fdsys/pkg/USCODE-2011-title42/pdf/USCODE-2011-title42-chap6A-subchapII-partG-sec264.pdf. Accessed 12 March 2015.
3. "A Proposed Approach to the Regulation of Cellular and Tissue-Based Products." 62 *FR* 9721 (4 March 1997).
4. 21 CFR Part 1271. FDA website. http://www.accessdata.fda.gov/scripts/cdrh/cfdocs/cfcfr/CFRSearch.cfm?CFRPart=1271. Accessed 12 March 2015

5. *Guidance for Industry: Regulation of Human Cells, Tissue, and Cellular and Tissue-Based Products (HCT/Ps) Small Entity Compliance Guide* (August 2007). FDA website. http://www.fda.gov/BiologicsBloodVaccines/GuidanceComplianceRegulatoryInformation/Guidances/Tissue/ucm073366.htm . Accessed 12 March 12 2015.
6. Form FDA 3356, Establishment Registration and Listing for HCT/Ps. FDA website. www.fda.gov/downloads/AboutFDA/ReportsManualsForms/Forms/UCM082428.pdf. Accessed 12 March 2015
7. FDA Electronic Human Cell and Tissue Establishment Registration (eHCTERS). FDA website. http://www.fda.gov/BiologicsBloodVaccines/GuidanceComplianceRegulatoryInformation/EstablishmentRegistration/TissueEstablishmentRegistration/ucm147970.htm. Accessed 12 March 2015.
8. *Guidance for Industry: Eligibility Determination for Donors of Human Cells, Tissue, and Cellular and Tissue-Based Products (HCT/Ps)* (August 2007). FDA website. http://www.fda.gov/BiologicsBloodVaccines/GuidanceComplianceRegulatoryInformation/Guidances/Tissue/ucm073964.htm . Accessed 12 March 2015.
9. *Guidance for Industry: Current Good Tissue Practice (CGTP and Additional Requirements for Manufacturers of Human Cells, Tissues, and Cellular and Tissue-Based Products (December 2011)* FDA website. http://www.fda.gov/downloads/BiologicsBloodVaccines/GuidanceComplianceRegulatoryInformation/Guidances/Tissue/UCM285223.pdf. Accessed 12 March 2015.
10. *Guidance for Industry: MedWatch Form FDA 3500A: Mandatory Reporting of Adverse Reactions Related to Human Cells, Tissue, and Cellular and Tissue-Based Products (HCT/Ps)* (November 2005). FDA website. http://www.fda.gov/BiologicsBloodVaccines/GuidanceComplianceRegulatoryInformation/Guidances/Tissue/ucm074000.htm . Accessed 12 March 2015.
11. SOPP 8508—*Procedures for Handling Adverse Reaction Reports Related to "361" Human Cells, Tissues, and Cellular and Tissue Based Products* (March 2008). FDA website. http://www.fda.gov/BiologicsBloodVaccines/GuidanceComplianceRegulatoryInformation/ProceduresSOPPs/ucm073048.htm. Accessed 12 March 2015.
12. Form FDA 3486, Biological Product Deviation Report. FDA website. http://www.fda.gov/downloads/AboutFDA/ReportsManualsForms/Forms/UCM061463.pdf. Accessed 12 March 2015.
13. FDA Electronic Biological Product Deviation Report (eBPDR) system. FDA website. http://www.fda.gov/BiologicsBloodVaccines/SafetyAvailability/ReportaProblem/BiologicalProductDeviations/default.htm -Accessed 19 June 2015.
14. FDA Direct Recall Classification (DRC) Program. FDA website. http://www.fda.gov/BiologicsBloodVaccines/SafetyAvailability/ReportaProblem/BiologicalProductDeviations/ucm172970.htm Accessed 19 June 2015.
15. Compliance Program 7341.002A: Inspection of Tissue Establishments, (covers human tissue recovered before 25 May 2005) FDA website. http://www.fda.gov/BiologicsBloodVaccines/GuidanceComplianceRegulatoryInformation/ComplianceActivities/Enforcement/CompliancePrograms/ucm095218.htm. Accessed 12 March 2015.
16. Compliance Program 7341.002: Inspection of Human Cells, Tissues, and Cellular and Tissue-Based Products (HCT/Ps). Covers human tissue recovered after 25 May 2005. FDA website. http://www.fda.gov/BiologicsBloodVaccines/GuidanceComplianceRegulatoryInformation/ComplianceActivities/Enforcement/CompliancePrograms/ucm095207.htm . Accessed 12 March 2015.
17. Compliance Program 7342.007 Addendum: Imported Human Cells, Tissues, and Cellular and Tissue-based Products (HCT/Ps). FDA website. http://www.fda.gov/BiologicsBloodVaccines/GuidanceComplianceRegulatoryInformation/ComplianceActivities/Enforcement/CompliancePrograms/ucm095250.htm. Accessed 12 March 2015.
18. *Guidance for Industry:BLA for Minimally Manipulated, Unrelated Allogeneic Placental/Umbilical Cord Blood Intended for Hematopoietic and Immunologic Reconstitution in Patients with Disorders Affecting the Hematopoietic System* (March 2014). FDA website. http://www.fda.gov/downloads/BiologicsBloodVaccines/GuidanceComplianceRegulatoryInformation/Guidances/CellularandGeneTherapy/UCM357135.pdf. Accessed 12 March 2015.
19. *Guidance for Industry and FDA Staff: IND Applications for Minimally Manipulated, Unrelated Allogeneic Placental/Umbilical Cord Blood Intended for Hematopoietic and Immunologic Reconstitution in Patients with Disorders Affecting the Hematopoietic System"* (March 2014). FDA website. http://www.fda.gov/BiologicsBloodVaccines/GuidanceComplianceRegulatoryInformation/Guidances/CellularandGeneTherapy/ucm388218.htm. Accessed 12 March 2015.
20. *Compliance Program Guidance Manual 7345.848:Inspection of Biological Drug Products* (October 2010). FDA website. http://www.fda.gov/BiologicsBloodVaccines/GuidanceComplianceRegulatoryInformation/ComplianceActivities/Enforcement/CompliancePrograms/ucm095393.htm. Accessed 12 March 2015.
21. FDA CBER Tissue & Tissue Products website. http://www.fda.gov/BiologicsBloodVaccines/TissueTissueProducts/default.htm. Accessed 12 March 2015.

Reading List

"Keeping Human Tissue Transplants Safe," *FDA Consumer Magazine*, May-June 2005 (http://permanent.access.gpo.gov/lps1609/www.fda.gov/fdac/features/2005/305_tissue.html. Accessed 12 March 2015.

Tissue and Tissue Product Questions and Answers. FDA website. http://www.fda.gov/BiologicsBloodVaccines/TissueTissueProducts/QuestionsaboutTissues/ucm101559.htm. Accessed 12 March 2015.

Frequently asked Questions About Transplant Safety, CDC website. http://www.cdc.gov/transplantsafety/overview/faq.html Accessed 12 March 2015.

Prebula R. "Current Good Tissue Practices; The Core Requirements when Donating Human Tissue," *FDLI Update*, November/December 2007.

Shapiro JK and Wesloloski BJ. "FDA's Regulatory Scheme for Human Tissue, A Brief Overview," *FDLI Update*, November/December 2007.

Weber DJ. "Understanding and Implementing Good Tissue Practices (GTPs)," *RAPS Regulatory Focus*, July 2008.

Weber DJ. "Navigating FDA Regulations for Human Cells and Tissue," *BioProcessing International*, 2(8): 22-26, 2004.

Wells MA. "Overview of FDA Regulation of Human Cellular and Tissue-Based Products," *Food and Drug Law Journal*, 52, 401-408, 1997.

Wells MA and Lazarus EF. "FDA Streamlines Licensure approach for Certain Cord Blood Products," *RAPS Regulatory Focus*, April 2010.

Wells MA, Anselmo C and Weiskopf R. "Are you ready for the FDA? How to Prepare for and Manage your FDA inspection," Fertility Nurse First, 2012, Issue 37.

Chapter 31

Regulating Regenerative Medicine: Cell Therapy, Gene Therapy and Tissue Engineering

By James Smith, DPhil Candidate, Brock Reeve, MBA, MPhil, Andy Carr, MA, ChM, Dsc, FRCS, FMedSci, and David A. Brindley, DPhil, MEng

OBJECTIVES

- ❑ Introduce the science behind cell therapy, gene therapy and tissue engineering
- ❑ Outline regulatory routes for human cells, tissues and cellular and tissue-based products (HCT/Ps)
- ❑ Outline regulatory routes for regenerative medicine combination products
- ❑ Outline regulation of point-of-care procedures and same surgical procedure exception
- ❑ Outline guidance pertaining to generation of cellular populations for therapeutic use, including collection of cells, cell culture procedures, cell banking and materials used in manufacture
- ❑ Outline guidance on characterization and release testing
- ❑ Outline preclinical and clinical considerations including clinical study objectives, study population selection, controlling and blinding, dosing and treatment and monitoring and follow-up
- ❑ Provide a comprehensive list of FDA guidance documents

REGULATIONS AND GUIDELINES COVERED IN THIS CHAPTER

- ❑ *Public Health Service Act* 42 USC 264, Section 361
- ❑ 21 CFR 1271 Human Cells, Tissues and Cellular and Tissue-Based Products
- ❑ *Public Health Service Act* 42 USC 262, Section 351
- ❑ 21 CFR 312 Investigational New Drug Application
- ❑ 21 CFR 812 Investigational Device Exemptions
- ❑ 21 CFR 3 Product Jurisdiction
- ❑ FDA Office of Combination Products. *Concepts for Comment Purposes Only—Not for Implementation; Number of Marketing Applications for a Combination Product*
- ❑ *Draft Guidance for Industry: Same Surgical Procedure Exception under 21 CFR 1271.15(b): Questions and Answers Regarding the Scope of the Exception*
- ❑ *Draft Guidance for Industry and FDA Staff: Minimal Manipulation of Human Cells, Tissues, and Cellular and Tissue-Based Products*
- ❑ *Guidance for Industry and FDA Staff—Devices Used to Process Human Cells, Tissues, and Cellular and Tissue-Based Products*

- ❑ *Guidance for Industry: Guidance for Human Somatic Cell Therapy and Gene Therapy*
- ❑ *Points to Consider in the Characterization of Cell Lines Used to Produce Biological Products*
- ❑ *Guidance for Industry: Preclinical Assessment of Investigational Cellular and Gene Therapy Products*
- ❑ *Guidance for Industry: Considerations for the Design of Early-Phase Clinical Trials of Cellular and Gene Therapy Products*
- ❑ *Guidance for Industry: Cellular Therapy for Cardiac Disease*
- ❑ *Guidance for Industry: Gene Therapy Clinical Trials—Observing Subjects for Delayed Adverse Events*

Introduction

"Regenerative medicine replaces or regenerates human cells, tissue or organs, to restore or establish normal function"[1] and has been identified by FDA as an emerging technology and important component of the strategic plan.[2] Regenerative medicine often is perceived as the use of stem cells to treat disease; however, it can be considered a group of cell- or gene-based technologies, employing not just stem cells, but other cell types as well as combinations of cells and other product types.[3] Although some definitions of regenerative medicine could include drugs to target endogenous stem cell populations or to regenerate or repair tissues more generally, here, regenerative medicine is taken to comprise cell therapy, gene therapy and tissue engineering, each of which is explained below. FDA refers to these as cellular, tissue and gene therapy (CGT) products. These diverse approaches have overlapping regulatory considerations and often utilize stem cells as a central component. Several CGT products have received marketing authorization in the US (**Table 31-1**). The regulation of such products poses unique challenges compared to other therapeutics, as the use of 'living' products carries greater uncertainty and unpredictability compared to other FDA-regulated products.[4] This chapter discusses the essential science behind regenerative medicine approaches, special considerations for developing a regulatory strategy and FDA requirements for regenerative medicine products.

Background on Regenerative Medicine

Cell Therapy

Cell therapy typically refers to the use of stem cells to regenerate tissue, either through direct differentiation into the host tissue or through indirect signaling to induce responses in the local tissue. Stem cells can be divided into two broad classes: pluripotent and multipotent. A pluripotent stem cell has the ability to differentiate into all specialized tissues, whereas a multipotent stem cell can only differentiate into a subset of tissue or cell types. Both pluripotent and multipotent cells currently are employed as therapies. Non-stem cells, such as chondrocytes, pancreatic islet cells and cardiomyocytes, also can be used therapeutically. Therapeutic cells may be autologous or allogeneic: autologous products use cells from a patient to treat that same patient, whereas allogeneic products use a donor's cells in other patients.

Historically, it has been assumed the primary mode of action (PMOA) of cell therapies is differentiation into host tissue; however, it is becoming apparent signals derived from transplanted cells play an extremely important therapeutic role.[5] This realization has led to the emergence of a new 'subset' of cell therapy: the use of extracellular vesicles, which are essentially a membrane-bound sample of the cellular cytosol.[6] Further, cell therapies may be used

Table 31-1. Summary of Select Revenue-Generating Regenerative Medicine Products Currently on the Market

Company	Lead Product(s)	Indication	Current Markets
Dendreon (Seattle, WA, US)	Provenge	Prostate cancer	US, EU
Organogenesis (Canton, MA)	Apligraf	Diabetic foot ulcers	US, Canada
	Dermagraft	Venous leg ulcers/ diabetic foot ulcers	US, Saudi Arabia
NuVasive (San Deigo, CA, US)	Osteocel Plus	Skeletal defects	US
Orthofix (Curaçao, Netherlands Antilles)	Trinity Evolution	Musculoskeletal defects	US
Genzyme (Cambridge, MA, US)	Carticel	Articular cartilage repair	US, EU
	Epicel	Severe burns	US, EU

Source: French A, Buckler RL, Brindley DA. Commercialization of regenerative medicine: learning from spin-outs. Rejuvenation Res. 2013 Apr:16(2): 164–70.

Table 31-2. Definition of Minimal Manipulation

Relevant Documentation	Guidance
21 CFR 1271 Human Cells, Tissues and Cellular and Tissue-Based Products Section 1271.3 *Draft Guidance for Industry and FDA Staff: Minimal Manipulation of Human Cells, Tissues, and Cellular and Tissue-Based Products*	(1) For structural tissue, processing that does not alter the original relevant characteristics of the tissue relating to the tissue's utility for reconstruction, repair, or replacement; and (2) For cells or non-structural tissues, processing that does not alter the relevant biological characteristics of cells or tissues
66 FR 5447 Human Cells, Tissues, and Cellular and Tissue-Based Products; Establishment Registration and Listing at 5457 *Draft Guidance for Industry and FDA Staff: Minimal Manipulation of Human Cells, Tissues, and Cellular and Tissue-Based Products*	Specific manipulations considered to be: • cutting • grinding • shaping • centrifugation • soaking in antibiotic solution • sterilization by ethylene oxide treatment or irradiation • cell separation • density gradient separation • lyophilization • freezing • cryopreservation • selective removal of B-cells, T-cells, malignant cells, red blood cells, or platelets

Source: *PAS 83: 2012 Developing human cells for clinical applications in the European Union and the United States.* 2012.

in combination with other products, such as devices or nanoparticles that mediate delivery of cells or protect them from immune attack.

Gene Therapy

Gene therapy can be defined as the treatment or alleviation of a disease by genetically modifying a patient's cells.[7] This modification can take place *in vivo*, with introduction of genetic material directly into the patient, or *ex vivo*, with cells being isolated from a patient, grown in culture and genetically manipulated, then transplanted back into the patient. *In vivo* gene therapy is being investigated for a variety of indications, including cystic fibrosis, blood disorders and immuno-deficiencies, where correction of a mutated gene can suppress and potentially cure disease. *Ex vivo* gene therapy commonly is used for cancer immunotherapy treatment. A patient's immune cells are genetically engineered and expanded essentially to attack tumor cells upon transplantation. Sipuleucel-T (Provenge; Dendreon Corporation, Seattle, WA), for example, uses genetically engineered dendritic cells to treat prostate cancer, and is approved in the US.[8]

Tissue Engineering

Tissue engineering refers to the use of combinations of cells, biomaterials, scaffolds and/or biologically active molecules to improve or regenerate functionality in tissues or organs. Considerable overlap exists between tissue-engineered products and cell therapies; however, tissue engineering typically employs complex substrates for cell and tissue growth and implies the generation of more complete tissues for transplantation than cell therapy. It also may include bioprinting, repopulating devascularized organs and some cell-free materials with or without growth factors. Various tissue-engineered treatments have been used in patients, although most are experimental and very costly.[9]

Human Cell and Tissue Products

Most regenerative medicine products incorporate cells or tissues as a core component and, as such, it is important to understand human cell and tissue product regulation. These regulations are covered in the chapter on Human Cell and Tissue Products; however, certain areas are worth highlighting. Notably, FDA does not require a separate regulatory approach for stem cell-based products compared to other cellular products.[10] Cell therapies generally are considered to be biologics and, therefore, they typically are subject to up to two regulatory regimes: public health legislation and pharmaceutical legislation (some products also are subject to medical device legislation (see section on Combination Products)). Some cell-incorporating products are regulated solely under Section 361 of the *Public Health Service Act* (*PHS Act*), which has authority over the transmission of communicable diseases. These products often are referred to as '361 products' and do not require premarket approval. A 361 product must meet the following conditions stated in 21 CFR 1271.10:

1. The human cells, tissues and cellular and tissue-based product (HCT/P) is minimally manipulated (**Table 31-2**).
2. The HCT/P is intended for homologous use only, as reflected by the labeling, advertising or other indications of the manufacturer's objective intent.

Table 31-3. 361 and 351 Product Classification and Regulation

	Criteria	Regulation
361 Product	• Minimal manipulation • Homologous use • Not combined with another article • Either no systemic effect and do rely on metabolic effect of living cells • Or have a systemic effect and rely on metabolic effect of living cells but are for autologous, first or second degree blood relative or reproductive use	• Section 361 of *PHS Act* • CFR 21 1271 • No premarket approval • Good Tissue Practice (GTP) compliance
351 Product: Biologic or Device	• Do not meet criteria for 361 products • Regulated as either a biologic or device, depending on the primary mode of action	• Section 351 of *PHS Act* • Biologics: 21 CFR 312 (Center for Biologics Evaluation and Research (CBER)/Office of Cellular, Tissue and Gene Therapies (OCTGT)) • Devices: 21 CFR 812 (Center for Devices and Radiological Health (CDRH)) • Premarket approval • GTP and Good Manufacturing Practice (GMP) compliance

Source: Coopman K. *From production to patient: challenges and approaches for delivering cell therapies.* StemBook [Internet]. 2014.

3. HCT/P manufacture does not involve the combination of the cells or tissues with another article, except water, crystalloids or a sterilizing, preserving or storage agent, provided the addition of water, crystalloids or the sterilizing, preserving or storage agent does not raise new clinical safety concerns with respect to the HCT/P.
4. Either:
   i. The HCT/P does not have a systemic effect and is not dependent on the metabolic activity of living cells for its primary function; or
   ii. The HCT/P has a systemic effect or is dependent on the metabolic activity of living cells for its primary function, and:
      a. is for autologous use
      b. is for allogeneic use in a first- or second-degree blood relative; or
      c. is for reproductive use

FDA's definition of minimal manipulation is provided in **Table 31-2**. In December 2014, FDA released *Draft Guidance for Industry and FDA Staff: Minimal Manipulation of Human Cells, Tissues, and Cellular and Tissue-Based Products*[11] to clarify some ambiguity in the definition. See the guidance document for a complete discussion.

If the 361 criteria are not met, the product is regulated under Section 351 of the *PHS Act* as a drug, biologic or device and, therefore, requires regulatory approval before marketing. Products regulated under Section 351 are referred to as '351 products' (**Table 31-3**).

Of the three main regenerative medicine areas outlined above, only cell therapies potentially could be regulated as 361 products. Gene therapies, as their primary function, have a systemic effect and are dependent on the metabolic activity of living cells, whereas tissue-engineered products involve combining cells with another article. These two product groups, therefore, will be regulated as 351 products. Cell therapies involving "the administration to humans of autologous, allogeneic, or xenogeneic living cells which have been manipulated or processed *ex vivo*"[12] are termed somatic cell therapies by FDA and are also 351 products. Gene therapies involving *ex vivo* manipulation of cells then transplanted back to the patient technically are considered a form of somatic cell therapy. Generally, cell, tissue and gene 351 products will be regulated by the Center for Biologics Evaluation and Research (CBER)/Office of Cellular, Tissue and Gene Therapies (OCTGT). However, as discussed in the section below, this is not always the case.

Combination Products

Combining cells with another article to form a combination product is common in both tissue engineering and cell therapy (**Table 31-4**). For cell therapy, the article typically is a device and may include devices for cell delivery or cell encapsulation once delivered (e.g., to protect transplanted cells from immune attack). Cells decorated with nanoparticles or loaded with payloads also would be considered combination products. For tissue-engineered products, similar combination products exist; however, more-complex biomaterials such as animal tissues and electrospun nanofibres also may be used.[13] Such biomaterials also may be products in their own right. This section covers general considerations for cell and device combination product regulation.

Devices incorporating HCT/Ps will be regulated as combination products, with the lead center for regulation depending on the product's PMOA. The PMOA is defined in 21 CFR Part 3, which details regulations for combination products' assignment to FDA centers, as:

"the single mode of action of a combination product that provides the most important therapeutic action of the combination product. The most important therapeutic action is the mode of action expected to make the greatest contribution to the overall intended therapeutic effects of the combination product."

A Request for Designation (RFD) must be submitted, following the process described in 21 CFR 3, to determine the center with primary jurisdiction, or lead center. The Office of Combination Products (OCP) also can be approached for product classification discussions, which may be useful in the early product development stages to inform the likely regulatory route. However, any informal OCP designations are not legally binding.[14]

For cell-incorporating devices, the designated office will be either CBER, if the cell component is considered to provide the PMOA, or the Center for Devices and Radiological Health (CDRH), if the device component provides the PMOA. In 'borderline' cases, where the PMOA cannot be determined, FDA first looks at previous products that may have posed similar safety and efficacy questions, and assigns the product to the same lead center to which the previous products were assigned. In the absence of a previous, comparable product, FDA assigns the product to the center considered to have the most expertise in products presenting similar perceived risks to the combination product.[15]

Therefore, there is no steadfast, certain route for stem cell technology device regulation in the US, as with other combination products. Each particular product requires individual assessment, with the decision largely depending on the PMOA. However, once a lead center is assigned, the secondary center remains involved in the review process, particularly with matters concerning the second component.

In the majority of cases, a single Investigational New Drug (IND) or Investigational Device Exemption (IDE) is required to begin clinical studies for products with a biologic or device PMOA, respectively. Regulations regarding IND applications are detailed in 21 CFR 312, and those for IDE applications in 21 CFR 812. In some cases, two marketing applications, i.e., a Biological License Application (BLA) and a Premarket Approval (PMA), may be necessary to ensure, from a regulatory perspective, safety, efficacy or adequate postmarket regulation. FDA released *Number of Marketing Applications for a Combination Product* for comment, in which the number of marketing applications required for combination products is discussed.[16] It details instances where two marketing applications might be required:

"when a "BLA for Further Manufacture"… is appropriate to ensure the identity, safety, purity and potency of certain biological products (e.g., cell and gene therapy, therapeutic proteins, monoclonal antibodies, blood products) when the combination product as a whole is being regulated under the device or drug provisions."

A BLA for further manufacture could be required because the *PHS Act* provides for licensing intermediate products used in the manufacture of specifically identified biological products; thus, if a biologic is combined with a device during manufacture, a second marketing application may be required in addition to the application for the product as a whole.[17] For potentially complex regulatory routes like this, engaging the relevant authority at an early stage is recommended.

Point of Care Autologous Therapies and Same Surgical Procedure Exemption

A particularly complex regulatory scenario occurs with devices intended for processing autologous cells intra-operatively,*[1]also called 'point of care' processing.[18] 21 CFR, Section 1271.15 states compliance with Part 1271 is not required "if you are an establishment that removes HCT/P's from an individual and implants such HCT/P's into the same individual during the same surgical procedure." In the draft guidance *Cell selection devices for point of care production of minimally manipulated autologous peripheral blood stem cells (PBSCs)*,[20] FDA outlines five specific criteria that support the removal and subsequent implantation of PBSCs in the same surgical procedure. It is assumed that these will apply to other stem cell types:

1. The cells are autologous and are intended for use for a specific clinical indication.
2. The cells are minimally manipulated.
3. The device is solely responsible for the production of the autologous cells (i.e., no other manufacturing steps take place outside of the device other than the recovery of the source cells)
4. The cells are used within a short period of time (i.e., they are not stored or shipped).
5. The device and selected cells are used only at the point of care (i.e., cell processing is performed at and by the clinical site where cells are directly administered).

When these five conditions are met, FDA does not require compliance with 21 CFR 1271, and no IND or BLA for the cellular product is warranted. The product is regulated as a device, not as a combination product. If no device is used, and the cellular product meets the above applicable criteria and is transplanted back into the patient during the

* Intra-operative means the cells are harvested, processed and used for their purpose within the same surgical procedure. Processing might include concentrating a particular cell-type from a tissue sample, with the aim of implanting the concentrated cells in another location. Such approaches have been used to heal bone defects by concentrating certain cells from bone marrow, for example.

Table 31-4. Examples of Potential Regenerative Medicine Combination Products

Category	Examples
Cell therapy product	• Cell incorporating delivery device, such as catheters for intra-arterial delivery or sprays for topical application • Cell encapsulation devices
Tissue-engineered product	• Scaffold for cell growth • Growth factors and cells • Biomaterial cell combinations • Electrospun nanofibres with bioactive molecules

same surgical procedure, the cell product qualifies for the exception in Section 1271.15. FDA recently released *Draft Guidance for Industry: Same Surgical Procedure Exception under 21 CFR 1271.15(b): Questions and Answers Regarding the Scope of the Exception,*[20] which clarifies this matter further.

Devices not requiring an IND or BLA for the cellular product can be assigned to either CDRH or CBER. FDA has released specific guidance on which devices will be regulated by which center in a jurisdictional update, *Guidance for Industry and FDA Staff: Devices Used to Process Human Cells, Tissues, and Cellular and Tissue-Based Products (HCT/Ps).*[21] The assignment depends on the device's intended use: if the therapeutic effect is mediated by the device's biologic output, the device most likely will be regulated by CBER. In contrast, if the device simply is intended to isolate or concentrate cells used for *in vitro* diagnostics (i.e., they are not re-implanted into the patient), the device likely will be regulated by CDRH.

Generating Cell Populations for Therapeutic Use

FDA has issued *Guidance for Industry: Guidance for Human Somatic Cell Therapy and Gene Therapy*, regarding cellular material used therapeutically.[22] Relevant generally and broadly applicable sections are summarized in **Table 31-5**.

Cell Collection

FDA has stated the following information should be included in the IND regarding cell collection for therapeutic use:

1. Cell type: Cell type should be classified as autologous, allogeneic or xenogeneic.
2. Donor selection criteria: Relevant donor characteristics such as age and sex should be specified. Allogeneic donors, at a minimum, should meet the standards for blood donors (as stated in *Points to Consider in the Collection, Processing, and Testing of Ex-Vivo-Activated Mononuclear Leukocytes for Administration to Humans*[23]), and state testing and acceptance criteria and procedures, exclusion criteria focusing on presence or likelihood of infection by infectious agents such as, HIV-1, HIV-2, hepatitis B and C, and HTLV-1 should be provided. Serological, diagnostic and clinical history data to be obtained from donors, and donor follow-up provisions should be provided, if applicable.
3. Tissue typing: For allogeneic donors, typing for polymorphisms such as blood type should be included, if appropriate, and the importance of immunological matching at major histocompatibility antigens between donor and recipient should be covered along with typing procedures and acceptance procedures.
4. Procedures: Details of procedures for collection of cells should be provided.

Cell Culture Procedures

The following should be included in the IND for cell culture procedures:

1. quality control procedures
2. culture media: all media components should be recorded and acceptance criteria established
3. adventitious agents in cell cultures: confirmation adventitious agent absence should be documented (For long-term culture, this should occur periodically.)
4. cell identity and heterogeneity monitoring: manufacturing and testing procedures to ensure identity and heterogeneity are controlled; quantitative assessments are recommended
5. characterization of therapeutic entity: if a particular molecular species, synthesized by the cells, is responsible for the therapeutic effect, evidence that a biologically active form is present should be provided
6. culture longevity: essential cultured cell population characteristics should be defined and monitored for stability over time; this profile should be used to define the limits of the culture period

Cell Banking

Many allogeneic cell therapy products rely on cell banking systems to generate product over time. Often, this involves a two-tiered approach comprising a master cell bank (MCB) from which working cell banks (WCB) are generated. Guidance for establishment of cell banks is available in *Draft Guidance for Industry: Points to Consider in the Characterization of Cell Lines Used to Produce Biological Products.*[24] The following information should be included in the IND:[25]

1. cell origin and history

Table 31-5. Summary of Important IND Information for Generation of Cell Populations for Therapeutic Use

Area	Recommended Information to Provide in IND
Collection of cells	Cell type, donor selection criteria, tissue typing and procedures used
Cell culture	Quality control procedures, culture media, adventitious agents, monitoring of cell identity and heterogeneity, characterization of therapeutic entity, culture longevity
Cell banking	Origin and history of cells, freezing/thawing procedures, genotypic/phenotypic characterization, testing for contaminating organisms, expiration dating, tests for thawed cells, tests for working cell banks
Manufacturing materials	Any materials that may affect safety, purity or potency of the final product, acceptable concentration limits of such materials

Source: http://www.fda.gov/BiologicsBloodVaccines/GuidanceComplianceRegulatoryInformation/Guidances/CellularandGeneTherapy/ucm072987.htm

2. freezing and thawing procedures and the number of vials preserved in one lot
3. cell line characterization by phenotypic and/or genotypic markers
4. contaminated organism testing: MCBs must be shown to be free of adventitious agents
5. expiration dating: information on how long the cells can remain frozen for should be provided
6. thawed cell tests: viability, identity, function, yield and sterility tests should be repeated after thawing and/or expanding cells
7. WCBs also should undergo testing for identity with phenotypic and/or genotypic markers if used

For autologous cell therapies, cell banking may not be practical; however, crucial final product characteristics also may need to be tested.

Manufacturing Materials

Any materials used during *in vitro* manipulation of cells that may affect the final product's safety, purity or potency must be defined clearly, with specifications determined for acceptable use during manufacture. Examples of such materials include antibodies, cytokines, serum, protein A, toxins and antibiotics. Procedures for testing each reagent grade's safety, purity and potency should be included. For clinical grade materials, less-extensive testing may be acceptable. If materials persist in the final product, concentration limits should be specified. Removal procedures for any persisting materials, and assays to quantify removal, should be detailed, and if some added components are present in the final product, toxicity assessments in animals or other systems may be required.

Characterization and Release Testing

The final product, as well as the manufacturing process, should undergo quality control (QC) testing. QC testing information for the final product and manufacturing process elements should be included in the IND.[26] Each lot, defined as "a quantity of material that has been thoroughly mixed in a single vessel," requires release testing based on set QC criteria. In the case of preparations intended solely for one individual, e.g., autologous therapy, large batches will not be produced, and lot testing procedures should be adjusted appropriately given batch size constraints. Procedure reproducibility can be measured based on lot-to-lot variability. The following characteristics should be tested before lot release:

- cell identity
- potency
- viability
- adventitious agent testing
- purity
- general safety tests

Lot-release testing also is required on frozen populations of cells thawed and expanded prior to patient application, as indicated above.

Reference Materials

Biologics often are complex products that cannot be completely defined.[27] For cell and gene therapies, this is particularly true, and manufacturing process QC, therefore, is an important requirement. However, challenges associated with characterization and comparability of such products lead to difficulties in designing an adequate QC program. In particular, establishing reference materials (RMs) is challenging.[28,29] RMs are essential to allow comparability between batches and measure product drift over time, a major concern for cell therapies. Many complex analytical methods are required to demonstrate manufacturing consistency; however, these analytical methods themselves require RM to demonstrate consistency over time, posing a further challenge. At an early product development stage, manufacturers should begin to develop in-house RMs to test the lot-release characteristics accurately.

Preclinical Recommendations

FDA recently released *Guidance for Industry: Preclinical Assessment of Investigational Cellular and Gene Therapy Products*,[30] which supersedes preclinical recommendations given in the 1998 *Guidance for Industry: Guidance for Human Somatic Cell Therapy and Gene Therapy*.[31] These recommendations do not apply to cell, tissue or gene products regulated as 361 products or to those regulated as medical devices. The guidance document notes, although the same general principles of pharmacology and toxicology apply to CGT products, certain concepts and terms either are not applicable or have not yet been defined adequately for CGT products. Therefore, traditional standardized approaches used for drug and device testing may not be appropriate for CGT products, and a flexible review process taking into account the product's biology and its intended clinical application may be more appropriate. The blistering pace of development in the field necessitates this flexible approach, and communication between the sponsor and OCTGT should begin early in product development. Central to the recommendations is the concept of establishing the product's benefit-risk ratio.

Despite the flexible approach, basic toxicological and pharmacological principles underpinning more traditional preclinical investigations still apply. As such, preclinical study objectives include, as stated in Part III A of *Guidance for Industry: Preclinical Assessment of Investigational Cellular and Gene Therapy Products*:

1. establishment of biological plausibility
2. identification of biologically active dose levels
3. selection of potential starting dose level, dose-escalation schedule and dosing regimen for clinical trials
4. establishment of feasibility and reasonable safety of the investigational product's proposed clinical route of administration (ROA)
5. support of patient eligibility criteria
6. identification of physiologic parameters to guide clinical monitoring
7. identification of potential public health risks (e.g., to the general public, caregivers, family members, close contacts (e.g., co-workers) and intimate contacts)

Detailed recommendations for general preclinical program design to achieve these objectives are given in Part III B and can be summarized broadly as follows:

- If possible, the CGT product used in preclinical studies should be the same as the one used in clinical studies. In some cases, where the product is species-specific, the use of an analogous product may be acceptable.
- Animal species selected should demonstrate similar biological responses to those expected in humans, and consideration must be given to the applicability of a particular animal model to the product in question. In some cases, more than one species may need to be tested. Animal models of disease and injury should be used to aid definition of the product's benefit-risk ratio. Information on the animal model's limitations and benefits should be provided. These recommendations apply to all studies in which animals are used.
- Proof-of-concept (POC) studies should be used to inform the 'benefit' component of benefit-risk ratio. Studies should include optimization of various dosing parameters and ROA, as well as characterizing putative mechanisms of action (MOA) and the product's functional activity. *In vitro* MOA and safety studies are strongly recommended to complement *in vivo* preclinical studies.
- Toxicology studies should identify, characterize and quantify potential toxicities at different doses, as well as identify potential means of resolving such toxicity. Many of the primary considerations for designing toxicology studies are similar to the requirements of POC studies, including the proposed clinical indication, studies already completed on similar products or the product itself, previous experience with the proposed delivery vehicle, MOA and properties of the CGT product, and the suitability of the animal species/model for the investigation. Secondary considerations center on the need to mimic the proposed clinical trial design, including appropriate animal numbers per gender, appropriate controls, multiple dose levels, dosing schedule reflecting that to be used in humans, ROA, multiple sacrifice points, safety endpoints and other product specific parameters (e.g., product fate, behavioral effects). All preclinical toxicology studies should be conducted in compliance with Good Laboratory Practice (GLP) as discussed in 21 CFR part 58,[32] where possible.
- Risks associated with the ROA should be assessed, and the ROA used in preclinical studies should, therefore, be identical to that proposed for clinical studies. The IND submission should include sufficient data and justification for the delivery system. If a device master file (MAF) has been submitted previously, a letter from the MAF holder granting FDA permission to cross-reference information in the MAF should be included. CDRH staff then will be asked to determine whether the MAF information is adequate to support a clinical trial. If no MAF exists or the information is insufficient, CDRH may be consulted to determine what information is necessary to support the device's use in a clinical trial.
- The principles of reduction, refinement and replacement (the "3Rs") of animal use should be followed as well as appropriate animal welfare provisions.

- Outstanding issues arising from later clinical trials may need to be addressed with additional preclinical studies (e.g., demonstrating the equivalence of a product from a modified manufacturing process to the product used in preclinical studies).
- Preclinical study reports must be submitted for each *in vivo* and *in vitro* preclinical safety study. Complete reports are not required for pharmacology/POC studies, but information to allow independent interpretation of the study results must be provided.

Additionally, Parts IV and V of *Guidance for Industry: Preclinical Assessment of Investigational Cellular and Gene Therapy Products* provide further specific considerations for investigational cell and gene therapy products, respectively.

Clinical Considerations

In 2013, FDA released *Draft Guidance for Industry: Considerations for the Design of Early-Phase Clinical Trials of Cellular and Gene Therapy Products,*[33] outlining its current thinking on designing early-stage clinical trials. This guidance applies only to 351 CGT products. FDA has not released specific guidance on later-stage CGT product clinical trials; general clinical trial guidance can be found elsewhere in this book. Therefore, this discussion is largely limited to early-stage clinical trials.

Part III of the draft guidance[34] outlines the three key features of CGT products that influence clinical trial design: product characteristics, manufacturing considerations, and preclinical considerations.

- Product characteristics: CGT products are relatively understudied, and their safety has been questioned, particularly given the fact some CGT products can persist for extended periods of time. CGT products may require invasive surgery or an investigational device for administration, adding risk to the procedure. Allogeneic cell products and gene vectors may elicit an immune response. As living products, cells may migrate and undergo malignant or benign transformation, and can be influenced by the microenvironment and change over time. Gene therapies carry risks of disrupting normal gene function and may lead to tumorigenic transformation. For *ex vivo* gene therapy products, considerations for cell and gene therapies apply.
- Manufacturing considerations: the complexities of the manufacturing process may put a practical limit on the quantity of product that can be produced, and as such, the range of doses or product concentration that can be used. Autologous therapies can be even more complex due to the need for a distinct manufacturing process for each patient.
- Preclinical considerations: as outlined in the previous section, preclinical studies supporting safety and appropriate benefit-risk of the CGT product

Objectives

Part IV of the *Draft Guidance for Industry: Considerations for the Design of Early-Phase Clinical Trials of Cellular and Gene Therapy Products*[35] outlines how these considerations impact CGT product clinical trial design. The primary aim of a Phase I trial to investigate the new product's safety. The three central objectives of early-stage CGT trials, according to Part IV A, are:

1. Dose exploration: for therapies addressing life-threatening diseases, a certain level of toxicity in a CGT product may be anticipated and acceptable. A major goal of early clinical trials, therefore, may be establishing a maximum tolerated dose (MTD). If toxicity is not expected to be substantial, dose exploration may focus instead on determining the optimal effective dose. Given practical GCT product manufacturing limitations, some trials instead may focus on characterizing safety of feasible doses.
2. Feasibility assessment: CGT products may require specialized ROA. Clinical trial design in this case should aim to identify and characterize any potential issues with the product's manufacture and administration
3. Activity assessments: assessing product potential activity and efficacy often is a secondary aim of the early preclinical study

Study Population

Part IV B of the *Draft Guidance for Industry: Considerations for the Design of Early-Phase Clinical Trials of Cellular and Gene Therapy Products,*[36] raises study population selection considerations. Study population choice should reflect the therapy's expected risks and potential benefits. The benefit-risk profile can be estimated based on previous preclinical or clinical studies; however, the clinical significance of any anticipated risk is dependent on the population receiving the product, as is the potential for benefit. In some cases, the use of healthy volunteers in early clinical trials may be appropriate; however, the possible risks associated with CGT products often include long-term effects and risks associated with the MOA so healthy subjects often are inappropriate. Therefore, a study population including patients affected by the condition the product is intended to treat is more suitable in many cases.

Selection of patient population based on disease stage or severity is complex. For more advanced disease, it may be easier to justify risks associated with treatment; however, if disease is so advanced even a slight decrease in function could lead to complete loss of function (e.g., vision), it may

Figure 31-1. Framework for Assessing Risk of Gene Therapy-Related Delayed Adverse Events

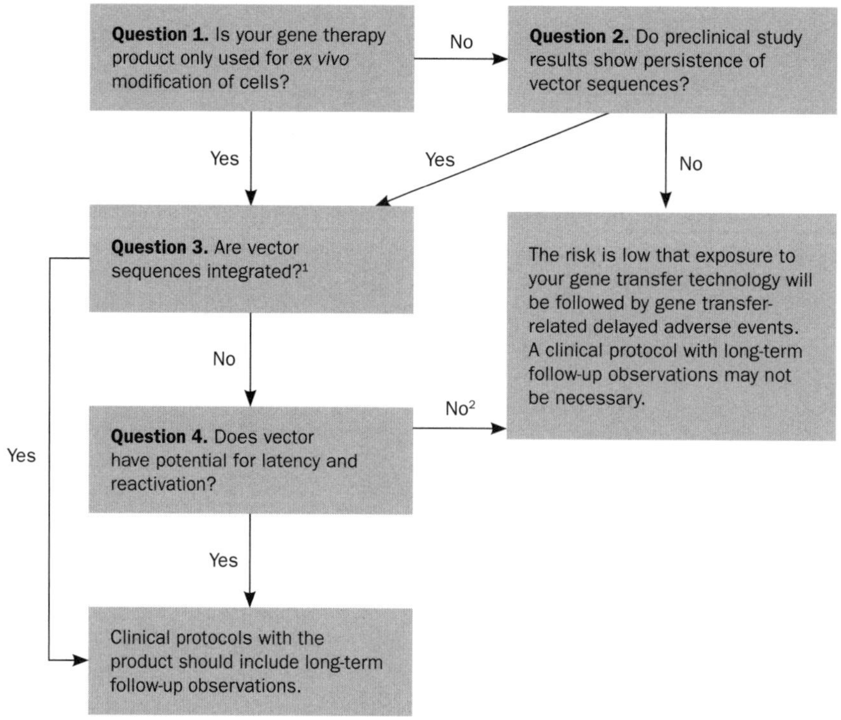

Source: http://www.fda.gov/BiologicsBloodVaccines/GuidanceComplianceRegulatoryInformation/Guidances/CellularandGeneTherapy/ucm072957.htm

be preferable to justify risk in less-diseased individuals in whom a loss of function could be tolerated. Furthermore, the potential benefit to the patients should be taken into account, as well as the influence the disease stage may have on the ability to detect evidence of benefit. For example, it may be challenging to interpret results from patients with late-stage disease if there are many confounding adverse events. Patients with a lack of other treatment options, for example those who have failed to respond to other available treatments, also may be used in CGT trials. In this case, the lack of other treatments should be evaluated properly.

Finally, for treatments aimed specifically at pediatric populations, special recommendations must be followed. 21 CFR 50 subpart D outlines the "Additional Safeguards for Children in Clinical Investigations."

Controlling and Blinding

As outlined in Part IV C of the *Draft Guidance for Industry: Considerations for the Design of Early-Phase Clinical Trials of Cellular and Gene Therapy Products,*[37] the use of controls and blinding for CGT trials is complicated by the fact some CGT products require administration via invasive procedures. For early-stage trials, in which the central aim is assessing efficacy, the risk of performing blinding in control subjects usually is not justifiable, as demonstration of efficacy is not necessary.

FDA has not issued specific guidance for later-stage clinical trials. However, Part IV C states the use of blinding and controls "might be considered for a later confirmatory trial." Also, in *Guidance for Industry: Cellular Therapy for Cardiac Disease,*[38] FDA notes a "sham control" (placebo surgery) may be particularly important for studies with subjective outcome measures that might be influenced by factors such as patient or observer expectations. Due to the additional risks of placebo surgery compared to traditional placebo drugs, trials may be designed to administer the product to control subjects after the study has ended, if proven effective.

In many treatments, placebo surgery generally is safer than the treatment arm and can be effective in demonstrating the efficacy of surgical procedures.[39] Although blinding can present challenges, it has been achieved successfully in many trials, including those of cell therapies.[40] FDA emphasises the importance of maintaining blinding in such studies.[41] Although recommended and effective, the placebo arm of some regenerative medicine products has proven problematic. In clinical trials of Sipuleucel-T (Provenge; Dendreon Corporation, Seattle, WA), for example, possible detrimental effects in subjects receiving the placebo treatment provoked much controversy. The potential effect of any placebo procedure should, therefore, be considered carefully to avoid such situations.

Given the frequently high cost of treating patients with CGT products, the use of control arms with the current standard of care may be required, as well as a placebo arm, to show cell-containing treatments are more effective than current, and possibly less expensive, treatments.

Dosing and Treatment

Parts IV D and E of *Draft Guidance for Industry: Considerations for the Design of Early-Phase Clinical Trials of Cellular and Gene Therapy Products*[42] outline considerations for dose selection and treatment plans, respectively. Initial dose selection is challenging and must take into account safety considerations as well as potential variability between the active dose administered to subjects (e.g., if the active cell subset in a cellular product is not known, or there are variable transduction rates for gene therapy products). In early-stage clinical trials, a one-time dosing regimen typically is used because most CGT products potentially can persist over long periods of time. When no data are available to establish a particular dose, staggered dosing between patients should be used to minimize risk. In later trials, different dosing regimens may be used once safe doses have been established. It is recommended those administering the treatment be adequately trained by an operator in each step of the administration process.

For patient-specific products, since the manufacturing process can take weeks or months, it is possible a patient enrolled in and eligible for a trial no longer will be eligible by the time the product is manufactured. The selection process may need to take factors into account that affect eligibility criteria to ensure patients meet the criteria at the time of administration.

Stopping rules should be included in early-phase trials due to the uncertainty surrounding potential CGT product adverse reactions. A stopping rule typically will detail a certain number or frequency of adverse events, after which some protocol component is changed or patient enrollment is suspended while the situation is assessed properly. In *Guidance for Industry: Cellular Therapy for Cardiac Disease,*[43] FDA similarly stresses the importance of including stopping rules in cellular therapy for cardiac disease, not necessarily limited to early-phase trials. On the other hand, positive results might warrant switching control arm patients to the active arm so they, too, receive the benefit. Both considerations must be made before the trial commences.

Monitoring and Follow-up of Early-Phase Trials

Part IV F of *Draft Guidance for Industry: Considerations for the Design of Early-Phase Clinical Trials of Cellular and Gene Therapy Products*[44] discusses monitoring and follow-up. General safety monitoring is required for all early-phase clinical trials; however, there are additional safety considerations for CGT products. Manufacturers should monitor potential product-specific issues unique to CGT products, including acute or delayed infusion reactions, autoimmunity, graft failure, GVHD, new malignancies, transmission of infectious agents from a donor and viral reactivation. Methods for *in vivo* tracking and monitoring may be required as, unlike traditional drugs that are metabolized, transplantation of live cells could lead to a host of issues including homing, engraftment, differentiation, trafficking and tumorogenesis, which, to a certain extent, can be assessed only after the cells have been transplanted.

The follow-up period for CGT products typically is recommended to be one year or more, although for some products, such as integrating gene therapies, the recommendation for long-term safety is to follow subjects for 15 years. Safety in gene therapy clinical trials has been particularly contentious, following the controversial death of Jesse Gelsinger in 1999.[45]

Delayed Adverse Events in Gene Therapy Trials

Guidance for Industry: Gene Therapy Clinical Trials—Observing Subjects for Delayed Adverse Events[46] outlines the criteria for gene therapy products that require long-term follow-up (up to 15 years). The framework for assessing the risk of gene therapy-related delayed adverse events, as detailed in the guidance, is provided in **Figure 31-1**. The

Table 31-6. Integration Properties of Current Commonly Used Gene Therapy Vectors in Clinical Trials

Vector Type	Propensity to Integrate[1]	Long-term Follow-up observations[2]
Plasmid	No	No
PoxVirus	No	No
Adenovirus	No	No
Adeno-associated virus[3]	No	No
Herpesvirus	No, but may undergo latency/ reactivation	Yes
Gammaretrovirus	Yes	Yes
Lentivirus	Yes	Yes

[1]Based on vector design (i.e., lack of any known mechanism to facilitate integration) as well as cumulative preclinical and clinical evidence suggesting that vector does not integrate or integrates only at very low frequencies.
[2]Specific circumstances showing persistent expression of the transgene, in the absence of integration, may be the basis for a conclusion that long-term follow-up observations are necessary to mitigate long-term risks to subjects receiving these vectors.
[3]Rep-negative vectors only.
Source: http://www.fda.gov/BiologicsBloodVaccines/GuidanceCompliance RegulatoryInformation/Guidances/CellularandGeneTherapy/ucm072957.htm

Table 31-7. Guidance Available for Regenerative Medicine Products (In Reverse Chronological Order)

Topic	Document	Year
Adipose tissue-derived cell and tissue products	*Draft Guidance for Industry: Human Cells, Tissues, and Cellular and Tissue-Based Products (HCT/Ps) from Adipose Tissue: Regulatory Considerations*	2014
Minimal manipulation	*Draft Guidance for Industry and Food and Drug Administration Staff: Minimal Manipulation of Human Cells, Tissues, and Cellular and Tissue-Based Products*	2014
Same surgical procedure exception	*Draft Guidance for Industry: Same Surgical Procedure Exception under 21 CFR 1271.15(b): Questions and Answers Regarding the Scope of the Exception*	2014
Virus or bacteria-based gene therapy and oncolytic therapy	*Draft Guidance for Industry: Design and Analysis of Shedding Studies for Virus or Bacteria-Based Gene Therapy and Oncolytic Products*	2014
Environmental issues	*Draft Guidance for Industry: Determining the Need for and Content of Environmental Assessments for Gene Therapies, Vectored Vaccines, and Related Recombinant Viral or Microbial Products*	2014
Cord blood products	*Guidance for Industry and FDA Staff: IND Applications for Minimally Manipulated, Unrelated Allogeneic Placental/Umbilical Cord Blood Intended for Hematopoietic and Immunologic Reconstitution in Patients with Disorders Affecting the Hematopoietic System*	2014
Preclinical assessment	*Guidance for Industry: Preclinical Assessment of Investigational Cellular and Gene Therapy Products*	2013
Early-phase clinical trials	*Draft Guidance for Industry: Considerations for the Design of Early-Phase Clinical Trials of Cellular and Gene Therapy Products*	2013
Knee cartilage repair and replacement	*Guidance for Industry: Preparation of IDEs and INDs for Products Intended to Repair or Replace Knee Cartilage*	2011
Cancer vaccines	*Guidance for Industry: Clinical Considerations for Therapeutic Cancer Vaccines*	2011
Cord blood products	*Guidance for Industry and FDA Staff: Investigational New Drug Applications for Minimally Manipulated, Unrelated Allogeneic Placental/Umbilical Cord Blood Intended for Hematopoietic Reconstitution for Specified Indications.*	2011
Potency	*Guidance for Industry: Potency Tests for Cellular and Gene Therapy Products*	2011
Cardiac disease	*Guidance for Industry: Cellular Therapy for Cardiac Disease*	2010
Immunogenicity assays	*Draft Guidance for Industry: Assay Development for Immunogenicity Testing of Therapeutic Proteins*	2009
Cord blood products	*Guidance for Industry:Minimally Manipulated, Unrelated Allogeneic Placental/Umbilical Cord Blood Intended for Hematopoietic Reconstitution for Specified Indications*	2009
Allogeneic pancreatic islet products	*Guidance for Industry: Considerations for Allogeneic Pancreatic Islet Cell Products*	2009
Chemistry, manufacturing and control (CMC) of gene therapy products	*Guidance for FDA Reviewers and Sponsors: Content and Review of Chemistry, Manufacturing, and Control (CMC) Information for Human Gene Therapy Investigational New Drug Applications (INDs)*	2008
CMC for cell therapy products	*Guidance for FDA Reviewers and Sponsors: Content and Review of Chemistry, Manufacturing, and Control (CMC) Information for Human Somatic Cell Therapy Investigational New Drug Applications (INDs)*	2008
Sterility testing	*Draft Guidance for Industry: Validation of Growth-Based Rapid Microbiological Methods for Sterility Testing of Cellular and Gene Therapy Products*	2008
Donor eligibility	*Guidance for Industry: Eligibility Determination for Donors of Human Cells, Tissues, and Cellular and Tissue-Based Products*	2007
Delayed adverse events in gene therapy	*Guidance for Industry: Gene Therapy Clinical Trials—Observing Subjects for Delayed Adverse Events*	2006
Retroviral vector gene therapy	*Guidance for Industry: Supplemental Guidance on Testing for Replication Competent Retrovirus in Retroviral Vector Based Gene Therapy Products and During Follow-up of Patients in Clinical Trials Using Retroviral Vectors*	2006
Cell and gene therapy	*Guidance for Industry: Guidance for Human Somatic Cell Therapy and Gene Therapy*	1998
CMC for autologous cell therapy	*Guidance for the Submission of Chemistry, Manufacturing, and Controls Information and Establishment Description for Autologous Somatic Cell Therapy Products*	1997

need for long-term follow up revolves around the propensity for any gene therapy to persist or reactivate over long periods of time. In particular, gene therapies involving integration into host cell DNA will require long-term follow up, as illustrated in **Table 31-6**. Further information on the specific requirements for delayed adverse event reporting can be found in the guidance document.

Additional Available Guidance for CGT Products

FDA has released many guidance and draft guidance documents, including guidance for specific indications and/or treatments. **Table 31-7** provides a comprehensive reference list of all available guidance for CGT products, based on information on the FDA website.

Summary

- The term 'regenerative medicine' describes a group of medicinal products comprising cell therapy, gene therapy and tissue engineering.
- Each of these product types is applicable to a variety of indications, although collectively, they pose regulatory challenges.
- HCT/P regulation is applicable to regenerative medicines. HCT/Ps can be regulated as either '361 products' or '351 products.' 351 products are regulated as drugs, biologics or devices.
- Combination products are regulated as 351 products, with the lead center determined by the product's PMOA.
- Some cell therapy products may be exempt from the IND requirement if they comply with the same surgical procedure exemption.
- IND submissions are required to include information on generation of CGT products, including the collection of cells, cell culture, cell banking and manufacturing materials.
- Characterization and release testing are essential for CGT products; however, there are challenges associated with these requirements, such as the generation of reference materials.
- FDA takes a flexible approach in evaluating preclinical data for CGT products, although the same underlying principles apply to CGT products as to more conventional therapeutics.
- Early-phase CGT product clinical trials follow similar principles to trials for more conventional products, although differences include the selection of study participants, the use of controls and blinding and dosing regimens used.
- Follow-up periods for CGT product clinical trials are typically at least one year; follow-up for some gene therapy products extend to 15 years.
- Minimal guidance is available on late-phase clinical trials specific to CGT products.
- FDA has released a large number of guidance documents for specific aspects/applications of CGT products and regenerative medicines.

References

1. Mason C, Dunnill P. "A brief definition of regenerative medicine." *Regen Med.* 2008 Jan;3(1):1–5.
2. Lee MH, Hyde J, Johnson C, Heidaran M, et al. "Translation of Regenerative Medicine Products Into the Clinic in the United States: FDA Perspective." *Tranlational Regenerative Medicine.* 2014. p. 49–74.
3. Mason C, Brindley DA, Culme-Seymour EJ, Davie NL. "Cell therapy industry: billion dollar global business with unlimited potential." *Regen Med.* 2011 May;6(3):265–72.
4. Davies BM, Rikabi S, French A, Pinedo-Villanueva R, Morrey ME, Wartolowska K, et al. "Quantitative assessment of barriers to the clinical development and adoption of cellular therapies: A pilot study." *J Tissue Eng.* 2014 Jan 1;5:2041731414551764.
5. Vishnubhatla I, Corteling R, Stevanato L, Hicks C, Sinden J. "The Development of Stem Cell-derived Exosomes as a Cell-free Regenerative Medicine." *J Circ Biomark.* 2014;1.
6. Smith JA, Ng KS, Mead BE, Dopson S, Reeve, B, Edwards J, Wood MJA, Carr AJ, Bure K, Karp JM and Brindley DA (2015). "Extracellular Vesicles Commercial Potential As Byproducts of Cell Manufacturing for Research and Therapeutic Use." Bioprocess International. 13 (4)s: 20-27
7. Amer MH. "Gene therapy for cancer: present status and future perspective." *Mol Cell Ther.* 2014 Sep 10;2(1):27.
8. Ibid.
9. Fisher MB, Mauck RL. "Tissue Engineering and Regenerative Medicine: Recent Innovations and the Transition to Translation." *Tissue Eng.* Part B Rev. 2013 Feb;19(1):1–13.
10. Fink DW. "FDA Regulation of Stem Cell Therapeutics." *Science.* 2009 Jun 26;324:1662.
11. FDA. *Draft Guidance: Cellular & Gene Therapy Guidances - Minimal Manipulation of Human Cells, Tissues, and Cellular and Tissue-Based Products.* FDA website. http://www.fda.gov/BiologicsBloodVaccines/GuidanceComplianceRegulatoryInformation/Guidances/CellularandGeneTherapy/ucm427692.htm. Accessed 4 May 2015.
12. FDA. *Guidance for Industry: Guidance for Human Somatic Cell Therapy and Gene Therapy.* FDA website. http://www.fda.gov/BiologicsBloodVaccines/GuidanceComplianceRegulatoryInformation/Guidances/CellularandGeneTherapy/ucm072987.htm. Accessed 4 May 2015.
13. Op cit 2.
14. FDA. Office of the Commissioner. About Combination Products—Frequently Asked Questions About Combination Products. FDA website. http://www.fda.gov/CombinationProducts/AboutCombinationProducts/ucm101496.htm. Accessed 4 May 2015.
15. Jennings J. "Combination Products." *Fundamentals of US Regulatory Affairs. 8th ed.* Regulatory Affairs Professionals Society; 2013. p. 311–8.
16. FDA. Concepts for Comment Purposes Only—Not for Implementation; Number of Marketing Applications for a Combination Product. FDA website. http://www.fda.gov/downloads/CombinationProducts/RequestsforComment/UCM108197.pdf. Accessed 4 May 2015.
17. Siegel EB. "Detailed Regulatory Approaches to development, Review and Approval. Development and Approval of Combination Products: A Regulatory Perspective". *John Wiley & Sons*; 2008.
18. Coelho MB, Cabral JMS, Karp JM. "Intraoperative Stem Cell Therapy." *Annu Rev Biomed Eng.* 2012;14:325–49.
19. FDA. *Draft Guidance for Industry: Cell Selection Devices for Point of Care Production of Minimally Manipulated Autologous Peripheral Blood*

Stem Cells (PBSCs). FDA website. http://www.fda.gov/OHRMS/DOCKETS/98fr/07d-0290-gdl0001.pdf. Accessed 4 May 2015

20. FDA. *Draft Guidance for Industry: Same Surgical Procedure Exception under 21 CFR 1271.15(b): Questions and Answers Regarding the Scope of the Exception.* FDA website. http://www.fda.gov/BiologicsBloodVaccines/GuidanceComplianceRegulatoryInformation/Guidances/Tissue/ucm419911.htm. Accessed 4 May 2015.
21. FDA. *Guidance for Industry and FDA Staff: Devices Used to Process Human Cells, Tissues, and Cellular and Tissue-Based Products (HCT/Ps).* FDA website. http://www.fda.gov/RegulatoryInformation/Guidances/ucm126052.htm. Accessed 4 May 2015.
22. Op cit 12.
23. FDA. Points to Consider in the Collection, Processing, and Testing of Ex-Vivo-Activated Mononuclear Leukocytes for Administration to Humans, 1989. FDA website. http://www.fda.gov/downloads/BiologicsBloodVaccines/GuidanceComplianceRegulatoryInformation/OtherRecommendationsforManufacturers/UCM062770.pdf. Accessed 4 May 2015.
24. FDA. Points to Consider in the Characterization of Cell Lines Used to Produce Biological Products, 1993. FDA website. http://www.fda.gov/downloads/BiologicsBloodVaccines/SafetyAvailability/UCM162863.pdf Accessed 4 May 2015.
25. Op cit 12.
26. Ibid.
27. Ibid.
28. French A, Bravery C, Smith J, Chandra A, Archibald P, Gold JD, et al. "Enabling Consistency in Pluripotent Stem Cell-Derived Products for Research and Development and Clinical Applications Through Material Standards." *Stem Cells Transl Med.* 2015 Feb 3.
29. Bravery CA, French A. "Reference materials for cellular therapeutics." *Cytotherapy.* 2014 Sep 1;16(9):1187–96.
30. FDA. *Guidance for Industry: Preclinical Assessment of Investigational Cellular and Gene Therapy Products.* FDA website. http://www.fda.gov/BiologicsBloodVaccines/GuidanceComplianceRegulatoryInformation/Guidances/CellularandGeneTherapy/ucm376136.htm. Accessed 4 May 2015.
31. Op cit 12.
32. Code of Federal Regulations Title 21. FDA website. http://www.accessdata.fda.gov/scripts/cdrh/cfdocs/cfcfr/CFRsearch.cfm?CFRPart=58. Accessed 4 May 2015.
33. FDA. *Draft Guidance for Industry: Considerations for the Design of Early-Phase Clinical Trials of Cellular and Gene Therapy Products* FDA website. dhttp://www.fda.gov/downloads/BiologicsBloodVaccines/GuidanceComplianceRegulatoryInformation/Guidances/CellularandGeneTherapy/UCM359073.pdf. Accessed 4 May 2015.
34. Ibid.
35. Ibid.
36. Ibid.
37. Ibid.
38. FDA. *Guidance for Industry: Cellullar Therapy for Cardiac Disease.* FDA website. http://www.fda.gov/downloads/BiologicsBloodVaccines/GuidanceComplianceRegulatoryInformation/Guidances/CellularandGeneTherapy/UCM164345.pdf. Accessed 4 May 2015.
39. Wartolowska K, Judge A, Hopewell S, Collins GS, Dean BJF, Rombach I, et al. "Use of placebo controls in the evaluation of surgery: systematic review." *BMJ.* 2014 May 21;348(May21 2):g3253–g3253.
40. Gross RE, Watts RL, Hauser RA, Bakay RA, Reichmann H, von Kummer R, et al. "Intrastriatal transplantation of microcarrier-bound human retinal pigment epithelial cells versus sham surgery in patients with advanced Parkinson's disease: a double-blind, randomised, controlled trial." *Lancet Neurol.* 2011 Jun;10(6):509–19.
41. Op cit 38.
42. Op cit. 33
43. Op cit 38
44. Op cit 33.
45. Stolberg SG. "The biotech death of Jesse Gelsinger." *New York Times Magazine.* 1999;28:136–40.
46. FDA. *Guidance for Industry: Gene Therapy Clinical Trials—Observing Subjects for Delayed Adverse Events.* FDA website. http://www.fda.gov/BiologicsBloodVaccines/GuidanceComplianceRegulatoryInformation/Guidances/CellularandGeneTherapy/ucm072957.htm. Accessed 4 May 2015

Recommended Reading

French A, Bravery C, Smith J, Chandra A, Archibald P, Gold JD, et al. "Enabling Consistency in Pluripotent Stem Cell-Derived Products for Research and Development and Clinical Applications Through Material Standards." *Stem Cells Transl Med.* 2015 February 3.

Lee MH,, Hyde J, Johnson C, Heidaran M, et al. "Translation of Regenerative Medicine Products Into the Clinic in the United States: FDA Perspective." *Translational Regenerative Medicine.* 2014. p. 49–74.

PAS 83: 2012 Developing human cells for clinical applications in the European Union and the United States—Guide (2012).

Acknowledgments

The authors wish to express our sincere thanks to the following organizations that have contributed to the CASMI Translational Stem Cell Consortium (CTSCC) as funding and events partners, without whom the consortium and the benefits it will bring to stem cell translation would be constrained: GE Healthcare, CCRM, Sartorius Stedim Biotech (formerly TAP Biosystems), Lonza, CIRM, SENS Research Foundation, UK Cell Therapy Catapult, NIH Centre for Regenerative Medicine, NYSCF, ThermoFisher Scientific, Eisai, Medipost (US), Medipost (Korea), Celgene, Roche and Oxford Biomedica. DA Brindley gratefully acknowledges personal funding from the Oxford Musculoskeletal NIHR BRU, the Said Foundation and the SENS Research Foundation. JA Smith gratefully acknowledges support from the CTSCC.

Disclosures

The content outlined herein represents the individual opinions of the authors and may not necessarily represent the viewpoints of their employers. DA Brindley gratefully acknowledges support from the SENS Research Foundation (Mountain View, CA). Brindley is a stockholder in Translation Ventures Ltd. (Charlbury, Oxfordshire, UK), a company that, among other services, provides cell therapy biomanufacturing, regulatory and financial advice to clients in the cell therapy sector. He is subject to the CFA Institute's Codes, Standards and Guidelines and, as such, must stress that this piece is provided for academic interest only and must not be construed in any way as an investment recommendation. Additionally, at the time of publication, DA Brindley and the organizations with which he is affiliated, may or may not have agreed and/or pending funding commitments from the organizations named herein.

Chapter 32

Laws and Regulations Pertaining to Pediatrics

Updated by Mitchell E. Parrish, JD, CIP, RAC

OBJECTIVES

- ❑ Review the history behind the regulatory framework governing pediatric products
- ❑ Learn how the *Best Pharmaceuticals for Children Act* (*BPCA*) functions
- ❑ Learn the *Pediatric Research Equity Act* (*PREA*) requirements
- ❑ Understand the difference between *BPCA* and *PREA*
- ❑ Know how the Pediatric Priority Review Voucher operates and incentives the development of products
- ❑ Review the *Pediatric Medical Safety and Improvement Act* requirements

LAWS, REGULATIONS AND GUIDELINES COVERED IN THIS CHAPTER

- ❑ *Guidance for Industry: General Considerations for the Clinical Evaluation of Drugs in Infants and Children* (September 1977)
- ❑ American Academy of Pediatrics Clinical Report: Guidelines for the Ethical Conduct of Studies to Evaluate Drugs in Pediatric Populations (April 2010)
- ❑ *Orphan Drug Act* of 1983
- ❑ *Guidance for Industry: The Content and Format for Pediatric Use Supplements* (May 1996)
- ❑ *Food and Drug Administration Modernization Act* of 1997
- ❑ *Best Pharmaceuticals for Children Act* of 2002
- ❑ *Pediatric Research Equity Act* of 2003
- ❑ *Food and Drug Administration Amendments Act* of 2007
- ❑ *Pediatric Medical Device Safety and Improvement Act* of 2007
- ❑ *Food and Drug Administration Safety and Innovation Act* of 2012
- ❑ 21 CFR 316 Orphan Drugs
- ❑ 21 CFR 50, Subpart D Protection of Human Subjects; additional safeguards for children in clinical investigations
- ❑ 21 CFR 201.23 Labeling; required pediatric studies
- ❑ 21 CFR 201.57(c)(9)(iv) Labeling; specific requirements on content and format of labeling for human prescription drug and biological products described in 201.56(b)(1); full prescribing information; use in specific populations; pediatric use

- ❑ 21 CFR 314.55 Applications for FDA approval to market a new drug; pediatric use information
- ❑ 21 CFR 314.50(d)(7) Applications for FDA approval to market a new drug; content and format of an application; technical sections; pediatric use section
- ❑ 21 CFR 314.81(b)(2) Applications for FDA approval to market a new drug; other postmarketing reports; reporting requirements; annual report
- ❑ *Draft Guidance for Industry: Pediatric Study Plans: Content of and Process for Submitting Initial Pediatric Study Plans and Amended Pediatric Study Plans* (July 2013)
- ❑ *Draft Guidance for Industry: How to Comply with the Pediatric Research Equity Act* (September 2005)
- ❑ *Guidance for Industry: Qualifying for Pediatric Exclusivity Under Section 505(A) of the Federal Food, Drug, and Cosmetic Act* (September 1999)
- ❑ *Draft Guidance for Industry and Review Staff: Pediatric Information Incorporated Into Human Prescription Drug and Biological Products Labeling* (February 2013)
- ❑ *Draft Guidance for Industry: Rare Pediatric Disease Priority Review Vouchers* (November 2014)
- ❑ *Guidance for Industry and Food and Drug Administration Staff: Premarket Assessment of Pediatric Medical Devices* (March 2014)
- ❑ ICH, *Clinical Investigation of Medicinal Products in the Pediatric Population E11* (July 2000)

Introduction

A well-worn but important phrase is "children are not small adults." This phrase is critical when calculating drug doses or assessing physiological parameters. Simply adjusting a drug's dose for a smaller person does not guarantee safety or effectiveness in a child, and a device that functions properly in adults may not perform the same in children due to differences in growth, metabolism and activity levels.

Due to the differences between children and adults, there is a significant medical need to understand and develop drugs and devices for pediatric populations. Despite this need, gaps in knowledge and products exist for a number of potential reasons:

- ethical concerns in enrolling pediatric patients in studies
- limited populations for certain diseases
- technical difficulties in conducting pediatric trials (e.g., developing assays that process very small amounts of blood)
- lack of suitable infrastructure for conducting pediatric trials (e.g., minimal validated pediatric assessment tools)
- limited marketing potential compared to adults (i.e., lack of incentives for companies to develop drugs for neonates, infants and children)

To combat these gaps, the US Food and Drug Administration (FDA) historically has produced a number of pediatric initiatives designed to expand and encourage the development of medical products in children, culminating with the *Food and Drug Administration Safety and Innovation Act (FDASIA)* of 2012.

History of Pediatric Initiatives

- 1972—Former FDA Commissioner Charles Edwards stated at the American Academy of Pediatrics (AAP) annual meeting that most prescription products used in children are given based on empirical evidence.
- 1973—The National Academy of Sciences issued a report calling for innovative investigative programs to provide information on the use of pharmacologic agents in the pediatric population.
- 1974—AAP issued a report commissioned by FDA on the evaluation of drugs to be used in the treatment of pregnant women, infants and children.
- 1975—Professor John Wilson of the Department of Pediatrics at LSU Medical Center published a survey of prescription drug package inserts noting that 78% of package inserts state the product either had not been studied in infants and children or had no pediatric statement.
- 1977—Publication of three documents related to pediatric research:
    - o FDA published *Guidance for Industry: General Considerations for the Clinical Evaluation of Drugs in Infants and Children.*
    - o National Commission on Pediatric Research issued *General Considerations for the Clinical Evaluation of Drugs in Infants and Children.*
    - o AAP issued *Guidelines for the Ethical Study of Drugs in Infants and Children.*
- 1979—FDA published a regulation adding a pediatric use subsection to the precautions section of the approved product package insert.

- 1983—The *Orphan Drug Act* established the precedent of incentives, provided by the federal government, to develop new therapeutics for underserved populations.
- 1994—The National Institute of Child Health and Development (NICHD) established the first national network for pediatric pharmacology.
- 1995—AAP revised *Guidelines for the Ethical Conduct of Studies to Evaluate Drugs in Pediatric Populations*.
- 1996—FDA issued *Guidance for Industry: The Content and Format of Pediatric Use Section*.
- 1996—The National Institutes of Health (NIH) initiated a policy of requiring NIH-funded clinical research to address applicability to pediatric populations.
- 1997—*The Food and Drug Administration Modernization Act (FDAMA)* established an incentive program for pediatric studies for medicinal products. Incentives, such as additional six months' exclusivity or patent extension, may be permitted after FDA issues a written request for relevant pediatric studies to the sponsor. The incentive is granted after a review confirms the study has been conducted in accordance with the FDA agreement. The program is limited to chemical moieties and excludes biological products and some antibiotics. Additionally, *FDAMA* generally encouraged the following:
  - o the development of medical and surgical devices for pediatric patients
  - o assurance drugs that are or will be prescribed for children are tested for safety and effectiveness in children.
  - o the review of study designs to ensure pediatric patients are protected and these studies result in medically and ethically appropriate data for pediatric therapeutics
- 1998—FDA published a regulation ("Pediatric Rule") mandating pediatric studies when the disease or condition is similar in adults and children, and if either widespread use is anticipated or the product is a therapeutic advance.
- 2002—The Federal Court in the District of Columbia invalidated the 1998 Pediatric Rule, holding FDA overstepped its authority in requiring pediatric testing unless the manufacturer can show it is highly unlikely the drug will be used in pediatric populations.
- 2002—The *Best Pharmaceuticals for Children Act (BPCA)* renewed the pediatric incentive program and established a program for the study of off-patent products through the NICHD.
- 2003—The *Pediatric Research Equity Act (PREA)* established the mandates of the 1998 Pediatric Rule as law for drugs and biological products, excluding products with Orphan Drug designation. (See the section on *PREA* below for details.)
- 2006—FDA, under the incentive programs defined in the *BPCA*, revised product package inserts for 118 products with new pediatric information.
- 2007—The *Food and Drug Administration Amendments Act (FDAAA)* became law and renewed, with modification, *PREA and BPCA* and introduced *the Pediatric Medical Device Safety and Improvement Act.*
- 2010—The *Patient Protection and Affordable Care Act* of 2010 expanded *BPCA* to include biologics.
- 2012 —The *Food and Drug Administration Safety and Innovation Act (FDASIA)* was signed into law and renewed and strengthened three essential pediatric research laws *(PREA, BPCA* and the *Pediatric Medical Device Safety and Improvement Act*). *FDASIA* also made *PREA* and *BPCA* permanent, so they no longer require reauthorization every five years. Finally, *FDASIA* created the Pediatric Priority Review Voucher Program to encourage the development of treatments for rare pediatric diseases.

The remainder of this chapter covers those initiatives key to understanding the current regulatory framework governing drugs, biologics and devices in pediatric populations: *BPCA*, *PREA*, the Priority Review Voucher Program and the *Pediatric Medical Device Safety and Improvement Act.* However, since each of these laws implicates research in children, it is important to first understand those FDA regulations governing studies in pediatric populations.

Pediatric Clinical Research Regulations

In addition to all protections afforded to adults in clinical research, children receive extra safeguards. These include restrictions on conducting studies in children unless an Institutional Review Board (IRB) approves the study and, in its approval, finds the study has an appropriate risk-benefit ratio:

- no greater than minimal risk (21 CFR 50.51)
- greater than minimal risk but presents the prospect of direct benefit to the individual child participating in the research (21 CFR 50.52)
- a minor increase over minimal risk but likely to yield generalizable knowledge about the child's disorder or condition (21 CFR 50.53)

If a study does not fall under one of the three risk-benefit ratios above, an IRB still may approve the study in children. However, to do so, the IRB must seek approval from the FDA commissioner and must find the research presents an opportunity to understand, prevent or alleviate a serious problem affecting the health or welfare of children. (21 CFR 50.54)

Best Pharmaceuticals for Children Act (BPCA)

BPCA is in Title V of *FDAAA*. *BPCA* incentivizes pediatric studies by providing a voluntary program through which a sponsor may obtain the benefit of extended marketing exclusivity and patent protection. This program begins with a "written request" and ends with FDA determining whether the terms of the written request were satisfied.

Initiating the Written Request

The majority of written requests start as proposed pediatric study requests. These requests outline a sponsor's idea for pediatric studies, which FDA may modify or reject. If the request is accepted, FDA then issues its formal written request.

Of its own initiative, FDA may issue written requests for pediatric clinical studies at any time, meaning the request need not be linked to an NDA, BLA or supplement. FDA only need issue one study request for more than one use of a drug, and as part of a written request, FDA may request preclinical studies. Requests may be for products still under initial development or already marketed. For marketed products, FDA may request studies of drugs that are on-patent or off-patent.

With on-patent study requests, the sponsor has 180 days to respond and can agree to conduct the studies or decline the request. If the sponsor declines, FDA may publicize the fact the sponsor has declined the written request. FDA also may refer its request to the Foundation for the National Institutes of Health (FNIH) for funding. FNIH is a congressionally created, but independent, nonprofit organization that raises private funds and works with all research sectors to support studies that further NIH's mission. If FNIH does not fund the studies under the request, *BPCA* directs FDA to consider whether to require the studies under *PREA* (discussed below).

With off-patent study requests, NIH, in consultation with FDA, develops a list of pediatric therapeutic priorities. FDA issues written requests based on these priorities. Sponsors have 30 days to respond to the request, which is a right of first refusal. If the sponsor declines the request, FDA refers its request to NIH. If NIH funds the study, the entity that conducts the study submits the study results and proposed labeling to FDA.

Written Request

The criteria for issuing a written request include:

- serious or life-threatening condition
- disease or condition frequency
- whether other therapeutic options are available
- how often the drug is used or expected to be used in the pediatric population
- whether adequate safety data are available to move into the pediatric population (based on animal studies and adult experience)
- whether there is an appropriate and acceptable benefit compared to the risks

The written request is a legal document requesting the sponsor to conduct studies in the pediatric population and may specify the following information:

- types and objectives of studies to be performed
- indications to be studied (indications can be those intended or approved for adults or for new indications not approved for adults)
- age groups and numbers of patients to be studied
- study endpoints, including pharmacokinetic, pharmacodynamic, safety and efficacy endpoints
- drug information, including dosage form, route of administration, regimen, need for development of age-appropriate formulation and documentation requirements
- statistical information, including statistical analyses to be performed
- provisions for labeling that may result from the study or studies
- format of reports to be submitted to FDA
- timeframe for satisfying the written request
- public disclosure requirements for the studies

A sponsor is considered to have completed a written request successfully if the requested studies are completed within the specified timetable and the sponsor meets any other terms of the request. Once the written request is satisfied, the sponsor submits a report addressing the information obtained from the studies and makes a claim for the sixth months' exclusivity. FDA determines whether exclusivity is earned, based on an evaluation of the report. Exclusivity determinations must be made and exclusivity awarded at least nine months prior to the underlying patent's expiration or market exclusivity being extended. The reported study results do not need to demonstrate the drug is safe and effective for the specified pediatric use or result in a labeling change. In some cases, pediatric studies yield valuable negative findings that warn a drug or biologic is not safe and should not be administered in specific pediatric populations.

Exclusivity

If granted, exclusivity attaches to the pediatric study drug's active moiety. The active moiety is "the molecule or ion, excluding those appended portions of the molecule that cause the drug to be an ester, salt..., or other noncovalent derivative...of the molecule, responsible for the physiological or pharmacological action of the drug substance" (21 CFR 314.108(a)). Based on this definition, different active ingredients and products may have a common active moiety. Therefore, sponsors receive marketing protection for not just the product and specific indications examined in the pediatric study, but also protection covering any of the sponsor's drug products containing the active moiety.

Sponsors who receive exclusivity must provide physicians and other healthcare providers with any new pediatric labeling information. Additionally, sponsors must submit adverse events to FDA for one year after exclusivity is awarded.

BPCA Dispute Resolution

If FDA recommends changes to the label based on studies under a written request, and the sponsor does not accept the recommendations, the issue is referred to the Pediatric Subcommittee for advice. If the Pediatric Subcommittee recommends label changes, and the sponsor declines, FDA may declare the product misbranded.

Public Information

FDA can publicize the fact the sponsor of a drug with exclusivity has declined a written request. Study reports in response to written requests are published in FDA dockets, as are the reviews of the study reports and recommended label changes. Summaries of clinical and pharmacology submissions also are published in the dockets and in the *Federal Register*. Finally, prominent public disclosure is required when a sponsor creates a pediatric formulation and fails to market it.

Pediatric Research Equity Act (PREA)

PREA is in Title IV of *FDAAA*. If *BPCA* is the carrot, *PREA* is the stick. Unlike *BPCA, PREA* is mandatory. *PREA* applies to marketing applications involving a new active ingredient, indication, dosage form, dosing regimen or route of administration for drugs or biologics. Drugs with an orphan drug designation for a rare disease or condition are exempt. Unless deferred or waived, the law requires pediatric studies in order to 1) "assess the safety and effectiveness of the drug product for the claimed indications in all relevant pediatric subpopulations," and 2) "to support dosing and administration for each pediatric subpopulation for which the drug is safe and effective" (21 CFR 314.55).

In order to satisfy *PREA*'s pediatric assessment requirement, sponsors must submit a "pediatric plan." A pediatric plan is a statement of intent outlining the applicant's planned pediatric studies or providng the grounds upon which a *PREA* waiver or deferral is sought. FDA encourages applicants to discuss their pediatric plans at Pre-Investigational New Drug (Pre-IND) application meetings, especially for products intended for life-threatening or severely debilitating diseases. For products not intended for treating life-threatening or severely debilitating diseases, applicants may submit and discuss their pediatric plans no later than the End-of-Phase 2 meeting. For more information about the pediatric plan, see FDA *Draft Guidance for Industry: How to Comply with the Pediatric Research Equity Act* (September 2005).

In addition to submitting a pediatric plan, a sponsor must conduct an annual review to document the plan's progress. If there is a lack of progress on the plan, the review must provide the reasons for such delay and plans for completing studies in a timely fashion.

Waiver

FDA may grant a full waiver from *PREA* for a number of reasons: pediatric studies are impossible or impracticable because, for example, the condition does not exist in children, or the number of pediatric patients overall is small; strong evidence suggests the drug or biologic would be ineffective or unsafe in children; or the drug or biologic does not represent a meaningful therapeutic benefit over existing therapies and is not likely to be used in a substantial number of pediatric patients. FDA has used 50,000 patients as representing a "substantial number."

FDA may grant a partial waiver for an age subset of the pediatric population using the same conditions and criteria that apply for a full waiver. A partial waiver also may be granted if reasonable attempts to produce a pediatric formulation for a particular subset of the pediatric population have failed. Sponsors must document why attempts to develop a pediatric formulation have failed, and this documentation is required to be made public via FDA's website. If a full or partial waiver is granted, FDA makes the waiver application publicly available.

Finally, while not a waiver, FDA may permit extrapolation in place of certain clinical studies in children. Extrapolation is utilizing data from adequate and well-controlled studies in adults, supplementing this data with other relevant information for children (e.g., pharmacokinetics and pharmacodynamics data) to show the drug's effect is expected to be similar in adults, and applying this data to the pediatric population. Extrapolation of data from adults to children under *PREA* generally refers only to efficacy and not to safety or dosing. Extrapolation also is permitted from one pediatric age group to another. For more information on extrapolation, see FDA *Draft Guidance for Industry and Review Staff: Pediatric Information incorporated Into Human Prescription Drug and Biologics Products Labeling* (February 2013).

Deferral

Of its own initiative, FDA may defer a sponsor's submission of required pediatric assessments until some time after the drug or biologic is approved for marketing. A sponsor also may request FDA to defer its submission. FDA may authorize a deferral when the drug or biologic is ready for approval in adults or when additional safety and effectiveness data are necessary. Sponsors who receive a deferral must provide FDA the reasons for deferral, describe planned or ongoing studies and provide schedules for their completion. The sponsor must report the progress of its studies annually. Typically, deferrals are tracked as a Phase 4 study or postmarketing commitment.

Marketed Products

For marketed drugs and biological products, *PREA* authorizes FDA to require pediatric assessments under certain circumstances. These circumstances may include the following: the drug or biologic is used for a substantial number of pediatric patients for the labeled indication, and the absence of adequate labeling poses significant risks to pediatric patients; or there is a reason to believe the drug or biologic represents a meaningful therapeutic benefit over existing therapies, and the absence of adequate safety data from clinical studies poses significant risks to pediatric patients. Pediatric plan requirements and waiver and deferral criteria are the same as those for investigational new drugs and biologics.

Exclusivity

Exclusivity under *BPCA* is granted only for the completion of a study or studies subject to a written request and for which reports are submitted and accepted by FDA. Exclusivity is not granted for required pediatric studies under *PREA* unless such studies are included as part of an FDA-issued written request under *BPCA*.

Rare Pediatric Disease Priority Review Vouchers

The rare pediatric disease priority review voucher program is contained in Title IX of *FDASIA*. This program provides a different incentive than the exclusivity offered by *BPCA* and pertains only to products for prevention and treatment of certain rare pediatric diseases. FDA interprets "rare pediatric disease" to mean "if the entire prevalence of the disease or condition in the U.S. is below 200,000 and if more than 50% of patients with the disease are 0 through 18 years of age," or if the product "is for an 'orphan subset' of a disease or condition that otherwise affects 200,000 or more persons in the U.S., and if this subset is primarily (i.e., more than 50%) comprised of individuals aged 0 through 18" (*Draft Guidance for Industry: Rare Pediatric Disease Priority Review Vouchers* (November 2014)).

To receive a pediatric priority review voucher, a sponsor must submit an application for a drug or biologic intended to prevent or treat a rare pediatric disease. The product may not contain any active ingredient previously approved in any drug or biologic application. Additionally, the application must be eligible for priority review and must rely on clinical data from studies of the product in the pediatric population. Once FDA grants a voucher to a sponsor of a qualifying approved "rare pediatric disease product application," the sponsor can sell or redeem the voucher with a subsequently filed NDA or BLA.

Pediatric Medical Device Safety and Improvement Act

The *Pediatric Medical Device Safety and Improvement Act* is in Title III of *FDAAA*.

Tracking Pediatric Device Approvals

Device studies and marketing applications must include an evaluation describing any pediatric subpopulations suffering from the disease or condition the device is intended to treat, diagnose or cure, and the number of affected pediatric patients, if readily available. If the course of the disease or condition and the device's effects are sufficiently similar in adult and pediatric patients, FDA has the specific authority to conclude adult data may be used to support a determination of a reasonable assurance of effectiveness in pediatric populations. A study may not be needed in each pediatric subpopulation if data from one subpopulation can be extrapolated to another.

FDA is required to provide an annual report to Congress containing information pertaining specifically to pediatric usage of devices. This permits tracking the number and types of devices approved specifically for children or for conditions that occur in children.

Humanitarian Device Exemptions

Devices may be exempt from the requirements to demonstrate effectiveness for treatment or diagnosis of diseases or conditions that affect fewer than 4,000 individuals. Additionally, sponsors are permitted to make a profit on devices approved under the Humanitarian Device Exemption (HDE) specifically designed to meet a pediatric need. This exemption from the usual HDE requirements is conditional, based on appropriate labeling for use in the pediatric population, and sets a limit on the number of devices that can be distributed annually (i.e., the annual distribution number (ADN)). The device distributor is obligated to notify FDA if the number of devices distributed during any calendar year exceeds the ADN. Distributors also must submit adverse event reports, which are to be reviewed and evaluated by the FDA Pediatric Advisory Committee and reported to Congress. Notably, this section defines pediatric populations as under the age of 21; subpopulations are defined in **Table 32-1**.

Encouraging Pediatric Medical Device Research

The NIH director is required to designate an office to serve as a point of contact to identify and access funding for pediatric medical device research. Moreover, NIH, FDA and the Agency for Healthcare Research and Quality (AHRQ) are required to submit a plan to expand pediatric medical device research. The plan must include a survey of pediatric healthcare providers to assess unmet pediatric medical device needs; provide a research agenda for improving pediatric medical device development and FDA clearance or approval of pediatric medical devices; and provide a plan for evaluating pediatric medical devices' short- and long-term safety and effectiveness.

Demonstration Grants for Improving Pediatric Device Availability

Demonstration grants for nonprofit consortia were established to facilitate the development, production, approval and distribution of pediatric devices. The consortia is required to coordinate with NIH to identify research issues that require further study and to coordinate with FDA to facilitate pediatric medical device approval. These grants aim to encourage innovation and connect qualified individuals with potential manufacturers; mentor and manage pediatric device projects from concept through development and marketing; assess the scientific and medical merit of medical device projects; and provide other assistance and advice consistent with the purposes of the *Pediatric Medical Device Safety and Improvement Act.*

Office of Pediatric Therapeutics and Pediatric Advisory Committee

FDA's Pediatric Advisory Committee has the authority to monitor medical devices and make recommendations for improving their availability and safety.

Postmarket Surveillance

For Class II or III devices expected to have significant pediatric usage, FDA may require a manufacturer to conduct postmarket surveillance. FDA may require a prospective surveillance period of more than 36 months for these devices as a condition of approval. Dispute resolution may be requested by a manufacturer.

Premarket Assessment of Pediatric Medical Devices

FDA assesses device safety and effectiveness in the pediatric population using the same regulatory basis, scientific approaches and processes as those for adult medical devices. However, special consideration is given to devices meant for use in pediatric patients.

Table 32-1. Definition of Pediatric Subpopulations

Pediatric Subpopulation	Approximate Age Range
Newborn	Birth to 1 month of age
Infant	1 month to 2 years of age
Child	2 to 12 years of age
Adolescent	12-21 years of age

The agency does not believe clinical pediatric study data are always necessary to demonstrate safety and effectiveness for devices intended for children. A number of factors are used to determine the need for clinical data, including the device's nature and its adult use history, whether known factors can be extrapolated to the pediatric population and the underlying disease or condition being treated. Well-designed bench and animal testing are sufficient in some cases. FDA may require pediatric studies in the following circumstances:

- supporting information from sources such as preclinical bench or animal testing, literature or adult clinical trials is inadequate to establish safety and effectiveness for the pediatric indication
- adult data are inadequate to predict pediatric risks and adverse events
- pediatric data are needed to validate device design modifications
- pediatric data are needed to develop an age-appropriate treatment regimen

If a device is modified to meet the needs of a pediatric population, the manufacturer must conduct a risk analysis of the changes and develop methods to address or mitigate the identified risks adequately. Indications for use should be supported by appropriate data for the targeted populations and subpopulations. Moreover, contraindications, warnings and precautions for devices intended for pediatric use should address the risks associated with the pediatric subject's age, size and maturity clearly, and alert the user to specific hazards associated with the device's use in the target population. Finally, any instructions for use provided specifically for the pediatric patient should be age appropriate with respect to written language and other visual and auditory tools. The labeling must be satisfactory for all pediatric subgroups.

Summary

- Throughout history, legal, regulatory and policy actions have been taken to encourage and require the development of medical products important for the health benefit of children. Most recently, these actions have culminated in *BPCA*, *PREA*, the rare priority disease voucher program and the *Pediatric Medical Device Safety and Improvement Act.*

- To conduct clinical research in children, an IRB must approve the research under one of four risk-benefit ratio categories captured in 21 CFR 50, Subpart D.
- *BPCA* incentivizes drug and biologics sponsors to develop products and labeling for children by offering extended marketing exclusivity and patent protection.
- *PREA* requires drug and biologics sponsors to develop products and labeling for children, although this requirement may be waived or deferred in certain circumstances.
- The rare pediatric disease priority review voucher program encourages drug and biologics sponsors to develop products for rare diseases in children by offering a voucher for priority review that may be sold or redeemed.
- The *Pediatric Medical Device Safety and Improvement Act* provides increased oversight of medical device development and use in children, as well as a number of initiatives designed to encourage the development of pediatric devices.

Chapter 33

Dietary Supplements and Homeopathic Products

Updated by Abhishek K. Gurnani, JD and Ashish R. Talati, JD, MS, RAC

OBJECTIVES

- ❑ Develop a broad understanding of the regulation of dietary supplements by the US Food and Drug Administration
- ❑ Understand the scope and types of claims permitted for dietary supplements products
- ❑ Understand basic current Good Manufacturing Practice regulations (CGMPs) for dietary supplements and recent FDA enforcement activity concerning CGMPs
- ❑ Understand the basic regulatory requirements for adverse event reporting concerning dietary supplements
- ❑ Develop a broad understanding of the regulation of homeopathic drug products by FDA and current regulatory activity with respect to homeopathic drug products

LAWS, REGULATIONS AND GUIDELINES COVERED IN THIS CHAPTER

- ❑ *Dietary Supplement and Health Education Act* of 1994 (*DSHEA*)
- ❑ 21 CFR 101.36 Nutrition labeling of dietary supplements
- ❑ 21 CFR 101.93 Structure/function claims
- ❑ 21 CFR 111 Current Good Manufacturing Practice in manufacturing, packaging, labeling, or holding operations for dietary supplements
- ❑ 21 CFR 190.6 Requirement for premarket notification of new dietary ingredients
- ❑ *Public Health Security and Bioterrorism Preparedness and Response Act* of 2002 (Public Law 107-188). 107th Congress
- ❑ 21 CFR 110.310: Prior notice of imported food under the Public Health Security and Bioterrorism Preparedness and Response Act of 2002
- ❑ *Guidance for Industry: A Dietary Supplement Labeling Guide* (April 2005)
- ❑ 21 CFR 190.6 New Dietary Ingredient Notifications
- ❑ *Guidance for Industry: Questions and Answers Regarding Adverse Event Reporting and Recordkeeping for Dietary Supplements as Required by the Dietary Supplement and Nonprescription Drug Consumer Protection Act* (October 2007; Revised June 2009; Revised September 2013)
- ❑ *Guidance for Industry: Substantiation for Dietary 403(r)(6) of the Federal Food, Drug, and Supplement Claims Made Under Section Cosmetic Act* (December 2008)

- "Claims That Can Be Made for Conventional Foods and Dietary Supplements" (September 2003)
- *Draft Guidance for Industry: Dietary Supplements: New Dietary Ingredient Notifications and Related Issues* (July 2011)
- FTC, *Dietary Supplements: An Advertising Guide for Industry*
- *Guidance for Industry: Evidence-Based Review System for the Scientific Evaluation of Health Claims* (January 2009)
- *Guidance for Industry: Iron-Containing Supplements and Drugs: Label Warning Statements Small Entity Compliance Guide* (October 2003)
- *Guidance for Industry: Notification of a Health Claim or Nutrient Content Claim Based on an Authoritative Statement of a Scientific Body* (June 1998)
- *Guidance for Industry: Evidence-Based Review System for the Scientific Evaluation of Health Claims* (January 2009)
- *Guidance for Industry: Food Labeling; Nutrient Content Claims; Definition for "High Potency" and Definition for "Antioxidant" for Use in Nutrient Content Claims for Dietary Supplements and Conventional Foods; Small Entity Compliance Guide* (July 2008)
- *Guidance for Industry: Statement of Identity, Nutrition Labeling, and Ingredient Labeling of Dietary Supplements; Small Entity Compliance Guide* (January 1999)
- *Guidance for Industry: Structure/Function Claims, Small Entity Compliance Guide* (January 2002)
- *Guidance for Industry: Evidence-Based Ranking System for Scientific Data* (January 2009)
- *Guidance for Industry: Interim Procedures for Qualified Health Claims in the Labeling of Conventional Human Food and Human Dietary Supplements* (July 2003)
- *Guidance for Industry: Prior Notice of Imported Food Questions and Answers* (Edition 3) (March 2014)
- *Guidance for Industry: Questions and Answers Regarding Establishment and Maintenance of Records* (Edition 5) (February 2012)
- *Draft Guidance for Industry: Questions and Answers Regarding the Labeling of Dietary Supplements as Required by the Dietary Supplement and Nonprescription Drug Consumer Protection Act* (Revised December 2008 and September 2009)
- *Guidance for Industry: Questions and Answers Regarding Food Allergens, Including the Food Allergen Labeling and Consumer Protection Act of 2004* (Edition 4) (October 2006)
- *Guidance for Industry: FDA Export Certificates* (July 2004)
- Compliance Policy Guide, Guidance for FDA and CBP Staff. Sec. 110.310 Prior Notice of Imported Food Under the Public Health Security and Bioterrorism Preparedness and Response Act of 2002 (May 2009)
- *Guidance for Industry: Questions and Answers Regarding Registration of Food Facilities* (Edition 6) (November 2014)
- "Criteria Needed With Request For Certificate Of Free Sale For Dietary Supplement(s), Infant Formula(s), & Medical Food(s)" (December 2006)
- Compliance Policy Guide 7132.15, Section 400.400 "Conditions Under Which Homeopathic Drugs May Be Marketed" (Revised March 1995)
- 21 CFR 207 Registration of producers of drugs and listing of drugs in commercial distribution
- 21 CFR 211 Current Good Manufacturing Practice for finished pharmaceuticals
- *Current Good Manufacturing Practice in Manufacturing, Packaging, Labeling, or Holding Operations for Dietary Supplements; Small Entity Compliance Guide* (December 2010)
- 21 CFR 201 Labeling of Drug Products
- *The Homeopathic Pharmacopoeia of the United States, Guidelines For Homeopathic Drugs*

Dietary Supplements

Controversies over the regulation of vitamin and mineral dietary supplement product dosages and health claims arose in the 1960s and 1970s.[1] Between 1941 and 1979, the US Food and Drug Administration (FDA) attempted to limit the dosages of dietary supplements that could be sold without a prescription, limit the claims that could be made and require a disclaimer on supplement products stating there was no scientific basis for the routine use of vitamins and minerals.[2,3] Litigation and, eventually, legislation limited FDA's ability to regulate supplements, resulting in no final rules enacted, and withdrawal of proposed rules.[4]

In November 1989, FDA first issued a warning against the use of L-tryptophan products and subsequently recalled them. There was growing evidence that linked L-tryptophan, an amino acid promoted to relieve occasional sleeplessness, among other things, to a serious but rare blood disorder, eosinophilia. In 1990, sufficient evidence had been developed to link the disorder to a product from a Tokyo firm, Showa Denko KK, which had introduced a new production method in early 1989. Unfortunately, by that time, 1,478 cases and 21 deaths due to eosinophilia linked to L-tryptophan use had been reported.[5]

Concurrently, the *Nutrition Labeling Education Act* (*NLEA*) was passed in 1990, requiring FDA to regulate food labeling and include references to dietary supplements. In the early 1990s, several bills were introduced in both the House and Senate that would have impacted the dietary supplement industry. One such bill introduced in the House was the *Nutrition Advertising Coordination Act* of 1991 (HR 1662 SC2). This bill was thought to threaten the future availability of vitamins and other supplements because it defined misbranding in part as a claim that "characterizes the relationship of any nutrient ... to a health-related condition."[6] Another bill, the *Dietary Supplement Consumer Protection Act* of 1993 (HR 2923 IH), also introduced in the House, stated a dietary supplement would be deemed unsafe unless the ingredient was "generally recognized, among experts qualified by adequate training and experience to evaluate its safety, as having been adequately shown through scientific procedures to be safe under the conditions of its intended use."[7] This provision was retroactive to products already on the market. The legislation further stated FDA would establish regulations stipulating the uses and "the maximum quantity which may be used or permitted in the dietary supplement."[8] This proposed legislation was interpreted as moving dietary supplements, which previously had been regulated as foods, into a regulatory status very similar to drugs.

While neither of these bills passed, the proposed legislation led the supplement and health foods industries to promote a public letter-writing campaign declaring FDA was seeking to regulate some dietary supplements as drugs, and in fact they were. In early 1991, David Kessler, MD, FDA commissioner at the time, created the Dietary Supplements FDA Task Force.[9] Kessler gave this task force the job of taking a new look at how FDA possibly could regulate dietary supplements and creating a proposal to best serve US citizens' public health. The Task Force was chaired by Gary Dykstra and its final report, finished in May of 1992, forever became known in the dietary supplement industry at the "Dykstra Report."[10]

The Dykstra Report included several generalized conclusions proposed by the Dietary Supplements Task force, focusing on safety as FDA's overriding concern in regulating dietary supplements. In addition, it recommended the industry assume the burden of ensuring these products' safety. The task force divided supplements into three main categories: 1) vitamins and minerals, 2) amino acid products and 3) all other types of dietary supplements. The primary recommendation for vitamins and minerals was to establish safe daily intake levels through rulemaking. These daily intake levels would provide a benchmark for some essential nutrients that are toxic when consumed in excess to avoid hazards associated with them. The recommendation for amino acids was analyzing each individual amino acid on a case-by-case basis; overall, the products would be regulated as drugs if any non-*NLEA* claims were associated with them. The final category, all other types of dietary supplements, was recommended to be regulated under the food additives provisions of the statute, unless drug claims were made for the product. The task force also recommended the establishment of Good Manufacturing Practices (GMPs), purity and identity standards and disintegration and dissolution standards to ensure bioavailability.

Although the Dykstra Report was completed in May 1992, it was not released by Kessler until many months later. The dietary supplement industry had been working on its own proposal, the *Dietary Supplement Health Education Act* (*DSHEA*), with the help of Senator Orin Hatch (R-UT), Representative Bill Richardson (D-NM) and Senator Tom Harkin (D-IA).[11] The public write-in campaign resulted in an estimated two million[12] letters to Congress, prompting passage of *DSHEA*.[13] The first paragraph of the executive summary in the Report of the Commission on Dietary Supplement Labels, states: "The *Dietary Supplement Health and Education Act* (*DSHEA* or the Act) of 1994 was enacted by Congress following public debate concerning the importance of dietary supplements in leading a healthy life, the need for consumers to have current and accurate information about supplements, and controversy over the Food and Drug Administration (FDA) regulatory approach to dietary supplements. President Clinton, in signing the legislation into law on October 25, 1994, said: After several years of intense efforts, manufacturers, experts in nutrition, and legislators, acting in a conscientious alliance with consumers at the grassroots level, have moved successfully to bring common sense to the treatment of dietary supplements under regulation and law."

In *DSHEA*, Congress defined dietary supplements and dietary ingredients; required ingredient and nutrition labeling; provided for claims and nutritional support statements that can be used for dietary supplements; outlined guidelines for information that can be provided on supplement products; and gave FDA the authority to establish GMP regulations for dietary supplements. In addition, *DSHEA* allowed the continued sale of dietary ingredients on the market as of 15 October 1994. The law also established a framework for assuring the safety of new dietary ingredients (NDIs).

Prior to 1994, vitamins, minerals and other dietary supplements were regulated as foods;[14] however, the passage of *DSHEA* led to creation of a new class of FDA-regulated products. In addition, the law allowed statements of nutritional support to be made regarding dietary supplement products. The resulting dietary supplement regulations promulgated by FDA are very similar to food regulations. Like foods, dietary supplements are not subject to agency approval prior to marketing. Dietary supplement product labels must include a supplement facts box similar, but not identical to, the nutrition facts boxes used on food products. Dietary ingredients not on the market as of 15 October 1994 must be the subject of NDI notifications similar in content to "generally regarded as safe" (GRAS) notifications for new food additives. Additionally, most nutrient content claims, established in *NLEA,* also may be used on dietary supplement products.

The dietary supplement industry has grown into a $32 billion dollar industry and is projected to increase to $60 billion dollars by the year 2021.[15] This exponential growth has been met with increased regulatory oversight, not only by FDA, but also by state regulatory bodies and consumer class action attorneys looking to reap the benefits of a now wealthy industry. The result is heightened enforcement of labeling and GMP regulations by regulatory bodies and constant litigation over dietary supplement product claims by plaintiffs' lawyers. With all the added attention on this expanding industry, even state attorneys general, who arguably once deferred to federal regulatory oversight, now have prosecuted a number of false advertising matters concerning dietary supplements.

Definition of Dietary Ingredients and Dietary Supplements

Dietary ingredients traditionally were viewed as essential vitamins, minerals and other nutrients, such as fats, carbohydrates and proteins. In 1990, *NLEA* added "herbs, or similar nutritional substances"[16] to the definition of dietary supplement. In *DSHEA*, this definition was expanded further as Congress defined dietary supplements as "products (other than tobacco) intended to supplement the diet that bear or contain one or more of the following dietary ingredients: (a) a vitamin; (b) a mineral; (c) an herb or other botanical; (d) an amino acid; (e) a dietary substance for use by man to supplement the diet by increasing the total dietary intake; or (f) a concentrate, metabolite, constituent, extract, or combination of any ingredient described in clause (A), (B), (C), (D), or (E).[17] Further, dietary supplements are products intended for ingestion, are not represented for use as a conventional food or as a sole item of a meal or the diet, and are labeled as dietary supplements."[18] This definition also excludes an article approved as a new drug, certified as an antibiotic, or licensed as a biologic.[19] It also precludes an article authorized for investigation as a new drug, antibiotic, or biologic for which substantial clinical investigations have been instituted and for which the existence of such investigations have been made public, unless the article was authorized for use as a dietary supplement or food before such approval.[20]

The prohibition on representing dietary supplements as conventional foods was underscored by the agency's 2009 publication of a guidance document regarding liquid dietary supplements.[21] FDA noted this guidance was issued to address the trend of marketing beverages as dietary supplements and including ingredients in beverages and conventional foods that are not GRAS. The guidance states in part, "Liquid products that suggest through their serving size, packaging, or recommended daily intake that they are intended to be consumed in amounts that provide all or a significant part of the entire daily drinking fluid intake of an average person in the U.S., are represented as beverages. In addition, the name of a product can represent the product as a conventional food. Product or brand names that use conventional food terms such as "beverage," "drink," "water," 'juice" or similar terms represent the product as a conventional food."

Lately, FDA has been more vocal about dietary supplement product classification and whether a product meets the definition of a dietary supplement under *DSHEA*. Recent FDA Warning Letters to industry have noted the following objections:

- "We note that some of your products are marketed as dietary supplements, but are marketed for topical use. Under section 201(ff)(2)(A)(i) of the Act [21 U.S.C. §321(ff)](2)(A)(i)], a dietary supplement is defined, among other things, as a product intended for ingestion. Topical products are not dietary supplements."[22]
- "You currently market [product omitted] as a dietary supplement. However, under section 201(ff)(3)(B)(ii) of the *FD&C Act* [21 U.S.C. §321(ff)(3)(B)(ii)], a dietary supplement may not include an article authorized for investigation as a new drug for which substantial clinical investigations have been instituted and made public, unless the article was

marketed as a dietary supplement or food before its authorization as a new drug."[23]

- "Section 201(ff)(1) of the Act (21 U.S.C. 321(ff)(1)) defines "dietary ingredient" as a vitamin, mineral, amino acid, herb or other botanical, or dietary substance for use by man to supplement the diet by increasing the total dietary intake, or a concentrate, metabolite, constituent, extract or combination of any dietary ingredient from the preceding categories. Synthetically produced dimethylamylamine is not a vitamin, mineral, amino acid, herb or other botanical. To the best of FDA's knowledge, synthetically produced dimethylamylamine is not commonly used as human food or drink; therefore, it is not a dietary substance for use by man to supplement the diet by increasing the total dietary intake. Further, synthetically produced dimethylamylamine is not a concentrate, metabolite, constituent, extract or combination of a dietary ingredient. Therefore, synthetically produced dimethylamylamine is not a dietary ingredient as defined in section 201(ff)(1) of the Act."[24]

"Grandfathered" Dietary Ingredients Versus New Dietary Ingredients

Under *DSHEA*, dietary ingredients may be in one of two categories: 1) a grandfathered or "old dietary ingredient" (ODI); or 2) a new dietary ingredient (NDI). *DSHEA* defined a "new dietary ingredient" as a dietary ingredient not marketed in the US before 15 October 1994. While *DSHEA* does not explicitly define "old dietary ingredients," from the definition of "new dietary ingredient," it can be concluded an old dietary ingredient is an ingredient marketed in the US prior to 15 October 1994. In determining whether a specific dietary ingredient is an ODI as opposed to an NDI, a company must show the dietary ingredient was marketed in the US prior to 15 October 1994. FDA considers marketing of a dietary ingredient to mean offering the dietary ingredient for sale as a dietary supplement, a bulk ingredient for use in dietary supplements or as an ingredient in a blend or formulation of dietary ingredients used in a dietary supplement.

The dietary ingredient must be offered for sale at a retail establishment, through a product catalog or pricing list, or through other means of advertising and promotion. Examples of documentation sufficient to show a marketing date prior to 15 October 1994 include sales records, manufacturing records, commercial invoices, magazine advertisements, mail order catalogues or sales brochures. The documentation should clearly show marketing took place in the US, the marketed ingredient's identity and form, and whether the ingredient was marketed as a dietary ingredient or for another purpose.[25]

New Dietary Ingredient Notifications

Dietary supplement ingredients and products are not subject to premarket approval; however, FDA must be notified prior to the introduction of any new dietary ingredient into the marketplace.[26] Notification must be given to the Office of Nutritional Products, Labeling and Dietary Supplements (ONPLDS) at least 75 days before introducing the NDI into interstate commerce. The notification must include, among other information:

- name and address of the manufacturer or distributor of the NDI or supplement product that contains the NDI
- NDI name, including the Latin binomial name of any herb or other botanical
- description of products that contain the NDI and the level of the NDI in the product; conditions of ordinary or recommended uses of the supplement
- history of use or other evidence establishing the dietary ingredient's safety under the conditions of use, including any citation to and reprint, copy or English translation of published articles or other evidence that is the basis upon which the distributor or manufacturer has concluded the NDI or product containing the NDI will reasonably be expected to be safe
- the signature of the person designated by the manufacturer or distributor of the NDI or dietary supplement containing the NDI

The dossier is a comprehensive summary of the ingredient, including a description of the ingredient's chemistry, its manufacturing process, its intended use and dosage level and a safety assessment to support the intended use and dosage level. Safety evidence can be in the form of human clinical studies or animal studies and also may include other *in vitro* studies to support a non-toxicity conclusion for the subject ingredient.

FDA recently has developed draft Form FDA 3880, which allows the electronic submission of a new dietary ingredient notification. Currently, FDA is inviting industry to comment on its plan for developing an electronic submission method.[27]

FDA customarily acknowledges and provides the date of receipt of the NDI notification. The date FDA provides is the notification filing date, and the NDI may not be introduced into interstate commerce for 75 days after the filing date. FDA will put the NDI notification, except of any trade secret or confidential information, "on public display" 90 days after receiving the submission. Although the NDI may be introduced into the marketplace 75 days after filing, this does not guarantee FDA agrees there is sufficient information to presume reasonable safety. As stated in 21 CFR 190.6(f), "Failure of the agency to respond to a notification does not constitute a finding by the agency that the NDI or the dietary supplement that contains the NDI is safe or is not adulterated under section 402 of the act."

In July 2011, FDA issued a draft guidance on NDI notifications and related issues.[28] The draft guidance met a considerable amount of industry backlash as it outlined safety requirements the industry believed to be in line with food additive regulations. The agency continues to review submitted NDI notifications in light of the 2011 draft guidance, which could be one of the reasons for the relatively high rejection rate of about 75%.[29] FDA's transparency initiative, FDA-TRACK, shows agency-wide performance on NDI notification reviews: http://www.accessdata.fda.gov/FDATrack/track?program=cfsan&id=CFSAN-ONLDS-Percentage-of-NDI-notification-reviews-to-which-FDA-objected. The agency agreed to re-review the draft guidance and accepted a substantial number of comments from industry. FDA aims to finalize the guidance for NDI notifications in 2015. This will provide industry with additional insight into FDA's position and review process and may result in an improved NDI acceptance rate.

Exemptions to the New Dietary Ingredient Notification Requirement

As discussed, if a dietary ingredient is an NDI, a notification is required to be submitted to FDA at least 75 days prior to marketing. However, there is an exemption to the NDI notification requirement if the NDI has been present in the food supply as an article used for food in a form in which the food has not been chemically altered. FDA, in its 2011 draft guidance, identified manufacturing processes it believes do not result in chemical alteration, and those that do amount to chemical alteration:

No Chemical Alteration

- minor loss of volatile components
- dehydration
- lyophilization
- milling
- formation of a tincture or a solution in water, a slurry, a powder or a solid in suspension do not chemically alter an ingredient[30]

FDA also provided examples it believes meets the "no chemical alteration" standard: 1) leaves or roots of a plant consumed as conventional food (e.g., broccoli or carrots) are dried and ground for sale in powder form; and 2) a tincture is made by soaking pears in aqueous ethanol. The mixture then is milled and dried into a powder that is placed in a capsule.[31]

Chemical Alteration:

FDA also provided manufacturing processes it believes to be chemical alteration, rendering the subject ingredient a new dietary ingredient:[32]

- a process that makes or breaks chemical bonds, such as hydrolysis or esterification, unless the bonds created by the process are reversed when the ingredient is dissolved in water (e.g., creation of a soluble salt) or during ingestion
- removal of some components of a tincture or solution in water (e.g., by chromatography, distillation or membrane filtration), which changes the chemical composition of the mixture
- use of solvents other than water or aqueous ethanol (tincture) to make an extract (Water and aqueous ethanol are specifically excluded from processes that chemically alter a food in the official legislative history of *DSHEA*. Other solvents alter the composition of the extract in significantly different ways, usually by extracting different types of constituents than are extracted using water and aqueous ethanol.)
- high temperature baking or cooking an ingredient that previously has not been baked or cooked, unless the process causes only minor loss of volatile components with no other changes to the ingredient's chemical composition
- changing an ingredient's manufacturing method such that the chemical composition is significantly different (e.g., changes that alter the composition of materials used to make the ingredient, use of a different solvent, use of a chromatographic matrix instead of a passive filter)
- application of nanotechnology resulting in new or altered ingredient chemical properties
- changing agricultural or fermentation conditions to alter the ingredient's chemical composition, such as sprouting garlic or fermenting yeast using a medium containing large amounts of sodium selenite to create large amounts of organic selenium compounds
- fermentation using a medium different from the one used to make conventional foods in the food supply (e.g., use of a defined commercial growth medium to produce a microorganism previously made by fermenting milk into dairy products like yogurt or cheese)
- use of a botanical ingredient at a different life stage than previously used (e.g., making an extract from unripe instead of ripe apples or using the mycelium instead of the fruiting body of a fungus)

Although it was met with criticism, the FDA draft guidance provides industry with FDA's current position on NDIs and NDI notifications. Should a company decide to submit an NDI notification, review of the draft guidance is imperative. Industry also can learn from FDA comments on other submissions through use of the American Herbal Product Association's (AHPA) online NDI database: http://ndi.npicenter.com/.

Additionally, companies that have achieved GRAS status, either through a self-affirmed GRAS or a GRAS notification to FDA, also may be exempt from the NDI notification requirement if the GRAS substance has been used in the food supply and is to be used as a NDI without chemical alteration.[33]

Labels and Labeling

Dietary supplement "labels" are "any display of written, printed, or graphic matter on the immediate container of any article, or any such matter affixed to any consumer commodity or affixed to or appearing upon a package containing any consumer commodity,"[34] and "labeling," "includes all written, printed, or graphic matter accompanying an article at any time while such article is in interstate commerce or held for sale after shipment or delivery in interstate commerce."[35] Dietary supplement product labeling regulations are found in 21 CFR 101.36.[36] This section frequently references 21 CFR 101.9,[37] which covers food labeling. Both food and dietary supplement labels must include a statement of identity; a net quantity of contents statement; an ingredient list; the manufacturer's, packer's or distributor's address; and a facts box declaring the nutrients present in the product. The regulations also specify key supplement fact design requirements (font size, line size, etc.) and other label size parameters.

Dietary supplement facts boxes are very similar to food label nutrition facts boxes. While both must list key nutrients when present at threshold levels defined by regulation, the order in which some of the nutrients must appear differs between foods and dietary supplements. Another key difference is nutrition facts boxes must list certain nutrients, such as fats, even when they are not present in the product; for dietary supplements, so called "zero-value" nutrients are not required to be listed in the facts box unless claims are being made about them. Supplement facts boxes also may list the quantities of dietary ingredients such as herbs, amino acids, concentrates or metabolites (see **Figure 33-1**).

FDA provides comprehensive dietary supplement labeling guidance outlining each requirement and referencing the associated regulation: http://www.fda.gov/Food/GuidanceRegulation/GuidanceDocumentsRegulatoryInformation/DietarySupplements/ucm2006823.htm.

Figure 33-1. Sample Supplement Facts Boxes

Supplement Facts
Serving Size: 1 capsule
Servings per container: 30

	Amount per serving	% Daily Value*
Vitamin A	2,500 IU	50%
Vitamin C	2.3 mg	4%
Vitamin D	165 IU	41%
Vitamin E	1.6 IU	5%
Thiamin	4.8 mg	320%
Riboflavin	2.2 mg	130%
Niacin	26 mg	130%
Vitamin B6	4.2 mg	210%
Vitamin B12	2.4 mcg	40%
Pantothenic acid	8.8 mg	88%
Calcium	11mg	1%
Iron	1.6 mg	9%
Magnesium	0.2 mg	<1%
Zinc	0.2 mg	1%
Selenium	15 mcg	21%
Copper	0.04 mg	2%
Manganese	0.03 mg	2%
Molybdenum	20 mcg	27%
Potassium	0.4 mg	<1%
Cobalt	10 mcg	†
Lecithin (from soybean)	14 mg	†
Rutin (from Dimorphandra mollis) (pods)	5 mg	†

*Percent Daily Values are based on a 2,000 calorie diet.
†Daily value not established.

INGREDIENTS. THIAMIN HYDROCHLORIDE, PYRIDOXINE HYDROCHLORIDE, CYANOCOBALMIN, SODIUM SELENITE, ASCORBIC ACID, NIACINAMIDE, RIBOFLAVIN, CALCIUM PANTOTHENATE, DICALCIUM PHOSPHATE, FERROUS FUMARATE, MAGNESIUM SULFATE, COPPER SULFATE, MANGANESE SULFATE, POTASSIUM SULFATE, COBALT SULFATE, SODIUM MOLYBDENATE, RUTIN, ZINC OXIDE, RETINYL PALMITATE, CHOLECALCIFEROL, DL-ALPHA TOCOPHEROL ACETATE, SOYBEAN OIL, GELATIN, BEESWAX, TITANIUM DIOXIDE, FD&C YELLOW # 5, FD&C BLUE #1, FD&C RED # 40.
ALLERGENS: CONTAINS SOY

Supplement Facts
Serving Size 1 Capsule

Amount Per Capsule	% Daily Value
Calories 20	
Calories from Fat 20	
Total Fat 2 g	3%*
Saturated Fat 0.5 g	3%*
Polyunsaturated Fat 1 g	†
Monounsaturated Fat 0.5 g	†
Vitamin A 4250 IU	85%
Vitamin D 425 IU	106%
Omega-3 fatty acids 0.5 g	†

* Percent Daily Values are based on a 2,000 calorie diet
† Daily Value not established

Ingredients. Cod liver oil, gelatin, water, and glycerin

Warning Statements

The regulations also cover certain warnings required on dietary supplement labels. The *Food Allergen Labeling and Consumer Protection Act* of 2004 (*FALCPA*) requires foods and dietary supplements to alert consumers to the presence of the any of the "major" allergens.[38] Congress defined "major allergens" as the eight foods responsible for 90% of food allergies: milk, eggs, fish, crustacean shellfish, tree nuts, peanuts, wheat and soybeans. Allergens must be declared by their common or usual name (i.e., milk, peanuts, wheat, etc.) and may be declared in either the ingredient list or in a separate statement. The species must be listed when fish, crustacean shellfish or tree nut allergens are declared.

Warnings, such as warnings for products containing added iron, also are mandated by the regulations,[39] while others, such as those directed at pregnant women or to keep the product out of reach of children, are common industry practice. Some warnings also may be provided based on the supplement ingredient's safety profile.

Claims Permitted on Dietary Supplement Products

Nutrient Content Claims

NLEA permitted nutrient content claims such as "high in fiber" or "rich source of vitamin C" on foods and dietary supplements. The guidelines for determining whether a product is eligible to bear such claims are found in the following sections of the CFR:

- 21 CFR 101.13 Nutrient content claims—general principles
- 21 CFR 101.54 Nutrient content claims for "good source," "high," "more," and "high potency"
- 21 CFR 101.56 Nutrient content claims for "light" or "lite"
- 21 CFR 101.60 Nutrient content claims for the calorie content of foods
- 21 CFR 101.61 Nutrient content claims for the sodium content of foods
- 21 CFR 101.62 Nutrient content claims for fat, fatty acid and cholesterol content of foods
- 21 CFR 101.65 Implied nutrient content claims and related label statements
- 21 CFR 101.67 Use of nutrient content claims for butter
- 21 CFR 101.69 Petitions for nutrient content claims

Health Claims

In addition, *NLEA* provided for the establishment of allowable health claims. Petitions for such claims may be made for foods, supplements or related ingredients when the ingredients' benefits have been documented in publicly available scientific literature. As a result, FDA has approved allowable health claims based on significant scientific agreement of data supporting the claims. Examples of claims include:

- Calcium—Regular exercise and a healthy diet with enough calcium help teen and young adult white and Asian women maintain good bone health and may reduce their high risk of osteoporosis later in life
- Soluble Fiber—Soluble fiber from foods such as oats, as part of a diet low in saturated fat and cholesterol, may reduce the risk of heart disease. A serving of oats supplies x grams of the 3 grams of soluble fiber from oats necessary per day to have this effect.

Specific information about allowable health claims can be found in the following regulations:

- 21 CFR 101.70 Petitions for health claims
- 21 CFR 101.71 Health claims: claims not authorized
- 21 CFR 101.72 Health claims: calcium and osteoporosis
- 21 CFR 101.73 Health claims: dietary lipids and cancer
- 21 CFR 101.74 Health claims: sodium and hypertension
- 21 CFR 101.75 Health claims: dietary saturated fat and cholesterol and risk of coronary heart disease
- 21 CFR 101.76 Health claims: fiber-containing grain products, fruits and vegetables and cancer
- 21 CFR 101.77 Health claims: fruits, vegetables and grain products that contain fiber, particularly soluble fiber, and risk of coronary heart disease
- 21 CFR 101.78 Health claims: fruits and vegetables and cancer
- 21 CFR 101.79 Health claims: folate and neural tube defects
- 21 CFR 101.80 Health claims: dietary noncariogenic carbohydrate sweeteners and dental caries
- 21 CFR 101.81 Health claims: soluble fiber from certain foods and risk of coronary heart disease (CHD)
- 21 CFR 101.82 Health claims: soy protein and risk of coronary heart disease (CHD)
- 21 CFR 101.83 Health claims: plant sterol/stanol esters and risk of coronary heart disease (CHD)

Provisions in the *Food and Drug Administration Modernization Act* of 1997 (*FDAMA*)[40] allow the use of claims based on current, published authoritative statements from "a scientific body of the United States with official responsibility for public health protection or research directly related to human nutrition." The law specifically notes some such authoritative scientific bodies include the National Academy of Sciences (NAS) or any of its subdivisions, the National Institutes of Health (NIH) and the Centers for Disease Control and Prevention (CDC). *FDAMA* further stated such claims could be made 120 days after submission of a notification of the claim. *FDAMA* claim notifications must include: the exact wording of the claim; a concise description of the basis for determining the requirements for an authoritative statement have been satisfied; a copy of the referenced authoritative statement; for a health claim, "a balanced representation of the scientific literature relating to the relationship between a nutrient and a disease or health-related condition to which the claim refers;" or, for a nutrient content claim, "a balanced representation of the scientific literature relating to the nutrient level to which the claim refers." FDA has issued guidance[41] but has not published specific regulations on *FDAMA* claims. Current authorized *FDAMA* claims cover:

- choline nutrient content claims
- fluoride and the risk of dental caries
- potassium and the risk of high blood pressure and stroke
- saturated fat, cholesterol and trans fat, and the risk of heart disease
- substitution of saturated fat with unsaturated fatty acids and risk of heart disease
- whole grain foods and the risk of heart disease and certain cancers

Qualified Health Claims

Yet another class of claims, "qualified health claims," has been created as a result of the court decision in *Pearson v. Shalala*. In this suit, FDA's general health claims regulations for dietary supplements and the agency's decision not to authorize health claims for four specific substance/disease relationships were challenged. A district court first ruled for FDA (14 F. Supp. 2d 10 (D.D.C. 1998)). However, on appeal, the US Court of Appeals for the DC Circuit reversed the lower court's decision (164 F.3d 650 (D.C. Cir. 1999)). The appeals court ruled the First Amendment does not permit FDA to reject health claims deemed potentially misleading unless the agency also determines no disclaimer would eliminate the potential deception. The disclaimers mentioned in the decision are what "qualify" the health claim. In general, qualified health claims are not supported by data meeting the standard of significant scientific agreement[42] required for health claims and are qualified by including a statement regarding the data's strength. Examples of qualified health claims include:

- Omega-3 Fatty Acids—Supportive but not conclusive research shows that consumption of EPA and DHA omega-3 fatty acids may reduce the risk of coronary heart disease. One serving of [Name of the food] provides [ ] gram of EPA and DHA omega-3 fatty acids. [See nutrition information for total fat, saturated fat, and cholesterol content.]
- B Vitamins—As part of a well-balanced diet that is low in saturated fat and cholesterol, Folic Acid, Vitamin B6 and Vitamin B12 may reduce the risk of vascular disease. FDA evaluated the above claim and found that, while it is known that diets low in saturated fat and cholesterol reduce the risk of heart disease and other vascular diseases, the evidence in support of the above claim is inconclusive.

Other qualified health claims cover the relationships between:

- selenium and cancer
- antioxidant vitamins and cancer
- phosphatidylserine and cognitive dysfunction and dementia
- nuts and heart disease
- walnuts and heart disease
- monounsaturated fatty acids from olive oil and coronary heart disease
- green tea and cancer
- chromium picolinate and diabetes
- calcium and colon/rectal cancer and calcium and recurrent colon/rectal polyps
- calcium and hypertension, pregnancy-induced hypertension and preeclampsia
- tomatoes and/or tomato sauce and prostate, ovarian, gastric and pancreatic cancers
- unsaturated fatty acids from canola oil and reduced risk of coronary heart disease
- corn oil and corn oil-containing products and a reduced risk of heart disease
- folic acid and neural tube birth defects[43]

Structure/Function Claims

DSHEA allowed statements of nutritional support for dietary supplements. Statements of nutritional support may discuss: the supplement's benefit in relation to a classic nutrient deficiency disease; the role of a nutrient or dietary ingredient in affecting the structure or function of the human body or its systems; the documented mechanism by which a nutrient or dietary ingredient acts to maintain the structure or function of the body; or general well-being supported from consumption of a nutrient or dietary ingredient. All such claims must be truthful, not misleading, supported by scientific data and accompanied by the following disclaimer: "This statement has not been evaluated by the Food and Drug Administration. This product is not intended to diagnose, treat, cure, or prevent any disease."[44]

If claims are made regarding nutrient deficiency diseases, such as scurvy from lack of vitamin C, the prevalence of the disease in the US must be disclosed. Since such nutrient deficiency diseases are rare, most claims made about dietary supplement products discuss the manner and/or mechanism by which a dietary ingredient affects or maintains human structure or function. Since dietary supplements may not be marketed to "diagnose, treat, cure, or prevent any disease," these so-called structure/function claims may describe only how the supplement affects or maintains the normal, healthy structure or normal, healthy function of the human body and its systems.

To assist industry in crafting acceptable structure/function claims, FDA has published regulations[45] and guidance[46] defining disease and providing criteria to evaluate whether dietary supplement claims are disease claims. The definition of "disease" is listed in 21 CFR 101.93(g)(1) as "damage to an organ, part, structure, or system of the body such that it does not function properly (e.g., cardiovascular disease), or a state of health leading to such dysfunctioning (e.g., hypertension); except that diseases resulting from essential nutrient deficiencies (e.g., scurvy, pellagra) are not included in this definition." Section 101.93(g)(2) lists 10 criteria for identifying statements are prohibited disease claims, which state explicitly or imply that a dietary supplement product:

1. has an effect on a specific disease or class of diseases
2. has an effect on the characteristic signs or symptoms of a specific disease or class of diseases, using scientific or lay terminology
3. has an effect on an abnormal condition associated with a natural state or process, if the abnormal condition is uncommon or can cause significant or permanent harm

4. has an effect on a disease or diseases through: a) the name of the product; b) a statement that the product contains an ingredient that is not listed in the definition of dietary ingredients and that has been regulated by FDA as a drug and is well known to consumers for its use or claimed use in preventing or treating a disease; c) citation of a publication or reference, if the citation refers to a disease use; d) use of the term "disease" or "diseased," except in general statements about disease prevention that do not refer explicitly or implicitly to a specific disease or class of diseases or to a specific product or ingredient; or e) use of pictures, vignettes, symbols or other means
5. belongs to a class of products that is intended to diagnose, mitigate, treat, cure or prevent a disease
6. is a substitute for a product that is a therapy for a disease
7. augments a particular therapy or drug action that is intended to diagnose, mitigate, treat, cure or prevent a disease or class of diseases
8. has a role in the body's response to a disease or to a vector of disease
9. treats, prevents or mitigates adverse events associated with a therapy for a disease, if the adverse events constitute diseases
10. otherwise suggests an effect on a disease or diseases

Dietary supplements may be marketed to affect certain conditions considered part of typical, everyday living due to their mild nature and infrequent occurrence. Such conditions are not considered diseases and typically resolve without requiring medical attention. They include occasional irregularity and mild stress due to everyday living and occasional sleeplessness. It is clear these same symptoms can indicate disease if they are not mild or occasional.

To legally make structure/function or any other type of claim about dietary supplement products, the manufacturer must have data to substantiate the claim. FDA has published a guidance on dietary supplement claim substantiation.[47] The guidance refers to the FTC standard of competent and reliable scientific evidence, defined in FTC case law as "tests, analyses, research, studies, or other evidence based on the expertise of professionals in the relevant area, that has been conducted and evaluated in an objective manner by persons qualified to do so, using procedures generally accepted in the profession to yield accurate and reliable results."[48] The level of substantiating evidence sufficient for a particular claim is affected by the claim's language and meaning, the quality of the studies and their relevance to the actual product, as well as the total body of evidence relating to the claim. The data substantiating product claims are not submitted to FDA but should be available if needed to answer any questions that may arise regarding the claim.

403(r)(6) Notifications

CFR Section 101.93 outlines the procedures for notifying FDA regarding use of structure/function statements on dietary supplement labels or labeling.[49] The regulations state:

> No later than 30 days after the first marketing of a dietary supplement that bears one of the statements listed in section 403(r)(6) of the Federal Food, Drug, and Cosmetic Act, the manufacturer, packer, or distributor of the dietary supplement shall notify the Office of Nutritional Products, Labeling and Dietary Supplements (HFS-810), Center for Food Safety and Applied Nutrition, Food and Drug Administration, 5100 Paint Branch Pkwy., College Park, MD 20740, that it has included such a statement on the label or in the labeling of its product. An original and two copies of this notification shall be submitted.[50]

With the notification, FDA requires: 1) the name and address of the manufacturer, packer, or distributor of the dietary supplement that bears the statement; 2) the text of the statement being made; 3) the name of the dietary ingredient or supplement that is the subject of the statement, if not provided in the statement's text; and 4) the name of the dietary supplement (including brand name). Claims are not endorsed by FDA, but the agency may issue a letter objecting to certain claims being made in the notification.

FDA very seldom initiates enforcement action based on noncompliance with Section 403(r)(6) alone. Objections related to this requirement usually are not raised by FDA through routine facility inspections or Form 483 observations, and Warning Letters rarely are addressed to companies based solely on a violation of the 403(r)(6) notification requirement. With little to no enforcement history concerning 403(r)(6) notifications, companies aware of this requirement that choose not to submit a notification to FDA likely do so having gauged the regulatory risk as minimal. In fact, a study completed by the Office of the Inspector General (OIG) of the Department of Health and Human Services identified several flaws in FDA's notification tracking system and the lack of adherence by industry to notification requirements.[51] The OIG study, completed in October 2012, analyzed 127 dietary supplements on the market marketed for weight loss or immune system support. The study's objective was to determine compliance with FDA regulations concerning structure/function claims, including the requirement to notify FDA within 30 days of use of the marketing claims. During the study, FDA could retrieve notification letters only for 21 of the 127 supplements studied and, among the 21 letters studied by OIG, 17 did not contain all the required information. Additionally, 11 letters contained structure/function claims that did not match claims listed on the product's label.

Third-Party Literature

Although dietary supplements may not be marketed to "diagnose, treat, cure or prevent any disease," many dietary ingredients—particularly herbs, botanicals and glandular extracts—historically have been used in various cultures' traditional and folk medicine. This body of information is difficult to use in dietary supplement promotional materials without violating regulations on allowable claims for dietary supplement products. *DSHEA* Section 403B makes provision for the use of "third-party literature" by stating "a publication, including an article, a chapter in a book, or an official abstract of a peer-reviewed scientific publication that appears in an article and was prepared by the author or the editors of the publication, which is reprinted in its entirety, shall not be defined as labeling when used in connection with the sale of a dietary supplement to consumers."[52]

The provision for using third-party literature goes on to list criteria to which the information must conform. Any articles, books or other literature used in the sale of dietary supplements must:

- be truthful and not misleading
- must be a reprint of an entire publication authored by someone other than the supplier or retailer
- not promote a particular manufacturer or brand of a dietary supplement
- be displayed or presented with other such items on the same subject matter, so as to present a balanced view of available scientific information on a dietary supplement
- be displayed physically separated from the dietary supplements
- not have appended to it any information by sticker or any other method

The act also states these criteria "shall not apply to or restrict a retailer or wholesaler of dietary supplements in any way whatsoever in the sale of books or other publications as a part of the business of such retailer or wholesaler."[53]

Although not stated in any regulation, industry has established a self-imposed rule called the "two click rule." Industry relies on this rule to establish a third-party literature website essentially is two hyperlinks (or clicks) from a retailer or distributor's website. FDA's position on this "rule" has not been explained indirectly or directly by the agency.

Federal Trade Commission Considerations

The Federal Trade Commission ("FTC") is charged dually with ensuring US consumers are protected from fraud, deception and unfair business practices and that a fair and competitive marketplace exists for businesses. The agency has investigative, enforcement and litigation authority over many areas impacting businesses and consumers daily. FTC's Division of Advertising Practices is the nation's enforcer of federal truth-in-advertising laws. Among other things, this division's law enforcement activities focus on claims for products promising health benefits including foods, drugs, medical devices and dietary supplements.

FDA works closely with FTC under a 1971 Memorandum of Understanding[54] governing how responsibilities are divided between the two agencies. FDA has primary responsibility for claims appearing on product labeling, including packaging, inserts and other promotional materials distributed at the point of sale. FTC has primary responsibility for claims made in advertising, including print and broadcast advertisements, infomercials, websites, catalogs and similar direct marketing materials.

The most basic FTC regulation requirement is all advertisements must be truthful, not misleading and appropriately substantiated. FTC's advertising guide for the supplement industry[55] provides detailed examples of claims, how to identify claims and ways to determine adequate levels of substantiation.

FTC evaluates product claims against a "reasonable basis" standard of substantiation.[56] Before disseminating an advertisement, the advertiser must substantiate all claims, express and implied, the ad conveys to reasonable consumers.[57] Whether a company has a reasonable basis depends on factors including: the involved product, the claim type, benefits of a truthful claim, the ease and cost of developing claim substantiation, a false claim's consequences and the amount of substantiation experts in the field regard as reasonable. The advertiser must possess at least the level of substantiation expressly or impliedly claims in the advertisement. When an ad does not make express or implied references to a certain level of support and, in the absence of other evidence indicating consumer expectations, it is assumed that the consumers expect the advertiser had a "reasonable basis" for making the claims.

National Advertising Review Considerations

More recently, use of the industry self-regulating advertising body, National Advertising Division (NAD), of the Council of Better Business Bureaus, has gained traction within the supplement industry. The NAD process allows for an advertising review process that is significantly less expensive than traditional litigation. NAD attorneys are experts in advertising review, and the process provides a quick, confidential way of leveling the playing field in terms of advertising. The process entails the filing of a challenge by a competitor and follow-up responses from the advertiser and challenger. NAD then reviews the entire record and determines whether there is a reasonable basis for the challenged product claims.

NAD stated it traditionally has looked at whether an advertiser has produced reliable and well-controlled clinical testing on the advertised product that can be verified readily in determining whether there is a reasonable basis for an establishment claim for a product. NAD does not require a specific number of tests to be conducted in support of an establishment claim and, instead focuses its analysis on the quality, consumer relevance and reliability of the scientific study offered in support of an advertiser's establishment claim.[58]

Other Regulations Impacting the Dietary Supplement Industry

The *Public Health Security and Bioterrorism Preparedness and Response Act* of 2002 (*Bioterrorism Act*)[59] amended the *FD&C Act* to require facilities that manufacture, process, hold or package food to register with FDA. FDA has stated, according to the *FD&C Act*, dietary supplements and dietary ingredients are "food" and therefore, facilities manufacturing these products must register.[60] Registration may be submitted electronically[61] or by mail or facsimile. As detailed in 21 CFR 1.232, the following information must be included to register a dietary supplement facility:

- facility name, full address and telephone number
- parent company name, address and telephone number, if the facility is a subsidiary
- owner, operator and agent in charge names, addresses and telephone numbers; foreign facilities also must provide the names, addresses and telephone numbers of their US agents
- emergency contact telephone number; foreign facilities also must provide emergency contact phone numbers for their US agents
- all trade names the facility uses
- applicable food product categories as identified in 21 CFR 170.3
- a statement in which the owner, operator or agent in charge certifies the information submitted is true and accurate; the person submitting the registration also must provide a statement certifying the information submitted is true and accurate if he or she is someone other than the owner, operator or agent in charge

Facility registrations must be updated within 60 days of any changes in the information submitted. In 2012, FDA completed an update of its Food Facility Registration Module (FFRM) (www.fda.gov/Food/GuidanceRegulation/FoodFacilityRegistration/default.htm).[62] Food facilities now are able to register biannually and update information via FDA's website instead of using Form FDA 3537. FDA also provides valuable question and answer and guidance documents on food facility registration: http://www.fda.gov/Food/GuidanceRegulation/GuidanceDocumentsRegulatoryInformation/FoodDefense/ucm331957.htm and http://www.fda.gov/Food/GuidanceRegulation/GuidanceDocumentsRegulatoryInformation/FoodDefense/ucm331959.htm.

The *Food Safety Modernization Act* (*FSMA*),[63] enacted on 4 January 2011, amended *FD&C Act* Section 415 to require facilities engaged in manufacturing, processing, packing or holding food for consumption in the US to submit additional registration information to FDA, including an assurance the agency will be permitted to inspect the facility at the times and in the manner permitted by the FD&C Act. *FD&C Act* Section 415, as amended by *FSMA*, also requires food facilities required to register with FDA to renew such registrations every other year and provides the agency the authority to suspend a food facility's registration in certain circumstances. Specifically, if FDA determines food manufactured, processed, packed, received or held by a registered food facility has a reasonable probability of causing serious adverse health consequences or death to humans or animals, the agency may suspend the registration of a facility that:

- created, caused or was otherwise responsible for such reasonable probability
- knew of, or had reason to know of, such reasonable probability; and packed, received or held such food

FDA provides *FSMA*-related advice through a series of guidance and question and answer documents that allow industry to understand the new regulations and implementation plan: http://www.fda.gov/Food/GuidanceRegulation/FSMA/ucm247559.htm.

Dietary Supplement GMPs

More than a decade after receiving authorization from Congress to establish CGMPs for dietary supplements, and four years after FDA published its proposed rule,[64] the agency released its final rule,[65] 21 CFR 111 Current Good Manufacturing Practice in manufacturing, packaging, labeling, or holding operations for dietary supplements ("dietary supplement CGMP rule"). Previously, dietary supplement manufacturing and distribution were regulated under "umbrella" CGMPs established for food generally and were not subject to individualized CGMPs. Although the general food CGMPs in 21 CFR 110 apply to a variety of food products, including dietary supplements, they do not address the unique characteristics of dietary supplements.

The dietary supplement CGMP rule in 21 CFR 111 establishes the minimum CGMPs necessary for activities related to manufacturing, packaging, labeling or holding dietary supplements to ensure product quality. The dietary supplement CGMP rule went into effect 24 August 2007. However, FDA phased in the rule based on the number of dietary supplement company full-time equivalent employees: 25 June 2008 for companies with more than 500 employees; June 2009 for companies with fewer than 500 employees; and June 2010 for companies with fewer than 20 employees.

The dietary supplement CGMP rule applies to all domestic and foreign establishments that manufacture, package, label or hold dietary supplements, including those involved with testing, quality control, packaging and labeling and distribution in the US. The rule does not apply to retail establishments holding dietary supplements only for purposes of direct retail sale to individual consumers, although this exception does not include a retailer's warehouse or other storage facility or a warehouse or other storage facility that sells directly to individual consumers. The dietary supplement CGMP rules do not apply to dietary ingredient suppliers.

The dietary supplement CGMP rule requires:

- written procedures for personnel (Subpart B)
- cleaning the physical plant, including pest control (Subpart C)
- calibrating instruments and controls (Subpart D)
- calibrating, inspecting and checking automated, mechanical or electronic equipment (Subpart D)
- maintaining, cleaning and sanitizing equipment and utensils (Subpart D)
- quality control operations, including conducting a material review and making a disposition decision (Subpart F)
- components, packaging, labels and labeling (Subpart G)
- laboratory operations (Subpart J)
- manufacturing operations (Subpart K)
- packaging and labeling operations (Subpart L)
- holding and distributing operations (Subpart M)
- returned dietary supplements (Subpart N)
- product complaints (Subpart O)

The dietary supplement CGMP rule is divided into 16 user-friendly question and answer subparts (Subparts A–P) and was published in *Federal Register* Volume 72, No. 121 on 25 June 2007. Each subpart is presented according to its specific operations to make it easier to find the relevant production and process control requirements.

The following outline is not intended to be complete or all-inclusive but does provide some key points:

- Establish minimum requirements for personnel, including rules to prevent microbial contamination from sick personnel, employee and supervisor qualifications and record retention (21 CFR 111.10, 21 CFR 111.12, 21 CFR 111.13 and 21 CFR 111.14).
- Establish minimum requirements for physical plant and grounds, equipment and utensils, design and construction, including requirements for written procedures, the use of automated, mechanical or electronic equipment, and record development, retention and maintenance (21 CFR 111.15, 21 CFR 111.16, 21 CFR 111.20, 21 CFR 111.23, 21 CFR 111.25, 21 CFR 111.27,21 CFR 111.30, 21CFR 111.35).
- Establish specifications in the production and process control system that will ensure dietary supplements meet the identity, purity, strength and composition established in specifications and are properly packaged and labeled as specified in the master manufacturing record (21 CFR 111.55, 21 CFR 111.60, 21 CFR 111.70, 21 CFR 111.75, 21 CFR 111.77).
- Permit the use of a "certificate of analysis" from a component supplier for specifications other than the identity of a dietary ingredient in lieu of having manufacturers conduct tests or examinations on all components received (21 CFR 111.75).
- Establish minimum requirements for representative samples and reserve samples (21 CFR 111.80, 21 CFR 111.83).
- Establish minimum requirements for quality control and require implementation of quality control operations to ensure the quality of a dietary supplement (21 CFR 111.105, 21 CFR 111.110, 21 CFR 111.113, 21 CFR 111.117,21 CFR 111.120).
- Require the preparation and use of a written master manufacturing record for each unique formulation of manufactured dietary supplement and for each batch size to ensure the manufacturing process is performed consistently and to ensure uniformity in the finished product from batch to batch (21 CFR 111.205, 21 CFR 111.210,21,CFR 111.123)
- Require design and conduct of all manufacturing operations of dietary supplements in accordance with adequate sanitation principles to prevent contamination of components or dietary supplements (21 CFR 111.355, 21 CFR 111.360, 21 CFR 111.365).
- Require testing of a subset of finished product batches, basing the testing system on either a sound statistical sampling plan or testing of all finished batches (21 CFR 111.75).
- Establish minimum requirements for the batch production record (21 CFR 111.255, 21 CFR 111.260).
- Require the establishment and use of laboratory control processes related to establishing specifications and to the selection and use of testing and examination methods (21 CFR 111.303, 21 CFR 111.310, 21 CFR 111.315, 21 CFR 111.320, 21 CFR 111.325).
- Establish minimum requirements for packaging and labeling operations to assure the quality of the dietary supplement and that the dietary supplement is packaged and labeled as specified in the master

manufacturing record (21 CFR 111.160, 21 CFR 111.415).
- Require reserve samples of dietary supplements to be held in a manner that protects against contamination and deterioration (21 CFR 111.465).
- Require holding of components and dietary supplements under appropriate conditions of temperature, humidity and light so that the identity, purity, strength and composition of the components and dietary supplements are not affected and are protected against mix-up, contamination or deterioration (21 CFR 111.455).
- Establish minimum quality control operations required for returned dietary supplements and require identification and quarantine of returned dietary supplements until quality control personnel conduct a material review and make a disposition decision (21 CFR 111.130, 21 CFR 111.503, 21 CFR 111.510, 21 CFR 111.515, 21 CFR 111.525, 21 CFR 111.530, 21 CFR 111.535).
- Require a qualified person to investigate any "product complaint" that involves a possible failure of a dietary supplement to meet any CGMP requirement, with oversight by quality control personnel (21 CFR 111.553, 21 CFR 111.560).
- Establish minimum requirements for records and recordkeeping (21 CFR 111.605, 21 CFR 111.610).
- Require records associated with the manufacture, packaging, labeling or holding of a dietary supplement to be kept for one year beyond the shelf life dating or, if shelf life dating is not used, for two years beyond the date of distribution of the last batch of dietary supplements associated with those records (21 CFR 111.605).

FDA examined the dietary supplement CGMP rule's economic implications as required by the *Regulatory Flexibility Act* (5 U.S.C. 601–612) and determined the rule would have a significant economic impact on a substantial number of small entities. In compliance with Section 212 of the *Small Business Regulatory Enforcement Fairness Act* (Public Law 104–121), FDA has released a Small Entity Compliance Guide (SECG)[66] stating in plain language the requirements of the 21 CFR 111 regulations. FDA issued this SECG as Level 2 guidance consistent with the agency's Good Guidance Practices regulation (21 CFR 10.115(c)(2)). This SECG restates, in simplified format and language, FDA's requirements for Current Good Manufacturing Practice in Manufacturing, Packaging, Labeling or Holding Operations for Dietary Supplements, including the requirements for a Petition to Request an Exemption from 100% Identity Testing of Dietary Ingredients. In addition, the SECG includes several FDA recommendations from the dietary supplement CGMP rule so the guidance in those recommendations is readily accessible to small businesses.

On 15 December 2010, FDA took new steps aimed at keeping consumers safe from harmful products marketed as dietary supplements and containing undeclared or deceptively labeled ingredients. The new steps include: a letter from the FDA commissioner to the dietary supplement industry emphasizing its legal obligation and responsibilities to prevent tainted products from reaching the US market;[67]and a new rapid public notification system (RSS Feed) on its website to more quickly warn consumers about these products.[68] Companies that make or distribute tainted products may receive Warning Letters and/or face enforcement actions, such as product seizures, injunctions and criminal prosecution. Responsible individuals also may face criminal prosecution.

With the implementation of *FSMA*, FDA has renewed its focus on GMP compliance in the dietary supplement industry. Facilities are inspected routinely by FDA, and dietary supplement GMP compliance remains one of the most prevalent comments by FDA following inspection. Traditionally, inspections are assigned by FDA on a risk-based, case-by-case initiative. In other words, a company routinely receiving Form 483 observations regarding GMP compliance or has received a Warning Letter from FDA can expect to be inspected on an annual basis. Those who have not received such feedback from FDA and generally are found to be compliant may be inspected on a less strict schedule.

The dietary supplement industry currently is made up of a number of private label distributors that utilize contract manufacturers to manufacturer, pack, label and distribute their products. In some instances, the product label owner does not even see the product before it is sent to a fulfillment warehouse. Recently, FDA has taken a strong stance in dealing with private label distributors that incorrectly believe GMP obligations do not apply to contract manufacturers.

In a Warning Letter to a dietary supplement distributor, FDA noted "[a]s a distributor that contracts with other manufacturers to manufacture, package, or label dietary supplements that your firm releases for distribution under your firm's name, your firm has an obligation to know what and how manufacturing activities are performed so that you can make decisions related to whether your dietary supplement products conform to established specifications and whether to approve and release the products for distribution [72 Fed. Reg. 34752, 34790 (Jun. 25, 2007)]. Your firm introduces or delivers, or causes the introduction or delivery, of dietary supplement products into interstate commerce in their final form for distribution to consumers. As such, your firm has an overarching and ultimate responsibility to ensure that all phases of the production of that product are in compliance with dietary supplement CGMP requirements."[69] Thus, private label distributors also should ensure their practices, albeit with minimal involvement, are compliant with GMP regulations.

Requirements such as returned product review, complaints and product review before dissemination to consumers likely will apply. Industry can continue to expect increased FDA enforcement of dietary supplement GMPs moving forward with the rolling implementation of *FSMA* initiatives.

Adverse Event Reporting

In April 2001, the Office of the Inspector General (OIG) developed a report identifying the then current parameters for dietary supplement adverse event reporting to be "an inadequate safety valve."[70] As such, there was an apparent need for legislation to protect consumers and provide a system for adverse events reporting.

On 22 December 2006, President George W. Bush signed into law the *Dietary Supplement and Nonprescription Drug Consumer Protection Act* (Pub. L. 109-462, 120 Stat. 3469). This law amends the *FD&C Act* with respect to adverse event reporting and recordkeeping for dietary supplements and nonprescription drugs marketed without an approved application. The manufacturer, packer or distributor whose name (pursuant to Section 403(e)(1) of the *FD&C Act*) appears on the label of a dietary supplement marketed in the US is required to submit all serious adverse event reports associated with the dietary supplement's use in the US to FDA. The effective date for compliance with the requirements of this law was 22 December 2007.

An "adverse event" is "any health-related event associated with the use of a dietary supplement that is adverse." A "serious adverse event" is an adverse event that results in death, a life-threatening experience, inpatient hospitalization, a persistent or significant disability incapacity, a congenital anomaly or birth defect, a medical or surgical intervention, based on reasonable medical judgment, to prevent an outcome described above.

The *Dietary Supplement and Nonprescription Drug Consumer Protection Act* usually refers to the entity (manufacturer, packer or distributor) required to submit a serious adverse event report to FDA as the "responsible person." Serious adverse event reports, as well as all follow-up reports of new medical information received within one year after the initial report, must be submitted to FDA on MedWatch Form 3500A along with a copy of the dietary supplement label and any other attachments no later than 15 business days after the report is received by the responsible person. However, voluntary reports of adverse events associated with a dietary supplement may be submitted on MedWatch Form 3500, the voluntary reporting form.

FDA requires mandatory reports using MedWatch Form 3500A for serious adverse events associated with the use of dietary supplements to be submitted in hard copy by mail only. FDA currently does not accept dietary supplement serious adverse event reports electronically or by facsimile.

The following five data elements,[71] at minimum, are necessary for FDA to avoid duplication in its adverse event reports database and to interpret the significance of adverse events, facilitate follow-up and detect fraud:

- an identifiable injured person
- an identifiable initial reporter
- responsible person's identity and contact information (i.e., the manufacturer, packer or distributor submitting the serious adverse event report to FDA)
- a suspect dietary supplement
- a serious adverse event or fatal outcome

If a serious adverse event involves multiple dietary supplements manufactured, packaged or distributed by the same responsible person, the responsible person should submit only one serious adverse event report to FDA on Form 3500A. If a serious adverse event involves multiple suspect dietary supplements manufactured, packaged or distributed by more than one responsible person (e.g., manufacturers A and B), and if the event is reported to one of the responsible persons (manufacturer A), that responsible person (manufacturer A) should submit a serious adverse event report to FDA, identifying both its own product(s) and manufacturer B's product(s) in the Suspect Product section (Section C) of Form 3500A. In such a case, manufacturer A should send manufacturer B a copy of the submitted Form 3500A, including manufacturer A's report number. Manufacturer B need not submit a separate report to FDA for the serious adverse event unless manufacturer B has information about the serious adverse event that was not provided to FDA in manufacturer A's report. If manufacturer B does have such information, it must be reported to FDA as a follow-up report of new medical information, accompanied by a copy of manufacturer A's serious adverse event report. It is not necessary for manufacturer B to submit its own separate serious adverse event report on Form 3500A.

If the serious adverse event involves a nonprescription drug product marketed without an approved application and a dietary supplement also manufactured, packaged or distributed by the same responsible person, and the initial reporter views each product as suspect, the responsible person should submit one report about the serious adverse event to both the Center for Drug Evaluation and Research (CDER) and the Center for Food Safety and Applied Nutrition (CFSAN). The report should include information about both suspect products in Section C of the form and should use one manufacturer report number. There is no requirement to provide a sample of the dietary supplement to FDA with the adverse event report, and the agency does not recommend a sample be submitted unless requested. Instructions for completing MedWatch Form 3500A to report a serious adverse event associated with a dietary supplement can be found on FDA's website (http://www.fda.gov/Safety/MedWatch/HowToReport/DownloadForms/ucm149236.htm).

The responsible person must maintain records related to each serious adverse event report for six years. These records should include, at minimum, copies of the following:

- the responsible person's serious adverse event report to FDA on MedWatch Form 3500A, with attachments
- any new medical information about the serious adverse event received by the responsible person
- any reports to FDA of new medical information related to the serious adverse event
- communications between the responsible person and the initial reporter
- any other person(s) who provided information related to the adverse event

Any new medical information received within one year of the initial report must be submitted to FDA within 15 business days of receipt. Dietary supplements labeled on or after 22 December 2007 need to include a domestic address or domestic telephone number at which the responsible person can receive reports of adverse events.[72] Products that do not include such information (such as those imported from foreign manufacturers) will be deemed "misbranded" and subject to FDA regulatory action.

While the adverse event process has been enhanced by legislation and enforcement by FDA, the current process still has its pitfalls. Another OIG report analyzed 127 weight loss and immune dietary supplements,[73] finding 28% of the companies contacted from the pool of supplements failed to register with FDA as required. Of the companies that failed to register, 72% failed to provide complete and accurate information through registration. 20% of the labels analyzed did not provide required telephone numbers or addresses, undermining the adverse event process.

Import and Export Regulations

The *Bioterrorism Act* of 2002, Section 307, added Section 801(m) to the *FD&C Act*, requiring FDA to receive prior notice for food imported or offered for import into the US. Prior notice is notification to FDA an article of food, including animal feed or pet food, is being imported or offered for import into the US in advance of the food article's arrival at the US border. Section 801(m) also provides, if an article of food arrives at the port of arrival with inadequate prior notice (e.g., no prior notice, inaccurate prior notice or untimely prior notice), the food is subject to refusal of admission under Section 801(m)(1) of the act and may not be delivered to the importer, owner or consignee.

Prior notice must be submitted to FDA electronically via either the US Customs and Border Protection (Customs) Automated Broker Interface (ABI) of the Automated Commercial System (ACS) or FDA's Prior Notice System Interface (FDA PNSI). Prior notice must be received and confirmed electronically by FDA no more than five days before arrival and, as specified by the mode of transportation below, no less than: 1) two hours before arrival by land by road; 2) four hours before arrival by air or by rail; 3) eight hours before arrival by water; 4) the time consistent with the timeframe established for the mode of transportation for an article of food carried by or otherwise accompanying an individual if it is subject to prior notice.

Instructions for submitting prior notice and information on prior notice of imported foods can be found on the FDA website (www.fda.gov/Food/GuidanceRegulation/ImportsExports/Importing/ucm2006836.htm). Additional information on Customs' procedures for prior notice can be found at http://www.cbp.gov/. Failure to submit prior notice by a person who imports or offers for import an article of food is a prohibited act under Section 301(ee) of the act (21 U.S.C. 331(ee)) and could result in the US bringing civil, criminal and debarment actions against him or her. When it is consistent with the agency's public protection responsibilities, and depending on the nature of the violation, FDA gives individuals and firms an opportunity to take voluntary and prompt corrective action before initiating regulatory actions.[74] Accordingly, FDA may elect to refuse prior notices or send compliance letters to give the responsible parties warning before pursuing other regulatory actions, e.g., injunction, prosecution, etc. The regulatory actions for violations include:

- refusal under Section 801(m) of the act for no prior notice, inaccurate prior notice or untimely prior notice
- hold under Section 801(l) of the act for importing or offering for import food from a foreign facility that is not registered under section 415 of the act
- injunction under Section 302 of the act
- prosecution under Sections 301 and 303 of the act
- debarment under Section 306 of the act
- Customs seizure and assessment of civil monetary penalties for violation of any laws enforced by Customs and Border Protection, including 19 U.S.C. 1595a(b), against any person who directs, assists financially or otherwise, or is in any way concerned in the importation of any merchandise contrary to law

The *Bioterrorism Act* requires domestic and foreign facilities manufacturing, processing, packing or holding food for consumption in the US to register with FDA. In addition, the act amended *FD&C Act* Chapter VIII by adding Section 801(l), which requires any food for human and animal consumption from an unregistered foreign facility imported or offered for import to be held at the port of entry until the foreign facility has been registered.

In addition, the *Bioterrorism Act*, Section 305, added Section 415 to the *FD&C Act* to require domestic and foreign facilities manufacturing, processing, packing or holding food for human or animal consumption in the US to register with FDA. Dietary supplements and dietary ingredients are regulated as foods by FDA. The *Bioterrorism Act* makes failure to register a prohibited act under Section 301 of the *FD&C Act*.

Owners, operators or agents in charge of domestic or foreign facilities manufacturing, processing, packing or holding foods for human or animal consumption in the US are required to register the facility with FDA. Domestic facilities are required to register whether or not food from the facility enters interstate commerce.

Foreign facilities manufacturing, processing, packing or holding food also are required to register unless food from that facility undergoes further processing (including packaging) by another foreign facility before the food is exported to the US. However, if the subsequent foreign facility performs only a minimal activity, such as putting on a label, both facilities are required to register. Foreign facilities are required to designate a US agent for purposes of the registration regulation. The US agent acts as a communications link between FDA and the foreign facility. FDA will treat representations by the US agent as those of the foreign facility and will consider information or documents provided to the US agent equivalent to providing the information or documents to the foreign facility.

Registrants must register using Form FDA 3537. Registrations can be submitted in hard copy format by mail, electronically via the Internet, on CD-ROM or by fax. Instructions for completing Form FDA 3537 and additional information on registration of food facilities can be found on FDA's website (www.fda.gov/Food/GuidanceRegulation/FSMA/ucm314178.htm).

Section 801(e)(1) of the *FD&C Act* states a food intended for export must not be deemed to be adulterated or misbranded under the act if it: (a) accords to the specifications of the foreign purchaser; b) is not in conflict with the laws of the country to which it is intended for export; c) is labeled on the outside of the shipping package saying it is intended for export; and d) is not sold or offered for sale in domestic commerce.[75] Dietary ingredients and dietary supplements for export are subject to Section 801(e)(1) of the act and would be subject to the notification and recordkeeping requirements of 21 CFR 1.101.[76]

Currently, FDA issues the "certificate of free sale" as an export certificate for food, including dietary supplements legally marketed in the US.[77] The criteria needed to request a certificate of free sale for dietary supplements can be found at www.food-drug.com/fda_expoert_certificate.htm. A certificate of free sale is only issued for products manufactured in the US. The requirements for prior notice do not apply to dietary supplements that are imported and then exported without leaving the port of arrival until export.

FDA Detentions

Products are subject to detention and review upon entry into the US. FDA works closely with Customs to ensure imported products are compliant with the *FD&C Act*. Upon entry of a shipment, the product is designated with a hold, detention or "may proceed" from FDA. In cases where products are held or detained, FDA issues a Notice of Action identifying its position on the products in the shipment. At that point, the importer of record can either request refusal of the shipment and re-export the noncompliant goods, respond to FDA stating its position that the goods are in compliance with the *FD&C Act* or request reconditioning of the goods to bring the products into compliance. Product reconditioning is completed through use of FDA Form 766 and must identify the corrective action being taken, the place where the corrective action is being taken and how long the corrective action will take. FDA is not obligated to accept a reconditioning proposal but customarily does so in instances where goods can be brought into compliance easily.

FDA Import Alerts

Should a product be refused due to noncompliance, a company risks being placed on FDA's Import Alert List (http://www.fda.gov/ForIndustry/ImportProgram/ImportAlerts/). Import Alerts are established for a variety of noncompliance reasons, including misbranded labeling, adulterations through filth, pesticides or undeclared drug ingredients, and through preemptive initiatives, such as seafood safety. For example, Import Alert 16-131 authorizes the detention "without physical examination of all shipments of aquacultured catfish, Basa (*Pangasius sp*), shrimp, dace, and eel from the People's Republic of China (CN), except for the firms identified in the Green List to this alert."[78] Firms may apply for removal from an import alert after certain guidelines are met. The application must include a persuasive petition assuring FDA the products or the issues that gave rise to the Import Alert in the first place have been resolved. If a product has been placed on a detention without physical examination because it appears violative under Section 801(a)(1) or (2), FDA customarily requires a follow-up establishment inspection in addition to analysis of samples from representative shipments.[79] For products automatically detained because they appear violative under Section 801(a)(3), a minimum of five consecutive nonviolative commercial shipments should be entered before FDA may consider the appearance of the violation has been sufficiently overcome. At least one of the five consecutive, nonviolative shipments must be audited by FDA to ensure the validity of the analysis.

FDA's *Regulatory Procedures Manual*, "Chapter 9 Import Operations and Actions," provides valuable insight into operational guidelines from FDA to its staff. Industry can benefit from reviewing this manual for import regulations and operations. While the manual does not provide specifics on what constitutes an adequate petition for removal, generally one must submit US Customs Form 3461 or US Customs Form 7501, Commercial Invoices, Packing Lists, Bill of Lading and any laboratory analysis (if applicable) for each of the five nonviolative shipments. FDA's Division of Import Operations (DIO) is charged with review of petitions for removal from import alerts.

Homeopathic Products

The term "homeopathy" is derived from the Greek words *homeo* (similar) and *pathos* (suffering or disease). Homeopathy is the practice of treating the syndromes and conditions constituting disease with remedies that have produced similar syndromes and conditions in healthy subjects.[80]

History of Homeopathy in Food and Drug Law

As both the chief sponsor of the *FD&C Act* and a homeopathic physician, Senator Royal Copeland of New York amended the *Food and Drugs Act* of 1906 by defining "drug" to include those homeopathic drugs listed in the *Homeopathic Pharmacopoeia of the United States* (*HPUS*).

For five decades (from 1938–88), homeopathic drugs were sold in a regulatory vacuum. FDA action was based on institutional understanding and informal agreements between agency officials and industry members. From 1982–88, the industry, professional and consumer members of the community through the American Homeopathic Pharmacists Association worked with FDA in the development of a regulatory framework called a Compliance Policy Guide, CPG 7132.15 "Conditions under which homeopathic drugs may be marketed." CPG 7132.15 provides guidance on the regulation of over-the-counter (OTC) and prescription homeopathic drugs, and delineates those conditions under which homeopathic drugs ordinarily may be marketed in the US.

FDA does not regulate homeopathic drugs in precisely the same way as conventional or allopathic drugs; in fact, the agency treats homeopathic drugs, both prescription and OTC, quite differently. Unlike conventional drugs, homeopathic drugs are not subject to premarket approval, which involves filing a new drug application (NDA) in order to market the drug. Furthermore, unlike other OTC drugs, which are either required to be submitted for OTC review or filed in an NDA, OTC homeopathic drugs are not subject to the FDA review process. Like some drug OTC products, homeopathic drugs need to comply with a monograph.

The FDA Compliance Policy Guide, CPG 7132.15 and *HPUS* form the basis for the regulation of homeopathic drugs in the US.[81]

Definition of Homeopathic Drugs

A homeopathic drug is any drug labeled as being homeopathic that is listed in *HPUS*, an addendum to it or its supplements. Homeopathic drug potencies are specified in terms of dilution, i.e., 1x (1/10 dilution), 2x (1/100 dilution), etc. Homeopathic drug products must contain diluents commonly used in homeopathic pharmaceuticals. Drug products containing homeopathic ingredients in combination with non-homeopathic active ingredients are not homeopathic drug products.

Homeopathic drugs generally must meet the standards for strength, quality and purity set forth in *HPUS*. *HPUS* is declared a legal source of information on homeopathic drug products in Section 201(g)(1) of the *FD&C Act*. *HPUS* is a compilation of standards for source, composition and preparation of homeopathic drugs, which the *FD&C Act* also recognized as an official compendium. Section 201(j) of the act (21 U.S.C. §321) defines the term "official compendium" as the "official *United States Pharmacopoeia*, official *Homeopathic Pharmacopoeia of the United States*, official *National Formulary* or any supplement to them."

Introduction to the Homeopathic Pharmacopoeia Convention of the United States (HPCUS)

The Homeopathic Pharmacopoeia Convention of the United States (HPCUS) is a nongovernmental, nonprofit, scientific organization composed of experts who have appropriate training and experience and have demonstrated additional knowledge and interest in the principles of homeopathy. HPCUS is an autonomous body that works closely with FDA and homeopathic organizations. The HPCUS board appoints a Monograph Review Committee (MRC), a Pharmacopoeia Revision Committee (PRC) and a Council on Pharmacy to assist in its ongoing responsibilities.

HPCUS is responsible for the production and constant updating of *HPUS*. *HPUS* is published as the *Homeopathic Pharmacopoeia of the United States Revision Service*. *HPUS* is "written" by a group of pharmacists, physicians and lay people who meet three to six times a year to review monographs and pharmacy procedures. The *HPUS Revision Service*, also known as the subscription service, began in December 1988. One or two revisions are published each year. Annual subscription updates are required to keep the *HPUS Revision Service* current and official.

HPUS is divided into two sections: General Pharmacy and Drug Monographs. General Pharmacy contains all official manufacturing procedures for all official homeopathic dosage forms as well as labeling guidelines and administrative information. In addition, criteria and procedures for inclusion in *HPUS* are published. *HPUS* contains approximately 1,300 individual monographs of official drug substances. Each monograph lists complete identifying data for the drug as well as specific manufacturing standards.

The *HPUS* online database is a powerful tool that provides quick access to all *HPUS* publications. The database includes the most current monograph and quality control specifications, along with real-time updates. To access the *HPUS* online database, visit www.hpus.com.

The HPUS Approval Process

To be included in *HPUS*, a drug must have sufficient clinical data or "drug proving" to show efficacy. In a homeopathic drug proving, a homeopathically prepared substance is administered to healthy volunteers to produce the symptoms specific to that substance and thereby reveal its inherent curative powers. During a homeopathic drug proving, the goal is to provoke temporary symptoms associated with the homeopathic medication. These symptoms then are arranged to form a symptom pattern or "remedy picture" specific to that particular homeopathic substance and provide the basis for a better understanding of its possible effects in patients. To be eligible for inclusion in *HPUS*, the drug must meet the first three criteria and at least one of the latter four (4, 5, 6 or 7):

1. HPCUS has determined the drug is safe and effective.
2. The drug must be prepared according to the specifications of the General Pharmacy and relevant sections of *HPUS*.
3. The submitted documentation must be in an approved format as set forth in the relevant sections of *HPUS*.
4. The therapeutic use of a new and nonofficial homeopathic drug is established by a homeopathic drug proving and clinical verification acceptable to HPCUS.
5. The therapeutic use of the drug is established through published documentation the substance was in use prior to 1962. This documentation must include the symptom picture, including subjective and any available objective symptoms.
6. The drug's therapeutic use is established by at least two adequately controlled, double-blind clinical studies using the drug as the single intervention; and the study is accompanied by adequate statistical analysis and adequate description of the symptom picture acceptable to HPCUS, including the subjective symptoms and, where appropriate, the objective symptomatology.
7. The drug's therapeutic use is established by: data gathered from clinical experience encompassing the symptom picture and pre- and post-treatment, including subjective and any available objective symptoms; or data documented in the medical literature (all sources of medical literature may be considered on a case-by-case basis) subjected to further verification (statistical and/or other forms of verification).

Homeopathic drug provings on healthy volunteers are carried out according to Hahnemann's classical directions and also adhere to the current regulations for conventional clinical trials Clinical verification of all or part of the symptom picture established in a homeopathic drug proving is designed to demonstrate further a homeopathic medication's potential clinical applicability. Clinical verification also may use a variety of methodologies in a prospective or retrospective fashion. The design and sample size will vary on a case-by-case basis, depending on what is being verified (symptom picture, keynotes or a specific clinical indication). The responsibility for a scientifically sound clinical verification protocol lies with the sponsor. The study design for clinical verification of the symptoms gathered in a drug proving should be submitted to the MRC and the PRC for review prior to beginning clinical verification. For additional information, refer to the HPCUS Guidelines for Homeopathic Drug Provings, HPCUS Outline for Protocols for Homeopathic Drug Provings and HPCUS Guidelines for Clinical Verification on the HPUS website. To be considered for inclusion in *HPUS*, a monograph must adhere to the specified format and be accompanied by documentation verifying it meets *HPUS* inclusion eligibility criteria.

A sponsor desiring to have monographs considered for inclusion in *HPUS* must submit them to the editor. If the monographs are acceptable, the editor will forward them, with any comments and accompanying documentation, to the chairman of the MRC. The MRC will review each monograph comprehensively and recommend its categorization under one of three headings: approved for publication in *HPUS*; deferred for presentation of additional data; or not approved for publication in *HPUS*.

The editor will publish the list of monographs the MRC has recommended for the approved category and those in the not-approved category, and the reasons for the actions taken, in an appropriate medium such as the *Journal of the American Institute of Homeopathy*, *Homeopathy Today* or *American Homeopathy*. The editor also will forward the annotated monographs, the monograph list and any accompanying documentation to the PRC chairman. A minimum of 90 days, beginning on the 15th of the month the monograph list is published, is permitted for comments from the general public. At the end of the 90-day period, any public comments received by the editor will be forwarded to the PRC chairman. The PRC will review each monograph and recommend categorization under one of three headings: approved for publication in *HPUS*; deferred for presentation of additional data; or not approved for publication in *HPUS*. The board of directors reviews and acts on MRC and PRC recommendations. If acceptable, the monograph is granted final approval for inclusion in *HPUS*, and the secretary notifies the sponsor of the board's decision.

Labeling and Advertising

All homeopathic products are drugs within the meaning of the *FD&C Act* and, therefore, are subject to applicable FDA regulations for labeling, advertising and promotion. Homeopathic drug product labeling must comply with the provisions of Sections 502 and 503 of the *FD&C Act* and 21 CFR 201. The label shall contain, in prominent type, the word "HOMEOPATHIC" or "Homeopathic."

The Statement of Ingredients must appear in accordance with Section 502(e) of the *FD&C Act* and 21 CFR 201.10. Labeling must bear a statement of the quantity and amount of ingredient(s) in the product in conformance with Section 502(b) of the act and 21 CFR 201.10, expressed in homeopathic terms, e.g., 1x, 2x. On each label and package, the letters "HPUS" should be appended to the name of each official drug present in the product, e.g., "Arnica Montana 3X HPUS." In addition, the following statement must appear at the end of the label's formula section when all product(s) contained therein are official: "The letters 'HPUS' indicate that the component(s) in this product is (are) officially monographed in the *Homeopathic Pharmacopoeia of the United States*. The designation 'HPUS' is restricted (or may be appended only) to those substances (or Homeopathic Drug Products) whose monographs have been reviewed by the Convention and have been approved for publication in the current Pharmacopoeia by the Board of Directors."

Other general labeling requirements include the manufacturer, packer or distributor's name and place of business, in conformance with Section 502(b) and 21 CFR 201.1, adequate directions for use (Section 502(f) and 21 CFR 201.5) and Established Name (Section 502(e)(3) of the *FD&C Act* and 21 CFR 201.10). The label and labeling must be in the English language as described and provided for under 21 CFR 201.15(c)(1), although it is permissible for industry to include the labeling in both English and Latin.

Prescription homeopathic drug product labels shall bear a statement of identity (21 CFR 201.50), declaration of net quantity of contents (21 CFR 201.51), a statement of the recommended or usual dosage (21 CFR 201.55) and information described under 21 CFR 201.56 and 21 CFR 201.57. An exemption from adequate directions for use under Section 503 is applicable only to prescription drugs. All prescription homeopathic drug products must bear the prescription legend, "Caution: Federal law prohibits dispensing without prescription" (Section 503(b)(1)), and a package insert bearing complete labeling information for the homeopathic practitioner must accompany the product.

OTC homeopathic drug product labels must comply with the principal display panel provision (21 CFR 201.62) and the statement of identity (21 CFR 201.61) shall conform to the provisions for declaring net quantity of contents under 21 CFR 201.62. OTC homeopathic drugs intended for systemic absorption, unless specifically exempted, must bear a warning statement in conformance with 21 CFR 201.63(a). Other warnings, such as those for indications conforming to those in the OTC drug final regulations, are required as appropriate.

Homeopathic products intended solely for self-limiting disease conditions amenable to self-diagnosis (of symptoms) and treatment may be marketed OTC. Homeopathic products offered for conditions not amenable to OTC use must be marketed as prescription products. The criteria specified in Section 503(b) of the *FD&C Act* apply to the determination of prescription status for all drug products, including homeopathic drug products. If *HPUS* specifies a distinction between nonprescription and prescription status of products based on strength that is more restrictive than Section 503(b) of the act, the more stringent criteria will apply.

Any drug included in *HPUS* is considered "official," and those not included in *HPUS* are "nonofficial." Any official drug can be sold without any further manufacturer documentation. Nonofficial drugs require the manufacturer to produce a proving or sufficient clinical data for FDA to make a determination as to whether the drug was, in fact, homeopathic.

If any homeopathic drug is promoted significantly beyond the recognized or customary practice of homeopathy, FDA's health fraud policy priorities and procedures will apply (CPG 7150.10 "Health Fraud-Factors in Considering Regulatory Action" 5 June 1987).

Recently, FDA has increased its enforcement of homeopathic regulations with respect to advertising. In Warning Letters to industry, the agency has stated clearly "under the CPG, only homeopathic products intended solely for self-limiting disease conditions amenable to self-diagnosis (of symptoms) and treatment may be marketed OTC. Homeopathic products offered for conditions not amenable to OTC use must be marketed as prescription products."[82] However, FDA does not specify its position on the diseases it considers to be self-limiting or those not amenable to OTC use. This matter remains a somewhat gray area with respect to homeopathic regulations.

Members of industry who solely rely on homeopathic literature provings as a base for their intended use and product claims have now started implementing a disclaimer on their products. Such a disclaimer discloses to consumers the product's uses are based on homeopathic literature provings and have not been studied through a clinical trial.

Establishment Registration With FDA

FD&C Act Section 510 *Act* requires manufacturers, repackers and relabelers engaging in the manufacture, preparation, propagation, compounding or processing of human drugs (including homeopathics) to register their establishment(s) and submit a listing of every product in commercial distribution with FDA. Registration is submitted using an electronic system, instructions for which can be found at http://www.fda.gov/Drugs/GuidanceComplianceRegulatoryInformation/DrugRegistrationandListing/ucm078801.htm. Although registration information must be submitted to FDA, the agency does not review the electronic registration application and product information for compliance with FDA homeopathic drug regulations.

Good Manufacturing Practices

All firms manufacturing, preparing, propagating, compounding or otherwise processing homeopathic drugs must register as drug establishments in conformance with *FD&C Act* Section 510 and 21 CFR 207.[83]

Homeopathic drug products must be manufactured in conformance with current Good Manufacturing Practices, *FD&C Act* Section 501(a)(2)(B) and 21 CFR 211. However, the unique nature of these drug products has led to two exemptions to this requirement. First, homeopathic drugs need not have expiration dating (21 CFR 211.137). Second, FDA proposed an amendment exempting homeopathic drug products from the requirement for laboratory determination of identity and strength of each active ingredient prior to the drug's release and distribution (21 CFR 211.165). Until there is a final ruling on this proposed testing requirement amendment, FDA has a policy of not enforcing this regulation against homeopathic drugs.

Recent Events in the Homeopathic Industry

On 20–21 April 2015, FDA held a public hearing to obtain additional information and comments from industry and other stakeholders concerning the use of human drug products labeled as homeopathic. The public hearing also discussed FDA's current regulatory framework for these products. The hearing included presentations from agency representatives, educational institutions and members of industry and industry trade associations.

FDA currently is seeking written comments from all interested parties in response to a proposed rule printed in the *Federal Register* on 27 March 2015.[84] Among other information, FDA requested input on the following:

- consumer and healthcare provider attitudes toward homeopathic human drug and biological products
- data sources to be identified or shared with FDA so the agency can assess homeopathic drug and biological product risks and benefits better
- appropriateness of current enforcement policies under the Compliance Policy Guide to protect and promote public health in light of the tremendous growth in the homeopathic drug market (Are there alternatives to the Compliance Policy Guide's current enforcement policies that would inform FDA's regulatory oversight of drugs labeled as homeopathic?)
- any current Compliance Policy Guide areas that could benefit from additional clarity
- information regarding the homeopathic product regulation in other countries that could inform FDA's thinking in this area
- appropriate regulatory processes for evaluating homeopathic OTC human drug products, for a wide variety of indications never considered for OTC use under a formal regulatory process
- given the wide range of indications for these products processes companies currently use to evaluate whether homeopathic products, including their indications for use are appropriate for OTC marketing adequacy of information available to consumers and healthcare providers to make informed decisions about homeopathic drug products

In setting up the proposed rule and public hearing, FDA noted the homeopathic drug market initially was a multimillion dollar industry when the Compliance Policy Guide was published in 1988. However, the industry ballooned to nearly $2.9 billion dollars in sales in 2007.[85] This recent FDA initiative could be a signal FDA plans additional regulatory oversight of homeopathic drugs.

FTC also is hosting a workshop 21 September 2015 to evaluate advertising for OTC homeopathic products. FTC seeks to bring together medical professionals, industry representatives, consumer advocates and government regulators to discuss mass-market advertising of homeopathic drugs. In announcing this workshop, FTC also noted growth of the industry from a multimillion-dollar to a multibillion-dollar market.

Summary

- Dietary supplements are regulated as a class of food products and may be marketed to support the normal, healthy structure or function of the human body and its systems.
- Dietary supplements are subject to GMP regulations and adverse event reporting requirements and manufacturing, packing, relabeling and warehousing facilities must be registered with FDA; however, product listing and premarket approval are not required.
- Homeopathic products are a class of drug products regulated through a Compliance Policy Guide.
- Homeopathic drug products are not subject to the NDA process. They are subject to approval by the Homeopathic Pharmacopoeia Convention of the United States (HPCUS) or must conform to a monograph published in the *Homeopathic Pharmacopoeia of the United States* (HPUS).

- Homeopathic drug products must comply with labeling regulations found in 21 CFR 201.
- Homeopathic manufacturing establishments must be registered and products must be listed with FDA.

References

1. Pray WS. *A History of Nonprescription Product Regulation*, Pharmaceutical Products Press, New York (2003).
2. "Chapter II: Background on dietary supplements." Commission on Dietary Supplement Labels. Office of Disease Prevention and Health Promotion website. http://www.health.gov/dietsupp/ch2.htm. Accessed 8 May 2015.
3. "Vitamin and Mineral Drug Products for Over-the-Counter Human Use." *Federal Register*, Vol 44, No. 53, p. 16126 (16 March 1979).
4. Pray WS. "The FDA, Vitamins, and the Dietary Supplement Industry." *US Pharm*. 2008;33(10):10–15.
5. Op cit 1.
6. *Nutrition Advertising Coordination Act* of 1991 (HR 1662 SC2).
7. *Dietary Supplement Consumer Protection Act* of 1993 (HR 2923 IH).
8. Op cit 3.
9. *The Dietary Supplements Task Force Final Report,* Dept. of Health and Human Services, Public Health Service, Food and Drug Administration, 1992.
10. Interview Mr. Loren Isrealsen, JD, Executive Director UNPA, 1 October 2009.
11. Ibid.
12. Soller RW. "Regulation in the Herb Market: The Myth of the 'Unregulated Industry.'" *HerbalGram*. 2000;49:64 American Botanical Council.
13. *Dietary Supplement Health and Education Act* of 1994 (Public Law 103-417, 103rd Congress).
14. FDA information on *Dietary Supplement Health and Education Act* of 1994, 1 December 1995. FDA website. www.fda.gov/Food/DietarySupplements/default.htm. Accessed 8 May 2015.
15. "Nutritional Supplements Flexing Muscles as Growth Industry." Forbes website. 18 April 2013. http://www.forbes.com/sites/davidlariviere/2013/04/18/nutritional-supplements-flexing-their-muscles-as-growth-industry/. Accessed 8 May 2015.
16. *Nutrition Labeling Education Act* of 1990 (Public Law 101-535, 101st Congress).
17. 21 USC 321(ff)(1) Definitions; "dietary supplement." GPO website. http://www.gpo.gov/fdsys/pkg/USCODE-2010-title21/pdf/USCODE-2010-title21-chap9-subchapII-sec321.pdf. Accessed 8 May 2015.
18. Op cit 6.
19. 21 USC 321(ff)(3)(B)(i). Definitions; "dietary supplement." GPO website. http://www.gpo.gov/fdsys/pkg/USCODE-2010-title21/pdf/USCODE-2010-title21-chap9-subchapII-sec321.pdf. Accessed 8 May 2015.
20. 21 USC 321(ff)(3)(B)(ii). Definitions; "dietary supplement." GPO website. http://www.gpo.gov/fdsys/pkg/USCODE-2010-title21/pdf/USCODE-2010-title21-chap9-subchapII-sec321.pdf. Accessed 8 May 2015.
21. *Draft Guidance for Industry: Factors that Distinguish Liquid Dietary Supplements from Beverages, Considerations Regarding Novel Ingredients, and Labeling for Beverages and Other Conventional Foods* (December 2009). FDA website. www.fda.gov/Food/GuidanceRegulation/GuidanceDocumentsRegulatoryInformation/DietarySupplements/ucm196903.htm. Accessed 8 May 2015.
22. Warning letter to dōTERRA International, LLC dated 22 September 2014. FDA website. http://www.fda.gov/iceci/enforcementactions/warningletters/2014/ucm415809.htm. Accessed 8 May 2015.
23. Warning letter to Descor LLC dated 19 August 2014. FDA website. http://www.fda.gov/iceci/enforcementactions/warningletters/2014/ucm413627.htm. Accessed 8 May 2015.
24. Warning letter to Regeneca, Inc. dated 28 August 2012. FDA website. http://www.fda.gov/iceci/enforcementactions/warningletters/2012/ucm318069.htm. Accessed 8 May 2015.
25. Section IV A 8. *Draft Guidance for Industry: Dietary Supplements: New Dietary Ingredient Notifications and Related Issues* (July 2011). FDA website. http://www.fda.gov/food/guidanceregulation/guidancedocumentsregulatoryinformation/dietarysupplements/ucm257563.htm . Accessed 8 May 2015.
26. 21 CFR 190.6 Requirement for premarket notification. GPO website. www.gpo.gov/fdsys/pkg/CFR-2011-title21-vol3/pdf/CFR-2011-title21-vol3-part190-subpartB.pdf. Accessed 8 May 2015.
27. *Draft Form FDA 3880: Electronic New Dietary Ingredient Notification (NDIN) Submission.* FDA website. http://www.fda.gov/Food/DietarySupplements/NewDietaryIngredientsNotificationProcess/ucm356620.htm. Accessed 8 May 2015.
28. *Draft Guidance for Industry: Dietary Supplements: New Dietary Ingredient Notifications and Related Issues* (July 2011). FDA website. http://www.fda.gov/food/guidanceregulation/guidancedocumentsregulatoryinformation/dietarysupplements/ucm257563.htm. Accessed 8 May 2015.
29. "FDA Has No Objections to One in Four NDI Notifications. Nutritional Outlook. 16 June 2014. http://www.nutritionaloutlook.com/140616/NDI. Accessed 8 May 2015.
30. Section IV B 3. *Draft Guidance for Industry: Dietary Supplements: New Dietary Ingredient Notifications and Related Issues* (July 2011). FDA website. http://www.fda.gov/food/guidanceregulation/guidancedocumentsregulatoryinformation/dietarysupplements/ucm257563.htm . Accessed 8 May 2015.
31. Op cit. 16
32. Section IV B 4. *Draft Guidance for Industry: Dietary Supplements: New Dietary Ingredient Notifications and Related Issues* (July 2011). FDA website. http://www.fda.gov/food/guidanceregulation/guidancedocumentsregulatoryinformation/dietarysupplements/ucm257563.htm . Accessed 8 May 2015.
33. Section IV B 2. *Draft Guidance for Industry: Dietary Supplements: New Dietary Ingredient Notifications and Related Issues* (July 2011). FDA website. http://www.fda.gov/food/guidanceregulation/guidancedocumentsregulatoryinformation/dietarysupplements/ucm257563.htm . Accessed 8 May 2015.
34. 21 CFR 1.3(b). Definitions; Label. FDA website. www.accessdata.fda.gov/scripts/cdrh/cfdocs/cfcfr/CFRSearch.cfm?fr=1.3. Accessed 8 May 2015.
35. 21 CFR 1.3(a). Definitions, Labeling. FDA website. www.accessdata.fda.gov/scripts/cdrh/cfdocs/cfcfr/CFRSearch.cfm?fr=1.3. Accessed 8 May 2015.
36. 21 CFR 101.36. Nutrition labeling of dietary supplements. FDA website. www.accessdata.fda.gov/scripts/cdrh/cfdocs/cfcfr/CFRSearch.cfm?fr=101.36. Accessed 8 May 2015.
37. 21 CFR 101.9 Nutrition labeling of food. FDA website. www.accessdata.fda.gov/scripts/cdrh/cfdocs/cfcfr/cfrsearch.cfm?fr=101.9. Accessed 8 May 2015.
38. *Food Allergen Labeling Consumer Protection Act* of 2004 (Public law 108-282).
39. 21 CFR 101.17(e). Good labeling warning, notice, and safe handling statements; dietary supplements containing iron or iron salts.. FDA website. http://www.accessdata.fda.gov/scripts/cdrh/cfdocs/cfcfr/CFRSearch.cfm?fr=101.17. Accessed 8 May 2015.
40. *Food and Drug Administration Modernization Act* of 1997 (*FDAMA*) (Public Law 105-115).
41. Section 303. *FDA Modernization Act of 1997 (FDAMA)*. FDA website. http://www.fda.gov/RegulatoryInformation/Legislation/FederalFoodDrugandCosmeticActFDCAct/SignificantAmendmentstotheFDCAct/FDAMA/FullTextofFDAMAlaw/default.htm#SEC. 303 3. Accessed 8 May 2013.

42. 21 CFR 101.14(c). Health claims: general requirements; Validity claims. FDA website. www.accessdata.fda.gov/scripts/cdrh/cfdocs/cfcfr/CFRSearch.cfm?fr=101.14. Accessed 8 May 2015.
43. "Qualified Health Claims." FDA website. http://www.fda.gov/Food/IngredientsPackagingLabeling/LabelingNutrition/ucm2006877.htm. Accessed 8 May 2013.
44. Op cit 6.
45. 21 CFR 101.93 Certain types of statements for dietary supplements. FDA website. www.accessdata.fda.gov/scripts/cdrh/cfdocs/cfcfr/CFRsearch.cfm?fr=101.93. Accessed 8 May 2015.
46. *Guidance for Industry: Structure/Function Claims Small Entity Compliance Guide* (January 2002). FDA website. www.fda.gov/Food/GuidanceRegulation/GuidanceDocumentsRegulatoryInformation/DietarySupplements/ucm103340.htm. Accessed 8 May 2015.
47. *Guidance for Industry: Substantiation for Dietary Supplement Claims Made Under Section 403(r)(6) of the Federal Food, Drug, and Cosmetic Act* (December 2008). FDA website. www.fda.gov/Food/GuidanceRegulation/GuidanceDocumentsRegulatoryInformation/DietarySupplements/ucm073200.htm. Accessed 8 May 2015.
48. Ibid.
49. Op cit. 45.
50. 21 CFR 101.93(a)(1). Certain types of statements for dietary supplements. FDA website. www.accessdata.fda.gov/scripts/cdrh/cfdocs/cfcfr/CFRsearch.cfm?fr=101.93. Accessed 8 May 2015.
51. "Dietary Supplements: Structure/Function Claims Fail To Meet Federal Requirements (October 2012)." Department of Health and Human Services, Office of Inspector General. Office of Inspector General website. http://www.nutriwatch.org/09Reg/oig_2012.pdf. Accessed 8 May 2015.
52. "Section 5 Dietary Supplement Claims, Dietary Supplement Labeling Exemptions," *Dietary Supplement Health and Education Act* of 1994 (Public Law 103-417, 103rd Congress).
53. Op cit 6.
54. Memorandum of Understanding Between Federal Trade Commission and the Food and Drug Administration, Federal Register, Vol 36, No. 180, 16 September 1971.
55. Federal Trade Commission, *Dietary Supplements: An Advertising Guide for Industry*. FTC website. https://www.ftc.gov/system/files/documents/plain-language/bus09-dietary-supplements-advertising-guide-industry.pdf. Accessed 8 May 2015.
56. Pfizer, Inc., 81 F.T.C. 23 (1972), *see also* FTC Policy Statement Regarding Advertising Substantiation Program, 1984.
57. Thompson Medical Co., 104 F.T.C. 648 (1984), *aff'd*, 791 F.2d 189 (D.C. Cir. 1986).
58. *Unilever United States, Inc.* (Dove® Deep Moisture body Wash), NAD Case #5599 (June 3, 2013).
59. *Public Health Security and Bioterrorism Preparedness and Response Act* of 2002 (Public law 107-188).
60. *Guidance for Industry: Questions and Answers Regarding Registration of Food Facilities* (Edition 6) (November 2014). FDA website. http://www.fda.gov/Food/GuidanceRegulation/GuidanceDocumentsRegulatoryInformation/FoodDefense/ucm331959.htm. Accessed 8 May 2015.
61. "Registration of Food Facilities." FDA website. www.fda.gov/Food/GuidanceRegulation/FoodFacilityRegistration/default.htm. Accessed 8 May 2015.
62. Food, Registration. FDA website. www.fda.gov/Food/GuidanceRegulation/FSMA/ucm314178.htm. Accessed 8 May 2015.
63. *The FDA Food Safety Modernization Act of 2011* (Public Law 111-353).
64. 68 *Fed. Reg.* 12158 (13 March 2003). Current Good Manufacturing Practice in Manufacturing, Packing, or Holding Dietary Ingredients and Dietary Supplements. GPO website. www.gpo.gov/fdsys/pkg/FR-2003-03-13/pdf/03-5401.pdf. Accessed 8 May 2015.
65. 21 CFR Part 111 Current Good Manufacturing Practice in manufacturing, packaging, labeling, or holding operations for dietary supplements; final rule. FDA website. www.accessdata.fda.gov/scripts/cdrh/cfdocs/cfcfr/cfrsearch.cfm?cfrpart=111. Accessed 8 May 2015.
66. *Current Good Manufacturing Practice in Manufacturing, Packaging, Labeling, or Holding Operations for Dietary Supplements; Small Entity Compliance Guide* (December 2010). FDA website. www.fda.gov/Food/GuidanceRegulation/GuidanceDocumentsRegulatoryInformation/DietarySupplements/ucm238182.htm. Accessed 8 May 2015.
67. FDA News Release: Tainted products marketed as dietary supplements potentially dangerous (15 December 2010). FDA website. www.fda.gov/NewsEvents/Newsroom/PressAnnouncements/ucm236967.htm. Accessed 8 May 2015.
68. Tainted Products That are Marketed as Dietary Supplements RSS Feed. FDA website. www.fda.gov/AboutFDA/ContactFDA/StayInformed/RSSFeeds/TDS/rss.xml. Accessed 8 May 2015.
69. Warning letter to Pristine Bay LLC dba Vianda dated 26 April 2013. FDA website. http://www.fda.gov/ICECI/EnforcementActions/WarningLetters/2013/ucm350469.htm. Accessed 8 May 2015.
70. "Adverse Event Reporting for Dietary Supplements: An Inadequate Safety Valve (April 2011)." Department of Health and Human Services, Office of Inspector General. Office of Inspector General website. https://oig.hhs.gov/oei/reports/oei-01-00-00180.pdf. Accessed 8 May 2015.
71. *Guidance for Industry: Questions and Answers Regarding Adverse Event Reporting and Recordkeeping for Dietary Supplements as Required by the Dietary Supplement and Nonprescription Drug Consumer Protection Act* (October 2007; Revised June 2009; Revised September 2013). FDA website. www.fda.gov/Food/GuidanceRegulation/GuidanceDocumentsRegulatoryInformation/DietarySupplements/ucm171383.htm. Accessed 8 May 2015.
72. *Guidance for Industry: Questions and Answers Regarding the Labeling of Dietary Supplements as Required by the Dietary Supplement and Nonprescription Drug Consumer Protection Act* (December 2007; Revised December 2008 and September 2009). FDA website. http://www.fda.gov/Food/GuidanceRegulation/GuidanceDocumentsRegulatoryInformation/DietarySupplements/ucm179018.htm. Accessed 8 May 2015.
73. "Dietary Supplements: Companies May Be Difficult To Locate In An Emergency (October 2012." Department of Health and Human Services, Office of Inspector General. Office of Inspector General website. https://oig.hhs.gov/oei/reports/oei-01-11-00211.pdf. Accessed 8 May 2015.
74. Compliance Policy Guide, *Guidance for Industry and CBP Staff: Sec. 110.310 Prior Notice of Imported Food Under the Public Health Security and Bioterrorism Preparedness and Response Act* of 2002 (May 2009). FDA website. www.fda.gov/Food/GuidanceRegulation/GuidanceDocumentsRegulatoryInformation/FoodDefense/ucm153055.htm. Accessed 8 May 2015.
75. *FD&C Act*, Section 801 (21 USC 381) Imports and exports. GPO website. http://www.gpo.gov/fdsys/pkg/USCODE-2010-title21/html/USCODE-2010-title21-chap9-subchapVIII-sec381.htm. Accessed 8 May 2015.
76. 21 CFR 1.101 Notification and recordkeeping. FDA website. www.accessdata.fda.gov/scripts/cdrh/cfdocs/cfcfr/CFRSearch.cfm?fr=1.101. Accessed 8 May 2015.
77. FDA Export Certificates to Foreign Governments FAQs. FDA website. www.fda.gov/downloads/Drugs/GuidanceComplianceRegulatoryInformation/ImportsandExportsCompliance/UCM318409.pdf. Accessed 8 May 2015.
78. Import Alert 16-131; Detention Without Physical Examination of Aquacultured Catfish, Basa, Shrimp, Dace, and Eel from China – Presence of New Animal Drugs and/or Unsafe Food Additives. FDA website. http://www.accessdata.fda.gov/cms_ia/importalert_33.html. Accessed 8 May 2015.
79. Regulatory Procedures Manual April 2013; Chapter 9 Import Operations and Actions. FDA website. http://www.fda.gov/downloads/ICECI/ComplianceManuals/RegulatoryProceduresManual/UCM074300.pdf. Accessed 8 May 2015.

80. Compliance Policy Guide 7132.15, Sec. 400.400, "Conditions Under Which Homeopathic Drugs May Be Marketed." FDA website. www.fda.gov/ICECI/ComplianceManuals/CompliancePolicyGuidanceManual/ucm074360.htm. Accessed 8 May 2015.
81. *Homeopathic Pharmacopoeia of the United States*, "The Regulation of Homeopathic Medicines." HPUS website. www.hpus.com/regulations.php. Accessed 8 May 2015.
82. Warning Letter to Standard Homeopathic Company, Inc. dated 25 September 2013. FDA website. http://www.fda.gov/ICECI/EnforcementActions/WarningLetters/2013/ucm370015.htm. Accessed 8 May 2015.
83. "Drug Registration and Listing System (DRLS & eDRLS)." FDA website. www.fda.gov/Drugs/GuidanceComplianceRegulatoryInformation/DrugRegistrationandListing/default.htm. Accessed 8 May 2015.
84. FDA Notice of Public Hearing; Request for Public Comments. 80 Fed. Reg. 16327 (Docket No. FDA-2015-N-0450) (March 27, 2015).
85. Nahin, R. L., P. M. Barnes, B. J. Stussman, and B. Bloom, "Costs of Complementary and Alternative Medicine (CAM) and Frequency of Visits to CAM Practitioners: United States, 2007."*National Health Statistics Reports;* no 18. Hyattsville, MD: National Center for Health Statistics, 2009.

Recommended Reading

21 CFR Part 1 Subpart I: Prior Notice of Imported Food Under the Public Health Security and Bioterrorism Preparedness and Response Act of 2002. FDA website. www.accessdata.fda.gov/scripts/cdrh/cfdocs/cfcfr/CFRSearch.cfm?CFRPart=1&showFR=1&subpartNode=21:1.0.1.1.1.7. Accessed 8 May 2015.

21 CFR 101.93 Certain types of statements for dietary supplements. FDA website. www.accessdata.fda.gov/scripts/cdrh/cfdocs/cfcfr/CFRsearch.cfm?fr=101.93. Accessed 8 May 2015.

Public Health Security and Bioterrorism Preparedness and Response Act of 2002 (Public Law 107-188, 107th Congress). FDA website. www.fda.gov/regulatoryinformation/legislation/ucm148797.htm. Accessed 8 May 2015.

New Dietary Ingredient in Dietary Supplements. FDA website. www.fda.gov/Food/DietarySupplements/ucm109764.htm. Accessed 8 May 2015.

Guidance for Industry: Substantiation for Dietary Supplement Claims Made Under Section 403(r) (6) of the Federal Food, Drug, and Cosmetic Act (December 2008). FDA website. www.fda.gov/Food/GuidanceRegulation/GuidanceDocumentsRegulatoryInformation/DietarySupplements/ucm073200.htm. Accessed 8 May 2015.

"Label Claims for Conventional Foods and Dietary Supplements" (December 2013). FDA website. www.fda.gov/Food/IngredientsPackagingLabeling/LabelingNutrition/ucm111447.htm. Accessed 8 May 2015.

Guidance for Industry: Evidence-Based Review System for the Scientific Evaluation of Health Claims - Final (January 2009). FDA website. www.fda.gov/Food/GuidanceRegulation/GuidanceDocumentsRegulatoryInformation/LabelingNutrition/ucm073332.htm. Accessed 8 May 2015.

Guidance for Industry: Iron-Containing Supplements and Drugs: Label Warning Statements Small Entity Compliance Guide (October 2003). FDA website. www.fda.gov/Food/GuidanceRegulation/GuidanceDocumentsRegulatoryInformation/DietarySupplements/ucm073014.htm. Accessed 8 May 2015.

Guidance for Industry: Notification of a Health Claim or Nutrient Content Claim Based on an Authoritative Statement of a Scientific Body (June 1998). FDA website. www.fda.gov/Food/GuidanceRegulation/GuidanceDocumentsRegulatoryInformation/LabelingNutrition/ucm056975.htm. Accessed 8 May 2015.

Guidance for Industry: Food Labeling; Nutrient Content Claims; Definition for "High Potency" and Definition for "Antioxidant" for Use in Nutrient Content Claims for Dietary Supplements and Conventional Foods Small Entity Compliance Guide (July2008). FDA website. www.fda.gov/Food/GuidanceRegulation/GuidanceDocumentsRegulatoryInformation/LabelingNutrition/ucm063064.htm. Accessed 8 May 2015.

Guidance for Industry: Statement of Identity, Nutrition Labeling, and Ingredient Labeling of Dietary Supplements Small Entity Compliance Guide (January 1999). FDA website. www.fda.gov/Food/GuidanceRegulation/GuidanceDocumentsRegulatoryInformation/DietarySupplements/ucm073168.htm. Accessed 8 May 2015.

Guidance for Industry: Structure/Function Claims Small Entity Compliance Guide (January 2002). FDA website. www.fda.gov/Food/GuidanceRegulation/GuidanceDocumentsRegulatoryInformation/DietarySupplements/ucm103340.htm. Accessed 8 May 2015.

Guidance for Industry: Interim Procedures for Qualified Health Claims in the Labeling of Conventional Human Food and Human Dietary Supplements (July 2003). FDA website. www.fda.gov/Food/GuidanceRegulation/GuidanceDocumentsRegulatoryInformation/LabelingNutrition/ucm053832.htm. Accessed 8 May 2015.

Draft Guidance for Industry: Prior Notice of Imported Food Questions and Answers (Edition 3) (May 2014). FDA website. www.fda.gov/Food/GuidanceRegulation/GuidanceDocumentsRegulatoryInformation/FoodDefense/ucm078911.htm. Accessed 8 May 2015.

Guidance for Industry: Questions and Answers Regarding Establishment and Maintenance of Records by Persons Who Manufacture, Process, Pack, Transport, Distribute, Receive, Hold or Import Food (Edition 5) (February 2012). FDA website. www.fda.gov/Food/GuidanceRegulation/GuidanceDocumentsRegulatoryInformation/FoodDefense/ucm292746.htm. Accessed 8 May 2015.

Guidance for Industry: Questions and Answers Regarding Adverse Event Reporting and Recordkeeping for Dietary Supplements as Required by the Dietary Supplement and Nonprescription Drug Consumer Protection Act (October 2007; Revised June 2009; Revised September 2013). FDA website. http://www.fda.gov/Food/GuidanceRegulation/GuidanceDocumentsRegulatoryInformation/ucm171383.htm. Accessed 8 May 2015.

Draft Guidance for Industry: Questions and Answers Regarding the Labeling of Dietary Supplements as Required by the Dietary Supplement and Nonprescription Drug Consumer Protection Act (December 2007; Revised December 2008; Revised September 2009). FDA website. www.fda.gov/Food/GuidanceRegulation/GuidanceDocumentsRegulatoryInformation/DietarySupplements/ucm179018.htm. Accessed 8 May 2015.

Guidance for Industry: Questions and Answers Regarding Food Allergens, including the Food Allergen Labeling and Consumer Protection Act of 2004 (Edition 4); Final Guidance (October 2006). FDA website. www.fda.gov/Food/GuidanceRegulation/GuidanceDocumentsRegulatoryInformation/Allergens/ucm059116.htm. Accessed 8 May 2015.

Clarke JH. *A Dictionary of Practical Materia Medica.* (3 vol.). London (U.K.): The Homeopathic Publishing Co.; 1902.

Chapter 34

Cosmetics

Updated by Vic Mencarelli

OBJECTIVES

- ❑ Understand the classifications of cosmetics
- ❑ Understand the basic regulations covering cosmetic product sales in the US
- ❑ Understand the requirements for products at the cosmetic-drug interface
- ❑ Understand FDA harmonization efforts with international regulatory agency partners and their impact on US requirements
- ❑ Understand the basic role on-package claims play in FDA enforcement activities and the interplay between FDA and FTC
- ❑ Review developments in the more recent trends in cosmetics including natural and organic claims as well as nanotechnology-based ingredients

REGULATIONS, GUIDANCES AND FDA ENFORCEMENT POLICIES FOR THE COSMETICS INDUSTRY

- ❑ 21 CFR 1 (General enforcement regulations)
- ❑ 21 CFR 250.250 Requirements for drugs and cosmetics – hexachlorophene
- ❑ 21 CFR 700–740—Cosmetics
- ❑ Cosmetic Good Manufacturing Practice Guidance
- ❑ Cosmetics Labeling Manual
- ❑ Intercenter Agreement Between the Center for Drug Evaluation and Research and the Center for Food Safety and Applied Nutrition to Assist in Implementing the Drug and Cosmetic Provisions of the Federal Food, Drug, and Cosmetics Act for Products That Purport to be Cosmetics but Meet the Statutory Definition of a Drug
- ❑ FDA Recall Policy for Cosmetics
- ❑ *Fair Packaging and Labeling Act*
- ❑ *Federal Trade Commission Act* section 13
- ❑ Memorandum of Understand Between the Federal Trade Commission and the Food and Drug Administration Concerning Exchange of Information (FDA—225-71-8003)
- ❑ International Standard *ISO 22716 Cosmetics – Good Manufacturing Practices (GMP) – Guidelines on Good Manufacturing Practices*
- ❑ International Conference on Cosmetic Regulation
- ❑ FDA Sunscreen Monograph
- ❑ FDA Skin Protectant Monograph

Introduction

Since the skin is the body's single largest organ, it is no wonder the US Food and Drug Administration (FDA) is involved in regulating cosmetic products in the marketplace. The surprise is that the regulation generally is left to the industry to self-regulate, with FDA taking action only where necessary to protect the public from hazardous products. Under Title 21 of the United States Code (USC), FDA was given authority in 1938 under the *Federal Food, Drug, and Cosmetic Act* (*FD&C Act*) for regulating cosmetic products. "Cosmetics" as defined at 21 USC 321(i) are "... (1) articles intended to be rubbed, poured, sprinkled, or sprayed on, introduced into, or otherwise applied to the human body or any part thereof for cleansing, beautifying, promoting attractiveness, or altering the appearance, and (2) articles intended for use as a component of any such articles; except that such term shall not include soap."[1] While the statute itself does not specifically define the term "soap," FDA has defined it within the regulations found at 21 CFR 701.20, which explains a "soap" is one that meets the following three conditions:

- composed mainly of "alkali salts of fatty acids" and
- those alkali salts must be the only material with cleansing activity and
- the label and marketing of the product must be as a soap

In essence, if the product is a soap, it is not regulated at all by FDA, but instead the product will be regulated by the Consumer Product Safety Commission.[2]

Based on the definition, in the author's experience, it has become fairly standard to consider any product that has no real or long-acting activity on the body to be a cosmetic under the regulations. For example, products such as face make-up (eye shadow, rouge, lipsticks) would all meet the definition of promoting attractiveness. Fragrances and perfumes also would seem to meet the definition of a cosmetic product without too much discussion. Moisturizing lotion, the sole purpose of which is to provide moisture to skin, would appear to be a cosmetic as well. As an illustrative list, the following generally are considered by FDA to be cosmetic products[3]:

- baby products
- bath preparations
- eye makeup preparations
- fragrance preparations
- hair preparations (non-coloring such as styling products)
- hair color preparations
- makeup preparations (not for the eye such as rouge, blush, concealer, lipstick)
- manicuring preparations
- oral hygiene products (not including fluoride-containing products, which are regulated as drugs)
- personal cleanliness products
- shaving preparations
- skin care preparations (lotions, creams, powder, sprays)
- suntan preparations (not sunscreens, which are regulated as drugs) that may require additional warnings on the labeling

However, in recent years, there is a stronger movement within the industry to make claims such as "anti-aging" or "skin protectant" that may slide into the regulation of products as "drugs." The key here is the definition of a "drug" under the *FD&C Act*, which includes items recognized by one of the official pharmacopoeias (*US Pharmacopoeia, Homoeopathic Pharmacopoeia of the US, National Formulary*) or any supplement to them; any article "intended for use in the diagnosis, cure, mitigation, treatment, or prevention of disease in man...;" articles other than foods that are intended to impact the structure or function of the body; and any article intended for use as a component of the previous items[4] (see specifically 21 USC 321(g)(1)). Thus, it is possible some of the products making anti-aging claims or even skin protectant claims could be considered (and have been considered) to be drugs by FDA.

Both the cosmetic and drug definitions within the *FD&C Act* include not only the products sold to the ultimate consumer but also the ingredients of these consumer products.[5] The importance of this point cannot be stated strongly enough to those whose work is a step back from the consumer in the supply chain—ingredients used in products regulated by FDA also may be regulated by FDA.

Over the past several years there have been multiple attempts in Congress to further define and increase FDA's regulatory authority over cosmetics. Most recently, several obligations were discussed for inclusion in the 2015 FDA appropriations bill for cosmetics. The original House of Representatives' bill included:

- review of several Time and Extent Applications (TEAs) for sunscreen active ingredients (some of which have been pending with FDA for more than a decade)
- the development of a "Trusted Trader" program to allow more efficient and expeditious clearance of imported products
- a request for a report from FDA on the current policy for "natural" claims
- a direction to the FDA Office of Cosmetics and Colors (OCAC) to respond by 15 March 2015 to a Citizen's Petition relating to levels of lead in cosmetics

The original Senate appropriations bill included:

- encouragement to ensure sufficient personnel are assigned to import inspection and clearance

- an expectation to continue FDA support of research into the environmental, health and safety aspects of nanotechnology in FDA-regulated products
- the same requirement for OCAC to respond to the lead in cosmetics' Citizen's Petition
- a requirement to initiate a bilateral dialogue with Chinese regulators
- promotion of international harmonization and trade for cosmetics
- finalizing the sunscreen labeling rule and issuing a proposed rule for regulating testing and labeling standards for sunscreen sprays[6]

As these bills demonstrate, even updated regulatory requirements through the appropriations route have not changed the definition of what is considered a cosmetic or what legal authorities FDA can utilize against cosmetics significantly. However, in the 113th Congress, several legislative bills were submitted to eliminate the use of plastic microbeads,[7–8] eliminate animal testing for cosmetics[9] and eliminate the sale of products tested on animals.[10] Another bill was intended to ensure the safe use of cosmetics; this piece of legislation had more far-reaching goals, including:

- updated labeling requirements
- introduction of establishment and registration fees
- notification, non-distribution and recall of adulterated or misbranded cosmetics
- mandatory serious adverse event reporting
- creation of an assumption that a product meets the standard for safety as required by the legislation if the product contains only ingredients deemed to be safe or safe with restrictions, provided the restrictions are met from a list created by FDA, subject to limited exceptions where FDA may require a brand owner to demonstrate safety where specific chemical types are used or potentially harmful byproducts can be generated from ingredient reactivity or the secretary of the Department of Health and Human Services has reason to believe the product does not meet the standard[11]

Adulteration of Cosmetics

Under present requirements for cosmetics, there are six specific ways in which FDA can find a product to be adulterated (21 USC 361):

- containing any poisonous or deleterious substance that may render it injurious to the consumer under normal or usual use
- consisting in whole or in part of any filthy, putrid or decomposed substance
- preparing, packing or holding under insanitary conditions whereby it may become contaminated with filth or whereby it may be rendered injurious to health
- the container is composed of any poisonous or deleterious substance
- containing an unsafe color additive within the meaning of 21 USC 379e(a)[12]

Under each of these is a fairly broad level of FDA interpretation. For example, what is considered a poisonous or deleterious substance? There are obvious poisons, but it would seem the term "any" would include a more far-reaching subset of ingredients. FDA also has used the putrid or decomposing substance portion of the definition to include products found to have microbiological contamination. Insanitary conditions also could be used for microbial contamination issues, since the product was somehow contaminated, and the contamination portion of the definition generally is expected to be for inappropriate cleaning or sanitizing of equipment or poor company GMP enforcement.[13] More importantly, several products have been held under FDA's Detention Without Physical Examination (DWPE) program at the point of import for use of colorants not certified under FDA's certified color program from OCAC.[14]

It also should be understood FDA has outlawed the use of certain specific materials in any form for cosmetics by regulation. Under 21 CFR 700.11-700.23, FDA has determined the following ingredients are unacceptable (and therefore adulterating) in cosmetics:[15]

- biothionol (causes photosensitivity)
- mercury and mercury-containing compounds (known toxicity)
- vinyl chloride (acute toxic by inhalation)
- halogenated salicylanilides (causes photosensitivity and can cross-sensitize)
- zirconium in aerosols (causes granulomas in skin and upon inhalation also in the lung)
- chloroform (carcinogenic)
- methylene chloride (causes tumors)
- chlorofluorocarbon propellants (environmental issues)

Additionally, under 21 CFR 700.27, the use of prohibited cattle materials including specified risk materials (brain, skull, eyes, trigeminal ganglia, spinal cord, vertebral column (excluding vertebrae of the tail, the transverse process of the thoracic and lumbar vertebrae, and the wings of the scrum), and the dorsal root ganglia of cattle 30 months and older as well as the tonsils and distal ileum of the small intestine of all cattle), the small intestine, any material from nonambulatory disabled cattle, any material from cattle not inspected and passed for human consumption or any mechanically separated material wherein the product is finely comminuted resulting from the mechanical separation and removal of most of the bone from attached skeletal muscle of cattle carcasses as described in the specification found at 9 CFR 319.5 are unacceptable in cosmetics.[16]

Earlier, it was noted that FDA does not approve products before they come to market, and the definition of the term "cosmetic" includes the ingredients used to manufacture such products. However, there is one, and only one area where FDA specifically approves not only the ingredient but every single production batch of the ingredient for use in cosmetics. Colorants designated by the format "FD&C XXXXX #" or "D&C XXXXX #," where the X's are the color imparted by the colorant, and the # is a serially incremented number for the color (for example "FD&C Red 4"), are actually batch-tested by FDA for approval prior to being allowed on the market.[17] Any ingredient purporting to be FD&C or D&C colorants not previously tested and approved by FDA are considered adulterated.[18]

Misbranding of Cosmetics

A related issue is misbranding of cosmetics. However, to understand the "misbranding" provisions, it is equally essential to understand the requirements for cosmetic product labels under the *FD&C Act*. The following are required label components for any cosmetic product sold in the US[19]:

- a list declaring the ingredients used that may appear on any appropriate panel using letters not smaller than 1/16 of an inch using the following resources in descending order of predominance of the ingredient down to 1% in the formulation:
  - a name specified under 21 CFR 701.30 as adopted by the FDA commissioner
  - Cosmetic Ingredient Dictionary (with specific exclusions)
  - *US Pharmacopeia*
  - *National Formulary*
  - *Food Chemicals Codex*
  - USAN and the USP dictionary of drug names
  - a name generally recognized by the consumer
  - chemical or technical name or description
- where a product is both a cosmetic and over-the-counter drug, the active ingredient must be specified as required in 21 CRFR 201.66(c)(2) and (d), while the other cosmetic ingredients must be declared as required in 21 CFR 201.66(c)(8) and (d)
- a statement of identity in bold type on the principal display panel as defined in 21 CFR 701.10
- name and place of business of the responsible person placing the product on the market
- declaration of the net quantity of package contents

The place of business of the responsible company must be the physical address of the company unless the company is listed in the current telephone directory for the area in which the facility is located. In this instance, only the city and state of the company address must appear such that a consumer could obtain the physical address from the telephone directory listing.[20] According to 21 USC 362, a cosmetic is misbranded when:[21]

- labeling is false or misleading in any particular
- packaged, the label fails to bear the name and place of business of the responsible party and an accurate statement of quantity of the contents either in terms of weight, measure or numerical count
- any required information is not prominently and conspicuously placed relative to other non-required information
- containers are made or filled in such a way as to be misleading
- a color additive is not labeled as required under 21 USC 379e unless the color additive is marketed solely for use in hair dyes
- packaging or labeling is in violation of any regulation as promulgated under section 1472 or 1473 of title 15.

There is only one instance where a company can place a product on the market for which safety is not previously assured. For a product with a questionable safety profile, the regulations at 21 CFR 740.10 can be placed conspicuously on the packaging to avoid an FDA misbranding charge. The warning is specifically noted in the regulation and should be quoted directly as:

> "*Warning*—The safety of this product has not been determined."[22]

This can become an issue for the company if, in the future, the safety of an ingredient is called into question unless:

- the safety of the ingredient had been substantiated prior to the development of the new information and
- the new information does not demonstrate a specific hazard to human health and
- adequate additional studies are underway to determine the safety profile of the ingredient[23]

While the use of the warning statement above is a potential defense against an FDA misbranding charge, the regulations specifically state at 21 CFR 740.10(c) this is not an exemption from a potential adulteration charge under the *FD&C Act*.[24]

While many regulatory professionals can explain the importance of FDA regulations and authority easily for many of the product groups regulated by FDA, it is equally important, especially in certain areas of FDA regulation such as cosmetics, to understand the important role the US Federal Trade Commission (FTC) plays in managing advertisements of these products. A recurring Memorandum of Understanding (MOU) between FDA and FTC[25] has continued to define the responsibilities for each agency. FDA,

Table 34-1. Examples of Claims That Misbrand or Adulterate Cosmetic Products

Date Issued	Company	Issues Involved
2011-05-24	Allure Labs Inc.[27]	Unapproved new drugs positioned as cosmetics • Eyelash follicle stimulation • Improves length and thickness of lashes
2011-08-22	Brazilian Blowout[28]	Adulterated cosmetic • Formaldehyde exposure Misbranded cosmetic • Formaldehyde not declared on label (in fact, formaldehyde content is specifically disclaimed)
2012-10-05	Avon Products[29]	Website claims • Starts rebuilding collagen in 48 hours • Helps tighten the connections between skin's layers
2014-07-08	Dr. Bronner's Magic Soap[30]	Unapproved new drug • Ingredient improves blood cholesterol by increasing the ratio of HDL to LDL cholesterol

under the current MOU, has authority to bring actions for violations of the *FD&C Act* and set governmental policy relating to what constitutes a cosmetic product and the requirements for product labeling under the *FD&C Act*. FTC accepts the responsibility for regulating advertisements of the products. This includes such issues as claims and claims support and superiority-type claims. This is not to imply FDA will not review advertisements or less "traditional" labeling (labeling not directly affixed to product, such as advertisements on Internet sites or even print or television advertisements) but, generally, most cosmetic advertisement enforcement seems to be conducted by FTC.

Cosmetic Product Claims

Based on both the *FD&C Act* and FDA's implementing regulations, the product claims determine the product's regulatory classification and requirements. As noted previously in the definitions, it is easy to understand how important the claims made on product packaging are to determining how the product is going to be regulated. Looking at a specific set of examples for the same fictional product may assist in understanding this point:

1. This ultra-moisturizing, light-weight, fragrance-free lotion goes on smooth, rubs in easily and leaves no greasy after-feel, thereby leaving your skin soft, smooth and pampered.
2. This ultra-moisturizing, light-weight, fragrance-free lotion goes on smooth, rubs in easily and leaves no greasy after-feel, thereby protecting your skin from the impacts of wind, cold, heat and dryness.

Looking at example 1, it would appear the product should be regulated as a cosmetic as the claims all appear to lead to promotion of attractiveness. If example 2 is analyzed, it is highly likely FDA could use this as evidence the product is intended to be used as a drug because the claim "protecting your skin" is among several areas of the allowed claims under the Skin Protectant monograph.[26]

While FDA reviews each product claim, in general, the agency takes a holistic approach to determining into which category a product rightfully fits under the regulations and the statute. Understanding this is a key point in the regulatory professional's review of labeling, websites, advertisements, press releases, etc. The key generally is prominence and preponderance of the evidence to determine how the product is regulated. A single statement, as noted in example 2 above, would provide evidence of intended drug function but potentially could be mitigated by other statements or by lessened prominence, thereby changing the product classification to a cosmetic. Several Warning Letters have been issued in the last few years in which FDA has taken specific claims and the context in which the agency finds them to categorize the products as "drugs" for regulatory purposes (see **Table 34-1**).

As noted above, FTC also handles situations where questions of efficacy arise. The complaints here can arise as original complaints made specifically by FTC under its authority as provided in the *Federal Trade Commission Act* to eliminate unfair competition by overstatement of claims or unsubstantiated superiority claims, or such claims can be initiated at the request of either the National Advertising Division of the Better Business Bureau (NAD) or through a complaint lodged by a competitor and subsequently investigated either by NAD or FTC.[31] FTC's general requirement is for either adequate scientific substantiation of the claim or adequate and reasonable disclaimers to place the claim in proper and reasonable context. Importantly, if the claim requires further context-creating disclaimers or explanations, the disclaimer's prominence should be reasonable in relation to the original claim's prominence.[32] For example, a claim made by a very large, front-of-pack bold-type highly differentiable contrasting color would not receive disclaimer credit if the disclaimer is noted by an "*" and the contextual information is found at the bottom of the rear or bottom panel in smaller, less-distinguishable color contrast. On the other hand, well-placed, well-worded and easily differentiable type, even if slightly smaller in relation to the original claim, can mitigate any misleading tendency for the claim. While FTC generally does manage the regulation of advertising, FDA still requires all information on the label to be truthful and not misleading. Based on FDA's expansive definition of labeling in its compliance policy guide, it often is possible for advertisements to be considered as labeling, especially on Internet sites. As noted previously, any misleading or false statement on labeling is sufficient for FDA to consider the product misbranded and, therefore, could provide FDA with the impetus to initiate a misbranding charge.[33]

In an unexpected twist, several companies have begun a new era of defending their products from competitors who push the allowed claim limits. In the past few years, several companies have taken advantage of the *Lanham Act* to do something they previously could not do legally—sue competitors to require their labels to conform more accurately to federal regulations under the legal theory of unfair competition. Traditionally, labeling lawsuits between competitors under the *FD&C Act* have been dismissed for lack of legal authority to sue because the act has no private right of action and specifically states that all attempts to enforce the *FD&C Act* must be "by and in the name of" the US.[34] In the most recent and most widely publicized case in 2014, POM, the owner of POM Wonderful, successfully sued Coca Cola, who owns Minute Maid juices, for unfair competition under the *Lanham Act*. This case went all the way to the US Supreme Court, which found in favor of POM's petition that Coca Cola had violated the *Lanham Act* by unfairly creating an implied label claim that the Minute Maid product was primarily or at least largely pomegranate juice when, in fact, the Minute Maid formula contained significantly smaller amounts of pomegranate juice. This was the first instance of which the author is aware in which a competitor was able to successfully challenge an implied label claim and win the case.[35]

In a second case, also in 2014, the US Court of Appeals for the Federal Circuit took the unusual step of deciding a case that had nothing at all to do with patent rights for which that Court was originally established. The case, Allergan, Inc. v Athena Cosmetics, Inc., led the Federal Circuit to review the rightful regulatory classification of a product based on California's *Unfair Competition Law*. Again, this was unexpected because of the express preemption of labeling lawsuit conflicts based on the *FD&C Act* requirement that any attempt to enforce the act be by the US and not a competitor. However, Allergan put forth a legal theory the product could not be sold legally in the US (including California) because it was a drug, and more importantly, a new drug for which FDA had never granted approval. Athena Cosmetics argued the lawsuit really meant to try to interfere with FDA's statutory discretion as to whether to regulate a product in interstate commerce. In fact, Athena argued the product was never required to be removed by FDA and, therefore, the suit was an unacceptable way to eliminate competition based on the *FD&C Act*. The Federal Circuit sided with Allergan finding the suit was filed legally, there was nothing in the *FD&C Act* or the California statute to preempt the lawsuit from being filed, the summary judgment in the lower court in California was correct, and there could be no dispute as to the intended product activity (to affect the structure of eye lashes). While most of the Federal Circuit decision favored Allergan, there was one small piece of good news for Athena—the Federal Circuit vacated the order insofar as the order was for a "nationwide" injunction. The Federal Circuit decided it would be too far-reaching for a California district court to determine national policy and, therefore, only allowed the injunction to stand in California. The judges on the panel determined nationwide enforcement was properly the realm of FDA.[36]

Products at the Drug-Cosmetics Interface

While many companies continue to reference "cosmeceutical" products in their advertising, this term has never been accepted or defined by either FDA or the *FD&C Act* and, therefore, has no regulatory meaning.[37] However, several product categories can find themselves at the drug-cosmetic regulatory interface. For example, the product in example 2 above, discussing cosmetic claims, could be one. Besides this example, other examples might include products such as moisturizing or color makeups with sunscreen active ingredients added, or products that provide cooling relief to sunburned skin specifically made with botanical ingredients such as aloe vera, etc.[38] The problems with these products do not necessarily end with the assignment to the regulatory category under which they will be analyzed. This decision also can impact the manner in which the product is required to be labeled. For example, cosmetic products without active ingredients, which are considered cosmetics only, require the specific label information above (name/location of the responsible party, descending order of predominance ingredient listing, net contents statement and statement of identity). On the other hand, when a product is classified as a drug, even the order of ingredients can change; an over-the-counter drug requires a drug facts box (see Chapter 17 Over-the-Counter Drug Products), and even the names used for the ingredients may differ. The other problem is determining whether a product qualifies as a drug-cosmetic product. These products contain both active ingredients and claims that qualify the product as drugs (i.e., active ingredients) as well as other claims that make the product a cosmetic.[39] An example of such a product might be a moisturizing sunscreen product. The sunscreen active ingredient contents and SPF claims would require the product to be managed as a drug, while the moisturizing claim would qualify the product as a cosmetic. In this instance, the labeling is blended. A drug facts box is required with any required elements included, but the "Other ingredients" section of the drug facts box will have ingredients listed in the order and nomenclature of cosmetics.[40]

Other popular claims for cosmetics over the past several years include claims of "cruelty free" or "no animal test" claims, organic personal care products, "Designed for the Environment," Natural Products Association (NPA) and other "natural" certifications (e.g., EcoCert, SOIL programs), biodegradable claims, and non-GMO/verified non-GMO claims. Each of these is dealt with in more specific detail later in this chapter.

Cosmetic Good Manufacturing Practices

There currently is no requirement in the *FD&C Act* for cosmetic products to be manufactured, stored, shipped or processed under Good Manufacturing Practice (GMP) principles. However, FDA has stated companies adhering to a GMP program likely will have fewer significant inspectional difficulties and findings.[41] As noted previously, several attempts have been made to pass legislation that would change this to a requirement for cosmetics product manufacturers. So far none of these attempts has succeeded.[42]

One reason for this may well be attempts by the industry itself to promote such a GMP program policy. For example, the Personal Care Products Council (PCPC), formerly known as the Cosmetics, Toiletries and Fragrances Association (CTFA), has for several decades published both test methods and interpretation guidelines for areas such as cosmetic quality assurance, cosmetic microbiology, cosmetic environmental programs, cosmetic toxicological reviews and other areas. FDA has been an active and willing commenter on the documents before their publication, and many FDA comments have been taken and included or at minimum acknowledged within the text of the final published document. Much of the PCPC guidance is based on FDA's own compliance policy as announced in FDA's GMP Policy guidance document for cosmetic products.[43]

In addition to the industry guidelines and FDA's own GMP Policy guidance, the international community has adopted an international standard that provides further GMP guidance. This document, ISO 22716, has been used by many countries to update their laws and regulations of cosmetics to include such a GMP requirement.[44] In some countries, before a product is accepted for import, a foreign company is required to attest to compliance with ISO 22716. This standard, approved through the processes of the International Standards Organization, with member countries both great and small, developed and developing, has been articulated as the standard for such jurisdictions as the EU and Japan. While not adopting the standard in the strictest sense of the term, FDA has stated that compliance with ISO 22716 will go far to avoiding significant findings during inspections centering on GMP issues.

Facility and Product Registration

Under the current law, FDA does not have the authority to require any facility, company or trader to register with the agency or to require the company to notify FDA of the formulation of their products if they are only producing, selling or representing cosmetic products. However, FDA has been given authority to initiate a program of voluntary cosmetic facility registration and product registration. FDA has codified these regulations under 21 CFR 720. While this is not a mandatory reporting requirement, if a company plans to initiate such reporting, it must follow all of the requirements and also ensure it is providing the necessary information and updating that information as though it were a legal requirement.[45]

FDA has suggested the information provided by the cosmetics industry is extremely helpful to the agency in understanding the current state of the industry as well as the number of companies and products on the market.[46] FDA has set up a web portal (http://www.fda.gov/Cosmetics/RegistrationProgram/default.htm) that can be used to upload information on the company, its facilities and its product formulations. The information provided in the database is relatively straightforward but needs to be entered carefully, using FDA's ingredient codes for the formulations. These codes identify the ingredient at the CAS number level so FDA can identify the ingredients currently in use in cosmetics better, as well as industry's propensity to use specific ingredients. This is also helpful to the Cosmetic Ingredient Review Expert Panel's (CIR) work assessing the safety of cosmetic ingredients.

CIR is an independent group of toxicologists, pharmacists and physicians that meets four to five times per year to review available information on the safety of cosmetic product ingredients. CIR is funded by the cosmetic industry, and an industry liaison from PCPC as well as a liaison from FDA and a liaison from a large consumer interest group attend the meetings. Meetings generally are open to the public unless there is a specific reason a portion of the meeting must be conducted in private.[47] CIR has reviewed hundreds of ingredients for safety, and their decisions are published in peer-reviewed journals.[48] To determine what ingredients are to be reviewed for a particular work year session, CIR uses FDA's Voluntary Cosmetics Reporting Program data to identify the ones used most frequently. These generally are considered the ingredients used most regularly in the industry, and CIR usually prioritizes the ingredients with the highest usage for review. In general, CIR informs the public of meeting dates and lists the reports to be reviewed and finalized at each meeting. Additionally, there is a 60-day public comment period after the final report is accepted by CIR for publication to obtain any additional information or comments from the community at large. In addition, CIR typically determines the priority ingredient list to be reviewed the next year in the fall of the current year.[49]

Even though the reporting program is voluntary, FDA has seen a fair number of companies registering their facilities and products. Since the program's online launch in December 2005, FDA has had more than 1,000 facilities registered and almost 42,000 active product formulations reported. Approximately 20,000 product registrations have been discontinued by companies, and almost 2,100 others have been rejected by the program for technical reasons. More impressively, since the program's initiation in 1972, more than 1,800 facilities have been registered, with more than 48,000 active product formulations, while almost 72,000 formulas have been discontinued, and more than 2,100 product registrations have been rejected.[50] Considering this program is entirely voluntary, it would appear industry is embracing the information exchange with the agency.

Importing and Exporting Cosmetics

Exporting Cosmetics

To export cosmetics, the products must meet the requirements of the country to which they are being shipped. In addition, many countries require some form of proof the product is freely sold and has been manufactured in a manner to ensure it is safe for use. This typically is accomplished by a Certificate of Free Sales (COFS). FDA is the only US government agency approved to provide COFS documentation for products it regulates. However, FDA has extremely long lead-time requirements for COFs because this is not one of its current areas of concentration.[51] To fill in the gaps, many non-governmental organizations, especially PCPC and the Independent Cosmetics Manufacturers and Distributors (ICMAD), have begun issuing documents with FDA's approval.

PCPC and ICMAD are both cosmetics industry trade associations. PCPC will issue COFS documents on any product that, according to US law, is a cosmetic. PCPC takes the position products that are combination cosmetics and drugs and legally required to meet FDA drug regulation requirements must be certified by FDA and are drugs by law and regulatory definitions. Therefore, PCPC will not issue a COFS for sunscreens or skin protectant products. Since so many products have sunscreen or skin protectant claims, and since PCPC will only offer this service to "Council member" companies,[52] PCPC often is not an option for COFS documentation.

ICMAD protocol looks not at US law but at the laws of the country to which products are exported. In this case, a product like a sunscreen or skin protectant that is regulated by FDA as a drug in the US but will be regulated by the importing country as a cosmetic product is eligible for ICMAD COFS documentation.[53]

Besides a COFS document, there are two categories of foreign countries: "authority" countries, where the document simply must be authenticated by the issuer, and "legalization" countries, where the document must be accepted and recognized by the foreign nation's US embassy.[54] Obviously, the easier category is countries that simply require authentication, since this can be accomplished by the US exporting company and the COFS document issuer. A "legalization" country that requires the COFS document to be accepted and approved by its US embassy adds time and expense to obtaining documentation.[55] Additionally, several countries require all supporting documentation to be authenticated through their US embassies, which takes more time.[56] When necessary, these delays can cause issues with the timing of documentation availability and the product arriving at the foreign nation's point of import. It is highly recommended the company work with its partners in the importing countries to understand what requirements might exist and the lead time required to obtain necessary shipment documentation. More importantly, it is essential the company provides product information that will match product labels at the port of entry; otherwise, it is possible (and in some countries likely) the products will not be released for sale.

Imported Cosmetics

As with products being exported, all products being imported into the US must comply with US law. This includes proper labeling, the name and address of the manufacturer's US-based representative, and the other requirements as discussed previously regarding misbranding and adulteration.[57]

Possibly the single most important piece of this puzzle is the requirement to have a US-based representative responsible for accepting the product. This person is legally responsible for the product being imported into the US and must abide by all regulations and requirements. Usually, this also is the contact point for labeling. This means the product typically is labeled as being "Distributed by XXXX Company, US City, US State." It is important to understand the person or legal entity who agrees to take responsibility for the product is actually responsible for any product failure to meet US legal requirements and regulations.[58]

Compliance and Enforcement

As stated above, all enforcement currently is based on postmarket surveillance. There is no specific premarket approval requirement for cosmetic products and, even for ingredients, premarket approval is required only for colorants.

Effectively, this means FDA does not have the authority to do anything in a premarket form.

While all enforcement and compliance initiatives are postmarket, FDA does have the authority to inspect facilities engaged in cosmetic product manufacturing.[59] Again, a large part of this is postmarketing and is heavily dependent on the Voluntary Cosmetics Reporting Program information provided to the agency. This information is important because it actually aids FDA in prioritizing inspections properly. While FDA has the ability to go into any facility engaged in producing any consumer product it regulates, it is difficult to locate these facilities unless they are registered. One thing that assists the agency is that a number of companies manufacture not just cosmetics but also over-the-counter pharmaceuticals like sunscreens and skin protectants that are regulated as drugs and have mandatory facility registration requirements.

As with all FDA enforcement areas, there are multiple layers of results.[60] A company could have no significant issues found during any inspection. It could have been issued a Form FDA-483 with fundamental compliance problems noted by an inspector during a particular timeframe that need to be corrected. If the noncompliances are significant, the company can expect to receive either an Untitled Letter or a Warning Letter. These are serious regulatory actions and require sufficient resources to respond. Not only is this a significant issue from a regulatory perspective, it is also a public relations issue since these letters are published on FDA's website. While FDA-483s also are publicly available, more information and knowledge are required to find them. Warning Letters are easily accessible by the public from FDA's main webpage.[61] In the worst cases, where regulatory findings are very serious, FDA has been known to ask the Department of Justice (DOJ) to file civil and criminal charges against not only the company but also the company's principal owners and management. This becomes an even greater issue for those specifically charged, because resolution of these problems can involve further punishment, up to and including debarment, which eliminates the person's ability to work in an FDA-regulated industry at any level and in any capacity for periods up to permanent lifetime bans.[62] In addition to these specific actions, it also is possible for FDA to request court injunctions and effectively shut down the business until charges are adjudicated, and those responsible are formally brought to justice.

Products that are imported have an additional layer of possible enforcement, the import alert. This is known as "Detention Without Physical Examination" (DWPE). A product placed on DWPE essentially is stopped from entering the country through an "administrative hold," when FDA determines the product or the manufacturer has violated the law in some way, leading to the agency finding "an appearance of adulteration" of the product. The key concept here is FDA requires only the appearance of adulteration for a product to be denied entry, and then the company or responsible person must prove the product is compliant with the law. This is far different from the requirements for a domestically manufactured product, where FDA must have specific evidence of adulteration to support and sustain an adulteration charge. It is equally important to note that once a product is on the DWPE list, it is extremely difficult to remove the company or product from it. An example of a DWPE for cosmetics is Import Alert 66-38,[63] which lists products promoted as "anti-aging," and 53-17,[64] for products that evidently have unacceptable microbiological profiles. A list of all current import alerts can be found at http://www.accessdata.fda.gov/cms_ia/industry_53.html.

Regulatory professionals also should understand that, at present, FDA has no authority to order a company to recall a product from the market. However, FDA will work with companies who voluntarily initiate market withdrawals and recalls to ensure the public is informed, as necessary, of the actions and also will work with the company to properly word any press releases published by the company with regard to a recall or withdrawal and post these to their website to further ensure public awareness of the recall. While the agency does not have recall authority, it does have the authority to ask DOJ to initiate court proceedings to obtain a court-ordered recall or market withdrawal. This typically is considered if a product poses serious hazards to consumers, and FDA does not do this routinely because most cosmetic manufacturers work with the agency to avoid such significant censure. In addition to FDA asking DOJ to initiate court proceedings for recalls, DOJ also can request the court to take any other action it or the court finds necessary or relevant to the current situation.[65]

Section 351(k) of the US *FD&C Act* states explicitly that any attempt to enforce the act's requirements must be by and in the name of the US. In other words, no one other than FDA, through DOJ, can bring a case in federal court to enforce *FD&C Act* requirements, including GMP compliance, labeling requirements, or any other specific US requirement for cosmetics.[66] However, in 2014, the US Supreme Court decided a case known commonly as *POM Wonderful*, in which a company sued a competitor under the *Lanham Act* that makes it illegal to engage in unfair business practices. The case, more fully described earlier in this chapter, determined that while a company cannot be forced to comply with the *FD&C Act*, it can be sued under the *Lanham Act* if the product labeling or other particulars are false and could be considered unfair business practices.[67] Regulatory professionals are not required to be lawyers, but it often is helpful for the company regulatory team to review all documentation using the question, "Does this information provide anything that could be challenged as unfair business practices?"

Recent "New" Issues for Cosmetics

Several new areas of cosmetics have been considered in recent years. These include areas such as "organic" cosmetics, "natural" claims, "GMO-free" cosmetics, and even "gluten-free" and "nano-free" cosmetics. The regulatory professional dealing with these types of claims should obtain independent third-party certification of the claim; this is not only essential from a marketing standpoint but also provides the greatest defense against potential legal action by FDA, FTC or competitors under *Lanham Act* claims. Each of these is discussed below, as are some additional areas that recently have become important to the cosmetics industry.

Organic Cosmetics

When most think about organic products, they invariably think of foods. The US Department of Agriculture (USDA) was charged in the early portion of the millennium with creating a program for verifying products are "organic" or "made with organic," through documentation review. When the National Organic Program (NOP) was created, USDA also invited companies in other areas, including cosmetics, to work on a program that would meet USDA NOP requirements.[68] Many companies, including Burt's Bees and others, made significant investments in bringing their quality programs up to new required NOP levels to obtain individual product certifications that would allow the company to use the NOP seal on its product packaging, product literature and advertising. After USDA announced it had reviewed the new law, allowing it to issue the seal, it informed industry it had made a mistake and was not authorized to allow or disallow any labeling on cosmetics because they are regulated by FDA, and withdrew the offer to certify cosmetic products under the NOP. As might be expected, companies immediately began trying to overturn the new decision with the basic argument they had invested significant money, time and work to bring their documentation processes into compliance with the new requirements to obtain the seal. When USDA would not return to the original position of certifying cosmetics, those companies filed a legal action in federal court to require USDA to review, approve (if applicable) and allow the use of the seal on cosmetic products. The companies claimed since the *Federal Register* listing had set in motion an agreement for a government agency to provide a service to industry, that government agency could not renege on the agreement by stating it had made a mistake and could not provide the service.[69] Some cosmetic products approved under the USDA NOP can be found in both niche stores and major organic retailers, and more and more can be found in the aisles of mainstream mass merchants. Importantly, the regulatory professional always must remember even products meeting USDA's NOP requirements for organic also require compliance with general FDA cosmetic regulations.[70]

The USDA NOP program has significant issues for certain product categories such as bath soaps, body washes, shampoos and conditioners. The problem results from the extremely limited pallet of "non-organic" items that can be used in USDA NOP-certified products and the limited options for preservation of these formulations.[71] Besides the USDA NOP organic certification, which allows the USDA seal to be used when the organic percentage reaches 95% when water and salt (sodium chloride only) are eliminated from the formula,[72] industry created the NSF/ANSI 305 standard that is held as the "American National Standard for cosmetics products made with organic ingredients." This program has a more expansive pallet of non-organic inputs and also requires the product to contain 70% organic material when water, salt and minerals are excluded from the formulation.[73] With NSF/ANSI 305, the product claiming to be organic or to contain organic ingredients in which a product contains only 70% organic ingredients when properly excluding the water, salt and minerals, can be challenged in certain states, notably in California where the *California Organic Products Act* (*COPA*) is a mirror image of the USDA program, which does not allow the exclusion of minerals.[74] This means a product containing exactly (or almost exactly) 70% organic content when excluding water, salt and minerals likely will fall below the 70% threshold in California if any minerals are included in the formula, because they will be considered part of the "non-organic" and "non-excluded" ingredients in the formula, so the calculation denominator will include the minerals.

Natural Cosmetics

One of the most difficult issues for a regulatory professional is when an "undefined" claim is made for a product. There is no better example than the "natural" claim. FDA has been asked on several occasions in Citizen's Petitions under 21 CFR 20, and the original drafts of several legislative texts have included a requirement, for the agency to provide a formal definition through rulemaking for the term "natural."[75-76] Currently, all non-legislative efforts have failed, with FDA arguing it does not have sufficient personnel to create such a definition through rulemaking, and it is not an agency priority. Seemingly, this means there is little chance of getting a definition of the term "natural" for regulatory use without either an absolute mandate from Congress or Congress stepping in and providing a formal legal definition through legislative action. Each of these options has different efficiencies and difficulties. A definition forced on industry through specific legislative action would benefit industry because the definition would be provided through a law and, therefore, likely would lead to a more far-reaching definition and deference from the courts. Unfortunately, this also could be envisioned as too restrictive (or possibly too passive), defining the term and making its use either impossible if too restrictive, or meaningless if too passively defined. Requiring FDA to provide a regulatory definition under a time table that is part of a legislative mandate would provide the agency with the necessary legal coverage to specifically define the term and make it difficult for FDA to be challenged insofar as the legal right to initiate such a definition in rulemaking. However, the requirement could cause internal issues with regard to FDA personnel and staff being forced to utilize time and effort in less prominent areas of its mission. On the negative side, when rules are required to be promulgated within a specifically defined time limit, they may be difficult for the industry to understand or align with. Consequently the industry and FDA may not have the same understanding of what is acceptable according to the definition and what is not, which would lead to something no one wants—"regulation by enforcement action."

Free From Claims

In the past 15–20 years, industry has seen a significant increase in the "free from" claims that seem to find their way onto just about every product in the cosmetics aisles at both niche stores and mass markets and even luxury outlets. For example, the famous issue of parabens being linked to breast cancer about 20 years ago[77] led to almost immediate action by marketing departments, creating a flurry of new development requests for research and development teams to eliminate the use of parabens in products. One of the problems with such a request is the teams could identify fairly easily which formulas had "intentionally added" parabens, meaning the parabens were added as specific ingredients in the formula; however, it was not necessarily as easy to determine which ingredients in the formula also might have contained parabens to preserve them. FTC has taken the stance that "free from" claims need to be truly free from,[78] meaning the product cannot have any detectable parabens. This further caused issues for the suppliers of ingredients who were now expected to provide ingredients with preservatives other than parabens that could protect the ingredient and continue to provide the same ingredient shelf life as the paraben formula. Some two decades later, it is possible to look at a product shelf in almost any category and find claims such as "GMO free" or "gluten free," even in cosmetics. These claims can be made if the ingredient review shows no GMO or gluten in the formula's ingredients. However, there also are third-party certifiers such as the Non-GMO Project[79] and Gluten Free Certifying Organization[80] that will review (and in some cases even test) the ingredients and the products independently, as well as review production procedures and processes to show they truly are "free from" the specific claimed material and allow the use of a seal recognized by consumers.

Nanotechnology

Nanotechnology has created an equally difficult situation for cosmetic companies. Take the most simplistic and obvious example: a company wants to create a mineral blush. One of the most common color adjusting ingredients in such products is titanium dioxide. This is true for several reasons, but one of those is the idea the company could, in theory, also claim a sunscreen activity for the product if it uses sufficient levels of titanium dioxide to obtain an allowable SPF response. Additionally, since titanium dioxide is white, it also is a good color adjusting ingredient if the product color needs to be lightened. Currently, in the US, there is no regulatory definition of the term "product of nanotechnology," which causes further difficulty in documenting and acceptably defining the term on labeling and in advertisements. While FDA has produced a guidance document on this issue, a guidance document cannot establish a regulatory definition.[81] Considering the case of a sunscreen product that is an OTC, larger particles of titanium dioxide lead to the appearance of white pasty faces that were made famous in the beach movies in the 1960s. The physical property that leads to this is the size of the titanium dioxide particles. The smaller the particles are, the less obvious the white pasty appearance from the sunscreen. But the lack of a regulatory definition of what is considered a product of nanotechnology makes a regulatory professional's job more difficult. One solution is for companies to use the EU definition.[82] There is some basis for this, especially since FDA and EU regulators have been meeting through the International Conference on Cosmetics Regulations (ICCR), which brings together regulatory agencies from the US, EU, Canada, Japan and now several additional countries, either as participants or observers to develop a more global regulatory scheme for cosmetics and lessen industry trade barriers.[83] However, while this would make sense from a regulatory perspective, there is no guarantee such a definition would be accepted by a court if any legal action were to be filed against the company.

International Harmonization

FDA is involved in several specific areas of global harmonization for cosmetic products. As noted above, it is a member of ICCR,[84] the US-Canada Regulatory Form (USCRF),[85] the International Conference on Harmonization (ICH)[86-87] and is an observer in the International Standards Organization (ISO).[88] Each of these gives FDA an opportunity to influence regulatory science internationally and to discuss and even learn from colleagues in other governments and from industry. For example, ICCR actually offers FDA the opportunity to interact with other regulators (specifically from Canada, Europe, and Japan as well as other newer members and observers, including Brazil and China) and with industry (PCPC, Cosmetics Europe, Canadian Cosmetics, Toiletries and Fragrances Association and the

Japan Cosmetic Industry Association). These meetings occur routinely and have resulted in several FDA guidance documents to assist international industry (and, by extension, US industry) in understanding how to avoid running afoul of the agency and regulations.

In addition to the work in ICCR, FDA has been active in reviewing ISO documentation. For example, FDA has used portions of the ISO 22716 document to further define and enunciate its position on US GMP expectations for cosmetics. While it is true FDA does not have the authority to require GMP activities in the US cosmetics sector, it also is true the agency still expects a certain level of GMP awareness and activity even in cosmetics. This is because FDA still is responsible for cosmetic safety. Additionally, poor or non-adherence to GMP principles can lead to products being considered adulterated according to the *FD&C Act*.

FDA already is involved in many specific areas of international harmonization, but it might need to become more so. For example, the US currently is engaged in several "Free Trade" agreements with jurisdictions including the EU, Japan, South America and Korea.[89] These discussions (especially the negotiation with the EU) include topics such as how to further harmonize the requirements for cosmetic products as a way to further eliminate any perceived trade barriers. Also, with the number of major cosmetics companies and even smaller companies pushing their goods into international export, the author believes FDA's involvement in these activities is a positive step.

While usually not entirely within the regulatory professional's purview, he or she needs to understand implications surrounding such issues as international relations and treaties. Two immediate examples are the Nagoya Protocol on Prior Informed Consent and Access and Benefits Sharing, and the requirements to disclose whether or not a publically traded company complies with prohibitions on obtaining certain materials from African war zones.

Nagoya Protocol

At the beginning of the millennium, the United Nations entertained and brokered an international treaty that extended the requirements of the previously negotiated Convention on Biodiversity. The new protocol requires the treaty's signatories and acceding countries to provide within their national laws for checking to ensure biological materials (what the treaty calls genetic resources) and traditional knowledge of how to use these resources are, when obtained from other signatory countries, collected in a way to provide for (1) prior informed consent through (2) mutually agreed terms with (3) contractually agreed access and benefit sharing for the countries involved. There are some significant implications for the cosmetics industry since the protocol took effect in October 2014 in the EU.[90] The rules for access and benefit sharing are different for each country, and there are differences, even among EU Member States regarding the Competent Authorities. Several countries have chosen to have either the patent office or the office handling product registration serve as the checkpoint. If the company cannot prove the treaty's requirements have been met, this could result in the denial or revocation of a patent or registration, or both.[91] While the US currently is not a signatory to the treaty, any company doing international business needs to consider the implications of these requirements and the impact of possible noncompliance both legally (liability, loss of patent rights, loss of market approval or acceptance) and on the company's reputation (poor news coverage regarding claims of "bio-piracy").

Conflict Minerals

Several significant issues exist with sourcing ingredients internationally. For example, current laws enforced by the US Securities and Exchange Commission (SEC) require publicly traded companies to certify annually the company has not obtained ingredients or certain reactants to create ingredients from countries actively involved in civil war in Africa. These ingredients are called "conflict minerals" because combatants in those areas are financing the costs of their conflicts from mining these minerals. These filings are required annually, when the company prepares and files SEC Form 10-K. Dangers here include criminal prosecution for company officials if the filing is not submitted or is inaccurate in any respect.[92]

Summary

Ultimately, the keys to determining what requirements apply (drug, cosmetic, device, combination) to a product are the labeling and advertisements associated with the product. This has been where FDA traditionally has looked, and there is no reason to believe this will change in the future. It is just as important to understand several different government agencies potentially may have some jurisdiction over the company's product. These can include USDA, FDA, FTC and EPA. Besides these agencies, several other groups can be brought into the mix, such as organic certifying agents or agencies, natural product certifying agents or agencies and even CIR or other groups that review products for safety and, in some cases, magazines (e.g., *Consumer Reports*) reviewing product efficacy.

Regulatory professionals in the cosmetics sector must understand claims' regulations and not allow those claims to change the classification of company products from cosmetics to drugs. All information should be reviewed in view of how the agency will consider the products. FDA reviews product labeling and any other information readily available to consumers, including the Internet and advertising both in print and other electronic media. Regulatory professionals in the area also must work to understand and provide the best recommendations possible to ensure the company remains compliant and understands the risks inherent in any problematic or questionable claims. As important as claims are in protecting the company from regulatory action, necessary documentation to support any package claims is equally important. This support can take the form of test data, instrumental data, consumer perception questionnaires, literature documentation, supplier ingredient documentation or any combination thereof. The professional should view claims with an eye toward determining whether the claim is supported and how best to support it. When regulatory professionals are briefed on new projects early in formula development, they have the best opportunity to provide the most effective counsel to the project team and work with the team to determine how to support the claims or reword problematic claims most effectively.

References

1. *Federal Food, Drug, & Cosmetics Act of 1938 (FD&C Act)*, Chapter II. FDA website. http://www.fda.gov/RegulatoryInformation/Legislation/FederalFoodDrugandCosmeticActFDCAct/FDCActChaptersIandIIShortTitleandDefinitions/default.htm. Accessed 1 February 2015.
2. Title 21 Code of Federal Regulations. FDA website. http://www.accessdata.fda.gov/scripts/cdrh/cfdocs/cfcfr/CFRSearch.cfm. Accessed 1 February 2015.
3. 21 CFR 720.4. FDA website. http://www.accessdata.fda.gov/scripts/cdrh/cfdocs/cfcfr/CFRSearch.cfm. Accessed 1 February 2015.
4. Op cit 1.
5. Ibid.
6. Karst K. "As Senate and House Lawmakers Slog Through FDA Appropriations Bills, FDA's To-Do List Grows." FDA Law Blog website. http://www.fdalawblog.net/fda_law_blog_hyman_phelps/2014/05/as-senate-and-house-lawmakers-slog-through-fda-appropriations-bills-fdas-to-do-list-grows.html. Accessed 1 February 2015.
7. S. 2902 (113th): *A Bill To prohibit the sale or distribution of certain cosmetics containing synthetic plastic microbeads.* Government Printing Office (GPO) website. http://www.gpo.gov/fdsys/pkg/BILLS-113s2902is/pdf/BILLS-113s2902is.pdf. Accessed 1 February 2015.
8. H.R. 4895 (113th): *A Bill To prohibit the sale or distribution of cosmetics containing synthetic plastic microbeads.* GPO website. http://www.gpo.gov/fdsys/pkg/BILLS-113hr4895ih/pdf/BILLS-113hr4895ih.pdf. Accessed 1 February 2015.
9. H.R. 4148 (113th): *A Bill To phase out cosmetic animal testing and the sale of cosmetics tested on animals.* GPO website. http://www.gpo.gov/fdsys/pkg/BILLS-113hr4148ih/pdf/BILLS-113hr4148ih.pdf. Accessed 1 February 2015.
10. Ibid.
11. H.R. 1385 (113th): *A Bill To amend title VI of the Federal Food, Drug, and Cosmetic Act to ensure the safe use of cosmetics, and for other purposes.* GPO website. http://www.gpo.gov/fdsys/pkg/BILLS-113hr1385ih/pdf/BILLS-113hr1385ih.pdf. Accessed 1 February 2015.
12. Op cit 1.
13. Warning Letter Vienna Beauty Products 17 May 2012. FDA website. http://www.fda.gov/iceci/enforcementactions/warningletters/2012/ucm313452.htm. Accessed 1 February 2015.
14. Import Alert 45-02. FDA website. http://www.accessdata.fda.gov/cms_ia/importalert_118.html. Accessed 1 February 2015.
15. 21 CFR sections 700.11-700.23. FDA website. http://www.accessdata.fda.gov/scripts/cdrh/cfdocs/cfcfr/CFRSearch.cfm?CFRPart=700&showFR=1&subpartNode=21:7.0.1.2.10.2. Accessed 1 February 2015.
16. Ibid.
17. 21 CFR Part 74. FDA website. http://www.accessdata.fda.gov/scripts/cdrh/cfdocs/cfcfr/CFRSearch.cfm?CFRPart=74. Accessed 1 February 2015.
18. 21 CFR 80.37. FDA website. http://www.accessdata.fda.gov/scripts/cdrh/cfdocs/cfcfr/CFRSearch.cfm?fr=80.37. Accessed 1 February 2015.
19. 21 CFR part 701. FDA website. http://www.accessdata.fda.gov/scripts/cdrh/cfdocs/cfcfr/CFRSearch.cfm?CFRPart=701. Accessed 1 February 2015.
20. 21 CFR 701.12. FDA website. http://www.accessdata.fda.gov/scripts/cdrh/cfdocs/cfcfr/CFRSearch.cfm?fr=701.12. Accessed 1 February 2015.
21. 21 CFR 701.1. FDA website. http://www.accessdata.fda.gov/scripts/cdrh/cfdocs/cfcfr/CFRSearch.cfm?fr=701.1. Accessed 1 February 2015.
22. 21 CFR 740.10. FDA website. http://www.accessdata.fda.gov/scripts/cdrh/cfdocs/cfcfr/CFRSearch.cfm. Accessed 1 February 2015.
23. Ibid.
24. Ibid.
25. "Memorandum of Understanding Between Federal Trade Commission and the Food and Drug Administration," *Federal Register*, Vol 36, No. 180. 16 September 1971.
26. "Skin Protectant Drug Products for Over-the-Counter Human Use; Final Monograph." *Federal Register*, Vol. 68, No. 107, 4 June 2003.
27. Warning Letter Allure Laboratories, Inc. 24 May 2011. FDA website. http://www.fda.gov/iceci/enforcementactions/warningletters/2011/ucm257013.htm. Accessed 1 February 2015.
28. Warning Letter Brazilian Blowout 22 August 2011. FDA website. http://www.fda.gov/ICECI/EnforcementActions/WarningLetters/2011/ucm270809.htm. Accessed 1 February 2015.
29. Warning Letter Avon Products, Inc. 5 October 2012. FDA website. http://www.fda.gov/ICECI/EnforcementActions/WarningLetters/2012/ucm323738.htm. Accessed 1 February 2015.
30. Warning Letter Dr. Bronner's Magic Soaps 8 July 2014. FDA website. http://www.fda.gov/ICECI/EnforcementActions/WarningLetters/2014/ucm408739.htm. Accessed 1 February 2015.
31. Federal Trade Commission website. http://www.ftc.gov/about-ftc/what-we-do/enforcement-authority. Accessed 1 February 2015.
32. "Marketers Settle FTC Charges That They Used Deceptive Ads In Promoting Products for Mole and Wart Removal, Anti-Aging and Weight Loss." 23 December 2014. FTC website. http://www.ftc.gov/news-events/press-releases/2014/12/marketers-settle-ftc-charges-they-used-deceptive-ads-promoting. Accessed 1 February 2015.
33. "Labeling Requirements." FDA website. http://www.fda.gov/cosmetics/labeling/regulations/default.htm. Accessed 1 February 2015.
34. *Title 21 United States Code section 337.* GPO website. http://www.gpo.gov/fdsys/pkg/USCODE-2010-title21/pdf/USCODE-2010-title21-chap9-subchapIII-sec337.pdf. Accessed 1 February 2015.
35. *POM Wonderful LLC v. Coca-Cola Co.* No. 12-761. US Supreme Court website. http://www.supremecourt.gov/opinions/13pdf/12-761_6k47.pdf. Accessed 1 February 2015.
36. *Allergan, Inc. v. Athena Cosmetics, Inc.* No 2010-1396. US Court of Appeals, Federal Circuit. FindLaw.com website. http://caselaw.findlaw.com/us-federal-circuit/1568579.html. Accessed 1 February 2015.
37. "Cosmeceutical." FDA website. http://www.fda.gov/cosmetics/labeling/claims/ucm127064.htm. Accessed 1 February 2015.
38. "Is It a Cosmetic, a Drug, or Both? (Or Is It Soap?)" FDA website. http://www.fda.gov/Cosmetics/GuidanceRegulation/LawsRegulations/ucm074201.htm. Accessed 1 February 2015.
39. Ibid.
40. Ibid.
41. "Good Manufacturing Practice (GMP) Guidelines/Inspection Checklist." Updated 24 April 2008. FDA website. http://www.fda.gov/Cosmetics/GuidanceRegulation/GuidanceDocuments/ucm2005190.htm. Accessed 1 February 2015.
42. Op cit 11.

43. Op cit 41.
44. International Standards Organization. "International Standard ISO 22716: Cosmetics—Good Manufacturing Practices (GMP)—Guidelines on Good Manufacturing Practices." 15 May 2008.
45. Title 21 CFR Part 720. FDA website. http://www.accessdata.fda.gov/scripts/cdrh/cfdocs/cfcfr/CFRSearch.cfm?CFRPart=720&showFR=1. Accessed 1 February 2015.
46. "Voluntary Cosmetic Registration Program." FDA website. http://www.fda.gov/Cosmetics/RegistrationProgram/default.htm. Accessed 1 February 2015.
47. "About the Cosmetic Ingredient Review." Cosmetic Ingredient Review (CIR) website. http://www.cir-safety.org/about. Accessed 1 February 2015.
48. "Find Ingredient Reviews and Documents." CIR website. http://www.cir-safety.org/ingredients. Accessed 1 February 2015.
49. *Cosmetic Ingredient Review Procedures*. October 2010. Part D Section 30 Annual Ingredient Priority List and Review Process. CIR website. http://www.cir-safety.org/how-does-cir-work. Accessed 1 February 2015.
50. "Registration Reports." FDA website. http://www.fda.gov/cosmetics/registrationprogram/registrationreports/default.htm. Accessed 1 February 2015.
51. "Information for Cosmetic Exporters: FAQs." FDA website. http://www.fda.gov/Cosmetics/InternationalActivities/Exporters/ucm2005217.htm. Accessed 1 February 2015.
52. "Certificates of Free Sale." Personal Care Products Council (PCPC) website. http://www.personalcarecouncil.org/member-industry-resources/certificates-free-sale. Accessed 1 February 2015.
53. "Certificates of Free Sale." Independent Cosmetics Manufacturers and Distributors (ICMAD) website. http://www.icmad.org/programs/certificates-of-free-sale. Accessed 1 February 2015.
54. Ibid.
55. Ibid.
56. Ibid.
57. "Information for Cosmetic Importers." FDA website. http://www.fda.gov/Cosmetics/InternationalActivities/Importers/ucm2005215.htm. Accessed 1 February 2015.
58. Ibid.
59. "Inspection of Cosmetics." FDA website. http://www.fda.gov/Cosmetics/ComplianceEnforcement/ComplianceResources/ucm136455.htm. Accessed 1 February 2015.
60. *Compliance Program Guidance Manual: Cosmetics Program; Import and Domestic*. FDA website. http://www.fda.gov/downloads/Cosmetics/GuidanceRegulation/GuidanceDocuments/UCM208412.pdf. Accessed 1 February 2015.
61. "Inspections, Compliance, Enforcement, and Criminal Investigations: Warning Letters." FDA website. http://www.fda.gov/ICECI/EnforcementActions/WarningLetters/default.htm. Accessed 1 February 2015.
62. "FDA Debarment List (Drug Product Applications)." FDA website. http://www.fda.gov/ICECI/EnforcementActions/FDADebarmentList/ucm2005408.htm. Accessed 1 February 2015.
63. "Import Alert 66-38." FDA website. http://www.accessdata.fda.gov/cms_ia/importalert_188.html. Accessed 1 February 2015.
64. "Import Alert 53-17." FDA website. http://www.accessdata.fda.gov/cms_ia/importalert_136.html. Accessed 1 February 2015.
65. "FDA Recall Policy for Cosmetics." FDA website. http://www.fda.gov/Cosmetics/ComplianceEnforcement/RecallsAlerts/ucm173559.htm. Accessed 1 February 2015.
66. Op cit 1.
67. Op cit 35.
68. USDA. Agricultural Marketing Service National Organic Program. "Cosmetics, Body Care Products, and Personal Care Products." April 2008. USDA website. http://www.ams.usda.gov/AMSv1.0/getfile?dDocName=STELPRDC5068442. Accessed 8 February 2015.
69. "Fighting for Organic Integrity in Body Care." Dr. Bronner's Magic Soap website. https://www.drbronner.com/impact/activism/organic-integrity/coming-clean-campaign/. Accessed 8 February 2015.
70. "Organic" Cosmetics." FDA website. http://www.fda.gov/Cosmetics/Labeling/Claims/ucm203078.htm. Accessed 8 February 2015.
71. Op cit 68.
72. *Title 7 Part 205—National Organic Program Subpart D—Labels, Labeling, and Market Information*. 7 USC 205.302 Calculating the percentage of organically produced ingredients. eCFR website. http://www.ecfr.gov/cgi-bin/text-idx?SID=f708590627e019de44692e3927dd8e6e&node=se7.3.205_1302&rgn=div8. Accessed 8 February 2015.
73. *NSF/ANSI 305: Organic Personal Care Products*. Available from NSF International or American National Standard Institute.
74. *California Organic Products Act of 2003*. Food and Agriculture Code Sections 46000-46029 and Health and Safety Code Sections 110810-110959. Section 110838. California Department of Food and Agriculture website. http://www.cdfa.ca.gov/is/docs/copa2003.pdf. Accessed 8 February 2015.
75. "Food: Agency Summary Memorandum Re: Consultation with Calgene, Inc., Concerning FLVR SAVR™ Tomatoes." FDA website. http://www.fda.gov/food/foodscienceresearch/biotechnology/submissions/ucm225043.htm. Accessed 8 February 2015.
76. "Letter to the Personal Care Products Council and Independent Cosmetics Manufacturers and Distributors Concerning the Proposed Draft Legislation." FDA website. http://www.fda.gov/aboutfda/centersoffices/officeoffoods/cfsan/cfsanfoiaelectronicreadingroom/ucm388296.htm. Accessed 8 February 2015.
77. "Parabens." The Campaign for Safe Cosmetics website. http://safecosmetics.org/article.php?id=291. Accessed 8 February 2015.
78. "Guides for the Use of Environmental Marketing Claims ('Environmental Guides' or 'Green Guides')." Title 16 CFR Part 260. Federal Trade Commission website. http://www.ftc.gov/enforcement/rules/rulemaking-regulatory-reform-proceedings/guides-use-environmental-marketing-claims. Accessed 8 February 2015.
79. "Everyone Deserves an Informed Choice." Non-GMO Project website. http://www.nongmoproject.org/about/. Accessed 8 February 2015.
80. "About the Gluten Intolerance Group." Gluten Intolerance Group website. http://www.gfco.org/. Accessed 8 February 2015.
81. "Considering Whether an FDA-Regulated Product Involves the Application of Nanotechnology." June 2014. FDA website. http://www.fda.gov/regulatoryinformation/guidances/ucm257698.htm. Accessed 8 February 2015.
82. "Nanomaterials." European Commission Directorate General Environment website. http://ec.europa.eu/environment/chemicals/nanotech/index_en.htm. Accessed 8 February 2015.
83. "International Cooperation on Cosmetics Regulations (ICCR)." Last update, 11 December 2014. FDA website. http://www.fda.gov/cosmetics/internationalactivities/iccr/default.htm. Accessed 8 February 2015.
84. Ibid.
85. "Office of International Programs." Last updated 15 September 2014. FDA website. http://www.fda.gov/AboutFDA/CentersOffices/OfficeofGlobalRegulatoryOperationsandPolicy/OfficeofInternationalPrograms/default.htm. Accessed 8 February 2015.
86. "International Conference on Harmonization (ICH) in the Office of Pharmaceutical Science (OPS)." Last updated 1 April 2009. FDA website. http://www.fda.gov/aboutfda/centersoffices/officeofmedicalproductsandtobacco/cder/ucm128047.htm. Accessed 8 February 2015.
87. Op cit 83.
88. "Draft Guidance for Industry: Cosmetic Good Manufacturing Practices." Last updated June 2013. FDA website. http://www.fda.gov/regulatoryinformation/guidances/ucm353046.htm. Accessed 8 February 2015.
89. Op cit 85.

90. "The Nagoya Protocol on Access and Benefit-Sharing." Last updated 28 January 2015. Convention on Biodiversity website http://www.cbd.int/abs/. Accessed 8 February 2015.
91. "Questions and answers on access and benefit-sharing." 10 June 2014. European Commission website. http://europa.eu/rapid/press-release_MEMO-14-411_en.htm. Accessed 8 February 2015.
92. "FACT SHEET: Disclosing the Use of Conflict Minerals." Last updated 29 July 2014. SEC website. http://www.sec.gov/News/Article/Detail/Article/1365171562058#.VNeOHcItGM8. Accessed 8 February 2015.

Chapter 35

Veterinary Products

Updated by Adria Tyndall, RAC

OBJECTIVES

- ❑ Understand the definition, agency jurisdiction and regulations for different veterinary product types
- ❑ Identify the appropriate regulatory approval pathway and required elements for each submission type

LAWS, REGULATIONS AND GUIDELINES COVERED IN THIS CHAPTER

- ❑ *Federal Food, Drug and Cosmetic Act* of 1938
- ❑ *Animal Drug Amendments* of 1968
- ❑ *Animal Medicinal Drug Use Clarification Act* of 1994
- ❑ *Animal Drug User Fee Act* of 2003
- ❑ *Animal Drug User Fee Amendments* of 2013
- ❑ *Animal Generic Drug User Fee Act* of 2008
- ❑ *Minor Use and Minor Species Animal Health Act* of 2004
- ❑ *Generic Animal Drug and Patent Term Restoration Act* of 1988
- ❑ *Virus-Serum-Toxin Act* of 1913
- ❑ *Federal Insecticide, Fungicide, and Rodenticide Act* of 1972
- ❑ 9 CFR, Chapter 1, Subchapter E-Animals and Animal Products-Viruses, Serums, Toxins and Analogous Products; Organisms and Vectors
- ❑ 21 CFR 25, Environmental Impact Considerations
- ❑ 21 CFR 201, Labeling
- ❑ 21 CFR 211, Current Good Manufacturing Practice for Finished Pharmaceuticals
- ❑ 21 CFR 225-226, Current Good Manufacturing Practice for Medicated Feeds, Type A Medicated Articles
- ❑ 21 CFR 501, Animal Food Labeling
- ❑ 21 CFR 510, New Animal Drugs
- ❑ 21 CFR 511, New Animal Drugs for Investigational Use
- ❑ 21 CFR 514, New Animal Drug Applications
- ❑ 21 CFR 515, Medicated Feed Mill License
- ❑ 21 CFR 516, New Animal Drugs for Minor Use and Minor Species
- ❑ 21 CFR 530, Extralabel Drug Use in Animals

- ❑ 21 CFR 558, New Animal Drugs for Use in Animal Feeds
- ❑ 21 CFR 573, Food Additives Permitted in Feed and Drinking Water of Animals
- ❑ 21 CFR 582, Substances Generally Recognized as Safe
- ❑ 21 CFR Chapter 1300, Drug Enforcement Administration Definitions
- ❑ 40 CFR, Chapter 1, Subchapter E, Pesticide Programs
- ❑ *Guidance for Industry 57: Preparation and Submission of Veterinary Master Files* (January 1995)
- ❑ *Guidance for Industry 61: FDA Approval of New Animal Drugs for Minor Uses and for Minor Species* (May 2008)
- ❑ *Guidance for Industry 82: Development of Supplemental Applications for Approved New Animal Drugs* (October 2002)
- ❑ *Guidance for Industry 108: How to Register with the CVM Electronic Submission System* (February 2013)
- ❑ *Draft Guidance for Industry 132: The Administrative New Animal Drug Application Process* (November 2002)
- ❑ *Guidance for Industry 170: Animal Drug User Fees and Fee Waivers and Reductions* (October 2008)
- ❑ *Guidance for Industry 173: Animal Drug Sponsor Fees Under the Animal Drug User Fee Act (ADUFA)* (February 2005)
- ❑ *Guidance for Industry 200: Small Entities Compliance Guide (SECG) for Designation of New Animal Drugs for Minor Uses/Minor Species* (July 2014)
- ❑ *Guidance for Industry 201: SECG for Index of Legally Marketed Unapproved New Animal Drugs for Minor Species* (July 2014)
- ❑ *Guidance for Industry 209: The Judicious Use of Medically Important Antimicrobial Drugs in Food-Producing Animals* (April 2012)
- ❑ *Draft Guidance for Industry 227: Two-Phased Chemistry, Manufacturing and Controls (CMC) Technical Sections* (October 2014)
- ❑ Veterinary Services Memorandum Number 800.50: Basic License Requirements and Guidelines for Submission of Materials in Support of Licensure (February 2011)
- ❑ Veterinary Services Memorandum 800.52: Export Certificates and Certificates of Licensing and Inspection for Animal Biological Products (April 2001)
- ❑ Veterinary Services Memorandum 800.101: US Veterinary Biological Product Permits for Distribution and Sale (June 2013)

Introduction

Regulated veterinary products in the US are diverse and include drugs, biologics, food and medicated feeds, devices, grooming aids and pest control products. The regulations and marketing approvals vary not only by product type, but by whether the intended use is for companion animals, food-producing animals or minor species. Veterinary products are regulated by the Center for Veterinary Medicine (CVM) within the US Food and Drug Administration (FDA), the US Department of Agriculture (USDA) and the Environmental Protection Agency (EPA). This chapter provides a fundamental overview of the agencies, regulations, application types and compliance considerations for US veterinary products.

To manufacture, distribute and sell veterinary products in the US, it is important to classify the product to identify the appropriate jurisdiction and regulations. **Table 35-1** may be used in conjunction with the information throughout this chapter to identify the pertinent regulations and associated filing types.

Drugs

Veterinary drugs are regulated by CVM. The *Animal Drug Amendments* to the *Food, Drug, and Cosmetic Act* (*FD&C Act*) in 1968 added provisions to ensure animal drugs are safe and effective for intended use and do not result in unsafe residues in food for human consumption. Two main processes regulate the distribution and use of animal drugs. The Investigational New Animal Drug (INAD) filing allows interstate shipment of drugs for experimental use in animal clinical trials. The New Animal Drug Application (NADA), Abbreviated New Animal Drug Application (ANADA) and

Conditional New Animal Drug or Indexing for Minor Use and Minor Species allow legal marketing and distribution of the new animal drug.

INAD

The Office of New Animal Drug Evaluation (ONADE) within CVM is responsible for the review of new animal drug applications and oversight of the drug development process. Communication with FDA is encouraged early and often throughout the product development process, which begins when the sponsor initiates an INAD. An INAD must be submitted to the agency prior to shipping product for clinical study use. This dynamic file, updated throughout the development process, contains technical sections including protocols and data related to clinical studies that eventually will support a NADA or ANADA.

The INAD exempts products from US law, allowing drug shipment for experimental use in animal clinical studies prior to marketing approval without violating the *FD&C Act*. The sponsor or distributor is responsible for the following 21 CFR 511 requirements:[1]

- labeling product with the statement "Caution. Contains a new animal drug for use only in investigational animals in clinical trials. Not for use in humans. Edible products of investigational animals are not to be used for food unless authorization has been granted by the US Food and Drug Administration or by the US Department of Agriculture."
- ensuring drug is shipped only to qualified investigators and maintaining records, including investigator names and addresses, shipment dates, quantity and batch code for two years after shipment and delivery
- ensuring the drug is used in testing as outlined in the INAD, is not used in humans, and records and investigator reports are retained for two years after the investigation's termination or NADA approval
- monitoring the investigation and reporting any findings suggesting hazards related to the drug's safety to FDA and all investigators
- environmental impact, including a claim for categorical exclusion per 21 CFR 25.30 or 25.33 or completion of an environmental assessment per 21 CFR 25.40
- submission of any information deemed necessary to protect the public health
- submission of a Notice of Claimed Investigational Exemption (NCIE) with each drug shipment, including:
    - identity
    - labeling
    - clinical investigator name and address
    - number of animals to be treated
    - if used for food animals, a commitment the animals will not be used for food without prior authorization, start and end dates for treatment and dosing information
    - statement identifying transfer of any obligation to a contract research organization

The sponsor may request ongoing review of documents within the INAD to obtain feedback on intended protocols or studies. A sponsor also may request a phased review of the new drug application, having individual technical sections of the INAD reviewed and deemed complete prior to submitting an administrative NADA for marketing approval.

NADA

To introduce a new drug into interstate commerce, an approved marketing application or exemption through the *Minor Use Minor Species Act* is required. An NADA is the application for drug approval for sale and distribution. It includes data demonstrating the drug's safety and effectiveness in the target animal and its safety for humans who may consume products from the treated animal.

CVM does not require applicants to submit an NADA as one complete package. Instead, applicants may submit individual completed technical sections or components to the INAD file for technical review. NADA data requirements remain the same whether a phased approach is used or not. For example, the applicant may submit data and information as they are compiled, including the drug's target animal safety and effectiveness, human food safety and labeling. When all technical sections have been submitted for phased review, and CVM has issued a "technical section complete" letter for each, the manufacturer submits an administrative NADA with pertinent user fees. The chemistry, manufacturing and controls (CMC) section also may also be submitted in two phases, although CVM prefers a single submission.[2]

Information required for an NADA includes several technical sections: target animal safety, effectiveness, human food safety (if applicable), CMC and environmental impact. 21 CFR 514 specifies the following administrative requirements for an NADA:[3]

- product identification
- table of contents and summary
- three copies of each product labeling piece with adequate directions for use
- components and composition
- manufacturing methods, facilities and controls
- representative product samples
- analytical methods for new animal drug residues in or on food, and proposed tolerance or withdrawal period
- evidence to establish safety and effectiveness

Table 35-1. Summary of Veterinary Product Types

Product Type	Definition	Jurisdiction	Regulatory Filing(s)	Reference to Legal Definition and Regulations
Drug	an article intended for use in the diagnosis, cure, mitigation, treatment or prevention of disease and intended to affect the structure or any function of the body	FDA CVM	New Animal Drug Application (NADA) Abbreviated New Animal Drug Application (ANADA) Conditional New Drug Application	*FD&C Act*, Section 201(g) 21 CFR 510
New Animal Drug	any drug intended for use in animals other than man, including any drug intended for use in animal feed but not including the animal feed, the composition of which is such that the drug is not generally recognized as safe and effective for the use under the conditions prescribed, recommended or suggested in the labeling thereof	FDA CVM	NADA	*FD&C Act*, Section 201(v) 21 CFR 510 21 CFR 514
Generic Animal Drug	a drug that has the same ingredients in the same concentrations, and is bioequivalent to the approved Reference Listed New Animal Drug	FDA CVM	ANADA	*FD&C Act*, Section 201(v) 21 CFR 510 21 CFR 514
Investigational New Animal Drug	a new chemical entity being investigated as a new animal drug or a drug being investigated for an indication for which it is not currently approved	FDA CVM	Investigational New Animal Drug (INAD) file Generic Investigational New Animal Drug (JINAD) file	*FD&C Act*, Section 201(v) 21 CFR 511
Drug for Minor Use or Minor Species	Minor use is the intended use of a drug in a major species for a disease that occurs infrequently or in limited geographic areas and in only a small number of animals annually. A minor species is any animal species other than humans and major animal species, which include cattle, horses, swine, chickens, turkeys, dogs and cats.	FDA CVM	Conditional NDA Indexing	*FD&C Act*, Section 571 and 572 21 CFR 516
Animal Feed	articles used for food or drink or components of any such article	FDA CVM	no premarket approval required may require Generally Recognized as Safe (GRAS) notification or food additive petition if food contains novel ingredients	*FD&C Act*, Section 201(w) 21 CFR 501 21 CFR 570 21 CFR 571 21 CFR 573 21 CFR 582 21 CFR 584 21 CFR 589
Type A Medicated Article	a mixture of one or more drug substances with suitable vehicle intended for use in animal feed and intended for further manufacturing	FDA CVM	NADA ANADA	*FD&C Act*, Section 201(v) 21 CFR 226 21 CFR 558
Type B Medicated Feed	a product intended for the manufacture of other medicated feeds from a Type A Medicated Article or another Type B Medicated Feed	FDA CVM	approved veterinary feed directive labeling from Type A medicated article may require GRAS notification or food additive petition if food contains novel ingredients	*FD&C Act*, Section 201(w) 21 CFR 225 21 CFR 558

Product Type	Definition	Jurisdiction	Regulatory Filing(s)	Reference to Legal Definition and Regulations
Type C Medicated Feed	a dilution of a Type A medicated Article or Type B Medicated Feed which is intended as the final feed product	FDA CVM	approved veterinary feed directive labeling from Type A medicated article may require GRAS notification or food additive petition if food contains novel ingredients	*FD&C Act*, Section 201(w) 21 CFR 225 21 CFR 558
Veterinary Devices	an instrument, apparatus, implement, machine, contrivance, implant, in-vitro reagent, intended for use in diagnosis of disease or in the cure, mitigation, treatment or prevention of disease which is intended to affect the structure or function of the body, but which does not achieve primary intended purpose through chemical action and is not dependent upon being metabolized	FDA CVM FDA Center for Devices and Radiologic Health (CDRH)	no premarket approval required radiation-emitting devices must be registered with FDA CDRH	*FD&C Act*, Section 201(h)
Grooming Aids	cosmetic articles intended to cleanse and beautify animals	none	no application required, may require drug application if therapeutic claims are made	none
Veterinary Biologic	all viruses, serums, toxins or analogous products of natural or synthetic origin which are intended for use in the treatment of animals which act primarily through the direct stimulation, supplementation, enhancement or modulation of the immune system or immune response	USDA [a]	US Veterinary Biological Product License Veterinary Biological Product Permit	9 CFR, Chapter 1, Subchapter E-Animals and Animal Products-Viruses, Serums, Toxins and Analogous Products; Organisms and Vectors
Pesticides	a substance or mixture of substances intended for preventing, destroying, repelling or mitigating any pests; this excludes animal drugs, new animal drugs and animal feeds as defined per the FD&C Act	EPA	Pesticide Product Registration	40 CFR, Chapter 1, Subchapter E, Pesticide Programs

[a] *The USDA regulates Veterinary Biologic Products with an immunological mechanism. Other veterinary products of biological origin are regulated by the FDA as drugs.*

- veterinary feed directive (if applicable)
- applicant's commitment to label and market the drug under the conditions stated in the NADA
- commitment the methods, facilities and controls as described in the application conform to current Good Manufacturing Practices (CGMPs)
- a statement of compliance or noncompliance with Good Laboratory Practices (GLPs) per 21 CFR 58
- environmental impact, including a claim for categorical exclusion per 21 CFR 25.30 or 25.33 or completion of an environmental assessment per 21 CFR 25.40

A Freedom of Information (FOI) Summary also is required per 21 CFR 511.11, which summarizes the studies used as a basis for approval. The FOI Summary is made available publicly to comply with the *Freedom of Information Act*.

NADAs are subject to user fees per the *Animal Drug User Fee Act* (*ADUFA*). Fiscal year 2015 user fees are $400,600 for an original application and $200,300 for a supplemental application with safety and effectiveness data. ONADE reviews the NADA to determine whether the animal drug should be approved for marketing based on the drug's effectiveness for the purposes claimed. *ADUFA II* established an end-review-amendment (ERA) process that allows FDA reviewers to work with the sponsor to amend pending applications to decrease the number of review cycles. *ADUFA III* established the following performance goals for 2014–18:[4]

- Refuse to File notification will occur within 30 days of the submission date for applications that are insufficient or otherwise unacceptable quality for review.
- Refuse to Review notifications for insufficient INADs will occur within 60 days of submission.

- FDA will review and act on 90% of NADAs and INADs within 180 days from date of submission for complete or incomplete applications. An application is incomplete if substantial data or information is required to complete a comprehensive review.
- FDA will review and act on 90% of NADAs and INADs within 220 days from date of submission for applications requiring additional non-substantial data to complete the application, and for which an ERA is requested electronically before day 180 but sponsor fails to file by day 210. If a sponsor files an amendment after day 210, the amendment is ineligible for consideration as an ERA, the 345 day performance goal will not apply and a complete letter will be issued by day 220 for the original application.
- FDA will review and act on 90% of INADs within 270 days of the submission date for applications with an ERA requested by the agency on or before day 180 and submitted by the sponsor on or before day 210.
- FDA will review and act on 90% of NADAs within 345 days of the submission date for applications with an ERA requested by the agency on or before day 180 and submitted by the sponsor on or before day 210.

If ONADE determines the NADA information shows the product is safe and effective for its intended use, it makes a recommendation to the CVM director. If the director agrees with the recommendation, the application is approved, a notice of the approval is published in the *Federal Register* and the new animal drug is listed in the pertinent section of 21 CFR 520–529.

Each approved animal drug manufacturer must submit information to FDA regarding patents covering the animal drug or its intended method of use and the agency is required to make this information public. The *Generic Animal Drug and Patent Term Restoration Act* of 1988 (*GADPTRA*) provides market exclusivity periods to products newly approved under NADAs, similar to the exclusivity awarded to certain newly approved drugs for human use to allow recovery of patent term time lost during clinical development and review. New animal drugs typically have five years of marketing exclusivity. FDA publishes a list of all animal drug products approved for safety and effectiveness, and updates the list monthly. This list of Approved Animal Drug Products, the *Green Book*, is available on FDA's website.[5]

ANADA

A generic animal drug is one with the same ingredients in the same concentrations and bioequivalent to the approved Reference Listed New Animal Drug (RLNAD). CVM cannot approve generic versions of drugs still protected by patent or marketing exclusivity and will not review an ANADA until the RLNAD has been marketed for four of the five exclusivity period years. Further, the center will not approve ANADAs based on drugs withdrawn from the market for safety or efficacy reasons. Bioequivalence studies are performed under a Generic Investigational New Animal Drug (JINAD) filing, which is similar to INAD requirements. Suitability petitions may be requested for products differing from the RLNAD in strength, dosage form, route of administration or components.

The ANADA contains the following information: [6]

- RLNAD identity
- RLNAD patent status
- copies of RLNAD labeling and proposed generic drug labeling
- ingredient list, which should be identical unless a suitability petition is included
- bioequivalence data or bioequivalence waiver
- human food safety data, as applicable
- CMC
- environmental impact assessment
- FOI summary

Generic drug applications are subject to user fees and performance standards under the *Animal Generic Drug User Fee Act* (*AGDUFA*). The Fiscal 2015 user fee is $189,200 for certain active drug combinations requiring clinical data per 21 U.S.C. 360b(d)(4) and $94,600 for all other applications. The following performance goals have been established for 2014–18:[7]

- Refuse to File notification will occur within 30 days from date of submission for applications insufficient or otherwise unacceptable quality for review.
- Refuse to Review notifications for insufficient JINADs will occur within 60 days of submission.
- FDA will review and act on 90% of ANADAs within 270 days of date of submission.
- FDA will review and act on 90% of JINAD protocols without substantial data within 100 days.
- FDA will review and act on 90% of JINAD scientific data sections within 270 days.
- FDA will review and act on 90% of Administrative ANADAs after review of JINAD files within 100 days of submission.

Postapproval Changes

Per 21 CFR 514.8, the sponsor of an approved NADA or ANADA must notify FDA of each change in any condition established in the application beyond those variations provided for in the application to ensure the marketed product still meets safety and efficacy requirements. Changes may include, but are not limited to: manufacturers, manufacturing process, equipment, composition, specifications or analytical methods. The notification type and supporting data requirements are based on the type of change and its potential to impact the drug's quality, identity, safety, purity and potency.[8] Major and moderate changes require a supplement to be submitted prior to marketing the changed product; minor changes may be reported in the annual Minor Changes and Stability Report (MCSR).

There are four reporting categories for postapproval changes:

- Prior Approval Supplement (PAS)—For major changes, the sponsor submits a supplement that CVM must approve before the drug manufactured with the change may be distributed.
- Changes Being Effected in 30 Days Supplement (CBE-30)—For moderate changes, the sponsor submits a supplement and, if there is no response from CVM within 30 days of receiving the supplement, the drug manufactured with the change may be distributed.
- Changes Being Effected Supplement (CBE)—For moderate changes, the sponsor submits a supplement and may distribute the drug made using the change upon CVM's receipt of the supplement.
- Annual Report—Minor changes made during the year may be documented in the MCSR. The drug may be distributed prior to CVM notification.

Adverse Event Reporting and Postapproval Reporting

After approval, the sponsor of an approved NADA or ANADA is responsible for continued product monitoring and reporting per all provisions outlined in 21 CFR 514.80.[9] Manufacturers must report serious, unexpected adverse events to CVM within 15 working days of becoming aware of them. The manufacturer must investigate the event and submit a follow up report. These events are reported on the Veterinary Adverse Drug Reaction, Lack of Effectiveness, Product Defect Report (Form FDA 1932) and submitted through the FDA electronic gateway.[10] Manufacturers also must submit Transmittal of Periodic Reports and Promotional Material for New Animal Drugs periodically, reporting postmarketing surveillance experience and other information for new animal drugs every six months for the first two years after the drug's approval and annually thereafter.[11]

In addition, product and manufacturing defects or failures related to stability must be reported to the FDA District Field Office or local FDA resident post within three working days of the manufacturer becoming aware a defect may exist. The manufacturer may initially submit information via telephone, and follow up with submission of Form FDA 1932.

Minor Use Minor Species (MUMS)

The *MUMS Act* of 2004 is similar in principle to the human *Orphan Drug Act*. It provides incentives to sponsors to address the lack of FDA-approved drugs for treating rare disorders of major veterinary species (minor use) and less-common animal species (minor species) under a veterinarian's care.[12]

MUMS defines minor species as all animals other than major species (cattle, horses, swine, chickens, turkeys, dogs and cats). Minor species include zoo animals, ornamental fish, parrots, ferrets and guinea pigs. Some animals of agricultural importance also are considered minor species for the purpose of MUMS, including sheep, goats, consumable fish and honeybees. The *MUMS Act* creates three major incentives: conditional approval, indexing and designation.

Conditional Approval

A sponsor of a veterinary drug for a minor use or minor species can apply for conditional approval, allowing the sponsor to market the drug before collecting all necessary effectiveness data but only after demonstrating the drug is safe in accordance with FDA standards and has a reasonable expectation of efficacy. The drug sponsor can keep the product on the market for up to five years through annual renewals while collecting the required efficacy data. This provision is managed by ONADE.

Indexing

CVM can designate unapproved new drugs as legally marketed for a minor species by adding the intended use to the Index of Legally Marketed Unapproved New Animal Drugs for Minor Species (the Index). Standards and procedures to establish the index are contained in 21 CFR 516. The index is published on FDA's website and maintained by the Office of Minor Use and Minor Species Animal Drug Development.[13,14] Under the Indexing rule, CVM:

- grants investigational exemptions for indexing purposes
- determines new animal drug eligibility for indexing consideration
- approves the selection of qualified expert panels to review drug safety and efficacy data
- reviews expert panels' findings, issues final decisions and publishes the index

Designation

Similar to *Orphan Drug Act* provisions for human drugs, CVM may designate a drug as eligible for monetary incentives and extended marketing exclusivity. The manufacturer of the drug under development for a minor use or minor species is eligible for safety and effectiveness data development grants and seven years of marketing exclusivity upon the drug's approval or conditional approval for the minor use or minor species.[15]

Labeling

Veterinary drug labeling is submitted for FDA approval in the NADA or ANADA application. Animal drug labels are required to contain the same elements as human drug labels per 21 CFR 201. Additionally, the label must state the condition for use and the product is for "veterinary use only." FDA-approved drugs also display the NADA number or ANADA number. Veterinary labeling follows the Structured Product Labeling format and may be submitted electronically through FDA's electronic listing system.[16]

Over-the-Counter Products

Upon application review, FDA will determine whether the drug's status is over-the-counter (OTC) or prescription. A prescription product can be dispensed only by order of a licensed veterinarian. An OTC drug may be used safely and effectively without a veterinarian's supervision with adequate directions for use. Prescription animal drugs are labeled with an "Rx," and the package label must state: "Caution: Federal law restricts this drug to use by or on the order of a licensed veterinarian." New animal drug listings in 21 CFR 520– 529 describe the specification, conditions for use and indications for use, and describe whether the product is limited to use by prescription.[17]

Scheduled Drugs

Like human drugs, veterinary drugs containing an active ingredient with a high potential for human abuse and/or dependence may be classified as a controlled substance. When a new animal drug has a stimulant, depressant or hallucinogenic effect on the central nervous system and may have potential for abuse, FDA will forward the application information to the attorney general to determine whether the drug is to be scheduled.[18] In addition to FDA regulations, controlled substance manufacture and distribution is enforced by the US Drug Enforcement Agency (DEA). Scheduled drugs are classified as Schedule I, II, III, IV or V, with Schedule I products having the highest potential for abuse and dependence and Schedule V having the lowest potential. Manufacturers, distributors, dispensers and practitioners are required to have a controlled substance license, security practices and appropriate distribution records relating to controlled substances. The scheduled drug's label must contain the DEA schedule in addition to all other required label elements.[19]

Veterinary Master Files

Veterinary Master Files (VMF) are equivalent to Drug Master Files (DMF) and contain specific technical information for a facility, component or process used in a veterinary drug's manufacture. For ANADAs or NADAs, the sponsor may reference a DMF or a VMF by obtaining a Letter of Authorization from the DMF or VMF holder. This letter authorizes FDA to review the VMF's data to support the animal drug application while protecting any confidential information the VMF contains. The VMF is neither approved nor disapproved and is reviewed only when referenced in a new drug application. VMF types are aligned to DMF types and currently not subject to user fees. A VMF database is maintained on FDA's website. VMFs may be inactivated or withdrawn at the holder's request. An annual update is required for VMFs, and the file is withdrawn if it has not been updated in five years.[20, 21]

Veterinary Master File types are:

- Type I: no longer used (formerly manufacturing site, facilities, operating procedures and personnel)
- Type II: manufacturing information for bulk drug substance or intermediates used in the manufacture of the bulk drug substance, medicated articles, medicated feeds or manufacturing information for finished dosage forms
- Type III: packaging materials
- Type IV: excipient, color, flavor, essence or material used in product preparation
- Type V: manufacturing site, facilities, personnel, operating procedures and sterilization process validation to support sterile dosage form and sterile bulk drug manufacture

Electronic Submissions

In 2011, FDA introduced an electronic gateway for veterinary product submissions. To register for the CVM Electronic Submission System, Form FDA 3538 must be submitted to the agency. The following documents and applications may be submitted through the Electronic Submission Gateway, and templates for the eSubmitter are available on FDA's website:[22,23]

- INAD and JINAD
- NADA and ANADA
- NCIE
- adverse event reports

Drug Compliance

Licenses, Registrations and Fees

Drug establishments must register first with FDA through the Electronic Drug Registration and Listing System (eDRLS) within five days of beginning operations and renew registration annually between 1 October and 31 December of each year.[24] Firms must list any drug products and submit labeling through the Structured Product Listing (SPL) system.[25] At the time of the registration, the firm also will be responsible for the payment of annual establishment, sponsor and product fees per *ADUFA* and *AGDUFA*. For Fiscal 2015:

- *ADUFA* annual establishment fee is $104,150, the sponsor fee is $94,450 and the product fee is $8,075.
- *AGUDFA* sponsor fees are prorated based on the number of approved abbreviated applications and range from $40,450 to $80,900; the product fee is $8,500.[26]

GMP Manufacturing and Inspections

Veterinary drugs are subject to the same CGMPs as human drugs in 21 CFR 211. Facility inspections are conducted regularly by FDA to verify establishments are operating under CGMPs; inspections also may be for-cause or preapproval (PAI) for new drug applications. FDA maintains Compliance Policy Guides (CPG) explaining current agency policies on regulatory issues and to guide inspection staff on standards to be applied when assessing compliance. Veterinary CPGs can be found in Chapter 6 of CVM's Compliance Manual.[27] CVM's Compliance Program Manuals, while non-binding to the public, instruct FDA inspectors how to conduct inspections and may be referenced by an establishment when preparing for an inspection.[28]

Additional Standards

United States Pharmacopoeia (USP)

USP and the *National Formulary* (*NF*) are recognized as the official US compendia for human and animal drugs under the *FD&C Act*. The two compendia are published together as the *USP-NF*. Monographs for drug substances and formulations are contained in the *USP*, and excipient monographs are contained in the *NF*.

Under *FD&C Act* requirements, ingredients, manufactured products and compounded preparations must have the strength, quality and purity specified in the relevant *USP* and *NF* monographs. The monographs include the ingredient or preparation name; definition; packaging; storage and labeling requirements; and the specification. The specification is a series of analytical tests, procedures and acceptance criteria. Certain tests and procedures require the use of official *USP* Reference Standards. *USP-NF* general chapters describe in detail analytical tests and procedures referenced in multiple monographs.

International Cooperation on Harmonization of Technical Requirements for Registration of Veterinary Medicinal Product (VICH)

VICH harmonizes requirements among the US, Japan and the EU, similar to the International Conference for Harmonisation's (ICH) role for human medicines. VICH publishes guidelines on topics such as biologics, pharmaceuticals, pharmacovigilance, quality, safety and efficacy on its website.[29] Additionally, draft guidelines are published for stakeholder feedback. FDA aligns with and adopts the standards and requirements contained in the VICH and many CVM guidance documents for data requirements in new animal drug applications are based on VICH.

Extra-Label Use and Illegal Residues

The *Animal Medicinal Drug Use Clarification Act* of 1994 (*AMDUCA*) allows veterinarians to prescribe certain approved animal drugs for extra-label uses and approved human drugs for animals under certain conditions. Extra-label use refers to the use of an approved drug in a manner not in accordance with the approved labeling.

Under *AMDUCA*, any extra-label use must be by or on the order of a veterinarian in accordance with an appropriate medical rationale, must not result in violative residues in food-producing animals and must be in conformance with additional restrictions in 21 CFR 530.[30] Specific drugs identified in 21 CFR 530.41 are prohibited from extra-label use. To avoid volatile residues in food-producing animal products, veterinarians may obtain appropriate withdrawal times for drugs administered extra-label by consulting the Food Animal Residue Avoidance Databank (FARAD), a congressionally mandated risk management program under USDA jurisdiction and supported by several universities.[31]

Per 21 CFR 530.13, an animal drug may be compounded from an approved animal or human drug if no animal or human drug is available in the correct dosage form or concentration. The compounding operation must utilize adequate processes and procedures to ensure the product is safe and effective, and be of appropriate scale (e.g., the compounding pharmacy should not be producing products at a manufacturing scale without approved prescriptions, as they are not operating as a manufacturer under CGMP).[32]

USDA's Food Safety and Inspection Service (FSIS) is responsible for inspecting meat and poultry products in slaughter and egg processing plants and establishments that further process meat and poultry products to ensure the wholesomeness of these products. FSIS reports detection of violative drug residues in meat and poultry to CVM. In the event unapproved drugs or illegal amounts of drug residue are found in tissues of food-producing animals, the responsible operator is subject to enforcement action by FDA, including Warning Letters.

Animal Feeds, Medicated Feeds and Type A Medicated Articles

Feeds are intended either solely to meet an animal's nutritional requirements (non-medicated feeds) or as a means to administer drugs (medicated feeds) orally. CVM is responsible for both non-medicated animal feeds, including pet foods, and medicated feeds.

Animal feeds, like human foods, must be pure and wholesome, contain no harmful or deleterious substances, and be labeled truthfully per 21 CFR 501. Additionally, canned pet foods must be processed in conformance with the low-acid canned food regulations per 21 CFR 113. Non-medicated animal feeds generally do not require FDA approval before they are marketed, provided they are made from either approved food additive ingredients per 21 CFR 573 or those generally recognized as safe (GRAS) for their intended use per 21 CFR 582. The *Dietary Supplement and Health Education Act* (*DSHEA*) does not apply to animal nutritional supplements.[33] Substances marketed as human dietary supplements fall under the pre-*DSHEA* regulatory scheme when marketed for animals and are considered food, food additives, GRAS items or new animal drugs, depending on their intended use. However, CVM often has exercised regulatory discretion and waived food additive petitions or NADAs for such articles when they are determined not to present animal or human safety concerns.

If a food substance, other than a food, is intended to treat or prevent disease or to affect the body's structure or function, it falls within the *FD&C Act*'s definition of a drug and is subject to an approved NADA before it can be marketed. Under 21 CFR 558, FDA recognizes Type A Medicated Articles, Type B Medicated Feeds and Type C Medicated Feeds, which are required to be listed in the eDRLS.

Drugs for use in food are subject to the Veterinary Feed Directive (VFD) and are categorized as VFD drugs. These drugs are available only under a veterinarian's direction and supervision. The veterinarian issues a VFD order to the client, and the order is filled by a licensed VFD manufacturer or distributor. The client, veterinarian and manufacturer all maintain VFD order records. Extra-label VFD drug use by anyone, including veterinarians, is prohibited.[34]

Type A Medicated Articles are mixtures of one or more drug substance(s) with suitable vehicles. They are used to facilitate active drug component dilution and admixture with animal feed before administration. The manufacture of a Type A Medicated Article requires CVM approval of either an NADA or ANADA. Type A Medicated Articles are divided into two categories. Category I includes those drugs that require no withdrawal period at the lowest use level in each species for which they are approved. Category II includes those drugs that require a withdrawal period at the lowest level for at least one species for which they are approved, or are regulated on a "no-residue" basis or with zero tolerance due to drug residue carcinogen concerns. Type A Medicated Articles are intended solely for use in manufacturing another Type A Article (e.g., mixing two Type A Medicated Articles containing different drug substances to manufacture a third Type A Medicated Article) or a Type B or Type C Medicated Feed. Labeling for the Type B and Type C Medicated Feeds utilizing a Type A medicated article is required to be included with the NADA. Type A Medicated Article CGMPs are found in 21 CFR 226.

Type B Medicated Feeds contain either a Type A Medicated Article or another Type B Medicated Feed, plus a substantial quantity of nutrients (not less than 25% of the total weight), and are intended solely for use in manufacturing another Type B Medicated Feed or a Type C Medicated Feed. Before being fed to animals, a Type B Medicated Feed must be diluted substantially with one or more nutrients to produce a nutritionally appropriate and medically safe Type C Medicated Feed for administration.

Type C Medicated Feed contains an active drug component(s) and is intended either to be offered as a complete animal feed, administered on top of other feed or offered free-choice in conjunction with other feed to supplement the animal's total daily ration. Type C Mediated Feed is produced by substantially diluting a Type A Medicated Article, a Type B Medicated Feed or another Type C Medicated Feed. Medicated feed CGMPs are found in 21 CFR 225.

Feed manufacturing facilities must hold a medicated feed mill license to manufacture a Type B or Type C Medicated Feed from Category II, Type A Medicated Articles. No license is required if drug use is limited to Category I drugs (all types) and Type B sources of Category II drugs. FDA routinely inspects medicated feed mills and Type A Medicated Article manufacturers.[35]

Veterinary Devices

CVM has jurisdiction over medical devices for veterinary use; however, these devices are given regulatory discretion and are not subject to the same premarket approval, registration and listing requirements as medical devices intended for use in humans. Veterinary devices are not subject to performance standards.

Veterinary devices that are not safe, effective or properly labeled are deemed to be adulterated and/or misbranded under *FD&C Act* Sections 501 and 502. Thus, it is the manufacturer and/or distributor's responsibility to ensure these veterinary devices are safe, effective and properly labeled. Veterinary device labeling must not be false or misleading and must bear directions for use adequate for each target animal group for which the device is intended. Devices not complying with the *FD&C Act* may be subject to seizure, and firms and individuals responsible for marketing these illegal devices may be subject to other penalties under the act, including fines.[36]

Although the Quality System Regulation for devices outlined in 21 CFR 820 is applicable only to medical devices for humans, CVM recommends ≠veterinary device manufacturers become familiar with these regulations and be guided by them in manufacturing and assembling their devices. CVM also recommends labeling be submitted for agency review to avoid misbranding.

Diagnostics used in safety testing of foods derived from animals may be regulated by the Center for Food Safety and Applied Nutrition (CFSAN) under product-specific regulations and guidelines. Additionally, veterinary electronic devices emitting radiation are subject to the *Radiation Control for Health and Safety Act* of 1968, which contains various performance and safety standards, and must be registered with the Center for Devices and Radiologic Health (CDRH).

Grooming Aids

Cosmetic articles intended to cleanse and beautify animals are referred to as animal grooming aids. Grooming aids formulated only to cleanse or beautify animals are not subject to federal regulation, as the *FD&C Act* definition of cosmetic applies only to articles for use in humans. CVM is concerned with the safety of such products and tracks complaints and adverse reactions. If animal grooming aids are labeled with direct or implied therapeutic claims, they may fall under the definition of drugs under the *FD&C Act*.

Guidance Documents and Current Agency Initiatives

CVM maintains a database of non-binding guidance documents available on FDA's website, representing the agency's current thinking on a variety of topics related to veterinary products.

FDA and global regulatory authorities currently are focused on the judicious use of antibiotics in food-producing animals. Antimicrobial products historically have been used in animal food and feed for production purposes such as weight gain. As many of these antibiotics also may be used in humans, the overuse in animals may promote the development of drug resistant bacteria. FDA is working with industry to revise labeling to remove production indications for certain drugs and to ensure certain antibiotics are only used under the direction of a licensed veterinarian.. More information on this initiative can be found in *Guidance for Industry 213*.[37,38]

Unapproved animal drugs remain a priority for FDA. Some veterinary drugs on the market, including those listed under FDA establishment registrations, are not the subjects of approved NADAs or ANADAs and have not demonstrated safety and efficacy. Many of these have historical precedence for use, and in some cases, are the standards of care, although they are not grandfathered or on the GRAS list. FDA encourages manufacturers to submit applications for New Animal Drugs, and manufacturers of unapproved drugs have received Warning Letters requiring marketing to be halted until an application is submitted and approved. FDA plans to develop a CVM guidance document on marketed unapproved new animal drugs in 2015.[39,40]

Biologics

Veterinary biologics are defined in the *Virus-Serum-Toxin Act* (*VSTA*) as viruses, serums, toxins or analogous products of natural or synthetic origin intended for use in the treatment of animals and acting primarily through the direct stimulation, supplementation, enhancement or modulation of the immune system or immune response.[41] USDA is responsible for the approval and regulation of veterinary biologics that act through an immunological or otherwise unknown mechanism, regardless of the target species (e.g., products for both companion and production animals are regulated through USDA). CVM is responsible for regulating products of biologic origin meeting the *FD&C* definition of drugs, and not acting through an immunological mechanism, including antimicrobials, corticosteroids and hormones. A Memorandum of Understanding between FDA and USDA details specific product category jurisdiction and provides a process in the event a product in development requires jurisdictional clarification.[42] Veterinary biologics regulated by FDA are under CVM jurisdiction and follow the same regulatory and approval pathway as other animal drugs.

USDA Veterinary Biologics

USDA veterinary biologics are regulated by the Center for Veterinary Biologics (CVB) in the Animal and Plant Health Inspection Service (APHIS). CVB enforces *VSTA* provisions to ensure pure, safe, potent and effective veterinary biologics are available for the diagnosis, prevention and treatment of animal diseases. CVB develops or approves appropriate product release standards and procedures, issues licenses and permits, monitors and inspects products and facilities and controls veterinary biologic field tests and batch release.

Biological Product License

To manufacture and distribute a veterinary biologic in the US, a US Veterinary Biologics Establishment License and US Veterinary Biological Product License are required. The establishment license is obtained in conjunction with the product license (e.g., an establishment license will not be issued without an associated product). The Veterinary Biological Product License application requirements are outlined in Veterinary Services (VS) Memorandum 800.50. This memorandum references several other VS Memoranda and regulations providing specific instructions and guidance for the preparation of each of the following items to be included in the application: [43]

- APHIS Form 2003 Application for US Veterinary Biological Product License
- production outline
- master seed and cell reports for each microorganism and cell stock used in the production of biological products (Reports describe testing performed to evaluate purity, identity and safety of seed and cell, source and passage history.)
- Summary Information Formats (SIFs) for master seeds to be used in producing new live biological products and those produced by recombinant DNA technology (The SIF includes safety and identity data including biocontainment requirements.)

- protocols for studies of host animal immunogenicity, safety, backpassage, shed/spread and interference (It is recommended the protocols are submitted to the CVB for comments 60 days prior to conducting the study.)

Applicants also must submit product development data and information including:

- in-process procedures and corresponding validation reports
- host animal immunogenicity/efficacy reports
- potency test development reports
- product safety reports
- stability reports
- APHIS Form 2008-Veterinary Biologics Production and Test Reports for prelicensing serials (numbered lots) of product (three consecutive serials)
- labeling and data to support approval of label claims

CVB does not require a product license application to be submitted as one complete package. Instead, applicants may submit individual, completed licensing sections for technical review. For example, the applicant may submit the license application and outline of production, field safety and labeling separately when the necessary data and information have been compiled for each.

CVB's Policy, Evaluation and Licensing unit (CVB-PEL) reviews production facility and biological product license applications and issues licenses. This unit also reviews product importation permit applications and establishes licensing, testing and permit requirements and procedures.

During the application process, product samples are selected and shipped to CVB as described in 9 CFR 113.3. CVB-PEL laboratories conduct prelicense testing, test development and standardization and postlicense quality control monitoring. During prelicense testing, the laboratories assay parent materials (master seeds and cells) and final product. CVB-PEL tests master seed and master cell stock purity and identity. Initial product serials are tested for purity and potency to ensure quality product is reproducible and product tests are appropriate and transferrable.[44]

The *VSTA* does not require ingredients and manufactured products to conform to *USP* and *NF* monograph standards. Instead, the manufacturer must test all serials in accordance with the filed outline of production prior to sale and report results to CVB's Inspection and Compliance (CVB-IC) unit. Results are compared with CVB-PEL testing. Certain serials are selected for additional CVB-PEL testing, and each satisfactory batch is released by CVB-IC for market distribution. CVB-IC is responsible for facilities inspections, product inspections and oversight of adverse event reporting and investigations.

Labeling

Veterinary biologics' labeling requirements are specified in 9 CFR 112. Finished product labels include:[45]

- product name as filed in the product license
- name and address of producer and US permittee if product is manufactured by a foreign establishment
- product license or permit number assigned by USDA
- storage temperature recommendation
- full instructions on proper use
- applicable warning statements
- recommendation for use in food-producing animals
- expiry date, doses, recoverable quantity of the final container and serial number
- restriction statement, such as restricted to use by veterinarian

Biologics Establishment License

All domestic facilities producing USDA-regulated veterinary biologics must obtain a US Veterinary Biologics Establishment License. Facilities are subject to initial and periodic USDA inspection. To maintain the license, the establishment must be manufacturing an approved veterinary biologic product. If a facility has not manufactured a biologic product in five years, the license is forfeited. The requirements for initial licensure are outlined in 9 CFR 102.3 and VS Memorandum 800.50:[46]

- APHIS Form 2001, Application for US Veterinary Biologics Establishment License
- articles of incorporation for applicant and applicable subsidiaries
- water quality statement
- APHIS Form 2003 and supporting documents for US Veterinary Biological Product License
- APHIS Form 2007, Qualifications of Veterinary Biologics Personnel
- facility blueprints

After reviewing the establishment license application and supporting documents, CVB-IC will inspect the facility before licensure. The license is issued only when the product to be manufactured in the establishment is qualified for licensure.

Imports and Exports

Licensed veterinary biologics may be exported by domestic veterinary biologics facilities. Export certificates for these products may be obtained by submitting APHIS form 2017 to CVBIC per 9 CFR 112.2 (e). Further guidance on this procedure may be found in VS Memo 800.52.[47]

The requirements for importing veterinary biologics are outlined in 9 CFR 104. Imports are distributed under a Veterinary Biological Product Permit for distribution and sale. Each product shipment is required to be accompanied by a copy of the permit. Unlike domestically manufactured products, Biologics Establishment Licenses and Biological Product Licenses are not issued to the manufacturer. A US permittee residing in or owning a business in the US is responsible for the application, compliance and handling of the imported product. Veterinary Biological Product Permit requirements are listed in VS Memo 800.101:[48]

- The foreign manufacturer is required to undergo USDA inspection within 24 months of product sale, and at any time the facility changes significantly, at the permittee's expense.
- The imported Veterinary Biologic Permit Application is contained in APHIS Form 2005. Much of the data required for the Biologics Product License are required for the permit, with the following additions:
  - o studies for adjuvant safety, field safety and diagnostic kit field evaluation based on US data
  - o Summary of Information Format for each master seed, master cell and final or finished product for products that must assess risk of introduction of foreign animal disease
  - o certification the product is originating from a region free from certain transmittable animal diseases per 9 CFR 94

A permittee number is assigned for all products imported from the same source. The permittee is responsible for establishing a US quarantine facility to hold the serial until it is released by CVB-IC for distribution. A permit may be revoked if the product has not been imported for five years.

Compliance

USDA-regulated veterinary biologics are not required to be manufactured to drug product CGMP per 21 CFR 211. The following are the analogous regulations for veterinary biologics:

- facility requirements per 9 CFR 108
- packaging and labeling requirements per 9 CFR 112
- production requirements per 9 CFR 114
- record and reporting requirements per 9 CFR 116

An adverse event, defined as any undesirable occurrence after the veterinary biologic product's use, including illness or reaction, may be reported to the product manufacturer or directly to CVB. Upon the report's receipt, USDA conducts an investigation to determine whether the product is deficient. In the event a marketed product fails to meet required regulatory standards, a recall must be issued within two days.

Pesticides Regulated by the Environmental Protection Agency

Pesticides administered to animals, including topical flea products, fly sprays, ear tags, insecticide dips and pesticide feeds are regulated by EPA under the *Federal Insecticide, Fungicide and Rodenticide Act* (*FIFRA*). A pesticide is defined as a substance or mixture of substances intended for preventing, destroying, repelling or mitigating any pests, excluding animal drugs, new animal drugs and animal feeds as defined per the *FD&C Act*.[49] Products used to treat internal parasites, or that treat external parasites but work systemically in an animal, are regulated as drugs, while products used to treat external parasites and applied externally are regulated as pesticides.

Pesticide regulations primarily are concerned with safety to humans handling the product and environmental impact from the product's manufacture, use and disposal. New pesticide product manufacturers are required to submit an application containing scientific data defined in 40 CFR 158 and 161. The application includes chemistry and manufacturing information, environmental risks and administrative information. Applications may be submitted electronically, and application fees are payable as defined in the *Pesticide Registration Improvement Act* (*PRIA*).[50]

When a new pesticide product is under development, or an existing product is intended for a use outside the current labeling, an experimental use permit is required for its shipment or sale. Experimental use permit requirements are outlined in 40 CFR 172. For animal products, tests may be conducted only on animals that will not be used for food or feed unless a product tolerance or exemption for tolerance exists.

Labeling requirements for pesticide products are outlined in 40 CFR 156. Labels must be placed conspicuously on the immediate container, be legible and in English. The label must include:[51]

- product name
- producer or registrant name and address
- net contents
- product registration number
- producing establishment number
- ingredient statement
- hazard and precautionary statements
- directions for use
- use classifications

Any establishment manufacturing pesticides is required to register as a pesticide-producing establishment with EPA (40 CFR 167) prior to beginning operations using Form EPA 3540-8. Establishments are assigned a unique number, and changes to any information submitted in the form must be reported within 30 days. Pesticide establishments are required to submit an initial report on manufacturing and distribution of pesticide products within 30 days of initial registration and annually thereafter, even if no pesticides are produced in a particular year. The establishment registration remains active until the producer requests its termination or the establishment fails to submit an annual report. Facility inspections are carried out by the federal or state EPA, and the inspection frequency varies based on the local jurisdiction's policies.[52]

EPA regulates the import and export of pesticide products. All imported pesticides for use in the US must be registered with EPA and labeled per EPA guidelines. A Notice of Arrival (NOA) Form 3540-1 must be submitted to the EPA regional office for approval prior to shipment and the approved form must accompany the shipment for customs review. Pesticides may be produced in the US for export only if they are not registered with EPA. These products require a signed statement from the foreign purchaser acknowledging the product's regulatory status in the US. This statement is shipment-specific for each exporter, product and foreign purchaser. The statement is filed with EPA, and a copy is transmitted to the authority of the foreign purchaser.[53]

The *FD&C Act* authorizes EPA to set maximum pesticide residue limits for foods or animal feed. Pesticide residues in foods are monitored, and the limits are enforced by FDA (fruits and vegetables, seafood) and USDA's FSIS (meat, milk, poultry, eggs and agricultural foods). Extra-label or unregistered pesticide use is prohibited unless EPA grants an emergency exception.

Summary

- Veterinary products in the US include drugs, biologics, food and medicated feeds, devices, grooming aids and pest control products.
- Veterinary product regulations and marketing approvals vary not only by product type, but whether the intended use is for companion animals, food-producing animals or minor species.
- New animal drugs are reviewed and approved by CVM through the submission of an NADA.
- *GADPTRA* requires a generic animal drug product sponsor to submit and receive approval of an ANADA prior to marketing.
- Animal drugs must be produced under CGMP conditions per 21 CFR 211.
- Animal foods and medicated feeds are regulated by CVM. Non-medicated animal foods typically do not require premarket approval. Type A Medicated Articles are subject to NADA and ANADA applications. Type B and C Medicated feeds require special labeling and use under the VFD.
- Veterinary medical devices are subject to regulatory discretion.
- Animal grooming aids intended to cleanse and beautify animals are not regulated by FDA but may be considered new animal drugs if they have direct or implied therapeutic claims.
- Veterinary biologics are licensed through USDA's CVB, which is responsible for licensing the facility and the product. Samples of all licensed biological products are submitted to CVB for testing and approval prior to sale.
- Veterinary products applied to treat external pests and insects are considered pesticides and are regulated by EPA.

Disclaimer: Adria Tyndall's contribution was provided based on her individual knowledge and expertise. Her participation in preparing this chapter should not be construed as a statement or opinion by Catalent Pharma Solutions on this topic.

References

1. 21 CFR 511. FDA website. http://www.accessdata.fda.gov/scripts/cdrh/cfdocs/cfcfr/CFRSearch.cfm?fr=511.1. Accessed 9 March 2015.
2. CVM *Draft Guidance for Industry 227: Two Phased Chemistry, Manufacturing and Controls.* October 2014. FDA website. http://www.fda.gov/downloads/AnimalVeterinary/GuidanceComplianceEnforcement/GuidanceforIndustry/UCM419043.pdf. Accessed 9 March 2015.
3. 21 CFR 514. FDA website. http://www.accessdata.fda.gov/scripts/cdrh/cfdocs/cfcfr/CFRSearch.cfm?fr=514.1. Accessed 9 March 2015.
4. *Animal Drug User Fee Act Reauthorization Performance Goals and Procedures-Fiscal Years 2014 through 2018.* FDA website. http://www.fda.gov/downloads/ForIndustry/UserFees/AnimalDrugUserFeeActADUFA/UCM343226.pdf. Accessed 9 March 2015.
5. Approved Animal Drug Products (*Green Book*). FDA website. http://www.fda.gov/AnimalVeterinary/Products/ApprovedAnimalDrugProducts/default.htm. Accessed 9 March 2015.
6. *Generic Animal Drug and Patent Term Restoration Act* (*GADPTRA*). FDA website. http://www.fda.gov/AnimalVeterinary/GuidanceComplianceEnforcement/ActsRulesRegulations/ucm049100.htm. Accessed 9 March 2015.
7. *Animal Generic Drug User Fee Act Reauthorization Performance Goals and Procedures Fiscal Years 2014 through 2018.* FDA website. http://www.fda.gov/downloads/ForIndustry/UserFees/AnimalGenericDrugUserFeeActAGDUFA/UCM343235.pdf. Accessed 9 March 2015.
8. *Guidance for Industry 83: Chemistry Manufacturing and Controls Changes to an Approved NADA/ANADA.* May 2007. http://www.fda.gov/downloads/AnimalVeterinary/GuidanceComplianceEnforcement/GuidanceforIndustry/UCM052415.pdf. Accessed 9 March 2015.
9. 21 CFR 514.80. FDA website. http://www.accessdata.fda.gov/scripts/cdrh/cfdocs/cfcfr/CFRSearch.cfm?fr=514.80. Accessed 9 March 2015.
10. Veterinary Adverse Event Reporting for Manufacturers. FDA Website. http://www.fda.gov/AnimalVeterinary/SafetyHealth/ReportaProblem/ucm212682.htm. Accessed 9 March 2015.
11. Op cit 9.
12. "Designation of New Animal Drugs for Minor Uses or Minor Species: Final Rule." *Federal Register* Volume 72:143, 26 July 2007. http://www.gpo.gov/fdsys/pkg/FR-2007-07-26/html/E7-14444.htm. Accessed 9 March 2015.
13. Drug Indexing. FDA website. http://www.fda.gov/AnimalVeterinary/DevelopmentApprovalProcess/MinorUseMinorSpecies/ucm070206.htm. Accessed 09 March 2015.
14. *Guidance for Industry 201: Small Entities Compliance Guide. The Index of Legally Marketed Unapproved Animal Drugs for Minor Species.* July 2014. http://www.fda.gov/downloads/AnimalVeterinary/GuidanceComplianceEnforcement/GuidanceforIndustry/UCM224589.pdf. Accessed 9 March 2015.
15. *Guidance for Industry 200: Small Entities Compliance Guide. Designation of New Animal Drugs for Minor Uses/Minor Species.*

July 2014. http://www.fda.gov/downloads/AnimalVeterinary/GuidanceComplianceEnforcement/GuidanceforIndustry/UCM224588.pdf. Accessed 9 March 2015.
16. Electronic Animal Drug Product Listing Directory. FDA website. http://www.fda.gov/ForIndustry/DataStandards/StructuredProductLabeling/ucm191015.htm. Accessed 9 March 2015.
17. Animal Drugs. FDA website. http://www.fda.gov/AnimalVeterinary/ResourcesforYou/ucm268128.htm. Accessed 10 March 2015.
18. Op cit 3.
19. 21 CFR 1300, Definitions. FDA website. http://www.accessdata.fda.gov/scripts/cdrh/cfdocs/cfcfr/CFRSearch.cfm?CFRPart=1300&showFR=1. Accessed 10 March 2015.
20. Veterinary Master Files. FDA website. http://www.fda.gov/AnimalVeterinary/DevelopmentApprovalProcess/ucm071808.htm. Accessed 10 March 2015.
21. *Guidance for Industry 57: Preparation and Submission of Veterinary Master Files.* January 1995. FDA website. http://www.fda.gov/downloads/AnimalVeterinary/GuidanceComplianceEnforcement/GuidanceforIndustry/UCM052373.pdf. Accessed 10 March 2015.
22. *Guidance for Industry 108: How to Register with the CVM Electronic Submission System to Submit Information in Electronic Format Using the FDA Electronic Submissions Gateway.* February 2013. FDA website. http://www.fda.gov/downloads/AnimalVeterinary/GuidanceComplianceEnforcement/GuidanceforIndustry/UCM052649.pdf. Accessed 10 March 2015.
23. Electronic Submissions. FDA website. http://www.fda.gov/AnimalVeterinary/DevelopmentApprovalProcess/ElectronicSubmissions/default.htm. Accessed 10 March 2015.
24. 21 CFR 207. FDA website. http://www.accessdata.fda.gov/scripts/cdrh/cfdocs/cfcfr/CFRSearch.cfm?CFRPart=207&showFR=1. Accessed 10 March 2015.
25. Op cit 16.
26. "FDA Announces FY 2015 Animal Drug User Fee Rates for ADUFA and AGDUFA." July 2014. FDA website. http://www.fda.gov/AnimalVeterinary/NewsEvents/CVMUpdates/ucm407375.htm. Accessed 10 March 2015.
27. Compliance Policy Guides, Chapter 6 –Veterinary Medicine. FDA website. http://www.fda.gov/ICECI/ComplianceManuals/CompliancePolicyGuidanceManual/ucm117042.htm. Accessed 10 March 2015.
28. CVM Compliance Programs. FDA website. http://www.fda.gov/AnimalVeterinary/GuidanceComplianceEnforcement/ComplianceEnforcement/ucm112583.htm. Accessed 10 March 2015.
29. VICH website. http://www.vichsec.org/. Accessed 10 March 2015.
30. 21 CFR 530. Extralabel Drug Use in Animals. FDA website. http://www.accessdata.fda.gov/scripts/cdrh/cfdocs/cfcfr/CFRSearch.cfm?CFRPart=530&showFR=1. Accessed 10 March 2015.
31. Food Animal Residue Avoidance Databank. www.farad.org. Accessed 10 March 2015.
32. Compliance Policy Guide Section 608.400. Compounding of Drugs for Use in Animals. FDA website. http://www.fda.gov/iceci/compliancemanuals/compliancepolicyguidancemanual/ucm074656.htm. Accessed 10 March 2015.
33. Docket 95N-0308, "Inapplicability of the Dietary Supplement Health and Education Act to Animal Products." *Federal Register* 61:78.22 April 1996. http://www.gpo.gov/fdsys/pkg/FR-1996-04-22/pdf/96-9780.pdf. Accessed 10 March 2015.
34. Veterinary Feed Directive. FDA website. http://www.fda.gov/AnimalVeterinary/DevelopmentApprovalProcess/ucm071807.htm. Accessed 10 March 2015.
35. Medicated Feeds. FDA website. http://www.fda.gov/AnimalVeterinary/Products/AnimalFoodFeeds/MedicatedFeed/default.htm. Accessed 10 March 2015.
36. How FDA Regulates Veterinary Devices. FDA website. http://www.fda.gov/AnimalVeterinary/ResourcesforYou/ucm047117.htm. Accessed 10 March 2015.
37. Judicious Use of Antimicrobials. FDA website. http://www.fda.gov/AnimalVeterinary/SafetyHealth/AntimicrobialResistance/JudiciousUseofAntimicrobials/default.htm. Accessed 10 March 2015.
38. *Guidance for Industry 213. New Animal Drugs and New Animal Drug Combination Products Administered in or on Medicated Feed or Drinking Water of Food-Producing Animals: Recommendations for Drug Sponsors for Voluntarily Aligning Product Use Conditions with GFI#209.* December 2013. http://www.fda.gov/downloads/AnimalVeterinary/GuidanceComplianceEnforcement/GuidanceforIndustry/UCM299624.pdf. Accessed 10 March 2015.
39. What You Need to Know: FDA-Approved vs. Unapproved Animal Drugs. FDA website. http://www.fda.gov/downloads/AnimalVeterinary/GuidanceComplianceEnforcement/ComplianceEnforcement/UnapprovedAnimalDrugs/UCM289711.pdf. Accessed 10 March 2015.
40. Guidances Under Development for 2015. FDA Website. http://www.fda.gov/AnimalVeterinary/GuidanceComplianceEnforcement/GuidanceforIndustry/ucm042451.htm. Accessed 10 March 2015.
41. 9 CFR 101.2. Definitions. US Government Printing Office Website. http://www.ecfr.gov/cgi-bin/text-idx?SID=2c898e688e33d3d393622 7187468e3f8&node=pt9.1.101&rgn=div5#se9.1.101_12. Accessed 11March 2015.
42. APHIS Agreement # 04-9100-0859-MU, FDA Serial # 225-05-7000, Memorandum of Understanding Between APHIS USDA and the FDA Department of Health and Human Services, February, 2013. http://www.aphis.usda.gov/animal_health/vet_biologics/publications/APHIS_FDA_biologics_MOU.pdf. Accessed 11 March 2015.
43. Veterinary Services Memorandum Number 800.50. February 2011. USDA website. http://www.aphis.usda.gov/animal_health/vet_biologics/publications/memo_800_50.pdf. Accessed 11 March 2015.
44. Policy Evaluation and Licensing Unit. USDA website. http://www.aphis.usda.gov/wps/portal/aphis/home/?urile=wcm%3apath%3a%2Faphis_content_library%2Fsa_our_focus%2Fsa_animal_health%2Fsa_vet_biologics%2Fsa_about_vb%2Fct_vb_pel. Accessed 11 March 2015
45. 9 CFR 112. Packaging and Labeling. US Government Printing Office website. http://www.ecfr.gov/cgi-bin/text-idx?SID=4b43932781726 1d2eb240c35161980d9&node=pt9.1.112&rgn=div5. Accessed 11 March 2015.
46. Op cit 43.
47. Veterinary Services Memorandum 800.52. April 2011. USDA website. http://www.aphis.usda.gov/animal_health/vet_biologics/publications/memo_800_52.pdf. Accessed 11 March 2015.
48. Veterinary Services Memorandum 800.101. June 2013. USDA website. http://www.aphis.usda.gov/animal_health/vet_biologics/publications/memo_800_101.pdf. Accessed 11 March 2015.
49. 40 CFR 152.3. Definitions. Government Printing Office website. http://www.ecfr.gov/cgi-bin/text-idx?tpl=/ecfrbrowse/Title40/40cfr152_main_02.tpl. Accessed 11 March 2015.
50. *PRIA* Fees. EPA website. http://www2.epa.gov/pria-fees/fy-201415-fee-schedule-registration-applications#registration. Accessed 11 March 2015.
51. 40 CFR 156. Labeling Requirements for Pesticides and Devices. Government Printing Office website. http://www.ecfr.gov/cgi-bin/text-idx?SID=6be8df12dc7bccf96b03df772662f526&node=pt40.2 4.156&rgn=div5 Accessed 11 March 2015.
52. Pesticide Establishment Registration and Reporting. EPA website. http://www2.epa.gov/compliance/pesticide-establishment-registration-and-reporting. Accessed 11 March 2015.
53. Import and Export Trade Requirements. EPA website. http://www.epa.gov/oppfead1/international/trade/. Accessed 11 March 2015.

Recommended Reading

CVM/ONADE Reviewer's Chapter. FDA website. http://www.fda.gov/animalveterinary/guidancecomplianceenforcement/policiesproceduresmanual/ucm046623.htm. Accessed 11 March 2015.

AAVPT/CVM Animal Drugs in Feeds Workshop May 2013. [Recording]. FDA website. http://www.fda.gov/animalveterinary/products/animalfoodfeeds/ucm355400.htm. Accessed 11 March 2015.

AAVPT Veterinary Drug Regulatory Life Cycle Course, March 2011. [Recording]. FDA website. http://www.fda.gov/AnimalVeterinary/DevelopmentApprovalProcess/ucm249768.htm. Accessed 11 March 2015.

Guidance for Industry. FDA website. http://www.fda.gov/AnimalVeterinary/GuidanceComplianceEnforcement/GuidanceforIndustry/default.htm. Accessed 11 March 2015.

American Veterinary Medical Association. AVMA website. https://www.avma.org/Pages/home.aspx. Accessed 11 March 2015.

Animal Health Institute. AHI website. http://www.ahi.org/. Accessed 11 March 2015.

Generic Animal Drug Alliance. GADA website. http://www.gadaonline.org/. Accessed 11 March 2015.

VICH. VICH website. http://www.vichsec.org/. Accessed 10 March 2015.

American Feed Industry Association. AFIA website. http://www.afia.org/. Accessed 11 March 2015.

Chapter 36

Food Products

Updated by Edward A. Steele, Charles Breen, Elizabeth Campbell, Robert Martin, PhD

OBJECTIVES

- ❑ Provide an overview of requirements for marketing an FDA-regulated food in the US
- ❑ Understand the basics of food labeling requirements and voluntary elements
- ❑ Develop a broad understanding of the mechanisms available for the use of new ingredients and color additives in compliance with regulatory requirements
- ❑ Explain food adulteration standards and major sanitation programs, including Good Manufacturing Practice, Hazard Analysis and Critical Control Point (HACCP) and Preventive Controls Mandated by the *Food Safety Modernization Act* (*FSMA*)
- ❑ Describe administrative requirements for food facilities, such as facility registration, prior notice, recordkeeping and reporting of reportable foods

LAWS, REGULATIONS AND GUIDELINES COVERED IN THIS CHAPTER

- ❑ *Federal Food, Drug, and Cosmetic Act* of 1938, as amended (codified at 21 USC §301 *et al*)
- ❑ Section 304 [21 USC §334]
- ❑ Section 321 Definitions
- ❑ Section 331 Prohibited Acts
- ❑ Sections 341–350f Food
- ❑ Section 374 Inspection
- ❑ Section 379e Color Additives
- ❑ *Guidance for Industry: Recommendations for Submission of Chemical and Technological Data for Direct Food Additive Petitions* (March 2006, revised March 2009)
- ❑ *Guidance for Industry: Summary Table of Recommended Toxicological Testing for Additives Used in Food* (June 2006)
- ❑ GAO Report: *Food Safety: FDA Should Strengthen Its Oversight of Food Ingredients Determined to Be Generally Recognized as Safe (GRAS)* (February 2010)
- ❑ GRAS Self-determination Inventory Database
- ❑ *Food Allergen Labeling and Consumer Protection Act* of 2004 (P.L. 108-282)
- ❑ *Public Health Security and Bioterrorism Preparedness and Response Act* of 2002 (P.L. 107-188)
- ❑ *Food and Drug Administration Modernization Act* of 1997 (P.L. 105-115)

- *Food Safety Modernization Act* of 2011 (Public Law 111-353)
- *Dietary Supplement Health Education Act* of 1994 (P.L. 103-417)
- *Nutrition Labeling and Education Act* of 1990 (P.L. 101-535)
- *Orphan Drug Act* of 1983, §5 (P.L. 97-414)
- FDA *FSMA Frequently Asked Questions, Proposed Rule cGMPs and HACCP for Human Foods* (March 2013)
- *Tariff Act* of 1930 (codified at 19 USC 1304)
- 9 CFR 317 Meat labeling, marking devices and containers
- 21 CFR 1 General enforcement regulations
- 21 CFR 7 Enforcement policy
- 21 CFR 70–82 Color additives
- 21 CFR 100–190 Food for human consumption
- FDA's Biotechnology Policy of 1992
- *Guidance for Industry: Regulation of Genetically Engineered Animals Containing Heritable Recombinant DNA Constructs* (January 2009)
- USDA's "A Guide to Federal Food Labeling Requirements for Meat and Poultry Products"(August 2007)
- *Food Action Defect Levels Handbook*
- *Guidance for Industry: A Food Labeling Guide* (Revised October 2009)
- *Guidance for Industry: Frequently Asked Questions About GRAS* (December 2004)
- *Foods Derived from Genetically Engineered Plants* (April 2013)
- *Summary of Qualified Health Claims Subject to Enforcement Discretion*
- *Guidance for Industry: Frequently Asked Questions About Medical Foods* (Revised May 2007)

Introduction

The US Food and Drug Administration (FDA) is the federal agency charged with regulation of most food and food-related products. FDA derives its authority to regulate foods primarily from the *Federal Food, Drug, and Cosmetic Act* of 1938 (*FD&C Act*), as amended.[1] The *FD&C Act* defines "food" broadly to mean:

> "(1) articles used for food or drink for man or other animals, (2) chewing gum, and (3) articles used for components of any such article."[2]

As a result of this broad definition, FDA's regulation of food covers not just conventional human food but also any individual component of food, ingredients, pet food and animal feed. Under the *Dietary Supplement and Health Education Act* of 1994 (*DSHEA*),[3] dietary supplements also are regulated under the general umbrella of "foods," although they are subject to a number of labeling and ingredient requirements specific to dietary supplements. Regulation of dietary supplements is discussed in more detail in Chapter 33.

FDA implements the *FD&C Act* and establishes regulations to prevent food from adulteration, ensuring foods are safe, wholesome and sanitary. FDA also regulates the misbranding of food labels and labeling, ensuring products are honestly, accurately and informatively represented to the public. Within FDA, food is regulated by the Center for Food Safety and Applied Nutrition (CFSAN).

Although FDA regulates most foods, it does not regulate all foods. The US Department of Agriculture (USDA) has jurisdiction over meat, poultry and commercially processed egg products, as well as combination products (e.g., meat stew, pizza with meat toppings), depending on the meat or poultry content. Within USDA, the Food Safety and Inspection Service (FSIS) is responsible for the inspection, safety and labeling of these products. Further, although FDA regulates bottled water, the US Environmental Protection Agency (EPA) regulates tap water, and the US Alcohol and Tobacco Tax and Trade Bureau (TTB) regulates most alcohol products.

FDA also does not regulate all aspects of food products. For example, although FDA regulates food labeling, the agency works with the Federal Trade Commission (FTC) to regulate food advertising, with FTC taking the lead on most enforcement actions.[4] Fruits, vegetables and other plants are regulated by USDA's Animal and Plant Health Inspection Service (APHIS) to prevent the introduction of plant diseases and pests into the US. USDA's Agricultural Marketing Service (AMS) administers the National Organic Program, which develops, implements and administers national standards for organic agricultural products and accredits the certifying agents who inspect organic operations.

Moreover, FDA works jointly with numerous federal, state and local agencies to regulate various aspects of foods and specific food categories. For example, FDA works cooperatively with states and other agencies, such as the Centers for Disease Control and Prevention (CDC), to address outbreaks of foodborne illness. The following provides more detail on some agencies and other jurisdictions responsible for some aspect of food regulation or working cooperatively with FDA on food matters:

- States are the primary regulators for restaurants, farms and retail establishments, including grocery stores. States work cooperatively with FDA to regulate milk and shellfish and also are involved in the regulation of weights and measures.
- FTC works with FDA to regulate all advertising, ensuring advertisements are truthful and not misleading for consumers. Within FTC, the Bureau of Consumer Protection has a mandate to protect consumers against unfair, deceptive or fraudulent practices.
- EPA establishes pesticide tolerances (acceptable residues) for food and animal feed, while FDA enforces compliance with pesticide tolerances. EPA also establishes maximum contaminant levels in public drinking water.
- TTB, formerly the Bureau of Alcohol, Tobacco, and Firearms (ATF), enforces labeling and other regulatory requirements for beer, wine and distilled spirits.
- US Customs and Border Protection (CBP) works with FDA to regulate imported food (and other FDA-related imported products).

Food Ingredients and Packaging (Food Additives)

Unlike its regulation of drugs or medical devices, FDA has very limited authority to regulate food before it goes on the market. One significant exception is regulation of food and color additives, which must be approved by FDA as safe for intended uses prior to marketing. The term "food additive" includes not just ingredients intentionally added to the food but also any substance used in the production process that could reasonably end up in the food, including packaging that could leach into food and even lubricants used on machinery that touches food during processing.

FDA must issue a regulation to approve a new food additive. For this reason, it can be important to determine whether a substance falls within any of the several exemptions from the agency's food additive definition.

What is a food additive?

Stripping out the exclusions, the broad definition of a food additive is:

> "Any substance the intended use of which results or may reasonably be expected to result, directly or indirectly, in its becoming a component or otherwise affecting the characteristics of any food...."[5]

The definition requires two key determinations. What is the intended use of the substance? When used as intended, can the substance reasonably be expected to end up in the food or affect the food in any way?

Substances such as cleaning solvents used on food processing machinery or packaging materials may be food additives if they could "reasonably be expected" to end up in the food in any amount or otherwise affect the food. The definition specifically states, "any substance intended for use in processing, manufacturing, packing, processing, preparing, treating, packaging, transporting or holding food" and "any source of radiation intended for any such use" can be a food additive.[6]

Regulations approving direct food additive uses—direct addition of a substance to food—can be found in 21 CFR part 172 and part 173. Regulations approving food additives that may indirectly become a food component can be found at 21 CFR 175–178. Regulations approving the use of radiation on food can be found at 21 CFR 179.

What is not a food additive?

The *FD&C Act* specifically excludes the following types of substances from the definition of a food additive:

- any substance Generally Recognized as Safe (GRAS) for its intended uses by scientific experts qualified to evaluate its safety
- pesticide chemical residues
- pesticides
- color additives
- new animal drugs
- new dietary ingredients (i.e., ingredients for use in dietary supplements)
- "Prior Sanction:" any substance approved or sanctioned for use prior to 6 September 1958 under the *FD&C Act*, the *Federal Meat Inspection Act* of 1906 or the *Poultry Products Inspection Act* of 1957[7]

Any substance that falls within any of these seven exclusions need not be approved as a food additive prior to use, although it may be subject to other regulations, depending on the substance type. For example, pesticides are approved for use by EPA,[8] and color additives must be approved by FDA under the color additive approval process in a different section of the *FD&C Act*.[9]

Most exclusions from the food additive definition apply to defined substance categories—a substance either is or is not an approved pesticide or color additive and, if not, may be a food additive. The exclusion for GRAS substances, however, is more fluid; it depends on the available evidence supporting the safety of the substance's intended use. Because a GRAS substance need not be approved by regulation prior to use in food, determining whether a substance is GRAS or is a food additive is important in developing new food products.

How is a food additive approved?

A food additive is deemed unsafe and cannot be used in food unless FDA has issued a regulation setting out the conditions under which the food additive can be used safely.[10] For a food additive to be deemed "safe," FDA must determine that under the intended conditions of use, the additive presents a "reasonable certainty of no harm."

Once a substance is determined to be a food additive, it must be approved through the food additive process unless it falls into one of two limited categories: a food-contact substance (FCS) or a food additive intended solely for investigational use. The exception for investigational use rarely is used and requires FDA to issue a regulation allowing the exception.[11] The FCS substance notification process is discussed in more detail later in this chapter.

Any person may petition FDA to issue a regulation approving a food additive for a particular use. A food additive petition must include:

- the food additive's chemical identity and composition
- the conditions of the additive's proposed uses
- data about the additive's intended physical or technical effect and the quantity required to produce such effect
- methods for determining the additive's quantity in food
- full reports of investigations made regarding the additive's safe use[12]

FDA also may request information on the additive's production methods, samples of the additive and its components or the food on which it will be used.

FDA must publish a notice in the *Federal Register* within 30 days of receiving a complete food additive petition. The agency then has 90 days (which may be extended to no more than 180 days) from petition filing to publish a regulation approving the food additive's use or issue an order denying the petition.[13] Any person adversely affected by a food additive petition's approval or denial may file objections within 30 days after the order approving or denying the petition is published.[14] FDA must respond to the objections, including any request for a public meeting, "as soon as practical."

FDA cannot approve a food additive petition if a fair evaluation of the data fails to establish the additive's proposed use will be safe, or the data show the proposed additive's use would deceive consumers or otherwise result in food adulteration or misbranding.[15] FDA has significant discretion to use its scientific judgment in evaluating data to determine whether a food additive's use is safe. For example, in determining safety, the agency may consider the additive's probable consumption level, its cumulative effect in the diet and other safety factors recognized by experts to be appropriate. FDA has issued guidance documents to aid stakeholders regarding requirements for establishing safety of use:

- *Guidance for Industry: Frequently Asked Questions About GRAS*[16]
- *Guidance for Industry: Recommendations for Submission of Chemical and Technological Data for Direct Food Additive Petitions*[17]
- *Guidance for Industry: Summary Table of Recommended Toxicological Testing for Additives Used in Food*[18]

FDA has no discretion, however, if a food additive is determined to induce cancer. The "Delaney Clause" in Section 409(c) of the *FD&C Act* states the agency cannot approve any food additive's use as safe if the food additive is found: 1) to induce cancer in man or animals when ingested; or 2) is found, by appropriate tests, to induce cancer in man or animals by methods other than ingestion.[19]

The Delaney Clause applies when FDA determines there is any risk the additive may induce cancer, regardless of how small the risk.[20] Only two limited exceptions to the application of the Delaney Clause have been recognized. Courts have held it does not apply where a constituent of a food or color additive is deemed to be a carcinogen, unless the food or color additive itself is determined to induce cancer.[21] The Delaney Clause also does not apply to certain food additives intended for use as ingredients of feed for animals raised for food production.[22]

Food additive approvals apply to the additive generally and are not intended to be proprietary to a particular product. The food additive regulation will specify the conditions of use, which may limit the amounts of the additive, the types of foods in which it can be used or even labeling requirements for the additive's use.

FCS Notifications

The *FD&C Act* was amended in 1997 to allow FCS products approved for use on food to go through a notification process rather than requiring FDA to issue a regulation.[23] An FCS is any substance used as a component of materials used in manufacturing, packing, packaging, transporting or holding food not intended to have a technical effect on the food. This definition includes such substances as paper, plastics, adhesives, lubricants and coatings used in food containers or packaging. It also includes food processing equipment, production aids, sanitizers, antimicrobials and colors used in packaging.

FDA requires any FCS product to be determined to be safe for its intended use before it is permitted to be sold in the US. Safety is dictated by the regulatory status of each component that comprises the FCS. New FCS product components and uses require premarket notification to FDA prior to marketing in the US.

The determination of how an FCS is regulated depends on its chemical composition. It is the FCS manufacturer's responsibility to ensure food contact materials comply with the specifications and limitations in all applicable authorizations. Individual FCS components' identity, specifications and limitations are regulated by provisions in the Code of Federal Regulations, the *Federal Register*, Effective Food Contact Notifications, Prior Sanctioned Letters, GRAS Notices, Threshold of Regulations Exemptions and FDA enforcement actions, such as import refusals, import alerts, Warning Letters, etc.

Anyone may submit a food contact notification to FDA. The agency has 120 days to review the notification. The agency may issue an objection or non-acceptance letter during the 120 days if it has safety concerns about the proposed FCS use. Before issuing an objection or non-acceptance letter, the agency typically contacts notifiers to request more information or to permit the notifier to withdraw the notification. If FDA does not issue an objection or non-acceptance letter within 120 days, the food-contact notification becomes effective on the 120-day date. At that point, FDA sends a letter to the notifier confirming the effective date. Approvals under the food-contact notification process are proprietary—they extend only to the specific proprietary substance and use in the notification, not to other identical substances. During the 120-day review period, the information submitted in the notification cannot be disclosed publicly by FDA. Similarly, FDA cannot disclose information related to a notification that is withdrawn prior to the end of the 120-day review period.

GRAS Substances

As described above, any GRAS substance is not a food additive and, therefore, does not have to be approved through the food additive process prior to use. Substances used in food prior to 1958 also can be deemed GRAS, based on their common use in food, rather than requiring consensus on the scientific data,[24] but this basis for GRAS determination rarely is used anymore.

The *FD&C Act* does not set out how FDA is to determine whether a substance is GRAS. Moreover, the *FD&C Act* does not require FDA to approve a substance as GRAS prior to its use in food, so the agency only has authority to challenge whether a substance is, in fact, GRAS after it is used in food. As a result, a sponsor may self-determine the GRAS status of a substance and use it in food. Many food manufacturers, however, will require suppliers to support the assertion a substance is GRAS to avoid the risk of FDA challenging the substance's GRAS status after the product is on the market.

To help those seeking to determine whether a substance is GRAS, FDA issued *Guidance for Industry: Frequently Asked Questions About GRAS* in December 2004, discussing how the agency evaluates whether a substance is GRAS. The agency also has published regulations in 21 CFR Parts 182–186 affirming the GRAS status of certain substances. Due to limited resources, FDA rarely issues such regulations. Instead, the agency has implemented a voluntary GRAS notification process to provide manufacturers some support for a GRAS assertion about a substance.

FDA has taken the position that a GRAS substance (other than substances used in food prior to 1958) must have scientific data and information supporting its safe use is of the same quantity and quality as needed for a food additive petition's approval, must be widely available and must have expert consensus the data establishes the substance's safe use. GRAS determinations cannot be based on private, proprietary data.

Under the GRAS notification program, FDA will review GRAS claims for a substance. GRAS notifications should include a substance description (including chemical identity and properties), applicable conditions of use and the basis for the GRAS determination, including discussion of the scientific information supporting the product's safe use and information supporting experts' consensus on its safe use. FDA typically will consult with the notifier during its notification review. FDA does not approve GRAS notifications. However, at the conclusion of its review, the agency may issue a letter indicating it does not question the basis for the GRAS determination. Alternatively, the agency may issue a letter concluding it does not believe the notification provides a sufficient basis for a GRAS determination. Because the GRAS notification process is voluntary, FDA is not bound by any timeline in completing its review but seeks to complete its review within 180 days.

Independent GRAS Determination

Self-determination of a substance's GRAS status is referred to as an "independent GRAS determination." Typically, an independent GRAS determination does not involve FDA, and the stakeholder is not required by law to notify FDA of its determination before adding the substance to food.

Recently, the GRAS process, and independent GRAS determinations in particular, have received increased scrutiny.[25–28]

Issues raised concerning independent GRAS determinations include transparency, FDA's lack of knowledge of what is added to the food supply, conflict of interest, etc. There are others who do not believe the GRAS process is "broken" to the extent described. Nevertheless, other stakeholders are taking steps to address these issues.[29,30]

As of 3 March 2015, FDA has posted receipt of 562 GRAS Notices on its website, while an estimated 1,000–3,000 independent GRAS Notices have been made for substances now in the food supply and dietary supplements. At the time of publication, these issues still are being discussed, and it is quite possible congressional action may be required.

Color Additives

A "color additive" is defined as any dye, pigment or other substance that can impart color to a food, drug or cosmetic, or to the human body, except any substance FDA determines is intended solely for a use other than coloring.[31] All color additives (except cosmetic hair dyes[32]) are subject to premarket approval.[33] In addition, all color additives must be properly declared on food labels and beverage labels. Unlike food additives, there is no GRAS exemption from the definition of color additives.

FDA issues regulations listing color additives that have been approved as safe for their intended uses.[34] FDA's review of color additive petitions is similar to the review of food additive petitions. The petitioner must submit data demonstrating the new color additive's safety and suitability for its intended uses. As is the case for food additives, there is a Delaney Clause for color additives that prohibits FDA from determining a color additive is safe for any use that will result in the additive being ingested if the agency finds it induces cancer when ingested by man or animals, or it is found by appropriate tests to induce cancer in man or animals through a method other than ingestion.

As a condition of use, some approved color additives require batch certification by FDA before they can be sold. Certification generally is required by FDA when the composition of the additive needs to be controlled to protect public health. Synthetic organic dyes, lakes[35] and pigments must be batch certified, whereas color additives derived from plant or mineral sources generally are exempt from batch certification.

As with food additives, the approved conditions of use for certain color additives may extend to labeling requirements. In addition, regulations governing food color additive labeling can be found in 21 CFR 101.22.

Biotechnology and Genetically Modified Organisms

Biotechnology refers to the techniques scientists use to modify the genetic material of microorganisms, plants or animals to achieve a desired trait. Common use of the terms "biotechnology" and "genetically engineered" in the US is limited to foods produced using recombinant DNA or gene splicing.

FDA's Biotechnology Policy, published in 1992, is limited to foods derived from new plant varieties. FDA recommends those developing a bioengineered food consult with the agency during development to discuss relevant safety, nutritional or other regulatory issues. FDA also recommends developers submit a scientific and regulatory assessment of the food for agency review. FDA has proposed a rule that would require developers to submit such an assessment to FDA 120 days before a bioengineered food is marketed. The rule has not been finalized, so no requirement to this effect currently is in place. Bioengineered plants also may be subject to regulation by APHIS.

In January 2009, FDA issued *Guidance for Industry: Regulation of Genetically Engineered Animals Containing Heritable Recombinant DNA Constructs*. In the guidance, FDA takes the position a recombinant DNA (rDNA) construct in a genetically engineered (GE) animal and intended to affect the animal's structure or function meets the definition of an animal drug and is subject to premarket approval requirements. The guidance further states developers of GE animals must demonstrate the construct is safe for the GE animals' health and, if they are food animals, the construct and its products are safe for human consumption.

In April 2013, FDA published *Foods Derived from Genetically Engineered Plants*; this covered Questions & Answers on Food from GE Plants, Background on GE Plants for Food and Feed, Draft Guidance on Voluntary Labeling, FDA Policy Statement on Foods Derived from New Plant Varieties and Consultation Procedures.

Misbranding: Food Labeling and Claims

Under *FD&C Act* Section 403(a), a food is misbranded if its label or labeling is false or misleading in any particular, if it is offered for sale under the name of another food or if it is an imitation of another food without proper labeling.[36] A "label" is defined to include any "written, printed, or graphic matter upon the immediate container of any article."[37] "Labeling" is broader and includes "all labels and other written, printed, or graphic matter (1) upon any article or any of its containers or wrappers, or (2) accompanying such article."[38] Labeling has been interpreted by FDA and the courts to include flyers, brochures and displays proximate to the product in a store. FDA has interpreted labeling further to include information on a website from which a product can be purchased, and even information on websites reachable through links on a website where the product can be purchased.

In addition, FDA regulations include formal standards of identity for many kinds of food including: milk and cream; cheese and related cheese products; frozen desserts; bakery products; cereal flours and related products; macaroni and noodle products; canned fruits; canned fruit juices; fruit butters, jellies, preserves and related products; fruit pies; canned vegetables; vegetable juices; frozen vegetables; eggs and egg products; fish and shellfish; cacao products; tree nut and peanut products; beverages; margarine; sweeteners and table syrups; and food dressings; and flavorings. These regulations prevent the intentional substitution of ingredients without declaring those ingredients in labeling (e.g., using an unlisted, less-expensive ingredient to reduce the cost of manufacturing). The standards of identity require products to contain the ingredients mandated by the standard.

The *FD&C Act* prohibits misbranded foods from being introduced, delivered or received in interstate commerce.[39] FDA has authority to take action against a product if the label or labeling fails to identify "material facts."[40] Everything on a product's label or labeling must be truthful and cannot be misleading.

FDA regulates labeling for all foods, except those within USDA's jurisdiction (meat, poultry and cracked egg products). No label preapproval is required by FDA; however, the agency has promulgated extensive regulations governing food labeling. The labeling rules governing foods regulated by USDA are similar to FDA's requirements; however, label preapproval is required for most products within USDA's jurisdiction.

There are two primary areas of food labeling regulation: required elements and voluntary claims. All food labels must contain certain uniform elements to provide meaningful information to consumers in a manner that allows easy comparison between products. Many products also bear voluntary claims promoting their benefits or usefulness.

Mandatory Labeling Elements

The *FD&C Act* establishes requirements for numerous statements that must appear on a food product's label. Food labeling is required for most packaged foods, such as breads, cereals, canned and frozen foods, snacks, desserts and drinks. Labeling requirements are very specific, often requiring near-exact placement in a mandated size on a specific component of a certain label.

Food labels must contain five primary elements (unless subject to limited exemptions):

- statement of identity
- net quantity of contents
- Nutrition Facts
- ingredient statement
- manufacturer's statement

Additional labeling requirements are applicable to certain products, e.g., juice content, country of origin, use of irradiation, allergen declaration, mandated warnings and labeling of infant formulas. Certain label statements are prohibited, such as unapproved nutrient content and health claims and statements that are otherwise false or misleading.

The required information must appear on one of two label panels. The "principal display panel" (PDP), a product's primary label, is the "part of a label that is most likely to be displayed, presented, shown, or examined under customary conditions of display" for sale.[41] The PDP must contain the product's statement of identity and net weight. In addition, the PDP may include the ingredient statement, manufacturing statement and nutrition information. Many product labels also contain an "information panel," which is typically the "part of the label immediately contiguous and to the right of the principal display panel."[42] No intervening material is permitted between the PDP and the information panel unless the panel immediately to the right of the PDP is too small to accommodate the required information. The information panel generally includes the manufacturing statement, ingredient declaration and nutrition information.

Statement of Identity

All products must bear a product identity statement prescribed by either a standard of identity, a common or usual name or an appropriately descriptive term or "fanciful" name.[43] Additionally, products deemed imitations of other foods must be labeled as such.

Standards of Identity

The *FD&C Act* authorizes FDA to establish standards of identity for foods.[44] Standards of identity define what a given food product is, its name and the ingredients that must be used, or may be used, in the food's manufacture. Food standards ensure consumers get what they expect when they purchase certain food products, providing predictability that a product labeled, for example, as "ice cream" is actually ice cream and not some other frozen dairy product. Once a standard of identity is established, any food purporting to be the standardized food must comply with the standard of identity, and a food may not bear the standardized name if it does not comply with the standard. The standards of identity are codified in 21 CFR Parts 130–169.

Common or Usual Name

A standard of identity does not exist for all types of foods. To ensure consistency and predictability for consumers, the common or usual name of a product must "accurately identify or describe the basic nature of the food or its characterizing properties or ingredients."[45] Regulations establish common or usual name requirements for particular foods, which are less rigid than standards of identity, but nonetheless must be followed when labeling these types of foods. These regulations are contained in 21 CFR 102.

Descriptive or Fanciful Name

When neither a standard of identity nor a common or usual name is available for a food, the statement of identity is permitted to be a descriptive term, or if the nature of the food is obvious, a fanciful name.[46] For example, the brand name of many soft drinks serves as their statement of identity because the nature of the product is commonly understood.

Imitation

If a food resembles a traditional food and is a substitute for the traditional food, but is nutritionally inferior to that food, it must be labeled as an imitation.[47] A food is considered nutritionally inferior if, for example, it contains less protein or a lesser amount of any essential vitamin or mineral. Products that are not nutritionally inferior and are a substitute for and resemble another food can use a different name that is not false or misleading rather than imitation labeling, such as using the phrase "whipped topping" to identify a product like Cool Whip that would otherwise be called "Imitation Whipped Cream."

Net Quantity of Contents

A net quantity of contents statement, expressed in terms of weight, measure, numerical count or a combination of numerical count and weight or measure, must appear in the lower 30% of the PDP.[48] The statement must declare the package's contents in both English and metric units, typically using pounds and grams for solids and fluid ounces and milliliters for liquids. Detailed requirements mandate the statement's type size and placement; it must appear as a "distinct item" separated from other printed label information. This statement must be accurate, although reasonable variations from stated weight are permitted for either statistical variations occurring during production under Good Manufacturing Practices or from loss or gain of moisture during distribution. As noted earlier, state and local authorities also are very active in regulating net quantity statements.

Nutrition Labeling

Regulations established to implement the *Nutrition Labeling and Education Act* of 1990 specify detailed substantive and technical requirements for food nutrition labeling.[49] The embodiment of these detailed regulations is the Nutrition Facts panel. FDA places great importance on maintaining uniformity in the presentation of information in the Nutrition Facts panel. Regulations dictate such details as font sizes, indentations, use of bolding and even the width of lines in the Nutrition Facts panel. Only those nutrients listed in FDA's nutrition regulations, as mandatory or voluntary components of the nutrition label, may be included in the Nutrition Facts label as directed in 21 CFR 101.9(c). In addition to numerous other requirements, a food's nutrition label must:

- specify the serving size (based on reference amounts customarily consumed)
- identify nutrients required to be declared
- follow specific formatting and type size requirements

Under the regulations, certain nutrients must be declared on the Nutrition Facts panel, while other nutrients may be declared voluntarily. FDA may evaluate products to confirm whether the product contains the level of nutrients declared on the nutrition panel, while recognizing there will be some variability in foods' inherent nutritional composition.

In 2014, FDA proposed revising Nutrition Facts content and formatting to take into account up-to-date scientific information and dietary guidance.[50] Among the areas addressed in the proposed changes are mandatory nutrients, optional nutrients, Daily Values, serving sizes and formatting. FDA's proposal would have the final changes to Nutrition Facts become effective two years after the final rule is published. Manufacturers should follow FDA's progress on these changes to be able to make the required revisions in a timely manner.

Ingredient Statement

The ingredients added to a product must be listed by name in the ingredient statement in descending order of predominance by weight.[51] Ingredients present at less than 2% of the total can be exempt from the descending order of predominance requirement. If an ingredient contains multiple components and has an established name, the manufacturer may either declare the name of the multicomponent ingredient followed by a parenthetical listing of each component by name or list each component in descending order in the ingredient statement without identifying the name of the multicomponent ingredient itself. A small number of ingredients are eligible for "and/or" labeling when the ingredient may or may not be included in the product. There also are specific regulations governing the declaration of spices, flavors and colors.

Importantly, the *Food Allergen Labeling and Consumer Protection Act* of 2004 (*FALCPA*)[52] requires manufacturers to declare in plain language the presence of any major food allergen, specifically egg, wheat, milk, soy, fish, shellfish (crustaceans), peanuts and tree nuts.[53] The presence of the allergen may be declared in the ingredient statement or through the statement "Contains: (name of the allergen)" immediately after the ingredient statement. The declaration for tree nuts, seafood and shellfish must indicate the particular species, while for other allergens, manufacturers are not required to specify the species (for example, "Contains: Wheat, Milk, Cashews, Cod and Shrimp"). FDA has not regulated the use of advisory allergen statements, such as "Processed in plant that also processes peanuts;" such statements are voluntary but must not be misleading.

Manufacturer's Statement

The label must contain a manufacturing statement identifying the manufacturer, packer or distributor.[54] The company's actual corporate name must appear on the label, as well as its city, state and zip code. If the company is not listed in the city or telephone directory, its street address also must appear on the label. Unless it is misleading, it is acceptable to list the principal place of business instead of the actual place of manufacture. If the name on the label is not that of the manufacturer, it must be qualified with a phrase such as "distributed by," "packed for" or "imported by."

Additional Requirements Imposed by USDA/FSIS

Labeling for foods regulated by FSIS must contain the information above plus:

- an inspection legend and establishment number (in the form of a logo that looks like a USDA mark)[55]
- special handling instructions for products requiring refrigeration or freezing[56]
- safe handling instructions for products not considered ready-to-eat[57]

Another distinction from FDA requirements is USDA-regulated product labels must be preapproved by FSIS prior to use.[58]

However, FSIS published a new regulation allowing generic approval of labels.[59] Manufacturers no longer need to obtain a sketch approval requiring a label application to be submitted directly to FSIS. Under generic labeling, statements defined in FSIS regulations or the *Food Standards and Labeling Policy Book* will not require prior approval. Labels with special claims such as "vegetarian fed" or "no added antibiotics" still will need to be submitted to FSIS for approval. Once the agency approves such labels, the company does not have to resubmit them for approval if it later adds statements defined in FSIS regulations (e.g., a defined nutrient content claim, such as "low fat"). Companies still need to submit labels bearing certain claims, such as organic, natural or animal-raising, as well as labels for temporary approval; products produced under religious exemption; and products for export only that bear allowable labeling deviations.

Country of Origin Labeling

USDA and CBP regulate separate Country of Origin (COO) labeling requirements that affect many food products, including most imports. The *Farm Bills* of 2002 and 2008 mandated Country of Origin Labeling (COOL) for certain products. The final rule for all covered commodities (7 CFR Part 60 and Part 65) went into effect 16 March 2009. The COOL program is administered by USDA's Agricultural Marketing Service (AMS). The rules require labeling at retail to indicate the country of origin for certain covered commodities (i.e., muscle cuts and ground beef, lamb, chicken, goat and pork; wild and farm-raised fish and shellfish; perishable agricultural commodities (specifically fresh and frozen fruits and vegetables); macadamia nuts; pecans; peanuts; and ginseng).[60] Excluded from USDA COOL requirements are "processed food items," defined as retail items derived from a covered commodity that has "undergone specific processing resulting in a change of character" or has been "combined with at least one other covered commodity." For example, breaded fish sticks; fruit cups containing cantaloupe, watermelon and honeydew; and cured hams all are considered to be processed food items and are exempt from COOL requirements.

Almost all imported products, whether or not exempt from USDA COOL requirements, still are required to be marked with country of origin labeling under the *Tariff Act* of 1930,[61] enforced by CBP.[62] For example, although a bag of frozen peas and carrots is considered a processed food item and thus is exempt from USDA COOL requirements, if the peas and carrots are of foreign origin, CBP requires the product's bag or its shipping container to be marked with country of origin information. CBP's COO requirements apply only until the product reaches its ultimate purchaser in the US, which may be a business that further manufactures the goods, rather than a consumer. Thus, because CBP's restrictions allow labeling on shipping containers and do not transfer upon food processing, they do not have the same impact on consumers as USDA's requirements.

Voluntary Labeling Information

Manufacturers may choose to make claims on their food labels about their products' attributes or benefits. FDA has comprehensive requirements regarding claims, requiring authorization prior to use of nutrient content claims and health claims by regulation or by notification under the *Food and Drug Administration Modernization Act* of 1997 (*FDAMA*).[63] Qualified health claims are authorized by letters placed on FDA's website. FDA also regulates structure/function claims, which do not require approval prior to use.

A product's intended use will determine whether it is subject to regulation as a food, dietary supplement or drug. Claims made for a product are key to determining its intended use. For example (and as explained in more detail below), a claim that a product treats or prevents a disease or abnormal health condition subjects it to regulation as a drug, while the claim that a product "maintains healthy cholesterol for people with normal cholesterol" is a permissible food structure/function claim. Because most drugs cannot be marketed until they have received premarket approval under the *FD&C Act*, food companies must avoid making claims that would subject their products to regulation as new drugs.

Nutrient Content Claims

A nutrient content claim describes the level of a nutrient using terms such as "free," "high" and "low," or compares the level of a nutrient in a food to that of another food, using terms such as "more," "reduced" and "lite."[64] For example, the statements "zero calorie" and "high in fiber" are nutrient content claims. Under the *FD&C Act*, a food is deemed misbranded if it bears a nutrient content claim, unless FDA has issued a regulation authorizing the claim, and the claim is made in a manner consistent with the regulation.[65] Nutrient content claims can be expressed or implied and typically are based on the reference amount customarily consumed for the food at issue. Generally, there must be an established daily value for the nutrient that is the subject of the claim. Special labeling also is required for products that exceed designated "disclosure levels" for fat, saturated fat, cholesterol and sodium, using a statement such as "See nutrition information for fat content," for a food where the level of fat exceeds the disclosure level, and a nutrient content claim is made.

Health Claims

A health claim describes the relationship between a substance (food or food component) and a disease or health-related condition.[66] For example, the statement, "While many factors affect heart disease, diets low in saturated fat and cholesterol may reduce the risk of this disease," is a model health claim. Health claims are limited to claims about reducing disease risk and cannot be claims about the cure, mitigation, treatment or prevention of disease. Since only drugs may bear claims that a product cures, mitigates, treats or prevents a disease (or unapproved health claims), such claims signal the product is intended for use as a drug.[67] FDA will regard a food product bearing such claims as violative of the *FD&C Act* as both a misbranded food and as an unapproved new drug.

As noted, foods are deemed misbranded if they bear a health claim not authorized by FDA. Health claims must be supported by significant scientific agreement to be established by regulation. Foods are ineligible for health claims if they exceed disqualifying levels of certain nutrients (total fat, saturated fat, cholesterol and sodium), which are the same as the disclosure levels for nutrient content claims. Approved health claims are listed in the regulations at 21 CFR 101.72–101.83 and include claims relating such substances and diseases as calcium and osteoporosis and sodium and hypertension.

Qualified Health Claims

For claims for which there is no significant supporting scientific agreement, manufacturers can petition to make "qualified health claims." The *FD&C Act* does not approve health claims with less than significant scientific agreement. Following court decisions striking down FDA's denial of certain health claims on First Amendment grounds, the agency established a petition process for qualified health claims.

Though not requiring significant scientific agreement, such claims must be supported by scientific evidence. FDA has issued extensive guidance on how it evaluates scientific evidence for health claims and qualified health claims. If FDA agrees the scientific evidence supports a qualified health claim, the agency will provide claim language for which it will exercise enforcement discretion. The claim language is tailored to convey the level and quality of the science supporting the claim accurately, e.g., "Supportive but not conclusive research shows that eating 1.5 ounces per day of walnuts, as part of a low saturated fat and low cholesterol diet and not resulting in increased caloric intake, may reduce the risk of coronary heart disease. See nutrition information for fat and calorie content." These statements often are so qualified as to not be useful. For example, in response to a petition for qualified health claims regarding a relationship between consumption of green tea and a reduced risk of certain cancers, FDA permitted the following claim:

> "Two studies do not show that drinking green tea reduces the risk of breast cancer in women, but one weaker, more limited study suggests that drinking green tea may reduce this risk. Based on these studies, FDA concludes that it is highly unlikely that green tea reduces the risk of breast cancer."

FDAMA Nutrient Content and Health Claims

FDAMA allows nutrient content and health claims to be made on the basis of statements issued by authoritative bodies such as the National Institutes of Health or the National Academy of Sciences.[68] FDA takes the position these claims must meet the same standard of evidence (significant scientific agreement) as FDA-approved health claims. To make a *FDAMA*-based claim, a notification must be filed with FDA at least 120 days prior to introducing the food bearing the claim into interstate commerce. The notification must include the exact words of the claim, a copy of the authoritative statement on which the claim is based and a balanced representation of the scientific literature supporting the nutrient/disease relationship. During the 120-day period, FDA may notify the person wishing to make the claim if any of the required information has not been submitted. After 120 days, the claim may be used until FDA either issues a regulation prohibiting or modifying the claim or takes enforcement action.[69]

Structure/Function Claims

Structure/function claims describe the role of substances intended to affect the normal structure or function of humans.[70] Such claims assume a person is healthy and just wants to maintain that good health. For example, the statement "Calcium maintains strong bones" is a structure/function claim. FDA authorization is not required prior to use of structure/function claims; however, such claims cannot be false or misleading or fail to reveal any material facts. Additionally, the claims must derive from the nutritional value of the product bearing the claim. Structure/

function claims may characterize the mechanism by which substances act to maintain such structure or function (e.g., "Fiber provides bulk which maintains bowel regularity").

Structure/function claims may not explicitly or implicitly link the relationship to a disease or health-related condition. For example, it is permissible to make the claim a substance supports memory but not to make the claim the substance reduces memory loss. The one exception to this rule is claims are permitted to describe a benefit related to a nutrient deficiency disease (e.g., Vitamin C and scurvy), as long as the statement also provides information about how widespread such a disease is in the US.

Dietary Guidance

Dietary guidance statements are made to assist and encourage individuals in making better food choices and establishing healthier eating patterns. For example, the statement, "Diets rich in fruits and vegetables reduce the risk of certain cancers," is an acceptable dietary guidance statement. Although a dietary guidance statement can mention a specific disease, the disease cannot be linked to a specific food or a specific substance in food. The recommendations of recognized government (e.g., US Surgeon General, National Cancer Institute) or private professional health organizations (e.g., American Heart Association) provide the basis for dietary guidance. FDA has never codified the requirements for these statements but has addressed this issue in preambles to regulations and in guidance documents.

Medical Foods

A "medical food" is a food "formulated to be consumed or administered under supervision of a physician and which is intended for the specific dietary management of a disease or condition for which distinctive nutritional requirements are established by medical evaluation."[71] FDA has issued limited guidance on medical foods (see *Guidance for Industry: Frequently Asked Questions About Medical Foods* (Revised May 2007). In general, however, to be a medical food, the product must, at a minimum, be: a food for oral or tube feeding; labeled for the dietary management of a specific medical disorder, disease or condition with distinctive nutritional requirements; and must be intended for use under medical supervision.[72]

The main distinction between medical foods and other foods is in labeling. Medical foods are not subject to labeling requirements for nutrient content claims and health claims. In other words, medical foods may bear nutrient content claims and health claims without prior FDA approval, so long as the claims are truthful and not misleading. Medical food labels must bear a statement of identity, a statement of net quantity, a manufacturer statement, a list of ingredients and allergen labeling. Nutrition labeling requirements do not apply.

For more information on medical foods, see Chapter 38.

Foods for Special Dietary Uses

Foods for special dietary uses are foods "for supplying particular dietary needs which exist by reason of a physical, physiological, pathological or other condition, including but not limited to the conditions of diseases, convalescence, pregnancy, lactation, allergic hypersensitivity to food, underweight, and overweight."[73] Under 21 CFR 105.3, foods containing artificial sweeteners to reduce calories or available carbohydrates, or for use by diabetics, are considered foods for special dietary use. These products must bear nutrition labeling as required for conventional foods.

Infant Formula

Infant formulas must bear the label information required for other foods except Nutrition Facts. There are specific nutrient content requirements for infant formula and separate requirements for nutrition labeling in Part 107 of FDA regulations.[74] Infant formula labels must have several additional types of information, including directions for preparation and use both in words and as pictograms, as well as "use by" dates.[75]

Also in 21 CFR Part 107 are special provisions for "exempt infant formulas." These are infant formulas represented for use by infants who have inborn errors of metabolism or low birth weight, or who otherwise have unusual medical or dietary problems. These special provisions allow, among other things, different nutrient content depending on the needs of the infant.

Adulteration: Food Sanitation and Safety

Food may be deemed adulterated if it consists of any "filthy, putrid, or decomposed substance or if it is otherwise unfit for food," or if it has been "prepared, packed or held under insanitary conditions" whereby it may have been contaminated with filth or rendered injurious to health. The statute also lists a number of other less common conditions that may render a food adulterated.

Basically, a poisonous or deleterious substance is anything in food that could cause harm, whether the substance is physical (such as a shard of glass), chemical (lead) or biological (salmonella). Whether a substance in a food is an "added substance" or a naturally occurring substance will determine the standard FDA must meet to prove adulteration.

Courts essentially have held any act of man that causes the presence of the substance in the food renders the substance an "added substance." For example, the US Court of Appeals for the Fifth Circuit has affirmed that mercury in swordfish is an "added substance" where evidence established any amount of the mercury resulted from industrial pollution.[76]

Unavoidable Poisonous or Deleterious Substances in Food

Some poisonous or deleterious substances in food are unavoidable, such as aflatoxins in peanuts. The *FD&C Act* recognizes some such substances may be unavoidable, and the statute provides a mechanism for the agency to establish allowable tolerances for them.[77] However, because such tolerances must be established by resource-intensive formal rulemaking, the agency has not issued a new tolerance for decades. Instead, FDA has a procedure for establishing what it calls "regulatory limits" that establishes levels at which an unavoidable added substance may render a food injurious to health.[78] Although regulatory limits can be established by notice and comment rulemaking, which is significantly easier than formal rulemaking, the agency has never set a regulatory limit. Instead, the agency has issued action levels for certain poisonous or deleterious substances. Action levels are unenforceable guidances that represent the agency's current thinking as to what level of the substance may render it injurious to health. An action level has no legal effect, so in any enforcement action, the agency must prove the level of the substance in the food may render it injurious to health—simply providing evidence that the action level was exceeded is not sufficient.

Current Good Manufacturing Practices (CGMPs)

FDA's CGMPs for food manufacturing, packing or holding are set out in 21 CFR 110. Failure to follow CGMPs is a determining factor in whether a food is adulterated because it was manufactured under conditions that rendered it unfit for food[79] or was prepared, packed or held under insanitary conditions whereby the food may have been contaminated with filth or rendered injurious to health.[80] The *Food Safety Modernization Act* (*FSMA*) revised 21 CFR Part 110 requirements. FDA proposes to remove Part 110 for all businesses to be in compliance with the new requirements of the new Part 117 (78n FR3672).[81]

The regulations set out CGMPs for personnel, buildings and facilities, equipment and production and process controls. 21 CFR 110 also provides for "defect action levels," which establish maximum allowable levels of certain types of contamination that may result despite CGMP compliance. For example, FDA's *Food Defect Action Level Handbook* sets out the maximum levels of insect fragments or rodent hair that may be present in wheat flour.[82] FDA also has separate CGMP regulations for bottled water in 21 CFR 129.

HACCP—Juice and Seafood Products

Whereas all USDA-regulated products (meat, poultry and processed eggs) are required to implement Hazard Analysis and Critical Control Point (HACCP) controls for the safety of their products, FDA currently requires HACCP only for juice and seafood product producers. FDA's HACCP regulations require juice and seafood producers to conduct an analysis to identify food safety hazards reasonably likely to occur. If the analysis concludes such hazards exist, the producer is required to implement a HACCP plan that:

- identifies the possible hazards
- lists all critical control points (CCPs) for controlling each hazard while the product is in the producer's control
- lists critical limits that must be met at each CCP to control the hazard
- lists monitoring procedures and frequency for compliance with the critical limits
- includes any corrective actions to be taken in the event of a deviation from a critical limit
- lists verification procedures for the adequacy of the HACCP plan
- establishes a recordkeeping system that documents the monitoring of compliance with the critical limits

Under HACCP regulations, records must be maintained for a minimum of one year, and two years for some products with longer shelf lives. FDA has access to review and copy all records required to be maintained by HACCP regulations.

Acidified and Low-Acid Canned Foods

Stringent processing controls are established for acidified and low-acid foods in hermetically sealed containers, such as metal cans, bottles and flexible pouches. For convenience, these are referred to as canned foods. These foods must be processed to achieve commercial sterility and eliminate viable spores of *Clostridium botulinum*. FDA requires manufacturers producing certain shelf-stable, aseptically sealed low-acid canned or acidified foods to obtain a Food Canning Establishment (FCE) registration.

In addition, manufacturers must file documentation with FDA for each process used in producing foods subject to these requirements. These submissions are known as "Process Filings," and each is assigned a unique "Submission Identifier" (SID).

Manufacturing requirements for low-acid canned foods are set out in 21 CFR 113, and those for acidified foods are in 21 CFR 114. In addition to the specific GMPs set out in 21 CFR 113 and 114, acidified and low-acid canned food manufacturers must register with FDA and file the scheduled processes they intend to use to ensure product safety with the agency.[83]

FSMA

On 4 January 2011, President Obama signed *FSMA* into law.[84] This act was aimed at refocusing FDA's regulatory oversight of food production from a reactive stance to a preventive role. It reaffirms manufacturers' responsibility to make safe food, and gave the agency recall authority, administrative detention and facility registration suspension authority. *FSMA* requires all food processors not already covered by HACCP or acidified and low-acid canned food regulations to conduct a risk-based hazard analysis. If a significant hazard is reasonably likely to occur, in the absence of control measures, the firm must establish a preventive control program. The law also required FDA to propose and enact regulations to ensure the safe harvesting and handling of raw produce; increased agency oversight of imported foods; required FDA to increase inspections; and allowed a program of user fees for re-inspections, mandatory recalls and import activities. FDA was assigned the task of preparing various regulations, rulemakings and guidance documents to facilitate compliance with the act. The process of promulgating regulations is ongoing.

FSMA's provisions focus on five main areas:

- authority to require human and animal food processors and produce growers, unless specifically exempted, to establish formal programs to prevent food safety problems
- capacity to rapidly detect and respond to food safety problems
- imported food safety
- establish a third-party accreditation process
- provide guidance for the regulated community to achieve compliance with *FSMA*

Perhaps the most significant change in the legislation is a requirement for food companies to take preventive steps to avoid food contamination. Manufacturers now are required to analyze their processes for each type of food produced, identify the critical points at which the food could become contaminated and implement procedures (documented in written food-safety plans) designed to prevent contamination. If the food processor's risk-based hazard analysis does not identify significant hazards reasonably likely to occur in the absence of control(s), a food safety preventive control plan is not required.

Another significant change is the law gave FDA the right to order companies to recall tainted food if a company will not or cannot conduct its own recall. Previously, the agency only could request a company to undertake a recall. Additionally, the bill contains provisions requiring:

- FDA to inspect food manufacturers more frequently
- FDA to create a pilot program to trace outbreaks back to their source quickly
- FDA to establish product safety standards
- importers to verify incoming foods meet US food-safety guidelines

Every producer of a food type for which one or more significant hazards reasonably can be expected to occur in the absence of control(s) is required to adopt a written food safety plan that includes an internal inspection system with detailed recordkeeping. Effective dates for pending *FSMA* regulations will be based on the firm's size by dollar volume, with large firms having the shortest time to comply, and small and very small firms having longer periods. At the time of publication, the specific size and timing details are pending issuance of the final regulation.

Facilities manufacturing a food type for which one or more significant hazards reasonably are likely to occur in the absence of control(s) must specify potential problems that could affect their products' safety and document steps the facility will take to eliminate or significantly reduce the likelihood of those problems causing consumers harm.

FSMA explicitly identifies food producers and manufacturers as having primary responsibility for food safety. In addition to responding to events, FDA's role now extends to regulating programs food manufacturers have established to prevent food safety problems before they arise.

FSMA calls for FDA to establish and enforce science-based standards for safe fruit and vegetable production and harvesting. Those standards will consider both natural and man-made risks to fresh produce safety. Previously, FDA had limited authority over raw agricultural commodities.

The law also calls for more frequent inspections and for the secretary of the Department of Health and Human Services to determine which food facilities are high risk, and encourages the secretary to work with officials at the state, tribal and local levels to implement the law.

Foods and facilities posing a greater risk to food safety will get the most attention—with inspections mandated not less than once every three years. Although not part of *FSMA*, the agency also has published draft regulations to implement the *Sanitary Food Transportation Act* of 2005. These proposals are pending at the time of publication.

Finally, every two years, FDA is required to provide industry guidance on the most important food contaminants, based on evaluations (and re-evaluations) of data and other studies.

Inspections, Recalls and Enforcement

FDA inspections, compliance, enforcement and recalls generally are covered in other chapters of this book. Addressed here are aspects of these FDA functions particular to foods.

FDA has the authority to inspect any factory, warehouse, establishment or vehicle in which food is manufactured, processed, packed or held for introduction into interstate commerce (excluding small farms and restaurants), as well as all pertinent equipment, finished and unfinished materials, containers and labeling therein.[85] FDA also may inspect and copy records relating to the manufacture, processing, packing, distribution, receipt, holding or importation of food if the agency has a reasonable belief the food is adulterated and presents a threat of serious adverse health consequences or death, in humans or animals (SAHCODHA). In other words, if the food meets the standard for a Class I recall,

FDA has the authority to require this degree of records access.[86] FDA does not have the authority to inspect or copy financial data, sales data or other data not related to the food's safety.[87]

FDA's recall authorities under 21 CFR 7 apply equally to food products and other products. One aspect specific to foods failure to label a major food allergen's presence in a food product is cause for a Class I recall.

As noted above, *FSMA* gave FDA the authority to require food product recalls. This authority comes into effect if a food product is deemed to present "a reasonable probability that an article of food (other than infant formula) is adulterated under section 402 or misbranded under section 403(w) and the use of or exposure to such article will cause serious adverse health consequences or death to humans or animals" and if the manufacturer will not voluntarily or cannot recall the product.

FDA may take enforcement action to seize or enjoin the continued distribution of adulterated or misbranded food. In addition, the agency can charge each violation as a misdemeanor subject to imprisonment of not more than one year and a fine of up to $1,000. If the violation was committed with the intent to defraud or mislead, FDA can charge a criminal felony, with penalties of up to three years in prison and a fine of up to $10,000.

The Reportable Food Registry

In 2007, Congress amended the *FD&C Act* to establish a Reportable Food Registry (RFR). If a registered food facility owner, operator or agent in charge determines an article of food (other than infant formula or pet food or feed) that has been in the facility is likely to meet the standard for a Class I recall (reasonable probability of SAHCODHA), the firm is required to file a report with the registry within 24 hours of the determination. The only exception to the reporting requirement is if the adulteration originated in the facility, was detected prior to transfer of the food to any other person and was corrected or the food destroyed. The report must be filed electronically through FDA's MedWatchPlus portal and must provide certain information regarding the food and the adulteration, including contact information for the immediate previous source of the food and the immediate subsequent recipient in the supply chain. FDA then may require notification of the identified persons in the supply chain. FDA is paying increased attention to the requirement for a firm making an RFR follow-up report with the results of a root cause analysis to determine how a hazardous food was able to leave its control. The RFR requirements took effect 8 September 2009.

Food Defense

The *Public Health Security and Bioterrorism Preparedness and Response Act* of 2002 (*Bioterrorism Act*)[88] amended the *FD&C Act* to provide several new authorities for FDA to protect against any possible attack on the food system or other food safety emergency. Provisions of the *Bioterrorism Act* include facility registration, prior notice of imports and administrative detention authority. Under *FSMA*, FDA is proposing regulations covering mitigation strategies for preventing intentional adulteration. These regulations are pending at the time of publication.

Facility Registration

All food facilities must be registered with FDA. A "food facility" is any facility engaged in manufacturing, processing, packing or holding food for consumption in the US.[89] The registration requirement extends to the last foreign facilities to engage in manufacturing or packaging of food to be imported to the US, provided such processing is more than *de minimis*.[90]

The requirement does not apply to farms, retail food establishments (such as supermarkets), restaurants, fishing vessels or facilities regulated exclusively by USDA.[91]

The registration must provide, among other information, the types of food manufactured, packed or held at the facility and a 24-hour emergency contact. FDA issues each facility a unique registration number.[92] Failure to register is a prohibited act under the *FD&C Act*. The information provided with each registration is exempt from public disclosure under the *Freedom of Information Act*. *FSMA* required food facilities to renew their FDA Food Facility Registrations between 1 October 2012 and 31 December 2012, and between October 1 and December 31 of every even numbered year thereafter.

Prior Notice of Imported Food

FDA must receive prior notice of the import of any FDA-regulated food into the US. Excluded foods include meat, poultry and egg products regulated by USDA; products imported for export; and those imported for personal use only.[93] Prior notice time requirements vary by the transportation method: two hours if by road, four hours if by rail, four hours if by air and eight hours if by water.[94] Prior notice must be submitted electronically through links on FDA's website www.fda.gov/. A backup facsimile system is available in case the electronic gateway is unavailable. Food submitted without prior notice may be refused for import.[95]

Administrative Detention

FSMA amended FDA's authority to administratively detain food. The old standard allowed FDA, upon issuance of a detention order, to detain any article of food found to present a threat of SAHCODHA during an inspection, examination or investigation.[96] The new threshold for detention is finding a reasonable belief a food is in violation of the *FD&C Act*.[97] The detention may not exceed 20 calendar days, but up to 10 more days may be authorized if necessary to institute a seizure or injunction action.[98] Any person who can claim the detained food can appeal a detention order challenging the determination the food is in violation of the *FD&C Act*.[99]

Summary

- FDA regulates most foods. Exceptions include meat, poultry and processed egg products, which are regulated by USDA, and tap water and alcohol, which are regulated by EPA and TTB, respectively. FDA also does not regulate all aspects of food; for example, it regulates food labeling, and FTC regulates food advertising. EPA sets pesticide tolerances, and FDA enforces them. FDA primarily regulates food processing and manufacturing, whereas states are the primary regulators of restaurants, farms and retail establishments.
- Under the *FD&C Act*, FDA's regulatory authority over foods can be divided into two major categories: adulteration of food and misbranding of food labels and labeling.
- Food may be deemed adulterated for a variety of reasons set out in the *FD&C Act*, including poisonous or deleterious substances in the food, filthy or insanitary conditions under which the food was produced or use of unapproved food additives in the food. FDA has set out CGMPS for sanitation in the production of food. Seafood and juice production are regulated through HACCP principles set out by regulation.
- In general, food labeling is misbranded if it is false or misleading in any particular. FDA's food labeling regulations set out detailed requirements governing mandatory labeling such as ingredient, nutrition and allergen labeling. FDA regulations also govern how certain types of voluntary labeling—primarily claims such as structure/function claims and nutrient content claims—may be made. Nutrient content and health claims cannot be made on foods unless FDA has approved the claims.
- Food additives must be preapproved by regulation for specific uses. GRAS substances are exempted from the definition of food additives and, therefore, do not require premarket approval for use. FDA provides a voluntary GRAS notification program for those seeking some assurance the agency agrees a substance is GRAS.
- Color additives also require FDA premarket approval for specific uses prior to use in any FDA-regulated product. FDA requires batch approval of certain types of color additives.
- Recent food defense amendments require all food facilities to be registered with FDA. In addition, FDA must receive prior notice of any food being imported into the US for distribution. Since September 2009, food facilities also are required to report to FDA whenever the facility determines food manufactured, processed, packed or held there presents a reasonable probability of a serious adverse health consequence or death.
- *FSMA* will change how FDA regulates foods dramatically. It is designed to prevent problems from occurring before food products enter or are offered for sale in the US.

Appreciation: The authors acknowledge the excellent work done by Dr. Nigel Andre Sean Hernandez, the previous author of this chapter on Food Products.

References

1. The *FD&C Act* is codified at 21 USC § 301 *et al.*
2. 21 USC §321(f).
3. P.L. 103-417 (Oct. 25, 1994).
4. The distinction between "labeling" and "advertising" is discussed in more detail under Misbranding: Food Labeling and Claims. Generally, "labeling" includes the food label and all materials "accompanying" the food where sold (such as brochures, displays, or information on websites where the product can be purchased). "Advertising" is, broadly, any marketing of the product that is not labeling.
5. 21 USC §321(s).
6. Ibid.
7. Ibid.
8. See 21 USC §346a.
9. See 21 USC §379e.
10. 21 USC §348(a).
11. See 21 USC §348(j).
12. 21 USC §348(b).
13. 21 USC §348(c)(1)-(2).
14. 21 USC §348(f).
15. 21 USC §348(c)(3).
16. *Guidance for Industry: Frequently Asked Questions About GRAS.* FDA website. http://www.fda.gov/Food/GuidanceRegulation/GuidanceDocumentsRegulatoryInformation/ucm061846.htm. Accessed 2 April 2015.
17. *Guidance for Industry: Recommendations for Submission of Chemical and Technological Data for Direct Food Additive Petitions.* FDA website. http://www.fda.gov/Food/GuidanceRegulation/GuidanceDocumentsRegulatoryInformation/ucm124917.htm. Accessed 2 April 2015.
18. *Guidance for Industry: Summary Table of Recommended Toxicological Testing for Additives Used in Food.* FDA website. http://www.fda.gov/Food/GuidanceRegulation/GuidanceDocumentsRegulatoryInformation/ucm054658.htm. Accessed 2 April 2015.
19. 21 USC §348(c)(3)(A).
20. *Les v. Reilly*, 968 F.2d 985 (9th Cir. 1992) (food additives); *Public Citizen v. Young*, 831 F.2d 1108 (D.C. Cir. 1987) (color additives).
21. See *Scott v. Food and Drug Administration*, 728 F.2d 322 (6th Cir. 1984); *Public Citizen v. Young*, 831 F.2d 1108, 1118-19 (D.C.Cir. 1987).
22. See 21 USC §348(c)(3)(A).
23. Codified at 21 USC §348(a)(3).
24. See 21 USC §321(s).
25. GAO Report: Food Safety: FDA Should Strengthen Its Oversight of Food Ingredients Determined to Be Generally Recognized as Safe (GRAS). February 2010. Publication No. GAO-10-246. GAO website. http://www.gao.gov/products/GAO-10-246. Accessed 2 April 2015.

26. Navigating the US Food Additive Regulatory Program. *Compr Rev Food Sci Food Safety.*2011;10(6):342-368; Food and Drug Administration (US). 2009b. GRAS notice inventory. Wiley website. http://onlinelibrary.wiley.com/doi/10.1111/j.1541-4337.2011.00166.x/full. Accessed 2 April 2015.
27. Conflicts of Interest in Approvals of Additives to Food Determined to Be Generally Recognized as Safe: Out of Balance. Neltner TG Alger HM,; O'Reilly JT, Krimsky S, Bero LA, Maffini MV. *JAMA Intern Med.* 2013; 173 22):2032-2036. doi:10.1001/jamainternmed.2013.10559.
28. "Generally Recognized As Secret" 2014. NRDC website.: http://www.nrdc.org/food/safety-loophole-for-chemicals-in-food.asp. Accessed 2 April 2015.
29. "GRAS Self-determination Inventory Database." 6 October 2014 http://www.aibmr.com/resources/GRAS-database.php. Accessed 2 April 2015.
30. Grocery Manufacturer Association press announcement "GMA Announces Industry Initiative on Ingredients Added to Food" 28 August 2014. GMA website. http://www.gmaonline.org/news-events/newsroom/grocery-manufacturer-association-announces-industry-initiative-on-ingredien/. Accessed 2 April 2015.
31. 21 USC §321(t).
32. See 21 USC §361(e). Cosmetics are discussed in detail in Chapter 32.
33. 21 USC §379e(a).
34. See generally 21 CFR 70–82.
35. In the context of color additives, a "lake" is a form of color additive that is extended on a substratum to make it water insoluble.
36. 21 USC §343.
37. 21 USC §321(k).
38. 21 USC §321(m).
39. *FD&C Act,* Section 331(a), (b), (c).
40. *FD&C Act,* Section 321(n).
41. 21 CFR 101.1.
42. 21 CFR 101.2(a).
43. 21 CFR 101.3.
44. *FD&C Act,* Section 401.
45. 21 CFR 102.5(a).
46. 21 CFR 101.3(b)(3).
47. 21 CFR 101.3(e).
48. 21 CFR 101.105.
49. 21 CFR 101.9.
50. 79 FR 11880 and 11990, March 3, 2014
51. 21 CFR 101.4.
52. P.L. No. 108-282.
53. *FALCPA* §203.
54. 21 CFR 101.5.
55. 9 CFR 317.2(c)(5).
56. 9 CFR 317.2(k).
57. 9 CFR 317.2(l).
58. 9 CFR 317.4; see also "A Guide to Federal Food Labeling Requirements for Meat and Poultry Products," FSIS, August 2007.
59. 78 FR 66826, 7 November 2013.
60. The final rule became effective on 16 March 2009 and is codified in 7 CFR 60 and 65. 74 *Fed Reg.* 2658 (15 January 2009).
61. 19 USC 1304.65.
62. 19 CFR 134.11
63. *FDAMA* refers to the *Food and Drug Administration Modernization Act* of 1997, which, among other amendments, provided for health and nutrient content claims based on statements issued by authoritative government bodies, like the National Academies of Science or the National Institutes of Health.
64. 21 CFR 101.13.
65. *FD&C Act,* Sections 403(r)(1)(A) and 403(r)(2).
66. 21 CFR 101.14.
67. 21 USC §321(g).
68. 21 USC §343(r)(3)(C).
69. 21 USC §343(r)(3)(D).
70. 21 CFR 101.93.
71. *Orphan Drug Act* §5, codified at 21 USC 360ee(b)(3).
72. Food Labeling; Reference Daily Intakes and Daily Reference Values; Mandatory Status of Nutrition Labeling and Nutrition Content Revision proposed rule 56 *Fed. Reg.* 60366 at 60377, 27 November 1991.
73. Op cit 60.
74. 21 CFR Part 107
75. 21 CFR Part 107, Subpart B.
76. *United States v. Anderson Seafoods, Inc.*, 622 F.2d 157, 159-60 (5th Cir. 1980)
77. 21 USC §346.
78. 21 CFR 109.
79. 21 USC §342(a)(3).
80. 21 USC §342(a)(4).
81. FDA FSMA Frequently Asked Questions, Proposed Rule CGMPs and HACCP for Human Foods. FDA website. http://www.fda.gov/downloads/Food/GuidanceRegulation/UCM345224.pdf. Accessed 27 February 2015.
82. FDA. Defect Levels Handbook. FDA website. http://www.fda.gov/food/guidanceregulation/guidancedocumentsregulatoryinformation/ucm056174.htm. Accessed 2 April 2015.
83. 21 CFR 108.25 (acidified foods) and 108.35 (low acid canned foods).
84. 71. P.L. 111–353 (4 January 2011).
85. 21 U.S.C. §374.
86. 21 USC §350c.
87. 21 USC §374.
88. P.L. 107-188.
89. 21 USC §415
90. 21 CFR 1.226(a).
91. 21 CFR 1.226.
92. 21 CFR 1.232.
93. 21 CFR 1.277.
94. 21 CFR 1.279.
95. 21 CFR 1.283.
96. 21 CFR 1.378.
97. Section 304 [21 USC §334] Seizure.
98. 21 CFR 1.379.
99. 21 CFR 1.401.

Chapter 37

Companion Diagnostics

Updated by Maham Ansari, MS, RAC

OBJECTIVES

- ❑ Define personalized medicine and how companion diagnostics fit into the new personalized medicine paradigm
- ❑ Define a companion diagnostic
- ❑ Understand FDA policy development on companion diagnostics and where it stands today
- ❑ Understand the role of both diagnostic and drug companies in the development and FDA approval of companion diagnostics
- ❑ Learn requirements of companion diagnostics during the investigational phase
- ❑ Learn submission requirements and interaction between the different FDA centers
- ❑ Understand postapproval responsibilities of both diagnostic and drug companies in relation to the companion diagnostic
- ❑ Learn about emerging technologies like next generation sequencing

LAWS, REGULATIONS AND GUIDELINES COVERED IN THIS CHAPTER

- ❑ *Guidance for Industry and Food and Drug Administration Staff: In Vitro Companion Diagnostic Devices* (August 2014)
- ❑ *Draft Guidance for Industry, Food and Drug Administration Staff, and Clinical Laboratories: Framework for Regulatory Oversight of Laboratory Developed Tests (LDTs)* (October 2014)
- ❑ *Draft Guidance for Industry, Food and Drug Administration Staff, and Clinical Laboratories: FDA Notification and Medical Device Reporting for Laboratory Developed Tests (LDTs)* (October 2014)
- ❑ *Guidance for Industry and Food and Drug Administration Staff, Requests for Feedback on Medical Device Submissions: The Pre-Submission Program and Meetings with Food and Drug Administration Staff* (February 2014)
- ❑ Medical Device Reporting 21 CFR Part 803, Subpart E
- ❑ Quality System Regulation 21 CFR Part 820

Note: This chapter expands on Chapter 20 Medical Device Submissions and Chapter 23 In Vitro Diagnostics Submissions and Compliance

Introduction

As defined by the Personalized Medicine Coalition (PMC), "Personalized Medicine" refers to the use of diagnostic tools to identify specific biological markers, often genetic, to help determine which medical treatment will be appropriate for each patient.[1] Although the personalized medicine concept is not new, this approach is shaping the new paradigm for modern medicine whereby the biological and genetic elements unique to each person and his or her disease will dictate the most accurate diagnosis, thus leading to the right treatment.[2] This does not entail literal creation of drugs and medical devices unique to each patient,[3] but in fact causes patient "stratification," which means classifying individuals into subpopulations that differ in their susceptibility to a particular disease or their response to a specific treatment due to some characteristic. The ultimate goal of personalized medicine is to provide the right treatment in the right dose to the right patient at the right time.

Personalized medicine most commonly involves the use of two medical products: a diagnostic device and a therapeutic product, to improve patient outcomes. The diagnostic devices created for patient stratification often are in vitro diagnostics (IVDs), generally assays for the measurement of genetic factors, and *in vivo* tests, such as electroencephalography (EEG), electrocardiography (EKG) or diagnostic imaging equipment. Considerable attention currently is being paid to the use of genetic tests to guide therapeutic decisions. These genetic tests or IVDs, when intended to predict which patients are most likely to benefit from a particular drug therapy and assist in the clinical decision on what constitutes the "right drug" for each patient, are known as companion diagnostics (CDx). Today, CDx stand at the heart of personalized medicine.

The aim of this chapter is to summarize the US Food and Drug Administration's (FDA) approach to regulation of CDx, emerging FDA regulation trends and technological advances and the roles and responsibilities of both the diagnostic and therapeutic (drug) partners in co-development of a companion diagnostic and a targeted therapeutic.

What is a Companion Diagnostic?

According to FDA, "An IVD companion diagnostic device is an in vitro diagnostic device that provides information that is essential for the safe and effective use of a corresponding therapeutic product."[5] Per this definition, FDA strongly recommends contemporaneous development, i.e., the CDx is co-developed and approved alongside the corresponding therapeutic; however, the agency recognizes this approach is not always possible.

The most common technologies currently prevalent in the companion diagnostic market are polymerase chain reaction, in-situ hybridization and immunohistochemistry, largely within the area of oncology. While the one test-one drug paradigm currently is the most popular, next generation sequencing (NGS)-based companion diagnostic tests are predicted to capture a larger market share in chronic and life-threatening diseases in the future. These are elaborated on further in this chapter.

Policy Development

Although potential benefits of personalized medicine and CDx are very clear and obvious, the laws and regulations governing these technologies are far more complex and play a large role in determining the pace of development and adoption of these technologies. FDA's role in this is of particular importance.

Early Days to Present

The need for a clear companion diagnostic regulatory path has been a great concern since the first therapeutic product with an accompanying diagnostic (Herceptin®) was approved six months apart from Dako's diagnostic test (HercepTest™) in 1998. While Herceptin made the promise of personalized medicine clear, in the following years, other diagnostic companies followed Dako in obtaining approval on HER2 assays (the genetic marker linked to Genentech's Herceptin), including Ventana, Life Technologies and Leica Biosystems.

The HercepTest approval was the first instance in which FDA linked a specified assay's intended use to a specific drug requiring contemporaneous approval when no such policy existed at the time. In April 2005, FDA released the preliminary *Drug-Diagnostic Co-development Concept Paper*, which never was made final. This was replaced in July 2011 by *Draft Guidance for In Vitro Diagnostic Companion Diagnostic Devices*. At that time, FDA policy on companion diagnostics took a more definitive shape, and the agency approved several companion diagnostics that confirmed the guidance's key thinking; these included Roche Molecular Systems' COBAS 4800 BRAF V600 Mutation Test (P110020-Zelboraf), Abbott Molecular's VYSIS ALK Break Apart FISH Probe Kit (P110012-Xalkori) and QIAGEN's *therascreen*® EGFR RGQ PCR Kit (P120022) and *therascreen*® KRAS RGQ PCR Kit (P110030-Erbitux and P110027-Vectibix). For reference and convenience, FDA provides a page on its website of approved IVD-companion diagnostic devices: http://www.fda.gov/MedicalDevices/ProductsandMedicalProcedures/InVitroDiagnostics/ucm301431.htm.[5]

Table 37-1 outlines the main FDA guidance documents available on personalized medicine and companion diagnostics.

Current Policy

With the release of the final guidance, *Guidance for Industry and Food and Drug Administration Staff: In Vitro Companion Diagnostic Devices* in August 2014, replacing the 2011 draft version, the long-awaited US companion diagnostic

Table 37-1. Principal FDA Policy and Guidance Documents

Publication Date	Title
April 2005	Draft Preliminary Concept Paper: Drug-Diagnostic Co-Development Concept Paper
July 2011	*Draft Guidance for Industry and Food and Drug Administration Staff: In Vitro Companion Diagnostic Devices*
December 2012	*Draft Guidance for Industry: Enrichment Strategies for Clinical Trials to Support Approval of Human Drugs and Biological Products*
January 2013	*Guidance for Industry: Clinical Pharmacogenomics: Premarket Evaluation in Early Phase Clinical Studies and Recommendations for Labeling*
August 2014	*Guidance for Industry and Food and Drug Administration Staff: In Vitro Companion Diagnostic Devices*
In Process	*Guidance on Drug-Diagnostic Co-development*

policy finally was established. This final guidance sets the new paradigm for FDA regulation of companion diagnostics, with the goal of helping companies identify the need for companion diagnostics at an earlier stage in the drug development process and plan for drug and companion diagnostic co-development. The guidance's ultimate goal is to stimulate early collaborations that will result in faster access to promising new treatments for patients living with serious and life-threatening diseases.[6]

The final guidance generally is very similar to the draft version, with a few notable clarifications such as defining the word 'essential' when the use of the diagnostic device is "required" in the therapeutic product's labeling (final guidance footnote 6). A notable difference is FDA's position regarding combination products in the context of companion diagnostics. The final guidance's language is much stronger, with the agency emphasizing that even if products could constitute a combination product, separate marketing applications for the drug and diagnostic still are mandatory, while the draft guidance stated a single application may be submitted.

In the final guidance for Novel Therapeutic Products, FDA requires the companion diagnostic to be developed and approved or cleared contemporaneously so it will be available for use when the therapeutic product is approved. The therapeutic will not be approved until the IVD is cleared, and the companion diagnostic also will be included in the therapeutic's labeling. The guidance document also discusses cases when prior companion diagnostic approval is not required, such as when the therapeutic is intended to treat serious or life-threatening conditions. All these are to be reviewed by FDA on a case-by-case basis, and the guidance notes supplements to an approved therapeutic product application to update that product's labeling will not be approved until the companion diagnostic is cleared, unless a serious safety issue arises.

Since the diagnostic's proper use is critical to the proper use of its associated therapeutic product, FDA's Office of In Vitro Diagnostics and Radiological Health (OIR) maintains the companion diagnostic takes on the drug's risk profile and therefore classifies them as Class III devices requiring Premarket Approval (PMA). While the guidance does mention there can be cases where a companion diagnostic can be a 510(k) instead of a PMA, it does not go into any detail about what circumstances might make this possible, especially noting most CDx devices approved in the US thus far have required PMAs. An example of this, and also an exception to FDA's contemporaneous approval policy, was the approval of Vertex's Kayldeco. Kayldeco is approved for the treatment of cystic fibrosis (CF) for patients who have a mutation in their CF gene called the G551D mutation. Kayldeco is not effective in patients with CF with two copies of the F508del mutation (F508del/F508del) in the CF gene. If the patient's genotype is unknown, the drug's labeling states an FDA-cleared CF mutation test should be used to detect the presence of the G551D mutation. In this case, several FDA-cleared CF tests included detection of these mutations in their indications. Although FDA determined it was in the interest of public health not to require a separate diagnostic approval in the case of Kayldeco, the agency has determined in other cases an existing 510(k) clearance is insufficient to ensure safe and effective device use as a companion diagnostic. If a 510(k)-cleared product will be used to select patients during a pivotal trial, it is important the study sponsor has a discussion with the Center for Drug Evaluation and Research (CDER) or the Center for Biologics Evaluation and Research (CBER) and the Center for Devices and Radiological Health (CDRH) to ensure any companion diagnostic device requirements are known early in the development process.

The final guidance is very general and leaves some open questions such as not covering details of the co-development process itself and other aspects such as diagnostic test analytical and clinical validation requirements. FDA also is currently developing guidance on drug-diagnostic co-development that is expected to provide more insight into the agency's thinking and bridge some gaps in the final guidance.

Due to the complexity and logistical issues that arise in the co-development of drugs and diagnostic tests, a defined regulatory path for approving such product combinations would mark a significant step forward. FDA's dedication

Figure 37-1. Drug-Diagnostic Co-Development Process

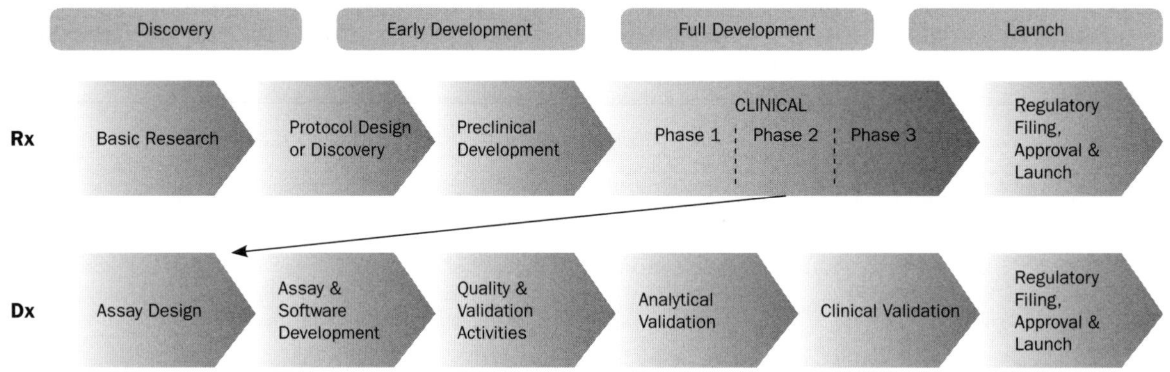

to personalized medicine is evident in the creation of the Personalized Medicine staff and director in the Office of In Vitro Diagnostics and Radiological Health (OIR) and CBER's efforts to help coordinate regulatory oversight between centers to ensure efficient personalized medicine product review. In October 2013, FDA released, *Paving the Way for Personalized Medicine: FDA's Role in a New Era of Medical Product Development,* which describes many of the personalized medicine developments and impending advances.[7,8] More recently, President's Obama's *Precision Medicine Initiative* promises the US government's commitment to personalized medicine and opens avenues for more funding to overcome challenges in this area.

Policy on LDTs

Traditionally, diagnostic tests fall into two main categories: diagnostic kits and laboratory developed tests (LDTs). The former, being in vitro diagnostic devices, are regulated by the FDA as medical devices. For LDTs, the agency has exercised what it describes as "enforcement discretion" and does not regulate them actively. The Centers for Medicare and Medicaid Services (CMS) has regulated laboratories, including those developing LDTs, under the *Clinical Laboratory Improvement Amendments* (*CLIA*) since 1988.[9] Although *CLIA* addresses laboratory testing processes, it does not assess their safety and effectiveness, i.e., the analytical and clinical validity of diagnostic tests. These are covered under the *Food, Drug, and Cosmetic Act* (*FD&C Act*) and enforced by FDA through its premarket clearance and approval process.

After years of debate and discussion on FDA's LDT oversight, on 3 October 2014, FDA released two draft guidance documents: *Framework for Regulatory Oversight of Laboratory Developed Tests (LDTs)* (the Framework Guidance) and *FDA Notification and Medical Device Reporting for Laboratory Developed Tests (LDTs)*,[10] rejecting any petitions challenging FDA's authority to regulate LDTs and announcing the agency could regulate LDTs as devices and do so through guidance documents and not rulemaking. (see Chapter 23 In Vitro Diagnostics Submissions and Compliance for more information.)

FDA now intends to take a risk-based approach in regulating LDTs. This means there will be three LDT groups: LDTs subject to full enforcement discretion; LDTs subject to partial enforcement discretion; and LDTs subject to full FDA regulation. Companion diagnostics are defined in the guidance as high-risk LDTs (Class III medical devices) and therefore are subject to full regulation. For all currently marketed LDTs with the same intended use as companion diagnostics, premarket submissions are required to be submitted 12 months after the guidance is finalized. If the appropriate premarket submission (generally a PMA) is made within the 12-month period after the draft guidance's release, FDA intends to continue exercising enforcement discretion while the premarket submission is under agency review, to avoid interrupting patient access. FDA intends to begin enforcing premarket review requirements immediately upon publication of the final guidance document for all new high-risk LDTs. Medical device reporting (MDR) requirements (21 CFR Part 803, Subpart E) will be enforced beginning six months after the guidance's finalization. Although FDA predicts the guidance documents will be finalized by the end of 2015, it is possible that the final documents may be significantly different.

The Drug-Diagnostic Co-Development Concept

The drug-diagnostic co-development process is complex and comes with a set of challenges companies must address before a perfect model can be achieved. While some larger organizations like Roche and Abbott, through having expertise in both drugs and diagnostics, are co-developing their products in-house, the vast majority of diagnostic and therapeutic products come from separate companies. The drug-device firms that partner need to account for the fact that each has a completely different model based on development platforms employing different technologies. A drug's development timeline is much longer than that for the diagnostic, and the question remains, at what point in the development process should the drug company approach a diagnostics firm? Early engagement between partners and with FDA is essential for co-development success. **Figure 37-1** illustrates the drug diagnostic co-development process.

Selecting Partners

Most companion diagnostic projects begin when a drug company identifies the need for a diagnostic and decides to seek the assistance of a diagnostics partner. Typically, the drug company provides substantial funds for the project and controls project scheduling. Business and economic factors make this the most likely case, but regulatory factors also are involved. For example, there is an imbalance under current FDA policy between the labeling requirements of a targeted therapeutic and a diagnostic. The targeted therapeutic generally requires an "FDA-approved diagnostic" in its labeling, but companion diagnostic labeling refers to a specific drug. As a consequence, while drug companies have some latitude to work with multiple partners or no partner at all, it is difficult for diagnostic companies to proceed beyond early development with a CDx project without identifying a drug partner.

Much of the early work on a companion diagnostic project involves the drug company finding the right partner(s) and establishing the right agreements. Many criteria may shape the drug company's final decision; at minimum, the right diagnostic partner will have both the technical ability and the appropriate rights to test for a particular analyte or gene. For example, a drug company may discover it needs to test for a particular gene, but the rights to test for this gene (or the bulk of the information pertaining to the gene) are owned exclusively by one diagnostics company or by a small number of companies. If this is the case, the drug partner is unlikely to have broad latitude in selecting a diagnostics partner; essentially, it will be impossible to submit a regulatory application without securing the rights-holder's permission. Fortunately, for most analytes and genes, there are no such ownership claims. When this is the case, the drug company will need to choose a diagnostics partner with the technical ability to detect the marker linked to use of the drug and the right infrastructure and business relationships to support the drug postapproval. The diagnostic company's track record in previous companion diagnostic approvals also may be considered.

Role of Drug Partner

The drug company must provide as much information as possible on both the disease biology and the drug's action to allow the diagnostic company to understand precisely what the test needs to measure and what performance characteristics (such as cut-offs) the test needs to demonstrate. It will be very important for the drug company's biomarker scientists to work closely with the diagnostic development scientists to ensure the proper requirements are captured prior to use in a pivotal clinical trial. If additional development activities are performed after the diagnostic is used in a pivotal trial, the results from that trial could be compromised, and additional studies might be required. It is not always practical to complete diagnostic development prior to the pivotal trial, but it is highly advisable to know what impact development may have on project schedule and budget. This is why the timing of the partnership for properly aligning the development of both products, as discussed earlier, plays a vital role in the co-development program's success.

Role of Diagnostic Partner

The diagnostic partner's role is to develop a test that will measure an analyte or analytes with the necessary precision to inform the drug's treatment decisions. This work needs to be performed in a manner and to standards that will facilitate FDA approval. Specifically, the diagnostic company must develop the product under design controls and also comply with other Quality System Regulation (QSR, 21 CFR Part 820) requirements, including software validation.

Presubmission Activities

Meetings With Drug Review Branch (CDER or CBER)

Early meetings about the companion diagnostic typically occur in the context of the drug's review. It is the responsibility of the drug review branch (CDER or CBER) to determine whether the investigational study design is appropriate to allow eventual approval of the therapy. One key discussion point will be whether the drug should be studied in a "selected" group of patients (either marker-negative or marker-positive) or an "unselected" group (both marker-negative and marker-positive patients). Selected designs are becoming more common, as they often allow a more efficient selection process. FDA tends to prefer unselected designs, however, making it possible to reach a more meaningful determination of whether marker status predicts the drug's efficacy. Generally, FDA is inclined to resist a selected design unless selection addresses a specific safety issue.

Meetings with the drug review branch typically include personnel from the device review branch, usually CDRH, or in certain cases, CBER, depending on the center regulating the diagnostic. Device review personnel are invited to early-stage drug review meetings so there is broad understanding across the relevant FDA groups regarding issues with both the drug and the diagnostic test.

Meetings With Device Review Branch (CDRH or CBER)

Once a drug moves past Phase 2, and it appears the marker may be important to the drug's safe and effective use, the drug review branch typically will recommend the drug company set up a meeting with the device review branch (CDRH or CBER). The device review branch will be responsible for ensuring the diagnostic product performs appropriately, and all studies demonstrating both nonclinical and clinical performance have been completed to the appropriate standard. Early discussions will include required analytical studies (i.e., limit of detection (LoD), precision, linearity, interfering substances, cross-contamination).The LoD study almost always is a key discussion issue. The assay detection limit needs to be determined by the biology of the disease and the drug. The final LoD determination will require coordination and agreement between both FDA review branches.

It is now the norm to have the drug review branch attend early meetings with the device review branch. Depending on the situation, a drug company may choose to have a meeting with the device review group prior to selecting a diagnostic partner. These meetings may help the drug company understand regulatory requirements and make a more informed partner choice. In other situations, it may be more efficient to engage device review personnel after a diagnostic partner is selected. To facilitate partner selection, discussions with the device review branch and coordination with the diagnostic partner, more and more drug companies are creating an in-house companion diagnostics departments and hiring personnel with diagnostic backgrounds, particularly within the diagnostic regulatory and development areas.

Investigational Device Exemptions vs. Investigational New Drugs

An Investigational Device Exemption (IDE) is not required for many IVDs but often is required in a companion diagnostic study. In the early days of companion diagnostics, the drug company incorporated the relevant device information into its Investigational New Drug (IND) application in lieu of submitting a parallel IDE. More recently, device review branches have been requesting device companies to prepare a separate IDE that is approved in parallel with the IND. Submitting a parallel IDE appears to address challenges with information-sharing across the centers and provide some efficiency for each center in tracking reviews and approvals separately.

The key information to include in a companion diagnostic IDE is the data that support investigational product use for select patients for the trial. This typically is a subset of the analytical testing ultimately required for PMA approval. The IDE also must contain the drug study protocol and key study documentation such as the Informed Consent Form. Although the protocol will be for the drug study (not a separate device study), the IDE must provide information on the site(s) that will perform the assay (rather than the investigators who will administer the drug). By restricting the IDE scope to the assay-running sites, it will be easier to know whether the IDE or IND needs to be updated as the trial proceeds. The ultimate responsibility for adhering to Good Clinical Practices (GCPs) falls to the study sponsor, typically the drug partner. Even so, the diagnostic partner may take on some responsibility to ensure the test is being run appropriately and does not change during the trial.

PMA and NDA

The diagnostic information from the trial will need to be incorporated into the NDA or Biologics License Application (BLA) for the therapy. Since the study sponsor handles the clinical database, the drug partner typically has the diagnostic information needed for an NDA or BLA once the trial is completed. However, the diagnostic partner should be prepared to respond to requests if any issues are noted with diagnostic testing during or after the trial. Apart from providing incidental support, it is not typical for the diagnostic partner to be involved with the drug submission.

Although the diagnostic partner does not have much involvement with the drug partner's submission, typically, the reverse is not true. The diagnostic partner will need several key pieces of information from the drug partner before filing the PMA or 510(k). Because the diagnostic's clinical utility is inherent to the drug's safe and effective use, the drug partner's safety analysis is germane to documenting that use. In some cases, the diagnostic may have undergone additional development or design change subsequent to the pivotal trial. If this is the case, it will be necessary to conduct a bridging study to show concordance between the clinical trial assay and the assay being submitted for approval. Meeting this requirement will involve the drug partner, because the safety analysis must be repeated with the assay to be commercialized to ensure the version change has not affected the basis for clinical utility.

Normally, companion diagnostics are Class III (high-risk) devices requiring a PMA, and new therapies typically require an NDA or BLA. To ensure FDA has adequate time to review both submissions, diagnostic companies typically submit a modular PMA. The modular PMA approach allows the diagnostic company to submit the PMA in pieces (modules) while the clinical trial is ongoing. For example, the diagnostic information on quality systems and manufacturing, software and analytical studies could be submitted and reviewed during the study. Then, when the clinical data are ready, the final clinical PMA module is submitted at the same time as the NDA. This approach allows FDA to keep the reviews in sync and, hopefully, be ready to approve both the drug and device at the same time.

Currently, if either the drug or device falls behind in the review process, there is a high risk that the paired products will be held up for review until both can be approved contemporaneously. However, the risks are not the same for both parties, and delays can realign incentives dramatically. A companion diagnostic device cannot be approved without the drug, but the reverse is not always true. There is no formal process yet for resolving companion diagnostic submission sync issues. The "correct" policy answer is both approvals must wait, as each product is only safe and effective in the context of the other. Practically speaking, FDA faces political and public health pressures to approve certain therapies, and this can lead to "creative" thinking on such policies; such exceptions are reflected in the final companion diagnostic guidance.

Postapproval

At the time of publication, companion diagnostics still are new enough that there is not enough definitive information to determine how certain postapproval responsibilities and issues will be handled.

Labeling

Targeted therapeutic labels are not required to reference a particular manufacturer's companion diagnostic device, only to include a reference the diagnostic is an FDA-approved or -cleared test. On the other hand, companion diagnostic labeling must mention the specific drug with which it is intended to be used, except in cases where evidence is sufficient to conclude the companion diagnostic is appropriate for use with a class of therapeutic products. However, this labeling policy explicitly leaves open the possibility additional diagnostic products may be approved for the same marker after the drug has been approved. The good news, as noticed in cases such as HER2, is although multiple companies have gained approval to market diagnostics intended for use with the same drug, they have done well.

The labeling of both the drug and diagnostic components of a companion diagnostic assume both products will be commercially available at the same time. It is not clear yet what would happen if FDA were to pull one of these paired products off the market. It is even more challenging to contemplate what should happen if one product were removed from the market voluntarily or not meaningfully offered for sale in the first place.

Any changes to drug labeling, such as addition of a new indication, would call for contemporaneous approval of a PMA supplement or a new or special 510(k) for its companion diagnostic (unless the change to drug labeling is urgent and safety related, at which point the requirement for contemporaneous approval is waived). All the scenarios mentioned here prove the relationship between the drug and diagnostic partners is an ongoing relationship and expected to last throughout the lifecycle of both products.

Reimbursement

The transition from development to commercialization is another challenge. Regulatory approval does not necessarily clear an assay's path to market. Coverage and payment policies—whether in government programs like Medicare or those of private payers—play an equally important role. Current systems largely consider drugs and diagnostics via separate evaluation and payment processes; this can lead to significant challenges, such as successful reimbursement of the drug but not its companion diagnostic, or vice versa.

While payers recognize personalized medicine's benefits, they increasingly are seeking additional evidence of a test's clinical utility. Unlike the pharmaceutical industry where reimbursement is value-based, until recently, payments for molecular diagnostic tests in the US were predictable and standardized, relying on payments based on "stacked codes."[11] Now this has been shifted to unique reimbursement or Z-Code per biomarker.[12] While this is a step toward establishing a value-based reimbursement price for each molecular diagnostic based on its impact on healthcare costs and patient outcome, payment and reimbursement policy changes have led to significant disruptions for laboratories and developers of personalized medicine products.[13] Pharmaceutical companies and their diagnostic partners need to collaborate very closely to generate the necessary evidence and obtain adequate reimbursement. Therefore, it is important to assess reimbursement requirements at early stages and identify potential entry strategies to maximize the chance of market access following regulatory approval.

Adverse Events

Adverse event (AE) reporting in the world of personalized medicine is not a very transparent process at this time. Misdiagnosis can result in delayed treatment, unnecessary treatment or lack of treatment, potentially leading to the recall of the diagnostic, which could result in further disruption in treatment. Therefore, the drug and diagnostic partners should work very closely to determine the cause of the AE. This could be the result of a physician or pathologist error, an issue with the drug's safety and effectiveness or failure of the companion diagnostic test kit to meet its performance specifications.

Future of CDx—Next Generation Sequencing

NGS-based companion diagnostics are predicted to be one of the major drivers in the companion diagnostics market in the near future due to their capability to identify multiple genes at a single time. NGS end results are superior when compared to other technologies, as NGS provides a wider definition of genome sequencing. A single NGS test can identify thousands, even millions of genetic variants, and, therefore, can be used to diagnose or predict an individual's risk of developing many different conditions or diseases. A number of NGS-platform diagnostic firms currently are engaged in developing NGS-based companion diagnostic tests for other chronic and life-threatening diseases and are entering into strategic acquisitions and collaborations with pharmaceutical firms. For example, companies like Thermo Fisher Scientific and Illumina already have entered partnerships with multiple pharmaceutical firms to develop universal next-generation sequencing-based oncology tests for solid tumors that will serve as companion diagnostic tests for several drug programs in one panel. The rapid adoption of NGS-based companion diagnostic tests gradually may make the one drug-one test-one disease paradigm obsolete.

This is challenging from a regulatory standpoint because the current guidelines focus on a one drug-one test concept, and no guidelines exist on validating multiple gene platforms. Since 2011, FDA has been evaluating its regulatory approach to NGS, has hosted several public workshops examining various aspects of NGS and has interacted extensively with scientists and other subject matter experts at conferences and in other professional venues.[14] In 2013, FDA cleared the first NGS instrument as well as two NGS tests for Cystic Fibrosis (Illumina MiSeqDx™; Cystic Fibrosis 139 Variant and Clinical Sequencing Assays).[15] In early 2015, FDA published a preliminary discussion paper on the topic and soon after followed it up through public comment at a meeting on NGS technology. As a result of this meeting, FDA intends to determine the types of changes, if any, it should initiate with respect to its oversight of NGS tests and communicate its findings and conclusions to the public.

Conclusion

Although FDA has come a long way in developing and refining its policies on companion diagnostic regulation, the complexity of co-development and the rapid pace of new emerging technologies like NGS nonetheless pose a challenge in developing policy aligned with the current landscape, leaving the agency to try to keep pace. At this point, while the final guidance is a great starting point for companies looking into contemporaneous drug-diagnostic development, FDA strongly recommends companies involve the agency in discussions very early in the co-development process, as each new product will be assessed on a case-by-case basis based on the agency's current thinking.

References

1. About. Personalized Medicine Coalition website. http://www.personalizedmedicinecoalition.org/About_Us/About_PMC. Accessed 8 March 2015.
2. Ansari M. "The Regulation of Companion Diagnostics: A Global Perspective." *Therapeutic Innovation & Regulatory Science*. Vol. 47; pp. 405-415. (2013).
3. Priorities for Personalized Medicine; President's Council of Advisors on Science and Technology (September 2008). White House website. www.whitehouse.gov/files/documents/ostp/PCAST/pcast_report_v2.pdf. Accessed 8 March 2015.
4. *Guidance for Industry and Food and Drug Administration Staff: In Vitro Companion Diagnostic Devices* (August 2014). FDA website. http://www.fda.gov/downloads/MedicalDevices/DeviceRegulationandGuidance/GuidanceDocuments/UCM262327.pdf. Accessed 8 March 2015.
5. List of Cleared or Approved Companion Diagnostic Devices (In Vitro and Imaging Tools). FDA website. http://www.fda.gov/MedicalDevices/ProductsandMedicalProcedures/InVitroDiagnostics/ucm301431.htm. Accessed 8 March 2015.
6. Companion Diagnostics. FDA website. http://www.fda.gov/MedicalDevices/ProductsandMedicalProcedures/InVitroDiagnostics/ucm407297.htm. Accessed 8 March 2015.
7. *The Case for Personalized Medicine*. Personalized Medicine Coalition. 4th Edition. 2014. Personalized Medicine Coalition website. http://www.personalizedmedicinecoalition.org/Userfiles/PMC-Corporate/file/pmc_the_case_for_personalized_medicine.pdf. Accessed 8 March 2015.
8. *Paving the Way for Personalized Medicine: FDA's Role in the New Era of Medical Product Development*. FDA website. http://www.fda.gov/downloads/ScienceResearch/SpecialTopics/PersonalizedMedicine/UCM372421.pdf. October 2013. Accessed 8 March 2015.
9. *Draft Guidance for Industry, Food and Drug Administration Staff, and Clinical Laboratories: Framework for Regulatory Oversight of Laboratory Developed Tests (LDTs)* (October 2014). FDA website. http://www.fda.gov/downloads/MedicalDevices/DeviceRegulationandGuidance/GuidanceDocuments/UCM416685.pdf. Accessed 8 March 2015.
10. *Draft Guidance for Industry, Food and Drug Administration Staff, and Clinical Laboratories: FDA Notification and Medical Device Reporting for Laboratory Developed Tests (LDTs)* (October 2014). FDA website. http://www.fda.gov/downloads/medicaldevices/deviceregulationandguidance/guidancedocuments/ucm416684.pdf. Accessed 8 March 2015.
11. Op cit. 7.
12. Op cit. 2.
13. Op cit. 7.
14. Optimizing FDA's Regulatory Oversight of Next Generation Sequencing Diagnostic Tests—Preliminary Discussion Paper. FDA website. http://www.fda.gov/downloads/MedicalDevices/NewsEvents/WorkshopsConferences/UCM427869.pdf. Accessed 28 February 2015.
15. Ibid.

Chapter 38

Medical Foods

Updated by Maruthi Prasad Palthur, PhD, PMP, RAC (US)

OBJECTIVES

- ❑ Develop a broad understanding of medical foods' statutory definition and criteria
- ❑ Understand the basics of regulations and labeling requirements pertinent to medical foods
- ❑ Understand the basic regulatory requirements for medical food manufacturing
- ❑ Develop a broad understanding of the regulation of medical foods

LAWS, REGULATIONS AND GUIDELINES COVERED IN THIS CHAPTER

- ❑ *Orphan Drug Act* of 1983 (Public Law 97-414)
- ❑ *Orphan Drug Amendments* of 1988 (Public Law 100-290)
- ❑ *Nutrition Labeling and Education Act* of 1990 (Public Law 101-535)
- ❑ *Food Allergen Labeling and Consumer Protection Act* of 2004 (Public Law 108-282)
- ❑ *Fair Packaging and Labeling Act* of 1966 (Public Law 89-755)
- ❑ *Federal Food, Drug, and Cosmetic Act* of 1938 (codified as amended at 21 U.S.C. § 301 *et al)*
- ❑ *Food Allergen Labeling and Consumer Protection Act* of 2004 (Public Law 108-282)
- ❑ *Food Safety Modernization Act* of 2011 (Public Law 111-353)
- ❑ *Food and Drug Administration Amendments Act* of 2007 (Public Law 110-085)
- ❑ 21 CFR 350 Vitamins and minerals
- ❑ 21 CFR 101 Food Labeling
- ❑ 21 CFR 101.9 Nutrition labeling of food
- ❑ 21 CFR 343 Misbranded food
- ❑ 21 CFR 110 Current Good Manufacturing Practice in manufacturing, packing, or holding human food
- ❑ 21 CFR 113 Thermally processed low-acid foods packaged in hermetically sealed containers
- ❑ 21 CFR 108 Emergency permit control
- ❑ 21 CFR 1, Subpart H Registration of food facilities
- ❑ 21 CFR 350f Reportable food registry
- ❑ 21 CFR 107.240 Notification requirements

- ❑ 21 CFR 172 Food additives permitted for direct addition to food for human consumption
- ❑ 21 CFR 73 Listing of color additives exempt from certification
- ❑ 21 CFR 74 Listing of color additives subject to certification
- ❑ 21 CFR 170.30 Eligibility for classification as Generally Recognized As Safe
- ❑ 21 CFR 182 Substances Generally Recognized As Safe
- ❑ 21 CFR 184 Direct food substances affirmed as Generally Recognized As Safe
- ❑ 21 CFR 186 Indirect food substances affirmed as Generally Recognized As Safe
- ❑ 21 CFR 107.50 Terms and conditions
- ❑ 21 CFR 106 Infant formula requirements pertaining to current good manufacturing practice, quality control procedures, quality factors, records and reports, and notifications
- ❑ 21 CFR 107 Infant formula
- ❑ Compliance Program 7321.002. Medical Foods Program – Import and Domestic (24 August 2006)
- ❑ Compliance Program 7321.006. Infant Formula Program – Import and Domestic (31 July 2006)
- ❑ *Draft Guidance for Industry: Frequently Asked Questions About Medical Foods; Second Edition* (May 1997; May 2007; Revised August 2013)
- ❑ *Guidance for Industry: Questions and Answers Regarding Food Allergens, including the Food Allergen Labeling and Consumer Protection Act of 2004 (Edition 4); Final Guidance* (October 2006)
- ❑ *Guidance for Clinical Investigators, Sponsors, and IRBs Investigational New Drug Applications (INDs)—Determining Whether Human Research Studies Can Be Conducted Without an IND* (September 2013)
- ❑ *Guidance for Industry: Frequently Asked Questions about GRAS* (December 2004)
- ❑ *Guidance for Industry: Questions and Answers Regarding the Reportable Food Registry as Established by the Food and Drug Administration Amendments Act of 2007* (September 2009)

Introduction

Food is one of the most basic human needs. Traditionally, food has been viewed as a means of providing nutrients to maintain homeostasis and sustenance. As a response to advances in food sciences and health-related research, some foods have adopted a different connotation of promoting health and reducing the risk of disease, beyond meeting basic nutritional needs. In the course of this evolution, a special category of foods with an emphasis on nutritional intervention to meet the distinctive nutritional requirements or metabolic deficiencies of a particular disease state has emerged. These foods are distinguished from the broader category of foods and are formulated specially for the specific dietary management of a disease or condition. These foods are unique because they cannot be classified as either conventional foods or prescription drugs, thereby requiring the concept of a distinct class of foods. At the global level, the approach to defining and regulating this unique category of foods is heterogeneous. In the US, these products are regulated as "medical foods."

Historical Regulation of Medical Foods

In the *Federal Register* of 22 November 1941 (6 FR 5921), the US Food and Drug Administration (FDA) for the first time promulgated a regulation using the term "special dietary uses." 'Special dietary uses,' as applied to food for man, means particular (as distinguished from general) uses of food, and means, among other things, "uses for supplying particular dietary needs which exist by reason of a physical, physiological, pathological or other condition, including but not limited to the conditions of disease, convalescence, pregnancy, lactation, allergic hypersensitivity to food, underweight, and overweight."

Before 1972, FDA regulated products for dietary management in disease conditions as drugs under Section 201(g)(1)(B) of the *Federal Food, Drug, and Cosmetic Act* (*FD&C Act*) because of their role in mitigating serious adverse effects of the underlying diseases. The statutory definition of "special dietary use" in Section 411(c)(3) of the act (21 U.S.C. 350(c)(3)) was added in 1976 (Pub. L. 94–278).[1] It defines this term as a particular use for which a food purports or is represented to be used, including, but not limited to the following: (a) supplying a special dietary need that exists by reason of a physical, physiological, pathological or other condition, including but not limited to the condition of disease, convalescence, pregnancy, lactation, infancy, allergic hypersensitivity to food, underweight, overweight or the need to control intake of sodium; (b) supplying a vitamin, mineral, or other ingredient for use by man to supplement his diet by increasing the total dietary intake; and (c) supplying a special dietary need by reason of being a food for use as the sole item of the diet.

Congress amended the *Orphan Drug Act* (Pub. Law. 97-414) of 1983.[2] The *Orphan Drug Amendments* of 1988 (Pub. Law. 100-290) enacted for the first time a statutory definition of "medical food."[3] Although Congress provided a statutory definition for medical foods, the legislative history of the *Orphan Drug Amendments* does not discuss the definition and, therefore, does not provide any further information regarding the types of products this definition was intended to cover. The *Nutrition Labeling and Education Act* (*NLEA*) of 1990 (Pub. Law 101-535) incorporated the definition of medical foods contained in the *Orphan Drug Amendments* of 1988 into *FD&C Act* Section 403(q)(5)(A)(iv) (21 U.S.C. 343(q)(5)(A)(iv)) and exempted medical foods from the nutrition labeling, health claim and nutrient content claim requirements applicable to other foods.[4] The final rule on mandatory nutrition labeling (58 *FR* 2079 at 2151, 6 January 1993) exempted medical foods from the nutrition labeling requirements and incorporated the statutory definition of a medical food into the regulations at 21 CFR 101.9(j)(8). In this regulation, FDA enumerated criteria intended to clarify the characteristics of medical foods.[5] In 1996, FDA proposed an Advance Notice of Proposed Rulemaking (ANPR) on regulating medical foods, which subsequently was withdrawn due to lack of activity, lack of resources and changes in priorities.[6] FDA provided guidance on medical foods in May 1997, which was revised in May 2007 and August 2013.[7] Effective 24 August 2006, FDA issued a Compliance Program Guidance Manual specific to medical foods.[8]

Since 1972, the legislative and regulatory history of medical foods has reflected FDA's efforts to develop a regulatory framework to manage the distinctive nutritional requirements resulting from health conditions while ensuring the safety and nutritional adequacy of medical foods.

Statutory Definition and Criteria

"Medical food," as defined in Section 5(b) of the *Orphan Drug Act* (21 U.S.C. 360ee(b)(3)), is "a food which is formulated to be consumed or administered enterally under the supervision of a physician and which is intended for the specific dietary management of a disease or condition for which distinctive nutritional requirements, based on recognized scientific principles, are established by medical evaluation."[9] The agency advises it considers the statutory definition of medical foods to narrowly constrain the types of products that fit within this food category.

The criteria clarifying the statutory definition of a medical food can be found at 21 CFR 101.9(j)(8).[10] A food is a medical food and exempt from nutrition labeling only if:

- It is a specially formulated and processed product (as opposed to a naturally occurring foodstuff used in its natural state) for the partial or exclusive feeding of a patient by means of oral intake or enteral feeding by tube.
- It is intended for the dietary management of a patient who, because of therapeutic or chronic medical needs, has limited or impaired capacity to ingest, digest, absorb or metabolize ordinary foodstuffs or certain nutrients, or who has other special medically determined nutrient requirements, the dietary management of which cannot be achieved by the modification of the normal diet alone.
- It provides nutritional support specifically modified for the management of the unique nutrient needs that result from the specific disease or condition, as determined by medical evaluation.
- It is intended to be used under medical supervision.
- It is intended only for a patient receiving active and ongoing medical supervision wherein the patient requires medical care on a recurring basis for, among other things, instructions on the use of the medical food.

Conditions for Which a Medical Food Could Be Labeled and Marketed

Medical foods are distinguished from the broader category of foods for special dietary use and foods that make health claims by the requirement that medical foods are intended to meet distinctive nutritional requirements of a disease or condition and be used under medical supervision, and are intended for the specific dietary management of a disease or condition. The term "medical foods" does not pertain to all foods fed to sick patients. In addition, medical foods are not those simply recommended by a physician or other healthcare professional as a component of an overall diet to manage the symptoms or reduce the risk of a disease or medical condition.[11]

Medical foods are intended for the specific dietary management of a disease or condition for which distinctive nutritional requirements are based on recognized scientific principles and are established by medical evaluation. In addition, FDA's regulations clarifying the statutory definition of a medical food specify such a product is a food intended to be used under medical supervision and intended only for a patient receiving active and ongoing medical supervision wherein the patient requires medical care on a recurring basis for, among other things, instructions on the use of the medical food (21 CFR 101.9(j)(8)(iv) and (v)). Medical foods must be intended for a patient who has a limited or impaired capacity to ingest, digest, absorb or metabolize ordinary foodstuffs or certain nutrients, or who has other special medically determined nutrient requirements, the dietary management of which cannot be achieved by the modification of the normal diet alone (21 CFR 101.9(j)(8)(ii)).

FDA generally considers inborn metabolism errors to be diseases or conditions a medical food could be used to manage. Therefore, if a product meets the definition of a medical food, FDA generally would consider a product labeled and marketed for inborn metabolism errors to meet the regulatory criteria for a medical food. FDA generally would not consider a product labeled and marketed for classical nutrient deficiency diseases typically managed through dietary modification or dietary supplementation to meet a medical food's regulatory criteria (21 CFR 101.9(j)(8)(iii)). In addition, FDA generally would not consider a product labeled and marketed for overall diet therapy or dietary modification to meet the medical food regulatory criteria. Conventional foods and naturally occurring foodstuff are not formulated and processed especially for the specific dietary management of a disease or condition with distinctive nutritional requirements; hence, regardless of their nutrient values, they would not meet the medical food regulatory criteria (21 CFR 101.9(j)(8)(i)).

Due to their intended use in supplying the distinctive nutritional needs of patients who are ill or otherwise medically vulnerable, it is essential medical foods be formulated appropriately for the particular disease or condition for which they are labeled. If the product, as formulated and consumed, does not meet those distinctive requirements, it would violate the act. Medical foods cannot be labeled or marketed for a disease or condition that can be managed solely by a normal diet alone.

Labeling

Medical foods are regulated, as are other foods, under the provisions of the *FD&C Act* and the *Fair Packaging and Labeling Act* (*FPLA*) of 1966 (Pub. Law 89-755).[12] Their labeling must comply with all food labeling requirements except those specific requirements from which medical foods are exempt. As a component of the broader category of foods, medical foods must comply with the general food labeling requirements of 21 CFR 101.[13] Medical foods must contain the following mandatory label information and conformation requirements:

- a statement of identity (21 CFR 101.3)
- an accurate statement of the net quantity of contents (21 CFR 101.105)
- name and place of business of the manufacturer, packer or distributor (21 CFR 101.5)
- complete list of ingredients, listed by their common or usual name and in descending order of predominance (21 CFR 101.4)
- all words, statements and other information required by or under authority of the act to appear on the label or labeling shall appear thereon in the English language (21 CFR 101.15(c) (1))
- any representation in a foreign language requires all mandatory label information be repeated in each foreign language used on the label (21 CFR 101.15(c) (2))
- conformance with the principal display panel requirements (21 CFR 101.1), the information panel requirements (21 CFR.101.2) and the misbranding of food requirements (21 CFR 101.18)

As part of the broader category of packaged foods regulated under the *FD&C Act*, the *Food Allergen Labeling and Consumer Protection Act* (*FALCPA*) of 2004 (Pub. Law 108-282) requires medical foods labeled after 1 January 2006 to comply with *FALCPA*'s food allergen labeling requirements.[14] However, medical foods are exempted from the labeling requirements for health claims and nutrient content claims under *NLEA* (21 U.S.C. 343(q)(5)(A)(iv)).[15]

Under the *FD&C Act*, the manufacturer or distributor is responsible for ensuring the medical food is not adulterated or misbranded. Medical foods are misbranded if their labeling is false and misleading.[16] Claims may be misleading not only because of affirmative representations made in the labeling, but also because labeling fails to reveal material facts in the light of such representations with respect to possible consequences when used under the conditions of use prescribed in the labeling. FDA also regards medical foods to be misbranded if they are labeled and marketed as medical foods but do not meet the statutory definition of a medical food in Section 5(b) of the *Orphan Drug Act* (21 U.S.C. 360ee(b)(3)) or the criteria set forth in 21 CFR 101.9(j)(8).

The *Orphan Drug Act* states medical foods must be formulated to be consumed or administered enterally under the supervision of a physician. FDA does not interpret either the *Orphan Drug Act* or FDA's implementing regulations at 21 CFR 101.9(j)(8) to require medical foods to be made available by prescription only.[17] Medical foods are not prohibited by federal law from being dispensed without a prescription. Therefore, the use of the statement "Rx only" in medical food labeling would misbrand it under *FD&C Act* Section 403(a)(1) because it would be a false statement about the product. However, FDA would not object to the use of labeling language to communicate medical foods are to be consumed or administered enterally under the supervision of a physician. National Drug Code (NDC) numbers are intended for uniquely identifying drugs and should not be used in labeling medical foods. The presence of an NDC number on a medical food may be a false or misleading representation that misbrands the product under *FD&C Act* Section 403(a)(1).[18]

Registration and Manufacturing Provisions

Medical foods are not drugs and, therefore, are not subject to any regulatory requirements that specifically apply to drugs. Medical foods do not have to undergo premarket review or approval. A clinical investigation intended only to evaluate a food's nutritional effects, including medical foods, would not require an Investigational New Drug application (IND). However, an investigation intended to evaluate other effects of such food on the structure or function of the body would require an IND.[19] An investigation intended to evaluate a medical food's effects on a disease would require an IND. However, if the medical food is being fed to subjects simply for nutritional purposes during a study examining the effects of another intervention, the medical food's use in the study would not trigger the need for an IND, although the study might require an IND or Investigational Device Exemption (IDE) for the intervention being studied.[20]

Medical foods must comply with all applicable FDA requirements for foods. Individual medical food products do not have to be registered with FDA; however, food facilities must be registered (21 CFR Part 1 Subpart H).[21] Medical foods are "food" and, accordingly, any facility engaged in manufacturing, processing, packing or holding medical foods for consumption in the US must register with FDA. Facilities do not have to identify their specific medical food products to FDA when they register, and the agency does not maintain a list of medical food products. Instructions for food facility registration can be found on FDA's food facility registration web page.[22]

Medical foods must comply with food manufacturing requirements, including current Good Manufacturing Practice (CGMP) regulations in manufacturing, packing or holding human food (21 CFR 110).[23] If applicable, medical foods must comply with regulations specific to the product formulation and processing, such as the Thermally Processed Low-Acid Foods Packaged in Hermetically Sealed Containers regulations (21 CFR part 113), Acidified Foods regulations (21 CFR part 114) and Emergency Permit Control regulations (21 CFR part 108).[24-26] The adulteration provisions of *FD&C Act* Section 342 are applicable to medical foods.[27]

Any ingredient added to a medical food must be safe, suitable and comply with all applicable *FD&C Act* provisions and applicable FDA regulations. Any additive to a medical food should comply with FDA's food additive regulations (21 CFR 172),[28] and a color additive in accordance with the color additive regulations (21 CFR 73 and 21 CFR 74).[29,30] Medical foods must be comprised of a substance generally recognized, by qualified experts, to be safe under the conditions of its intended use, Generally Recognized As Safe (GRAS) (21 CFR 170.30 and 21 U.S.C. 321(s)).[31,32] In addition, medical foods may contain a substance authorized by a prior sanction issued by FDA (21 CFR 170.3(l)). FDA has several lists of GRAS substances codified in 21 CFR 182, 21 CFR 184 and 21 CFR 186.[33-35] Importantly, these lists are not all inclusive. Because the use of a GRAS substance is not subject to premarket review and approval by FDA, it is impracticable to list all substances used in food on the basis of the GRAS provision. Other ingredients may achieve GRAS status through affirmation or the GRAS notification program.[36] Additional information on food additives and GRAS ingredients can be found on FDA's food ingredients, packaging and labeling web page.[37]

Medical foods also may include infant formulas used for inborn metabolism errors regulated as exempt infant formulas under *FD&C Act* Section 412(h)(1) (21 CFR 107.50).[38] If the medical food product also is intended for use as an infant formula, additional statutory and regulatory requirements apply. These additional requirements are found in *FD&C Act* Section 412 and FDA's implementing regulations in 21 CFR 106 and 21 CFR 107.[39,40] Additional regulatory information and guidance can be found on FDA's infant formula guidance web page.[41]

Compliance Program

FDA has a specific medical foods compliance program.[42] The compliance program enables FDA inspectors to: obtain information regarding the manufacturing/control processes and quality assurance programs employed by domestic medical food manufacturers through establishment inspections; collect domestic and import surveillance samples of medical foods for nutrient and microbiological analyses; and take action when significant *FD&C Act* (or related regulations) violations are discovered. If the medical food product also is intended for use as an infant formula, the domestic and foreign establishments are subject to additional compliance with *FD&C Act* Section 412 requirements.[43]

Provisions of the Reportable Foods

A "reportable food" is a food article (other than a dietary supplement or infant formula) for which there is a reasonable probability the use of, or exposure to, such food article will cause serious adverse health consequences or death to humans or animals.[44] Medical foods are subject to the reportable food provisions. The populations that consume medical foods, often as the sole or major nutrition source, are extremely vulnerable, e.g., elderly, patients with serious illnesses and patients in intensive care units. FDA interprets the definition of reportable food to include those foods that would meet the definition of a Class I recall situation. A Class I recall situation is one in which there is a reasonable probability the use of, or exposure to, a violative product will cause serious adverse health consequences or death (21 CFR 7.3(m)(1)).[45]

Registered food facilities that manufacture, process, pack or hold food for human or animal consumption in the US under *FD&C Act* Section 415(a) (21 U.S.C. 350d) are required to report when there is a reasonable probability the use of, or exposure to, a food article will cause serious adverse health consequences or death to humans or animals. A responsible party is required to submit a report to FDA through the reportable food electronic portal as soon as practicable, but in no case more than than 24 hours after determining an article of food is a reportable food (*FD&C Act* Section 417(d)(1)). The Reportable Food Registry (RFR) was established by the *Food and Drug Administration Amendments Act* of 2007 (Pub. Law 110-085) Section 1005. The RFR is an electronic portal for industry to report when there is reasonable probability a food article will cause serious adverse health consequences.[46] Additional regulatory information and guidance can be found on FDA's reportable food registry guidance and regulatory information web page.[47]

Adverse Event Reporting

Reporting serious adverse events, product quality problems, product use errors or therapeutic nonequivalence or failure suspected to be associated with the use of medical food in the course of clinical care is voluntary. Form FDA 3500 should be used by healthcare professionals and consumers to report adverse events voluntarily. An industry member can file a voluntary adverse event report through an electronic MedWatch online voluntary reporting form[48] or paper voluntary MedWatch form that can be mailed to FDA.[49] Instructions for completing Form FDA 3500 can be found on FDA's Form 3500 instructions web page.[50] FDA now is providing a consumer-friendly version of the 3500 Form as Form FDA 3500B, which is customized to make the form's completion by non-health professionals or consumers easier.[51]

Conclusion

- Medical foods are distinguished from the broader category of foods.
- Medical foods should meet the statutory definition of a medical food in the *Orphan Drug Act* (21 U.S.C. 360ee(b)(3)) and the criteria set forth in 21 CFR 101.9(j)(8).
- Medical food is "formulated to be consumed or administered enterally under the supervision of a physician and which is intended for the specific dietary management of a disease or condition for which distinctive nutritional requirements, based on recognized scientific principles, are established by medical evaluation."
- Medical foods cannot be labeled or marketed for a disease or condition that can be managed by a normal diet alone.
- Medical foods are foods and, therefore, must comply with all applicable FDA requirements for foods.
- Medical foods are not drugs and, therefore, are not subject to any regulatory requirements that apply specifically to drugs.
- Medical foods do not have to undergo premarket review or approval by FDA.
- Individual medical food products do not have to be registered with FDA; however, food facilities must be registered.
- Any ingredient added to a medical food must be safe, suitable and comply with all applicable provisions of the *FD&C Act* and applicable FDA regulations.
- Medical foods must comply with the requirements for the manufacture of foods, including current Good Manufacturing Practices regulations in manufacturing, packing or holding human food (21 CFR 110).
- Under the *FD&C Act*, the manufacturer or distributor is responsible for ensuring the medical food is not adulterated or misbranded.
- Medical food labeling must comply with all food labeling requirements, except those specific requirements from which medical foods are exempt.
- Medical foods are misbranded if their labeling is false and misleading.
- Medical foods are misbranded if their labeling bears the statement "Rx only" and/or National Drug Code (NDC) numbers.
- Medical foods are subject to the reportable foods provisions.
- FDA has a specific medical foods compliance program.
- Reporting serious adverse events, product quality problems, product use errors or therapeutic nonequivalence or failure suspected to be associated with the use of medical food in the course of clinical care is voluntary.
- If the medical food product also is intended for use as an infant formula, additional infant formula statutory and regulatory requirements apply.

References

1. Federal Food, Drug, and Cosmetic Act Amendments: Vitamins and Minerals (Public Law 94-278). NIH website. http://history.nih.gov/research/downloads/PL94-278.pdf. Accessed 18 February 2015.
2. *Orphan Drug Act* of 1983 (Public Law 97-414). NIH website. http://history.nih.gov/research/downloads/PL97-414.pdf. Accessed 18 February 2015.
3. *Orphan Drug Amendments* of 1988 (Public Law 100-290). GPO website. www.gpo.gov/fdsys/pkg/STATUTE-102/pdf/STATUTE-102-Pg90.pdf. Accessed 18 February 2015.
4. *Nutrition Labeling and Education Act* of 1990 (Public Law 101-535). GPO website. www.gpo.gov/fdsys/pkg/STATUTE-104/pdf/STATUTE-104-Pg2353.pdf. Accessed 18 February 2015.
5. 21 CFR 101.9(j)(8). GPO website. www.gpo.gov/fdsys/pkg/CFR-2012-title21-vol2/pdf/CFR-2012-title21-vol2-sec101-9.pdf. Accessed 18 February 2015.

6. Regulation of Medical Foods, Advance notice of proposed rulemaking. *Federal Register* Vol. 61, No. 231, 60661–60671. GPO website. www.gpo.gov/fdsys/pkg/FR-1996-11-29/pdf/96-30441.pdf. Accessed 18 February 2015.
7. *Draft Guidance for Industry: Frequently Asked Questions About Medical Foods; Second Edition (May 1997; May 2007; Revised August 2013).* FDA website. www.fda.gov/downloads/Food/GuidanceRegulation/GuidanceDocumentsRegulatoryInformation/MedicalFoods/UCM362995.pdf. Accessed 18 February 2015.
8. Compliance program 7321.002. Medical Foods Program – Import and Domestic (August 24, 2006). FDA website. www.fda.gov/downloads/Food/ComplianceEnforcement/UCM073339.pdf. Accessed 18 February 2015.
9. Op cit 3.
10. Op cit 5.
11. Op cit 7.
12. *Fair Packaging and Labeling Act* (Pub. Law 89-755). GPO website. www.gpo.gov/fdsys/pkg/STATUTE-80/pdf/STATUTE-80-Pg1296.pdf. Accessed 18 February 2015.
13. 21 CFR 101. FDA website. www.accessdata.fda.gov/scripts/cdrh/cfdocs/cfcfr/CFRSearch.cfm?cfrpart=101. Accessed 18 February 2015.
14. *Guidance for Industry: Questions and Answers Regarding Food Allergens, including the Food Allergen Labeling and Consumer Protection Act of 2004 (Edition 4); Final Guidance (October 2006).* FDA website. www.fda.gov/downloads/Food/GuidanceRegulation/UCM301394.pdf. Accessed 18 February 2015.
15. 21 U.S. Code § 343 - Misbranded food. FDA website. www.gpo.gov/fdsys/pkg/USCODE-2011-title21/pdf/USCODE-2011-title21-chap9-subchapIV-sec343.pdf. Accessed 18 February 2015.
16. Ibid.
17. Op cit 7.
18. Ibid.
19. *Guidance for Clinical Investigators, Sponsors, and IRBs Investigational New Drug Applications (INDs) — Determining Whether Human Research Studies Can Be Conducted Without an IND (September 2013).* FDA website. www.fda.gov/downloads/Drugs/Guidances/UCM229175.pdf. Accessed 18 February 2015.
20. Ibid.
21. 21 CFR 1, Subpart H. FDA website. www.accessdata.fda.gov/scripts/cdrh/cfdocs/cfCFR/CFRSearch.cfm?CFRPart=1&showFR=1&subpartNode=21:1.0.1.1.1.6. Accessed 18 February 2015.
22. Registration of Food Facilities. FDA website. http://www.fda.gov/Food/GuidanceRegulation/FoodFacilityRegistration/default.htm. Accessed 18 Feb 2015.
23. 21 CFR 110. FDA website. www.accessdata.fda.gov/scripts/cdrh/cfdocs/cfcfr/CFRSearch.cfm?CFRPart=110. Accessed 18 February 2015.
24. 21 CFR part 113. Thermally Processed Low-Acid Foods Packaged in Hermetically Sealed Containers. FDA website. http://www.accessdata.fda.gov/scripts/cdrh/cfdocs/cfcfr/CFRSearch.cfm?CFRPart=113. Accessed 18 February 2015.
25. 21 CFR 114. Acidified Foods. FDA website. www.accessdata.fda.gov/scripts/cdrh/cfdocs/cfcfr/CFRSearch.cfm?CFRPart=114. Accessed 18 February 2015.
26. 21 CFR 108.Emergency Permit Control. FDA website. www.accessdata.fda.gov/scripts/cdrh/cfdocs/cfcfr/CFRSearch.cfm?CFRPart=108. Accessed 18 February 2015.
27. 21 U.S.C. 342. GPO website. www.gpo.gov/fdsys/pkg/USCODE-2011-title21/pdf/USCODE-2011-title21-chap9-subchapIV-sec342.pdf. Accessed 18 February 2015
28. 21 CFR 172. FDA website. www.accessdata.fda.gov/scripts/cdrh/cfdocs/cfcfr/CFRSearch.cfm?CFRPart=172. Accessed 18 February 2015.
29. 21 CFR 73. FDA website. www.accessdata.fda.gov/scripts/cdrh/cfdocs/cfCFR/CFRSearch.cfm?CFRPart=73. Accessed 18 February 2015.
30. 21 CFR 74. FDA website. www.accessdata.fda.gov/scripts/cdrh/cfdocs/cfcfr/CFRSearch.cfm?CFRPart=74. Accessed 18 February 2015.
31. 21 CFR 170.30. FDA website. http://www.accessdata.fda.gov/scripts/cdrh/cfdocs/cfCFR/CFRSearch.cfm?fr=170.30. Accessed 18 February 2015.
32. 21 U.S.C. 321(s). FDA website. www.fda.gov/RegulatoryInformation/Legislation/FederalFoodDrugandCosmeticActFDCAct/FDCActChaptersIandIIShortTitleandDefinitions/ucm086297.htm. Accessed 18 February 2015.
33. 21 CFR 182. FDA website. www.accessdata.fda.gov/scripts/cdrh/cfdocs/cfcfr/CFRSearch.cfm?CFRPart=182. Accessed 18 February 2015.
34. 21 CFR 184. FDA website. www.accessdata.fda.gov/scripts/cdrh/cfdocs/cfcfr/CFRSearch.cfm?CFRPart=184. Accessed 18 February 2015.
35. 21 CFR 186. FDA website. www.accessdata.fda.gov/scripts/cdrh/cfdocs/cfcfr/CFRSearch.cfm?CFRPart=186. Accessed 18 February 2015.
36. *Guidance for Industry: Frequently Asked Questions About GRAS* (December 2004). FDA website. www.fda.gov/Food/GuidanceRegulation/GuidanceDocumentsRegulatoryInformation/IngredientsAdditivesGRASPackaging/ucm061846.htm. Accessed 18 February 2015.
37. Food Ingredients, Packaging & Labeling. FDA website. www.fda.gov/Food/IngredientsPackagingLabeling/default.htm. Accessed 18 February 2015.
38. 21 CFR 107.50. FDA website. www.accessdata.fda.gov/scripts/cdrh/cfdocs/cfCFR/CFRSearch.cfm?CFRPart=107&showFR=1&subpartNode=21:2.0.1.1.7.3. Accessed 18 February 2015.
39. 21 CFR 106. FDA website. www.accessdata.fda.gov/scripts/cdrh/cfdocs/cfcfr/CFRSearch.cfm?CFRPart=106. Accessed 18 February 2015.
40. 21 CFR 107. FDA website. www.accessdata.fda.gov/scripts/cdrh/cfdocs/cfCFR/CFRSearch.cfm?CFRPart=107. Accessed 18 February 2015.
41. Infant Formula Guidance Documents and Regulatory Information. FDA website. www.fda.gov/Food/GuidanceRegulation/GuidanceDocumentsRegulatoryInformation/InfantFormula/default.htm. Accessed 18 February 2015.
42. Op cit 8.
43. Compliance Program 7321.006: Infant Formula Program – Import and Domestic (July 31, 2006). FDA website. www.fda.gov/downloads/Food/GuidanceComplianceRegulatoryInformation/ComplianceEnforcement/ucm073349.pdf. Accessed 18 February 2015.
44. 21 U.S.C. 350f. GPO website. http://www.gpo.gov/fdsys/pkg/USCODE-2010-title21/pdf/USCODE-2010-title21-chap9-subchapIV-sec350f.pdf. Accessed 18 February 2015.
45. *Guidance for Industry: Questions and Answers Regarding the Reportable Food Registry as Established by the Food and Drug Administration Amendments Act of 2007* (September 2009). FDA website. www.fda.gov/Food/GuidanceRegulation/GuidanceDocumentsRegulatoryInformation/RFR/ucm180761.htm. Accessed 18 February 2015.
46. Reportable Food Registry for Industry. FDA website. www.fda.gov/Food/ComplianceEnforcement/RFR/default.htm. Accessed 18 February 2015.
47. Reportable Food Registry Guidance Documents and Regulatory Information. FDA website. www.fda.gov/food/guidanceregulation/guidancedocumentsregulatoryinformation/rfr/default.htm. Accessed 18 February 2015.
48. MedWatch Online Voluntary Reporting Form. FDA website. www.accessdata.fda.gov/scripts/medwatch. Accessed 18 February 2015.
49. Form FDA 3500. FDA website. www.fda.gov/downloads/AboutFDA/ReportsManualsForms/Forms/UCM163919.pdf. Accessed 18 February 2015.

50. Instructions for Completing Form FDA 3500. FDA website. www.fda.gov/Safety/MedWatch/HowToReport/DownloadForms/ucm149236.htm. Accessed 18 February 2015.
51. Form FDA 3500B. FDA website. www.fda.gov/downloads/AboutFDA/ReportsManualsForms/Forms/UCM349464.pdf. Accessed 18 February 2015.

Recommended Reading

Draft Guidance for Industry: Frequently Asked Questions about Medical Foods; Second Edition (May 1997; May 2007; Revised August 2013). FDA website. http://www.fda.gov/downloads/Food/GuidanceRegulation/GuidanceDocumentsRegulatoryInformation/MedicalFoods/UCM362995.pdf. Accessed 18 Feb 2015.

Compliance program 7321.002. Medical Foods Program – Import and Domestic (2006). FDA website. http://www.fda.gov/downloads/Food/ComplianceEnforcement/UCM073339.pdf. Accessed 18 Feb 2015.

Guidance for Industry: Questions and Answers Regarding Food Allergens, including the Food Allergen Labeling and Consumer Protection Act of 2004 (Edition 4); Final Guidance (October 2006). FDA website. http://www.fda.gov/downloads/Food/GuidanceRegulation/UCM301394.pdf. Accessed 18 Feb 2015.

Guidance for Industry: Questions and Answers Regarding the Reportable Food Registry as Established by the Food and Drug Administration Amendments Act of 2007 (September 2009). FDA website. http://www.fda.gov/Food/GuidanceRegulation/GuidanceDocumentsRegulatoryInformation/RFR/ucm180761.htm. Accessed 18 Feb 2015.

Guidance for Clinical Investigators, Sponsors, and IRBs Investigational New Drug Applications (INDs) — Determining Whether Human Research Studies Can Be Conducted Without an IND (September 2013). FDA website. http://www.fda.gov/downloads/Drugs/Guidances/UCM229175.pdf. Accessed 18 Feb 2015.

Food and Drug Administration, Compliance Program 7321.006: Infant Formula Program – Import and Domestic (July 31, 2006). FDA website. www.fda.gov/downloads/Food/GuidanceComplianceRegulatoryInformation/ComplianceEnforcement/ucm073349.pdf. Accessed 18 February 2015.

Kaur M: Medical foods from natural sources: Springer Science & Business Media; 2008.

Fernandes J, Saudubray J-M, Van Den Berghe G, Walter JH: Inborn metabolic diseases: diagnosis and treatment: Springer Science & Business Media; 2006.

Brown A: Understanding food: Principles and preparation: Cengage Learning; 2014.

Whitney EN, Cataldo CB, Rolfes SR: Understanding normal and clinical nutrition: Wadsworth Publishing Company, Inc.; 1998.

Nestle M: Food politics: How the food industry influences nutrition and health, Vol. 3: Univ of California Press; 2013.

Hark L, Deen D, Morrison G: Medical nutrition and disease: a case-based approach: John Wiley & Sons; 2014.

Alpers DH: Manual of nutritional therapeutics: Lippincott Williams & Wilkins; 2008.

Chapter 39

FDA Inspection and Enforcement

Updated by Anthony P. Schiavone and Andrew P. Zeltwanger, MS

OBJECTIVES

- ❑ Understand FDA's inspectional authority
- ❑ Understand the inspection process
- ❑ Understand FDA's enforcement authority and penalties under the *Food, Drug, and Cosmetic Act* and FDA regulations

LAWS, REGULATIONS AND GUIDELINES COVERED IN THIS CHAPTER

- ❑ *Federal Food, Drug, and Cosmetic Act* of 1938
- ❑ Applicable Parts of 21 CFR
- ❑ FDA Regulatory Procedures Manual
- ❑ FDA Investigations Operations Manual

Introduction

The US Food and Drug Administration (FDA), under its mandate to protect public health and safety, has broad powers to enforce the *Food, Drug, and Cosmetic Act* (*FD&C Act*) and the regulations stemming from it. While these powers are broad, they are not limitless. Firms whose products are regulated by FDA should understand both the source of the agency's authority and the processes by which it is enforced. Such knowledge will improve the firm's ability to work with FDA, to avoid product issues that may arise and to quickly resolve any issues that do.

According to FDA's own website, it "is responsible for protecting the public health by assuring the safety, efficacy, and security of human and veterinary drugs, biological products, medical devices, our nation's food supply, cosmetic, and products that emit radiation." FDA traces its roots back to the Patent Office in 1848 and has existed in a form we are familiar with today since the 1930s. Under the *FD&C Act*, FDA wields significant power to enforce the statutes and regulations enacted to protect the public health. This chapter discusses the source of FDA's enforcement authority, the inspection process and potential civil and criminal penalties.

The *FD&C Act*[1] was promulgated in 1938, and, as its name suggests, provides the legal framework for the manufacture and sale of foods, drugs, cosmetics as well as biologicals, medical devices and tobacco products. Under the *FD&C Act*, FDA was established[2] and charged with the tasks of promoting public health by promptly and efficiently reviewing clinical research and taking appropriate action on the marketing of regulated products in a timely manner,[3] as well as ensuring these regulated products are safe and effective (where applicable).[4]

FDA's creation and mandate center on protecting the public health. Achieving that goal requires FDA to have a wide variety of expertise, as well as a broad level of oversight, from product inception through manufacturing and marketing. Under the *FD&C Act*, FDA is granted authority to enforce the act's laws, but also to promulgate regulations that more clearly define manufacturers' duties under the act. Specifically, Title 21 in the Code of Federal Regulations (CFR) is reserved for FDA regulations.

FDA's enforcement powers are broad but still subject to jurisdictional boundaries. In general, FDA has jurisdiction over any regulated products introduced into the stream of interstate commerce.

FD&C Act Section 331[5] defines a list of prohibited acts for which FDA may pursue enforcement actions under its jurisdiction. These provisions apply across the spectrum of products FDA regulates, including pharmaceuticals, biologics, devices and combination products. For the purposes of this discussion, the following prohibited acts are the most salient and cited most frequently:[6]

- the introduction or delivery for introduction into interstate commerce of any food, drug, device, tobacco product or cosmetic that is adulterated or misbranded
- the adulteration or misbranding of any food, drug, device, tobacco product or cosmetic in interstate commerce
- the receipt in interstate commerce of any food, drug, device, tobacco product or cosmetic that is adulterated or misbranded, and the delivery or proffered delivery thereof for pay or otherwise
- the refusal to permit entry or inspection as authorized by *FD&C Act* Section 374
- the manufacture within any territory of any food, drug, device, tobacco product or cosmetic that is adulterated or misbranded
- forging, counterfeiting, simulating or falsely representing, or without proper authority using any mark, stamp, tag, label or other identification device authorized or required by regulations promulgated under the provisions of *FD&C Act* Section 344 or 379e
- making, selling, disposing of or keeping in possession, control or custody, or concealing any punch, die, plate, stone or other thing designed to print, imprint or reproduce the trademark, trade name or other identifying mark, imprint or device of another or any likeness of any of the foregoing upon any drug or container or labeling thereof so as to render such drug a counterfeit drug
- the doing of any act that causes a drug to be a counterfeit drug, or the sale or dispensing, or the holding for sale or dispensing, of a counterfeit drug
- the alteration, mutilation, destruction, obliteration or removal of the whole or any part of the labeling of, or the doing of any other act with respect to, a food, drug, device, tobacco product or cosmetic, if such act is done while such article is held for sale (whether or not the first sale) after shipment in interstate commerce and results in such article being adulterated or misbranded
- the failure to register in accordance with *FD&C Act* Section 360 or 387e, the failure to provide any information required by Section 360(j), 360(k), 387e(i) or 387e(j) of the act, or the failure to provide a notice required by *FD&C Act* Section 360(j)(2) or 387e(i)(3)
- the failure or refusal to comply with any requirement prescribed under *FD&C Act* Section 360h, 360j(g), 387c(b), 387g, 387h or 387o
- the failure or refusal to furnish any notification or other material or information required by or under *FD&C Act* Section 360i, 360j(g), 387d, 387i or 387t
- the failure or refusal to comply with a requirement under *FD&C Act* Section 360l or 387m
- the failure to comply with any requirements of the provisions of, or any regulations or orders of the secretary, under *FD&C Act* Section 360b(a)(4)(A), 360b(a)(4)(D) or 360b(a)(5)

Adulteration and misbranding are the most common issues noted by FDA as a result of inspections. A drug, biologic or device is considered adulterated by FDA if: it was produced under unsanitary conditions or contains filthy, putrid or decomposed substances; it was not manufactured in compliance with applicable Good Manufacturing Practices (GMPs); its container is made of a poisonous or deleterious substance that may cause its contents to be harmful to health; its strength or purity differs from an official compendium or that which is advertised; it is a non-exempt Class III device without premarket approval; or it is a banned device. As the previous scenarios suggest, adulteration is related most closely to the right to market and the conditions under which a product is manufactured.

Misbranding, however, applies to deficiencies in labeling and other product information. For instance, a drug, device or biologic would be considered misbranded by FDA if: it were found to bear false or misleading labeling; the product label fails to include required information, such as manufacturer or accurate quantity; the product is a drug and its label fails to establish the name of the drug, established name or the quantity and proportion of each active ingredient; the label fails to provide adequate warnings or instructions for use; the label provides improper dosage information that may be dangerous to health; the product was produced in a facility not listed or registered (as applicable) by FDA; or it is a device without a 510(k) clearance or a Premarket Approval (PMA).

Inspection

As stated above, FDA has authority to enter and inspect under 21 USC 374. This statute provides basic authority for establishment inspections and permits FDA to enter and inspect at reasonable times, within reasonable limits and in a reasonable manner, establishments or vehicles used to process, hold or transport food, drugs, devices, tobacco products or cosmetics. While the statute does not define the term "reasonable" specifically, FDA interprets the term to grant it authority to inspect "what is reasonably necessary to achieve the objective."[7]

FDA conducts inspections for many reasons. These may include routine inspections to monitor compliance with Good Clinical Practices, Good Laboratory Practices, current Good Manufacturing Practices (CGMPs), or adherence to the Quality System Regulations. The agency also conducts directed inspections (as a result of a complaint or other specific matter), or inspects to check for recall effectiveness. Inspections also often are conducted to close out a Warning Letter or to resolve other enforcement actions. There is a general requirement for FDA to inspect every two years, but resource constraints have caused the agency to focus its efforts on high-risk products, sites with lackluster inspection histories and uninspected new facilities.

Domestic inspections require the inspector to provide a properly completed Form FDA 482 to the top management official present at the site (or designate). The FDA inspector also should provide his or her credentials at this time. While it is not permitted to make a photocopy,[8] a firm may record the badge/ID number and inspector's name for future reference. The top management official should ensure at this time the inspector is a government official with authority to inspect and determine which agency the inspector represents. The properly completed Form 482 is not a search warrant; however, FDA may obtain a warrant in situations where a firm refuses to allow FDA to voluntarily enter and inspect, or the agency has reason to believe the firm will refuse inspection. Any federal enforcement officer (such as an FDA inspector) may request a search warrant from a federal court. In the case of refusal to permit inspection, FDA must provide a federal magistrate with probable cause a crime is being committed by a person upon whom the warrant will be served, or there are records or other evidence relating to the commission of a crime.

It is worth noting, while FDA's jurisdiction traditionally extended only to establishments located within the US, the *Food and Drug Administration Safety and Innovation Act* of 2012 (*FDASIA*) extended the agency's jurisdiction to any violation of the *FD&C Act* if a product is intended for import into the US. Additionally, FDA now may enter into agreements with foreign governments to recognize inspections of FDA-registered establishments outside the US to permit risk-based inspections. Of note, starting in January 2014, FDA began participating in a Medical Device Single Audit Program (MDSAP) pilot alongside other international partners. FDA will accept the MDSAP audit reports as a substitute for routine agency inspections. The MDSAP pilot is intended to allow MDSAP-recognized auditing organizations to conduct a single audit of a medical device manufacturer that will satisfy the relevant requirements of the medical device regulatory authorities participating in the pilot program.[9]

Generally, the scope of an inspection is dependent on the inspection's reason and the site's inspectional history. Findings during the inspection inform the process and may increase scrutiny and broaden the inspection. The basic purpose of an inspection is to determine a firm's compliance with laws and regulations enforced by FDA, and the agency has wide latitude to perform its inspection. As discussed later in this chapter, evidence of violations found during an inspection may be used to support any of the various enforcement pathways at FDA's disposal, including actions in federal court.

Inspection Limits

Limits are imposed on FDA when reviewing and collecting evidence during an inspection. Generally, FDA may not collect the following:

- financial and pricing information
- personnel data, except data necessary to show employees are qualified to perform their regulated functions
- sales data—except shipment information
- research data other than those subject to FDA inspection

Photographs are another tool FDA may attempt to use during an inspection. It is somewhat unclear as to whether FDA may take photographs if the firm objects; however, the agency cites the 1986 Dow Chemical case, which holds in part that "when Congress invests an agency with enforcement and investigatory authority, it is not necessary to identify explicitly each and every technique that may be used in the course of executing the statutory mission."[10] The agency additionally cites as authority *US v. Acri Wholesale Groceries*, where photos were taken without objection during a warrantless warehouse inspection and subsequently used in a criminal prosecution. The court allowed the photos to be admitted as evidence because taking them was reasonable in the context of the inspection, and the defendants failed to object to the obvious photography.[11] FDA generally will respect a corporate policy against photography; however, should the inspector be adamant about obtaining photographic evidence, it may seek court intervention. If, after consulting counsel, the firm permits the inspector to take photographs, it should clearly note its objection and carefully document (with photographs of its own or a written narrative of the agency's actions) what the inspector is photographing.

FDA may request a firm to read and sign or listen to the reading of an affidavit[12] during or at the conclusion of an inspection or ask the firm to attest to the accuracy of any observations made. This acknowledgment may be used in further enforcement actions. FDA does not have authority to require this.

Inspection Procedures

FDA uses a systems approach to ensure CGMPs and Quality Systems Regulations are being followed. The systems approach allows more judicious use of FDA's limited resources by streamlining the process. During an inspection, the agency is looking at specific systems to determine whether they are "in a state of control." FDA looks at seven systems—management responsibility; design control; Corrective and Preventive Actions (CAPA); production and process controls; records and document change controls; material controls; facilities and equipment controls. The agency almost always looks at the CAPA system, and depending on the level of inspection, will review one or more of the seven subsystems.

During the inspection, an inspector may discuss daily findings with responsible management. At the close of the inspection, the inspector will discuss their findings verbally and in writing. Significant observations will be documented on Form FDA 483, if necessary.

Form 483

As the result of an establishment inspection, the inspector may have findings he or she considers significant; these observations are made when the investigator believes "conditions or practices observed indicate that any food, drug, device, or cosmetic have been adulterated or are being prepared, packed, or held under conditions whereby they may become adulterated, misbranded, or rendered injurious to health."[13]

Form 483 observations are presented to the site's top management at the conclusion of the inspection. At this time, the investigator will discuss the observations with management and solicit comments from the firm. During this discussion, the firm has an opportunity to identify any potential errors, ask for clarification and indicate any corrective actions already taken or planned. Specifically for medical device establishment inspections, but also at the investigator's discretion in other inspections, the form may be annotated. The annotations include: reported corrected, not verified; corrected and verified; promised to correct; and under consideration. Other information, such as timeframes for correction, also may be included. This is the firm's only opportunity to make changes to the Form 483. Close daily monitoring of an inspection is important to prevent any surprises upon receiving Form 483. Once the inspector has closed the inspection, the form may not be changed.

Once a firm has received 483 observations, it generaly has 15 working days to respond to the agency, in writing, detailing its corrective action plan. Firms should take this opportunity to explain their plan, what has been done and implemented, and provide a reasonable period of time in which the remaining corrective actions will be completed. For serious issues, where it may take months for the firm to complete and implement a corrective action plan for an observation or series of observations, the agency may request periodic status updates. Providing a detailed action plan, following through as promised in response to 483 observations and developing objective evidence or corrective or remedial activities may minimize the potential the agency will issue a Warning Letter or pursue other enforcement actions.

Establishment Inspection Reports

The Establishment Inspection Report (EIR) is the report issued by FDA after the close of the inspection. It provides a narrative review of the inspection, the inspector's findings and includes any additional evidence taken by FDA to support its findings. It relates the reasons for the inspection, site inspectional history, proof of interstate commerce, agency jurisdiction, what was covered during the inspection and any discussions with management and any refusals. Exhibits, such as photographs or copies of documents obtained by the inspector will be attached to the EIR. The EIR also will provide detail about any samples taken by the agency for testing or as evidence of adulteration. This report, along with any other products of the inspection (such as a Form 483), may be used in subsequent enforcement actions. The EIR may be delayed if FDA is contemplating enforcement action.

Once issued, the EIR classifies the inspection as No Action Indicated (NAI), Voluntary Action Indicated (VAI) or Official Action Indicated (OAI). NAI requires no additional action by the firm or FDA, and a finding of VAI likely will not require additional action by FDA if the firm completes its voluntary corrective actions; these likely will be reviewed at the next inspection (whether standard biennial or directed). If the EIR is classified as OAI, additional enforcement may occur, and dates for the next inspection will be recommended.

FDA Enforcement

Civil Enforcement

Keeping in mind FDA's main purpose is protecting the public health, the agency has an arsenal of tools available to compel compliance, to remove a product from the stream of commerce and to punish the bad actors. While it has this authority, FDA much prefers to work with a manufacturer to solve noncompliance issues. Administrative enforcement typically is FDA's first line of defense. This is authorized by statute or regulation and represents a non-judicial path that does not require involvement by the Department of Justice (DOJ) or other agency. **Table 39-1**[14] shows some of the more common agency forms of administrative enforcement.

FDA usually begins the proceedings above after a field inspection, which can be directed or a normal biennial inspection. Concurrence with the center (i.e., Center for Devices and Radiological Health (CDRH), Center for Biologics Evaluation and Research (CBER) or Center for Drug Evaluation and Research (CDER)) usually is required. For more severe enforcement actions, the Office of the Chief Counsel is consulted.

FDA enforcement can be split into two categories: civil and criminal. Civil enforcement refers to a wide array of

Table 39-1. FDA Enforcement Actions

Recalls*	Device Ban, Repair, Replacement or Notification	Debarment	Import Detention
Clinical Investigator Disqualification	Product approval suspension	Restitution	Civil monetary penalties
Notices of Violation (Form 483 observations resulting from an Inspection)	Warning Letters	Untitled Letters	Publicity
License suspension or revocation	Administrative detentions	Application Integrity Policy	483 observations

**21 CFR 810; 21 USCXXX*

tools the agency has at its disposal to ensure continued compliance with applicable laws and regulations.

Warning Letters

The agency generally prefers firms to comply voluntarily with the law. In certain circumstances where regulatory significance and the nature of the violation do not immediately place the public at harm, FDA's practice is to give individuals or firms an opportunity to take prompt, voluntary corrective action before the agency commences an enforcement action. FDA accomplishes this by issuing a Warning Letter. The Warning Letter is issued to accomplish two goals. First, there is an expectation most individuals or firms will comply with the law voluntarily, and the Warning Letter provides a firm with notice of noncompliance and an opportunity to remedy the situation.

The second goal is to establish prior notice. Prior notice is used to strengthen FDA's position in later enforcement actions by establishing responsible individuals continued violating the law despite having been warned by FDA or another agency (state, municipal or other federal agencies). Warning Letters are only one way to establish prior notice; other methods include, but are not limited to: issuance of Form FDA 483—list of observations—at the conclusion of an inspection, recall classification notification letters, discussion of observations with management by an FDA investigator (documented in the EIR) or other properly documented discussions with the agency.[15]

Other Correspondence (Untitled Letters)

For violations not meeting the threshold of regulatory significance required for the issuance of a Warning Letter, the agency may issue an Untitled Letter. This type of letter is distinguished from a Warning Letter in that it is not titled; does not include a statement indicating it will be shared with other federal agencies for use when awarding contracts; does not warn that failure to take prompt action to correct the situation may result in enforcement action; does not require district follow up; and requests, rather than requires, a written response from the firm within a reasonable amount of time.[16] Even though not required, firms still are encouraged to address the agency's concerns. An Untitled Letter is considered "prior notification," and failure to address a minor violation as a result of an Untitled Letter could lead to a Warning Letter or other enforcement action in the future.

Recalls

Recall procedures are covered in Chapter 21. This section, however, briefly examines FDA's power to mandate a recall in light of its enforcement power. Manufacturers or distributors may initiate a recall at any time to fulfill their obligation to protect the public health from products that present a risk of injury or gross deception, or are otherwise defective. However, FDA has the authority to order or mandate a recall, under various sections of the law. It accomplishes this through a written order to the firm. Generally, FDA-mandated recalls relate to a violative product causing an imminent or substantial risk to public health. FDA will exercise this authority when a firm refuses to initiate a recall of its own accord or fails to initiate a recall when requested by the agency.

Seizures

FDA is authorized to seize adulterated or misbranded product pursuant to the *FD&C Act.*[17] Seizure occurs under a supplemental Admiralty and Maritime rule, and begins with the US Government filing a Complaint of Forfeiture and obtaining a Warrant of Arrest, directing US Marshals to take possession of the article at issue, which could be a drug, device, food item or any other article regulated by FDA. A proper claimant may litigate on behalf of the seized article or, if none comes forward, the US is entitled to condemnation and forfeiture by default. Of note in this proceeding is the seized article is given the status of a "defendant" for purposes of the judicial action. In order for FDA to exercise its seizure authority, it must work through the Department of Justice to file the case.

FDA internally classifies the types of seizures it uses—mass and open-ended seizures, multiple seizures and lot-specific seizures. Mass and open-ended seizures occur when the agency seizes all FDA-regulated product at an establishment or facility as a result of the product being held in the same environment, such as "filthy conditions," or all the product being manufactured under the same conditions (this could be significant nonconformance with GMPs). Multiple seizures occur when FDA seizes the same product in more than one district court, generally to prevent continued distribution of a violative product (usually presenting a risk to health). Finally, lot-specific seizures involve a specific lot or lots of a violative product in a single location.

Once product is seized, FDA provides three options for its disposition. First, a claimant can do nothing. The effect of doing nothing is the agency (government) moves for default judgment, condemnation and forfeiture or destruction under a Default Decree. A Default Decree may be granted after a set period of time (usually 30 days) elapses without response from a proper claimant. Once a Default Decree has been granted, the government can dispose of the articles.

The next option is a Consent Decree of Condemnation. After filing a proper claim to the seized property, the claimant can agree to enter into a Consent Decree, which may provide for reconditioning the seized articles. Said reconditioning must bring the articles into compliance and usually is done under FDA supervision. A bond is required, most often twice the retail value of the seized goods, and the entire bond may be forfeited if the firm fails to abide by the Consent Decree.

Finally, a claimant may contest the seizure by filing a verified statement of interest in the seized articles and an answer within 20 days, denying all or part of the government allegations. This then proceeds as a normal civil trial, and the final decision will be determined by the court after considering the case.

Injunctions

FDA may seek an injunction against a firm in violation of the *FD&C Act* or regulations. An injunction is a civil judicial proceeding initiated to stop or prevent violation of the law. An injunction's effect is to prevent a firm from distributing the enjoined products unless the injunction is lifted. FDA will consider an injunction for any significant compliance failure but, most often, when a health hazard is identified. According to the *Regulatory Procedures Manual*, FDA considers several scenarios when contemplating an injunction. First, there is a determination of whether there is a "current and definite" risk to health or a gross consumer deception requiring FDA to stop the practice. An injunction also is more likely if FDA has requested or mandated a recall, and the firm has refused to comply or is not completing the recall at the level or with the urgency the agency expects. Firms with chronic noncompliance that have failed repeatedly to remedy their violations, regardless of safety or consumer fraud concerns, could face injunction.

FDA has three paths when seeking to enjoin a firm from further distribution of violative product: the agency may seek a temporary restraining order (TRO), preliminary injunction and/or a permanent injunction. The TRO is an immediate process, used to control an emergency. It temporarily stops distribution of the allegedly violative product, providing the agency with 10 days to gather sufficient noncompliance evidence (with the possibility for a 10-day extension) prior to a hearing for a preliminary injunction. This is used by FDA in cases where the agency believes a violation is so serious it requires immediate control to protect the public health.

With or without a TRO, the agency may seek a preliminary injunction. The preliminary injunction remains in effect according to order of court, but may stand indefinitely or until the case is settled, a permanent injunction is granted or the parties consent to entry of a decree. A preliminary injunction proceeds according to normal civil court processes.

Finally, FDA may seek a permanent injunction, through a hearing or settlement agreement. As with a preliminary injunction, a permanent injunction granted through a hearing proceeds according to the normal civil court processes. An affected firm also may agree, through a settlement agreement, to be permanently enjoined from distributing allegedly violative products. Once decreed, a firm is enjoined from distributing the products at issue unless the order is lifted by the court.

FDA uses injunctions mainly in cases where repeated notice has not yielded improvement or remedy of violations. Adequate notice and evidence are required, and the timeliness of FDA's request is weighed by the issuing court.

Civil Money Penalties

Civil money penalties (CMP) are authorized under various sections of the *FD&C Act* and the *Public Health Service Act*. CMPs can be assessed for a variety of reasons, including, but certainly not limited to: false or misleading advertisements, destruction of required records, submitting false or misleading clinical trial information, submitting false information in applications to FDA.[18] Current maximum penalty amounts can be found in the tables of 21 CFR 17.2.

Disqualification of Clinical Investigators

FDA has the power and authority to prevent an investigator from participating in clinical studies that will be used to provide information for a regulatory submission. If FDA has information, generally obtained through a Bioresearch Monitoring (BIMO) inspection, which indicates an investigator or sponsor-investigator has repeatedly or deliberately failed to comply with the applicable Good Clinical Practice requirements and regulations (such as 21 CFR Parts 312, 314 and 812), 21 CFR Part 50 or 21 CFR Part 56 or repeatedly has submitted deliberately to FDA or to the sponsor false information in any required report, CDRH, CBER or CDER may provide written notice to the investigator of the alleged noncompliance. The investigator then is afforded an opportunity to explain the matter (in writing or an informal meeting, at the investigator's option). Successful explanation to the applicable center will result in discontinuance of the disqualification proceeding. However, should the investigator fail to supply adequate reasons for his or her alleged noncompliance, that investigator will be disqualified. Disqualification renders an investigator ineligible to conduct any clinical investigation to support an application for a research or marketing permit for products regulated by FDA, including drugs, biologics, devices, new animal drugs, foods, including dietary supplements, which bear a nutrient content claim or a health claim, infant formulas, food and color additives and tobacco products. An investigator may be reinstated by the FDA commissioner if the investigator provides sufficient assurances any clinical investigation supporting an application for a research or marketing permit for products regulated by FDA will be conducted solely in compliance with the provisions of the applicable part of the CFR.

Debarment

FDA possesses statutory authority to ban or debar individuals and companies from the drug industry if those individuals and companies are convicted of certain felonies or misdemeanors related to drug products. Once individuals have been subjected to debarment, they may no longer work for anyone with an approved or pending drug product application at FDA. Debarred companies may no longer submit abbreviated drug applications. Civil Money Penalties also may be levied in cases where an individual was debarred as a result of generic drug approval application fraud (21 USC 355a-335c).

Criminal Enforcement

For the most egregious violations of statutes or regulations, the *FD&C Act* provides for criminal prosecution; however, FDA does not prosecute its own cases. Instead, the potential criminal case is forwarded to FDA's Office of Criminal Investigation for an initial review and investigation. If it is decided a criminal case should proceed against the corporation or individual, FDA involves the Department of Justice (DOJ), which handles the actual prosecution.

FDA's legal authority to bring a criminal case against an individual stems from the 1975 Supreme Court case *United States v. Park*. In this case, it was held the government can seek to obtain misdemeanor convictions of a company official for alleged violations of the *FD&C Act*, even if the official was unaware of the violation.[19] No knowledge or intent is required in this type of prosecution; instead, the *FD&C Act* "imposes the highest standard of care and permits conviction of responsible corporate officials who, in light of this standard of care, have the power to prevent or correct violations of its provisions."[20]

FDA considers multiple factors when deciding to recommend prosecution of a corporate officer, including: whether the violation involves actual or potential risk to public health; whether the violation is serious, obvious and widespread; whether the violation reflects a pattern of illegal behavior or shows a failure to heed prior warnings or notifications; the quality and quantity of legal and factual support; and whether the proposed prosecution is a prudent use of agency resources.[21]

In most cases where a criminal prosecution is sought against an individual or company, a Section 305 hearing will be held. This hearing is formally noticed and generally informal, affording a person the opportunity to provide information to the agency to assuage its concerns and stop the agency from further pursuing the prosecution with the Department of Justice. In situations where evidence has been altered or destroyed, the potential defendant is a flight risk or felony proceedings are being sought through a grand jury, a 305 hearing will not be held.

A potential affirmative defense to prosecution is a guaranty. This provides a safe harbor from prosecution.[22] A guaranty is a statement the articles delivered by the guarantor are not adulterated or misbranded under the *FD&C Act*. 21 CFR Part 7 explains a guaranty expires when the covered products are delivered by the person or firm providing the guaranty into the receiving firm's possession. If the products subsequently become misbranded or adulterated, the receiving firm no longer is protected by the safe harbor provision, and the firm may be held accountable for this misbranding or adulteration.

Other Agencies

FDA enforces statutes and regulations under the *FD&C Act*. However, other agencies have authority to take actions in relation to companies and products generally overseen by FDA. For example, the Consumer Product Safety Commission regulates child-resistant packaging. Similarly, the Securities and Exchange Commission will step in when traditionally FDA-regulated materials are misleading to investors. The Federal Trade Commission regulates over-the-counter advertising for foods, drugs, cosmetics and devices. Additionally, state agencies also may take enforcement actions to enforce state statutes and regulations.

Summary

FDA has statutory and regulatory authority granting it wide latitude to enforce the laws and regulations for which it is responsible. Perhaps its most versatile weapon is the establishment inspection. This power allows FDA to inspect a firm's compliance firsthand and gives the agency the opportunity to examine the facility, records and personnel. FDA inspects to protect the public health. The product, industry and the site's inspectional history, among other factors, will determine the type of inspection and the depth of inspection that will be performed.

Firms should remember the agency's power to inspect is not unlimited and should understand those limitations. Providing solid policies and procedures for employees tasked with handling FDA inspections and ensuring all employees are properly trained will contribute to a smooth inpection.

Firms that fail to comply voluntarily with the *FD&C Act* and attendant regulations can face enforcement actions from a Warning Letter, civil money penalties and criminal prosecution. FDA, with cause and with the aid of other federal agencies such as the Department of Justice, can seize violative product or enjoin a firm from further distribution of misbranded or adulterated products. However, regardless of the power it wields, FDA expects companies to comply voluntarily with the regulations and take proactive measures to maintain their products' integrity.

References

1. 21 U.S.C 301, et seq.
2. 21 U.S.C. 393(a).
3. 21 U.S.C. 393(b)(1).
4. 21 U.S.C. 393(b)(2).
5. 21 U.S.C. 331, et seq.
6. Ibid.
7. IOM Chapter 5.
8. 18 USC 701.
9. Medical Device Single Audit Program (MDSAP) Pilot. FDA website. http://www.fda.gov/medicaldevices/internationalprograms/mdsappilot/default.htm. Accessed 22 June 2015.
10. *Dow Chemical v. United State* 476 US 227 (1986).
11. *United States of America v. Acri Wholesale Grocery Company, A Corporation, and JOSEPH D. ACRI and ANTHONY ACRI, Individuals,* U.S. District Court for Southern District of Iowa. 409 F. Supp. 529. (1976).
12. An affidavit is a written statement sworn to or affirmed before a person with authority ot witness the oath. Black's Law Dictionary.
13. IOM 5.2.3
14. Chapter 36 8th edition of Fundamentals of US regulatory Affairs.
15. Regulatory Procedures Manual 10-2-4.
16. Ibid page 33.
17. 21 USC 334.
18. Op cit 1.
19. *US v. Park* 421, US 658 (1975).
20. Ibid.

Chapter 40

Healthcare Fraud and Abuse Compliance

Updated by H. Carol Saul

OBJECTIVES

- Provide overviews of state and federal laws directed at preventing waste, fraud and various other abuses by life sciences firms
- Explain types of fraud
- Provide overview of amendments to the existing laws
- Provide examples of circumstances that might trigger concerns under these laws
- Identify consequences of violating these laws
- Identify compliance methods and tools to combat healthcare fraud and abuse

LAWS, REGULATIONS AND GUIDELINES COVERED IN THIS CHAPTER

- *Federal Food, Drug, and Cosmetic Act* of 1938
- *Guidance for Industry: Good Reprint Practices for the Distribution of Medical Journal Articles and Medical or Scientific Reference Publications on Unapproved New Uses of Approved Drugs and Approved or Cleared Medical Devices* (January 2009)
- *False Claims Act* of 1863 (*FCA*)
- Federal and state Anti-Kickback Laws
- Federal and state Physician Self-Referral Laws (*Stark Law*)
- Pharmaceutical Research and Manufacturers of America Code on Interactions with Healthcare Professionals (PhRMA Code) Advanced Medical Technology Association Code (AdvaMed Code)
- Price Reporting Laws
- Medicaid Drug Program
- Federal Upper Limit
- Public Health Service Program
- Federal Government Ceiling Price
- Medicare Part B
- Medicare Part D
- State sales and marketing compliance laws
- *Physician Payment Sunshine Act* of 2009
- *Patient Protection and Affordable Care Act* of 2010

Introduction

Healthcare fraud and abuse have become a primary focus of regulators in recent years and have led to the loss of billions of dollars annually. Since Medicare and Medicaid make up more than 20% of the federal budget, it is not surprising these programs are susceptible to fraud.

Life sciences firms selling items ultimately utilized in the healthcare industry are subject to laws directed at preventing waste, fraud and various other abuses. Any company providing goods or services reimbursed under Medicare, Medicaid or other federal healthcare programs may be subject to civil or criminal penalties under federal laws including the *Medicare and Medicaid Patient Protection Act* of 1987 (*Federal Anti-Kickback Statute*), the Ethics in Patient Referrals Act (*Stark Law)*, the *False Claims Act* (*FCA*) and US Food and Drug Administration (FDA) regulations. Companies providing goods or services reimbursed by state healthcare programs, or even by individuals or private payers, may find themselves subject to similar, but usually not identical, state laws. This chapter introduces several key risk areas for pharmaceutical and medical device manufacturers, with the aim of identifying illustrative, but not exhaustive, patterns that may, if not properly managed, lead to allegations of fraud, waste or abuse. It also discusses the common types of fraud being reported every year, the proactive enforcement measures the federal government is taking to curb these activities and key measures for fraud avoidance.

Off-Label Promotion

FDA seeks to ensure drug and device safety and efficacy. This means most drugs and devices must be approved or cleared by FDA prior to promotion or marketing. As part of this process, FDA approves or clears drugs and devices for certain uses or indications. The agency generally prohibits manufacturers of new drugs or medical devices from promoting or marketing products for any use FDA has not approved or cleared. According to FDA, an approved new drug marketed for an unapproved use is an unapproved new drug with respect to that use. Specifically, an approved drug or device or an uncleared device marketed for an unapproved use is considered to be misbranded. If the manufacturer promotes a drug or device for any unapproved or uncleared indication, commonly called "off-label promotion," it may violate both FDA laws and the *FCA*.

FDA recognizes off-label use can be appropriate and valuable to patient care. In fact, drugs and devices commonly are used for off-label indications with good results. Thus, the statutes allow for off-label use by physicians as part of the professional practice of medicine. Drugmakers currently are pushing for the right to speak to doctors regarding unapproved uses for their products, arguing truthful speech should be protected under the First Amendment. In May 2015, Amarin Pharma sued FDA, claiming it has a constitutional right to share such information with physicians.

The litigation involves Amarin's only product, Vascepa, a prescription omega-3 fatty acid, approved by FDA for use in patients with extremely high levels of triglycerides. Amarin sought to expand the drug's reach to a wider population, but FDA denied the request. Specifically, Amarin wanted to share with physicians a 2011 clinical trial indicating Vascepa lowered triglycerides in patients with persistently high levels. The litigation is ongoing and could have an impact on the future of drug marketing and FDA's drug approval process.

FDA understands there must be some room for free exchange of educational and scientific information in order to advance the cause of science and healthcare. For example, in FDA's *Guidance for Industry: Good Reprint Practices for the Distribution of Medical Journal Articles and Medical or Scientific Reference Publications on Unapproved New Uses of Approved Drugs and Approved or Cleared Medical Devices* (January 2009), the agency allows dissemination of certain scientific information by manufacturers, with constraints designed to ensure these exchanges are not used as subterfuges for off-label promotion. Most companies have implemented processes and procedures that apply when disseminating off-label information, to ensure adherence to FDA guidance.

The *FCA* may be implicated by off-label promotion. This law imposes civil liability for filing a false or fraudulent claim to be reimbursed by the government. Penalties under the *FCA* include treble damages, plus an additional civil penalty of $5,500 to $11,000 for each false claim filed. The steep per-claim civil monetary penalties and treble damages under the *FCA* mean low-valued claims nevertheless can result in significant fines. The *FCA* also allows any person or party who has knowledge of the wrongdoing and brings it to court (a "relator" or "whistleblower") to receive between 15% and 30% of the judgment or settlement's monetary proceeds.

In addition, the *FCA* applies to companies that "cause" a false claim to be filed. For example, in April 2012, McKesson Corp. agreed to pay $190 million to settle a lawsuit alleging the company inflated prices of hundreds of prescription drugs, which in turn caused state Medicaid programs to overpay millions of dollars in reimbursements (http://www.justice.gov/opa/pr/mckesson-corp-pays-us-more-190-million-resolve-false-claims-act-allegations).

Because the general rule is Medicare and Medicaid will provide reimbursement for a drug or device only when it is prescribed for an approved use, when a company markets a drug or device for an unapproved use, the government may argue such marketing "caused" a healthcare professional to file a claim with Medicare or Medicaid for an off-label use. One exception to this general rule is Medicare Part B payments when an off-label use of the drug is supported in major drug compendia or by clinical evidence in authoritative medical literature.

The federal government takes an aggressive stance regarding the enforcement of off-label promotion and has obtained some significant judgments against manufacturers for the practice. These cases typically arise from sales and marketing practices designed to persuade healthcare providers to prescribe products for off-label uses. For example, in January 2009, the Department of Justice (DOJ) accepted a guilty plea from Eli Lilly and Co. and fined the company $515 million. This fine was in addition to a civil settlement of approximately $800 million. These criminal and civil settlements resulted from a claim that Eli Lilly promoted its drug, Zyprexa, for the treatment of dementia, Alzheimer's, depression, anxiety, sleep problems and behavioral symptoms such as agitation, aggression and hostility, despite the fact that Zyprexa was approved only for the treatment of psychotic disorders and bipolar disorder. Similarly, in April 2009, Nichols Institute Diagnostics, a subsidiary of Quest Diagnostics Inc., pled guilty to a felony misbranding charge in violation of the *Food, Drug, and Cosmetic Act* of 1938 (*FD&C Act)* and agreed to pay a criminal fine of $40 million as part of a $302 million global settlement with the federal government. In its guilty plea, the defendant admitted, over approximately a six-year period, beginning in May 2000, it had marketed a misbranded test. The misbranding claim was premised on the allegation the defendant distributed marketing materials describing the Advantage Intact PTH Assay as having "excellent correlation" to another assay—despite the fact it was aware the Advantage Intact PTH Assay was not providing consistently equivalent results.

Other cases illustrating off-label marketing risks are emerging. In December 2012, Amgen Inc. (Amgen) pled guilty to illegally introducing a misbranded drug, Aranesp, into interstate commerce, resulting in a global settlement in which Amgen agreed to pay $762 million. Aranesp is an erythropoiesis-stimulating agent approved by FDA at calibrated doses for particular patient populations suffering from anemia. To increase sales of Aranesp, Amgen was alleged to have sold the drug illegally, with the intent the drug be used at off-label doses and for an off-label treatment FDA had never approved. In addition, the government alleged Amgen promoted two other drugs, Enbrel and Neulasta, for off-label uses and doses not approved by FDA and not properly reimbursable by federal programs (http://www.justice.gov/opa/pr/amgen-inc-pleads-guilty-federal-charge-brooklyn-ny-pays-762-million-resolve-criminal).

In November 2013, Johnson & Johnson agreed to pay $1.391 billion to resolve allegations resulting from its off-label marketing and kickbacks for Risperdal and Invega. Invega is an antipsychotic drug approved for the treatment of schizophrenia and schizoaffective disorder. The government alleged, from 2006 through 2009, Johnson & Johnson and a subsidiary marketed the drug for off-label indications and made false and misleading statements about its safety and efficacy.

The government also alleged Johnson & Johnson and its subsidiary marketed Risperdal to control the behaviors and conduct of elderly nursing home residents, children and individuals with mental disabilities. The government alleged the defendants were aware Risperdal posed serious health risks for the elderly, including an increased risk of strokes, and patients taking Risperdal had an increased risk of developing diabetes, but had downplayed these risks. Johnson & Johnson also allegedly promoted the antipsychotic drug for use in children and individuals with mental disabilities, even though Risperdal posed certain health risks to children. Furthermore, the complaint alleged, despite FDA warnings and increased health risks, the defendants used an "ElderCare sales force" to market Risperdal aggressively, targeting nursing homes and doctors who treat the elderly. As a result of these actions, the government alleged the defendants caused false claims to be submitted to federal healthcare programs (http://www.justice.gov/opa/pr/johnson-johnson-pay-more-22-billion-resolve-criminal-and-civil-investigations).

CareFusion is a California-based medical technology company that manufactures, markets and sells ChloraPrep, an antiseptic applied to a patient's skin prior to surgery or injection. In a complaint against CareFusion, the State and qui tam relator alleged CareFusion had promoted the sale of ChloraPrep products for uses not approved by FDA, some of which were not medically accepted indications. In addition, the government alleged CareFusion knowingly made and/or disseminated unsubstantiated representations about the use of ChloraPrep products. In January 2014, CareFusion agreed to pay $40.1 million to resolve these allegations (http://www.justice.gov/opa/pr/carefusion-pay-government-401-million-resolve-allegations-include-more-11-million-kickbacks)

In addition to monetary relief, FDA may seek an injunction to prohibit a company from manufacturing and distributing an unapproved drug. For example, in April 2009, FDA announced it was barring Neilgen Pharmaceuticals Inc., its parent company Advent Pharmaceuticals Inc. and two of its officers from manufacturing and distributing any unapproved, adulterated or misbranded drugs. According to FDA, the unapproved drugs (primarily prescription cough and cold products) had not undergone the agency's drug approval process. Accordingly, the companies failed to establish the drugs' safety and effectiveness, and FDA had not reviewed the directions for use and related label warnings' adequacy and accuracy. As part of the consent decree with FDA, Neilgen and Advent were ordered to destroy their existing drug supplies and expressly prohibited from commercially manufacturing and distributing any new drugs without the agency's approval. The companies also were required to consult with outside experts who could provide guidance regarding appropriate compliance standards, and to obtain written authorization from FDA before resuming operations. They face the prospect of steep financial penalties for any future violations. While the failure to obtain FDA approval makes this an extreme case, the enforcement action demonstrates the significant business disruption that can result from violating FDA regulatory requirements.

It also is important to note claims of off-label promotion are not levied exclusively against manufacturers. For example, in 2006, DOJ charged a psychiatrist with conspiring with the manufacturer of a drug called Xyrem to promote the drug for off-label uses. According to the indictment, the manufacturer of Xyrem, Orphan Medical Inc., paid the psychiatrist thousands of dollars for promoting Xyrem for off-label uses at various speaking engagements. As a result, both the company and the physician were charged. Orphan Medical paid $20 million to settle civil and criminal charges, and in 2008, the physician pled guilty to misbranding.

Kickbacks

Patients rely on their physicians to recommend the best treatments, drugs and devices. Indeed, patients cannot obtain prescription medical products without a referral or order from a medical professional. Thus, the physician-patient relationship is regarded as a special, fiduciary relationship in which the physician's motivating concern is to act in the patient's best interest. Remunerative relationships (such as consulting arrangements) between manufacturers and physicians who make referrals for or order the manufacturers' products can create an apparent or real conflict of interest, thereby potentially tainting referral decisions.

This is the underlying concern of the federal *Anti-Kickback Statute.* Generally, the criminal statute prohibits intentionally soliciting, offering or receiving any remuneration (including any kickback, bribe, discount or rebate) in return for referring an individual to a person for the furnishing of any item or service for which payment may be made under a federal or a federally-funded state healthcare program such as Medicare or Medicaid. For example, the *Anti-Kickback Statute* prohibits the provision of remuneration to a physician to induce or reward him or her for writing prescriptions for a particular product. A violation may be found if only one purpose of the remuneration was to induce the referral or purchase. The mandatory penalties for violations of this statute are severe, and a party found guilty of violating the *Anti-Kickback Statute* is guilty of a felony and may be subject to a prison term of up to five years, with the potential for additional criminal fines up to $25,000 per violation. Civil penalties for violation of the *Anti-Kickback Statute* include fines of up to $50,000 per violation and a civil assessment of up to three times the amount of a kickback. In addition, a party that has violated the statute is excluded from participation in Medicare, Medicaid and other federal healthcare programs. For life sciences companies, this means Medicare and Medicaid will no longer provide reimbursement for the company's products. Pursuant to the *Patient Protection and Affordable Care Act* of 2010 (*PPACA*), violations of the *Anti-Kickback Statute* became *per se* violations of the *False Claims Act.* In addition, *PPACA* amended the *Anti-Kickback Statute* to provide that a person does not have to have actual knowledge of the law or a specific intent to violate the act. Basically, this change means even unintentional violations of the *Anti-Kickback Statute* can be grounds for a finding of fraud.

Application of the *Anti-Kickback Statute* is complex. Nevertheless, many common business arrangements involving remuneration between manufacturers and referral sources can be structured to comply with the statute by using one of the currently available 23 safe harbors provided by regulations. For example, a "safe harbor" to the *Anti-Kickback Statute* can protect arrangements with consultants, speakers and advisory board members providing services to companies. It is important all remunerative relationships (i.e., transfers of value through compensation or otherwise) between manufacturers and their customers and others in a position to generate business for the manufacturer be properly vetted for compliance with the *Anti-Kickback Statute* and structured to meet applicable safe harbors.

There are many examples of investigations and prosecutions under the *Anti-Kickback Statute.* These actions typically arise from cases where a device or pharmaceutical manufacturer gives something, such as excessive compensation or luxurious travel, to a physician or another person in a position to recommend its product, and it appears the reason behind the remuneration is to induce the recipient to recommend or order the manufacturer's product. Notably, it is not unusual to see a prosecution involving allegations a company made improper payments to a physician to induce the physician to prescribe products for off-label uses, thereby violating both the prohibition against off-label promotion and the *Anti-Kickback Statute.*

These cases often involve payments to physicians, but also can involve payments to other parties in a position to promote the manufacturer's product. For example, one prosecution reaching a settlement agreement in May 2015 involved a large pharmacy benefit manager, Medco. The government alleged Medco violated the *Anti-Kickback Statute* by soliciting and accepting payments from pharmaceutical companies for favorable formulary placement, and by paying kickbacks to induce health plans to award Medco contracts to provide mail order pharmacy benefits for the plans' beneficiaries. In *United States ex rel. Kester v. Novartis Pharm. Corp.*, the US and 11 states alleged Novartis Pharmaceuticals Corporation violated the *Anti-Kickback Statute* by paying kickbacks in the form of cash rebates and patient referrals to certain specialty pharmacies in connection with two of its drugs, Exjade and Myfortic. In *United States ex rel. Ruscher v. Omnicare, Inc.*, the relator brought a law suit against Omnicare Inc., alleging a kickback scheme wherein Omnicare induced and retained business from skilled nursing facilities that provided services to a high volume of Medicare Part D/Medicaid patients, in exchange for which Omnicare forfeited its payments for pharmaceuticals dispensed to Medicare Part A patients.

Many states have adopted their own versions of the *Anti-Kickback Statute*. These laws may affect arrangements involving items or services not reimbursed under a governmental program. Also, these state laws may implicate slightly different behavior than the federal statute. The existence of these state anti-kickback statutes means all remunerative relationships with referral sources should be scrutinized for compliance with both state and federal law. Generally, where remuneration tracks volume or value of referrals or purchases, a red flag should be raised, and counsel should be consulted.

Physician Self-Referrals

Increasingly, physicians have branched out from the practice of medicine to provide ancillary services to their patients, such as laboratory tests, pharmaceuticals, durable medical equipment, therapy, imaging and lithotripsy. Some physicians may own interests in hospitals or other facilities to which they refer patients, or in device companies producing products used by their patients. While this practice seems like a natural evolution—and can be beneficial to the extent it increases accessibility or quality or spurs innovation—it also has the potential for creating a conflict of interest. The financial interest provides the physician with an incentive to direct patients to purchase services or products from an entity in which he or she has an interest, despite the fact these products or devices may not be needed or may not be the best or most economical product available to the patient.

The *Stark Law* (named for its primary sponsor, US Representative Pete Stark of California) and its associated complex regulations address this concern by prohibiting physician referrals to entities in which the physician, or an immediate family member, has an ownership or compensation interest for certain "designated health services" reimbursed by Medicare or Medicaid, except in certain specified circumstances. The *Stark Law* is a strict liability statute, which means a violation can be found even in the absence of intent. As with the *Anti-Kickback Statute*, many states have adopted their own variants of the *Stark Law* and prohibit self-referrals in the same or similar circumstances as prohibited by the federal law. Of course, not all of these arrangements will be problematic; rather, they may fall under one of numerous statutory or regulatory exceptions. However, all these arrangements require careful attention.

In 2014, Halifax Hospital Medical Center and Halifax Staffing agreed to pay $85 million to resolve alleged violations of the *Stark Law* and *FCA*. The government alleged Halifax violated the *Stark Law* pursuant to its contract with six medical oncologists containing an incentive bonus that included the value of prescription drugs and tests the oncologists ordered and billed to Medicare (http://www.beckershospitalreview.com/legal-regulatory-issues/10-largest-false-claims-stark-law-and-anti-kickback-settlements-of-2014.html). Additionally, in April 2013, Paul Lux, MD, agreed to pay $63,900 for alleged violations of the *Stark Law* and *Anti-Kickback Statute*. The Office of Inspector General (OIG) alleged Lux received compensation from a medical device manufacturer in the form of payments under a clinical registry contract (http://oig.hhs.gov/fraud/enforcement/cmp/kickback.asp).

Physician-owned distributors (PODs) also have faced regulatory scrutiny. A POD is "any physician-owned entity that derives revenue from selling, or arranging for the sale of, implantable medical devices and includes physician-owned entities that purport to design or manufacture, typically under contractual arrangements, their own medical devices or instrumentation." In June 2011, the Senate Finance Committee published an inquiry regarding the legitimacy of POD arrangements, noting these arrangements may create unlawful financial incentives. Subsequently, on 26 March 2013, OIG issued a Special Fraud Alert addressing the issue of PODs, explaining any opportunity for a referring physician to earn a profit could be a violation of the *Anti-Kickback Statute*. In addition, OIG described PODs as "inherently suspect."

On 8 October 2013, in response to OIG's statement against PODs, Reliance Medical Systems, a Utah distributorship, filed a Complaint for Declaratory Relief against OIG and the Department of Health and Human Services (DHHS). Specifically, the complaint alleged the Special Fraud Alert violated Reliance's First Amendment rights because classifying a physician-owned business as "inherently suspect" discourages business owners from speaking to physicians about working together. In February 2014, the District Court for the Central District of California dismissed Reliance's complaint on the basis Reliance had not demonstrated an injury-in-fact as required to confer standing.

Currently under litigation is the first *FCA* action filed by the government against a POD. On 8 September 2014, the US filed two complaints to recover civil penalties against Reliance Medical Systems, Dr. Aria Sabit, two Reliance distributorships—Apex Medical Technologies and Kronos Spinal Technologies, and the companies' owners. The complaints allege Apex Medical and Kronos Spinal paid physicians to induce them to use Reliance spinal implants. The government alleged the Reliance claims submitted to Medicare were therefore tainted by kickbacks (http://www.justice.gov/opa/pr/united-states-pursues-claims-against-neurosurgeon-spinal-implant-company-physician-owned).

PhRMA Code and AdvaMed Code

In addition to laws governing manufacturers' conduct, trade organizations have adopted voluntary codes of ethics. The Pharmaceutical Research and Manufacturers of America (PhRMA) adopted a voluntary marketing code to govern the pharmaceutical industry's relationships with physicians and other healthcare professionals. The PhRMA Code on Interactions with Healthcare Professionals originally took effect in 2002 and was revised and made more stringent in 2009. Similarly, the Advanced Medical Technology Association (AdvaMed) issued its Code of Ethics on Interactions with Health Care Professionals (the AdvaMed Code) in 2005 and revised it in 2009 to coincide with the PhRMA Code revisions.

Both the PhRMA and AdvaMed Codes have established standards for manufacturers' interactions with healthcare professionals. For example, the codes discuss gifts, entertainment, the use of consultants, support of third-party conferences and grants. While not law, the government has recognized these codes as providing appropriate guidance to the industry. Additionally, a number of states have enacted laws requiring or recommending compliance with the codes.

Bad Reimbursement Advice

Manufacturers of complex or innovative products often provide reimbursement advice to their customers. Liability can arise from advice that is faulty or perceived as promoting over-utilization. For example, in *United States v. Augustine Medical Inc.*, the government alleged a manufacturer directed its customers to bill Medicare in a manner that obscured its product's true nature, because it believed if Medicare knew exactly what product was being billed, it would reimburse for the product at a less-favorable rate. As a result, Augustine Medical and various individuals associated with the company faced criminal and civil enforcement actions. The company eventually settled all claims against it. However, certain Augustine Medical executives pled guilty to criminal charges related to withholding facts used to determine rights to Medicare payments, and each received probation and incurred a significant fine. Companies should take care to provide only objective and accurate reimbursement information and remind customers of their duty to confirm reimbursement policies before submitting claims to avoid a similar investigation.

Price Reporting Fraud

Pharmaceutical manufacturers are required to report drug prices under a number of different government programs using several different methodologies (e.g., Average Manufacturer Price, Best Price, Average Sales Price, Average Wholesale Price and Wholesale Acquisition Cost). Additionally, sponsors of programs operating under Medicare Part D are required to report all price concessions (e.g., rebates or discounts) obtained from manufacturers to the Centers for Medicare and Medicaid Services (CMS). Allegations a pharmaceutical manufacturer defrauded Medicare or Medicaid (or another government program) often are premised on the alleged inaccuracy of various pricing reports. Charges of misconduct can arise in connection with, for example, inaccurate reporting or characterization of discounts or rebates. Allegations of "marketing the spread"—where manufacturers report their Average Wholesale Price to Medicare as "x" but sell to physicians at "x-y," thereby yielding a windfall gain to physicians—have been prosecuted aggressively. Similarly, causes of action based on concealment of Best Price (where manufacturers do not report certain discounts to the states in connection with their Best Price reporting obligations under Medicaid) also have been popular theories for prosecution.

In 2006, Schering-Plough entered into a civil settlement to resolve potential liability stemming from the company's alleged private labeling of one of its products, K-Dur. The government alleged Schering-Plough had private-labeled K-Dur for an HMO client. The company then sold the product at a lower price than the Schering-labeled version of the product. The government alleged when Schering calculated its Best Price for the product, it failed to consider the lower private label price.

Additionally, in 2003, GlaxoSmithKline entered into an $87 million civil settlement regarding its potential liability for allegedly reporting inaccurate best prices for Flonase and Paxil. The government alleged Glaxo Wellcome had private-labeled Flonase for an HMO customer. The company then sold the drug to the HMO with a label displaying the HMO's NDC number at a discounted price and distribution. SmithKline Beecham also had entered into a repackaging agreement with the HMO customer, allegedly providing Paxil in bulk quantities to be repackaged and relabeled by the HMO under its own NDC number. In their Best Price calculations for the products, Glaxo Wellcome and SmithKline Beecham did not include the private label or bulk sales for repackaging. The government alleged these sales should have been taken into account when the companies reported their Best Price.

Beyond ensuring the integrity of data generated and submitted for government reimbursement purposes, accurate compliance with the various price reporting programs requires attention to periodic filing and reporting requirements. The key federal programs to which pharmaceutical manufacturers may need to submit price reporting data include the Medicaid Drug Program, Federal Upper Limit (applicable to multiple source drugs under Medicaid), Public Health Service Program, Federal Government Ceiling Price (applicable only to single-source and innovator multiple-source drugs), Medicare Part B and Medicare Part D (outpatient drug program).

Patient Protection and Affordable Care Act

The *PPACA*, variously known as the *Affordable Care Act, Health Insurance Reform, Healthcare Reform* or *Obamacare*, is a federal statute was signed by President Obama on 23 March 2010. The dual goals of *PPACA* are to reduce the number of uninsured people in the US and control healthcare costs. The act also strengthens the government's arsenal for combating healthcare fraud, waste and abuse.

PPACA's new rules have been implemented to help reduce fraud and waste and also to increase federal sentencing guidelines for people and companies involved in fraud. The law strengthens screening requirements for providers and suppliers who pose high risks. *PPACA* provides funding for enhanced data-mining tools and technologies to understand and analyze trends and predict fraudulent areas more precisely. *PPACA* also provides major funding (approximately $350 million over a period of 10 years) to boost anti-fraud efforts.

The Physician Payment Sunshine Act

A section of *PPACA*, known as the *Physician Payment Sunshine Act* (re-labeled the "National Physician Payment Transparency Program," or "Open Payments") requires drug and device manufacturers to make annual public disclosures of certain payments or other transfers of value to a physician or a teaching hospital.

By 1 October 2011, the entity charged with collecting such reports, DHHS, was required to establish procedures for submitting information and making public disclosure. The initial data gathering window was 1 August–31 December 2013, with the first reports due to CMS by 31 March 2014. The information was made available on 30 September 2014 on the Open Payments website at http://www.cms.gov/OpenPayments/Explore-the-Data/Dataset-Downloads.html. Pursuant to the CMS Final Rule, the specific data collected included the following categories of information: consulting fees, compensation for services other than consulting, gifts, entertainment, honoraria, food, travel, education, charitable contributions, research, royalty or license, current or prospective ownership or investment interest, direct compensation for serving as faculty or as a speaker for a medical education program, grants, or any other nature of the payment or other transfer of value as defined by the secretary.

Under the *Physician Payment Sunshine Act*, the transfer of anything with a value greater than $10, or $100 in the annual aggregate, must be reported. However, there are a number of exemptions from this reporting obligation. For example, gifts of educational materials directly benefitting patients or intended for patient use need not be reported. Manufacturers who fail to report are subject to significant civil monetary penalties ranging of $1,000–$100,000 per undisclosed transfer.

On 31 October 2014, as part of the 2015 Medicare Physician Fee Schedule publication, a number of revisions were published as a final rule. Notably, the final rule deleted the reporting exemption previously allowed for compensation to physician speakers at accredited or certified continuing education events. Previously, there was an exemption for indirect payments to physicians speaking at continuing education programs sponsored by certain accredited organizations. According to CMS, this change will create a consistent reporting requirement and provide clarity for consumers who can access the data.

In addition, the final rule aligns the reporting requirements for certain information pertaining to devices and medical supplies with the requirements for drugs and biologicals, requiring the marketed names for not only drugs and biologicals but also for all devices and medical supplies to be reported. Specifically, the final rule requires the marketed name and therapeutic area or product category of the related covered drugs, devices, biologicals or medical supplies to be reported, unless the payment or other transfer of value is not related to a particular covered or non-covered drug device, biological or medical supply. Additionally, applicable manufacturers and group purchasing organizations (GPOs) now will be required to report stock, stock options or any other ownership interests as distinct payment categories or forms.

Notably, the *Sunshine Act* preempts duplicative state reporting requirements. However, any additional and more-stringent reporting requirements states may choose to impose are not preempted.

Other Patterns of Fraud

Phantom Billing

This type of fraud includes billing for tests never performed on the patient. It also may include inappropriate or unnecessary billing of procedures never conducted. There may be cases where the patient is billed for equipment that was not ordered during the course of treatment. Charging Medicare or Medicaid higher prices while providing the patient with cheaper and lower quality products is another aspect of phantom billing. Additionally, there may be instances where a Certificate of Medical Necessity (CMN) may be completed by the drug or equipment supplier instead of the physician.

Code Jamming

This fraud results from a laboratory using a fake diagnosis code to make a patient eligible for Medicare or Medicaid coverage http://medicarefraudcenter.org).

Upcoding

This involves inflating bills by using false diagnosis billing codes that show the patient suffers from medical complications and/or needs more-expensive treatment than is true. In this instance, the provider intentionally uses a higher paying code on the claim form for a patient and asserts the patient was treated with a more expensive procedure or required the use of more costly devices during the treatment than were actually used.

A $31 million settlement was reached in 2000 with Community Health Systems, arising from allegations of upcoding by a hospital in Brentwood, TN, stemming from misuse of eight different codes, including those for pneumonia, septicemia, certain cardiac conditions, and respiratory failure and ventilators between 1 January 1994 and 31 December 1997 (Source: http://medicarefalseclaims.com/?page_id=358).

In 2009, the US Department of Justice began an investigation of Medicare claims for kyphoplasty after two former employees of Kyphon Inc. brought *FCA* allegations saying Kyphon actively recommended hospitals perform kyphoplasty on an inpatient basis, increasing the cost of the procedure by up to $10,000. Also in 2009, Johns Hopkins Bayview Medical Center Inc. settled *FCA* allegations by two hospital employees who claimed employees were reviewing inpatient charts that could be falsified with laboratory results to indicate additional medical problems. Hospital physicians then were told to make erroneous diagnoses in the medical charts to inflate the severity of the medical conditions, resulting in the facility being able to claim a higher reimbursement rate from the Maryland Health Services Cost Review Commission (http://www.myquitamlawsuit.com/index.aspx?id=upcoding).

Unbundling

This type of fraud usually is found in laboratory billing, where bills are submitted in unbundled parts, thus making the overall amount billed higher than the original required total. Certain types of tests are lower cost because they frequently are used by physicians and are intended to be "bundled" for reduced cost. Under unbundling, the healthcare provider artificially increases the total by billing each test separately. This type of fraud also is known as "fragmentation."

Reflex Testing

In this type of fraud, a laboratory runs certain tests automatically and bills the amount to Medicare. These tests are run even though the physician never prescribed or requested them. These cases are discovered when proper physician documentation is not sent to the laboratories.

Defective Testing

This results when the physician has prescribed certain tests to be carried out but the laboratory or clinic is unable to conduct them due to a lack of the appropriate technology or the absence of necessary equipment. The laboratory or clinic still bills the prescribed tests to Medicare.

State Laws Relating to Sales and Marketing

A number of state legislatures have sought new approaches to contain healthcare costs, track interactions between manufacturers and healthcare practitioners and generally reduce healthcare fraud. These approaches include laws requiring marketing activity and expenditure reporting and regulating interactions between manufacturers and healthcare professionals. California, Connecticut, Maine, Massachusetts, Minnesota, Montana, Nevada, West Virginia, Vermont and the District of Columbia have such laws. For the most part, these laws are triggered when a manufacturer interacts with a healthcare professional licensed in one of these states, including such situations as a national conference (e.g., may wish to invite a physician licensed in Maine to attend a dinner after a conference in another state) or may engage a healthcare professional licensed in one of the states to serve on an advisory board or speaker's bureau.

Table 40-1 includes the laws of the states mentioned above. Companies are cautioned to monitor these laws for revisions and to watch for the promulgation of new laws by other states.

Useful Compliance Tools to Avoid Fraudulent Activities

Office of Inspector General (OIG)

OIG was organized to combat waste, abuse and fraud taking place in the Medicare and Medicaid programs. Following are some duties carried out by OIG, which investigates instances of fraud, waste and mismanagement that may constitute either criminal wrongdoing or violation of DHHS and Broadcasting Board of Governors regulations. Familiarity with these tools and publications can help pharmaceutical and device manufacturers avoid risk under the laws discussed in this chapter.

Health Care Fraud Prevention and Enforcement Action Team (HEAT)

Since 2009, the Health Care Fraud Prevention and Enforcement Action Team (HEAT) has played a vital role in preventing fraudulent activities. HEAT's activities include harnessing resources across the government to help prevent fraud and waste, cracking down on individuals and organizations who abuse the system, reducing overall healthcare costs and improving quality of care by preventing fraud.

Operation HEAT has led to a significant increase in the number of individuals charged with healthcare fraud. Criminals convicted of fraudulent activities are facing tougher and longer sentences. More information on the HEAT initiative can be found at www.stopmedicarefraud.gov/aboutfraud/heattaskforce/index.html. In addition,

Table 40-1. State Laws on Manufacturer Interaction With Healthcare Providers

California	**CA HLTH & S § 119402**. Adoption of Comprehensive Compliance Program by pharmaceutical companies; annual dollar limits on certain items; drug samples; annual declaration of compliance. **CA WEL & INST § 14107.2**. Kickbacks, bribes or rebates; punishment.
Connecticut	**CT ST § 21a-70e.** Pharmaceutical or medical device manufacturing company. Adoption of code on interaction with health care professionals and comprehensive compliance program.
District of Columbia	**DC CODE § 48-833.01.** Requirement to disclose prescription drug marketing costs. **DC CODE § 48-833.02.** Manner of reporting. **DC CODE § 48-833.03.** Content of annual report by manufacturer or labeler. **DC CODE § 48-833.04.** Department reports. **DC CODE § 48-833.05.** Confidentiality; public information. **DC CODE § 48-833.06.** Penalty. **DC CODE § 48-833.08.** Report. **DC CODE § 48-843.03.** Establishment of the Pharmaceutical Education Program.
Maine	**ME ST T. 22 § 2685.** Prescription drug academic detailing program. **ME ST T. 22 § 2700-A**. Prohibitions.
Massachusetts	**MA ST 111 § 4N.** Prescription drugs outreach and education program for physicians, pharmacists and other health care professionals. **MA ST 111N § 2.** Marketing code of conduct; adoption; prohibited practices. **MA ST 111N § 3.** Violations of marketing code of conduct prohibited. **MA ST 111N § 4.** Adoption of marketing code of conduct by pharmaceutical or medical device manufacturing company; training program; annual audits; investigation and correction of noncompliance; compliance officer. **MA ST 111N § 5.** Annual submission of compliance information. **MA ST 111N § 6.** Disclosure of data relating to provision of economic benefits valuing fifty dollars or greater. **MA ST 111N § 7.** Enforcement; penalties. **MA ST 175H § 3.** Solicitation, improper inducement to use goods, facilities, services, or products covered by insurance. **MA ST 175H § 7.** Restitution; attorneys fees, costs.
Minnesota	**MN ST § 62J.23.** Provider conflicts of interest. **MN ST § 151.29.** Violation a misdemeanor. **MN ST § 151.461.** Gifts to practitioners prohibited. **MN ST § 151.47.** Wholesale drug distributor licensing requirements.
Montana	**MT ST § 37-2-102.** Practices declared unlawful between drug companies and medical practitioners. **MT ST § 37-2-103.** Practices declared unlawful between medical practitioners and pharmacies. **MT ST § 45-6-313.** Medicaid fraud.
Nevada	**Nev. Rev. Stat. Ann. § 639.570.** Employees of wholesalers or manufacturers; adoption of marketing code of conduct; training; investigation policies; submission of information to Board; Board to report certain information to Governor and Legislature; duties of Board.
Vermont	**18 V.S.A. § 4631a.** Expenditures by manufacturers of prescribed products.
West Virginia	**W. Va. CSR § 206-1-3.** Required Disclosure. **W. Va. CSR § 206-1-4.** Discretionary Disclosure.

Source: http://www.ncsl.org/research/health/marketing-and-advertising-of-pharmaceuticals.aspx

current HEAT Task Force updates are available at www.stopmedicarefraud.gov/newsroom/index.html.

One vital component of HEAT, the Medicare Fraud Strike Force, includes a team of analysts, investigators and prosecutors constantly on the lookout for emerging or migrating fraud schemes. Since 2007, the Medicare Fraud Strike Force has charged more than 1,400 defendants who billed Medicare more than $4.8 billion. In May 2014, Attorney General Eric Holder and DHHS Secretary Kathleen Sebelius announced a Medicare Fraud Strike Force takedown in six cities that resulted in charges against 90 individuals for their alleged participation in a Medicare fraud scheme involving approximately $260 million. The Medicare Fraud Strike Force recently expanded to nine cities: Baton Rouge, Brooklyn, Chicago, Dallas, Detroit, Houston, Los Angeles, Miami and Tampa.

Fraud Detection Technology

Fraud Detection Technology—Fraud Prevention Systems (FPS) employ predictive analytic technology to identify and track suspicious or fraudulent billing patterns. They use sophisticated mathematical and statistical algorithms and models to identify suspicious behavior. The systems analyze information from multiple data sources, such as Medicare. FPS systems run predictive models against all Medicare claims nationwide before the final payment is made to

Figure 40-1. Fraud Detection Technology

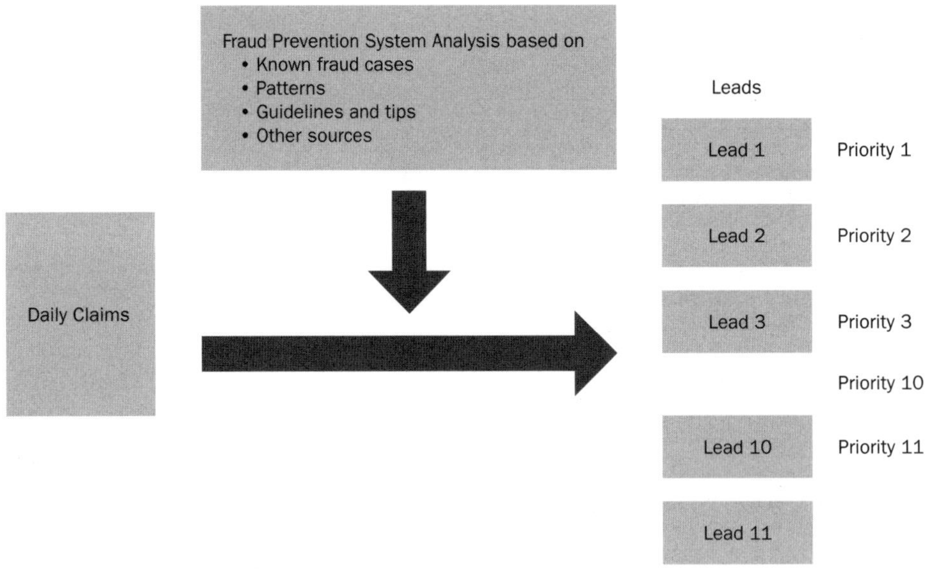

detect any deviation in billing patterns and other suspicious activities. When an FPS system detects irregularities or any suspicious activities, it generates reports providing leads and further data to investigate. The system automatically prioritizes the leads to help conduct investigations of high risk zones or entities (See **Figure 40-1**).

Senior Medicare Patrols

Since 1997, the Administration on Aging (AoA) has funded Senior Medical Patrol (SMP) projects to recruit and train senior citizens and retired personnel to help the government recognize and report fraudulent activities to authorities. The Obama administration has expanded the Senior Medicare Patrol task force by providing more funding for these groups. These patrols educate and authorize their colleagues to identify, prevent and report healthcare fraud.

Compliance Program Guidance

In July 1999, OIG published *Compliance Program Guidance for the Durable Medical Equipment, Prosthetics, Orthotics and Supply Industry*, identifying seven fundamental elements applicable to an effective compliance program. The guidance is intended to assist suppliers of durable medical equipment, prosthetics, orthotics and supplies and their agents and subcontractors to develop effective controls and processes to promote adherence to applicable federal and state laws, regulations and other program requirements. In addition, in May 2003, OIG published *Compliance Program Guidance for Pharmaceutical Manufacturers* in an effort to promote voluntary compliance programs for the healthcare industry. Companies that develop, manufacture, market and sell pharmaceuticals or biological products should use the compliance guidance to develop and implement procedures to promote adherence to statutes, regulations and requirements governing federal healthcare programs.

OIG Work Plans

Another tool for companies seeking to avoid healthcare fraud is the OIG Work Plan, published annually and describing various projects the Office of Audit Services, Office of Evaluation and Inspections, Office of Investigations and Office of Counsel to the Inspector General will address during the fiscal year. Projects include those planned in CMS. The work plan also provides information on state and local government use of federal funding and functional areas of the Office of the Secretary of Health and Human Services.

The 2015 work plan focused on a number of areas related to pharmaceutical and medical device manufacturers. Specifically, OIG noted it will review Medicare claims to identify costs resulting from additional use of medical services associated with defective medical devices and Medicare B payments for blood glucose test strips, lancet supplies and immunosuppressive drugs billed with a service modifier "KX." In addition, OIG will review claims for nebulizers and related drugs and frequently replaced medical equipment, to determine whether the claims were for medically necessary products and supported in accordance with Medicare requirements. OIG also will determine the effects of the competitive bidding program on Medicare beneficiaries' access to certain types of durable medical equipment.

Further, OIG will describe trends in Part D billing in 2006–14, including commonly used opioid drugs. OIG also will determine whether states have established adequate accountability and internal controls for collecting Medicaid rebates on physician-administered drugs, and review drug manufacturers' treatment of authorized generic sales in their Medicaid drug rebate program AMP calculation. The work plan also describes a number of activities focusing on drug prices, including review of Medicare Part B drug prices by comparing average sales prices to average manufacturer prices and identifying drug prices exceeding a designated threshold. It also includes a project to analyze generic drug prices over a period of time to determine whether prices increased more than the increases in inflation as measured by the consumer price index for urban consumers.

Summary

Life sciences firms selling items ultimately utilized in the healthcare industry are subject to laws directed at preventing waste, fraud and various other abuses. While a multitude of scenarios exist under which a life sciences company can find itself in trouble, attention should be focused on avoiding common enforcement targets, including: engaging in off-label promotion; giving illegal kickbacks; involvement in prohibited physician self-referrals; distributing misleading reimbursement advice; failing to comply with price reporting obligations; and failing to adhere to state sales and marketing laws. This chapter is designed to increase awareness of these risk areas, so the regulatory professional can help his or her company avoid them. It also aims to depict the latest countermeasures the federal government is taking to combat fraud, abuse and waste.

Recommended Reading

Advanced Medical Technology Association, *Code of Ethics on Interactions with Health Care Professionals*, http://advamed.org/res/112/advamed-code-of-ethics-on-interactions-with-health-care-professionals. Accessed 15 June 2015.

DHHS Administration on Aging website. http://www.aoa.gov/. Accessed 23 June 2015.

Office of Inspector General, *Compliance Guidance*, http://oig.hhs.gov/compliance/compliance-guidance/index.asp. Accessed 15 June 2015.

Pharmaceutical Research and Manufacturers of America, *Code on Interactions with Healthcare Professionals*, http://www.phrma.org/sites/default/files/pdf/phrma_marketing_code_2008.pdf.

Medicare & Medicaid Fraud Reporting Center website, http://medicarefraudcenter.org/. Accessed 23 June 2015.

STOP Medicare Fraud website. http://www.stopmedicarefraud.gov/. Accessed 23 June 2013.

HealthCare.gov website. http://www.healthcare.gov/. Accessed 23 June 2015.

Chapter 41

Regulatory Information Resources in Review

By Auresa Thomas, PhD, RAC (US, Global)

OBJECTIVES

- ❑ Become familiar with information resources relevant to the healthcare regulatory industry
- ❑ Learn where to access and retrieve publicly available government, industry and association resources to build regulatory intelligence
- ❑ Recognize the value of meetings and continued learning programs available for professional knowledge and development

Introduction

Two persistent challenges for the regulatory professional include remaining informed and dealing with constant change. The regulatory profession is characterized by both lateral job changes and promotions, as well as frequent mergers among pharmaceutical, medical device and biologics companies. In addition, it is not uncommon for a regulatory professional's career to begin in the pharmaceutical industry and then transition to the device arena, or for professionals to switch from devices to combination products. The regulatory field's dynamics, in terms of internal personnel moves, external enterprise decisions and changes to the regulatory landscape, require vigilance to stay abreast of healthcare industry information. As such, proactive management of information resources is a valuable objective for a regulatory team concerned with functioning effectively to maintain regulatory compliance. In addition, within the regulatory field, the transition to digital transactions and electronic data has resulted in increased reliability, trustworthiness, usability and portability of online information technology tools.

Given the fluidity of the regulatory environment, both domestically and globally, the regulatory professional is expected to know how to synthesize dynamic information and develop regulatory strategy based on multiple information streams: print (e.g., books and magazines), static electronic (e.g., e-newsletters and government websites) and interactive electronic resources (i.e., social medial and webinars). This chapter discusses the value of each information stream and provides a comprehensive review of resources available to build US regulatory intelligence and support product substantiation.

Regulatory Intelligence

US Governing Law

An integral component of a regulatory professional's work is to stay informed of the latest regulatory and legislative developments. This section reviews readily accessible electronic regulatory and legislative documents.

The Government Printing Office (GPO) is the official federal bookstore for US government publications. GPO is the primary resource for gathering, cataloging, producing, providing, authenticating and preserving published information in all its forms for the executive, legislative and judicial branches of the federal government.[1] Publications pertaining to regulatory healthcare topics may be accessed through a search using the keywords "FDA" or "Food and Drug Administration" and "DHHS" or "Department of Health & Human Services" combined with more specific terms such as "pharmaceutical," "clinical" or "drug industry." GPO's Federal Digital System (FDsys) provides free electronic access to legislative resources, including Congressional bills, the *Congressional Record*, public and private law and the US Code; executive sources, such as the Code of Federal Regulations (CFR), the *Federal Register*

(FR) and presidential materials; and judicial sources, including the Supreme Court, trial and appellate court cases, opinions, oral arguments and decisions.

The *FR*, published daily (except on weekends and federal holidays) by the Office of the Federal Register, National Archives and Records Administration, and made accessible by GPO, serves as the official daily publication for rules, proposed rules, executive orders, presidential documents and federal agency and organization notices. The 2015 *FR* is Volume 80 and may be searched separately or in conjunction with prior years dating back to 1994 (Volume 59). Individuals also may register for a free daily email containing the *FR* table of contents.[2] The CFR codifies general and permanent rules published in the *FR*, and is divided into 50 titles representing broad areas subject to federal regulation. Each CFR volume is updated yearly and issued quarterly. Titles are divided into chapters, usually bearing the issuing agency's name. Chapters, in turn, are subdivided into parts covering specific regulatory areas (e.g., 21 CFR 316.24 = Title 21—Food and Drugs, Chapter I—Food and Drug Administration, Department of Health and Human Services, Subchapter D—Drugs for Human Use, Part 316—Orphan Drugs, Subpart C—Designation of an Orphan Drug, Section 316.24—Granting orphan-drug designation.). CFR records on FDsys span 1996 to the current year. Documents are available as ASCII text, HTML and PDF files.[3]

In addition to the *FR* and CFR, FDsys provides access to numerous databases, including the *Congressional Record*, the US Code, Congressional bills, Statutes at Large and public and private laws. FDsys serves as the official source of legislation and regulations; however, reference information for FDA legislation, rules, regulations, guidance documents, administrative FDA proceedings and rule-making documents, standards and the electronic reading room reside on FDA's website.[4] The electronic reading room provides a collection of publicly releasable FDA agency records. FDA manages dockets, administrative FDA proceedings and rule-making documents, through a searchable Federal Dockets Management System (FDMS). The FDMS allows the public to search and download documents and post feedback to agencies.[5] In 1995, the Library of Congress created the THOMAS database at the direction of the 104th Congress to make federal legislation publicly available. THOMAS offers a vast range of government resources, including databases to search bill resolutions; bill and amendment summaries; bills across multiple Congresses; public laws searchable by number; House and Senate roll call votes; legislation by sponsor; congressional activity databases; the *Congressional Record*; days-in-session calendars; committee reports; and treaties.[6]

Importers and exporters of FDA-regulated products must be familiar with applicable US trade laws. These products are regulated by the *Federal Food, Drug, and Cosmetic Act* (*FD&C Act*), per Chapter VIII: FDA Imports and Exports, the *FD&C Act*, Sections 801 and 802, the US Code (as it relates to the *FD&C Act*, patent infringement and several additional matters), CFR (Title 21) and US Customs and Border Protection (CBP) regulations.

CBP, a bureau of the Department of Homeland Security, regulates and enforces US regulations on trade and customs. It maintains a trademark recording system, Intellectual Property Rights Search (IPRS) database, for trademarks registered with the US Patent and Trademark Office (PTO).[7] The CBP website also provides a searchable repository of *FR* notices related to product importation into the US. The Customs Rulings Online Search System (CROSS) is a database allowing the retrieval of trade-related rulings and legal decisions issued by CBP from 1989 to present.[8] In 2011, CBP released a "Letter to Industry" to review the medical and non-medical radiation-emitting electronic product import entry review process. The letter discusses the voluntary use of Affirmations of Compliance (AofC) codes during the import entry process to provide product identification and show compliance with specific FDA product requirements.[9] CBP resources support a company's efforts to enforce its intellectual property rights on trademarks, copyright and patents.

Along with CBP, the Bureau of Industry and Security (BIS), an agency of the US Department of Commerce, monitors and regulates the import and export of goods across US borders. BIS manages and enforces export control and treaty compliance, including those related to anti-boycott laws under *Export Administration Act* provisions. BIS makes unofficial electronic Export Administration Regulations (EAR) files accessible on its website, while the *FR* provides the official text. BIS makes boycott guidelines (43 FR 3454, 44 FR 66272, 49 FR 18061 and 52 FR 2511) accessible on its website. In addition, foreign boycott requests or acts of compliance with such boycotts that do not align with US policy, are reportable on the BIS website.[10]

US Government Agencies

This section features government agency websites offering additional healthcare product regulatory information. A regulatory professional's decision-making process is shaped by several federal agency regulations and guidelines. This chapter will not go into detail about all these governmental bodies, but **Table 41-1** provides the websites where further information can be gained about these agencies.

The US Department of Health and Human Services (DHHS) is the US federal agency whose mission is to protect the health of all US citizens and provide essential human services. The office of the secretary and its subdivisions carry out DHHS' initiatives while 11 operating agencies perform a broad range of tasks and services, from conducting research and ensuring food and drug safety to funding grants and programs and managing health insurance. The specific operating agencies include: the Administration for Children and Families (ACF), Administration on Community Living (ACL), Agency for Healthcare Research and Quality (AHRQ), Agency for Toxic Substances and Disease Registry (ATSDR), Center for Medicare & Medicaid Services (CMS), Centers for Disease Control and Prevention (CDC), Food and Drug Administration (FDA), Health Resources and Services Administration (HRSA), Indian Health Service (HIS), National Institutes of Health (NIH) and Substance Abuse and Mental Health Services Administration (SAMHSA). Further discussion focuses on FDA.

FDA consists of nine centers and offices, each of which provides a website offering detailed regulatory information. The Center for Drug Evaluation and Research (CDER), Center for Devices and Radiological Health (CDRH), Center for Biologics Evaluation and Research (CBER), Center for Food Safety and Applied Nutrition (CFSAN) and Center for Veterinary Medicine (CVM) homepages all offer product-specific topical coverage, spotlighted center links, recalls and alerts, approvals and clearances, news and announcements, resources targeting industry, consumers and healthcare professionals, links to program area coverage, a search box and contact information. The FDA website also provides several convenient listings, which include but are not limited to the Humanitarian Device Exemptions Listing, FDA Debarment List (Drug Product Applications) and Clinical Investigators—Disqualification Proceedings.

A few other particularly helpful resources found on FDA's website are the Office of Regulatory Affairs (ORA) and the Office of Combination Products (OCP) pages. OCP's website is designed to assist users in classifying their products. Consequently, this page provides an overview of OCP, a section with links to further information, including the combination products page, guidance documents, information pertaining to the request for designation process, performance reports and contact information. The ORA page features a spotlight section, ORA news, links to resources and requested documents, recalls and alerts and a link to the ORA *Freedom of Information Act* (*FOIA*) electronic reading room. The FOI page contains links to frequently asked questions; how to make an *FOIA* request; *FOIA* fees; online payments; an electronic reading room; annual reports; the *Privacy Act*; reference materials; and contacts and links to other *FOIA* requester centers.

As an added resource, FDA hosts training modules on its website on CBER, CDRH, guidances, nonclinical studies and clinical investigations to foster transparency between FDA and academia, industry and clinical investigators, and to promote public health by ensuring the safety and quality of regulated medical products.[11] A subset of these learning tools is offered in French and Spanish to service the international audience. In addition, FDA periodically hosts online webinars with senior FDA officials speaking on specific topics and attendees given the opportunity to ask questions. Recent topics have included drug shortages, over-the-counter (OTC) medicines and drug trial snapshots.[12]

The US Consumer Product Safety Commission (CPSC) is another agency deeply impacting product development decisions. CPSC's primary mission is to protect the public from unreasonable risks of injury or death from a broad range of consumer products. For example, its poison prevention packaging standards and testing procedures, as well as its child-resistant and senior-friendly packaging guidelines, determine how OTC and prescription drugs and physician samples must be packaged.

Last, the US Federal Trade Commission (FTC) addresses issues related to enforcing appropriate business competition and monitoring anticompetitive practices. FTC's Bureau of Consumer Protection is specifically responsible for handling fraudulent and dishonest consumer protection activities, which encompass advertising and e-commerce oversight. Advertising and consumer safety also are key priorities for healthcare product regulatory professionals.

Online Commercial and Government Databases

An integral component of a regulatory professional's work is to stay informed about the latest regulatory and legislative developments. The resources reviewed in this section highlight noteworthy governmental database tools to support these monitoring and surveillance responsibilities. Numerous commercial, fee-based, web-based databases and free, federal, web-based databases are available to support the regulatory professional's legislative tracking and regulatory analysis responsibilities.

Federal Government Databases—Agency Resources

Many federal agencies have built their own specialized databases to monitor specific regulatory issues and provide public access to biomedical, clinical and other useful government resources. The beginning of this chapter discusses databases housing US Governing Law (e.g., THOMAS, CROSS and FDsys). Further review will highlight repositories useful for manufacturer and device registrations, submission preparation and postmarket surveillance. This section focuses primarily on the databases created within FDA's centers.

CDER and CDRH have developed the largest number of database systems, with some overlap between CDER and CBER. CVM and CFSAN also have developed some unique databases. Due to chapter length constraints, however, this summary will review only selected center databases. A comprehensive list of all the agency's databases and corresponding website addresses is provided in **Table 41-3**.

Table 41-1. Agencies, Organizations, Institutes, Centers and Offices Associated With Healthcare Product Regulation

Organization	Website	Subject Coverage
US Consumer Product Safety Commission (CPSC)	www.cpsc.gov	Safety Education, Recalls, Poisoning, Packaging, Labeling, Drugs, Children's Products
	www.cpsc.gov/en/Regulations-Laws–Standards	Regulations, Laws, Bans, Guidances, Standards, *Federal Register* Notices
US Environmental Protection Agency (EPA)	www.epa.gov	Environment Health, Public Health, Chemicals, Air Pollutants, Medical Waste
US Department of Health and Human Services (DHHS)	www.hhs.gov	Public Health, Food Safety, Drugs, Medical Devices, Biologics, Blood and Vaccines Devices, Cosmetics, Radiation Emitting Products, Combination Products, Grants and Funding, Research, Health Insurance
Assistant Secretary for Preparedness and Response (ASPR)	www.phe.gov	Public Health and Medical Disasters and Emergencies
Administration of Community Living (ACL)	www.acl.gov	Aging and Disability Population
Agency for Healthcare Research and Quality (AHRQ)	www.ahrq.gov	Research and Resources on Outcomes, Cost, Safety, Access and Quality of Healthcare
Centers for Disease Control (CDC)	www.cdc.gov	Disease Control and Prevention
National Institute for Occupational Safety and Health (NIOSH)	www.cdc.gov/niosh	Prevention of Workplace Illness and Injury
Agency for Toxic Substances and Disease Registry (ATSDR)	www.atsdr.cdc.gov	Harmful Exposures and Diseases Related to Toxic Substances
Centers for Medicare & Medicaid Services (CMS)	www.cms.gov	Medicare, Medicaid and Children's Health Insurance Program (CHIP) coverage
US Food and Drug Administration (FDA)	www.fda.gov	Public Health, Regulations, Food, Drugs, Medical Devices, Biologics, Vaccines, Tissue and Tissue Products, Blood and Blood Components, Cosmetics, Animal and Veterinary Products
Center for Biologics Evaluation and Research (CBER)	www.fda.gov/BiologicsBloodVaccines	Vaccines, Blood and Biologics
Center for Drug Evaluation and Research (CDER)	www.fda.gov/Drugs	Drugs
Center for Devices and Radiological Health (CDRH)	www.fda.gov/MedicalDevices	Medical Devices
Center for Food Safety and Applied Nutrition (CFSAN)	www.fda.gov/AboutFDA/CentersOffices/OfficeofFoods/CFSAN	Food and Cosmetics Safety
Center for Veterinary Medicine (CVM)	www.fda.gov/animalveterinary	Animal and Veterinary Products
Office of Combination Products (OCP)	www.fda.gov/CombinationProducts	Combination Products
Freedom of Information (FOI) Electronic Reading Room	www.fda.gov/RegulatoryInformation/foi/ElectronicReadingRoom	Frequently Requested FDA Documents
Information for the FDA-Regulatory Industry	www.fda.gov/forindustry	Information for Companies
Health Resources and Services Administration (HRSA)	www.hrsa.gov	Healthcare Access
Indian Health Services (IHS)	www.ihs.gov	Public Health of Federally Recognized American Indians and Alaska Natives
National Institutes of Health (NIH)	www.nih.gov	Biomedical and Clinical Research Resources
Substance Abuse & Mental Health Services Administration (SAMHSA)	www.samhsa.gov	Behavioral Health: Substance Abuse and Mental Illness
US Small Business Association (SBA)	www.sba.gov	Congressional Advocacy, Federal Procurement, Training and Financing
International Conference on Harmonisation of Technical Requirements for Registration of Pharmaceuticals for Human Use (ICH)	www.ich.org	Drugs and Biologics

Organization	Website	Subject Coverage
International Medical Device Regulators Forum (IMDRF) (formerly Global Harmonization Task Force (GHTF))	www.imdrf.org	Medical Devices
	www.imdrf.org/documents/documents.asp	Archived Documents
World Health Organization (WHO)	www.who.int/en	Public Health, Drugs, Medical Devices, Biologics, Vaccines
	www.who.int/library/databases	
Medical Dictionary for Regulatory Activities (MedDRA)	www.meddra.org	Standardization of Medical Terminology for Adverse Events and Medication Errors Coding
Occupational Safety & Health Administration (OSHA)	www.osha.gov	Safety and Health in Workplace
Federal Trade Commission (FTC)	www.ftc.gov	Prevention of Fraud, Deception, and Unfair/ Anticompetitive Business Practices
US Nuclear Regulatory Commission (NRC)	www.nrc.gov	Radioactive Materials
US Patent and Trademark Office (PTO)	www.uspto.gov	Granting Patents, Registering Trademarks, Intellectual Property Law and Policy

Note: Website URLs are current at time of publication.

Three of CDER's most heavily searched databases focus on drug product approvals: the Approved Drug Products with Therapeutic Equivalence Evaluations (*Orange Book*) database, which lists drugs approved on the basis of safety and effectiveness; the National Drug Code Directory, a database of marketed prescription drugs listed by universal product identifiers; and the Drugs@FDA database, a searchable catalog of brand-name and generic prescription and OTC human drugs and biological therapeutic products approved since 1939. Drug manufacturing firms are required to register their sites with Drugs@FDA and re-register annually at the Drug Establishments Current Registration Site (DECRS) database. As a self-identification and Drug Establishment Registration and Drug Listing requirement, FDA requires human generic drug facilities to obtain Data Universal Numbering System (D-U-N-S) numbers for the facility or site and in some cases the registrant owner of the facility or site. Since 1963, D-U-N-S numbers, established by Dun & Bradstreet (D&B), have been used as business identifier.[13] The D-U-N-S number uniquely identifies the registrant and each physical location of the business's facility or site to FDA. Requests are made online. Typically, requests for new D-U-N-S numbers are processed in 20 business days, although a business can expedite the otherwise free service process for a nominal service fee. D&B hosts a public database for searching a company's D-U-N-S number.[14]

CDER's two clinically oriented databases are the Bioresearch Monitoring Information System, which identifies personnel engaged in Investigational New Drug (IND) studies; and the Clinical Investigator Inspection List Database, which contains data relevant to IND studies gathered by clinical investigator inspections.

CDER and CBER share the responsibility for reviewing postmarket safety reports submitted to the FDA Adverse Event Reporting System (FAERS), a database containing voluntarily submitted reports on approved drugs or therapeutic biologics products. CBER's other database systems include one for storing incoming Biological Product Deviation Reports and a Vaccine Adverse Event Reporting System (VAERS). Like the FAERS database, VAERS is based on a cooperative agency program between CBER and CDC to address vaccine safety.

CVM's Animal Drugs@FDA is comparable to CDER's Drugs@FDA and CDRH's 510(k) and PMA databases. This database allows users to search for approved animal drug products, suitability petitions, sponsors, the *Green Book*, CFR, *FR*, patents and exclusivity. In addition, FDA maintains its own Warning Letter database through its FOI office. The Warning Letter collection covers documents issued from November 1996 to present. The database can be searched by company, subject, issuing office or date.

CDRH has built and maintains more than 20 databases to monitor medical devices and radiological products. Its 510(k) Premarket Notification (PMN) database and its Premarket Approval (PMA) database are critical tools for device regulatory professionals. CDRH also has developed two adverse event reporting systems similar to CDER's FAERS database: the MAUDE (Manufacturer and User Facility Device Experience) database and the Medical Device Reporting (MDR) (formerly CDRH's Device Experience Network) database. MAUDE presents voluntarily submitted user facility medical device adverse event reports since 1991, distributor reports since 1993 and manufacturer reports since 1996. The MDR database consists of reports on devices that may have malfunctioned or caused a death or serious injury from 1984–96, when it was replaced by MAUDE.

Also, CDRH provides an integrated database offering a total lifecycle summary of a selected medical device. The Total Product Life Cycle (TPLC) database requires the user to

Table 41-2. Publisher Resources

Publisher	Website	Resources
International Electrotechnical Commission (IEC)	www.iec.ch	Newsletters, News Alerts, Standards, CDs
AdvaMed	www.advamed.org	News Alerts**
American National Standards Institute (ANSI)	www.ansi.org	Standards, Newsletters, Articles*
American Society for Quality (ASQ Quality Press)	www.asq.org	Journals, Books, Standards
American Society for Testing and Materials (ASTM)	www.astm.org	Standards, Journals, Research Reports, Symposia Papers, Proceedings, Manuals
Association for the Advancement of Medical Instrumentation (AAMI)	www.aami.org	Newsletters, Journals, CDs, Standards
Association of Clinical Research Professionals (ACRP)	www.acrpnet.org	Newsletters, Journals, Reports, White Papers, Directories*
Barnett International	www.barnettinternational.com	Books, Reference Manuals, Compendiums
Bentham Science	www.benthamscience.com	Books, Journals
Bureau of National Affairs (BNA)	www.bna.com/books	News Alerts, Newsletters*
CenterWatch	www.centerwatch.com	Newsletters, Books, Report, Guides, Data Libraries
CRC Online Press (Taylor & Francis Group)	www.crcpress.com	Books, Journals
Drug Information Association (DIA)	www.diahome.org	Newsletters, Journals, White Papers, Directories*
Elsevier Business Intelligence	pharmamedtechbi.com	Newsletters
FDAnews	www.fdanews.com	Newsletters, Books, Reports, White Papers, CDs*
Ferdic Inc.	www.fdareview.com	Newsletters
FierceMarkets	www.fiercemarkets.com	Newsletters
Food and Drug Law Institute (FDLI)	www.fdli.org	Newsletters, Books, Journals, White Papers, CDs*
Global Regulatory Press	globalregulatorypress.com	Journals
GMP Publications	www.gmppublications.com	Books, Handbooks, Manuals
Government Printing Office (GPO)	bookstore.gpo.gov	Newsletters, Books, Journals, Handbooks, Manuals, Guides*
Infinata	www.infinata.com	Newsletters, White Papers, Reports**
Institute for Electrical and Electronics Engineers (IEEE)	www.ieee.org	Standards, Books, Journals, Conference Publications
International Organization for Standardization (ISO)	www.iso.org	Journals, Standards, Handbooks, CDs
John Wiley & Sons	www.wiley.com/WileyCDA	Books, Journals
Majors.com	www.majors.com	Books
Medical Device Manufacturers Association (MDMA)	www.medicaldevices.org	News Alerts, Newsletters, Reports, White Papers, Directories*
Medtech Insight	www.medtechinsight.com	Newsletters, Reports
OMICS Group International	omicsgroup.org/journals/pharmaceutical-regulatory-affairs-open-access.php	Journals**
Outcomes LLC	www.outcomes-marketing.com	Newsletters**
Paternal Drug Association (PDA)	www.pda.org	Books, Journals, Directories*
Pharmaceutical-technology.com (Net Resources International)	www.pharmaceutical-technology.com	Newsletters, White Papers, Directories**
Regulatory Affairs Professionals Society (RAPS)	www.raps.org	Newsletters, Books, Guidances, Handbooks
SmartBrief	www.smartbrief.com	Newsletters**
Society of Clinical Research Associates (SoCRA)	www.socra.org	Newsletters, Journals, Manuals
Springer	www.springer.com	Books, Handbooks, Journals

Publisher	Website	Resources
The Organisation for Professionals in Regulatory Affairs (TOPRA)	www.topra.org	Newsletters
Thompson Publishers	www.thompson.com	Newsletters, Books, Reports, CDs
Thomson-Reuters (Life Sciences)	lifesciences.thomsonreuters.com	Articles, Reports, Databases*
Tradepub.com	www.tradepub.com	Books, Newsletters, White Papers**
UBM Canon	ubmcanon.com	News Alerts, Newsletters, Directories**
United States Pharmacopeia (USP)	www.usp.org	Books, Compendiums, Standards*
Wolters Kluwer (Law & Business; Health)	www.wolterskluwerlb.com/health	White Papers, Databases*

**Resource may be fee-based or free. **Resource is free.*
The absence of any asterisk indicates that the resource is fee-based. However, costs for members may differ.
Note: Website URLs are current at time of publication.

input the product code, regulation number or common device name to receive a summary of PMNs and/or PMAs, device problems and recalls by year, recall class and device class.

Other noteworthy CDRH databases include the *Clinical Laboratory Improvement Amendments* (*CLIA*) database, which represents commercially marketed FDA- and CDC-categorized in vitro diagnostic test systems; and the Establishment Registration database, which comprises domestic establishments engaged in the manufacture, preparation, propagation, compounding, assembly or processing of medical devices intended for human use and commercial distribution.

Recently, in collaboration with the National Library of Medicine (NLM), FDA released a web-based database, AccessGUDID, making medical device identification information publicly available. With the transition to unique device identifiers (UDI) by device labelers, the database will continue to populate with downloadable Global Unique Device Identifier Database (GUDID) data, which correspond to unique identifier content from the medical device label. Establishing UDI introduced Global Medical Device Nomenclature (GMDN), an internationally recognized identifier, as a requirement for labeling by FDA. The GMDN codes serve as a numerical identifier corresponding to a descriptor for a common device type. GMDN codes are purchased from the GMDN Agency, the entity that manages the categorization and creation of new GMDN terms.

In addition to the regulatory information available through FDA's databases, regulatory professionals requiring biomedical research can access PubMed, NLM's biomedical database, which includes more than 24 million citations from MEDLINE and other life science journals dating back to 1948. NLM also produces TOXNET, the toxicology data network, which consists of databases on toxicology, hazardous chemicals, environmental health and toxic releases. For molecular biology information, NLM's National Center for Biotechnology Information (NCBI) offers a comprehensive resource. Established in 1988, NCBI has created numerous public databases covering genetic sequencing and molecular processes affecting human health and disease and has developed software tools for analyzing genome data. Finally, the NIH's ClinicalTrials.gov site contains current information identifying federally and privately supported clinical trials for a range of diseases and conditions. The database includes 193,756 trials sponsored by NIH, other federal agencies and private industry conducted in all 50 states and 190 countries.

Another CDRH database is the Advisory Committee/Panel Meetings database, which contains both information about upcoming meetings and historical information with links to summaries and/or transcripts of recent past meetings.

A few additional recommended federal databases are RegInfo.gov, USA.gov and Regulations.gov. The Office of Management and Budget (OMB) and the General Services Administration (GSA), jointly produce RegInfo.gov. This website contains a catalog searchable by government agency to locate all the regulatory reviews conducted by OMB's Office of Information and Regulatory Affairs (OIRA). It also has a catalog of GSA's Regulatory Information Service Center's (RISC) semi-annually published Unified Agenda of Federal Regulatory and Deregulatory Actions dating back to late 1995. The Regulatory Plan is part of the fall edition of the Unified Agenda. The Regulatory Plan serves as a defining statement of the administration's regulatory and deregulatory policies and priorities, while the Unified Agenda provides information about regulations the government is considering or reviewing. USA.gov is the government's official portal to federal agency websites and information. This website is the product of an interagency initiative administered by the Government Accountability Office's (GAO) Office of Citizen Services and Communications. It provides a centralized database to locate information on US local, state and federal government agency websites. Regulations.gov is another valuable tool for locating government agency regulations, rulemakings or notices, and also is useful for finding, submitting and obtaining public comments on proposed *FR* regulations. A comment can be submitted directly via the website by accessing documents still open for public comment.

Table 41-3. Databases for Healthcare Product Regulatory-Related Intelligence

Database	Website	Subject Coverage
GOVERNMENT:		
CPSC/Consumer Product Safety Information Database	www.saferproducts.gov	Searchable reports and recalls related to consumer products
CPSC/National Electronic Injury Surveillance System (NEISS)	www.cpsc.gov/en/Research–Statistics/NEISS-Injury-Data	US sample of emergency room injury reports for consumer products
Federal Recalls	www.recalls.gov	Compilation of federal recalls: environmental, food, medicinal, cosmetic and consumer products
CMS/National and Local Coverage Determinations (NCD/LCD)	www.cms.gov/medicare-coverage-database/indexes/national-and-local-indexes.aspx	Medicare coverage
CMS/Open Payments	www.cms.gov/openpayments	Financial relationships between manufacturers/group purchasing organizations (GPOs) and hospitals/physicians
USA.gov	www.usa.gov	Federal information and services portal
	www.usa.gov/Topics/Reference-Shelf/forms.shtml	Federal forms and applications
NIH/NLM PubMed	www.pubmed.gov www.ncbi.nlm.nih.gov/pubmed	Bibliographic database of biomedical and life science journal articles at NIH/NLM
Regulations.gov	www.regulations.gov resources.regulations.gov/public/component/main	Public comments, agency regulatory agendas, federal regulations, federal notices and federal adjudications
GSA/OIRA/OMB Reginfo.gov	www.reginfo.gov/public/do/eAgendaSimpleSearch	Federal regulatory agendas/plans and regulatory/deregulatory actions
GPO Access: Federal Register and Code of Federal Regulations (CFR)	www.gpo.gov/fdsys	Legislative intelligence
Congress.gov	www.congress.gov	Federal legislative information: bills, records and reports
FDA Acronyms and Abbreviations	www.accessdata.fda.gov/scripts/cder/acronyms	General information
FDA Guidance Documents	www.fda.gov/RegulatoryInformation/Guidances	Guidance on FDA-regulated products
FDA/Inspections Database	www.accessdata.fda.gov/scripts/inspsearch	Compliance status of firms marketing FDA-regulated products
FDA/Warning Letter Archive	www.fda.gov/ICECI/EnforcementActions/WarningLetters	Warning letters
FDA/Medical Product Safety Network (MedSun)	www.accessdata.fda.gov/scripts/cdrh/cfdocs/Medsun/searchReport.cfm	Device regulatory intelligence: adverse event reporting
NIH/ClinicalTrials.gov	clinicaltrials.gov	Publicly and privately supported global clinical studies
National Cancer Institute (NCI) Clinical Trials	www.cancer.gov/clinicaltrials	NCI-sponsored clinical trial studies
NIH/ClinRegs	clinregs.niaid.nih.gov	Country-specific clinical research regulatory information
FDA/Global Unique Device Identification Database (GUDID)	gudid.fda.gov/gudid	FDA-regulated devices with unique identifier (not yet searchable)
	accessgudid.nlm.nih.gov	Public-access to GUDID (beta version)
FDA/Label Repository	labels.fda.gov	Drug regulatory intelligence: drug labels and other drug-specific information
FDA/Pediatric Labeling Information Database	www.accessdata.fda.gov/scripts/sda/sdNavigation.cfm?sd=labelingdatabase	Pediatric labeling information
FDA/Import Trade Auxiliary Communications System (ITACS)	itacs.fda.gov/app/welcomeToITACS.jsf	Import tracking
USPTO/Patent Database	appft.uspto.gov/netahtml/PTO	Patent databases
USPTO/Global Patent Search Network	gpsn.uspto.gov	International patent collections

Database	Website	Subject Coverage
GOVERNMENT:		
CPSC/Consumer Product Safety Information Database	www.saferproducts.gov	Searchable reports and recalls related to consumer products
USPTO/Patent Application Information Retrieval	portal.uspto.gov/pair/PublicPair	Issued patents and status of published patent applications
CBP/Intellectual Property Rights Search	www.dhs.gov/intellectual-property-rights-search	Intellectual property rights
FDA/Device Registration & Listing Module	www.access.fda.gov	FDA Unified Registration and Listing System (FURLS)
FDA/Biologics Export Certification Application & Tracking System		
FDA/CDRH Export Certification Application & Tracking System		
FDA/CVM Approved Animal Drug Products	www.accessdata.fda.gov/scripts/animaldrugsatfda	Drug regulatory intelligence: approved animal products
	www.fda.gov/AnimalVeterinary/Products/ApprovedAnimalDrugProducts/	*Green Book*: approved animal drug products
FDA/CVM Veterinary Recalls	www.fda.gov/AnimalVeterinary/SafetyHealth/RecallsWithdrawals	Drug regulatory intelligence: recalls
NIH and US Department of Agriculture (USDA)/ Dietary Supplement Ingredient Database	dietarysupplementdatabase.usda.nih.gov	Dietary Supplement Ingredient Database (DSID)
NIH and NLM/Dietary Supplement Label Database	www.dsld.nlm.nih.gov/dsld	Sample dietary supplement product labels
FDA/CDRH Product Classification	www.accessdata.fda.gov/scripts/cdrh/cfdocs/cfPCD/classification.cfm	Device regulatory intelligence: product codes and device classification
	www.accessdata.fda.gov/scripts/cdrh/cfdocs/cfPMN/denovo.cfm	Device regulatory intelligence: *de novo* classification orders
	www.accessdata.fda.gov/scripts/cdrh/cfdocs/cfPCD_RH/classification.cfm	Device regulatory intelligence: radiation-emitting electronic product codes
FDA/CDRH Premarket Clearances and Approvals	www.accessdata.fda.gov/scripts/cdrh/cfdocs/cfPMA/pma.cfm	Device regulatory intelligence: PMA
	www.accessdata.fda.gov/scripts/cdrh/cfdocs/cfpma/pmamemos.cfm	Device regulatory intelligence: PMA summary review memos
	www.accessdata.fda.gov/scripts/cdrh/cfdocs/cfPMN/pmn.cfm	Device regulatory intelligence: 510(k)
	www.accessdata.fda.gov/scripts/cdrh/cfdocs/cfHDE/hde.cfm	Device regulatory intelligence: approved Humanitarian Device Exemptions (HDEs)
	www.accessdata.fda.gov/scripts/cdrh/cfdocs/cfIVD/Search.cfm	Device regulatory intelligence: cleared or approved OTC in vitro diagnostic products
FDA/CDRH Establishment Registration & Listing	www.accessdata.fda.gov/scripts/cdrh/cfdocs/cfRL/rl.cfm	Device regulatory intelligence: medical devices and establishments registered with FDA
FDA/CDRH Establishment Inspections	www.accessdata.fda.gov/scripts/cdrh/cfdocs/cfTPLC/inspect.cfm	Device regulatory intelligence: establishment inspections
FDA/CDRH Recognized Consensus Standards	www.accessdata.fda.gov/scripts/cdrh/cfdocs/cfstandards/search.cfm	Device regulatory intelligence: federally recognized national and international medical device standards
FDA/CDER Postmarket Requirements and Commitments	www.accessdata.fda.gov/scripts/cder/pmc	Drug/Biologic regulatory intelligence: postmarket requirements, studies and clinical trials for approved products
FDA/CDRH 522 Postmarket Surveillance Studies	www.accessdata.fda.gov/scripts/cdrh/cfdocs/cfPMA/pss.cfm	Device regulatory intelligence: studies mandated under Section 522 of the *FD&C Act*
FDA/In Vitro Diagnostic Device Recalls	www.accessdata.fda.gov/scripts/cdrh/cfdocs/cfRES/IVDRes.cfm	Device regulatory intelligence: IVD recalls
FDA/CDRH Corrective Actions and Recalls	www.accessdata.fda.gov/scripts/cdrh/cfdocs/cfPCD_RH/rh_res.cfm	Device regulatory intelligence: radiation-emitting electronic products corrective actions
FDA/Medical Device Recalls	www.accessdata.fda.gov/scripts/cdrh/cfdocs/cfRES/res.cfm	Device regulatory intelligence: medical device recalls

Table 41-3. Databases for Healthcare Product Regulatory-Related Intelligence (con't.)

Database	Website	Subject Coverage
GOVERNMENT:		
CPSC/Consumer Product Safety Information Database	www.saferproducts.gov	Searchable reports and recalls related to consumer products
FDA/CDRH Medical Device Reporting (MDR)	www.accessdata.fda.gov/scripts/cdrh/cfdocs/cfmdr/search.CFM	Device regulatory intelligence: device-related adverse events and product problems
FDA/MedWatch	www.fda.gov/Safety/MedWatch	Safety Information and Adverse Event Reporting Program
FDA/CDRH Manufacturer and User Facility Device Experience (MAUDE)	www.accessdata.fda.gov/scripts/cdrh/cfdocs/cfmaude/search.cfm	Device regulatory intelligence: monitoring for device-associated deaths, serious injuries and/or malfunctions
FDA/CDRH Clinical Laboratory Improvement Amendments (CLIA)	www.accessdata.fda.gov/scripts/cdrh/cfdocs/cfCLIA/search.cfm	Device regulatory intelligence: certified clinical laboratory diagnostic test
FDA/CDRH CLIA-Waived Analytes	www.accessdata.fda.gov/scripts/cdrh/cfdocs/cfClia/analyteswaived.cfm	Device regulatory intelligence: waived clinical laboratory diagnostic test
FDA/CDRH Meetings/Panels	www.accessdata.fda.gov/scripts/cdrh/cfdocs/cfAdvisory/search.cfm	Device regulatory intelligence: Advisory Committee Meeting materials
FDA Meetings, Workshops and Conferences	www.fda.gov/NewsEvents/MeetingsConferencesWorkshops	Calendar of events and meeting materials
FDA/CDRH Total Product Life Cycle (TPLC)	www.accessdata.fda.gov/scripts/cdrh/cfdocs/cfTPLC/tplc.cfm	Device regulatory intelligence: PMA, 510(k), adverse events, and recalls
FDA/CDER FDA-Recommended Dissolution Methods	www.accessdata.fda.gov/scripts/cder/dissolution	Drug regulatory intelligence: methods recommended by the Division of Bioequivalence, Office of Generic Drugs
FDA/CDER Drugs@FDA Database	www.accessdata.fda.gov/scripts/cder/drugsatfda	Drug regulatory intelligence: approved products
FDA/CDER National Drug Code Directory	www.accessdata.fda.gov/scripts/cder/ndc	Drug regulatory intelligence: all drugs available for commercial distribution
FDA/CDER Drug Establishments Current Registration Site (DECRS) Database	www.accessdata.fda.gov/scripts/cder/drls	Drug regulatory intelligence: establishments registered with FDA
FDA/CDER Bioresearch Monitoring Information System (BMIS)	www.accessdata.fda.gov/scripts/cder/bmis	Biologics/Drug regulatory intelligence: responsible parties involved in Investigational New Drug (IND) studies
FDA/CDER Clinical Investigator Inspection List (CLIIL)	www.accessdata.fda.gov/scripts/cder/cliil/index.cfm	Device regulatory intelligence: clinical investigators involved with IND studies
FDA/CDER Adverse Event Reporting System (FAERS)	www.fda.gov/Drugs/GuidanceComplianceRegulatoryInformation/Surveillance/AdverseDrugEffects/ucm082193.htm	Biologics/Device regulatory intelligence: adverse event and medication error reports
NIH/NLM Toxicology Data Network (TOXNET)	www.toxnet.nlm.nih.gov	Scientific and regulatory intelligence on hazardous drugs and other chemicals
FDA/CDER Inactive Ingredients Database	www.accessdata.fda.gov/scripts/cder/iig/index.cfm	Drug regulatory intelligence: inactive ingredients for approved products
FDA/Substance Registration System	fdasis.nlm.nih.gov/srs/srs.jsp	Unique Ingredient Identifier (UNII) repository for FDA-regulated products
FDA/CDER Approved Drug Products with Therapeutic Equivalence Evaluations (Orange Book) Database	www.accessdata.fda.gov/scripts/cder/ob	Drug regulatory intelligence: approved products
FDA/Orphan Drug Designations and Approvals	www.accessdata.fda.gov/scripts/opdlisting/oopd	Drug regulatory intelligence: designations and approvals
FDA/Reported Drug Shortages and Discontinuations	www.accessdata.fda.gov/scripts/drugshortages	Drug regulatory intelligence: current and resolved drug shortages and discontinuations reported to FDA
FDA/Product-Specific Recommendations for Generic Drugs	www.fda.gov/Drugs/GuidanceComplianceRegulatoryInformation/Guidances/ucm075207.htm	Bioequivalence recommendations for specific products arranged by active ingredient
FDA/CBER Vaccine Adverse Event Reporting System (VAERS)	vaers.hhs.gov/index wonder.cdc.gov/vaers.html medalerts.org/	Drug regulatory intelligence: reports (unverified) of adverse events with US-licensed vaccines

Database	Website	Subject Coverage
GOVERNMENT:		
CPSC/Consumer Product Safety Information Database	www.saferproducts.gov	Searchable reports and recalls related to consumer products
FDA/Human Cell and Tissue Establishment Registration-Query	www.accessdata.fda.gov/scripts/cber/CFAppsPub/tiss	Registered Human Cell and Tissue Establishments
FDA/Blood Establishment Registration-Query	www.accessdata.fda.gov/scripts/cber/cfappspub	Registered Blood Establishments
FDA/ Electronic Biological Product Deviation Reporting (eBPDR) System	www.accessdata.fda.gov/scripts/cber/CFApps	Events for biologics, blood (or components), human cell, tissue and cellular and tissue-based product (HCT/P)
NON-GOVERNMENTAL:		
WHO/ISRCTN Registry	www.isrctn.com/search?q=	Clinical trial registry (proposed, ongoing or completed studies)
GovTrack.us	www.govtrack.us	Legislative intelligence on bills and congressional voting
Global Medical Device Nomenclature (GMDN) Agency	www.gmdnagency.com	Medical device identifiers

Note: Website URLs are current at time of publication.

Table 41-3 provides websites for federal databases useful in reviewing the following additional topics:

- Warning Letters and recalls
- adverse event reporting
- consumer product injury surveillance
- product and substance registration
- site registration and inspections
- guidances, consensus standards and drug recommendations
- product classification
- orphan drug designations
- postmarket requirements and studies
- nonclinical study recommendations
- clinical trials
- export certificates and import communications
- labeling: supplements, pediatrics and drugs
- Medicare coverage database and drug shortages
- supplement and inactive ingredients
- patents

Elsevier's PharmaPendium database, by comparison, provides drug safety data on FDA-approved drugs. This online resource affords researchers searchable access using the Medical Dictionary for Regulatory Activities (MEDRA) search terminology. It also incorporates animal and human study data from FAERS, preclinical and clinical studies, and postmarket data.[15] Regulatory professionals can use this database to obtain pharmacovigilance data to evaluate projected risks from PharmaPendium's FDA database.

Databases with Global Regulatory Coverage

Databases providing global coverage of country-specific regulations and guidelines also play an essential role in the regulatory professional's capability to monitor legislative developments, conduct regulatory analyses and understand compliance requirements for all phases of the drug, biologic and device product development lifecycles. These are invaluable tools when used in conjunction with other sources of regulatory expertise, from networking with colleagues to contacting consultants and/or communicating directly with government agency authorities. This section discusses several databases offering international regulatory information.

Publically launched in September 2014, NIAID's ClinRegs is designed to help clinical researchers navigate country-specific, regulatory information as they plan and implement clinical trials. ClinRegs, an online database was developed by NIH's National Institute of Allergy and Infectious Diseases (NIAID). The site is a central resource providing the research community with up-to-date regulatory information for multiple countries. Organized by country and topic areas, the site also allows users to compare countries' requirements side by side. Topic areas the website addresses include: clinical trial lifecycle, Competent Authority oversight, Ethics Committee oversight, informed consent, investigational products, specimens and sponsorship. ClinRegs currently includes clinical research regulatory information summarized in English for Brazil, China, India, Kenya, Liberia, Malawi, Peru, South Africa, Tanzania, Thailand, Uganda, Vietnam, Liberia, Sierra Leone, Guinea, the UK and US.[16]

The Tarius Regulatory Database, a fee-based subscription database service, enables regulatory professionals to stay informed about the latest legislative developments worldwide and to interpret regulations and guidelines applicable to global healthcare products. Tarius offers three product types: customized regulatory web portal, SAC Tracker and Medical Device 'Lite'. The customized database solution prescreens data from multiple global government and legislative websites based on product type and/or country, according to searches defined by a particular company or individual. SAC Tracker provides access to FDA Advisory Committees' scientific and technical updates provided by CDER, CBER and the Office of the Commissioner. Tarius provides analyses, summaries and voting results by way of newsletter or web portal. Medical Device 'Lite' includes continuously updated reference documents compiled from US and EU regulatory authorities and key international regulatory bodies (e.g., IMDRF and ISO).[17]

Thomson Reuters Cortellis' Intelligent Regulatory Database (IDRAC) is another fee-based global regulatory intelligence database of regulatory, legal and scientific information accessed by professionals who develop and register human drug and biologics products.[18] As is true of Tarius, IDRAC frequently updates its documents and provides expert analyses on key regulatory topics for more than 40 countries. Wolters Kluwer's MediRegs is also a provider of healthcare research products and software solutions for regulatory professionals.[19] The database includes a Pharmaceutical and Device Regulation Suite offering consolidated federal resources.

Clinical trial surveillance information also is accessible through Informa PLC's TrialTrove. This database contains a comprehensive repository of global ongoing clinical trials information. Clinical and regulatory professionals have access to global trial information organized by more than 180 disease groups through analyst monitoring of more than 30,000 data sources.[20] Like the Pipeline database product, TrialTrove offers users a research support service with direct access to Citeline analysts for no extra charge. Informa PLC's Pharmaprojects database also serves as a valuable source of pharmaceutical intelligence. This tool tracks more than 60,000 drugs in active development with a drug, company and therapy profile for each.[21] The drug profile contains product data, including therapies and indications by phase; originator and licensees; chemical data and structure; clinical trials; pharmacologies; country information; licensing opportunities and more.

Industry and International Standards

The International Organization for Standardization (ISO) is a key nongovernmental standards-producing organization, comprising a network of national standards institutes representing 163 countries, 3,368 technical bodies and a coordinating Central Secretariat in Geneva, Switzerland. ISO's catalog comprises more than 19,500 published international standards related to quality management, risk and many other drug and device lifecycle facets.[22] The American Society of Testing and Materials (ASTM) is a similar standards organization that produces Special Technical Publications, compilations, manuals, monographs, journals and handbooks on regulatory topics. The standards' publications focusing on healthcare regulatory issues may be found through a search of the following terms:

- biological
- biotechnology
- clinical
- pharmaceutical
- medical device
- medical instrumentation
- quality management
- regulatory

In the same manner, the United States Pharmacopeia (USP), an official public standards-setting authority for prescription, OTC medicines and US-manufactured healthcare products, develops documentary and quality reference standards. Its key publications include the *USP–National Formulary* (*NF*), the *USP Dietary Supplements Compendium* (*DSC*) and the *Food Chemical Codex (FCC)*. The *USP–NF* contains public pharmacopeial standards for medicines, dosage forms, drug substances, excipients, medical devices and dietary supplements. Similarly, the *DSC* offers standards and scientific information related to the development, manufacturing and testing of dietary supplements. The *FCC* provides standards for the identification and purity of food ingredients. The *DSC* is updated every three years, the *FCC* is published every two years and revision bulletins for the *USP-NF* are posted at the start of each month.[23]

Another valuable standards resource for regulatory professionals is IEEE, formerly the Institute of Electrical and Electronics Engineers, which develops and publishes conference proceedings, training materials, standards and publications central to regulatory research. It is the leading global professional association for the advancement of technology and the authority on biomedical engineering and medical devices. Similarly, the International Electrotechnical Commission (IEC) develops and publishes standards for electrical and electronic technologies.

Historically, FDA has joined forces with several standards organizations to improve the safety, interoperability and implementation of standards, e.g., the Association for the Advancement of Medical Instrumentation (AAMI) and the National Institute of Standards and Technology (NIST). Note FDA's enforced performance standards are not limited to the aforementioned organizations; the agency relies on a growing list of organizations, including the American National Standards Institute (ANSI), the Clinical Laboratory Standards Institute and the Underwriters

Laboratories Inc., among others, to ensure regulated products' safety and quality.

Global Harmonized Guidelines

Although this chapter focuses on US regulatory resources, a few global organizations are too important to overlook, given the critical US role within each of these groups in developing global guidelines. The International Conference on Harmonisation (ICH) is one of these global bodies. ICH brings together EU, US and Japanese regulatory bodies and pharmaceutical industry experts in the three regions to discuss scientific and technical aspects of product registration. ICH's safety, efficacy, quality and multidisciplinary guidelines are indispensable to pharmaceutical and biologics regulatory professionals (and medical device professionals with Q9 Quality Risk Management and guidelines on Clinical Trials and Human Subject Protection) in evaluating proposed products and ensuring regulatory compliance. ICH representatives include drug regulatory authorities from Australia, Brazil, China, Chinese Taipei, India, Republic of Korea, Russia, Singapore, the EU and the US, as well as the World Health Organization (WHO), which serves as an official observer. Six Regional Harmonisation Initiatives (RHIs) also are active participants in ICH meetings: Asia-Pacific Economic Cooperation (APEC), Association of Southeast Asian Nations (ASEAN), East African Community (EAC), Gulf Cooperation Countries (GCC), Pan American Network on Drug Regulatory Harmonization (PANDRH) and South African Development Community (SADC). Representatives from the EU, Japan, Canada, the US, WHO, the Pharmaceutical Research and Manufacturers of America (PhRMA) and International Federation of Pharmaceutical Manufacturers and Associations (IFPMA) serve on the ICH steering committee.[24] Since 1958, PhRMA has represented American biopharmaceutical research companies' interests in the alignment between medical research and policy, as they relate to addressing patient needs.[25]

US regulatory representatives also participate actively in the International Medical Device Regulators Forum (IMDRF), successor to the Global Harmonization Task Force on Medical Devices (GHTF). IMDRF is composed of medical device regulators from Australia, Brazil, Canada, China, Japan, Russia, the EU and the US, and is building the GHTF foundation. The World Health Organization (WHO) and APEC Life Sciences Innovation Forum (LSIF) Regulatory Harmonization Steering Committee are official observers to IMDRF.[26] The original GHTF documents embody harmonized regulatory practices for medical device safety, effectiveness, performance and quality. Device regulatory professionals can review these documents when evaluating device conformity assessment, quality management systems and postmarket surveillance issues surrounding their device products.

WHO provides worldwide leadership on health matters, shapes the health research agenda and sets United Nations' norms and standards. The US is an active WHO participant, particularly in the Essential Medicines and Pharmaceutical Policies Department, which develops, implements and monitors national medicines' policies and guidelines. It also participates in WHO's biologicals program, the goal of which is to ensure national regulatory authorities implement effective systems to ensure blood product and in vitro diagnostic device quality and safety. WHO's International Clinical Trials Registry Platform (ICTRP) compiles registered clinical trial information into a single, global search portal. Trials must register and be issued a primary identifier by one of WHO's primary registries or its data set. Upon request, WHO issues a secondary identifier, a Universal Trial Number (UTN), to registered clinical trials.[27] **Table 41-1** lists websites for these respective guideline repositories.

Book Publishers

Several companies specialize in print and electronic publications focused on healthcare regulatory topics. This section reviews industry, government, association and standards publishers targeting the healthcare regulatory profession and explains how to retrieve the most relevant resources using online catalogs. Because regulatory is an interdisciplinary profession, publishers primarily concentrating on scientific research and development (R&D), law, medicine, business or government, or possibly all of the above, also may produce publications with a regulatory focus.

CRC Online Press, John Wiley & Sons, Lippincott Williams & Wilkins/Wolters Kluwer Health, Majors.com and Springer are major publishing firms providing broad subject coverage and featuring a numerous publications directed at the regulatory profession. The CRC Online Press website contains regulatory publications under the general category of pharmaceutical science, which can be located in the subcategories: biotechnology/biopharmaceutical; cleaning and sterilization; clinical trials; computer software; drug delivery and development; drug discovery; laboratory; manufacturing and engineering; medical devices; quality assurance; regulations and standards; and training and validation. Similarly, John Wiley & Sons produces regulatory publications on drug submissions, clinical trials, drug safety evaluation, pharmaceutical manufacturing regulations, quality and preclinical development. Lippincott Williams & Wilkins, a division of Wolters Kluwer Health, also has publications on drug development, clinical trials and pharmaceuticals. Majors.com's publications focus on regulatory compliance; quality assurance; risk management; the *Health Insurance Portability and Accountability Act* (*HIPAA*); coding and reimbursement; administrative law and regulatory practice; pharmaceutical research; medical devices; biotechnology; chemistry, manufacturing and controls compliance; laboratory auditing; validation; and clinical research. Springer, by comparison, covers regulatory and toxicology issues such as pharmaceutical safety evaluation in its pharmaceutical science area. The following keywords are effective for searching these online catalogs:

- regulatory
- regulatory affairs
- regulatory healthcare
- pharmaceutical
- biotechnology
- medical device
- pharmacology

Other industry publishers focus on such specific areas as quality assurance and standards. For example, the American Society for Quality's (ASQ) Quality Press publishes books, standards and training materials relating to quality issues, and the Bureau of National Affairs (BNA) concentrates on legal aspects of regulatory affairs. Selected topics covered by BNA publications include pharmaceutical, biotechnology and health law, intellectual property and patent law.

Several industry publishers specialize in publications that focus entirely or largely on regulatory and compliance issues. Barnett International is one such company, publishing regularly updated reference manuals industry compendia to assist in complying with federal regulations. It also publishes regulatory industry executive analyses, question and answer guides on regulatory topics and a training series for regulatory professionals. FDAnews also prepares reference tools specifically aimed at pharmaceutical, biologics and medical device regulatory professionals. Its products include Code of Federal Regulations (CFR) compilations, an adverse event compliance series and publications on biologics, biosimilars and combination drug products. GMP Publications also targets the regulatory industry through its CFR pocket guides and Good Clinical Practice and Good Manufacturing Practice handbooks.

Thompson Publishing Group dedicates an entire product line to food and drug regulatory materials. These products generally consist of two-volume manuals containing regularly updated newsletters, an archive and special reports, in addition to access to other online resources. Topics include Good Clinical Practice, FDA advertising and promotion, FDA enforcement and medical device regulation.

Many associations, such as the Regulatory Affairs Professionals Society (RAPS) and the Food and Drug Law Institute (FDLI), publish materials intended for regulatory professionals available in their online bookstores. This book is a key example of one such RAPS' product. In addition, RAPS publishes regulatory affairs certification (RAC) preparatory materials for the US, Canadian, EU and Global exams; self-assessment exams for each certification; and books on topics key to the development of regulatory professionals. Also included in RAPS' bookstore are third-party publications of interest to regulatory professionals. FDLI, similarly, markets its own publications as well as third-party products addressing regulatory and legal topics. **Table 41-2** provides information on several additional book publishers.

Electronic Newsletters, Magazines and Journals

Industry Resources

In addition to books, reports and standards, a number of industry resources available to regulatory professionals monitor current events and advance their knowledge of healthcare product regulation. Regulatory professionals can stay informed and save time by reviewing these industry-specific publications, as the sources reviewed in this section cover a range of drug, device and biologic regulatory publications.

Many publishers produce multiple newsletters directed at different healthcare product sectors. For example, FDAnews publishes three free e-newsletters: *FDAnews Device Daily Bulletin, FDAnews Drug Daily Bulletin* and *The QMN Weekly Bulletin. FDAnews Device Daily Bulletin* monitors FDA regulatory, legislative and business news developments and selected international news affecting the medical device industry. *FDAnews Drug Daily Bulletin* provides parallel coverage for the pharmaceutical industry. *The QMN Weekly Bulletin* covers current quality management news, regulatory developments and inspection trends. Summaries in these publications offer brief but valuable perspectives on current regulatory management issues for drugs, devices and quality. Links to the full-text articles are listed below each summary. These links afford regulatory professionals an opportunity to obtain further information on a particular subject and learn about new resources. However, many of these publications require subscriptions. In addition to FDAnews' free e-newsletters, the company distributes 10 fee-based subscription newsletters. These include: *Clinical Trials Advisor, Drug GMP Report, Drug Industry Daily, Generic Line, International Medical Device Regulatory Monitor, International Pharmaceutical Regulatory Monitor* and *The GMP Letter.*

SmartBrief, an independent e-newsletter publisher, produces 25 industry-specific daily newsletters available free of charge with subscription. The company partners with trade associations and professional societies and publishes their newsletters. *FDLI SmartBrief* works with FDLI to reach food and drug industry professionals. Similarly, *AdvaMed SmartBrief* is issued in conjunction with the Advanced Medical Technology Association (AdvaMed) and targets medical device, diagnostic product and health information system professionals. AdvaMed is a lobbying/advocacy organization for the medical device and technology industry advancing global healthcare and increasing patient access to medical technology. AdvaMed also promotes policies encouraging high ethical standards, rapid product approvals, appropriate reimbursement and international market access. SmartBrief publication summaries are based on original information from news organizations and repackaged by the firm's editorial staff. Each newsletter typically covers top stories: healthcare in transition, hot topics, business and market trends, science and health policy, emerging technologies and product-specific and association-specific news. Regulatory professionals can use these publications to track current regulatory developments in time-saving compilations and obtain valuable competitive intelligence.

VertMarkets has established online community marketplaces for eight industry groups to connect buyers and suppliers. For each of its online industry communities, VertMarkets produces free bi-weekly email newsletters providing not only product offerings but also industry updates and the latest news to its members. The newsletters directed to regulatory professionals fall into the life sciences category and include the *BioProcess Online Newsletter, Drug Discovery Leader Online Newsletter, Life Sciences Leader Online Newsletter, Clinical Leader Online Newsletter, Laboratory Network Community Newsletter, Medical Device Online Community Newsletter* and *Pharmaceutical Online Newsletter*. Typical content includes top news stories, featured articles, featured downloads and product showcases.

FierceMarkets is another digital media company specializing in supporting business-to-business marketing in the life sciences, healthcare, IT, telecom and finance industries through its e-newsletters, websites, webinars and live events. *FiercePharma* is a daily e-newsletter focused on pharmaceutical company news and market development of FDA-approved products. In addition, the publication features FDA rulings, regulations, recalls, warnings, drug launches, drug safety information, pharmaceutical sales information and marketing news and activities of key industry professionals. *FierceBiotech* is another daily e-newsletter in the FierceMarkets' digital product family. It concentrates on drug discovery and clinical trials news as well as the latest biotechnology trends, breakthroughs and FDA approval updates. *FierceBiotechResearcher* reports on biotechnology research news, information and tools, with a special focus on the science of drug discovery. *FierceVaccines, FierceDrugDelivery, FierceDiagnostics, FierceCRO, FiercePharma Manufacturing FierceBiotechIT* and *FierceHealthcare* are the company's other seven e-newsletters within the healthcare division.

Another well-recognized, fee-based publisher is Informa, one of the largest publishers of business information for the pharmaceutical, biotechnology, medical devices and diagnostics industries. Its subsidiary, Informa Business Intelligence, distributes several e-newsletters monitoring business information and intelligence trends, technologies and companies in the medical device, diagnostics and biotech industry. The company's fee-based newsletters include *Medtech Insight, IN VIVO, Start-Up* and *The RPM Report. Medtech Insight* is particularly useful to regulatory professionals for its clinical and industry perspectives on products, procedures and technologies shaping the global medical technology market. *IN VIVO* provides in-depth analyses of marketing, R&D and regulatory and finance strategies in the biopharmaceutical, medical technology and diagnostics industries. *Start-Up* examines new product and leading-edge company and investment trends in the pharmaceutical, biotechnology, medical device and in vitro diagnostics industries. *The RPM Report* is a useful business resource for the biopharmaceutical regulatory professional. Its focuses primarily on FDA, the Centers for Medicare and Medicaid Services (CMS) and public sector issues.

F-D-C Reports Inc., a subsidiary of the Informa Business Intelligence Unit (formerly Elsevier Business Intelligence), is another newsletter publisher serving the healthcare product industry. F-D-C Reports publishes fee-based newsletters designed to clarify developments affecting US healthcare product and services marketing and regulation for industry executives, policymakers and analysts. Newsletters published by F-D-C Reports include: *The Pink Sheet/The Pink Sheet DAILY, Pharmaceutical Approvals Monthly, The Gold Sheet* and *PharmAsia News* in the pharmaceuticals and biotechnology category; *The Silver Sheet* and *The Gray Sheet* in the medical devices and diagnostics category; *The Tan Sheet* and *The Rose Sheet* in the consumer products category; and *Health News Daily* in the health policy and biomedical research category. Although the majority of its publications are fee-based, it does offer a complimentary subscription to a few of its weekly e-newsletters. One of these publications, *Medical Devices Today,* provides strategy, regulation, innovation and investment coverage from *The Gray Sheet, Medtech Insight, IN VIVO, Start-Up, The Silver Sheet, The Pink Sheet* and *Strategic Transactions.* The articles cover drug and business development, finance, strategy, regulation and reimbursement.

Another key regulatory publication by Informa is *SCRIP Regulatory Affairs (SRA,* formerly *Regulatory Affairs Journal Pharma/Devices). SRA* serves as a source of global news, commentaries and analyses of regulation in the pharmaceutical and biotechnology industries. The publication provides pharmaceutical regulatory intelligence on global regulations governing the development, launch and postmarket surveillance of medicines and combination products. Areas of coverage include: regulatory agencies and legislation, application requirements and guidelines, R&D, patents and intellectual property, international harmonization, pediatric legislation, pharmacovigilance, pharmacoeconomics and drug safety. Informa Healthcare also produces a broad range of fee-based industry news sources (e.g., *Scrip World Pharmaceutical News*), business and market research reports, R&D analytical tools and databases (e.g., Pharmaprojects and TrialTrove) and research journals (e.g., *Clinical Research & Regulatory Affairs, Drug Development and Industrial Pharmacy*).

The medical device industry also receives excellent web coverage through a number of free publications. *Medical Device & Diagnostic Industry (MD&DI)* is one of 13 magazines published by UBM Canon (formerly Canon Communications) focusing on the medical technology industry. *MD&DI* is a monthly magazine written exclusively for original equipment manufacturers of medical devices and in vitro diagnostic products. The publication supports industry efforts to comply with regulations, keep up-to-date on current events, improve manufacturing and design processes and understand market demand. *QMed Daily* is another UBM Canon publication available free of charge with membership to QMed, formerly Medical Device Link. *QMed Daily* is a daily e-newsletter reporting on top industry headlines and important FDA announcements and features articles on technology breakthroughs in the medical device industry worldwide. QMed also offers subscriptions to the *Consultants Corner* newsletter, which focuses on the development and commercialization of medical products, and the *MPMN Medtech Pulse* newsletter, which provides news on emerging medical technologies.

In addition, *Dickinson's FDAReview* is a monthly newsletter published by Ferdic Inc. providing in-depth analyses of the medical device and drug industries as well as FDA inspection and enforcement activities, including *Freedom of Information Act* (*FOIA*) daily logs and Warning Letter summaries. *FDAUpdate* is a weekly fax document containing *FR* updates pertaining to FDA rules and regulations; newly released Warning Letters; weekly filed Citizen Petitions; Advisory Committee proceedings and calendars; and late-breaking FDA and pharmaceutical product news. Free items also available on Dickinson's interactive website, *FDAWebview,* include FDA Warning Letters, *FR* notices and an FDA calendar.

A few other free electronic industry-specific resources worth mentioning briefly are *MedicalDeviceSummit, Today's Medical Developments Magazine*, *Marketing News*, in-PharmaTechnologist.com, *Pharmaceutical Technology Magazine*, PharmTech.com and Pharmafile.com. Clinical monitoring news is addressed in a free weekly e-newsletter entitled, *BioPharm Insight* and *BioPharm Clinical,* published by Infinata. The newsletter covers the latest information on clinical enrollments, clinical results, drug approvals, drug licensing and medical devices.

VirSci Corporation's *Pharma Marketing News* is a monthly newsletter for pharmaceutical and marketing professionals designed to keep subscribers informed about industry trends and innovations. It also offers a professional network for career advancement. Frequently covered topics include: physician marketing, sales and education, regulatory compliance, patient education and direct-to-consumer advertising and marketing. Outcomes LLC (formerly UBM Canon and Canon Communication) is another publisher offering a free monthly magazine, *Med Ad News*, and the site, *PharmaLive.com*, which provides news updates for the pharmaceutical industry. The magazine is an established resource for competitive business intelligence and marketing strategy information. Last, TradePub.com is excellent source for free healthcare and medical magazines, publications and newsletters covering the pharmaceutical and medical device industries and more.

Global Regulatory Press' *Journal of Medical Device Regulation* is yet another important resource for medical device regulatory professionals. This is a quarterly publication currently available only in electronic format. Regulatory professionals can monitor global regulatory developments through legislative changes summarized in each issue and obtain guidance from review articles analyzing current medical device regulatory and compliance issues.

The list of free and fee-based regulatory publications is long and varied, ranging from industry newsletters and peer-reviewed journals to association magazines. This section provides a snapshot of some of these resources. These publications, although not exhaustive of all available resources, provide regulatory professionals a solid basis for further independent research.

Association Resources

The majority of association publications are free with membership but require nonmembers to pay an annual membership fee. RAPS is one such association, publishing a monthly electronic magazine, *Regulatory Focus,* which is available to its members, with limited online guest access to selected articles. The magazine focuses on current regulatory issues affecting the drug, medical device and biological healthcare product sectors. As an offshoot from the magazine, RAPS provides daily (weekdays only) news briefings via *RF Today*, featuring summaries of the top regulatory news stories from around the world relating to pharmaceuticals, medical devices, biotechnology and the agencies that regulate them. Another RAPS member-based resource is a weekly e-newsletter, *RAPS Weekly Update*. Similarly, The Organisation for Professionals in Regulatory Affairs (TOPRA) publishes a members-only international journal, *Regulatory Rapporteur,* which provides current news and analyses on regulatory and legislative topics. TOPRA also issues a quarterly member newsletter, *In Touch*, which serves as an association news digest covering member and organizational activities.

In addition, FDLI publishes a quarterly magazine, the *Food and Drug Law Journal*, which is available free to members and by subscription to the public. The journal features articles on food, drug, cosmetic, medical device and healthcare technology industry regulation and legislation, implications of proposed regulations, policy trends and analyses of judicial decisions in food and drug law. Its members-only resource, *Update*, is issued bimonthly and contains the latest association and industry news, viewpoints on industry-specific trends, FDA agency developments and articles on various regulatory topics. In addition, FDLI publishes *Food and Drug Policy Forum to discuss policy, and Primers to provide guidance on trending topics in food and law.*

The Medical Device Manufacturers Association (MDMA) represents the interests of smaller, entrepreneurial medical technology companies through its advocacy and educational services. Its members-only publications include the Weekly MDMA Update and the Monthly Member Services Newsletter.

The Drug Information Association (DIA) publishes its official bimonthly journal, *Therapeutic Innovation & Regulatory Science* (formerly the *Drug Information Journal*). This newly launched journal encompasses drug, device and diagnostic innovations, global regulatory topics as well as pharmaceutical research and development issues. DIA produces *Global Forum*, a bimonthly magazine dedicated to global coverage of pharmaceutical and medical products from discovery and development to regulation, marketing and surveillance. *Global Forum* also delivers up-to-date association and member news. In addition, DIA'S e-newsletter, *DIA Daily*, provides news highlights and information about the pharmaceutical, biotechnology and medical device fields from thousands of global news sources.

The Parenteral Drug Association's (PDA) membership publication, *PDA Letter*, reports on science, technology, quality, regulatory affairs, association news and updates relevant to the PDA community. The *PDA Journal of Pharmaceutical Science and Technology* is a bimonthly publication containing peer-reviewed scientific and technical papers covering the pharmaceutical and biotech industries. The journal is distributed as a member benefit and also is available by subscription. *PDA Technical Reports* are global consensus documents addressing a range of topics relating to pharmaceutical production, validation and quality assurance. Expert task forces prepare the reports, which then are reviewed by technical forums and ultimately evaluated and approved by an advisory board and the PDA board of directors.

Within the biologics/biotechnology sphere, the Biotechnology Industry Organization (BIO) supports professionals engaged in the research and development (R&D) of new healthcare technology, biotechnology and related fields through its advocacy, business development and communications services. Its members-only publication, *BIO Newsletter* is published weekly and disseminated via email. The newsletter reports on organizational activities, professional perspectives on industry issues and member activities. In cooperation with the SmartBrief publisher, BIO also produces *BIO SmartBrief*, which focuses on news updates within the biotechnology industry.

The Society of Biomaterials is one of many professional scientific organizations in which regulatory professionals can participate to keep abreast of the latest innovations and technology relevant to their products. The society promotes progress in biomedical materials research and development. Members are afforded free access to its news magazine, *Biomaterials Forum*, which is available by subscription to nonmembers. The forum reports on current biomaterials community activities and includes book reviews, technical briefs and professional services information. The *Journal for Biomedical Materials Research* is the society's official journal and is a peer-reviewed publication provided free to members. It features clinical studies and research reports on a range of topics, including the preparation, performance and development of new biomaterials. *Applied Materials* is published as Part B of the journal. It contains peer-reviewed articles on device development, implant retrieval and analysis, manufacturing, regulation of devices, liability and legal issue, standards, reviews of device and clinical applications.

Two key associations in the clinical research area are the Association of Clinical Research Professionals (ACRP) and the Society of Clinical Research Associates (SoCRA). In addition to its free biweekly email newsletter, ACRP Wire, ACRP also publishes a bimonthly journal, the *Clinical Researcher* (formerly *The Monitor*), featuring peer-reviewed articles, association news and a guide to certification preparation courses and exams available only to members. SoCRA, like ACRP, is dedicated to the continuing education and development of its members and publishes the *SoCRA Source Journal*, a members-only quarterly publication containing scientific and professional articles; society news and events; and professional opportunities and services. Selected articles from past issues of the journal are available to the public on SoCRA's website. A comprehensive list of all the fee-based and free publisher resources reviewed and their corresponding website addresses is provided in **Table 41-2.**

Regulatory Collaboration: Meetings & Education

The delivery of safe, effective and high-quality healthcare products to the general public is the primary goal of any regulatory professional. With the increase in electronic submissions and online repositories, and the departmentalization of many healthcare businesses, a regulatory professional runs the risks of working in a silo. Thus, it is vital for regulatory professionals to seek opportunities for internal organizational collaboration, as well as externally across businesses, functional areas, product lines, customer-base and/or geography. Meetings and additional resources offered by industry, associations and FDA provide an opportunity for collaboration and innovation related to common challenges across businesses. Similarly, new or proven solutions to regulatory challenges can be provided by a consulting firm. This section discusses the benefits and role of associations, FDA public meetings and consulting firms to the regulatory professional.

Table 41-4. Societies, Trade Associations, Advocacy Groups and Associations Providing Learning Resources

Organization	Website	Learning Resources
American Association of Blood Banks (AABB)	www.aabb.org	e-Learning, Meetings, Webinars
American Association of Homeopathic Pharmacists (AAHP)	www.aahp.info	Webinars
American Association of Pharmaceutical Studies (AAPS)	www.aaps.org	e-Learning, Meetings, Webinars*
American Association of Tissue Banks (AATB)	www.aatb.org	Meetings, Webinars, Training, Certification
Association for the Advancement of Medical Instrumentation (AAMI)	www.aami.org	e-Learning, Meetings, Webinars Certifications*
Association of Clinical Research Professionals (ACRP)	www.acrpnet.org	e-Learning, Meetings, Webinars, Training, Certifications*
Advanced Medical Technology Association (AdvaMed)	www.advamed.org	e-Learning, Meetings, Webinars*
American Herbal Products Association (AHPA)	www.ahpa.org	e-Learning
Association of Medical Diagnostics Manufacturers (AMDM)	www.amdm.org	Meetings
American Society for Quality (ASQ)	www.asq.org	e-Learning, Meetings, Webinars, Training, Certifications*
Association of Veterinary Biologics Companies (AVBC)	www.avbc.net	Meetings
Biotechnology Industry Organization (BIO)	www.bio.org	Meetings
Consumer Healthcare Products Association (CHPA)	www.chpa.org	Meeting, Webinar, Training
Drug Information Association (DIA)	www.diahome.org	e-Learning, Meetings, Webinars, Training, Certificate Programs
Food and Drug Law Institute (FDLI)	www.fdli.org	Meetings
Generic Pharmaceutical Association (GPhA)	www.gphaonline.org	Meetings
Healthcare Distribution Management Association (HDMA)	healthcaredistribution.org	Meetings, Webinar*
Independent Cosmetic Manufacturers and Distributors (ICMAD)	www.icmad.org	Webinars*
Medical Device Manufacturers Association (MDMA)	www.medicaldevices.org	Meetings, Webinars*
Natural Products Association (NPA)	www.npainfo.org	Meetings, Webinars
Personal Care Product Council (PCPC)	personalcarecouncil.org	Meetings, Webinars
Parental Drug Association (PDA)	www.pda.org	e-Learning, Meetings, Training
Plasma Protein Therapeutics Association (PPTA)	www.pptaglobal.org	Meetings
Regulatory Affairs Professionals Society (RAPS)	www.raps.org	e-Learning, Meetings, Webinars, Training, Certification*
Society of Clinical Trials (SCT)	www.sctweb.org	Meetings, Webinars*
Society of Clinical Research Associates (SoCRA)	www.socra.org	e-Learning, Meetings, Training, Certifications
The Organisation for Professionals in Regulatory Affairs (TOPRA)	www.topra.org	e-Learning, Meetings, Degree Programs
World Medical Device Organization (WMDO)	www.wmdo.org	e-Learning, Certifications, Certificate Programs

**Resource may be fee-based or free.*
The absence of an asterisk indicates that the resource is fee-based. However, costs for members may differ.
Note: Website URLs are current at time of publication.

Associations and Continued Learning

The knowledge garnered from publications, government databases and other agency resources unquestionably has an integral place in a regulatory professional's career development. These resources enable the regulatory professional to monitor the latest news, track the status and development of laws, regulations and guidelines and engage in effective strategic product development.

In addition, associations are indispensable educational resources for regulatory professionals. Through the active participation of their members, these associations embody the immediate focus and future direction of the specific interest areas they serve. The organizations mentioned earlier in the chapter, including RAPS, DIA, TOPRA, BIO, AdvaMed, FDLI and ACRP, offer a broad variety of learning opportunities to their members. **Table 41-4** provides a comprehensive but not exhaustive list of associations providing learning resources for their members and/or non-members.

Most associations require a nominal membership fee, which grants individuals (or in some cases designated company representatives) access to member-only resources. These resources may include:

- discounts to the organization's resources, i.e., webinars and publications
- access to knowledge databases, reports, directories
- access to the latest news specific to the organization's focus via periodic newsletters, email updates and/or social media outlets
- access to education tools, i.e., e-learning and seminars
- access and/or discounts to the resources of partner associations
- access to member directories and online forums
- participation in meetings, trade shows and/or conferences
- involvement in special partnerships and/or meetings with direct interaction with compliance bodies and regulatory agencies
- networking with other professionals with similar expertise or regulatory interests
- assistance with business and/or regulatory activities
- advocacy for the professional and/or an organization's professional interests
- participation on committees influencing the organization's vision and direction

Participation in these associations grants access and opportunities for learning through professional networking, committee involvement and educational tools. Regulatory professionals can maintain their knowledge of the regulatory healthcare industry and/or fulfill core competency requirements by participating in e-learning courses, web-based training, interactive web-based webinars and/or online certificate programs.

Webinars may be open to members and nonmembers depending on the organization. These webinars offer live, virtual group learning sessions, in which the presenter(s), a subject matter expert, focuses on a specific topic and opens the floor to attendees for discussion and questions. Typically, the presentation is in Microsoft PowerPoint format, but also may reference a regulatory document, database or any other pertinent resource.

Alternatively, e-learning resources provide archived learning sessions accessible at the regulatory professional's convenience, where the learner sets the pace of the online coursework. RAPS, DIA and the World Medical Device Organization (WMDO) provide e-learning curricula culminating in a certificate. DIA offers certificates in clinical research, regulatory affairs, clinical safety and pharmacovigilance, project management and medical communications. WMDO provides educational opportunities to regulatory professionals in the medical device arena, with certificates in clinical evaluation, Asia-Pacific and EU medical device regulatory affairs and medical device monitoring. A combined medical device and pharmaceutical regulatory affairs certificate is offered by RAPS, as well as individual certificates within each topic. Formal postgraduate degree programs (online and classroom settings) are offered by several universities. Uniquely, TOPRA offers a Masters of Science in Regulatory Affairs, which is formally validated by the University of Hertfordshire. The program requires the completion of e-Learning modules on regulations, regulatory strategy, clinical operations, regulatory submissions and product development. It also requires the submission of a research-based dissertation.

Organizations such as the American Association of Tissue Banks (AATB), ACRP, ASQ, RAPS and SoCRA provide industry-recognized certifications specific to their respective specialties: tissue banking, clinical research, quality (i.e., auditing, engineering or improvement), regulatory affairs and clinical investigations, respectively. Certification typically requires achieving a passing score on an association-administered standardized exam offered several times throughout the year.

AATB, ACRP, ASQ, the Consumer Healthcare Products Association (CHPA), PDA and SoCRA provide face-to-face and/or virtual training sessions. CHPA serves as a trade association for manufacturers and distributors of OTC medicines and dietary supplements. They offer periodic face-to-face training sessions on compliance with current Good Manufacturing Practice (CGMP). PDA seeks to connect people, science and regulation through the development and coordination of scientific, technical and regulatory information germane to the pharmaceutical and biopharmaceutical communities. In support of its mission, PDA offers several courses in such areas as aseptic processing, filtration, environmental monitoring, biotechnology, microbiology, process validation and quality/regulatory affairs, among other topics.

Typically, association members have access to periodic association meetings and conferences where in-person classroom workshops and training sessions may be offered to registrants. Less didactic learning occurs at annual meetings, conferences or seminars held or co-sponsored by the associations listed in **Table 41-4**. These meetings allow regulatory professionals and other industry-related professionals to become acquainted, learn about key topics and engage in discussions related to changes in the regulatory healthcare industry over the course of one to seven days, depending on the meeting topics and organization's size. Note the American Herbal Products Association (AHPA), a scientific and regulatory advocate organization for herbs, botanicals and herbal products, and the Independent Cosmetic Manufacturers and Distributors (ICMAD) association, do not host meetings but participate in industry exhibits, trade shows and expos. WMDO also does not host or participate in meetings, as it focuses on distance, online learning.

In addition to offering formal learning options, associations enable professionals to engage in networking and information exchange with their colleagues through forums and online communities. Along with their periodic national meetings, numerous associations implement monthly or quarterly programming at the local, chapter level across the US to support ongoing networking and professional development activities. In concert, these association tools support the continued learning of the regulatory professional.

FDA Meetings

FDA accepts requests for formal meetings to discuss product development and regulatory submissions, and also sponsors and co-sponsors meetings, workshops and other events open to the general public. (Chapters 4 and 5 provide detailed discussions of FDA formal meetings and Advisory Committee Meetings, respectively.) FDA announces upcoming, scheduled sponsored and co-sponsored events, along with presentations by FDA representatives on its website. The website organizes the meeting announcements by topic (Advisory Committee calendar, animal and veterinary, biologics, combination products, cosmetics, drugs, food, medical countermeasures, medical devices, science and research and tobacco products), typically a month or more in advance. Attendance at FDA-sponsored events, whether in-person or via webcast (Adobe Connect, web conference software) requires registration, which is accepted on a first-come, first-serve basis due to limited seating. Registration is free. However, for co-sponsored events, registration and related fees may apply. FDA posts Advisory Committee Meeting announcements at least 15 calendar days before a meeting date in accordance with 41 CFR Section 102-3.150. In addition, FDA announces sponsored stakeholder meetings on its website a few days before the teleconference.[28]

Through these periodic stakeholder meetings, FDA aims to gain input from the general public, particularly consumer organizations, researchers, scientists and industry representatives, on public health actions and initiatives. Subsequent to meetings and workshops, FDA posts a text or PowerPoint version of presentations, meeting materials (*FR* notice, agenda and panelists) and/or webcasts on its website.

Consulting Firms

Regardless of a healthcare company's size, knowledge gaps arise within a regulatory team, warranting the need for an external consultant's expertise. These consultants execute a myriad of functions and offer knowledge in areas including, but not limited to product regulations, trade compliance, customs regulation, clinical research/trials, testing (laboratory or animal), data management, quality management, auditing, reimbursement, medical writing and due diligence. Hundreds of consulting companies exist to support industry needs during all product lifecycle phases. Numerous associations and media portals offer listings and rankings of consulting services. For example, QMED offers a directory of vetted consultants, organized by service for the medical device and in vitro diagnostics industry.[29] These directories serve as a starting point for identifying a consulting firm. In some cases, the consulting firm's website may serve as an online knowledge tool, e.g., the medical device consulting firm, Emergo Group Inc. offers an open-access digital library of articles, charts, reports, regulations and archived webinars.[30] In addition, Centerwatch, a service provider of clinical trials information, offers access to white papers, clinical trial databases and a directory of consulting firms/services.[31] Given the complexity and dynamism of the healthcare field, consultants' extensive knowledge can be a useful asset for a regulatory team.

Social Networking and Mobile Apps

The second generation of Internet-based services goes beyond static web content and commonly is referred to as Web 2.0. It encompasses social networking and other forms of dynamic and interactive information sharing by users. Given the pervasiveness of smart phones, tablets and other innovations in web and mobile technology, consumption of real-time, up-to-date information by end users of these devices goes beyond entertainment, and has important application for news and information retrieval. Users expect opportunities for community-based input and daily or minute-to-minute content-sharing in their respective professional fields. To complement the networking benefits of industry association memberships, regulatory professionals now can connect with colleagues through blogs and social networking websites. The regulatory professional has several options through which to receive information:

- Tumblr/Blogs/Microblogs—regularly updated journal entries designed to be read by a professional audience and representing the unique personality of the author or website; multimedia postings with commenting features (more information provided below)
- LinkedIn—microblogging/networking tool for professionals, organizations and businesses (more information provided below)
- RSS feeds—automated tracking of updates to favorite websites (more information provided below)
- Twitter—microblogging of videos, photos and status/activity updates, with commenting features Example: FDA Recalls and FDA MedWatch provide safety and recall updates[32]
- YouTube—public video sharing with captioning and commenting features Example: USPTO video series on applications[33]
- Facebook—microblogging/networking tool for sharing videos, photos and status/activity updates with commenting features Example: NIH Research Matters provides a weekly review of NIH-funded research[34]
- Google Plus+—microblogging/networking tool for sharing videos, photos and status/activity updates with commenting features Example: RAPS.org provides daily RAPS-specific and general regulatory news[35]

Government agencies and other industry associates already have adopted numerous Web 2.0 information tools, particularly social media outlets and information feeds, as a pathway to engage consumers, healthcare professionals and regulatory professionals. With the exception of the Plasma Protein Therapeutics Association (PPTA) and the Academy of Veterinary Behavior Technicians (AVBT), all other trade associations, advocacy groups and associations listed on **Table 41-4**, and all of the US agencies, organizations, institutes, centers and offices listed in **Table 41-1** utilize Web 2.0 tools (specifically social media). FDA provides web content devoted to staying informed via subscriptions,[36] RSS feeds and interactive media.[37]

RSS (Rich Site Summary, Really Simple Syndication) news feeds automatically track website content updates (news, blogs, audio, video and images), sending content to subscribers automatically. RSS allows users to collect and organize information from websites, commonly referred to as feeds. The RSS feed can be synched to Microsoft Outlook to receive scheduled email updates. RSS feed aggregators (also referred to as readers) are available for download, both commercially and open access. The RSS feed tool along with direct email subscriptions to government websites, organizations/societies and blogs offer the regulatory professional convenient periodic updates.

Some of the more popular blogs within the regulatory healthcare sector include: FDA Voice (official FDA blog); FDA Law Blog (Hyman, Phelps & McNamara PC); Biotech Blog (managed by Yali Friedman, PhD); Eye on FDA (RX for Pharma Industry Communications and Planning); and Medical Device and Diagnostic Industry (MDDI) blogs, including Device Talk. This list does not begin to scratch the surface of the widely available regulatory information; however, it is a good starting point.

In addition, regulatory professionals can participate in sites such as LinkedIn to establish public professional profiles, search for jobs, interact with colleagues, search for other regulatory professionals and join online regulatory groups. LinkedIn operates the world's largest professional network on the Internet, with more than 300 million members in over 200 countries and territories.[38] Joining the network is free and simply requires the user to create a profile summarizing his or her professional experience and accomplishments. The information a user chooses to make available publicly can be searched by other professionals within the LinkedIn network and used for the purpose of meeting and collaborating with other members.

LinkedIn hosts a multitude of regulatory groups supporting regulatory professionals' interaction. The Quality and Safety Regulatory Network on LinkedIn supports professionals working in quality assurance, regulatory and compliance in highly regulated industries. This group allows professionals to share experiences and expand their networks of people and ideas in quality, regulatory, safety, health, sustainability, risk and compliance for continuous improvement across multiple industries.[39] Similarly, the reg-info.com group on LinkedIn allows pharmaceutical professionals to share ideas and participate in a forum for issues related to regulatory intelligence and information gathering. This community also assists pharmaceutical professionals in finding regulatory intelligence information through links to key regulatory and related information sources.[40]

Other social networking sites, such as Pinterest, Instagram, Flickr and Foursquare, are not covered in this discussion, as they have not yet been adopted widely as useful platforms for regulatory intelligence and/or information sharing. Notably, mobile application technology has emerged within the last decade as a tool for quick, user-friendly information retrieval on smartphones. However, the adoption of downloadable mobile applications ("apps") for regulatory content still is in its nascent stage. In March 2015, FDA released the agency's first free, mobile app focused on relaying updates and the status of FDA drug shortages. In addition, the Emergo Group Inc. offers a free, mobile app providing access to regulatory intelligence, including the full text of the FDA QSR (21 CFR Part 820). Ultimately, the continued use of Web 2.0 technology and growing adoption of mobile apps will support increased interactions and collaboration across the regulatory field.

Summary

Regulatory professionals have improved their productivity, effectiveness and expertise significantly through ever-increasing access to an array of Internet-based regulatory resources. The ease with which regulatory information can be acquired is profound, compared to less than a decade ago when the only way to acquire similar information was through mail, fax and/or telephone. This chapter reviews a wide range of information resources and social networking tools available to regulatory professionals. The number of publications and databases, and government, association and industry web-based tools, as well as social networking opportunities developed in just the past few decades is staggering. The new challenge for regulatory professionals is to distill the essential knowledge they require from the vast storehouse of information available to perform their jobs as effectively as possible. This will require carefully managing subscriptions, becoming skilled in using relevant government and industry databases, making use of associations' educational resources to advance professional knowledge, leveraging the expertise of consulting firms as needed and using social networking tools with discipline and discernment. In this way, regulatory professionals will be certain to reap the greatest benefit from the abundant resources available, and thereby ensure the public receives safe, effective and quality healthcare products.

References

1. About GPO. GPO website. www.gpo.gov/about/. Accessed 21 January 2015.
2. Federal Register E-Mail Updates. National Archives website. http://www.archives.gov/federal-register/the-federal-register/email-signup.html. Accessed 21 January 2015.
3. GPO homepage. http://www.gpo.gov. Accessed 21 January 2015.
4. Regulatory Information. FDA website. http://www.fda.gov/RegulatoryInformation . Accessed 21 January 2015.
5. Regulations.gov home page. http://www.regulations.gov. Accessed 21 January 2015.
6. Congress.gov home page. http://thomas.loc.gov/ . Accessed 23 January 2015.
7. Intellectual Property Rights Search. Customs and Border Protection website. http://iprs.cbp.gov . Accessed 23 January 2015.
8. Customs Rulings Online Search System (CROSS) Data.gov website. https://catalog.data.gov/dataset/cbp-customs-rulings-online-search-system-cross . Accessed 23 January 2015.
9. Letter to Industry about Import Entry Review Process (September 6, 2011). FDA website. http://www.fda.gov/MedicalDevices/ResourcesforYou/Industry/ucm271180.htm. Accessed 3 February 2015.
10. https://www.bis.doc.gov/index.php/enforcement/oac. Accessed 21 January 2015.
11. Training and Continuing Education. www.fda.gov/Training. Accessed 30 June 2015.
12. Ask Us: FDA Basics Webinar Series. www.fda.gov/AboutFDA/Transparency/Basics/ucm197102.htm. Accessed 30 June 2015.
13. About Us and Dun & Bradstreet - FDA DUNS Request. www.dnb.com/government/duns-request.html. Accessed 30 June 2015.
14. D&B D-U-N-S® Number Lookup. www.dandb.com/dunsnumber-lookup. Accessed 30 June 2015.
15. PharmaPendium Interoperability. www.elsevier.com/solutions/pharmapendium/interoperability. Accessed June 30, 2015.
16. About ClinRegs. clinregs.niaid.nih.gov/about.php. Accessed 12 February 2015.
17. Tarius Solutions. www.tarius.com. Accessed 2 July 2015.
18. Cortellis Regulatory Intelligence Overview. thomsonreuters.com/en/products-services/pharma-life-sciences/regulatory-affairs/product-overview.htm. Accessed 30 June 2015.
19. Health home page. http://www.wolterskluwerlb.com/health Accessed 30 June 2015.
20. Trialtrove home page. citeline.com/products/trialtrove. Accessed 30 June 2015
21. Pharmaprojects home page. citeline.com/products/pharmaprojects. Accessed 30 June 2015
22. International Standard for Organization home page. iso.org. Accessed 21 January 2015.
23. About USP—An Overview. US Pharmacopeia website. www.usp.org/about-usp. Accessed 21 January 2015.
24. About ICH. www.ich.org. International Conference on Harmonisation website. Accessed 4 January 2015.
25. About PhRMA. http://www.phrma.org/about. Pharmaceutical Research and Manufacturers of America. Accessed 11 February 2015.
26. International Medical Device Regulators Forum home page. www.imdrf.org. Accessed 4 January 2015.
27. International Clinical Trials Registry Platform (ICTRP) home page. http://www.who.int/ictrp/en/. World Health Organization website. Accessed 11 February 2015
28. FDA Stakeholders Events home page. http://www.fda.gov/NewsEvents/MeetingsConferencesWorkshops/StakeholderMeetings/default.htm. FDA website. Accessed 11 February 2015.
29. Qualified Supplier Directory. www.qmed.com/supplier-categories/consultants. Accessed 2 July 2015
30. Resource Library for Medical Device Professionals. http://www.emergogroup.com/resources. Accessed 2 July 2015
31. Centerwatch News Resources. www.centerwatch.com/news-resources. Accessed 2 July 2015
32. FDA recalls Twitter site. FDA website. https://twitter.com/fdarecalls; FDA MedWatch twitter site. https://twitter.com/FDAMedWatch. Accessed 12 February 2015.
33. USPTO on youtube. https://www.youtube.com/user/USPTOvideo/videos. Accessed 12 February 2015.
34. NIH Research Matter. https://www.facebook.com/ResearchMatters. Facebook website. Accessed 12 February 2015.
35. Regulatory Affairs Professionals Society. https://plus.google.com/106321095709510076478/posts. Accessed 12 February 2015.
36. FDA Stay Informed. www.fda.gov/ForIndustry/FDABasicsforIndustry/ucm234630.htm. Accessed 1 July 2015.
37. FDA Interactive Media. www.fda.gov/NewsEvents/InteractiveMedia. Accessed 1 July 2015.
38. Linkedin home page. www.linkedin.com/about-us. Accessed 12 February 2015.
39. Linkedin Quality & Regulatory network. https://www.linkedin.com/groups?gid=80327. Accessed 12 February 2015.
40. reg-infor.com—Regulatory intelligence for pharma. https://www.linkedin.com/grp/home?gid=833547. Accessed 12 February 2015.

Comparative Matrix of Regulations Across Product Lines

FDA Centers		
	Source	**Centers**
Devices	www.fda.gov/MedicalDevices/default.htm	• Center for Devices and Radiological Health (CDRH) • Center for Biologics Evaluation and Research (CBER) for certain devices and in vitro diagnostics that involve blood collection.
Drugs	www.fda.gov/Drugs/default.htm	• Center for Drug Evaluation and Research (CDER)
Biologics	www.fda.gov/BiologicsBloodVaccines/default.htm	• Center for Biologics Evaluation and Research (CBER) • Center for Drug Evaluation and Research (CDER) for biological therapeutic products
Veterinary	www.fda.gov/AnimalVeterinary/default.htm	• Center for Veterinary Medicine (CVM)
Cosmetics	www.fda.gov/Cosmetics/default.htm	• Center for Food Safety and Applied Nutrition (CFSAN)
Foods	www.fda.gov/Food/default.htm	• Center for Food Safety and Applied Nutrition (CFSAN)
Tobacco	www.fda.gov/TobaccoProducts/default.htm	• Center for Tobacco Products (CTP)

FDA Requirements—Authority	
	Acts
Devices	• *Pure Food and Drugs Act* of 1906 • *Federal Food, Drug, and Cosmetic Act* of 1938 (*FD&C Act*) • *Fair Packaging and Labeling Act* of 1966 • *Medical Device Amendments* of 1976 • *Safe Medical Devices Act* of 1990 (*SMDA*) • *Medical Device Amendments* of 1992 • *FDA Export Reform and Enhancement Act* of 1996 (*FDERA*) • *FDA Modernization Act* of 1997 (*FDAMA*) • *Medical Device User Fee and Modernization Act* of 2002 (*MDUFMA*) • *Food and Drug Administration Amendments Act* of 2007 *(FDAAA)* • *Food and Drug Administration Safety and Innovation Act* of 2012 (*FDASIA*)
Drugs	• *Pure Food and Drugs Act* of 1906 • *Federal Food, Drug, and Cosmetic Act* of 1938 (*FD&C Act*) • *Fair Packaging and Labeling Act* of 1966 • *Durham-Humphrey Amendment* of 1951 • *Kefauver-Harris Drug Amendments* of 1962 • *Orphan Drug Act* of 1983 • *Drug Price Competition and Patent Term Restoration Act* of 1984 • *Prescription Drug Marketing Act* of 1987 • *Prescription Drug User Fee Act* of 1992 (*PDUFA*) • *FDA Export Reform and Enhancement Act* of 1996 • *FDA Modernization Act* of 1997 (*FDAMA*) • *Best Pharmaceuticals for Children Act* of 2002 (*BPCA*) • *The Pediatric Research Equity Act* of 2003 (*PREA*) • *Food and Drug Administration Amendments Act* of 2007 (*FDAAA*) • *Food and Drug Administration Safety and Innovation Act* of 2012 (*FDASIA*)
Biologics	• *Biologics Control Act* (also known as the *Virus-Toxin Act*) of 1902 • *Federal Food, Drug, and Cosmetic Act* of 1938 (*FD&C Act*) • *Public Health Service Act* of 1944 • *FDA Modernization Act* of 1997 (*FDAMA*) • *The Pediatric Research Equity Act* of 2003 (*PREA*) • *Food and Drug Administration Amendments Act* of 2007 *(FDAAA)* • *Biologics Price Competition and Innovation Act* of 2009 (*BPCIA*) • *Food and Drug Administration Safety and Innovation Act* of 2012 (*FDASIA*)

Major Guidelines		
	Source	**Major Guidelines**
Devices	www.fda.gov/MedicalDevices/DeviceRegulationandGuidance/GuidanceDocuments/default.htm www.fda.gov/MedicalDevices/DeviceRegulationandGuidance/Standards/default.htm	• Guidance documents • Blue Book Memoranda • Medical Device Quality Systems Manual • FDA Recognized Consensus Standards
	www.fda.gov/MedicalDevices/DeviceRegulationandGuidance/default.htm	• CDRH Device Advice website
Drugs	www.fda.gov/Drugs/GuidanceComplianceRegulatoryInformation/default.htm www.fda.gov/AboutFDA/CentersOffices/OfficeofMedicalProductsandTobacco/CDER/ManualofPoliciesProcedures/default.htm www.fda.gov/Drugs/DevelopmentApprovalProcess/Manufacturing/QuestionsandAnswersonCurrentGoodManufacturingPracticescGMPforDrugs/	• Guidance documents International Conference on Harmonisation (ICH) Guidelines • Manual of Policies & Procedures (MaPPs) (CDER) • Current Good Manufacturing Practices (cGMP) for Drugs: Reports, Guidances and Additional Information
Biologics	www.fda.gov/BiologicsBloodVaccines/GuidanceComplianceRegulatoryInformation/default.htm www.fda.gov/BiologicsBloodVaccines/GuidanceComplianceRegulatoryInformation/ProceduresSOPPs/default.htm	• Guidance documents • Guidelines • ICH Guidelines • Standard Operating Procedures and Policies (SOPPs) - CBER

Meetings With FDA		
	Source	**Content**

Devices	*Guidance for Industry and CDRH Staff: Early Collaboration Meetings Under the FDA Modernization Act* (February 2001)
	
	Guidance for Industry and FDA Staff: Requests for Feedback on Medical Device Submissions: The Pre-Submission Program and Meetings with FDA Staff (February 2014)
		Types of Meetings:
		• Formal early collaboration meetings
		  o Agreement Meeting—purpose is to reach concurrence on the key parameters of the investigational plan
		  o Determination—limited to PMAs/PDPs, purpose is to determine the type of valid scientific evidence required to demonstrate that a device is safe and effective for its intended use
		• Presubmission Meetings—provide the sponsor an opportunity to obtain feedback and advice prior to submitting an IDE or marketing application
		• Submission Issue Meetings—are held at a sponsor's request to discuss deficiencies identified by FDA during review of a premarket submission
		• PMA Day-100 Meetings—scheduled to occur 100 days after a PMA is accepted for filing, these meetings provide an opportunity to discuss the application's review status and obtain additional information to complete the PMA review.

Drugs	*Guidance for Industry: Formal Meetings Between the FDA and Sponsors or Applicants* (May 2009) *Draft Guidance for Industry: Formal Meetings Between the FDA and Sponsors or Applicants of PDUFA Products* (March 2015)	Type A meetings—those necessary for an otherwise stalled product development program to proceed (a "critical path" meeting) or to address an important safety issue. Type A meetings generally are reserved for dispute resolution, discussion of clinical holds, Special Protocol Assessments, or post-action meetings requested within three months after an FDA regulatory action (other than an approval). A Type A meeting should be held within 30 days of FDA's receipt of a written request. A meeting package should be submitted to FDA at the same time as the meeting request. Type B meetings—pivotal development meetings occurring prior to progression to the next development stage. FDA will schedule Type B meetings within 60 days of receipt of a written request. FDA expects the sponsor to submit a meeting package at least four weeks before the formal meeting. Type B meetings include: Pre-IND meetings, certain End-of-Phase 1 meetings, End of Phase 2 meetings/Pre-Phase 3 meetings, Pre-NDA/BLA meetings, REMS meetings and post-action meetings requested three or more months after an FDA regulatory action (other than an approval). Type C meetings— any other product development meeting not included in Type A or B. According to FDA guidance, the agency will schedule Type C meetings within 75 days of receipt of a written request. Type C meeting packages should be submitted to FDA at least four weeks before the formal meeting
Biologics	*Guidance for Industry: Formal Meetings Between the FDA and Sponsors or Applicants* (May 2009) *Draft Guidance for Industry: Formal Meetings Between the FDA and Sponsors or Applicants of PDUFA Products* (March 2015)	Same as Drugs

Product License, Listing Requirements and Establishment Registration			
	Source	**Forms**	**Content**
Devices	21 CFR 807 21 CFR 860	Electronic - FDA Unified Registration and Listing Systems (FURLS) website	• Initial establishment registration • Annual registration of device establishment • Product listing • Device Classification: Class I, Class II or Class III • Combination Products (Device/Biologic or Device/Drug) Who must register—All owners/operators of any establishment, foreign or domestically-owned, engaged in the manufacture, preparation, compounding or processing of a medical device; those who initiate and develop specifications, manufacture, repackage, relabel, restore and commercially distribute a device; and initial distributors (US agents of foreign manufacturers), but not domestic distributors. All registration and listing information (Annual, Initial or Updates) must be submitted electronically unless FDA grants a waiver. There is a Device Facility User Fee requirement associated with registration.
Drugs	21 CFR 207 21 CFR 320 21 CFR 328-369 21 CFR 316	Drug Registration and Listing System (eDRLS) through the Electronic Submission Gateway (ESG)	• Initial drug establishment registration • Annual update of drug/biologic establishment • Drug product listing (every June and December, or at the registrant's discretion when a change occurs)· • Prescription Drugs • Generic Drugs • Over-the-Counter Drugs • Orphan Drugs • Combination Products (Drug/Device or Drug/Biologic) Who must register—Unless specifically exempted by law or regulation, all establishments, foreign or domestic, that manufacture or process drugs in the US are required to be registered with FDA and all drugs marketed within the US, including imported drugs, are required to be listed with the agency. All registration must be submitted electronically in the Drug Registration and Listing system of the ESG, using the SPL format, unless FDA grants a waiver. There are user fees associated with Registration and/or listing for prescription and generic drugs
Biologics	21 CFR 207 21 CFR 601 21 CFR 607 21 CFR 1271	Electronic Submission Gateway (ESG) Blood—Form 2830 HCT/Ps—Form 3356	• Establishment registration • Annual update of drug/biologic establishment • Drug product listing • Product licensing Biologics License Application (BLA) • Blood and blood product establishment registration and product listings • Combination products (biologic/device or biologic/drug) Who must register—All manufacturers of biological drug products. All owners and operators of human blood and blood product establishments must register their establishment annually. Human cell, tissue and cellular and tissue-based product establishments. Registration for some products must be submitted electronically using the SPL format, unless FDA grants a waiver. For blood and blood products, registration may be by mail or through the Electronic Blood Establishment Registration and Product Listing system (eBER). For HCT/Ps, registration may be via mail or through the Electronic Human Cell and Tissue Establishment Registration (eHCTERS). User fees are associated with registration and/or listing for some products.

Premarket Approval Submissions			
	Source	**Forms**	**Premarket Approval (PMA) Submissions**
Devices	21 CFR 814	3514 · Premarket Submission Cover Sheet	**PMA Required for:** • Any Class III device not on the market prior to 28 May 1976 • Pre-1976 devices after FDA "calls" for PMA
			PMA Sections: • Copy of Medical Device User Fee Cover Sheet (Form 3601) • CDRH Submission Cover Sheet/table of contents (optional) • Summary of submission • Indications for use • Device description • Description of intended existing alternative practices and procedures for device • Description of marketing history (foreign) • Summary of nonclinical and clinical data • Discussion of safety and efficacy • Device Master Record • Performance standards • Technical section • Published and unpublished reports on device • Sample of device(s) • Proposed labeling • Environmental assessment • Financial Certification of Disclosure • Certification of Compliance with Requirements of ClinicalTrials.gov Data Bank
			PMA Approval Criteria: Substantial evidence of safety and efficacy, which includes adequate and well-controlled investigations User fees apply to original PMAs and certain types of PMA supplements. Small businesses are eligible for reduced or waived fees
			Approval Time Frames: • 15-day administrative review and 45-day filing review • FDA is charged with making a decision to approve or not approve within 180 calendar days following receipt of a complete PMA.
			Possible Outcomes: • Approval, not approvable, denial • Summary of safety and effectiveness (S&E) written with FDA approval for public dissemination
Drugs	21 CFR 314	356h	**NDA or Abbreviated New Drug Application (ANDA) Required for:** • Any new drug: o A new drug is any drug not generally recognized as safe and effective before 1938 • An approved drug may be considered a new drug if it: o Contains a new substance (active ingredient, excipient, carrier, coating or other component) o Is a new combination of already approved drugs o Proportion of ingredients has been changed o s a new intended use of drug o Dosage, method or duration of administration or application is changed
			ANDA versus NDA: The ANDA is an abbreviated new drug submission. The ANDA submission does not include preclinical (animal) and clinical (human) data to establish safety and effectiveness.
			NDA or ANDA Sections: • Summary volume • Chemistry, manufacturing and controls • Samples, methods validation and labeling • Nonclinical pharmacology and toxicology • Human pharmacokinetics and bioavailability • Microbiology • Clinical data • Statistical section • Case reports and tabulations • Patent information • Patent certification • Debarment certification • Field copy certification • User Fee Cover Sheet • Certification of Compliance with Requirements of ClinicalTrials.gov Data Bank

Premarket Approval Submissions			
	Source	**Forms**	**Premarket Approval (PMA) Submissions**
			Common Technical Document Format: • Module 1: Regional information (forms, waivers, patent information, etc.) • Module 2: Table of Contents, Introduction, Quality Overall Summary, Nonclinical Overview and Summaries, Clinical Overview and Summary • Module 3: Quality • Module 4: Nonclinical Study Reports • Module 5: Clinical Study Reports (and ISS/ISE for US submissions) User fees are applicable for both NDAs and ANDAs A fee waiver or reduction for: • The first NDA of a small business • Applications for orphan products (exemption) • Applications for drugs providing a benefit to public health, or applications where the fees constitute a barrier to innovation An NDA may be submitted as paper or electronically, electronic preferred. Based on final guidance published in May 2015, FDA will require all NDAs, ANDAs and BLAs to be submitted electronically using the eCTD format by 5 May 2017. Content of label must be submitted electronically in Structured Product Label (SPL) format
			NDA Approval Criteria: Substantial evidence of safety and efficacy, based on adequate and well-controlled investigations

			Approval Timeframes:
			• Within 60 days of receipt, FDA must determine whether an NDA can be filed
			• *PDUFA V* review goals:
			  o Priority NDA: six months from FDA's filing date (rather than six months from receipt date, as in previous *PDUFAs*)
			  o Standard NDA: 10 months from FDA's filing date

			Possible Outcomes: • Approval Letter • "Complete Response" letter that lists all review deficiencies and steps the applicant should take to address these deficiencies in a future submission before the application can be approved. Refusal to file letter • Notification the application is withdrawn • Summary Basis of Approval (SBA) is available to public
Biologics	21 CFR 601	356h	**BLA:** Similar to NDA, filed for all biologics
	21 CFR 601.2		The following specified categories have modified requirements: • Therapeutic DNA plasmid products • Therapeutic synthetic peptides of 40 or fewer amino acids • Monoclonal antibodies for in vivo use • Therapeutic recombinant DNA-derived products
			User fees are applicable
	21 CFR 601.25		**Approval Time Frames:** Same as Drugs
			Possible Outcomes: Same as Drugs

Premarket Notification Submission		
	Source	**Premarket Notification Submission**
Devices	21 CFR 807, Subpart (e)	**510(k) Premarket Notification:** • Pertaining to Section 510(k) of *Medical Device Amendments* (1976) to *FD&C Act* • Preamendment devices on the market prior to 28 May 1976 are grandfathered • Required for devices introduced into commercial distribution after 28 May 1976 that have been classified as Class I or Class II devices when the device is: o First introduced into market (not substantially equivalent to predecessor) o Already marketed but introduced for the first time by manufacturer o Already marketed but has a change or modification to the device that could significantly affect its safety or effectiveness such as changes in design, material, chemical composition, energy source, manufacturing process o Has new intended use
	21 CFR Parts 862-892	**Exemptions From Premarket Notification:** • Almost all Class I devices, except Restricted Devices • Many Class II devices • Custom devices (devices not commercially available and created for a specific patient, physician or dentist) • Distributors of 510(k)-cleared devices with written permission of the manufacturer or 510(k) holder Initial post-amendment distribution of a pre-1976 Class III device requires a 510(k)—until FDA calls for a PMA; the 510(k) must include Class III certification and summary of safety and effectiveness
		Substantial Equivalence (SE) compares a new device to a legally marketed "predicate" device. **Requirements:** • Same technological characteristics as predicate device, or • Different technological characteristics but raises no new or different questions of safety or effectiveness, and • Same intended use as predicate device
		510(k) Content/Format CDRH Submission Cover Sheet (Optional): • Trade, common or classification name • Establishment registration number of submitter • Device classification
		Application Contents: • Device User Fee Cover Sheet (Form 3601), Certification of Compliance with ClinicalTrials.gov (Form 3674) • Proposed labeling (device description, specifications, intended use, directions for use) • Substantial equivalence information (comparison to predicate device) • Data demonstrating what effect modification or new intended use has on safety and effectiveness • 510(k) summary or statement Application should be accompanied by an "ecopy," an exact duplicate of the paper submission, on a CD, DVD or a flash drive
		Data Requirements: • The need for performance data depends on device complexity and ability to demonstrate equivalence to predicate based on use and technological • FDA may require human clinical data in a 510(k) to demonstrate SE for certain higher-risk devices
		***SMDA* Provisions:** • Manufacturer must receive written SE order before commercial distribution • 510(k) must include 510(k) summary or statement • Summaries and statements are made public 30 days after SE notice
		510(k) Review: • Review begins when CDRH logs in the submission • 90-day statutory requirement for FDA review (often exceeded) • Request for additional information puts submission on hold—180 days to respond. If no response, the 510(k) is withdrawn. The 90-day clock restarts when FDA receives additional data

Premarket Notification Submission		
	Source	**Premarket Notification Submission**
		510(k) Paradigm: • Traditional 510(k): standard filing • Special 510(k): option where device modification does not affect its intended use • Abbreviated 510(k): alternative to traditional 510(k) where a guidance document exists that provides reasonable assurance that the device's safety and effectiveness have been established
		Possible Outcomes: • SE, NSE, request additional information, withhold decision until financial disclosure statement is submitted, advise the 510(k) is not required • SE determination implies "clearance" to market device, not "approval" to market device
Drugs		No comparable mechanism
Biologics		**510(k):** some products regulated by CBER are by definition "medical devices", primarily blood banking equipment and tests.
		Appropriate biologic "devices" are submitted as 510(k)s to CBER.
		See Devices for procedure

Reporting/Recordkeeping Requirements for PMA, NDA or BLA Submissions and Application Maintenance and Changes			
	Source	**Forms**	**Reporting/Recordkeeping Requirements**
Devices	21 CFR 814		• *PMA Amendment* adds information or modifies a pending application: o Resets 180-day "clock" for a major addition or change; and Includes additional voluntary information or additional information requested by FDA • *PMA Supplement* is used for changes or modifications to a PMA approved device: o Normal 180-day review cycle • *Special PMA Supplement—Changes Being Effected* o Limited supplement changes can be made once FDA has acknowledged the submission is being processed • *30-day Notice:* Used for changes in manufacturing procedures or method of manufacturing that affect safety or effectiveness (if information is insufficient, FDA will instruct the applicant what is needed and the supplement will become a 135-day supplement) • *Periodic Reports* are updates or changes post-approval, which do not affect S&E; submitted after approval letter, in annual report or as indicated by FDA
Drugs	21 CFR 314.60 21 CFR 314.70	356h	• *NDA Amendment* adds information or modifies a pending application o Extension of up to 180-day review clock for a major amendment o Minor amendments do not extend the review time • NDA Supplements are used to submit changes to an approved NDA • Manufacturing supplements/changes are submitted as: o Changes requiring prior approval o Changes Being Effected (CBE) in 30 days o Changes Being Effected (0) (Changes may be made before FDA approval of supplement) or o Changes via Annual Report (minor changes)
	21 CFR 314.50 (d)(5)(vi)(b) 21 CFR 314.80 21 CFR 314.81 21 CFR 314.80 (c)(2)	3500A 2252	**Reporting:** • 120-day Safety Update Report: Due 120 days after NDA filing • Postmarketing 15-day Alert Report: (15 calendar days) for serious and unexpected adverse events • NDA Annual Report: o Due within 60 days of anniversary of date of approval; o Includes distribution data, labeling, CMC changes, nonclinical data and clinical data • NDA Field Alert: Three working days for failed batches, mistaken identification, contamination, etc. • Periodic Adverse Drug Experience Reports: Quarterly for three years after approval and then annually
Biologics		3486	Same as Drugs • Amendment: Submission of additional information to an unapproved license application • Supplement: Submission of changes to an approved license application • Manufacturing Supplement: Same as drugs • Biologics Deviation Report
	21 CFR 600.80	3500A VAERS-1 – for vaccines	**Reporting:** • 15-day Alert Report (15 calendar days) for serious and unexpected adverse events • BLA/NDA Annual Reports
			• Periodic Adverse Experience/Event Reports: Quarterly for three years after approval and then annually
			• Distribution Reports: Quantity of product distributed in US; due every six months

Requirements and Submissions for Clinical Investigations			
	Source	**Forms**	**Requirements and Submissions for Clinical Investigations**
Devices	21 CFR 812 21 CFR 50 21 CFR 56	3674-ClinicalTrials.gov Data Bank 3514—CDRH Prmarket Review Submission Cover Sheet 3454/3455—Investigator Financial Disclosure	• Investigational Device Exemption (IDE) • Informed Consent • Institutional Review Board (IRB) Review and Approval of Protocol and Informed Consent • Good Clinical Practice (GCP) • An IDE permits a device to be shipped in Interstate commerce for clinical investigations to determine its safety and effectiveness. The IDE regulation exempts the device from: o Misbranding and adulteration o Establishment registration and device listing o 510(k)/PMA o Performance standards o Banned devices o Restricted devices o QSRs/GMPs (except for 820.30 requirements) o Records and reports All clinical investigations of devices to determine safety and effectiveness require an approved IDE (from IRB, or IRB and FDA, depending on risk). No FDA user fees are required for IDEs.
	21 CFR 812.2(b)		**IDE Time Frame:** FDA will review and approve, approve with modification or disapprove an IDE application within 30 days of receipt. Requirements vary based on risk level. The determination of significant risk versus nonsignificant risk is made by the sponsor and approved by the IRB, but may be decided by FDA.
			Nonsignificant Risk Device Studies Require: • An abbreviated IDE • IRB approval (IDE submission to FDA is not required) • Labeling: "CAUTION-Investigational Device. Limited by Federal (or US) Law to Investigational Use" • For IVDs: "For Investigational Use Only. The performance characteristics of this product have not been established" • Informed consent • Study monitoring • Appropriate records and reports
	21 CFR 812.2(a)		**Significant Risk Device Studies Require:** • All the requirements (above) for nonsignificant risk devices • IDE application and approval from FDA • Final report to FDA and IRB
	21 CFR 812.2(c)		**Exempted Investigations:** • IVDs if for laboratory research or if for human patients, provided a legally marketed IVD is used for confirmation • Custom devices • Devices shipped for animal research • Consumer preference testing if not for determining safety or efficacy • Devices intended for veterinary use only
	21 CFR 812.40-46 21 CFR 54.4		**Sponsor Responsibilities:** • Select qualified investigators • Control distribution of devices • Monitor studies • Ensure investigator receives IRB approval • Submit IDE to FDA (if required) • Ensure FDA and IRB(s) are promptly informed of significant new investigation information

Requirements and Submissions for Clinical Investigations			
	Source	**Forms**	**Requirements and Submissions for Clinical Investigations**
	21 CFR 812.60-66 and 21 CFR 56 21 CFR 812.100		**IRB Responsibilities:** • Review and approve studies • Review and approval of informed consent • Protect the safety and welfare of subjects • Determine whether the device is significant or nonsignificant risk
	21 CFR 812.110 21 CFR 54.4		**Investigator Responsibilities:** • Get IRB approval before study • Conduct study per agreement • Follow protocol and FDA regulations • Control and supervise device use • Obtain informed consent
Drugs	21 CFR 312 21 CFR 50 21 CFR 56	1571 3674 1572 3454/3455	• Investigational New Drug Application (IND) • Informed Consent • IRB Review and Approval of Protocol and Informed Consent • Good Clinical Practice (GCP) An IND is submitted to FDA for notification of the intention to conduct clinical studies with a new drug or biologic and to request an exemption for shipping the unapproved drug or biologic. Required for new dosage form, new route of administration, new concentrations, new sponsor or manufacturer or new indication.
	21 CFR 310 21 CFR 320		**IND Types:** • Investigator • Treatment—for experimental drugs showing promise in clinical testing for serious or immediately life-threatening conditions • Emergency **IND Categories:** • Commercial • Research (non-commercial)
			Important IND Sections: • Introductory statement • General investigational plan • Investigator's brochure • Protocol • CMC information • Pharmacology and toxicology • Previous human experience Based on final guidance published in May 2015, FDA will require all INDs to be submitted electronically using the eCTD format by 5 May 2018. No FDA User Fees are required for INDs
			IND Time Frame: Effective in 30 days from FDA receipt unless clinical hold is placed on the study.
	21 CFR 312.50–53 and 21 CFR 54.4	1572	**Sponsor Responsibilities:** • Select qualified investigators • Obtain investigator records (including Statement of Investigator (Form 1572), Protocol Signature Page, CVs, Financial Disclosure) • Control distribution of drugs • Monitor studies • Ensure investigator receives IRB approval • Submit IND/Protocol to FDA (if required)

Requirements and Submissions for Clinical Investigations			
	Source	**Forms**	**Requirements and Submissions for Clinical Investigations**
	21 CFR 56.108–110		**IRB Responsibilities:** • Review and approve studies • Review and approval of informed consent • Protect the safety and welfare of subjects • Ensure risk to subjects is minimized
	21 CFR 312.60		**Investigator Responsibilities:** Same as Devices
Biologics	21 CFR 312 21 CFR 50 21 CFR 56	1571 3674	• Investigational New Drug Application (IND) • Informed Consent • IRB Review and Approval of Protocol and Informed Consent • Good Clinical Practice (GCP)
			IND Timeframe: Same as Drugs
			Sponsor Responsibilities: Same as Drugs
			IRB Responsibilities: Same as Drugs
			Investigator Responsibilities: Same as Devices

Reporting/Recordkeeping Requirements for Clinical Investigations			
	Source	**Forms**	**Requirements and Submissions for Clinical Investigations**
Devices	21 CFR 812.140		**Investigator Records:** • Correspondence • Device receipt, use, disposition • Subject records including o Informed consent o Adverse device effects o Device exposure date and times o Protocol and other records
	21 CFR 812.140		**Sponsor Records:** • NSR/SR decision • Correspondence • Device shipment and disposition • Investigator agreements and financial disclosure • Adverse device effects • Investigator list • IRB list and other records
	21 CFR 812.150		**Investigator Reports:** • Unanticipated Adverse Device Effects (10 working days) • Withdrawal of IRB approval • Progress reports, at least annually • Deviations from investigational plan • Informed consent • Final report (due to sponsor and IRB within three months of study termination or completion)
	21 CFR 812.150		**Sponsor Reports:** • Evaluation of unanticipated ADEs (10 working days) • Withdrawal of IRB approval • Withdrawal of FDA approval • Current Investigator list • Progress reports, at least annually (for NSR, submit to all reviewing IRBs; for SR, to all reviewing IRBs and FDA) • Recall and device disposition • Informed consent • Final report (for SR, notify FDA within 30 working days of the completion or termination and submit final report to FDA and all reviewing IRBs and investigators within 6 months. For NSR final report to all reviewing IRBs within 6 months.) • Significant risk determination
	21 CFR 812.140		**Record Retention:** For two years after the latter of • Date of study completion or termination, or • Date that records are no longer needed to support a PMA or notice of completion of a PDP
Drugs	21 CFR 312.62		**Investigator Records:** • Correspondence • Investigational drug receipt, use, disposition • Case histories o Informed consent o Source documentation (case report forms and medical records) o Safety reports o Protocol and other records o Laboratory information

Reporting/Recordkeeping Requirements for Clinical Investigations			
	Source	**Forms**	**Requirements and Submissions for Clinical Investigations**
	21 CFR 312.57		**Sponsor Records:** • Correspondence • Investigational drug shipment and disposition • Investigator agreements and financial disclosure • Protocol and amendments • Clinical study report and publications • Monitoring and safety reports (serious adverse events) • Investigator list • IRB list and other records • Decoding and randomization records (if applicable)
	21 CFR 312.64		**Investigator Reports:** • Progress reports (to sponsor and IRB; at least annually) • Safety reports • Final (study closure) report • Financial disclosure reports
	21 CFR 312.31 21 CFR 312.32 21 CFR 312.33	1571 3674 1571 3500A 1571	**Sponsor Reports:** • IND Information Amendments o Information amendments to an IND, such as new toxicology, chemistry, or other technical information or discontinuance of a clinical investigation must be submitted not more than every 30 days. • IND Safety Reports—to FDA, as well as all participating investigators o Telephone report—seven calendar days (either by phone or fax) o Unexpected fatal or life-threatening adverse experience (AE) associated with the use of the drug, with follow-up written report within eight additional calendar days o Written reports—15 calendar days o Serious and unexpected AE associated with the use of the drug • IND Annual Reports o Must be submitted within 60 days of the anniversary date when the IND became effective
	21 CFR 312.57 21 CFR 312.62		**Record Retention:** • Sponsor two years after NDA approval or, if no application is to be filed or if the application is not approved for such indication, two years after the investigation is discontinued and FDA is notified. • Investigator: same as sponsor
Biologics			**Sponsor and Investigator Records:** Same as Drugs
			Reporting: Same as Drugs
			Record Retention: Same as Drugs

Labeling Requirements		
	Source	**Labeling Requirements**
Devices	21 CFR 801	**General Requirements:** • Name and place of business • Intended use • Adequate directions (in layman terms) • Prominence of statements • English language (exceptions: product solely distributed in Puerto Rico or territories in which English is not the predominant language) • Unique device identifier (UDI)
	21 CFR 809 16 CFR 1500	**IVD Labeling:** • Proprietary and established names • Intended use • Statement of warnings or precautions • Name and place of business of manufacturer, packer or distributor • Lot or control number • For reagents, storage instructions, ingredients and quantity of contents • For laboratory phase IVD, not represented as effective, label must include "For Research Use Only" • For products undergoing testing prior to full commercial release, label must include "For Investigational Use Only. The performance characteristics of this product have not been established." • Directions for Use Exemption for general use laboratory reagents where the product is labeled "For Laboratory Use"
	21 CFR 801	**Exemptions from Directions for Use:** • Prescription devices require this statement on the label: "Caution: Federal Law restricts this device to the sale by or on the order of a physician" • Retail exemption (devices delivered to end user by or on order of a physician) • Devices having commonly known directions to the ordinary individual • Devices for processing, repacking, or manufacturing if the label bears the statement: "Caution: For manufacturing, processing or repacking" • In vitro diagnostic products • Devices used in teaching, research, law enforcement (nonclinical use)
	21 CFR 812.5	**IDE Labeling:** • Label must display name and place of manufacturer prominently • Contents of package • Statement: "Caution: Investigational Device. Limited by Federal (or US) Law to Investigational Use" • No representation device is safe and effective for its investigational use
	21 CFR 820, Subpart K	**QSR/GMP Labeling Requirements:** • Label integrity (maintain legibility) • Separation of operations • Label inspections (for accuracy) and release • Storage (prevent mix-ups) • Control number, if required for traceability
Drugs	21 CFR 201–202 21 CFR 208	**General Requirements:** • Label must bear prominently name and place of manufacturer, packer or distributor • Identify the quantity and dosage • National Drug Code requested to appear on all drug labels and labeling • Adequate directions for lay persons to use • No misleading statements misrepresenting drug • Statement of all ingredients with accurate names and proportions • Claims must be supported with clinical data • Label must state "Rx Only" for approved prescription drugs • Drugs scheduled by DEA must bear classification on label • English language (exceptions: product solely distributed in Puerto Rico or territories in which English is not the predominant language) • Bar code labels (with some exceptions)

Labeling Requirements		
	Source	**Labeling Requirements**
	21 CFR 201.100	**Exemptions From Directions for Use:** • In the possession of a person regularly and lawfully engaged in the manufacture, transportation, storage or wholesale distribution of prescription drugs • In the possession of a retail, hospital or clinic pharmacy, or public health agency, that is engaged regularly and lawfully in dispensing prescription drugs • In the possession of a practitioner licensed by law to administer or prescribe such drugs • New drugs under IND exemption • Drugs having commonly known directions • Inactive ingredients • Prescription chemicals and other prescription components (label must include "For prescription compounding") • Drugs for processing, repacking or manufacturing if the label bears the statement: "Caution: For manufacturing, processing or repacking" • Drugs used in teaching, research, law enforcement (nonclinical use).
	21 CFR 312.26	**IND Labeling:** Immediate investigational drug package must have label "Caution—New drug limited by Federal (or US) law to Investigational Use"
	21 CFR 211, Subpart G	**GMP Label Requirements:** • Label integrity (meets specifications) • Storage (prevent label mix-ups; limited access to labels) • Separation of operations (between drug products or dosage forms) • Labeling materials (inspection) • Gang printing of labels for different drug products is prohibited • Area Inspections (prior to labeling operation) • Reconciliation of labels issued and labels used • Destruction of Labels (after batch and lot are complete or obsolete/outdated)
Biologics	21 CFR 600, 606, 610 21 CFR 208	**General Requirements:** • Proper name of the product • Name, address and license of manufacturer or distributor • Lot number and other lot identification (including expiration date and recommended individual dose) • Adequate directions for lay persons to use (Medication Guide) • Statement of all ingredients with accurate names and proportions • Label must state "Rx only" for approved prescription biologics Additional information and precautionary measures are required of labels for biologics, depending on the product.
	21 CFR 211, Subpart G	**GMP Label Requirements:** Same as Drugs

Promotion and Advertising			
	Source	**Form**	**Promotion and Advertising**
Devices	FTC Act Section 5, 15 US Code 45		**Advertising Regulated by Federal Trade Commission (FTC):** FTC covers nonrestricted device advertising and requires • Claim substantiation and • Ads that are fair and not misleading FDA covers restricted medical devices, as well as unapproved and uncleared devices used in investigational settings FDA can deem the device misbranded if advertising promotes an intended use that is inconsistent with or not included in the device labeling.
	21 CFR 820.120		**PMA:** • Labeling approved in PMA • Restricted medical devices must bear the statement "Caution: Federal law restricts this device to sale, distribution, and use by or on the order of a (indicate type of practitioner and, if applicable, required training/experience, and facilities to which the use is restricted)." • "Full disclosure" in ads (warnings, cautions, adverse effects, etc.)
Drugs	21 CFR 202		**Advertising Regulated by:** • Rx Drugs: CDER's Office of Prescription Drug Promotion (OPDP) • OTC Drugs: FTC Noncompliance with the advertising regulations causes the drug to be "misbranded"
	21 CFR 314.81 21 CFR 314.550	2253	**NDA:** • All advertising and promotional labeling must be filed to the NDA at the time of initial dissemination or publication. • For drugs approved for serious and life-threatening diseases under accelerated approval, launch materials are reviewed by FDA prior to dissemination; after 120 days following market approval, promotional material must be submitted at least 30 days prior to dissemination. • Changes in labeling are reported in the Annual Report to an approved NDA or a supplemental NDA.
			Rx Drug Advertising • Cannot make safety or efficacy claims before product approval • Can promote a new product is coming unless product carries a boxed warning • Cannot promote use of a product for an indication not in the labeling • Promotional items cannot suggest off-label uses • Cannot be false, misleading or lacking in fair balance • Product comparisons must be supported by substantial clinical experience • Advertising must include a brief summary of side effects, contraindications and effectiveness • Promotional labeling must include a copy of the instructions for use. • Reminder advertisements are exempt from the brief summary requirement.
Biologics	21 CFR 601.45	2253	Advertising Regulated by CBER's Advertising and Promotional Labeling Branch (APLB)
	21 CFR 601.12		**BLA:** Same as Drugs
	21 CFR 601.45		**Biologics Advertising:** • Concurrent notification rather than preapproval required. Exception—products under Accelerated Approval for serious and life-threatening diseases under accelerated approval. Their launch materials are reviewed by FDA prior to dissemination; after 120 days following market approval, promotional material must be submitted at least 30 days prior to dissemination.

Postmarketing Adverse Experience/Event and Medical Device Reporting			
	Source	**Form**	**Postmarketing Adverse Experience/Event and Medical Device Reporting**
Devices	21 CFR 803	3500A	**MDR Reportable Event:** • Information reasonably suggesting a device may have caused or contributed to a death or serious injury, or • A malfunction has occurred that would be likely to cause or contribute to a death or serious injury if the malfunction recurred
	21 CFR 803.50-803.56	3500A	**Manufacturers and Initial Distributors Must Report Within:** • Five working days of an event requiring remedial action to prevent unreasonable risk of substantial harm to public health or after becoming aware of a reportable event for which FDA has made a written request, or • 30 calendar days after the manufacturer becomes aware of a reportable event
	21 CFR 803.30-803.33	3500A 3419	**User Facility Reporting:** • Report death to FDA and manufacturer within 10 work days • Report serious injury to manufacturer only or to FDA if manufacturer is unknown within 10 work days, and • Report annually to FDA the total number of deaths and serious injuries, with attached details or copies of 3500A forms.
			Domestic Distributor Requirements: Recordkeeping only
Drugs	21 CFR 314.80		**Serious Adverse Drug Experience (SADE):** Any adverse drug experience occurring at any dose that results any of the following outcomes: • Causes death • Threatens life • Requires or prolongs existing hospitalization • Causes persistent or significant disability or incapacity • Induces congenital anomaly/birth defect • Important medical event
			Adverse Drug Experience (ADE): Any adverse event associated with the use of a drug, whether or not drug-related including: • Use of drug in professional practice • Drug overdose • Drug abuse or withdrawal • Failure of expected pharmacological action
		3500A 356h 356h	**Postmarketing 15-day Alert Reports** • Needs to be filed for ADE that is: o Both serious and unexpected (not in labeling) o Foreign or domestic • No later than 15 calendar days after initial notification • Sources of ADE/SADE o Manufacturer o Healthcare professional o Consumer o Distributor o Foreign use o Literature o User facility • Periodic Reports—quarterly for the first three years after approval. Reports to be submitted within 30 days of the close of the reporting period. • Annual Reports thereafter, with the reports to be submitted within 60 days of the anniversary of the issuance of the product approval.
Biologics	21 CFR 314.80, 600.80		**Adverse Experience (AE):** AE reporting is any event associated with the use of a biological product in humans, whether or not it is considered product-related including: • Use of the biological product in professional practice • Biological product overdose • Biological product abuse or withdrawal • Failure of expected pharmacological action
			Serious Adverse Drug Experience: Same as Drugs
		3500A VAERS-1	**Postmarketing 15-day Alert Reports:** Same as Drugs · Reporting requirements are the same as for drugs, except vaccine AEs are reported on Vaccine Adverse Event Reporting System (VAERS) form.

Good Manufacturing Practice (GMP)/ Quality System Regulation (QSR)		
	Source	**GMP**
Devices	21 CFR 820	**Quality System Regulation (QSR):** QSR aligns US requirements with international quality standards (ISO 13485), including management responsibility and review, design controls, purchasing controls, process validation, service record keeping and review, corrective and preventative action and statistical techniques. Eliminates the distinction for critical devices. Subparts: A. General Provisions (scope, definitions, quality system) B. Quality System Requirements (management responsibility, quality audit, personnel including consultants) C. Design Controls D. Document Controls E. Purchasing Controls F. Identification and Traceability G. Production and Process Controls (production and process controls; inspection, measuring and test equipment; process validation) H. Acceptance Activities (receiving, in-process and finished device acceptance, acceptance status) I. Nonconforming Product J. Corrective and Preventive Action K. Labeling and Packaging Control (device labeling, device packaging) L. Handling, Storage, Distribution and Installation M. Records (general requirements, Device Master Record, Device History Record, Quality System Record, complaint files) N. Servicing O. Statistical Techniques Failure to comply renders the device Adulterated
Drugs	21 CFR 210–211	**Current GMP for Finished Pharmaceuticals:** A. General Provisions (scope, definitions) B. Organization and Personnel (responsibilities of quality control unit, personnel qualifications, personnel responsibilities, consultants) C. Buildings and Facilities (design, construction, lighting, air filtration, HVAC, plumbing, sewage and refuse, washing and toilet facilities, sanitation, maintenance) D. Equipment (design, size, location, construction, cleaning and maintenance, automatic, mechanical and electronic equipment, filters) E. Control of Components and Drug Product Containers and Closures (receipt and storage; testing and approval/rejection; use of approved components, containers, and closures; retesting rejected components, containers, and closures) F. Production and Process Controls (written procedures, deviations, charge-in of components, yield calculation, equipment identification, sampling and testing of in-process materials and products, time limitations on production, control of microbiological contamination, reprocessing) G. Packaging and Labeling Control (materials examination and usage criteria, labeling issuance, packaging and labeling operations, tamper-resistant packaging, drug product inspection, expiration dating) H. Holding and Distribution (warehousing procedures, distribution procedures) I. Laboratory Controls (general requirements, testing and release for distribution, stability testing, special testing requirements, reserve samples, laboratory animals, penicillin contamination) J. Records and Reports (general requirements, equipment cleaning and use log, component and drug product container, closure and labeling records, master production and control records, batch production and control records, production record review, laboratory records, distribution records, complaint files) K. Returned and Salvaged Drug Products
Biologics	21 CFR 210–211	**Same as Drugs Plus Additional Requirements:**

Good Manufacturing Practice (GMP)/ Quality System Regulation (QSR)		
	Source	**GMP**
	21 CFR 600, 606, and 610	**Biological Products—Subparts:** A. General Provisions (definitions) B. Establishment Standards (personnel, physical establishment, equipment, animals and care, records, retention samples, reporting of product deviations, temperatures during shipment) C. Establishment Inspections (inspectors, time of inspection, duties of inspector) D. Reporting of Adverse Experiences (postmarket reporting of adverse experiences, distribution reports, waivers)
	21 CFR 610	**General Biological Products Standards—Subparts** A. Release Requirements (Tests prior to release required for each lot. Requests for samples and protocol, official release.) B. General Provisions (equivalent methods and processes, potency, general safety, sterility, purity, identity, constituent materials, total solids in serums, permissible combinations, cultures) C. Standard Preparations and Limits of Potency D. Mycoplasma (test for mycoplasma) E. Testing Requirements for Communicable Disease Agents (test requirements, donor deferral, restrictions on use for further manufacture of medical devices, use of reference standards by makers of test kits, HIV and HCV "lookback" requirements) F. Dating Period Limitations (date of manufacture, dating periods for licensed biologics) G. Labeling Standards (container label, package label, proper name, legible type, divided manufacturing responsibility to be shown, name of selling agent or distributor, products for export, bar code label requirements)
	21 CFR 606	**Current GMP for Blood and Blood Components—Subparts:** A. General Provisions (definitions) B. Organization and Personnel C. Plant and Facilities D. Equipment (equipment, supplies and reagents) E. Reserved F. Production and Process Controls (standard operating procedures, plateletpheresis, leukapheresis, plasmapheresis) G. Additional Labeling Standards for Blood and Blood Components (labeling, general requirements, container label, instruction circular) H. Laboratory Controls (laboratory controls and compatibility testing) I. Records and Reports (records, distribution and receipt, procedures and records, adverse reaction file, reporting of product deviations)

Complaint Files		
	Source	**Complaint Files**
Devices	21 CFR 820.198	**Written Procedures Required for:** • Receiving, reviewing and evaluating complaints by a formally designated unit • Processing all complaints uniformly in a timely manner • Documenting oral complaints upon receipt • Evaluating complaints to determine whether an MDR reportable event has occurred • Reviewing and investigating device service reports that identify a reportable MDR event immediately
		Requirements: • The written record shall include the following information, if known o Name of the device o Date complaint was received o Any unique device identifier (UDI) or universal product code (UPC), and any other device identification(s) and control number(s) used o Name, address and phone number of complainant o Nature and details of complaint o Date and results of investigation o Any corrective action taken o Reply to complainant Complaints that are MDRs must be identified clearly
	21 CFR 820.180	**Complaint Retention:** All records shall be retained for a period of time equivalent to the device's design and expected life, but in no case less than two years from the date of release for commercial distribution by the manufacturer. Complaint file must be available during GMP inspection
Drugs	21 CFR 211.198	**Written Procedures Required for:** • Handling both written and oral complaints • Review to determine whether the complaint represents a serious and unexpected adverse drug experience.
		Requirements: • The written record shall include the following information, if known o Name and strength of the drug product o Lot number o Name of complainant o Nature of complaint o Reply to complainant o Investigator finding or reason an investigation was not necessary
		Complaint Retention: • Written records involving a drug product shall be maintained until at least one year after the expiration date of the drug product, or one year after the date the complaint was received, whichever is longer. Complaint file must be available during an FDA GMP inspection
Biologics		Same as Drugs

FDA Inspections			
	Source	**Form**	**FDA Inspections**
Devices	*FD&C Act* Section 704 21 CFR 814.44–45		**FDA May Inspect All Companies That Manufacture, Process, Pack or Hold FDA-Regulated Products Including:** • Domestic manufacturing companies • Contract testing laboratories • Clinical study sponsors, monitors and investigator sites • IRBs • Contract Research Organizations (CROs) • Foreign companies
			Types of Inspections (Routine or For Cause): • GMP/QSR Compliance (routine surveillance, establishment license, or pre-approval) • GLP Compliance • GCP Compliance (Sponsor or investigational site)
			FDA May Not Inspect: • Sales data, except shipment information • Retail or hospital pharmacies regulated by state law • Financial and pricing information • Personnel files (other than qualifications) • Internal audit files • Research data other than those subject to FDA inspection
		482	**Inspector** should present credentials and a Notice of Inspection
		483	**Inspectional Observations**—Issued to management at the end of an inspection when an investigator(s) has observed any conditions that may constitute violations of the *FD&C Act* or related regulations Upon receipt of the 483, the manufacturer has 15 working days to respond, in writing, with detailed corrective action plan
		484	**Receipt for Samples**
			Establishment Inspection Report—Narrative review of the inspection, the inspector's findings and evidence to support FDA's findings. The EIR classifies the inspection as No Action Indicated (NAI), Voluntary Action Indicated (VAI) or Official Action Indicated (OAI).
Drugs	*FD&C Act* Section 704		**Same as Devices**
Biologics	PHS Act Section 262 21 CFR 600.20		**Same as Devices**

Lot and Batch Release Requirements		
	Source	**Lot and Batch Release Requirements**
Devices	21 CFR 820.80	Review the activities required in the Device Master Record (DMR) to ensure they are completed and signed-off, with date of finished device acceptance by a designated individual. Sterile devices require review of sterility test results before release
Drugs	21 CFR 211.165	Lot must comply with release specifications in compendia or as negotiated and approved by FDA during the application review and approval process. Acceptance criteria for the sampling and testing conducted by the quality control unit shall be adequate to assure batches of drug products meet appropriate specification and statistical quality control criteria for their approval and release.
Biologics	21 CFR 610.1	**Same as Drugs.** If product is subject to lot release (e.g., vaccines), lots cannot be distributed until they are released by CBER, which reviews samples and protocols.

Traceability Requirements		
	Source	**Traceability Requirements**
Devices	21 CFR 820.65 21 CFR 821	Traceability required for devices intended for surgical implant or a device to support or sustain life whose failure to perform when properly used in accordance with the instructions for use provided in the labeling can be reasonably expected to result in a significant injury. Procedures, documented in Device History Record, should be established to identify unit, lot or batch of finished devices and, where appropriate, key components with a control number that facilitates corrective action. In addition to traceability requirements, FDA has identified specific devices that require tracking, as specified in 21 CFR 821.1(a): the failure of the device would be reasonably likely to have serious adverse health consequences; or the device is intended to be implanted in the human body for more than one year; or the device is a life-sustaining or life-supporting device used outside a device user facility. The manufacturer should adopt a method of tracking to enable it to provide FDA with the following information for each device distributed: -within three working days of an FDA request, before distribution of a tracked device to a patient, the distributor name and contact information of the distributor(s) and the location of the device; -within 10 working days of an FDA request for tracked devices, after distribution or implantation, the UDI or other identifier, date shipped and date to patient, patient and physician information
Drugs	21 CFR 211, Subpart J *Drug Supply Chain Security Act* of 2013	All manufacturing records and QC test results, forward and backward traceability from raw materials to finished product In addition, Title II of the *Drug Quality and Security Act* of 2013 (*DQSA*), also called the *Drug Supply Chain Security Act* (*DSCSA*), adds a mandate to implement an electronic track and trace system to identify and trace certain prescription drugs throughout the US supply chain. Its requirements will be implemented in stages over 10 years. Two main provisions have 2015 deadlines: • 1 January 2015—manufacturers, repackagers and wholesale distributors must provide lot-level product tracing, transaction information, history, and statement • 1 July 2015—dispensers (primarily pharmacies) must provide lot-level product tracing, transaction information, history and statement
Biologics	21 CFR 211, Subpart J 21 CFR 600.12 21 CFR 606.160 21 CFR 1271.290	**Same as Drugs** Tracking of blood-derived products from collection through processing, storage and distribution Tracking of human cells, tissues, and cellular and tissue-based products requires establishing and maintaining a system to track all HCT/Ps from: (i) The donor to the consignee or final disposition; and (ii) The consignee or final disposition to the donor.

Retention of Product Samples		
	Source	**Retention of Product Samples**
Devices	21 CFR 58	No requirement for devices except where required by specific company procedures or GLP
Drugs	21 CFR 211.170	**Active Ingredient:** • Reserve sample consists of at least twice the quantity necessary for all tests required (except sterility and pyrogen testing) • Retention time depends on the active ingredient; in general, one reserve sample from each lot shall be retained for one year after expiration date of the last lot of the drug product containing the active ingredient
		Radioactive Active Ingredient: • Three months after the last lot if expiration dating period is less than 30 days or • Six months after the last lot if expiration dating period is more than 30 days • Samples for OTC drugs exempt from bearing an expiration date should be retained three years after distribution of the last lot
		The reserve sample of each lot of drug product must be stored under the same conditions as the label indicates and must be visually examined at least once per year
Biologics	21 CFR 600.13	• At least six months after the expiration date unless a different time period is specified in additional standards • Stored at temperatures and conditions to maintain identity and integrity • Quantity must be sufficient for examination and testing of potency • At least one final container as a final package

Import and Export Requirements			
	Source	**Form**	**Import and Export Requirements**
Devices	*FDERA*		**Import for Domestic Distribution:** Foreign establishments must meet US applicable medical device regulations, including establishment registration, device listing, QSR manufacturing, MDR and 510(k) or PMA, if applicable. Foreign manufacturers also must designate a US Agent who assists FDA communicating with the foreign establishment, responds to questions about the foreign establishment's devices imported to the US and assists FDA in scheduling inspections of the foreign establishment if FDA unable to contact the foreign establishment directly or expeditiously, FDA may provide documents to the US agent. An initial importer must register its establishment with FDA, follow MDRs, corrections and removals and tracking, if applicable.
	FD&C Act Sections 801–802		**Export:** Devices legally marketed in the US may be exported to anywhere in the world without prior FDA notification or approval. All devices not cleared for marketing in US must: • Meet the purchaser's specifications • Not conflict with the importing country's laws • Be labeled for export only • Not be sold in domestic commerce • May require Certificate of Exportability (COE) or Certificate of Foreign Government (CFG) Class III devices with no PMA require FDA approval to export Alternative (Section 802) for Class III devices with no PMA does not require FDA approval to export; only require "simple notification" – with restrictions Requests for Export Permit Letters and Simple Notifications can be submitted via CDRH Export Certification Application and Tracking System (CECATS).
Drugs	21 CFR 312.110 21 CFR 314.410		**Import for Domestic Distribution:** • Imports comply with requirements if subject to IND • In US, the sponsor, a qualified investigator or a domestic agent of foreign sponsor, can be consignee • New drug may be imported if it is the subject of an approved application • Foreign manufacturers of drug substances and drug products that wish to import products must have a US agent and are required to register with FDA
	FDERA		**Export of Investigational Drug** • Exports can be done under IND but not required • Each person who received drug should be an investigator named in application
			Export of Approved Drug: • New drug may be exported if it is the subject of an approved application • Exporter must be listed as supplier in approved application, and the drug substance intended for export meets the specifications of—and is shipped with—a copy of the labeling required for the approved drug product Anyone exporting a drug may submit an application for export certification for approved drug products, OTC products, unapproved drug products, homeopathic drugs and API or bulk drug substances. Submit request for Certificate of Pharmaceutical Product, using form 3613b
Biologics	*FDERA*		Same as Drugs Submit request through the Biologics Export Certificate Application and Tracking System (BECATS).

FDA Enforcement Options			
	Source	**Form**	**FDA Enforcement Options**
Devices	*FD&C Act* Sections 301–304 21 CFR 812.119 *Safe Medical Devices Act* of 1990	483	• Withdrawal of product approval • Criminal actions against investigator • Disqualified investigator • Inspections • Warning Letters • Untitled Letters • Adverse publicity • Recalls (mandatory and voluntary) • Alert List • Import alert • Civil monetaryy penalties • Application Integrity Policy (AIP) investigation and enforcement (third-party review of data) • Injunctions, seizures, criminal actions • Request to state agencies to take action
Drugs	*FD&C Act* Sections 301–304 *Generic Drug Enforcement Act of 1992*	483	**Same as Devices**, also: • Debarment of individuals or corporations • Dear Doctor letter
Biologics	*FD&C Act* Sections 301–304	483	**Same as Devices and Drugs**

Field Corrections and Recalls		
	Source	**Field Corrections and Recalls**
Devices	21 CFR 7 21 CFR 806 21 CFR 810	Enforcement/Recall Policy Medical Device Corrections and Removals Medical Device Recall Authority
	21 CFR 806	**Recall:** Recall Classification: Class I (most serious), II or III (least serious) assigned by FDA) Device recalls may be either voluntary (firm initiated or at FDA request) or mandatory by FDA order Mandatory Reports of Corrections/Removals (usually only Class I or II) required for any firm-initiated removal/correction conducted to: • Reduce risk to health posed by a device or • Remedy a violation of the *FD&C Act* caused by a device, which may present risk to health Written report required within 10 working days of removal/correction. Class III recalls have FDA recordkeeping, but not reporting requirements.
	21 CFR 810	**Mandatory Medical Device Recall:** Cease Distribution and Notification order is issued by FDA if the agency finds a reasonable probability a distributed device would cause serious adverse health consequences or death. The order requires a manufacturer to • Cease distribution • Notify healthcare professionals and user facilities • Instruct professionals and user facilities to cease use of the device If, after a chance for hearing and further review, FDA determines devices in distribution pose a risk, the agency may amend the order and require a recall.
		Recall Strategy Elements Must Include: • Depth of recall • Public warning • Effectiveness checks FDA will review the strategy and may suggest changes
Drugs	21 CFR 7 21 CFR 314.81	**Same as Devices Except:** NDA Field Alert—Within three working days, a field alert must be sent to FDA district office for distributed product that has contamination, change, deterioration or labeling causing mistaken identity. Recalls are voluntary and may be firm-initiated or requested by FDA. "FDA-requested" recall must begin immediately. For firm-initiated recall, notify district office and it will assign the recall to a class.
Biologics	21 CFR 7 21 CFR 600.14	**Same as Drugs Except:** Biologic Product Deviation Report (Form FDA 3486) —filed within 45 calendar days concerning any event, and information relevant to the event, associated with the manufacturing, to include testing, processing, packing, labeling or storage, or with the holding or distribution, of a licensed biological product, if that event meets all the following criteria: (1) Either: (i) represents a deviation from current Good Manufacturing Practice, applicable regulations, applicable standards or established specifications that may affect that product's safety, purity or potency; or (ii) represents an unexpected or unforeseeable event that may affect that product's safety, purity or potency; and (2) occurs in the sponsor's facility or another facility under contract with the sponsr; and (3) Involves a distributed biological product.

Corrective and Preventive Action Requirements		
	Source	**Corrective and Preventive Action Requirements**
Devices	21 CFR 820.100	Requires manufacturers to establish procedures for: • Analyzing processes, operations, audit reports, quality and service records, complaints, returned devices and other information to identify existing and potential causes of nonconforming product • Investigating the cause of nonconformities • Identifying the action needed to correct and prevent recurrence of nonconforming product • Verifying and validating the corrective and preventive action is effective • Implementing and recording changes in methods and procedures needed to effect the corrective and preventive action • Ensuring information related to nonconforming product and corrective and preventive action is disseminated to persons responsible for ensuring quality and preventing such problems • Submitting relevant information for management review
Drugs	21 CFR 211.22 *Guidance for Industry: Quality Systems Approach to Pharmaceutical CGMP Regulations* (September 2006)	**Same as Devices** Quality control unit approves or rejects all components and drug products and investigates errors or out-of-specification lots.
Biologics		**Same as Drugs**

Misbranding		
	Source	**Misbranding**
Devices	*FD&C Act* 501-502	**Failure to:** • File a 510(k) • Provide information as required • Have advertisements approved by FDA, if required • List device • Register establishment • Comply with notification or recall order or • Comply with postmarket surveillance order
	         FD&C Act Section 518	**Misbranding:** • False or misleading labeling including advertising and promotional materials • Label does not contain manufacturer's name and address in required prominence • Label does not contain quantity of contents • Required wording is not displayed prominently • Label does not contain adequate directions for use • Device is dangerous to health when used as prescribed • Product does not comply with color additive provision of the act • Device does not adhere to performance standard if applicable • Failure to comply (notification, reporting, recordkeeping) • Impression of official approval, based on registration and clearance of 510(k)
Drugs	*FD&C Act* 501-502 21 CFR 201	**Misbranding** • Labeling is false or misleading • Packaged form does not bear name of manufacturer, packer or distributor • Required information does not appear or is not prominently placed • Habit-forming substance does not bear habit-forming warning • Generic established name is less than one half the size of the trade/brand name • Not listed in official compendium • Packaging is misleading • Subject to deterioration without precautions • Labeling does not bear adequate directions for use • Drug is dangerous to health when used as suggested in the accompanying labeling • Antibiotic certificate of release, if required, was not issued • False or misleading advertisements or descriptive printed materials • Manufacturer not registered or drug not listed • Packaging or labeling does not comply with the *Poison Prevention Packaging Act* • Container is misleading
Biologics		Same as Drugs

Adulteration		
	Source	**Adulteration**
Devices	*FD&C Act* Section 501(a)–(d)	• Not manufactured under GMPs • Contaminated and defective product • Class III device for which PMA: o is not filed o is not approved or o has been suspended or withdrawn • Marketed Class III device without a PMA before FDA down-classified the device as Class I or II • Banned device • Strength, purity or quality fall below what they are represented to be • Not in conformance with a performance standard. • Contains unsafe color additives • Failure to comply with approved IDE requirements
Drugs	*FD&C Act* Section 501(a)–(d)	**If the Drug:** • Consists of filthy, putrid or decomposed substance • Has been prepared, packed or held under unsanitary conditions • Methods used in, or facilities or controls used for its manufacture do not conform to GMPs or • Strength differs from or purity is less than stated in the labeling • Mixture with or substitution of another substance
Biologics		**Same as Drugs**

Glossary

30-day Hold
Time period between filing a protocol under an IND and FDA approval to proceed with enrollment. Also, the time period between when a company submits an IND and when it can initiate a protocol. This timeline may be extended if FDA does not agree with the proposed protocol. (See "Clinical Hold.")

120-day Safety Report
Amendment to an NDA containing a safety update due 120 days after the NDA is filed.

180-day Exclusivity
Protects an ANDA applicant from competition from subsequent generic versions of the same drug product for 180 days.

505(b)(2) Application
An application submitted under section 505(b)(2) of the *FD&C Act* for a drug for which one or more of the investigations relied on by the applicant for approval of the "application were not conducted by or for the applicant and for which the applicant has not obtained a right of reference or use from the person by or for whom the investigations were conducted" (21 U.S.C. 355(b)(2)).

510(k)
Traditional 510(k): A premarket notification submitted to FDA to demonstrate the medical device to be marketed is as safe and effective or "substantially equivalent" to a legally marketed device. 510(k) refers to the section of the *FD&C Act* authorizing the submission of the premarket notification.

Special 510(k): A type of 510(k) submission for device modifications neither affecting the intended use nor altering its fundamental scientific technology. FDA processing time is 30 days.

Abbreviated 510(k): A type of 510(k) submission supported by conformance with guidance document(s), special controls or standards.

513(g) Request for Information
When it is unclear into which classification a device falls, a provision in Section 513(g) of the *FD&C Act* allows the device sponsor to request a classification determination and regulatory information from FDA. This requires a letter with a description of the device and a fee payment

515 Program Initiative
Created to facilitate reclassification action on the remaining pre-amendments Class III 510(k)s.

A

AABB
American Association of Blood Banks

ACBTSA
Advisory Committee on Blood and Tissue Safety and Availability

Accelerated Approval
Allows earlier approval of drugs to treat serious diseases and those filling an unmet medical need based on a surrogate endpoint.

Accredited Persons Program
FDA program accrediting third parties to conduct the primary review of 510(k)s for eligible devices.

ACE
Adverse Clinical Event

ACRP
Association for Clinical Research Professionals

Action Letter
Official communication from FDA informing an NDA or BLA sponsor of an agency decision; includes approvable, not approvable and clinical hold.

Active Ingredient
Any drug component intended to furnish pharmacological activity or other direct effect in the diagnosis, cure, mitigation, treatment or prevention of disease, or to affect the structure or any function of the body of man or other animals.

ADE
Adverse Drug Event or Adverse Drug Experience

ADME
Absorption, Distribution, Metabolism and Excretion

ADR
Adverse Drug Reaction

ADUFA
Animal Drug User Fee Act of 2003

ADUFA II
Animal Drug User Fee Amendments of 2008

ADUFA III
Animal Drug User Fee Amendments of 2013

Adulterated
Product containing any filthy, putrid or decomposed substance; or prepared under unsanitary conditions; or not made according to GMPs; or containing an unsafe color additive; or does not meet the requirements of an official compendium. (*FD&C Act*, SEC. 501 [351])

AdvaMed
Advanced Medical Technology Association

Advisory Committee
Committees and panels used by FDA to obtain independent expert advice on scientific, technical and policy matters.

AE
Adverse Event

AERS
See FAERS.

AFDO
Association of Food and Drug Officials

AGDUFA
Animal Generic Drug User Fee Act of 2008

AGDUFA II
Animal Generic Drug User Fee Act of 2013

AHRQ
Agency for Healthcare Research and Quality

AIA
America Invents Act of 2011

AIP
Application Integrity Policy. FDA's approach to reviewing applications that may be affected by wrongful acts raising significant questions regarding data reliability.

ALCOA
Attributable, legible, contemporaneous, original and accurate. Acronym used by FDA to describe data quality.

AMDUCA
Animal Medicinal Drug Use Clarification Act of 1994

Amendment
Additions or changes to an ANDA, NDA, BLA, PMA or PMA supplement still under review. Includes safety updates. Any updates to an IND or an IDE prior to approval are also called amendments.

AMS
Agricultural Marketing Service (USDA)

ANADA
Abbreviated New Animal Drug Application

Analyte
In a clinical trial, the part of the sample the test is designed to find or measure.

ANDA
Abbreviated New Drug Application. Used for generic drugs.

Animal Drugs@FDA
Database allowing users to search for approved animal drug products, suitability petitions, sponsors, the *Green Book*, CFR, *FR*, patents and exclusivity.

Animal Rule
Provides for approval of certain new drug and biological products based on animal data when adequate and well-controlled efficacy studies in humans cannot be ethically conducted because the studies would involve administering a potentially lethal or permanently disabling toxic substance or organism to healthy human volunteers and field trials are not feasible prior to approval.

Anti-Kickback Statute
Prohibits offering, paying, soliciting or receiving anything of value to induce or reward referrals or generate federal healthcare program business.

Annual Report
An annual periodic report or progress report required to be submitted to FDA. Depending on the type of application for which the report is submitted, it may include new safety, efficacy and labeling information; preclinical and clinical investigation summaries; CMC updates; nonclinical laboratory studies; and completed unpublished clinical trials.

ANPR
Advance Notice of Proposed Rulemaking

APhA
American Pharmacists Association

APHIS
Animal and Plant Health Inspection Service

API
Active Pharmaceutical Ingredient

APLB
Advertising and Promotional Labeling Branch (CBER)

Approved
FDA designation given to drugs, biologics and medical devices granted marketing approval.

AQL
Acceptable Quality Level

ASTM
American Society of Testing and Materials

ASQ
American Society for Quality (formerly ASQC)

ASR
Analyte Specific Reagents

ATF
Bureau of Alcohol, Tobacco, Firearms and Explosives

AUT
Actual Use Trials

B

BA/BE Studies
Bioavailability and bioequivalence studies.

Bad Ad Program
Truthful Prescription Drug Advertising and Promotion. Education program for healthcare providers to ensure prescription drug advertising and promotion is truthful and not misleading. Administered by CDER's Office of Prescription Drug Promotion (OPDP).

BACPAC
Bulk Actives Chemical Postapproval Changes

Banned Device
Device presenting a substantial deception, unreasonable risk of injury or illness, or unreasonable direct and substantial danger to public health.

BIMO
Bioresearch Monitoring Program

BIO
Biotechnology Industry Organization

Bioequivalence
The absence of a significant difference in the rate and extent to which the active ingredient or active moiety in pharmaceutical equivalents or pharmaceutical alternatives becomes available at the site of drug action when administered at the same molar dose under similar conditions in an appropriately designed study.

Biologic
A virus, therapeutic serum, toxin, antitoxin, vaccine, blood, blood component or derivative, allergenic product, protein (except any chemically synthesized polypeptide), or analogous product, or arsphenamine or derivative of arsphenamine (or any other trivalent organic arsenic compound) applicable to the prevention, treatment or cure of a disease or condition of human beings.

Biosimilar
Under the *BPCI Act*, a biological product may be demonstrated to be "biosimilar" if data show, among other things, the product is "highly similar" to an already-approved biological product.

Bioterrorism Act
Public Health Security and Bioterrorism Preparedness and Response Act of 2002

BLA
Biologics License Application

Blinded Study
Clinical trial in which the patient (single-blind) or patient and investigator (double-blind) are unaware of which treatment the patient receives. Involves use of multiple treatment groups such as other active, placebo or alternate dose groups. Sometimes referred to as "masked."

Boxed Warning
Drugs with special problems, particularly ones that may lead to death or serious injury, may have this warning information displayed within a box in the prescribing information. This often is referred to as a "boxed" or "black box" warning. Drugs with such boxed warnings are not permitted to have reminder ads.

BPCA
Best Pharmaceuticals for Children Act of 2002

BPCI Act
Biologics Price Competition and Innovation Act of 2009

BPDR
Biological Product Deviation Report

Breakthrough Therapy Designation
A new pathway to expedite the development of therapies showing substantial promise in early clinical trials. A drug company may seek Breakthrough Therapy designation if the drug is developed for a serious and life-threatening disease and preliminary clinical evidence shows the drug may offer substantial improvement over existing therapies on one or more clinically significant endpoints.

BsUFA
Biosimilar User Fee Act

C

CAPA
Corrective and Preventive Actions

CBE-30
Changes Being Effected in 30 days. A submission to an approved application reporting changes FDA has identified as having moderate potential to adversely affect drug product identity, strength, quality, purity and potency. The supplement must be received by FDA at least 30 days before product distribution.

CBER
Center for Biologics Evaluation and Research

CBP
US Customs and Border Protection

CDC
Centers for Disease Control and Prevention

CDER
Center for Drug Evaluation and Research

CDRH
Center for Devices and Radiological Health

CDx
Companion Diagnostic

CECATS
CDRH Export Certification Application and Tracking System

CF
Consent Form. Document used to inform a potential subject of the risks and benefits of a clinical trial per the Declaration of Helsinki. Sometimes referred to as ICF (Informed Consent Form) or ICD (Informed Consent Document).

CFG
Certificate to Foreign Government. Required by certain countries to prove an exported product can be legally marketed in the US.

CFR
Code of Federal Regulations

CFSAN
Center for Food Safety and Applied Nutrition

CGMP
Current Good Manufacturing Practice

CGT Products
Cellular and gene therapy products

CGTP
Current Good Tissue Practice

CH
Clinical Hold

CIOMS
Council for International Organizations of Medical Sciences

CIR
Cosmetic Ingredient Review

Class I Device
Low-risk device requiring general controls to ensure safety and effectiveness.

Class II Device
Requires general and special controls to ensure safety and effectiveness. Special controls may include guidance documents, mandatory performance standards, patient registries for implantable devices and postmarket surveillance. Requires 510(k), unless exempted; may require clinical trials.

Class III Device
Requires general controls and premarket approval (PMA); includes devices that are life-sustaining, life-supporting or pose significant potential for risk to patient, or are not substantially equivalent to Class I or Class II devices. PMAs almost always require clinical trials.

Clearance
Devices that receive marketing permission through the 510(k) process based on demonstrating substantial equivalence to a pre-amendment device or another device reviewed under section 510(k) of the *FD&C Act*.

CLIA
Clinical Laboratory Improvement Amendments of 1988

Clinical Hold
FDA order to delay proposed clinical investigation or suspend an ongoing investigation.

Clinical Investigator
A medical researcher in charge of carrying out a clinical trial's protocol.

ClinicalTrials.gov
A registry and results database of federally and privately supported clinical trials conducted in the US and around the world. Operated by NIH.

CLSI
Clinical and Laboratory Standards Institute (formerly National Committee for Clinical Laboratory Standards)

CMC
Chemistry, Manufacturing and Controls

CME
Continuing Medical Education

CMS
Centers for Medicare & Medicaid Services

COA
Clinical outcomes assessment. Directly or indirectly measures how patients feel or function and can be used to determine whether a drug has been demonstrated to provide a treatment benefit.

Codex Alimentarius Commission
Develops harmonized international food standards, guidelines and codes of practice to protect the health of consumers and ensure fair practices in the food trade.

COE
Certificate of Exportability. Required by certain countries for the export of unapproved devices not sold or offered for sale in the US; issued by FDA to the exporter.

Combination Product
Defined in 21 CFR 3.2(e) as a combination of two or more different types of regulated products, i.e.:
a drug and a device
a device and a biological product
a drug and a biological product
a drug, a device and a biological product

Commercial Distribution
Any distribution of a device intended for human use, which is offered for sale but does not include: internal or interplant transfer within the same parent, subsidiary or affiliate company any device with an approved exemption for investigational use.

Common Rule
Requires the research institution's IRB to ensure each research protocol contains adequate provisions to protect a subject during the course of the study.

Companion Diagnostic
An in vitro diagnostic device or an imaging tool providing information essential for the safe and effective use of a corresponding therapeutic product.

Complaint
Any written, electronic or oral communication alleging deficiencies related to a product's identity, quality, durability, reliability, safety, effectiveness or performance after release for distribution.

Component
Any ingredient or part intended for use in the manufacture of a drug, device, cosmetic, biologic or IVD product, including those not appearing in the finished product.

Consent Decree
Enforcement action carried out by the Justice Department. An agreement between FDA and a company outlining steps to correct CGMP violations by placing severe restrictions on company operations to ensure the firm comes into compliance.

COOL
Country of Origin Labeling. Requirements for source labeling for food products (USDA)

Cosmetic
Articles intended to be rubbed, poured, sprinkled or sprayed on, introduced into or otherwise applied to the human body or any part thereof for cleansing, beautifying, promoting attractiveness or altering appearance; and, articles intended for use as a component of any such article; except such term shall not include soap.

CPG
Compliance Policy Guide

CPGM
Compliance Program Guidance Manual

CPI
Critical Path Initiative

CPMP
Committee for Proprietary Medicinal Products (EU)

CPSC
Consumer Product Safety Commission

CRA
Clinical Research Associate

CRC
Clinical Research Coordinator

CRF
Case Report Form. Paper or electronic document used to record data collected in a clinical trial.

Critical Path Initiative
FDA's effort to stimulate and facilitate a national effort to modernize the scientific process through which a potential human drug, biological product or medical device is transformed from a discovery or "proof of concept" into a medical product.

CR Letter
Complete response letter. Communicates FDA's decision to a drug company its new drug application (NDA) or abbreviated new drug application (ANDA) to market a new or generic drug will not be approved in its present form.

CRO
Contract Research Organization

CSO
Consumer Safety Officer. Often the FDA contact person for sponsors. Also known as the regulatory project manager.

CTD
Common Technical Document

CTFA
Cosmetic, Toiletry and Fragrance Association

CTP
Center for Tobacco Products

Custom Device
A device:
deviating from devices generally available
deviating from an applicable performance standard or PMA requirement in order to comply with the order of a physician or dentist
not generally available in finished form for purchase or dispensing by prescription
not offered for commercial distribution through labeling or advertising, is intended for use by an individual patient named in the order of a physician or dentist, and ade in a specific form for that patient
intended to meet the special needs of the physician or dentist

CVB
Center for Veterinary Biologics (USDA)

CVM
Center for Veterinary Medicine (FDA)

D

DARRTS
Document Archiving, Reporting, and Regulatory Tracking System (CDER)

D&D
Design and Development Plan

DDT
Drug Development Tools

DEA
Drug Enforcement Administration

Dear Health Care Professional (DHCP) letter
Correspondence mailed by a manufacturer and/or distributor to physicians and/or other health care professionals to convey important information about drugs or devices. DHCP letters are considered promotional labeling and may be associated with recalls or device corrections or removals. These letters can be requested by FDA or initiated by the applicant.

Debarment
An official action in accordance with 21 CFR 1404 to exclude a person from directly or indirectly providing services in any capacity to a firm with an approved or pending drug or device product application. A debarred corporation is prohibited from submitting or assisting in the submission of any NDA or ANDA. Equivalent to disqualification for devices requiring a PMA submission.

Declaration of Helsinki
Ethical principles for medical research involving human subjects. Trials conducted under Good Clinical Practice generally follow the Declaration of Helsinki.

Default Decree
A court order entered when a seized article is not claimed or defended. The order condemns the article as being in violation of the law and provides for its destruction, donation to charity, sale or disposal as the court may elect to decree.

***De Novo* Process**
Provides a route to market for low to moderate risk medical devices, but have been classified in Class III because FDA has found them to be "not substantially equivalent" (NSE) to legally marketed predicate devices.

DESI
Drug Efficacy Study Implementation

DFUF
Device Facility User Fee

DHF
Design History File. Describes a finished device's design.

DHHS
Department of Health and Human Services

DHR
Device History Record. Contains a device's production history.

DIA
Drug Information Association

Discipline Review Letter
Used by FDA to convey early thoughts on possible deficiencies found by a discipline review team for its portion of the pending application at the conclusion of the discipline review.

DMC
Data Monitoring Committee

DMEPA
Division of Medication Error Prevention and Analysis (CDER)

DMF
Drug Master File. Submission to FDA that may be used to provide confidential detailed information about facilities, processes or articles used in the manufacturing, processing, packaging and storing of one or more human drugs.

DMPQ
Division of Manufacturing and Product Quality (CBER)

DMR
Device Master Record. Compilation of records containing a finished device's procedures and specifications.

DNCE
Division of Nonprescription Clinical Evaluation

DRC
Direct Recall Classification

DRLS
Drug Registration and Listing System

Drug
Any article intended for use in the diagnosis, cure, mitigation, treatment or prevention of disease in man.

Drugs@FDA
A searchable database of brand-name and generic prescription and OTC human drugs and biological therapeutic products approved since 1939.

"Drug Facts" Label
Labeling requirement for all nonprescription, over-the-counter (OTC) medicine labels with detailed usage and warning information so consumers can properly choose and use the products.

Drug Product
A finished dosage form (e.g., tablet, capsule, solution, etc.) containing an active drug ingredient. It generally, but not necessarily, also is associated with inactive ingredients. This includes a finished dosage form not containing an active ingredient but intended to be used as a placebo.

DQSA
Drug Quality and Security Act. Also called the *Compounding Quality Act.*

DSHEA
Dietary Supplement Health and Education Act of 1994

DSMICA
Division of Small Manufacturers, International, and Consumer Assistance (CDRH)

DSNDCA
Dietary Supplement and Nonprescription Drug Consumer Protection Act

DTC
Direct-to-Consumer (advertising)

D-U-N-S
Data Universal Numbering System. A unique nine-digit sequence provided by Dun & Bradstreet, which is specific to each physical location of an entity (e.g., branch, division and headquarter).

E

EA
Environmental Assessment

EAP
Expedited Access Pathway Program. A new voluntary program for certain medical devices demonstrating the potential to address unmet medical needs for life threatening or irreversibly debilitating diseases or conditions and subject to PMAs or *de novo* requests.

eBPDR
Electronic Biological Product Deviation Reports

EC
European Commission, European Community or Ethics Committee

ECO
Emergency Change Order

eCopy (CDRH)
Required format for medical device submissions to FDA. eCopy is an exact duplicate of the paper submission, created and submitted on a compact disc (CD), digital video disc (DVD) or a flash drive. The eCopy application must pass certain technical standards before it will be accepted by FDA for review.

eCTD
Electronic Common Technical Document

eDRLS
Electronic Drug Registration and Listing System

EFTA
European Free Trade Association

EIR
Establishment Inspection Report

EMA
European Medicines Agency (formerly European Medicines Evaluation Agency)

eMDR
Electronic Medical Device Reporting requirement for manufacturers and importers to submit MDRs to FDA in an electronic format FDA can process, review and archive. The two options for submitting eMDRs are eSubmitter or Health Level 7 Individual Case Safety Reports (HL7 ICSR).

Emergency Use IND
FDA authorization for shipping a drug for a specific emergency use for a life-threatening or serious disease for which there is no alternative treatment.

EPA
Environmental Protection Agency

ERS
Expedited Review Status. Program for veterinary products.

Establishment Listing and Registration
In accordance with 21 CFR 807, manufacturers (both domestic and foreign) and initial distributors (importers) of medical devices must electronically register their establishments with FDA. Manufacturers must also list their devices with FDA.

eSubmitter
Under the eMDR program, a free downloadable application allowing submission of MDRs one at a time. This option is suitable for low volume reporters.

ETASU
Elements to Ensure Safe Use

EU
European Union has 28 Member States: Austria, Belgium, Bulgaria, Croatia, Cyprus, Czech Republic, Denakr, Estonia, Finland, France, Germany, Greece, Hungary, Ireland, Italy, Latvia, Lithuania, Luxembourg, Malta, Netherlands, Poland, Portugal, Romania, Slovakia, Slovenia, Spain, Sweden and the UK. EU policies also apply to members of the European Free Trade Association: Iceland, Norway, Switzerland and Liechtenstein.

EUnetHTA
European network for Health Technology Assessment

Excipient
An ingredient contained in a drug formulation that is not a medicinally active constituent.

Expected Life
Time a device is expected to remain functional after being placed into service.

Expiration Date
Date printed on product label indicating the end of the product's useful life. Expiration period length is determined by stability studies and negotiated with FDA.

F

FAERS
FDA Adverse Event Reporting System. A database containing information on adverse event and medication error reports submitted to FDA (CDER).

FALCPA
Food Allergen Labeling and Consumer Protection Act of 2004

FAR
Field Alert Report

Fast Track
FDA program to facilitate the development and expedite the review of new drugs intended to treat serious or life-threatening conditions demonstrating the potential to address unmet medical needs. Accelerated NDA review.

FCA
False Claims Act

FCC
Federal Communications Commission

FD&C Act
Federal Food, Drug, and Cosmetic Act of 1938

FDA
Food and Drug Administration

FDAAA
Food and Drug Administration Amendments Act of 2007

FDA ESG
FDA Electronic Submissions Gateway. Enables the secure submission of regulatory information for review.

FDAMA
FDA Modernization Act of 1997

FDASIA
Food and Drug Administration Safety and Innovation Act of 2012

FDERA
Food and Drug Export Reform and Enhancement Act of 1996

FDLI
Food and Drug Law Institute

FIFRA
Federal Insecticide, Fungicide, and Rodenticide Act

FMECA
Failure Mode, Effects and Critical Analysis

FOIA
Freedom of Information Act

FPI
Full prescribing information

FPLA
Fair Packaging and Labeling Act

FPS
Fraud Prevention Systems

FR
Federal Register

FSIS
Food Safety and Inspection Service

FSMA
Food Safety Modernization Act of 2011

FSPCTA
Family Smoking Prevention and Tobacco Control Act of 2009

FTC
Federal Trade Commission

FURLS
FDA Unified Registration and Listing System for establishment registration of medical device operators and distributors.

G

GADPTRA
Generic Animal Drug and Patent Term Restoration Act of 1988

GAIN Act
Generating Antibiotic Incentives Now Act of 2011

GAO
Government Accountability Office

GCP
Good Clinical Practice. Regulations and requirements with which clinical studies must comply. These regulations apply to manufacturers, sponsors, clinical investigators and institutional review boards.

GDEA
Generic Drug Enforcement Act of 1992

GDUFA
Generic Drug User Fee Amendments

GE
Genetically engineered

Generic Drug
Drugs manufactured and approved after the original brand-name drug has lost patent protection. Sponsor files Abbreviated New Drug Application (ANDA) for marketing approval.

GGP
Good Guidance Practices

GINAD
Generic Investigational New Animal Drug

GLP
Good Laboratory Practice. Regulations governing the conduct of nonclinical laboratory studies supporting or intended to support applications for research or marketing applications.

GMP
Good Manufacturing Practices (for devices, see Quality System Regulation).

GPO
Government Printing Office and Group Purchasing Organization

GPR
General Purpose Reagents

Grandfathered
Tacit approval of drugs marketed before 1938 and devices marketed before May 1976.

GRADE
Grading of Recommendations Assessment, Development and Evaluation

GRAS(E)
Generally Recognized as Safe (and Effective)

Green Book
FDA-published listing of all animal drug products approved for safety and effectiveness. Updated monthly.

Group Purchasing Organization (GPO)
An entity consisting of two or more hospitals or other healthcare entities formed to offer its members access to purchasing contracts for health supplies (i.e., pharmaceuticals, biologics, medical/surgical equipment, laboratory supplies and other capital equipment).

GRP
Good Review Practice

GTP
Good Tissue Practice

Guidance
Documents published by FDA to provide current interpretation of regulations.

H

HAACP
Hazard Analysis and Critical Control Point (inspection technique)

Hatch-Waxman Act
Drug Price Competition and Patent Restoration Act of 1984

HCT/P
Human Cells, Tissues and Cellular and Tissue-Based Products

HDE
Humanitarian Device Exemption

Health Level 7 Individual Case Safety Reports (HL7 ISCR)
Under the eMDR program, this submission method allows reporters to submit MDRs either as a batch or individually as XML files from their own complaint handling system. The HL7 ICSR messaging standard supports the exchange of electronic data and enables the extraction of information directly from the reporter's database to populate and transmit MDRs to FDA's electronic secure gateway (ESG).

HeartNet
A subnetwork of MedSun (CDRH's adverse event reporting program) focusing on identifying, understanding and solving problems with medical devices used in electrophysiology laboratories.

HEAT
Health Care Fraud Prevention and Enforcement Action Team

HIPAA
Health Insurance Portability and Accountability Act of 1996, also known as the Privacy Rule, established the minimum federal requirements for protecting the privacy of individually identifiable health information.

HMO
Health Maintenance Organization

Homeopathic Drug
Any drug labeled as being homeopathic listed in the *Homeopathic Pharmacopeia of the United States* (*HPUS*), an addendum to it or its supplements. Homeopathy is based on the belief disease symptoms can be cured by small doses of substances producing similar symptoms in healthy people.

HPC-C
Hematopoietic progenitor cells derived from cord blood

HPCUS
Homeopathic Pharmacopoeia Convention of the United States

HPUS
Homoeopathic Pharmacopoeia of the United States

HTA
Health Technology Assessment

HUD
Humanitarian Use Device

Human Factors
The study or evaluation of how people use technology, specifically the interaction of human abilities, expectations and limitations with work environments and system design

I

IB
Investigator's Brochure

IC (ICF) (ICD)
Informed Consent (Form) (Document)

ICA
Intercenter Agreement

ICCBBA
International Council for Commonality in Blood Banking Automation

ICCR
International Cooperation on Cosmetic Regulations

ICH
International Conference on Harmonisation of Technical Requirements for Registration of Pharmaceuticals for Human Use (participants include Europe, Japan and US; observers include Australia and Canada).

IDE
Investigational Device Exemption

IDMC
Independent Data Monitoring Committee

IIAD
Inactive Ingredient Database

IMDRF
International Medical Device Regulators Forum. A voluntary group of medical device regulators from around the world who have come together to build on the foundational work of the Global Harmonization Task Force on Medical Devices (GHTF) and aims to accelerate international medical device regulatory harmonization and convergence.

Immunogenicity
The ability of a substance to provoke an immune response or the degree to which it provokes a response.

Inactive Ingredient
Any drug product component other than the active ingredient, such as excipients, vehicles and binders.

INAD
Investigational New Animal Drug (application)

INCI
International Nomenclature of Cosmetic Ingredients

IND
Investigational New Drug (application)

Information Amendment
Includes most submissions under an active IND, such as new protocols, final study reports, safety reports, CMC information, etc. The initial IND ends with 000; each serial amendment receives the next consecutive number.

INHATA
International Network of Agencies for Health Technology Assessment

INN
International Nonproprietary Names

Intended Use
Objective labeled use of a device.

Investigator IND
Protocol and IND submitted by an individual investigator instead of a manufacturer. A letter of authorization allows FDA to review the sponsor's DMF or cross-reference CMC information. The investigator, not the manufacturer, is responsible for maintaining the IND.

IOM
Investigations Operations Manual and Institute of Medicine

IRB
Institutional Review Board or Independent Review Board

IR Letter
A communication sent by FDA to an applicant during an application or supplement review to request further information or clarification needed or helpful in completing the discipline review.

ISO
International Organization for Standardization

IUO
Investigational Use Only

IVD
In Vitro Diagnostic

K

KidNet
A subnetwork of MedSun (CDRH's adverse event reporting program) focusing on identifying, understanding and solving problems with medical devices used in neonatal and pediatric intensive care units.

L

Label
Any display of written, printed or graphic matter on the immediate container or package of, or affixed to, any article.

Labeling
All written, printed or graphic matter accompanying an article at any time while such article is in interstate commerce or held for sale after shipment in interstate commerce; includes user manuals, brochures, advertising, etc.

LDT
Laboratory developed test. A subset of in vitro diagnostic devices are designed, manufactured and offered for clinical use by a single laboratory

LOA
Letter of Authorization. A letter from the holder of a Drug Master File to FDA, authorizing another party to reference the DMF (also Letter of Agreement).

LoD
Limit of Detection

Lookback Procedure
Donor screening procedure used by blood establishments to retrieve and quarantine units previously collected from a donor who originally tested negative for HIV or another infectious disease but subsequently tested positive at a later donation.

M

Major Statement
Refers to the presentation in a television or radio advertisement of a prescription drug's most important risks. This presentation must be spoken. It also can be included in the video part of television advertisements.

Market Withdrawal
Firm-initiated removal or correction of a device, drug or biologic product involving a minor violation of the *FD&C Act*, not subject to legal action by FDA, or which involves no violation, e.g., normal stock rotation practices, routine equipment adjustments and repairs, etc.

MAF
Device Master File. Analagous to a drug master file; submission to FDA that may be used to provide confidential detailed information about a medical device or a component used in the manufacture of a medical device to FDA in support of another party's obligation.

MAPP
Manual of Policies and Procedures. Approved instructions for internal practices and procedures followed by CDER staff to help standardize the new drug review process and other activities.

MAUDE
Manufacturer and User Facility Device Experience database. Contains reports of adverse events involving medical devices.

MCB
Master Cell Bank. A collection of cells of uniform composition derived from a single source prepared under defined culture conditions.

MCSR
Minor changes and stability report (for animal drugs). An annual report submitted to the application once each year within 60 days before or after the anniversary date of the application's original approval or on a mutually agreed upon date.

MDR
Medical Device Reporting

MDSAP
Medical Device Single Audit Program. Pilot program allowing FDA and other international partners to conduct a single audit of a medical device manufacturer that will satisfy the relevant requirements of the medical device regulatory authorities participating in the pilot program. FDA will accept the MDSAP audit reports as a substitute for routine agency inspections.

MDUFA III
Medical Device User Fee Amendments of 2012

MDUFMA
Medical Device User Fee and Modernization Act of 2002

MedDRA
Medical Dictionary for Regulatory Activities. Global standard international medical terminology designed to supersede or replace all other terminologies used within the medical product development process including COSTART and WHO-ART.

Medical Device
An instrument, apparatus, implement, machine, contrivance, implant, in vitro reagent or other similar or related article, including any component, part or accessory: recognized in the official *National Formulary* or *US Pharmacopeia*, or any supplement to them intended for use in diagnosis of disease or other conditions, or in cure, mitigation, treatment or prevention of disease in man or other animals intended to affect the structure or any function of the body of man or other animals, and which does not achieve its primary intended purposes through chemical action within or on the body of man or other animals, and which is not dependent upon being metabolized for the achievement of its primary intended purposes. (*FD&C Act* Section 201(h))

Medical Food
A food formulated to be consumed or administered enterally under the supervision of a physician and intended for the specific dietary management of a disease or condition for which distinctive nutritional requirements, based on recognized scientific principles, are established by medical evaluation.

Medication Guide
Paper handouts accompanying many prescription medicines, addressing issues specific to particular drugs and drug classes, which contain FDA-approved information to help patients avoid serious adverse events.

MedSun
Medical Product Safety Network. An adverse event reporting program for healthcare professionals launched in 2002 by CDRH.

MedWatch
FDA program for voluntary and mandatory reporting of AEs and product problems (Form FDA 3500 or 3500A).

Misbranded
Designation given to an incorrectly labeled product (i.e., false or misleading or fails to include information required by law). Other violations also may render a product misbranded (e.g., failure to obtain a 510(k) for a device).

MMA
Medicare Prescription Drug, Improvement and Modernization Act of 2003

Modular PMA
Allows a company to file the completed portions or modules of a PMA for an ongoing FDA review.

MOU
Memorandum of Understanding. An agreement between FDA and another country's regulatory authority allowing mutual recognition of inspections.

MSDS
Material Safety Data Sheet

MTD
Maximum Tolerated Dose

MUMS
Minor Use and Minor Species Animal Health Act of 2004

N

NADA
New Animal Drug Application

NAF
Notice of Adverse Findings

NAFTA
North American Free Trade Agreement

NAI
No Action Indicated. Most favorable FDA post-inspection classification.

NCE
New Chemical Entity

NCTR
National Center for Toxicological Research

NDA
New Drug Application

NDA Number
A six-digit number assigned by FDA to each application for new drug marketing approval in the US. A drug can have more than one application number if it has different dosage forms or routes of administration.

NDA Field Alert
Report filed with FDA within three working days of obtaining information on any distributed drug product with contamination, significant chemical or physical change, deterioration, batch failure or labeling causing mistaken identity.

NDC
National Drug Code. The first five digits identify establishment and last five digits identify drug name, package size and drug type.

NDF
New Dosage Form

Next-Generation Sequencing
Technologies that parallelize the genetic sequencing process, allowing the production of thousands or millions of sequences concurrently (also referred to as "high-throughput sequencing").

NF
National Formulary (incorporated into the *USP-NF*)

NICE
National Institute for Health and Care Excellence (UK)

NIDPOE
Notice of Initiation of Disqualification Proceedings and Opportunity to Explain Letter

NIH
National Institutes of Health

NLEA
Nutrition Labeling and Education Act of 1990

NLM
National Library of Medicine

NME
New Molecular Entity

NORD
National Organization for Rare Disorders

NOV
Notice of Violation letter

NRC
National Research Council or Nuclear Regulatory Commission

NSE
Not Substantially Equivalent. Designation for a device not qualifying for 510(k) clearance; generally requires a PMA.

NSR
Nonsignificant Risk

Nuremberg Code of 1947
A set of research ethics principles for human experimentation created as a result of atrocities involving medical experimentation on humans during World War II.

O

OAI
Official Action Indicated. Serious FDA post-inspection classification.

OBRR
Office of Blood Research and Review (CBER)

OC
Office of the Commissioner (FDA)

OCBQ
Office of Compliance and Biologics Quality (CBER)

OCC
Office of the Chief Counsel (FDA)

OCET
Office of Counterterrorism and Emerging Threats (FDA)

OCI
Office of Criminal Investigation (FDA)

OCP
Office of Combination Products (FDA)

OCTGT
Office of Cellular, Tissue and Gene Therapies (CBER)

ODA
Orphan Drug Act of 1983

ODE
Office of Device Evaluation (FDA)

OECD
Organization for Economic Cooperation and Development

Off-Label Drug Use
When a drug is used in a different way than described in the FDA-approved drug label.

Office of the Chief Scientist
Includes the following offices:
Office of Counterterrorism and Emerging Threats
Office of Regulatory Science and Innovation
Office of Scientific Integrity
Office of Scientific Professional Development
Office of Minority Health
Office of Women's Health
FDA's National Center for Toxicological Research

OFM
Office of Financial Management (FDA)

OGD
Office of Generic Drug Products (CDER)

OIG
Office of the Inspector General (FDA)

OIP
Office of International Programs (FDA)

OIR
Office of In Vitro Diagnostics and Radiological Health (formerly the Office of In Vitro Diagnostic Device Evaluation and Safety)

OIRA
Office of Information and Regulatory Affairs (OMB)

OMUMS
Office of Minor Use & Minor Species Animal Drug Development (CVM)

ONADE
Office of New Animal Drug Evaluation (CVM)

OND
Office of New Drugs (CDER)

ONDQA
Office of New Drug Quality Assessment (CDER)

ONPLDS
Office of Nutritional Products, Labeling and Dietary Supplements (CFSAN)

OOPD
Office of Orphan Products Development (FDA)

OPA
Office of Public Affairs (FDA)

OPDP
Office of Prescription Drug Promotion (CDER, formerly Division of Drug Marketing, Advertising, and Communications (DDMAC))

Open Label Study
A clinical trial in which subjects and investigators are aware of the treatment received.

ORA
Office of Regulatory Affairs (FDA); oversees FDA's field organization.

Orange Book
FDA-published listing of Approved Drug Products with Therapeutic Equivalence Evaluations generally known as generics (original print version had an orange cover).

Orphan Drug
Drugs for a disease or condition affecting fewer than 200,000 persons in the US or occurs in more than 200,000 and for which there is no reasonable expectation the drug development and manufacturing costs will be recovered from US sales.

OSB
Office of Surveillance and Biometrics (CDRH)

OSHA
Occupational Safety Health Administration

OSI
Office of Scientific Integrity (FDA)

OTC
Over-the-Counter. Nonprescription drugs receive this designation.

OTC Monograph
Rules for a number of OTC drug categories.

OVRR
Office of Vaccine Research and Review (CBER)

P

PADER
Periodic Adverse Drug Experiences Report

PAI
Preapproval Inspection

PAS
Prior Approval Supplement or Postapproval Study

PAT
Process Analytical Technology

PBRER
Periodic benefit-risk evaluation reports

PCPC
Personal Care Products Council (formerly Cosmetic, Toiletry and Fragrance Association)

PD
Pharmacodynamics. Study of the reactions between drugs and living structures.

PDA
Parenteral Drug Association

PDMA
Prescription Drug Marketing Act of 1987

PDP
Product Development Protocol (for medical devices) or Principal Display Panel (for product labels)

PDUFA
Prescription Drug User Fee Act of 1992

PDUFA II
Prescription Drug User Fee Act of 1997

PDUFA III
Prescription Drug User Fee Act of 2002

PDUFA IV
Prescription Drug User Fee Act of 2007

PDUFA V
Prescription Drug User Fee Act of 2012

Pediatric Rule
Requires manufacturers to assess the safety and effectiveness of certain drug and biological products in pediatric patients.

PEPFAR
President's Emergency Plan for AIDS Relief

Personalized Medicine
The tailoring of medical treatment to the individual characteristics, needs and preferences of a patient during all stages of care, including prevention, diagnosis, treatment and follow-up.

PGx
Pharmacogenomics. The study of variations of DNA and RNA characteristics as related to drug response.

Pharmaceutical Equivalents
Drug products containing the same active ingredient(s), same dosage form and route of administration and identical in strength or concentration.

Pharmacovigilance
Adverse event monitoring and reporting

PhRMA
Pharmaceutical Research and Manufacturers of America

Phase I
Initial clinical safety studies in humans. May be as few as 10 subjects, often healthy volunteers, includes PK, ADME and dose escalation studies. Usually open label.

Phase II
Well-controlled clinical trials of approximately 100–300 subjects who have the condition of interest, includes PK, dose ranging, safety and efficacy.

Phase III
Larger, well-controlled clinical trials of hundreds to thousands of subjects, including both safety and efficacy data. Generally, two well-controlled studies are needed to establish efficacy for drug products.

Phase IV
Postmarket clinical trials performed to support labeling and advertising or fulfill FDA safety requirements noted at the time of NDA approval.

PHI
Protected Health Information

PHS
Public Health Service

PI
Package Insert (approved product labeling) or Principal Investigator

PK
Pharmacokinetics. The study of the processes of ADME of chemicals and medicines.

Placebo
A drug product fashioned to look like an active drug but containing no active ingredient. Used in clinical trials to blind or mask the patient, investigator or both as to the treatment received.

PLR
Physician Labeling Rule

PMA
Premarket Approval. Marketing application required for Class III devices.
Traditional PMA: The complete PMA application is submitted to FDA at one time.
Modular: The complete contents of a PMA are broken down into well-delineated components (or modules) and submitted to FDA as soon as the applicant has completed the module, compiling a complete PMA over time.
Streamlined: A pilot program in the Division of Clinical Laboratory Devices. A complete PMA is submitted as in a traditional PMA; however, the Streamlined PMA is for a device in which the technology and use are well known to FDA.
Product Development Process (PDP): The clinical evaluation of a device and the development of necessary information for marketing approval are merged into one regulatory mechanism. Ideal candidates for the PDP process are those devices in which the technology is well established in industry.

PMC
Postmarketing commitment. Studies or clinical trials a sponsor has agreed to conduct but not required by a statute or regulation.

PMN
Premarket Notification. A premarket notification is also called a 510(k).

PMOA
Primary Mode of Action. The single mode of action of a combination product providing the most important therapeutic action of the combination product; used to assign a combination product to a lead FDA center.

PMR
Postmarketing Requirements. Studies and clinical trials sponsors are required to conduct under one or more statutes or regulations

PMS
Postmarketing Surveillance. Ongoing monitoring of the safety of approved medical products; may include Phase IV studies and AE reporting.

PNSI
Prior Notice System Interface. Used to provide prior notice for food products entering the US.

POCs
Physician-owned companies

PPA
Poison Prevention Act

PPACA
Patient Protection and Affordable Care Act of 2010

PPI
Patient Package Insert. Contains information for patients' understanding of how to use a drug product safely.

PPIA
Poultry Products Inspection Act

PREA
Pediatric Research Equity Act of 2003

Preclinical Studies
Animal studies of PK and toxicity generally performed prior to clinical studies. These studies must comply with GLP.

Pre-Sub Meeting
Provides the opportunity for an applicant to obtain FDA feedback prior to intended submission of an IDE or device marketing application.

Priority Review
FDA review category for drugs appearing to represent an advance over available therapy. NDA or BLA receives a faster review than standard applications.

PRO
Patient-reported outcome

Protocol
Document describing a clinical trial's objectives, design and methods. All GLP and GCP studies must follow a protocol.

PSUR
Periodic Safety Update Report

PTC
Points to Consider. Type of guidance published by FDA, usually by CBER.

PTCC
Pharmacology/Toxicology Coordinating Committee (CDER)

PTO
Patent and Trademark Office

***Public Health Security and Bioterrorism Preparedness and Response Act* of 2002**
Also known as *Bioterrorism Act*

PWR
Pediatric Written Request. *BPCA* authorizes FDA (in consultation with NIH) to issue a written request for the conduct of pediatric studies to holders of approved NDAs and ANDAs for drugs on the NIH list.

Q

QA
Quality Assurance

QALY
Quality Adjusted Life Year

QAU
Quality Assurance Unit

QC
Quality Control

QbR
Question-based review (CDER). Chemistry, Manufacturing, and Controls (CMC) evaluation of ANDAs incorporating the most important scientific and regulatory review questions focused on critical pharmaceutical attributes essential for ensuring generic drug product quality.

QdB
Quality by Design. This concept emphasized quality being built into a product with a thorough understanding of the product and process by which it is developed and manufactured along with a knowledge of the risks involved in manufacturing the product and how best to mitigate those risks.

QIDP
Qualified Infectious Disease Product

QoL
Quality of Life

QSIT
Quality System Inspection Technique

QSR
Quality System Regulation (21 CFR 820). Identifies GMPs for medical devices.

R

R&D
Research and Development

RAC
Reviewer Affairs Committee (CDER) or Regulatory Affairs Certification

RAPS
Regulatory Affairs Professionals Society

Rare Pediatric Disease Priority Review Voucher
A voucher FDA issues to the sponsor of a rare pediatric disease product application at the time of the marketing application approval. This voucher entitles the holder to designate a single human drug application submitted under *FD&C Act* Section 505(b)(1) or Section 351 of the *PHS Act* as qualifying for a priority review.

RCDAD
Relevant communicable disease agents and diseases

RCT
Randomized Clinical Trial or Randomized Controlled Trial

Real Time PMA Supplement
A supplement to an approved premarket application or premarket report under Section 515 requesting a minor change to the device, such as a minor change to the design of the device, software, sterilization or labeling, and for which the applicant has requested and the agency has granted a meeting or similar forum to jointly review and determine the status of the supplement.

Recall
A firm's removal or correction of a marketed product FDA considers to be in violation of the laws it administers and against which the agency would initiate legal action, e.g., seizure. Recall does not include a market withdrawal or a stock recovery.

Recall Classification
Assigned by FDA and applicable to firm-initiated device recalls based upon reasonable probability and relative degree of health hazard.
Class I: violative device would cause serious adverse health consequences
Class II: violative device may cause temporary or medically reversible adverse health consequences or such consequences are remote
Class III: violative device is not likely to cause adverse health consequences

Regulation
Refers to Code of Federal Regulations

REMS
Risk Evaluation and Mitigation Strategy

Restricted Device
A device restricted, by regulation, to sale, distribution and/or use only upon the written or oral authorization of a licensed practitioner or other conditions prescribed by the commissioner.

RFA
Request for Application

RFD
Request for Designation. A written submission to OCP requesting designation of the center with primary jurisdiction for a combination or non-combination product.

RFR
Request for Reconsideration. A request for OCP to reconsider an RFD determination.

RFR
Reportable Food Registry. An electronic portal used to report foods suspected of causing serious adverse health consequences.

RiskMAP
Risk Minimization Action Plan. A strategic safety program designed to meet specific goals and objectives in minimizing known risks of a product while preserving its benefits.

RLD
Reference Listed Drug. Drug product listed in the Approved Drug Products with Therapeutic Equivalence Evaluations book (also known as the *Orange Book*).

Rolling NDA Submission
Allows a company to file the completed portions of an NDA for an ongoing FDA review Only permitted for drugs and biologics granted Fast Track designation by FDA.

RPM
Regulatory Procedures Manual. A reference manual for FDA personnel containing information on internal procedures to be used in processing domestic and import regulatory and enforcement matters.

RTA Policy
Refuse to accept. FDA will conduct an acceptance review of all traditional, special or abbreviated 510(k)s and PMAs based on objective criteria using the applicable Acceptance Checklist to ensure the 510(k) or PMA is administratively complete.

RTF
Refusal to File. Letter sent by FDA when an incomplete NDA or ANDA is filed. FDA will not review the application until complete. Letter is sent within 60 days of submission.

RUO
Research Use Only

Rx
Prescription Use Only

Rx to OTC Switch
The process of transferring FDA-approved prescription medications to nonprescription, over-the-counter (OTC) products for the same dosage form, population and route of administration.

S

SAE
Serious Adverse Event

SBA
Summary Basis of Approval

SC
Study Coordinator

SD
Standard Deviation

SDWA
Safe Drinking Water Act

SE
Substantially Equivalent

S&E
Safety and Efficacy

SECG
Small entity compliance guide

Sentinel Initiative
FDA program aimed at developing and implementing a proactive system to complement existing systems the agency has in place to track reports of adverse events linked to the use of its regulated products.

Shelf Life
Maximum time a device will remain functional from the date of manufacture until it is used in patient care (See Expiration Date).

Significant Risk Device
An investigational device:
intended as an implant
represented to be for use in supporting or sustaining human life
for a use of substantial importance in diagnosing, curing, mitigating or treating disease or otherwise preventing impairment of human health and presents a potential for serious risk to the subject's health, safety or welfare

SMDA
Safe Medical Devices Act of 1990

SME
Significant Medical Event

SMP
Senior medical protocol

SNDA
Supplemental New Drug Application

SoCRA
Society of Clinical Research Associates

SOP
Standard Operating Procedure

Source Documents
Original documents and records containing information captured in a clinical study. Case Report Forms are monitored against source documents. Includes office charts, laboratory results, x-rays, etc.

SPA
Special Protocol Assessment

SPL
Structured Product Label. Content of package insert in XML format.

SR
Significant Risk (device)

Sponsor
Company, person, organization or institution taking responsibility for initiating, managing or financing a clinical trial.

SSED
Summary of Safety and Effectiveness Data. An FDA document intended to present a reasoned, objective and balanced summary of the scientific evidence, both positive and negative, that served as the basis of the decision to approve or deny the PMA.

SST
System Suitability Testing. Required by USP and FDA to check and ensure on-going performance of analytical systems and methods.

Standard Review
FDA review category for drugs with therapeutic qualities similar to those already approved for marketing.

Subject
Clinical trial participant; may be a healthy volunteer or a patient.

Subpart E
21 CFR 312. Accelerated review for life-threatening and severely debilitating illness.

Subpart H
21 CFR 314.500. Approval based upon a surrogate endpoint or a product approved with restrictions and/or requirements for Phase IV trials.

Substantial Equivalence
Comparison of a new device to a legally marketed predicate device; substantial equivalence establishes a device is as safe and as effective as another 510(k) cleared device.

Suitability Petition
A request to FDA to submit an ANDA for a product varying from a Reference Listed Drug in indication, strength, dosage form, route of administration, etc.

SUPAC
Scale Up and Post Approval Changes

Supplement (sNDA)
NDA submission for changes to an approved NDA, including SUPAC.

Supplement (sPMA)
PMA submission for changes to an approved PMA that affect the device's safety or effectiveness.

Surrogate Endpoint
A laboratory or physical sign used in trials as a substitute for a clinically meaningful endpoint that is a direct measure of how a patient feels, functions or survives and is expected to predict the effect of the therapy.

T

Target Product Profile (TPP)
A format for a summary of a drug development program described in terms of labeling concepts. A TPP can be prepared by a sponsor and shared with the appropriate FDA review staff to facilitate communication regarding a particular drug development program.

TEA
Time and extent application. Demonstrates a drug product can meet the statutory standard of marketing to a material extent and for a material time

Team Biologics
A group of specialized investigators who conduct routine and CGMP follow-up inspections of biological product manufacturers regulated by CBER. Partnership program between ORA and CBER.

TFM
Tentative Final Monograph

Third-Party Review
Under *FDAMA*, FDA has accredited third parties authorized to conduct the primary review of 510(k)s for eligible devices.

THOMAS
Public federal legislation database (Library of Congress)

TK
Toxicokinetics

Tobacco Control Act
The *Family Smoking Prevention and Tobacco Control Act* of 2009

TOPRA
The Organisation for Professionals in Regulatory Affairs

TPLC
Total product lifecycle

TPP
Target Product Profile

Transitional Device
Devices regulated as drugs prior to 28 May 1976, when the *Medical Device Amendments* were signed into law. Any device approved by the New Drug Application process now is governed by the PMA regulations.

Treatment IND (tIND)
Allows limited use of an unapproved drug for patients with a serious or life-threatening disease.

Truthful Prescription Drug Advertising and Promotion (Bad Ad Program)
Educational outreach program to help healthcare providers recognize misleading prescription drug promotion and provide them with an easy way to report this activity to the agency.

TSCA
Toxic Substances Control Act

TTB
Tax and Trade Bureau

U

UADE
Unexpected Adverse Device Effect. Any serious adverse effect on health or safety or any life-threatening problem or death caused by, or associated with, a device, if that effect, problem or death was not identified previously in nature, severity or degree of incidence in the investigational plan or application, or any other unanticipated serious problem associated with a device relating to the rights, safety or welfare of subjects.

UDI
Unique Device Identification. Requires a device's label to bear a unique identifier, unless an alternative location is specified by FDA or an exception is made for a particular device or group of devices.

Unexpected AE
An AE, the nature or severity of which is not described in the Investigator's Brochure (for an unapproved product) or in the package insert (for an approved product).

USAN
US Adopted Name

USANC
US Adopted Names Council

USC
US Code

USCA
US Code Annotated

USDA
US Department of Agriculture

User Fees
Fees authorized by Congress to fund various FDA activities. The fee schedule for different application types is published annually in the *Federal Register.* Initially established by the *Prescription Drug User Fee Act* and later extended to medical devices, generic drugs and animal drugs.

USP
United States Pharmacopeia

V

VA
Department of Veterans Affairs

VAERS
Vaccine Adverse Event Reporting System

VAI
Voluntary Action Indicated. Moderately serious FDA post-inspection classification.

VCRP
Voluntary Cosmetic Registration Program. FDA postmarket reporting system for use by manufacturers, packers and distributors of cosmetic products in commercial distribution in the US.

VICH
Veterinary International Conference on Harmonization

W

Warning Letter (WL)
Serious enforcement letter issued by FDA notifying a regulated entity of violative activity; requires immediate action within 15 days.

Warning Letter Database
Contains Warning Letters issued from November 1996 to present and searchable by company, subject, issuing office or date.

WCB
Working Cell Bank. Cells derived from one or more vials of cells from the master cell bank, which are expanded by serial subculture.

Well-Characterized Biologic
A biological product whose identity, purity, impurities, potency and quantity can be determined and controlled.

WHO
World Health Organization

Index

A

B

C

D

E

F

G

H

I

J

K

L

M

N

O

P

Q

R

S

T

U

V

W

Essential Regulatory Reference Guides

RAPS Fundamentals of Regulatory Affairs Series

The Fundamentals series presents complex information clearly and concisely, with easy-to-read charts and analysis by experts.

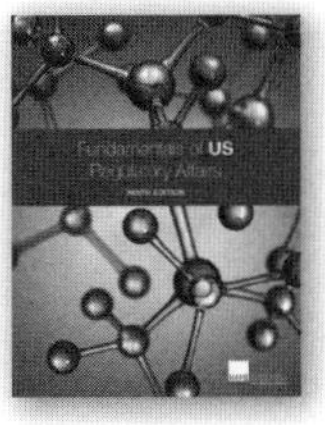

Fundamentals of US Regulatory Affairs, Ninth Edition

Healthcare product regulation is complex and changes often. Knowing how to navigate through the requirements and guidances goes a long way toward making your job easier and your work better. RAPS' *Fundamentals of US Regulatory Affairs, Ninth Edition*, has all the most current and accurate information in one place—making it the cornerstone of a good regulatory library:

- 41 chapters by 49 expert authors
- Enhanced matrix that clearly displays current regulations
- New chapters on Regulatory Strategy, Regulating Regenerative Medicine and User Fees

Fundamentals of EU Regulatory Affairs, Seventh Edition

Breaking down the complexities of EU regulations and directives, *Fundamentals of EU Regulatory Affairs* provides a comprehensive review of human and veterinary medicinal products, biologics, medical devices, cosmetics and food supplements, as well as the applicable international standards and guidances.

Fundamentals of International Regulatory Affairs, Second Edition

What are the implications of an international regulatory environment and how do you navigate this rapidly evolving landscape? *Fundamentals of International Regulatory Affairs* can help you find your way with a clear explanation of developments in the harmonization of requirements and regulations by international bodies including the ICH, IMDRF and WHO.

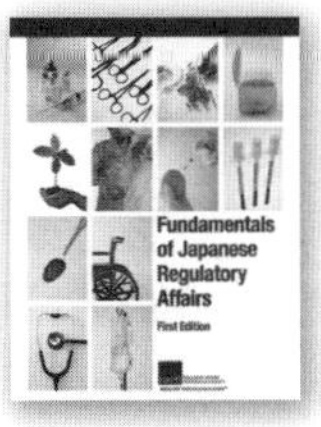

Fundamentals of Japanese Regulatory Affairs, Second Edition

Fundamentals of Japanese Regulatory Affairs answers the unique challenges of working on healthcare products in Japan. This English version provides a comprehensive source of information on submissions, licensing, and distribution requirements and postmarket obligations for drugs, biologics, medical devices and in vitro diagnostic products.

Fundamentals of Canadian Regulatory Affairs, Fourth Edition

A must-have for working in Canadian regulatory, this publication offers a robust index and glossary, as well as a detailed matrix of laws and guidances that will have pros and novices alike on the competitive edge of industry.

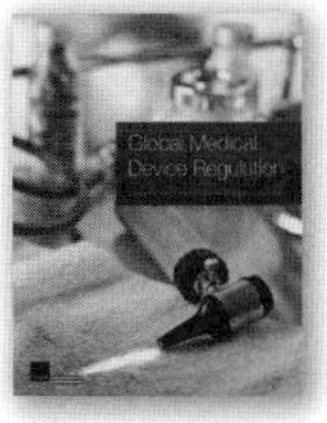

Global Medical Device Regulations, Second Edition

All the international medical device regulations from our Fundamentals series, compiled into a single edition for convenience. *Global Medical Device Regulations* takes you from introductory information about the global medical device scene through submissions, compliance, advertising and more from a global perspective.

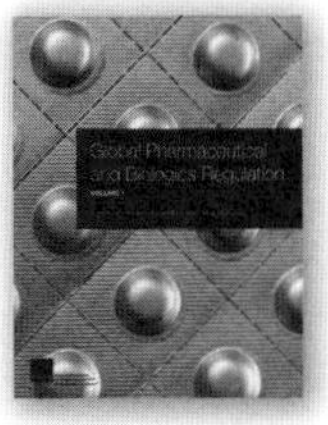

Global Pharmaceutical & Biologics Regulation, Vol. 1 & 2

The world of pharmaceutical and biological product regulations presents even seasoned regulatory pros with unique challenges. Overcome them with RAPS' guide to *Global Pharmaceutical and Biologics Regulation, First Edition.* Featuring materials adapted from RAPS' five book series Fundamentals of Regulatory Affairs, this resource is divided into two volumes. Volume 1 covers regulations in the US and international arena. Volume 2 addresses the EU, Canada and Japan.

Order your copies today at **RAPS.org/ fundamentals**